COMPREHENSIVE RENEWABLE ENERGY

COMPREHENSIVE RENEWABLE ENERGY

EDITOR-IN-CHIEF
Ali Sayigh
Chairman of WREC, Director General of WREN, and Chairman of IEI, Brighton, UK

VOLUME 3
SOLAR THERMAL SYSTEMS: COMPONENTS AND APPLICATIONS

VOLUME EDITOR
Soteris A. Kalogirou
Cyprus University of Technology, Limassol, Cyprus

ELSEVIER

AMSTERDAM BOSTON HEIDELBERG LONDON NEW YORK OXFORD
PARIS SAN DIEGO SAN FRANCISCO SINGAPORE SYDNEY TOKYO

Elsevier
Radarweg 29, PO Box 211, 1000 AE Amsterdam, The Netherlands
The Boulevard, Langford Lane, Kidlington, Oxford OX5 1GB, UK
225 Wyman Street, Waltham, MA 02451, USA

Copyright © 2012 Elsevier Ltd. All rights reserved.

4.04   Hydrogen Safety Engineering: The State-of-the-Art and Future Progress
Copyright © 2012 V Molkov

5.16   Renewable Fuels: An Automotive Perspective
Copyright © 2012 Lotus Cars Limited

The following articles are US Government works in the public domain and not subject to copyright:
1.19   Cadmium Telluride Photovoltaic Thin Film: CdTe
1.37   Solar Power Satellites
4.02   Current Perspective on Hydrogen and Fuel Cells
5.02   Historical Perspectives on Biofuels

No part of this publication may be reproduced, stored in a retrieval system or transmitted in any form or by any means electronic, mechanical, photocopying, recording or otherwise without the prior written permission of the publisher

Permissions may be sought directly from Elsevier's Science & Technology Rights Department in Oxford, UK: phone (+44) (0) 1865 843830; fax (+44) (0) 1865 853333; email: permissions@elsevier.com. Alternatively you can submit your request online by visiting the Elsevier web site at http://elsevier.com/locate/permissions, and selecting *Obtaining permission to use Elsevier material*

Notice
No responsibility is assumed by the publisher for any injury and/or damage to persons or property as a matter of products liability, negligence or otherwise, or from any use or operation of any methods, products, instructions or ideas contained in the material herein. Because of rapid advances in the medical sciences, in particular, independent verfication of diagnoses and drug dosages should be made.

British Library Cataloguing in Publication Data
A catalogue record for this book is available from the British Library

The Library of Congress Control Number: 2012934547

ISBN: 978-0-08-087872-0

For information on all Elsevier publications
visit our website at books.elsevier.com

Printed and bound in Italy

11 12 13 14 10 9 8 7 6 5 4 3 2 1

Working together to grow
libraries in developing countries

www.elsevier.com | www.bookaid.org | www.sabre.org

ELSEVIER   BOOK AID International   Sabre Foundation

Editorial: Gemma Mattingley, Joanne Williams
Production: Edward Taylor, Maggie Johnson

EDITOR-IN-CHIEF

Professor Ali Sayigh, BSc, DIC, PhD, CEng, a British citizen, graduated from Imperial College London and the University of London in 1966. He is a fellow of the Institute of Energy, a fellow of the Institution of Electrical Engineers, and is a chartered engineer.

From 1966 to 1985, Prof. Sayigh taught in the College of Engineering at the University of Baghdad and at King Saud University, Saudi Arabia, as a full-time professor, and also at Kuwait University as a part-time professor. From 1981 to 1985, he was Head of the Energy Department at the Kuwait Institute for Scientific Research (KISR) and expert in renewable energy at the Arab Organization of Petroleum Exporting Countries (AOPEC), Kuwait.

He started working in solar energy in September 1969. In 1984, he established links with Pergamon Press and became Editor-in-Chief of his first international journal, *Solar & Wind Technology*. Since 1990 he has been Editor-in-Chief of *Comprehensive Renewable Energy* incorporating *Solar & Wind Technology*, published by Elsevier Science Ltd., Oxford, UK. He is the editor of several international journals published in Morocco, Iran, Bangladesh, and Nigeria.

He has been a member of the International Society for Equitation Science (ISES) since 1973, founder and chairman of the ARAB Section of ISES since 1979, chairman of the UK Solar Energy Society for 3 years, and consultant to many national and international organizations, among them, the British Council, the Islamic Educational, Scientific and Cultural Organization (ISESCO), the United Nations Educational, Scientific and Cultural Organization (UNESCO), the United Nations Development Programme (UNDP), the Economic and Social Commission for Western Asia (ESCWA), and the United Nations Industrial Development Organization (UNIDO).

Since 1977 Prof. Sayigh has founded and directed several renewable energy conferences and workshops in the International Centre for Theoretical Physics (ICTP) – Trieste, Italy, Canada, Colombia, Algeria, Kuwait, Bahrain, Malaysia, Zambia, Malawi, India, the West Indies, Tunisia, Indonesia, Libya, Taiwan, UAE, Oman, the Czech Republic, Germany, Australia, Poland, the Netherlands, Thailand, Korea, Iran, Syria, Saudi Arabia, Singapore, China, the United States, and the United Kingdom.

In 1990 he established the World Renewable Energy Congress (WREC) and, in 1992, the World Renewable Energy Network (WREN), which hold their Congresses every 2 years, attracting more than 100 countries each time. In 2000, he and others in UAE, Sharjah, founded the Arab Science and Technology Foundation (ASTF) and regional conferences have been held in Sweden, Malaysia, Korea, Indonesia, Australia, UAE, and Libya, to name but a few. Prof. Sayigh has been running an annual international seminar on all aspects of renewable energy since 1990 in the United Kingdom and abroad. In total, 85 seminars have been held.

Prof. Sayigh supervised and graduated more than 34 PhD students and 64 MSc students at Reading University and the University of Hertfordshire when he was a professor from 1986 to 2004.

He has edited, contributed, and written more than 32 books and published more than 500 papers in various international journals and conferences.

In 2000–09, he initiated and worked closely with Sovereign Publication Company to produce the most popular magazine at annual bases called *Renewable Energy*, which was distributed freely to more than 6000 readers around the world. Presently, he is the editor-in-chief of *Comprehensive Renewable Energy*, coordinating 154 top scientists', engineers', and researchers' contributions in eight volumes published by Elsevier Publishing Company, Oxford, UK.

VOLUME EDITORS

Dr. Wilfried G. J. H. M. van Sark graduated from Utrecht University, the Netherlands, with an MSc in experimental physics in 1985, and with an MSc thesis on measurement and analysis of I–V characteristics of c-Si cells. He received his PhD from Nijmegen University, the Netherlands; the topic of his PhD thesis was III–V solar cell development, modeling, and processing. He then spent 7 years as a postdoc/senior researcher at Utrecht University and specialized in a-Si:H cell deposition and analysis. He is an expert in plasma chemical vapor deposition, both radio frequency and very high frequency. After an assistant professor position at Nijmegen University, where he worked on III–V solar cells, he returned to Utrecht University, with a focus on (single-molecule) confocal fluorescence microscopy of nanocrystals. In 2002, he moved to his present position as assistant professor at the research group Science, Technology and Society of the Copernicus Institute at Utrecht University, the Netherlands, where he performed and coordinated research on next-generation photovoltaic devices incorporating nanocrystals; for example, luminescent solar concentrators, as well as photovoltaic performance, life cycle analysis, socioeconomics, and policy development. He is member of the editorial board of Elsevier's scientific journal *Renewable Energy*, and member of various organizing committees of the European Union, the Institute of Electrical and Electronics Engineers (IEEE), and the SPIE PV conferences. He is author or coauthor of over 200 peer-reviewed journal and conference paper publications and book chapters. He has (co-)edited three books, including the present one.

Professor John K. Kaldellis holds a mechanical engineering degree from the National Technical University of Athens (NTUA) and a business administration diploma from the University of Piraeus. He obtained his PhD from NTUA (Fluid Sector) sponsored by Snecma–Dassault, France, and Bodossakis Foundation, Greece. He is currently the head of the Mechanical Engineering Department and since 1991 the director of the Soft Energy Applications and Environmental Protection Laboratory of the Technological Education Institute (TEI) of Piraeus. Prof. Kaldellis is also the scientific director (for TEI of Piraeus) of the MSc in Energy program organized by Heriot-Watt University and TEI of Piraeus. His scientific expertise is in the fields of energy and the environment. His research interests include feasibility analysis of energy sector applications; technological progress in wind, hydro, and solar energy markets; hybrid energy systems; energy storage issues; social attitudes toward renewable energy applications; and environmental technology–atmospheric pollution. He has participated in numerous research projects, funded by the European Union, European/Greek Industries, and the Greek State. Prof. Kaldellis has published six books concerning renewable energy applications and environmental protection. He is also the author of more than 100 scientific/research papers in international peer-reviewed journals and more than 300 papers for international scientific conferences. During the last decade, he was also a member of the Scientific Committee of the Hellenic Society of Mechanical–Electrical Engineers as well as a member of the organizing and scientific committee of several national and international conferences. He is currently a member of the editorial board of the *Renewable Energy International* journal and reviewer in more than 40 international journals in the energy and environment sector. He is the editor of the book *Stand-Alone and Hybrid Wind Energy Systems: Technology, Energy Storage and Applications* that has recently been published.

Dr. Soteris A. Kalogirou is a senior lecturer at the Department of Mechanical Engineering and Materials Science and Engineering at the Cyprus University of Technology, Limassol, Cyprus. He received his Higher Technical Institute (HTI) degree in mechanical engineering in 1982, his MPhil in mechanical engineering from the Polytechnic of Wales in 1991, and his PhD in mechanical engineering from the University of Glamorgan in 1995. In June 2011, he received the title of DSc from the University of Glamorgan.

For more than 25 years, he has been actively involved in research in the area of solar energy and particularly in flat-plate and concentrating collectors, solar water heating, solar steam generating systems, desalination, and absorption cooling. Additionally, since 1995, he has been involved in pioneering research dealing with the use of artificial intelligence methods, such as artificial neural networks, genetic algorithms, and fuzzy logic, for the modeling and performance prediction of energy and solar energy systems.

He has 29 books and book contributions and published 225 papers, 97 in international scientific journals and 128 in refereed conference proceedings. To date he has received more than 2550 citations on this work. He is Executive Editor of *Energy*, Associate Editor of *Renewable Energy*, and Editorial Board Member of another 11 journals. He is the editor of the book *Artificial Intelligence in Energy and Renewable Energy Systems*, published by Nova Science Inc.; coeditor of the book *Soft Computing in Green and Renewable Energy Systems*, published by Springer; and author of the book *Solar Energy Engineering: Processes and Systems*, published by Academic Press of Elsevier.

He has been a member of the World Renewable Energy Network (WREN) since 1992 and is a member of the Chartered Institution of Building Services Engineers (CIBSE), the American Society of Heating Refrigeration and Air-Conditioning Engineers (ASHRAE), the Institute of Refrigeration (IoR), and the International Solar Energy Society (ISES).

Dr. Andrew Cruden, a British citizen, was born in 1968. He obtained his BEng, MSc, and PhD in electrical engineering from the University of Strathclyde and CEng, MIEE Dr. Cruden is a past member of BSI GEL/105 Committee on Fuel Cells and Committee member of the IET Scotland Power Section. He is Director of the Scottish Hydrogen and Fuel Cell Association (SHFCA; www.shfca.org.uk) and Director of Argyll, Lomond and the Islands Energy Agency (www.alienergy.org.uk).

Dr. Cruden has been active in the field of hydrogen and fuel cells since 1995, when he acted as a consultant for Zevco Ltd., providing assistance with power electronic interfaces for early fuel cell systems. Later in 1998, he helped found the Scottish Fuel Cell Consortium (SFCC), supported by the Scottish Enterprise Energy Team, which ultimately developed a battery/fuel cell hybrid electric vehicle based on an AC Cobra kit car. The experience and contacts from the SFCC eventually gave rise to the formation of the Scottish Hydrogen and Fuel Cell Association (SHFCA), a trade body for the industry to promote and commercialize Scottish expertise in this field. Dr. Cruden was the founding chairman of the SHFCA.

Dr. Cruden is currently investigating alkaline electrolyzers in terms of improving their part load efficiency and lifetime when powered by variable renewable power sources, for example, wind turbines, as part of a £5 million EPSRC Supergen project on the 'Delivery of Sustainable Hydrogen' (EP/G01244X/1). He is also working with a colleague within Electronic and Electrical Engineering (EEE) at Strathclyde, studying the concept of vehicle-to-grid energy storage, as a mechanism not only to allow controlled load leveling on the power system, but also to potentially 'firm' up renewable energy generation. This work is supported by two research grants, an international E.On Research Initiative 2007 award and an ESPRC grant (EP/F062133/1).

Dr. Cruden is a senior lecturer within the Department of Electronic and Electrical Engineering at the University of Strathclyde. His current fields of research are modeling fuel cell and electrolyzer systems, fuel cell combined heat and power (CHP) systems, power electronic devices for interfacing both vehicular and stationary fuel cell systems, condition monitoring systems for renewable energy sources (i.e., wind turbines as part of EPSRC Supergen on Wind Energy Technologies, EP/D034566/1), and energy management systems for hybrid electric vehicles.

His areas of expertise include hydrogen-powered fuel cells and electrolyzers, energy storage for electric vehicles, and renewable energy generation.

Professor Dermot J. Roddy, BSc, PhD, CEng, FIET, joined Newcastle University as Science City Professor of Energy in 2008 after a period of some 20 years in the energy industry and petrochemical sectors. He is also Director of the Sir Joseph Swan Centre for Energy Research, which integrates energy research across Newcastle University and links with a powerful external industrial base in the energy sector. Outside of the university he is Chairman of Northeast Biofuels, Finance Director of the UK Hydrogen Association, and Vice-President of the Northern England Electricity Supply Companies Association. Prior to coming to Newcastle University, he was Chief Executive of Renew Tees Valley Ltd. – a company which he set up in 2003 to create a viable and vibrant economy in the Tees Valley based on renewable energy and recycling – where he was instrumental in a wide range of major renewable energy and low-carbon projects relating to biomass, biofuels, hydrogen, carbon capture and storage, wind, and advanced waste processing technologies. From 1998 to 2002, he ran the crude oil refinery on Teesside as a site director for a $5 billion turnover facility before moving to the Netherlands to work on Petroplus' international growth plans. Roddy's experience in the petrochemical industry began in 1985, involving a variety of UK and international roles in operations, engineering, and technology with ICI and others. Prior to that he developed leading-edge technology at Queen's University, Belfast, for optimization and control in aerospace applications.

André G. H. Lejeune was born on 2 August 1942 in Belgium. He was graduated in 1967 as a civil engineer, in 1972 as doctor in applied sciences (PhD), and in 1973 as master in oceanography in the University of Liège in Belgium. He was appointed full-time professor in the same university in 1976, and was visitor professor at the UNESCO–IHE Institute for Water Education in the Netherlands and Ecole Polytechnique Fédérale de Lausanne (EPFL) in Switzerland. Within the framework of his activities of professor, director of the Hydraulic Constructions and Hydraulic Research Laboratory, and expert, he took part in studies of dams and hydraulic structures and went on site in more than 90 countries of the world. In particular, he was for the last 6 years the chairman of the Technical Committee on Hydraulics for Dams in ICOLD (International Commission of Large Dams). He is a member of the Belgian Royal Academy of Sciences. He made his PhD thesis in hydraulic numerical modelization. This thesis received the Lorenz G. Straub Award in Minneapolis, USA (H. Einstein Jr. was a member of the Jury), and was used in particular by Chinese colleagues in the Three Gorges Project. Due to his practice and experience, he has a very complete knowledge of the hydraulic phenomena modelizations through both numerical and physical means.

With his wife, he has 3 children and 11 grandchildren. He likes books, tennis, and diving.

Thorsteinn I. Sigfusson is an internationally recognised physicist, educated in Copenhagen, Denmark, and Cambridge, UK. He is Director-General of the Innovation Center, Iceland and Professor of physics at the University of Iceland. He has been a visiting professor at Columbia University, New York, and he is currently the lead scientist in a prize-winning energy technology project performed at Tomsk Polytechnic University in Tomsk, Russia.

He has been a key figure in the introduction of new ideas and opportunities in the further greening of Icelandic society through the energy industry, and instrumental in the challenge of saving imported hydrocarbons by focusing on hydrogen from renewable energy.

He has started over a dozen start-up companies from research in Iceland and chaired various international societies in alternative energy. Among his achievements in geothermal energy is the construction of the world's largest solid-state thermoelectric generator powered with geothermal steam in southern Iceland. At the Innovation Center, Iceland, efforts are made to develop materials to withstand erosion in geothermal environments.

AbuBakr S. Bahaj is Professor of Sustainable Energy at the University of Southampton. After completing his PhD, he was employed by the University, progressing from a researcher to a personnel chair of Sustainable Energy. Over the past 20 years, Prof. Bahaj has established the energy theme within the University and directed his Sustainable Energy Research Group (SERG, www.energy.soton.ac.uk), which is now considered to be one of the United Kingdoms's leading university-based research groups in renewable energy and energy in buildings. He initiated and managed research in ocean energy conversion (resources, technologies, and impacts), photovoltaics, energy in buildings, and impacts of climate change on the built environment in the University. This work has resulted in over 230 articles published in academic refereed journals and conference series of international standing (see www.energy.soton.ac.uk).

Prof. Bahaj is the head of the Energy and Climate Change Division (ECCD) within the highly rated Faculty of Engineering and the Environment – Civil Engineering and the Environment – (www.civil.soton.ac.uk/research/divisions/divlist.asp?ResearchGroupID=1) (second in the United Kingdom, Research Assessment Exercise in 2008, with 80% of research judged to be either 'World Leading' or 'Internationally Excellent'). The aims of the Division and SERG are to promote and execute fundamental and applied research and preindustrial development in the areas of energy resources, technologies, energy efficiency, and the impact of climate change.

Prof. Bahaj is an experienced research team director and has many internationally focused research projects including collaborative projects in China, the European Union, the Middle East, and Africa. He also coordinated (2006–10) the United Kingdom's Engineering and Physical Sciences Research Council (EPSRC), Ecoregion Research Networks that aim to develop research themes and projects to study eco-city development encompassing resource assessment, technology pathways for the production and conservation of energy, planning, and social and economic studies required in establishing eco-regions in China and elsewhere (http://www.eco-networks.org). He is a founding member of the Sino-UK Low Carbon City Development Cooperation (LCCD) which aims to promote and undertake research into pathways for low-carbon development in Chinese cities. His work also encompasses an ongoing multimillion pound program in Africa, 'Energy for Development' for promoting and implementing village electrification systems, addressing villager's needs, and establishing coherent approaches to the commercial sustainability of the projects. This program is funded by the Research Councils and the UK Department for International Development (DFID; www.energyfordevelopment.net).

Prof. Bahaj is the editor-in-chief of the *International Journal of Sustainable Energy* and associate Editor of the *Renewable & Sustainable Energy Review*. He was on the editorial boards of the journals *Sustainable Cities and Society* and *Renewable Energy* (2005–11), and the United Kingdom's Institute of Civil Engineering journal *Energy* (2006–09). He was a member of the Tyndall Centre for Climate Change Research Supervisory Board (2005–10), and from 2001 to 2007 he was a member of the UK Government Department of Business, Enterprise and Regulatory Reform (now Department for Business Innovations and Skills, BIS), Technology Programmes Panels on Water (including ocean energy) and Solar Energy, now being administered by the Technology Strategy Board (TSB). Prof. Bahaj was the chair of the Technical Committees of the World Renewable Energy Congress – held in Glasgow (July 2008) and in Abu Dhabi (September 2010). He was a member of the Technical Committee of the 27th International Conference on Offshore Mechanics and Arctic Engineering (OMAE, 2008), a member of the management and technical committees of the European Wave and Tidal Energy Conferences (EWTEC, Porto, Portugal, September 2007; and Uppsala, Sweden, September 2009). He is also a member of the British Standards Institution (BSI) Committee GEL/82 on PV Energy Systems. Recently, at the invitation of the International Energy Agency, he has completed the 2008 status report on tidal stream energy conversion and in September 2009 was elected to chair the next EWTEC conference in the series – EWTEC2011 which was held in Southampton, 5–9 September 2011, and attended by around 500 participants.

To address training in the areas of energy and climate change Prof. Bahaj has coordinated and developed a set of MSc programs under the banner 'Energy and Sustainability' that address Energy Resources and Climate Change and Energy, Environment and Buildings.

CONTRIBUTORS FOR ALL VOLUMES

P Agnolucci
Imperial College London, London, UK

EO Ahlgren
Chalmers University of Technology, Gothenburg, Sweden

D Aklil
Pure Energy Center, Unst, Shetland Isles, UK

D-C Alarcón Padilla
Centro de Investigaciones Energéticas Medioambientales y Tecnológicas (CIEMAT), Plataforma Solar de Almeria, Almeria, Spain

K Alexander
University of Canterbury, Christchurch, New Zealand

S Alexopoulos
Aachen University of Applied Sciences, Jülich, Germany

A Altieri
UNICA – Brazilian Sugarcane Industry Association, São Paulo, Brazil

A Anthrakidis
Aachen University of Applied Sciences, Jülich, Germany

E Antolín
Universidad Politécnica de Madrid, Madrid, Spain

P Archambeau
University of Liège, Liège, Belgium

H Ármannsson
Iceland GeoSurvey (ISOR), Reykjavík, Iceland

MF Askew
Wolverhampton, UK

A Athienitis
Concordia University, Montreal, QC, Canada

G Axelsson
University of Iceland, Reykjavik, Iceland

V Badescu
Polytechnic University of Bucharest, Bucharest, Romania

AS Bahaj
The University of Southampton, Southampton, UK

P Banda
Instituto de Sistema Fotovoltaicos de Concentración (ISFOC), Puertollano, Spain

VG Belessiotis
'DEMOKRITOS' National Center for Scientific Research, Athens, Greece

P Berry
ADAS High Mowthorpe, Malton, UK

F Bidault
Imperial College London, London, UK

D Biro
Fraunhofer Institute for Solar Energy Systems, Freiburg, Germany

G Boschloo
Uppsala University, Uppsala, Sweden

C Boura
Aachen University of Applied Sciences, Jülich, Germany

E Bozorgzadeh
Iran Water and Power Resources Development Company (IWPCO), Tehran, Iran

CE Brewer
Iowa State University, Ames, IA, USA

M Börjesson
Chalmers University of Technology, Gothenburg, Sweden

RC Brown
Iowa State University, Ames, IA, USA

F Bueno
University of Burgos, Burgos, Spain

K Burke
NASA Glenn Research Center, Cleveland, OH, USA

LF Cabeza
GREA Innovació Concurrent, Universitat de Lleida, Lleida, Spain

L Candanedo
Dublin Institute of Technology, Dublin, Ireland

YG Caouris
University of Patras, Patras, Greece

UB Cappel
Uppsala University, Uppsala, Sweden

JA Carta
Universidad de Las Palmas de Gran Canaria, Las Palmas de Gran Canaria, Spain

P Chen
Dalian Institute of Chemical Physics, Dalian, China

DG Christakis
Wind Energy Laboratory, Technological Educational Institute of Crete, Crete, Greece

DA Chwieduk
Warsaw University of Technology, Warsaw, Poland

J Clark
University of York, York, UK

G Conibeer
University of New South Wales, Sydney, NSW, Australia

AJ Cruden
University of Strathclyde, Glasgow, UK

MC da Silva

B Davidsdottir
University of Iceland, Reykjavík, Iceland

O de la Rubia
Instituto de Sistema Fotovoltaicos de Concentración (ISFOC), Puertollano, Spain

E Despotou
Formerly of the European Photovoltaic Industry Association, Brussels, Belgium

BJ Dewals
University of Liège, Liège, Belgium

AL Dicks
The University of Queensland, Brisbane, QLD, Australia

R DiPippo
University of Massachusetts Dartmouth, Dartmouth, MA, USA

E Dunlop
European Commission DG Joint Research Centre, Ispra, Italy

NM Duteanu
Newcastle University, Newcastle upon Tyne, UK; University 'POLITEHNICA' Timisoara, Timisoara, Romania

LM Eaton
Oak Ridge National Laboratory, Oak Ridge, TN, USA

H-J Egelhaaf
Konarka Technologies GmbH, Nürnberg, Germany

T Ehara
Mizuho Information & Research Institute, Tokyo, Japan

B Erable
Newcastle University, Newcastle upon Tyne, UK; CNRS-Université de Toulouse, Toulouse, France

S Erpicum
University of Liège, Liège, Belgium

G Evans
NNFCC, Biocentre, Innovation Way, Heslington, York, UK

AFO Falcão
Instituto Superior Técnico, Technical University of Lisbon, Lisbon, Portugal

G Faninger
University of Klagenfurt, Klagenfurt, Austria; Vienna University of Technology, Vienna, Austria

GA Florides
Cyprus University of Technology, Limassol, Cyprus

ÓG Flóvenz
Iceland GeoSurvey (ISOR), Reykjavík, Iceland

RN Frese
VU University Amsterdam, Amsterdam, The Netherlands

Þ Friðriksson
Iceland GeoSurvey (ISOR), Reykjavík, Iceland

VM Fthenakis
Columbia University, New York, NY, USA; Brookhaven National Laboratory, Upton, NY, USA

M Fuamba
École Polytechnique de Montréal, Montreal, QC, Canada

A Fuller
University of Canterbury, Christchurch, New Zealand

LMC Gato
Instituto Superior Técnico, Technical University of Lisbon, Lisbon, Portugal

R Gazey
Pure Energy Center, Unst, Shetland Isles, UK

TA Gessert
National Renewable Energy Laboratory (NREL), Golden, CO, USA

MM Ghangrekar
*Newcastle University, Newcastle upon Tyne, UK;
Indian Institute of Technology, Kharagpur, India*

M Giannouli
University of Patras, Patras, Greece

EA Gibson
University of Nottingham, Nottingham UK

A Gil
Hydropower Generation Division of Iberdrola, Salamanca, Spain

SW Glunz
Fraunhofer Institute for Solar Energy Systems, Freiburg, Germany

JC Goldschmidt
Fraunhofer Institute for Solar Energy Systems ISE, Freiburg, Germany

R Gottschalg
Loughborough University, Leicestershire, UK

MA Green
The University of New South Wales, Sydney, NSW, Australia

J Göttsche
Aachen University of Applied Sciences, Jülich, Germany

J Guo
China Institute of Water Resources and Hydropower Research (IWHR), Beijing, China

A Hagfeldt
Uppsala University, Uppsala, Sweden

B Hagin
Ingénieur-Conseil, Lutry, Switzerland

K Hall
Technology Transition Corporation, Ltd., Tyne and Wear, UK

O Hamandjoda
University of Yaounde, Yaounde, Republic of Cameroon

AP Harvey
Newcastle University, Newcastle upon Tyne, UK

JA Hauch
Konarka Technologies GmbH, Nürnberg, Germany

D Heinemann
University of Oldenburg, Oldenburg, Germany

V Heller
Imperial College London, London, UK

GP Hersir
Iceland GeoSurvey (ÍSOR), Reykjavík, Iceland

T Heyer
Technical University of Dresden, Dresden, Germany

P Hilger
Aachen University of Applied Sciences, Jülich, Germany

B Hillring
Swedish University of Agricultural Sciences, Skinnskatteberg, Sweden

T Hino
CTI Engineering International Co., Ltd., Chu-o-Ku, Japan

LC Hirst
Imperial College London, London, UK

B Hoffschmidt
Aachen University of Applied Sciences, Jülich, Germany

H Horlacher
Technical University of Dresden, Dresden, Germany

N Hughes
Imperial College London, London, UK

SL Hui
Bechtel Civil Company, San Francisco, CA, USA

D Husmann
University of Wisconsin–Madison, Madison, WI, USA

JTS Irvine
University of St Andrews, St Andrews, UK

D Jacobs
Freie Universität Berlin, Berlin, Germany

Y Jestin
Advanced Photonics and Photovoltaics Group, Bruno Kessler Foundation, Trento, Italy

A Jäger-Waldau
Institution for Energy Transport, Ispra, Italy

S Jianxia
Design and Research Institute, Yangzhou City, Jiangsu Province, China

E Johnson
Pure Energy Center, Unst, Shetland Isles, UK

HF Kaan
TNO Energy, Comfort and Indoor Quality, Delft, The Netherlands

JK Kaldellis
Technological Education Institute of Piraeus, Athens, Greece

SA Kalogirou
Cyprus University of Technology, Limassol, Cyprus

HD Kambezidis
Institute of Environmental Research and Sustainable Development, Athens, Greece

M Kapsali
Technological Education Institute of Piraeus, Athens, Greece

M Karimirad
Norwegian University of Science and Technology, Trondheim, Norway

T Karlessi
National and Kapodistrian University of Athens, Athens, Greece

SN Karlsdóttir
Innovation Center Iceland, Iceland

D Al Katsaprakakis
Wind Energy Laboratory, Technological Educational Institute of Crete, Crete, Greece

O Kaufhold
Aachen University of Applied Sciences, Jülich, Germany

CA Kaufmann
Helmholtz Zentrum für Materialien und Energie GmbH, Berlin, Germany

KA Kavadias
Technological Education Institute of Piraeus, Athens, Greece

LL Kazmerski
National Renewable Energy Laboratory, Golden, CO, USA

A Kazmi
University of York, York, UK

K Kendall
University of Birmingham, Birmingham, UK

J Kenfack
University of Yaounde, Yaounde, Republic of Cameroon

R Kenny
European Commission DG Joint Research Centre, Ispra, Italy

HC Kim
Brookhaven National Laboratory, Upton, NY, USA

L Kloo
KTH—Royal Institute of Technology, Stockholm, Sweden

G Knothe
USDA Agricultural Research Service, Peoria, IL, USA

FR Kogler
Konarka Technologies GmbH, Nürnberg, Germany

D Kolokotsa
Technical University of Crete, Crete, Greece

K Komoto
Mizuho Information & Research Institute, Tokyo, Japan

E Kondili
Technological Education Institute of Piraeus, Athens, Greece

H Kristjánsdóttir
University of Iceland, Reykjavík, Iceland

LA Lamont
Petroleum Institute, Abu Dhabi, UAE

GA Landis
NASA Glenn Research Center, Cleveland, OH, USA

JGM Lee
Newcastle University, Newcastle upon Tyne, UK

G Leftheriotis
University of Patras, Patras, Greece

A Lejeune
University of Liège, Liège, Belgium

T Leo
FuelCell Energy Inc., Danbury, CT, USA

E Lester
The University of Nottingham, Nottingham, UK

E Lorenz
University of Oldenburg, Oldenburg, Germany

JW Lund
Geo-Heat Center, Oregon Institute of Technology, Klamath Falls, OR, USA

A Luque
Universidad Politécnica de Madrid, Madrid, Spain

BP Machado
Intertechne, Curitiba, PR, Brazil

FBL Mackay
GL Garrad Hassan, Bristol, UK

T-F Mahdi
École Polytechnique de Montréal, Montreal, QC, Canada

GG Maidment
London South Bank University, London, UK

A Malmgren
BioC Ltd, Cirencester, UK

C Manson-Whitton
Progressive Energy Ltd., Stonehouse, UK

Á Margeirsson
Magma Energy Iceland, Reykjanesbaer, Iceland

A Martí
Universidad Politécnica de Madrid, Madrid, Spain

M Martinez
Instituto de Sistema Fotovoltaicos de Concentración (ISFOC), Puertollano, Spain

S Mathew
University of Brunei Darussalam, Gadong, Brunei Darussalam

PH Middleton
University of Agder, Grimstad, Norway

R Mikalsen
Newcastle University, Newcastle upon Tyne, UK

D Milborrow
Lewes, East Sussex, UK

H Müllejans
European Commission DG Joint Research Centre, Ispra, Italy

V Molkov
University of Ulster, Newtownabbey, Northern Ireland, UK

M Moner-Girona
Joint Research Centre, European Commission, Institute for Energy and Transport, Ispra, Italy

PE Morthorst
Technical University of Denmark, Roskilde, Denmark

N Mortimer
North Energy Associates Ltd, Sheffield, UK

E Mullins
Teagasc, Oak Park Crops Research Centre, Carlow, Republic of Ireland

P Mulvihill
Pioneer Generation Ltd., Alexandra, New Zealand

DR Myers
National Renewable Energy Laboratory, USA

D Nash
University of Strathclyde, Glasgow, UK

GF Nemet
University of Wisconsin–Madison, Madison, WI, USA

H Nfaoui
Mohammed V University, Rabat, Morocco

T Nikolakakis
Columbia University, New York, NY, USA

X Niu
Changjiang Institute of Survey, Planning, Design and Research, Wuhan, China

B Norton
Dublin Institute of Technology, Dublin, Ireland

A Nuamah
The University of Nottingham, Nottingham, UK; RWE npower, Swindon, UK

B O'Connor
Aachen University of Applied Sciences, Jülich, Germany

O Olsson
Swedish University of Agricultural Sciences, Skinnskatteberg, Sweden

V Ortisi
Pure Energy Center, Unst, Shetland Isles, UK

H Ossenbrink
European Commission DG Joint Research Centre, Ispra, Italy

AG Paliatsos
Technological Education Institute of Piraeus, Athens, Greece

A Pandit
VU University Amsterdam, Amsterdam, The Netherlands

E Papanicolaou
'DEMOKRITOS' National Center for Scientific Research, Athens, Greece

A Paurine
London South Bank University, London, UK

N Pearsall
Northumbria University, Newcastle, UK

RJ Pearson
Lotus Engineering, Norwich, UK

RD Perlack
Oak Ridge National Laboratory, Oak Ridge, TN, USA

H Pettersson
Swerea IVF AB, Mölndal, Sweden

GS Philip
KCAET, Malapuram, Kerala, India

S Pillai
The University of New South Wales, Sydney, NSW, Australia

M Pirotton
University of Liège, Liège, Belgium

BG Pollet
University of Birmingham, Birmingham, UK

D Porter
Association of Electricity Producers, London, UK

A Pouliezos
Technical University of Crete, Hania, Greece

R Preu
Fraunhofer Institute for Solar Energy Systems, Freiburg, Germany

CM Ramos

C Rau
Aachen University of Applied Sciences, Jülich, Germany

AA Refaat
Cairo University, Giza, Egypt

TH Reijenga
BEARiD Architecten, Rotterdam, The Netherlands

AHME Reinders
Delft University of Technology, Delft, The Netherlands; University of Twente, Enschede, The Netherlands

G Riley
RWE npower, Swindon, UK

DJ Roddy
Newcastle University, Newcastle upon Tyne, UK

S Rolland
Alliance for Rural Electrification, Brussels, Belgium

A Roskilly
Newcastle University, Newcastle upon Tyne, UK

F Rubio
Instituto de Sistema Fotovoltaicos de Concentración (ISFOC), Puertollano, Spain

F Rulot
University of Liège, Liège, Belgium

L Rybach
GEOWATT AG, Zurich, Switzerland

M Santamouris
National and Kapodistrian University of Athens, Athens, Greece

J Sattler
Aachen University of Applied Sciences, Jülich, Germany

M Sauerborn
Aachen University of Applied Sciences, Jülich, Germany

TW Schmidt
The University of Sydney, Sydney, NSW, Australia

N Schofield
University of Manchester, Manchester, UK

REI Schropp
Utrecht University, Utrecht, The Netherlands

K Scott
Newcastle University, Newcastle upon Tyne, UK

SP Sen
NHPC Ltd., New Delhi, India

TI Sigfusson
Innovation Center, Reykjavik, Iceland

L Sims
Konarka Technologies GmbH, Nürnberg, Germany; Universität Augsburg, Augsburg, Germany

C Smith
NNFCC, Biocentre, Innovation Way, Heslington, York, UK

K Sæmundsson
Iceland GeoSurvey (ISOR), Reykjavík, Iceland

BK Sovacool
Vermont Law School, South Royalton, VT, USA

J Spink
Teagasc, Oak Park Crops Research Centre, Carlow, Republic of Ireland

JN Sørensen
Technical University of Denmark, Lyngby, Denmark

T Stallard
The University of Manchester, Manchester, UK

GS Stavrakakis
Technical University of Crete, Chania, Greece

R Steim
Konarka Technologies GmbH, Nürnberg, Germany

BJ Stokes
CNJV LLC, Washington, DC, USA

L Sun
KTH—Royal Institute of Technology, Stockholm, Sweden; Dalian University of Technology (DUT), Dalian, China

L Suo
Science and Technology Committee of the Ministry of Water Resources, Beijing, China

DT Swift-Hook
Kingston University, London, UK; World Renewable Energy Network, Brighton, UK

A Synnefa
National and Kapodistrian University of Athens, Athens, Greece

S Szabo
Joint Research Centre, European Commission, Institute for Energy and Transport, Ispra, Italy

MJY Tayebjee
The University of Sydney, Sydney, NSW, Australia

A Tesfai
University of St Andrews, St Andrews, UK

P Thornley
The University of Manchester, Manchester, UK

Y Tripanagnostopoulos
University of Patras, Patras, Greece

L Tsakalakos
General Electric – Global Research Center, New York, NY, USA

JWG Turner
Lotus Engineering, Norwich, UK

E Tzen
Centre for Renewable Energy Sources and Saving (CRES), Pikermi, Attica, Greece

T Unold
Helmholtz Zentrum für Materialien und Energie GmbH, Berlin, Germany

J van der Heide
imec vzw, Leuven, Belgium

P van der Vleuten
Free Energy Consulting, Eindhoven, The Netherlands

F Van Hulle
XP Wind Consultancy, Leuven, Belgium

GC van Kooten
University of Victoria, Victoria, BC, Canada

WGJHM van Sark
Utrecht University, Utrecht, The Netherlands

I Waller
FiveBarGate Consultants Ltd, Cleveland, UK

I Walsh
Opus International Consultants Ltd., New Zealand

Y Wang
Newcastle University, Newcastle upon Tyne, UK

T Wizelius
Gotland University, Visby, Sweden; Lund University, Lund, Sweden

LL Wright
University of Tennessee, Knoxville, TN, USA

H Xie
Changjiang Institute of Survey, Planning, Design and Research, Wuhan, China

M Yamaguchi
Toyota Technological Institute, Tempaku, Nagoya, Japan

P Yianoulis
University of Patras, Patras, Greece

EH Yu
Newcastle University, Newcastle upon Tyne, UK

H Yu
Newcastle University, Newcastle upon Tyne, UK

DP Zafirakis
Technological Education Institute of Piraeus, Athens, Greece

G Zaragoza
Centro de Investigaciones Energéticas Medioambientales y Tecnológicas (CIEMAT), Plataforma Solar de Almeria, Almeria, Spain

M Zeman
Delft University of Technology, Delft, The Netherlands

PREFACE

Comprehensive Renewable Energy is the only multivolume reference work of its type at a time when renewable energy sources are increasingly in demand and realistically sustainable, clean, and helping to combat climate change and global warming. Renewable energy investment has exceeded US$10 billion per year during the past 5 years. The World Renewable Energy Network (WREN) predicts that this figure is set to increase to US$20 billion per year by 2015.

As Editor-in-Chief, I have assembled an impressive world-class team of 154 volume editors and contributing authors for the eight volumes. They represent policy makers, researchers, industrialists, financiers, and heads of organizations from more than 80 countries to produce this definitive complete work in renewable energy covering the past, explaining the present, and giving the ideas and prospects of development for the future. There are more than 1000 references from books, journals, and the Internet within the eight volumes. *Comprehensive Renewable Energy* is full of color charts, illustrations, and photographs of real projects and research results from around the world. Each chapter has been painstakingly reviewed and checked for consistent high quality. The result is an authoritative overview that ties the literature together and provides the user with reliable background information and a citation resource.

The field of renewable energy research and development is represented by many journals that are directly and indirectly concerned with the field. But no reference work encompasses the entire field and unites the different areas of research through in-depth foundational reviews. *Comprehensive Renewable Energy* fills this vacuum, and is the definitive work for this subject area. It will help users apply context to diverse journal literature, aiding them in identifying areas for further research and development.

Research into renewable energy is spread across a number of different disciplines and subject areas. These areas do not always share a unique identifying factor or subject themselves to clear and concise definitions. This work unites the different areas of research and allows users, regardless of their background, to navigate through the most essential concepts with ease, saving them time and vastly improving their understanding so that they can move forward, whether in their research, development, manufacturing, or purchase of renewable energy.

The first volume is devoted to Photovoltaic Technology and is edited by Mr. Wilfried G. J. H. M. van Sark from the Netherlands. It consists of 38 chapters, written by 41 authors from Europe, the United States, Japan, China, India, Africa, and the Middle East. The topics covered range from the smallest applications to MW projects. A brief introduction and history is followed by chapters on finance and economics, solar resources, up- and downconversion, crystalline photovoltaic (PV) cells, luminescent concentrators, thin-film and multiple-junction plastic solar cells, dye-sensitized solar cells, bio-inspired converters, application of micro- and nanotechnology, building integrated photovoltaics (BIPV) application in architecture, and very large-scale PV systems. Without doubt, this is an impressive tour of an immense field.

Volume 2 is devoted to Wind Energy and is edited by Professor John K. Kaldellis from Greece. It consists of 22 chapters written by 22 authors, again from various parts of the world, covering all aspects of wind energy from small wind mills to very large wind farms. The volume includes chapters on the history of wind power, the potential of wind power, wind turbine development, aerodynamic analysis, mechanical and electrical loads, control systems, noise and testing, onshore and offshore wind systems, policy, industry, and special wind power applications.

Volume 3 is devoted to Solar Thermal Applications and the editor is Professor Soteris A. Kalogirou from Cyprus. It consists of 19 chapters written by 17 authors. All aspects of solar thermal energy and its applications are covered. The volume begins with solar energy as a source of heat and goes on to describe the history of thermal applications, low-temperature and high-temperature storage systems, selective coating, glazing, modeling and simulation, hot water systems, space heating and cooling, water desalination, industrial and agricultural applications, concentration power, heat pumps, and passive solar architecture. The authors have looked at the Sun from the thermal energy aspect and put together a very informative and up-to-date volume from which every interested person, no matter what their level of knowledge, can benefit.

Volume 4 is on Fuel Cells and Hydrogen Technology and is edited by Dr. Andrew Cruden from the United Kingdom. It consists of 14 chapters covering the following topics: introduction and perspectives on hydrogen and fuel cells; theory and application of alkaline fuel cells; application of proton exchange membrane (PEM) fuel cells; molten carbonate fuel cells; solid oxide fuel cells; microbial and biological fuel cells; storage of compressed gas and hydrogen; the economy and policy of hydrogen technology; hydrogen safety engineering and future progress; the use of hydrogen for transport; and hydrogen and fuel cell power electronics. The 14 chapters were written by 16 authors. All aspects of practice, innovative technology, and future guidelines for researchers and industry have been addressed in this definitive volume.

Volume 5 deals with the huge field of Biomass and Biofuels and is edited by Professor Dermot J. Roddy from the United Kingdom. This work consists of 21 chapters written by 23 authors, again covering all aspects of biomass and biofuels, including their past, present, and future. The volume explains the history and prospective future of biofuels; bioethanol development in Brazil; power generation from biomass; biomass co-firing stations; biomass world market; a critical assessment of biomass – combined heat and power (CHP) energy systems; the ethics of biofuel production – issues, constraints, and limitations; greenhouse gases life cycle analysis; six different solutions from gasification and pyrolysis; new processes in biomass-to-liquid technology; new processes in biofuel production; biofuels from waste materials; novel feedstocks and woody biomass; feedstocks with the potential of yield improvement; renewable fuels – an automotive prospective; and novel use of biofuels in a range of engine configurations. Under Expanding the Envelope, there are chapters on biochar, extracting additional value from biomass, and biomass to chemicals. Finally, the chapter on bioenergy policy development concludes the volume.

Volume 6 is concerned with Hydro Power and is edited by Professor André G. H. Lejeune from Belgium. This is the oldest of all the renewable energy applications and has progressed over the ages from pico-hydro of a few hundred watts to large- and mega-scale dams generating more than 3000 MW with innovative civil engineering capability. This volume consists of 18 chapters prepared by 21 authors. It contains introduction – benefits and constraints of hydropower, recent developments and achievements in hydraulic research in China, and the management of hydropower and its impacts through construction and operation. The volume then assesses nine hydropower schemes around the world: the Three Gorges Project in China; large hydropower plants of Brazil; hydropower in Iran – vision and strategy; the recent trend in developing hydropower in India; the evolution of hydropower in Spain; hydropower in Japan; hydropower in Canada; an overview of institutional structure reform of the Cameroon power sector and assessment; and hydropower reliability in Switzerland. Other important issues are covered: pumped storage power plants; simplified generic axial-flow microhydro turbines; the development of a small hydroelectric scheme at Horseshoe Bend, Teviot River, New Zealand; concrete durability in dam design structure; and long-term sediment management for sustainable hydropower.

Volume 7 deals with Geothermal Energy. The editor of this volume is Professor Thorsteinn I. Sigfusson from Iceland. The volume consists of 10 chapters, which are written by 15 different authors. It covers the following areas: introduction and the physics of geothermal resources and management during utilization; geothermal shallow systems – heat pumps; geothermal exploration techniques; corrosion, scaling, and material selection in geothermal power production; direct heat utilization of geothermal energy; geothermal power plants; geochemical aspects of geothermal utilization; geothermal cost and investment factors; and the role of sustainable geothermal development.

Volume 8 is devoted to Generating Electricity from the Oceans, edited by Professor AbuBakr S. Bahaj from the United Kingdom. It consists of six chapters written by five authors. The volume covers the historical aspects of wave energy conversion, resource assessment for wave energy, development of wave devices from initial conception to commercial demonstration, air turbines, and the economics of ocean energy.

One chapter is totally devoted to Renewable Energy Policy and Incentives. It is included in the first volume only. The author of this chapter is Mr. David Porter, Chief Executive of the Association of Electricity Producers in the United Kingdom, an author who has had vast experience of dealing with electricity generation in the United Kingdom over many years. He has advised the British Government on how to meet supply and demand of electricity and coordinate with all electricity producers regarding their sources and supply. The chapter outlines the types of mechanisms used to promote renewable energy and their use, the impact on their deployment, ensuring investor certainty, the potential for harmonizing support schemes, and the conclusion.

In short, my advice to anyone who wants to acquire comprehensive knowledge concerning renewable energy, no matter which subject or application, is that they should acquire this invaluable resource for their home, research center and laboratory, company, or library.

Professor Ali Sayigh BSc, DIC, PhD, FIE, FIEE, CEng
Chairman of WREC (World Renewable Energy Congress)
Director General of WREN (World Renewable Energy Network)
Chairman of IEI (The Institution of Engineers (India))
Editor-in-Chief of *Renewable Energy*
Editor-in-Chief of *Renewable Energy Magazine*

CONTENTS

Editor-in-Chief	v
Volume Editors	vii
Contributors for All Volumes	xi
Preface	xix

Volume 1   Photovoltaic Solar Energy

Renewable Energy

1.01	Renewable Energy Policy and Incentives *D Porter*	1

Photovoltaic Solar Energy

1.02	Introduction to Photovoltaic Technology *WGJHM van Sark*	5
1.03	Solar Photovoltaics Technology: No Longer an Outlier *LL Kazmerski*	13
1.04	History of Photovoltaics *LA Lamont*	31

Economics and Environment

1.05	Historical and Future Cost Dynamics of Photovoltaic Technology *GF Nemet and D Husmann*	47
1.06	Feed-In Tariffs and Other Support Mechanisms for Solar PV Promotion *D Jacobs and BK Sovacool*	73
1.07	Finance Mechanisms and Incentives for Photovoltaic Technologies in Developing Countries *M Moner-Girona, S Szabo, and S Rolland*	111
1.08	Environmental Impacts of Photovoltaic Life Cycles *VM Fthenakis and HC Kim*	143
1.09	Overview of the Global PV Industry *A Jäger-Waldau*	161
1.10	Vision for Photovoltaics in the Future *E Despotou*	179

1.11	Storage Options for Photovoltaics VM Fthenakis and T Nikolakakis	199

Resource and Potential

1.12	Solar Radiation Resource Assessment for Renewable Energy Conversion DR Myers	213
1.13	Prediction of Solar Irradiance and Photovoltaic Power E Lorenz and D Heinemann	239

Basics

1.14	Principles of Solar Energy Conversion LC Hirst	293
1.15	Thermodynamics of Photovoltaics V Badescu	315

Technology

1.16	Crystalline Silicon Solar Cells: State-of-the-Art and Future Developments SW Glunz, R Preu, and D Biro	353
1.17	Thin-Film Silicon PV Technology M Zeman and REI Schropp	389
1.18	Chalcopyrite Thin-Film Materials and Solar Cells T Unold and CA Kaufmann	399
1.19	Cadmium Telluride Photovoltaic Thin Film: CdTe TA Gessert	423
1.20	Plastic Solar Cells L Sims, H-J Egelhaaf, JA Hauch, FR Kogler, and R Steim	439
1.21	Mesoporous Dye-Sensitized Solar Cells A Hagfeldt, UB Cappel, G Boschloo, L Sun, L Kloo, H Pettersson, and EA Gibson	481
1.22	Multiple Junction Solar Cells M Yamaguchi	497
1.23	Application of Micro- and Nanotechnology in Photovoltaics L Tsakalakos	515
1.24	Upconversion TW Schmidt and MJY Tayebjee	533
1.25	Downconversion MJY Tayebjee, TW Schmidt, and G Conibeer	549
1.26	Down-Shifting of the Incident Light for Photovoltaic Applications Y Jestin	563
1.27	Luminescent Solar Concentrators JC Goldschmidt	587
1.28	Thermophotovoltaics J van der Heide	603
1.29	Intermediate Band Solar Cells E Antolín, A Martí, and A Luque	619
1.30	Plasmonics for Photovoltaics S Pillai and MA Green	641
1.31	Artificial Leaves: Towards Bio-Inspired Solar Energy Converters A Pandit and RN Frese	657

Applications

1.32	Design and Components of Photovoltaic Systems WGJHM van Sark	679
1.33	BIPV in Architecture and Urban Planning TH Reijenga and HF Kaan	697
1.34	Product-Integrated Photovoltaics AHME Reinders and WGJHM van Sark	709
1.35	Very Large-Scale Photovoltaic Systems T Ehara, K Komoto, and P van der Vleuten	733
1.36	Concentration Photovoltaics M Martinez, O de la Rubia, F Rubio, and P Banda	745
1.37	Solar Power Satellites GA Landis	767
1.38	Performance Monitoring N Pearsall and R Gottschalg	775
1.39	Standards in Photovoltaic Technology H Ossenbrink, H Müllejans, R Kenny, and E Dunlop	787

Volume 2 Wind Energy

2.01	Wind Energy – Introduction JK Kaldellis	1
2.02	Wind Energy Contribution in the Planet Energy Balance and Future Prospects JK Kaldellis and M Kapsali	11
2.03	History of Wind Power DT Swift-Hook	41
2.04	Wind Energy Potential H Nfaoui	73
2.05	Wind Turbines: Evolution, Basic Principles, and Classifications S Mathew and GS Philip	93
2.06	Energy Yield of Contemporary Wind Turbines DP Zafirakis, AG Paliatsos, and JK Kaldellis	113
2.07	Wind Parks Design, Including Representative Case Studies D Al Katsaprakakis and DG Christakis	169
2.08	Aerodynamic Analysis of Wind Turbines JN Sørensen	225
2.09	Mechanical-Dynamic Loads M Karimirad	243
2.10	Electrical Parts of Wind Turbines GS Stavrakakis	269
2.11	Wind Turbine Control Systems and Power Electronics A Pouliezos	329
2.12	Testing, Standardization, Certification in Wind Energy F Van Hulle	371
2.13	Design and Implementation of a Wind Power Project T Wizelius	391
2.14	Offshore Wind Power Basics M Kapsali and JK Kaldellis	431

2.15	Wind Energy Economics D Milborrow	469
2.16	Environmental-Social Benefits/Impacts of Wind Power E Kondili and JK Kaldellis	503
2.17	Wind Energy Policy GC van Kooten	541
2.18	Wind Power Integration JA Carta	569
2.19	Stand-Alone, Hybrid Systems KA Kavadias	623
2.20	Wind Power Industry and Markets PE Morthorst	657
2.21	Trends, Prospects, and R&D Directions in Wind Turbine Technology JK Kaldellis and DP Zafirakis	671
2.22	Special Wind Power Applications E Kondili	725

Volume 3 Solar Thermal Systems: Components and Applications

Solar Thermal Systems

3.01	Solar Thermal Systems: Components and Applications – Introduction SA Kalogirou	1
3.02	Solar Resource HD Kambezidis	27
3.03	History of Solar Energy VG Belessiotis and E Papanicolaou	85

Components

3.04	Low Temperature Stationary Collectors YG Caouris	103
3.05	Low Concentration Ratio Solar Collectors SA Kalogirou	149
3.06	High Concentration Solar Collectors B Hoffschmidt, S Alexopoulos, J Göttsche, M Sauerborn, and O Kaufhold	165
3.07	Thermal Energy Storage LF Cabeza	211
3.08	Photovoltaic/Thermal Solar Collectors Y Tripanagnostopoulos	255
3.09	Solar Selective Coatings P Yianoulis, M Giannouli, and SA Kalogirou	301
3.10	Glazings and Coatings G Leftheriotis and P Yianoulis	313
3.11	Modeling and Simulation of Passive and Active Solar Thermal Systems A Athienitis, SA Kalogirou, and L Candanedo	357

Applications

3.12	Solar Hot Water Heating Systems G Faninger	419
3.13	Solar Space Heating and Cooling Systems SA Kalogirou and GA Florides	449
3.14	Solar Cooling and Refrigeration Systems GG Maidment and A Paurine	481
3.15	Solar-Assisted Heat Pumps DA Chwieduk	495
3.16	Solar Desalination E Tzen, G Zaragoza, and D-C Alarcón Padilla	529
3.17	Industrial and Agricultural Applications of Solar Heat B Norton	567
3.18	Concentrating Solar Power B Hoffschmidt, S Alexopoulos, C Rau, J Sattler, A Anthrakidis, C Boura, B O'Connor, and P Hilger	595
3.19	Passive Solar Architecture D Kolokotsa, M Santamouris, A Synnefa, and T Karlessi	637

Volume 4 Fuel Cells and Hydrogen Technology

4.01	Fuel Cells and Hydrogen Technology – Introduction AJ Cruden	1
4.02	Current Perspective on Hydrogen and Fuel Cells K Burke	13
4.03	Hydrogen Economics and Policy N Hughes and P Agnolucci	45
4.04	Hydrogen Safety Engineering: The State-of-the-Art and Future Progress V Molkov	77
4.05	Hydrogen Storage: Compressed Gas D Nash, D Aklil, E Johnson, R Gazey, and V Ortisi	111
4.06	Hydrogen Storage: Liquid and Chemical P Chen	137
4.07	Alkaline Fuel Cells: Theory and Application F Bidault and PH Middleton	159
4.08	PEM Fuel Cells: Applications AL Dicks	183
4.09	Molten Carbonate Fuel Cells: Theory and Application T Leo	227
4.10	Solid Oxide Fuel Cells: Theory and Materials A Tesfai and JTS Irvine	241
4.11	Biological and Microbial Fuel Cells K Scott, EH Yu, MM Ghangrekar, B Erable, and NM Duteanu	257
4.12	Hydrogen and Fuel Cells in Transport K Kendall and BG Pollet	281
4.13	H_2 and Fuel Cells as Controlled Renewables: FC Power Electronics N Schofield	295
4.14	Future Perspective on Hydrogen and Fuel Cells K Hall	331

Volume 5 Biomass and Biofuel Production

Biomass and Biofuels

5.01	Biomass and Biofuels – Introduction *DJ Roddy*	1
5.02	Historical Perspectives on Biofuels *G Knothe*	11

Case Studies

5.03	Bioethanol Development in Brazil *A Altieri*	15
5.04	Biomass Power Generation *A Malmgren and G Riley*	27
5.05	Biomass Co-Firing *A Nuamah, A Malmgren, G Riley, and E Lester*	55

Issues, Constraints & Limitations

5.06	A Global Bioenergy Market *O Olsson and B Hillring*	75
5.07	Biomass CHP Energy Systems: A Critical Assessment *M Börjesson and EO Ahlgren*	87
5.08	Ethics of Biofuel Production *I Waller*	99
5.09	Life Cycle Analysis Perspective on Greenhouse Gas Savings *N Mortimer*	109

Technology Solutions – New Processes

5.10	Biomass Gasification and Pyrolysis *DJ Roddy and C Manson-Whitton*	133
5.11	Biomass to Liquids Technology *G Evans and C Smith*	155
5.12	Intensification of Biofuel Production *AP Harvey and JGM Lee*	205
5.13	Biofuels from Waste Materials *AA Refaat*	217

Technology Solutions – Novel Feedstocks

5.14	Woody Biomass *LL Wright, LM Eaton, RD Perlack, and BJ Stokes*	263
5.15	Potential for Yield Improvement *J Spink, E Mullins, and P Berry*	293

Technology Solutions – Novel End Uses

5.16	Renewable Fuels: An Automotive Perspective *RJ Pearson and JWG Turner*	305
5.17	Use of Biofuels in a Range of Engine Configurations *A Roskilly, Y Wang, R Mikalsen, and H Yu*	343

Expanding the Envelope

5.18	Biochar CE Brewer and RC Brown	357
5.19	Extracting Additional Value from Biomass MF Askew	385
5.20	Biomass to Chemicals A Kazmi and J Clark	395
5.21	Bioenergy Policy Development P Thornley	411

Volume 6 Hydro Power

Hydro Power

6.01	Hydro Power – Introduction A Lejeune	1

Constraints of Hydropower Development

6.02	Hydro Power: A Multi Benefit Solution for Renewable Energy A Lejeune and SL Hui	15
6.03	Management of Hydropower Impacts through Construction and Operation H Horlacher, T Heyer, CM Ramos, and MC da Silva	49

Hydropower Schemes Around the World

6.04	Large Hydropower Plants of Brazil BP Machado	93
6.05	Overview of Institutional Structure Reform of the Cameroon Power Sector and Assessments J Kenfack and O Hamandjoda	129
6.06	Recent Hydropower Solutions in Canada M Fuamba and TF Mahdi	153
6.07	The Three Gorges Project in China L Suo, X Niu, and H Xie	179
6.08	The Recent Trend in Development of Hydro Plants in India SP Sen	227
6.09	Hydropower Development in Iran: Vision and Strategy E Bozorgzadeh	253
6.10	Hydropower Development in Japan T Hino	265
6.11	Evolution of Hydropower in Spain A Gil and F Bueno	309
6.12	Hydropower in Switzerland B Hagin	343

Design Concepts

6.13	Long-Term Sediment Management for Sustainable Hydropower F Rulot, BJ Dewals, S Erpicum, P Archambeau, and M Pirotton	355
6.14	Durability Design of Concrete Hydropower Structures S Jianxia	377
6.15	Pumped Storage Hydropower Developments T Hino and A Lejeune	405

6.16	Simplified Generic Axial-Flow Microhydro Turbines A Fuller and K Alexander	435
6.17	Development of a Small Hydroelectric Scheme at Horseshoe Bend, Teviot River, Central Otago, New Zealand P Mulvihill and I Walsh	467
6.18	Recent Achievements in Hydraulic Research in China J Guo	485

Volume 7 Geothermal Energy

7.01	Geothermal Energy – Introduction TI Sigfusson	1
7.02	The Physics of Geothermal Energy G Axelsson	3
7.03	Geothermal Energy Exploration Techniques ÓG Flóvenz, GP Hersir, K Sæmundsson, H Ármannsson, and Þ Friðriksson	51
7.04	Geochemical Aspects of Geothermal Utilization H Ármannsson	95
7.05	Direct Heat Utilization of Geothermal Energy JW Lund	169
7.06	Shallow Systems: Geothermal Heat Pumps L Rybach	187
7.07	Geothermal Power Plants R DiPippo	207
7.08	Corrosion, Scaling, and Material Selection in Geothermal Power Production SN Karlsdóttir	239
7.09	Geothermal Cost and Investment Factors H Kristjánsdóttir and Á Margeirsson	259
7.10	Sustainable Energy Development: The Role of Geothermal Power B Davidsdottir	271

Volume 8 Ocean Energy

8.01	Generating Electrical Power from Ocean Resources AS Bahaj	1
8.02	Historical Aspects of Wave Energy Conversion AFO Falcão	7
8.03	Resource Assessment for Wave Energy EBL Mackay	11
8.04	Development of Wave Devices from Initial Conception to Commercial Demonstration V Heller	79
8.05	Air Turbines AFO Falcão and LMC Gato	111
8.06	Economics of Ocean Energy T Stallard	151
Index		171

3.01 Solar Thermal Systems: Components and Applications – Introduction

SA Kalogirou, Cyprus University of Technology, Limassol, Cyprus

© 2012 Elsevier Ltd. All rights reserved.

3.01.1	The Sun	2
3.01.2	Energy-Related Environmental Problems	3
3.01.2.1	Acid Rain	4
3.01.2.2	Ozone Layer Depletion	4
3.01.2.3	Global Climate Change	5
3.01.2.4	Renewable Energy Technologies	5
3.01.2.4.1	Social and economic development	6
3.01.2.4.2	Land restoration	6
3.01.2.4.3	Reduced air pollution	6
3.01.2.4.4	Abatement of global warming	6
3.01.2.4.5	Fuel supply diversity	6
3.01.2.4.6	Reducing the risks of nuclear weapons proliferation	6
3.01.3	Environmental Characteristics of Solar Energy	7
3.01.3.1	Equation of Time	8
3.01.3.2	Longitude Correction	8
3.01.3.3	Solar Angles	8
3.01.3.3.1	Declination angle, δ	10
3.01.3.3.2	Hour angle, h	11
3.01.3.3.3	Solar altitude angle, α	11
3.01.3.3.4	Solar azimuth angle, z	12
3.01.3.3.5	Sun rise and set times and day length	12
3.01.3.3.6	Incidence angle, θ	12
3.01.3.4	The Incidence Angle for Moving Surfaces	13
3.01.3.4.1	Full tracking	14
3.01.3.4.2	N–S axis tilted/tilt daily adjusted	14
3.01.3.4.3	N–S axis polar/E–W tracking	14
3.01.3.4.4	E–W axis horizontal/N–S tracking	16
3.01.3.4.5	N–S axis horizontal/E–W tracking	17
3.01.3.5	Sun Path Diagrams	17
3.01.4	Solar Radiation	18
3.01.4.1	Thermal Radiation	18
3.01.4.2	Transparent Plates	21
3.01.5	The Solar Resource	22
3.01.5.1	Typical Meteorological Year	22
3.01.5.2	Typical Meteorological Year – Second Generation	23
References		24

Glossary

Altitude angle The angle between the line joining the center of the solar disk to the point of observation at any given instant and the horizontal plane through that point of observation.

Azimuth angle Angle between the north–south line at a given location and the projection of the sun–earth line in the horizontal plane.

Declination Angle subtended between the earth–sun line and the plane of the equator (north positive).

Hour angle Angle between the sun projection on the equatorial plane at a given time and the sun projection on the same plane at solar noon.

Incident angle The angle between the sun's rays and a line normal to the irradiated surface.

Local solar time System of astronomical time in which the sun always crosses the true north–south meridian at 12 noon. This system of time differs from local clock time according to longitude, time zone, and equation of time.

Radiation Emission or transfer of energy in the form of electromagnetic wave.

Radiosity The rate at which radiant energy leaves a surface per unit area by combined emission, reflection and transmission (W/m^2).

Solar radiation Radiant energy received from the sun both directly as beam component and diffusely by scattering from the sky and reflection from the ground.
Sun-path diagram Diagram of solar altitude versus solar azimuth, showing the position of the sun as a function of time for various dates of the year.
Transmittance The ratio of the radiant energy transmitted by a given material to the radiant energy incident on a surface of that material. Depends on the angle of incidence.
Zenith angle Angular distance of the sun from the vertical.

3.01.1 The Sun

The sun is a sphere of intensely hot gaseous matter, which as shown in **Figure 1**, and has a diameter of 1.39×10^9 m. The sun is about 1.5×10^8 km away from earth so, as thermal radiation travels with the speed of light in vacuum, after leaving the sun, solar energy reaches our planet in 8 min and 20 s. As observed from the earth, the sun disk forms an angle of 32 min of a degree. This is important in many applications, especially in concentrator optics where the sun cannot be considered as a point source, and even this small angle is significant in the analysis of the optical behavior of the collector. The sun has an effective blackbody temperature of 5762 K [1]. The temperature in the central region is much higher and it is estimated at 8×10^6 to 40×10^6 K. In effect, the sun is a continuous fusion reactor in which hydrogen is turned into helium. The sun's total energy output is 3.8×10^{20} MW, which is equal to 63 MW m^{-2} of the sun's surface. This energy radiates outward in all directions. The earth receives only a tiny fraction of the total radiation emitted equal to 1.7×10^{14} kW [1]; however, even with this small fraction, it is estimated that 84 min of solar radiation falling on earth is equal to the world energy demand for 1 year. As seen from the earth, the sun rotates around its axis about once every 4 weeks.

Since prehistory, the sun has dried and preserved man's food. It has also evaporated sea water to yield salt. Since man began to reason, he has recognized the sun as a motive power behind every natural phenomenon. This is why many of the prehistoric tribes considered Sun as 'God'. Many scripts of ancient Egypt say that the Great Pyramid, one of man's greatest engineering achievements, was built as a stairway to the sun [2].

Man realized that a good use of solar energy was to his benefit, from prehistoric times. The Greek historian Xenophon in his 'memorabilia' records some of the teachings of the Greek Philosopher Socrates (470–399 BC) regarding the correct orientation of dwellings in order to have houses that were cool in summer and warm in winter.

Basically, all the forms of energy in the world as we know it are solar in origin. Oil, coal, natural gas, and woods were originally produced by photosynthetic processes, followed by complex chemical reactions in which decaying vegetation was subjected to very high temperatures and pressures over a long period of time [1]. Even the wind and tide energy have a solar origin since they are caused by differences in temperature in various regions of the earth.

The greatest advantage of solar energy as compared with other forms of energy is that it is clean and can be supplied without any environmental pollution. Over the past century, fossil fuels have provided most of our energy because these are much cheaper and more convenient than energy from alternative energy sources, and until recently, environmental pollution has been of little concern.

Twelve winter days of 1973 changed the economic relation of fuel and energy when the Egyptian army stormed across the Suez Canal on 12 October provoking an international crisis and for the first time, involved as part of Arab strategy, the threat of the 'oil weapon'. Both the price and the political weapon issues quickly came to a head when the six Gulf members of the Organizations of Petroleum Exporting Countries (OPEC) met in Kuwait and quickly abandoned the idea of holding any more price consultations with the oil companies, announcing that they were raising the price of their crude oil by 70%.

The reason for the rapid increase in oil demand occurred mainly because increasing quantities of oil, produced at very low cost, became available during the 1950s and 1960s from the Middle East and North Africa. For the consuming countries, imported oil was cheap compared with indigenously produced energy from solid fuels.

But the main problem is that proved reserves of oil, gas, and coal at current rates of consumption would be adequate to meet demand for another 40, 60, and 250 years, respectively. If we try to see the implications of these limited reserves, we will be faced with a situation in which the price of fuels will be accelerating as the reserves are decreased. Considering that the price of oil has become firmly established as the price leader for all fuel prices, then the conclusion is that energy prices will increase over the next decades at something greater than the rate of inflation or even more. Additional to this is also the concern about the environmental pollution caused by the burning of the fossil fuels. This issue is examined in Section 3.01.2.

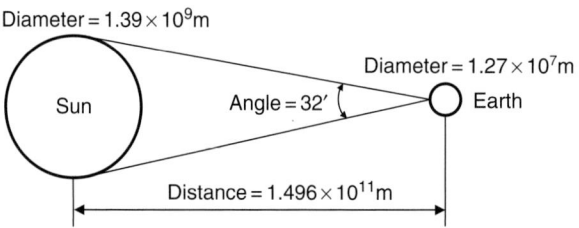

Figure 1 Sun–earth relationships.

In addition to the thousands of ways in which the sun's energy has been used by both nature and man through time, to grow food or dry clothes, it has also been deliberately harnessed to perform a number of other jobs. Solar energy is used to heat and cool buildings (both active and passive), to heat water for domestic and industrial uses, to heat swimming pool water, to power refrigerators, to operate heat engines, to desalinate seawater, to generate electricity, and many more.

There are many alternative energy sources that can be used instead of fossil fuels. The decision as to what type of energy source should be utilized, in each case, should be made on the basis of economic, environmental, and safety considerations. Because of the desirable environmental and safety aspects, it is widely believed that solar energy should be utilized instead of other alternative energy forms, even when the costs involved are slightly higher.

3.01.2 Energy-Related Environmental Problems

Energy is considered a prime agent in the generation of wealth and a significant factor in economic development. The importance of energy in economic development is recognized universally, and historical data verify that there is a strong relationship between the availability of energy and economic activity. Although at the early 1970s, after the oil crisis, the concern was on the cost of energy, during the past two decades the risk and reality of environmental degradation have become more apparent. The growing evidence of environmental problems is due to a combination of several factors and mainly is due to the increase of the world population, energy consumption, and industrial activities. Achieving solutions to environmental problems that humanity faces today requires long-term potential actions for sustainable development. In this respect, renewable energy resources appear to be one of the most efficient and effective solutions.

A few years ago, most environmental analysis and legal control instruments concentrated on conventional pollutants such as sulfur dioxide (SO_2), nitrogen oxides (NO_x), particulates, and carbon monoxide (CO). Recently however, environmental concern has extended to the control of hazardous air pollutants, which are usually toxic chemical substances which are harmful even in small doses, as well as to other globally significant pollutants such as carbon dioxide (CO_2). A detailed description of these gaseous and particulate pollutants and their impacts on the environment and human life is presented by Dincer [3, 4].

In June 1992, the United Nations Conference on Environment and Development (UNCED) held in Rio de Janeiro, Brazil, addressed the challenges of achieving worldwide sustainable development. The goal of sustainable development cannot be realized without major changes in the world's energy system. Accordingly, *Agenda 21*, which was adopted by UNCED, called for

> new policies or programs, as appropriate, to increase the contribution of environmentally safe and sound and cost-effective energy systems, particularly new and renewable ones, through less polluting and more efficient energy production, transmission, distribution, and use.

One of the most widely accepted definitions of sustainable development is:

> development that meets the needs of the present without compromising the ability of future generations to meet their own needs.

There are many factors that can help to achieve sustainable development, and nowadays, one of the main factors that must be considered is energy, and one of the most important issues is the requirement for a supply of energy that is fully sustainable [5, 6]. A secure supply of energy is generally agreed to be a necessary, but not a sufficient requirement for development within a society. Furthermore, for a sustainable development within a society, it is required that a sustainable supply of energy and effective and efficient utilization of energy resources are secured. Such a supply in the long term should be readily available at reasonable cost, be sustainable, and able to be utilized for all the required tasks without causing negative societal impacts. This is why there is a close connection between renewable sources of energy and sustainable development.

Sustainable development is a serious policy concept. In addition to the definition given above, it can be considered as development which must not carry the seeds of destruction because such development is unsustainable. The concept of sustainability has its origin in fisheries and forest management in which prevailing management practices, such as over fishing or single species cultivation, work for a limited time, then yield diminishing results and eventually endangers the resource. Therefore, sustainable management practices should not aim for maximum yield in the short run, but smaller yields that can be sustained over time.

Pollution depends on energy consumption. Today, the world daily oil consumption is 85 million barrels. Despite the well-known consequences of fossil fuel combustion on the environment, this is expected to increase to 123 million barrels per day by the year 2025 [7]. There are a large number of factors that are significant in the determination of the future level of the energy consumption and production. Such factors include population growth, economic performance, consumer tastes, and technological developments. Furthermore, governmental policies concerning energy and developments in the world energy markets will certainly play a key role in the future level and pattern of energy production and consumption [8].

In 1984, 25% of the world population consumed 70% of the total energy supply, while the remaining 75% of the population were left with 30%. If the total population was to have the same consumption per inhabitant, as the Organization for Economic Co-operation and Development (OECD) member countries have on average, it would result in an increase in the 1984 world energy demand from 10 TW to approximately 30 TW. An expected, increase in the population from 4.7 billion in 1984 to 8.2 billion in 2020 would even raise the figure to 50 TW.

The total primary energy demand in the world increased from 5536 billion TOE (TOE = tons of oil equivalent = 41.868 GJ (Giga, G = 10^9)) in 1971 to 10 345 billion TOE in 2002, representing an average annual increase of 2%. It is important however to note that the average worldwide growth from 2001 to 2004 was 3.7% with the increase from 2003 to 2004 being 4.3%. The rate of growth is rising mainly due to the very rapid growth in Pacific Asia that recorded an average increase of 8.6% from 2001 to 2004.

The major sectors of primary energy sources use include electrical power, transportation, heating, and industrial. The International Energy Agency (IEA) data show that electricity demand almost tripled from 1971 to 2002. This is because electricity is a very convenient form of energy to transport and use. Although primary energy use in all sectors has increased, their relative shares have decreased, except for transportation and electricity. The relative share of primary energy for electricity production in the world increased from about 20% in 1971 to about 30% in 2002 as electricity is becoming the preferred form of energy for all applications.

Fuelled by high increase in China and India, worldwide energy consumption may continue to increase at rates between 3% and 5% for at least a few more years. However, such high rates of increase cannot continue for a long period. Even at a 2% increase per year, the primary energy demand of 2002 would double by 2037 and triple by 2057. With such high energy demand expected 50 years from now, it is important to look at all available strategies to fulfill the future demand, especially for electricity and transportation.

At present, 95% of all energy for transportation is covered with oil, and as a consequence, the available oil resources and their production rates and prices will greatly influence the future changes in transportation. A possible replacement for oil is biofuels, such as ethanol, methanol, biodiesel, biogases, and hydrogen, if it could be produced economically from renewable energy sources to provide a clean transportation alternative for the future.

Natural gas will be used at increasing rates to compensate for the shortfall in oil production, so, it may not last much longer than oil itself at higher rates of consumption. Coal is the largest fossil resource available today but the most problematic due to environmental concerns. All indications show that coal use will continue to grow for power production around the world because of expected increases in China, India, Australia, and other countries. This however is unsustainable, from the environmental point of view, unless advanced clean coal technologies (CCTs) with carbon sequestration are deployed.

Another parameter that should be considered is the world population, which is expected to double by the middle of this century, and as economic development will continue to grow, the global demand for energy is expected to increase. Today much evidence exists, which suggest that the future of our planet and of the generations to come will be negatively impacted if humans keep degrading the environment at the present rate. Currently, three environmental problems are internationally known: the acid precipitation, stratospheric ozone depletion, and global climate change. These are analyzed in more detail below.

3.01.2.1 Acid Rain

This is a form of pollution depletion in which SO_2 and NO_x produced by the combustion of fossil fuels are transported over great distances through the atmosphere and deposited via precipitation on the surface of the earth, causing damage to ecosystems that are vulnerable to excessive acidity. Therefore, it is obvious that the solution to the issue of acid rain deposition requires an appropriate control of SO_2 and NO_x pollutants. These pollutants cause both regional and transboundary problems of acid precipitation.

It is well known that some energy-related activities are the major sources of acid precipitation. Nowadays, attention is also given to other substances such as volatile organic compounds (VOCs), chlorides, ozone, and trace metals that may participate in a complex set of chemical transformations in the atmosphere resulting in acid precipitation and the formation of other regional air pollutants. A number of evidences that show the damages of acid precipitation are reported by Dincer and Rosen [6]. Additionally, VOCs are generated by a variety of sources and comprise a large number of diverse compounds. Obviously, the more energy we spend, the more we contribute to acid precipitation; therefore, the easiest way to reduce acid precipitation is by reducing energy consumption.

3.01.2.2 Ozone Layer Depletion

The ozone present in the stratosphere, at altitudes between 12 and 25 km, plays a natural equilibrium-maintaining role for the earth, through absorption of ultraviolet (UV) radiation (240–320 nm) and absorption of infrared radiation [3]. A global environmental problem is the depletion of the stratospheric ozone layer that is caused by the emissions of CFCs, halons (chlorinated and brominated organic compounds), and NO_x. Ozone depletion can lead to increased levels of damaging UV radiation reaching the ground, causing increased rates of skin cancer and eye damage to humans and is harmful to many biological species. It should be noted that energy-related activities are only partially (directly or indirectly) responsible for the emissions that lead to stratospheric ozone depletion. CFCs play the most significant role in ozone depletion, which are mainly used in air conditioning and refrigerating equipment as refrigerants, and NO_x emissions which are produced by the fossil fuel and biomass combustion processes, the natural denitrification, and nitrogen fertilizers.

In 1998, the size of the ozone hole over Antarctica was 25 million km^2. It was about 3 million km^2 in 1993 [7]. Researchers expect the Antarctic ozone hole to remain severe in the next 10–20 years, followed by a period of slow healing. Full recovery is predicted to occur in 2050; however, the rate of recovery is affected by climate change [8].

3.01.2.3 Global Climate Change

The term greenhouse effect has generally been used for the role of the whole atmosphere (mainly water vapour and clouds) in keeping the surface of the earth warm. Recently however, it has been increasingly associated with the contribution of CO_2, which is estimated that contributes about 50% to the anthropogenic greenhouse effect. Additionally, several other gasses such as CH_4, CFCs, halons, N_2O, ozone, and peroxyacetylnitrate (also called greenhouse gasses) produced by the industrial and domestic activities can also contribute to this effect, resulting in a rise of the earth's temperature. Increasing atmospheric concentrations of greenhouse gasses increase the amount of heat trapped (or decrease the heat radiated from the earth's surface), thereby raising the surface temperature of the earth. According to Colonbo [9], the earth's surface temperature has increased by about 0.6 °C over the last century, and as a consequence, the sea level is estimated to have risen by perhaps. 20 cm. These changes can have a wide range of effects on human activities all over the world. The role of various greenhouse gasses is summarized in Reference 6.

The concentration of the most relevant greenhouse gasses in 2007 are presented in **Table 1** [10]. The capacity of the gasses tabulated in contributing to global warming is assessed by an indicator called global warming potential (GWP), which gives the relative contribution of each gas, per mass unit, compared to that of CO_2. As can be seen from **Table 1**, GWP depends on its lifetime in the atmosphere and on its interactions with other gasses and water vapor. One of the worst substances, which has a much extended lifetime in the atmosphere, is the chlorofluorocarbons (CFCs). This is proved by the high GWP.

Humans contribute, through many of their economic and other activities, to the increase of the atmospheric concentrations of various greenhouse gasses. For example, CO_2 releases from fossil fuel combustion, methane emissions from increased human activity, and CFC releases all contribute to the greenhouse effect. Predictions show that if atmospheric concentrations of greenhouse gasses, mainly due to fossil fuels combustion, continue to increase at the present rates, the earth's temperature may increase by another 2–4 °C in the next century. If this prediction proves correct, the sea level could rise by between 30 and 60 cm before the end of this century [9]. The impacts of such sea level increase could easily be understood and include flooding of coastal settlements, decrease the availability of fresh water for irrigation and other essential uses, and displacement of fertile zones for agriculture toward higher latitudes. Thus, such consequences could put in danger the survival of entire populations.

3.01.2.4 Renewable Energy Technologies

Renewable energy technologies produce marketable energy by converting natural phenomena into useful forms of energy. These technologies use the sun's energy and its direct and indirect effects on the earth (solar radiation, wind, falling water and various plants, such as biomass), gravitational forces (tides), and the heat of the earth's core (geothermal) as the resources from which energy is produced. These resources have massive energy potential; however, they are generally diffused and not fully accessible, most of them are intermittent, and have distinct regional variabilities. These characteristics give rise to difficult, but solvable, technical and economical challenges. Nowadays, significant progress is made by improving the collection and conversion efficiencies, lowering the initial and maintenance costs, and increasing the reliability and applicability of renewable energy systems.

A worldwide research and development in the field of renewable energy resources and systems has been carried out during the last two decades. Energy conversion systems that are based on renewable energy technologies appeared to be cost-effective compared to the projected high cost of oil. Furthermore, renewable energy systems can have a beneficial impact on the environmental, economic, and political issues of the world. At the end of 2001, the total installed capacity of renewable energy systems was equivalent to 9% of the total electricity generation [11]. By applying the renewable energy intensive scenario suggested by Johansen et al. [12], the global consumption of renewable sources by 2050 would reach 318 exajoules.

The benefits arising from the installation and operation of renewable energy systems can be distinguished into three categories: energy saving, generation of new working posts, and the decrease of environmental pollution.

The energy-saving benefit derives from the reduction in consumption of electricity and diesel which are used conventionally to provide energy. This benefit can be directly translated into monetary units according to the corresponding production or avoiding capital expenditure for the purchase of imported fossil fuels.

Another factor which is of considerable importance in many countries is the ability of renewable energy technologies to generate jobs. The penetration of a new technology leads to the development of new production activities contributing to the production,

Table 1 Major greenhouse gasses [10]

Greenhouse gas (GHG)	Chemical formula	GWP	Concentration 2007 (ppbv)	Lifetime (years)
Carbon dioxide	CO_2	1	383 000	Variable
Methane	CH_4	21	1 770	12
Nitrous oxide	N_2O	310	311	120
CFC-12	CCl_2F_2	6 200–7 100	0.503	102
HCFC-22	$CHClF_2$	1 300–1 400	0.105	12
Perfluoromethane	CF_4	6 500	0.070	50 000
Sulfur hexafluorine	SF_6	23 900	0.032	3 200

market distribution, and operation of the pertinent equipment. Specifically, in the case of solar energy collectors, job creation mainly relates to the construction and installation of the collectors. The latter is a decentralized process since it requires the installation of equipment in every building or every individual consumer.

The most important benefit of renewable energy systems is the decrease of environmental pollution. This is achieved by the reduction of air emissions due to the substitution of electricity and conventional fuels. The most important effects of air pollutants on the human and natural environment are their impact on the public health, agriculture, and ecosystems. It is relatively simple to measure the financial impact of these effects when they relate to tradable goods such as the agricultural crops; however, when it comes to nontradable goods, like human health and ecosystems, things become more complicated. It should be noted that the level of the environmental impact and therefore the social pollution cost largely depend on the geographical location of the emission sources. Contrary to the conventional air pollutants, the social cost of CO_2 does not vary with the geographical characteristics of the source as each unit of CO_2 contributes equally to the climate change thread and the resulting cost.

All renewable energy sources combined account for only 17.6% of electricity production in the world, with the hydroelectric power providing almost 90% of this amount. However, as the renewable energy technologies mature and become even more cost competitive in the future, they will be in a position to replace a major fraction of fossil fuels for electricity generation. Therefore, substituting fossil fuels with renewable energy for electricity generation must be an important part of any strategy of reducing CO_2 emissions into the atmosphere and combating global climate change.

The benefits of renewable energy systems can be summarized as follows [12].

3.01.2.4.1 Social and economic development
Production of renewable energy, particularly biomass, can provide economic development and employment opportunities, especially in rural areas, that otherwise have limited opportunities for economic growth. Renewable energy can thus help reduce poverty in rural areas and reduce pressures for urban migration.

3.01.2.4.2 Land restoration
Growing biomass for energy on degraded lands can provide the incentives and financing needed to restore lands rendered nearly useless by previous agricultural or forestry practices. Although lands farmed for energy would not be restored to their original condition, the recovery of these lands for biomass plantations would support rural development, prevent erosion, and provide a better habitat for wildlife than at present.

3.01.2.4.3 Reduced air pollution
Renewable energy technologies, such as methanol or hydrogen for fuel-cell vehicles, produce virtually none of the emissions associated with urban air pollution and acid deposition, without the need for costly additional controls.

3.01.2.4.4 Abatement of global warming
Renewable energy use does not produce carbon dioxide and other greenhouse emissions that contribute to global warming. Even the use of biomass fuels will not contribute to global warming as the carbon dioxide released when biomass is burned equals the amount absorbed from the atmosphere by plants as they are grown for biomass fuel.

3.01.2.4.5 Fuel supply diversity
There would be substantial interregional energy trade in a renewable energy-intensive future, involving a diversity of energy carriers and suppliers. Energy importers would be able to choose from among more producers and fuel types than they do today and thus would be less vulnerable to monopoly price manipulation or unexpected disruptions of supplies. Such competition would make wide swings in energy prices less likely, leading eventually to stabilization of the world oil price. The growth in world energy trade would also provide new opportunities for energy suppliers. Especially promising are the prospects for trade in alcohol fuels such as methanol derived from biomass and hydrogen.

3.01.2.4.6 Reducing the risks of nuclear weapons proliferation
Competitive renewable resources could reduce incentives to build a large world infrastructure in support of nuclear energy, thus avoiding major increases in the production, transportation, and storage of plutonium and other radioactive materials that could be diverted to nuclear weapons production.

Solar systems, including solar thermoelectric and photovoltaics (PV), offer environmental advantages over electricity generation using conventional energy sources. The benefits arising from the installation and operation of solar energy systems are environmental and socioeconomical.

From an environmental point of view, the use of solar energy technologies has several positive implications which include [13]:

- Reduction of the emission of the greenhouse gasses (mainly CO_2, NO_x) and of toxic gas emissions (SO_2, particulates)
- Reclamation of degraded land
- Reduced requirement for transmission lines within the electricity grid
- Improvement of the water resources quality

The socioeconomic benefits of solar technologies include:

- Increased regional/national energy independence
- Creation of employment opportunities
- Restructuring of energy markets due to penetration of a new technology and the growth of new production activities
- Diversification, security, and stability of energy supply
- Acceleration of electrification of rural communities in isolated areas
- Saving foreign currency.

It is worth noting that no artificial project can completely avoid some impact to the environment. The negative environmental aspects of solar energy systems include:

- Pollution stemming from production, installation, maintenance, and demolition of the systems
- Noise during construction
- Land displacement
- Visual intrusion.

These adverse impacts present difficult but solvable technical challenges.

The amount of sunlight striking the earth's atmosphere continuously is 1.75×10^5 TW. Considering a 60% transmittance through the atmospheric cloud cover, 1.05×10^5 TW reaches the earth's surface continuously. If the irradiance on only 1% of the earth's surface could be converted into electric energy with a 10% efficiency, it would provide a resource base of 105 TW, while the total global energy needs for 2050 are projected to be about 25–30 TW. The present state of solar energy technologies is such that single solar cell efficiencies have reached over 20% with concentrating PV at about 40% and solar thermal systems provide efficiencies of 40–60%.

Solar PV panels have come down in cost from about \$30 W^{-1} to about \$3 W^{-1} in the last three decades. At \$3 W^{-1} panel cost, the overall system cost is around \$6 W^{-1}, which is still too high for the average consumer. However, there are many off-grid applications where solar PV is already cost-effective. With net metering and governmental incentives, such as feed-in laws and other policies, grid-connected applications such as building-integrated photovoltaics (BIPV) have become cost-effective. As a result, the worldwide growth in PV production is more than 30% per year (average) during the past 5 years.

Solar thermal power using concentrating solar collectors was the first solar technology that demonstrated its grid power potential. A total of 354 MW_e solar thermal power plants have been operating continuously in California since 1985. Progress in solar thermal power stalled after that time because of poor policy and lack of R&D. However, the last 5 years have seen a resurgence of interest in this area, and a number of solar thermal power plants around the world are under construction. The cost of power from these plants (which is so far in the range of \$0.12–\$0.16 kWh^{-1}) has the potential to go down to \$0.05 kWh^{-1} with scale-up and creation of a mass market. An advantage of solar thermal power is that thermal energy can be stored efficiently and fuels such as natural gas or biogas may be used as back-up to ensure continuous operation.

In this volume, emphasis is given to solar thermal systems. Solar thermal systems are nonpolluting and offer significant protection to the environment. The reduction of greenhouse gasses is the main advantage of utilizing solar energy. Therefore, solar thermal systems should be employed whenever possible in order to achieve a sustainable future.

3.01.3 Environmental Characteristics of Solar Energy

As observed from earth, the path of the sun across the sky varies throughout the year. The shape described by the sun's position, considered at the same time each day for a complete year, is called the analemma and resembles a figure 8 aligned along a north/south axis. The most obvious variation in the sun's apparent position through the year is a north/south swing over 47° of angle (because of the 23.5° tilt of the earth axis with respect to the sun), called declination. The north/south swing in apparent angle is the main cause for the existence of seasons on earth.

Knowledge of the sun's path through the sky is necessary in order to calculate the solar radiation falling on a surface, the solar heat gain, the proper orientation of solar collectors, the placement of collectors to avoid shading, and many more which are not of direct interest here. The objective of this chapter is to describe the movements of the sun relative to the earth which give to the sun its east/west trajectory across the sky. The variation of solar incidence angle and the amount of solar energy received will be analyzed for a number of fixed and tracking surfaces. The solar environment in which a solar system works depends mostly on the solar energy availability. The general weather of a location is required in many energy calculations. This is usually presented as typical meteorological year (TMY) file.

In solar energy calculations, apparent solar time (AST) must be used to express the time of the day. AST is based on the apparent angular motion of the sun across the sky. The time when the sun crosses the meridian of the observer is the local solar noon. It usually does not coincide with the 12.00 o'clock time of a locality. In order to convert the local standard time (LST) to AST, two corrections are applied, the equation of time and longitude correction. These are analyzed below.

3.01.3.1 Equation of Time

Due to factors associated with the earth's orbit around the sun, the earth's orbital velocity varies throughout the year, so the AST varies slightly from the mean time kept by a clock running at a uniform rate. The variation is called the equation of time (ET). The equation of time arises because the length of a day, that is, the time required by the earth to complete one revolution about its own axis with respect to the sun, is not uniform throughout the year. Over the year, the average length of day is 24 h; however, the length of a day varies due to the eccentricity of the earth's orbit and the tilt of the earth's axis from the normal plane of its orbit. Due to the ellipticity of the orbit, the earth is closer to the sun on 3 January and furthest from the sun on 4 July. Therefore, the earth's orbiting speed is faster than its average speed for half the year (from about October–March) and slower than its average speed for the remaining half of the year (from about April–September).

The values of the equation of time as a function of the day of the year (N) can be obtained approximately from the following equation:

$$\mathrm{ET} = 9.87 \sin(2B) - 7.53 \cos(B) - 1.5 \sin(B) \text{ [min]} \quad [1]$$

$$\text{where} \quad B = (N-81)\frac{360}{364} \quad [2]$$

A graphical representation of eqn [1] is shown in **Figure 2** from which the equation of time can be obtained directly.

3.01.3.2 Longitude Correction

The standard clock time is reckoned from a selected meridian near the center of a time zone or from the standard meridian, the Greenwich, which is at longitude of 0 degrees. Since the sun takes 4 min to transverse one degree of longitude, a longitude correction term of 4(standard longitude – local longitude) should be either added or subtracted to the standard clock time of the locality. This correction is constant for a particular longitude and the following rule must be followed with respect to sign convention. If the location is east of the standard meridian, the correction is added to the clock time. If the location is west, it is subtracted. The general equation for calculating the AST is as follows:

$$\mathrm{AST} = \mathrm{LST} + \mathrm{ET} \pm 4\,(\mathrm{SL} - \mathrm{LL}) - \mathrm{DS} \quad [3]$$

where LST is local standard time, ET is equation of time, SL is standard longitude, LL is local longitude, and DS is daylight saving (it is either 0 or 60 min).

If a location is east of Greenwich, the longitude correction of eqn [3] is negative (–), and if it is west, it is positive (+). If a daylight saving time is used, this must be subtracted from the LST. The term DS depends on whether daylight saving is in operation (usually from end of March to end of October) or not. This term is usually ignored from this equation and considered only if the estimation is within the DS period.

3.01.3.3 Solar Angles

The earth makes one rotation about its axis every 24 h and completes a revolution about the sun in a period of 365.25 days approximately. This revolution is not circular but follows an ellipse with the sun at one of the foci. The eccentricity, e, of the earth's orbit is very small and is equal to 0.016 73. Therefore, the orbit of the earth round the sun is almost circular. The sun–earth distance, R, at perihelion (shortest distance, at 3 January) and aphelion (longest distance, at 4 July) is given by Garg [14]:

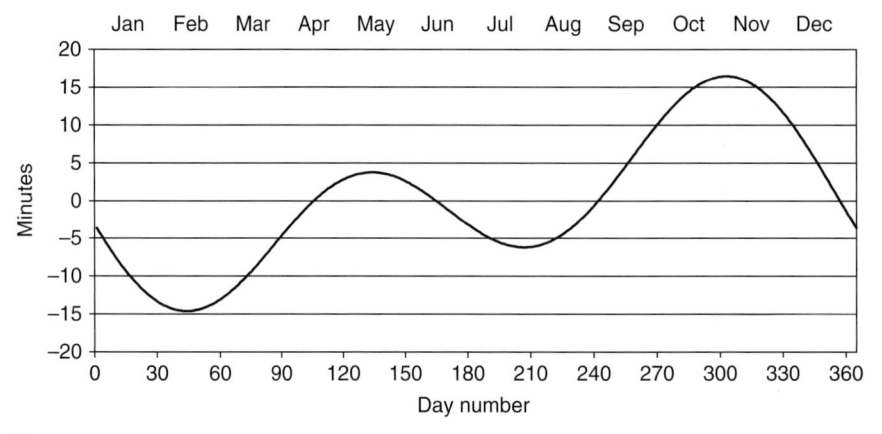

$$R = a(1 \pm e) \quad [4]$$

Figure 2 Equation of time.

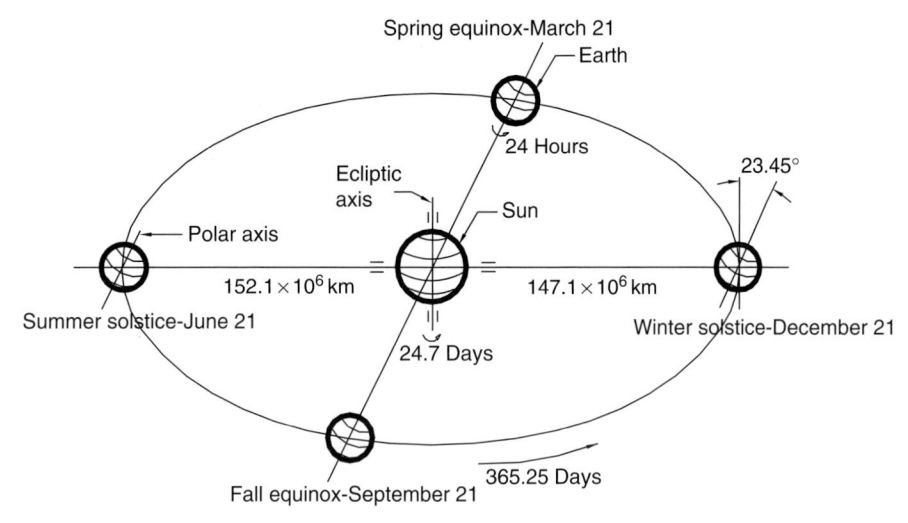

Figure 3 Annual motion of the earth about the sun.

where a is mean sun–earth distance which is $149.598\,5 \times 10^6$ km.

The plus sign in eqn [4] is for the sun–earth distance when the earth is at the aphelion position and the minus sign for the perihelion position. The solution of eqn [4] gives values for the longest distance equal to 152.1×10^6 km and for the shortest distance equal to 147.1×10^6 km as shown in **Figure 3**. The difference of the two distances is only 3.3%. The mean sun–earth distance, a, is defined as half the sum of the perihelion and aphelion distances.

The sun's position in the sky changes from day to day and from hour to hour. It is common knowledge that the sun is higher in the sky in summer than in winter. The relative motions of the sun and earth are not simple, but they are systematic and thus predictable. Once a year the earth moves around the sun in an orbit that is elliptical in shape. As the earth makes its yearly revolution around the sun, it rotates every 24 h about its axis, which is tilted at an angle of 23 degrees 27.14 min (23.45°) to the plane of the elliptic which contains the earth's orbital plane and the sun's equator as shown in **Figure 3**.

The most obvious apparent motion of the sun is that it moves daily in an arc across the sky, reaching its highest point at mid-day. As winter becomes spring and then summer, the sunrise and sunset points move gradually northward along the horizon. In the northern hemisphere, the days get longer as the sun rises earlier and sets later each day and the sun's path gets higher in the sky. At 21 June, the sun is at its most northerly position with respect to the earth. This is called the summer solstice and during this day the daytime is maximum. Six months later at 21 December, winter solstice, the reverse happens and the sun is at its most southerly position (see **Figure 4**). In the middle of the 6-months range, that is, at about 21 March and 21 September, the length of the day is equal to the length of the night. These are called spring and fall equinoxes, respectively. The summer and winter solstices are the opposite in the southern hemisphere; that is, summer solstice is on 21 December and winter solstice is on 21 June. It should be noted that all these dates are approximate and that there are small variations (difference of a few days) from year to year.

For the purposes of this chapter, the Ptolemaic view of the sun's motion is used in the analysis that follows for simplicity, that is, since all motion is relative, it is convenient to consider the earth fixed and to describe the sun's virtual motion in a coordinate system fixed on the earth with its origin at the site of interest.

For most solar energy applications, one needs reasonably accurate predictions of where the sun will be in the sky at a given time of day and year. In the Ptolemaic sense, the sun is constrained to move with two degrees of freedom on the celestial sphere; therefore, its position with respect to an observer on earth can be fully described by means of two astronomical angles, the solar altitude (a) and the solar azimuth (z). Following is a description of each angle together with the associated formulation.

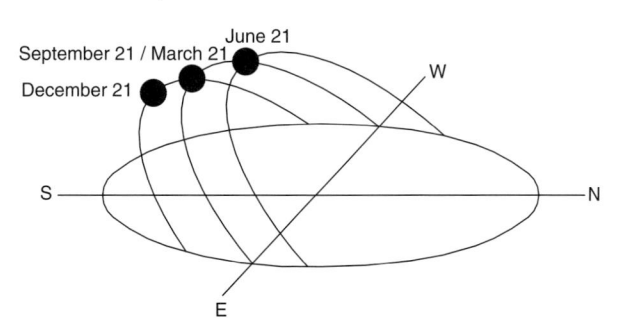

Figure 4 Annual changes in the sun's position in the sky (northern hemisphere).

Before giving the equations of solar altitude and azimuth angles, the solar declination and hour angles need to be defined. These are required in all other solar angle formulations.

3.01.3.3.1 Declination angle, δ

As shown in **Figure 3**, the earth axis of rotation (the polar axis) is inclined at an angle of 23.45° from the ecliptic axis, which is normal to the ecliptic plane. The ecliptic plane is the plane of orbit of earth around the sun. The solar declination angle is the angular distance of the sun's rays north (or south) of the equator, north declination designated as positive. As shown in **Figure 5**, it is the angle between the sun–earth center line and the projection of this line on the equatorial plane. Declinations north of the equator (summer in the Northern hemisphere) is positive and those south are negative. **Figure 6** shows the declination angle during the equinoxes and the solstices. As can be seen, the declination angle ranges from 0° at the spring equinox, to +23.45° at the summer solstice, to 0° at the fall equinox, to −23.45° at the winter solstice.

The variation of the solar declination angle throughout the year is shown in **Figure 7**. The declination angle δ, in degrees, for any day of the year (N) can be calculated approximately by the equation (ASHRAE, 2007):

$$\delta = 23.45 \sin\left[\frac{360}{365}(284 + N)\right] \qquad [5]$$

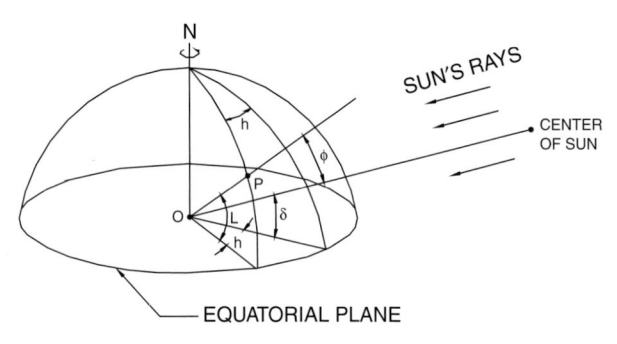

Figure 5 Definition of latitude, hour angle, and solar declination.

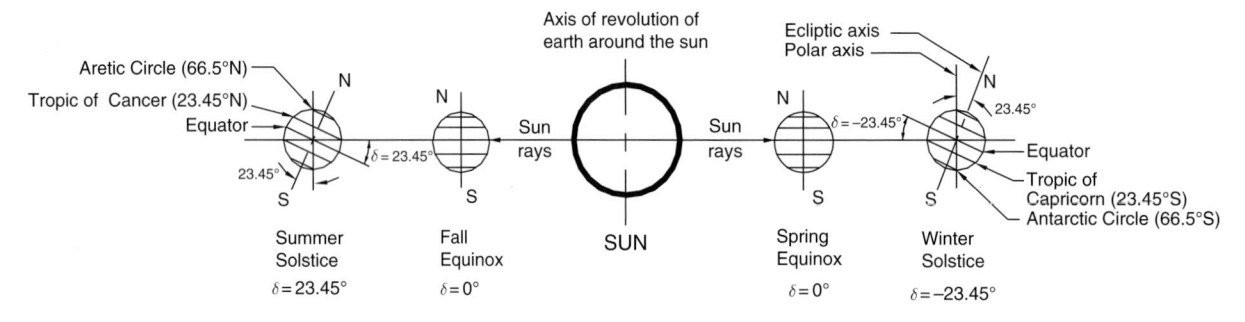

Figure 6 Yearly variation of solar declination angle.

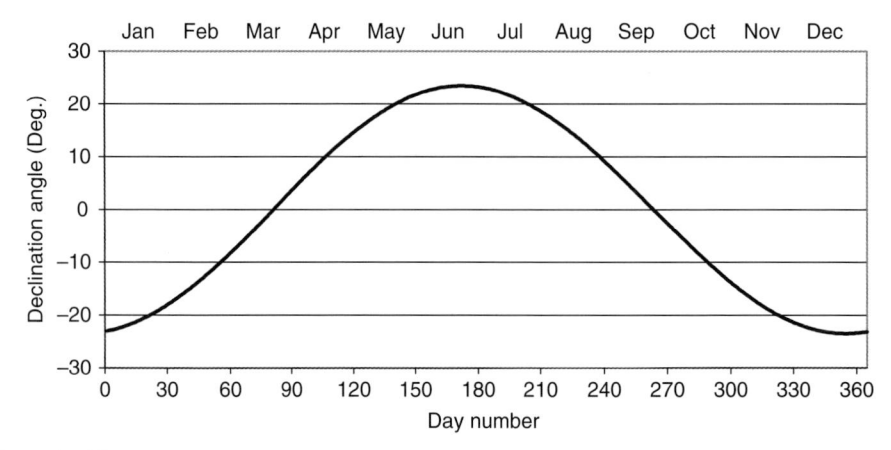

Figure 7 Declination angle of the sun.

Declination can also be given in radians by the Spencer formula [15]:

$$\delta = 0.006\,918 - 0.399\,912\,\cos(\Gamma) + 0.070\,257\,\sin(\Gamma) - 0.006\,758\,\cos(2\Gamma) + 0.000\,907\,\sin(2\Gamma) - 0.002\,697\,\cos(3\Gamma) \\ + 0.001\,48\,\sin(3\Gamma) \quad [6]$$

where Γ is called the day angle given by (in radians):

$$\Gamma = \frac{2\pi(N-1)}{365} \quad [7]$$

The solar declination during any given day can be considered constant in engineering calculations [16, 17].

As shown in **Figure 6**, the tropics of Cancer (23.45°N) and Capricorn (23.45°S) are the latitudes where the sun is overhead during summer and winter solstice, respectively. Another two latitudes of interest are the Arctic (66.5°N) and Antarctic (66.5°S) Circles. As shown in **Figure 6**, at winter solstice all points north of the Arctic Circle are in complete darkness, whereas all points south of the Antarctic Circle receive continuous sunlight. The opposite happens for the summer solstice. During spring and fall equinoxes, the North and South Poles are equidistant from the sun and daytime is equal to nighttime, which are both equal to 12 h.

3.01.3.3.2 Hour angle, h

The hour angle, h, of a point on the earth's surface is defined as the angle through which the earth would turn to bring the meridian of the point directly under the sun. In **Figure 5**, the hour angle of point P is shown as the angle measured on the earth's equatorial plane between the projection of OP and the projection of the sun–earth center-to-center line. The hour angle at local solar noon is 0, with each 360/24 or 15 degrees of longitude equivalent to 1 h, afternoon hours being designated as positive. Expressed symbolically, the hour angle in degrees is:

$$h = \pm 0.25\,(\text{number of minutes from local solar noon}) \quad [8]$$

where the + sign applies to afternoon hours and the − sign to morning hours.

The hour angle can also be obtained from the AST, that is, the corrected local solar time:

$$h = (\text{AST} - 12)15 \quad [9]$$

At local solar noon, AST = 12 and $h = 0°$. Therefore, from eqn [3], the LST (the time shown by our clocks at local solar noon) is:

$$\text{LST} = 12 - \text{ET} \mp 4(\text{SL} - \text{LL}) \quad [10]$$

3.01.3.3.3 Solar altitude angle, α

The solar altitude angle is the angle between the sun's rays and a horizontal plane as shown in **Figure 8**. It is related to the solar zenith angle Φ, being the angle between the sun's rays and the vertical. Thus:

$$\Phi + \alpha = \frac{\pi}{2} = 90° \quad [11]$$

The mathematical expression for the solar altitude angle is:

$$\sin(\alpha) = \cos(\Phi) = \sin(L)\sin(\delta) + \cos(L)\cos(\delta)\cos(h) \quad [12]$$

where L is local latitude, defined as the angle between a line from the center of the earth to the site of interest and the equatorial plane. Values north of the equator are positive and those of south are negative.

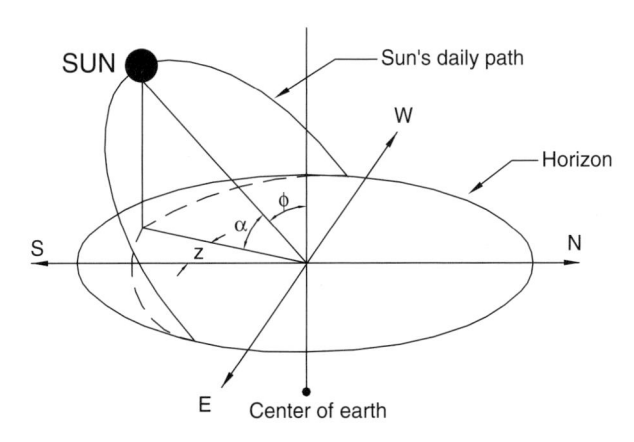

Figure 8 Apparent daily path of the sun across the sky from sunrise to sunset.

3.01.3.3.4 Solar azimuth angle, z

The solar azimuth angle z is the angle of the sun's rays measured in the horizontal plane from due south (true south) for the northern hemisphere or due north for the southern hemisphere; westward is designated as positive. The mathematical expression for the solar azimuth angle is:

$$\sin(z) = \frac{\cos(\delta)\sin(h)}{\cos(\alpha)} \qquad [13]$$

This equation is correct provided that $\cos(h) > \tan(\delta)/\tan(L)$ [18]. If not, it means that the sun is behind the E–W line as shown in **Figure 4**, and the azimuth angle for the morning hours is $-\pi + |z|$ and for the afternoon hours is $\pi - z$.

At solar noon, the sun is, by definition, exactly on the meridian, which contains the north–south line, and consequently, the solar azimuth is 0 degrees. Therefore, the noon altitude α_n is:

$$\alpha_n = 90° - L + \delta \qquad [14]$$

3.01.3.3.5 Sun rise and set times and day length

The sun is said to rise and set when the solar altitude angle is 0. So the hour angle at sunset, h_{ss}, can be found from solving eqn [12] for h when $\alpha = 0°$. Thus:

$$\sin(\alpha) = \sin(0) = 0 = \sin(L)\sin(\delta) + \cos(L)\cos(\delta)\cos(h_{ss})$$

$$\text{or} \quad \cos(h_{ss}) = -\frac{\sin(L)\sin(\delta)}{\cos(L)\cos(\delta)}$$

which reduces to:

$$\cos(h_{ss}) = -\tan(L)\tan(\delta) \qquad [15]$$

where h_{ss} is taken as positive at sunset.

Since the hour angle at local solar noon is 0, with each 15 degrees of longitude equivalent to 1 h, the sunrise and sunset time in hours from local solar noon is then:

$$H_{ss} - -H_{sr} = \frac{1}{15}\cos^{-1}[-\tan(L)\tan(\delta)] \qquad [16]$$

The day length is twice the sunset hour since the solar noon is at the middle of the sunrise and sunset hours. Thus, the length of the day in hours is:

$$\text{Day length} = \frac{2}{15}\cos^{-1}[-\tan(L)\tan(\delta)] \qquad [17]$$

3.01.3.3.6 Incidence angle, θ

The solar incidence angle, θ, is the angle between the sun's rays and the normal on a surface. For a horizontal plane, the incidence angle, θ, and the zenith angle, Φ, are the same. The angles shown in **Figure 9** are related to the basic angles shown in **Figure 5** with the following general expression for the angle of incidence [16, 17]:

$$\cos(\theta) = \sin(L)\sin(\delta)\cos(\beta) - \cos(L)\sin(\delta)\sin(\beta)\cos(z_s) + \cos(L)\cos(\delta)\cos(h)\cos(\beta) \\ + \sin(L)\cos(\delta)\cos(h)\sin(\beta)\cos(z_s) + \cos(\delta)\sin(h)\sin(\beta)\sin(z_s) \qquad [18]$$

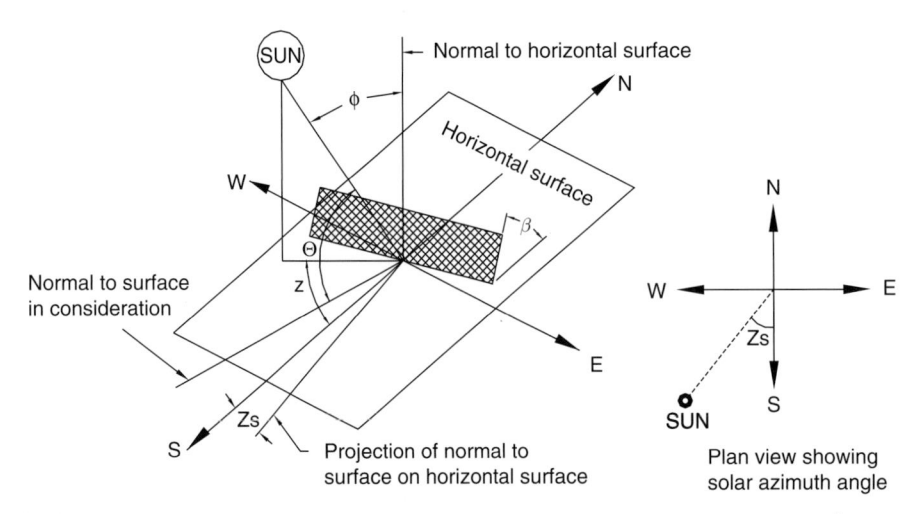

Figure 9 Solar angles diagram.

where β is surface tilt angle from the horizontal and z_s is surface azimuth angle, angle between the normal to the surface from true south, westward is designated as positive.

For certain cases, eqn [18] reduces to much simpler forms.

For horizontal surfaces, $\beta = 0°$ and $\theta = \Phi$, and eqn [18] reduces to eqn [12].
For vertical surfaces, $\beta = 90°$ and eqn [18] becomes:

$$\cos(\theta) = -\cos(L)\sin(\delta)\cos(z_s) + \sin(L)\cos(\delta)\cos(h)\cos(z_s) + \cos(\delta)\sin(h)\sin(z_s) \quad [19]$$

For south facing tilted surface in the northern hemisphere, $z_s = 0°$ and eqn [18] reduces to:

$$\cos(\theta) = \sin(L)\sin(\delta)\cos(\beta) - \cos(L)\sin(\delta)\sin(\beta) + \cos(L)\cos(\delta)\cos(h)\cos(\beta) + \sin(L)\cos(\delta)\cos(h)\sin(\beta)$$

which can be further reduced to:

$$\cos(\theta) = \sin(L-\beta)\sin(\delta) + \cos(L-\beta)\cos(\delta)\cos(h) \quad [20]$$

For a north facing tilted surface in the southern hemisphere, $z_s = 180°$ and eqn [18] reduces to:

$$\cos(\theta) = \sin(L+\beta)\sin(\delta) + \cos(L+\beta)\cos(\delta)\cos(h) \quad [21]$$

Equation [18] is a general relationship for the angle of incidence on a surface of any orientation. As it is shown in eqns [19]–[21], it can be reduced to much simpler forms for specific cases.

3.01.3.4 The Incidence Angle for Moving Surfaces

For the case of solar concentrating collectors, some form of tracking mechanism is usually employed to enable the collector to follow the sun. This is done in varying degrees of accuracy and modes of tracking as indicated in **Figure 10**.

Tracking systems can be classified by the mode of their motion. This can be about a single axis or about two axes (**Figure 10(a)**). In the case of a single axis mode, the motion can be in various ways, that is, east–west (**Figure 10(d)**), north–south (**Figure 10(c)**),

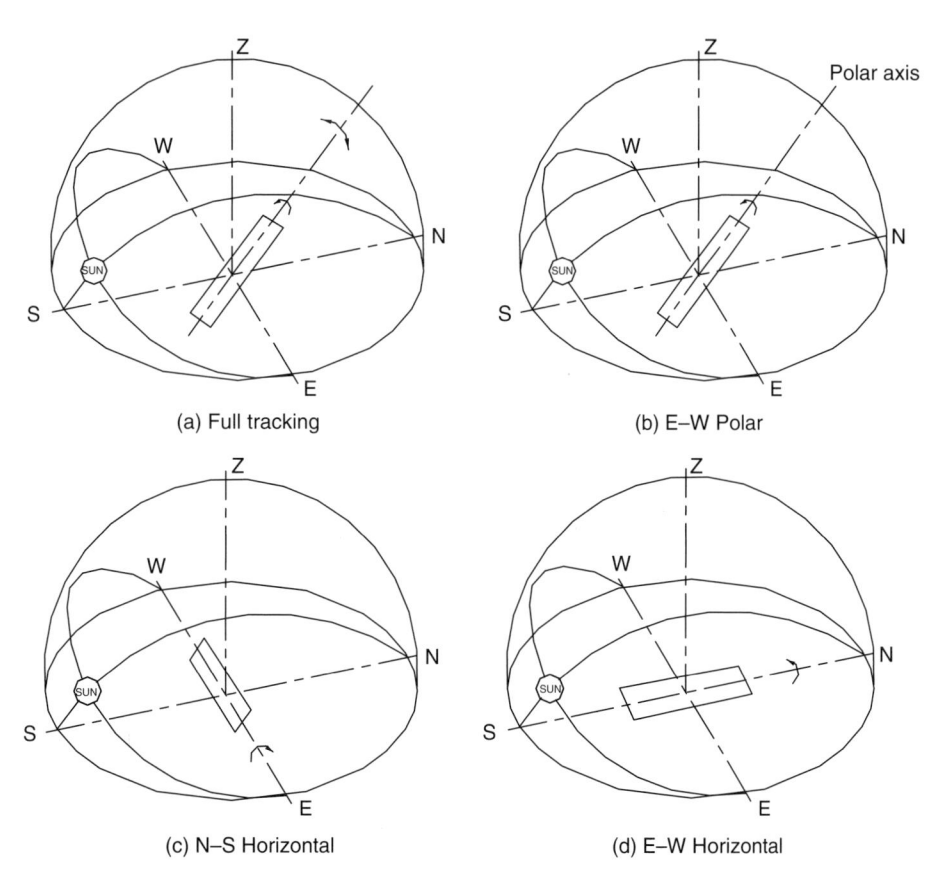

Figure 10 Collector geometry for various modes of tracking.

or parallel to the earth's axis (**Figure 10(b)**). The following equations are derived from the general eqn [18], and apply to planes moved as indicated in each case. For each mode, the amount of energy falling on a surface per unit area for the summer and winter solstices and the equinoxes for the latitude of 35° is investigated. This analysis has been performed with a radiation model, which is affected by the incidence angle and is different for each mode. The type of the model used here is not important as it is used for comparison purposes only.

3.01.3.4.1 Full tracking

For a two-axis tracking mechanism, keeping the surface in question continuously oriented to face the sun (see **Figure 10(a)**) will at all times have an angle of incidence θ equal to:

$$\cos(\theta) = 1 \qquad [22]$$

or $\theta = 0°$. This of course depends on the accuracy of the mechanism. The full tracking configuration collects the maximum possible sunshine. The performance of this mode of tracking with respect to the amount of radiation collected during 1 day under standard conditions is shown in **Figure 11**.

The slope of this surface (β) is equal to the solar zenith angle (Φ) and the surface azimuth angle (z_s) is equal to the solar azimuth angle (z).

3.01.3.4.2 N–S axis tilted/tilt daily adjusted

For a plane moved about a north–south axis with a single daily adjustment so that its surface normal coincides with the solar beam at noon each day, θ is equal to [17, 19]:

$$\cos(\theta) = \sin^2(\delta) + \cos^2(\delta)\cos(h) \qquad [23]$$

For this mode of tracking, we can accept that when the sun is at noon the angle of sun's rays and the normal to the collector can be up to 4° declination, as for small angles $\cos(4°) = 0.998 \sim 1$. **Figure 12** shows the number of consecutive days that the sun remains within this 4° 'declination window' at noon. As can be seen in **Figure 12**, the sun remains most of the time close to either the summer solstice or the winter solstice moving rapidly between the two extremes. For nearly 70 consecutive days, the sun is within 4° of an extreme position, spending only 9 days in the 4° window at the equinox. This means that a seasonally tilted collector needs be adjusted only occasionally.

The problem encountered with this and all tilted collectors, when more than one collector is used, is that the front collectors cast shadows on adjacent ones. This means that in terms of land utilization, these collectors lose some of their benefits when the cost of land is taken into account. The performance of this mode of tracking (see **Figure 13**) shows the peaked curves typical for this assembly.

3.01.3.4.3 N–S axis polar/E–W tracking

For a plane rotated about a north–south axis parallel to the earth's axis, with continuous adjustment, θ is equal to:

$$\cos(\theta) = \cos(\delta) \qquad [24]$$

This configuration is shown in **Figure 10(b)**. As can be seen, the collector axis is tilted at the polar axis, which is equal to the local latitude. For this arrangement, the sun is normal to the collector at equinoxes ($\delta = 0°$) and the cosine effect is maximum at the

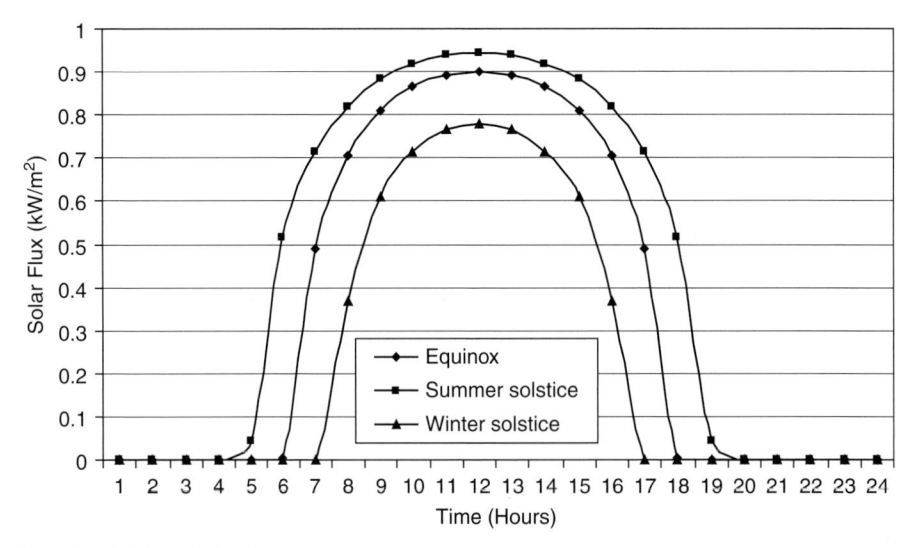

Figure 11 Daily variation of solar flux – full tracking.

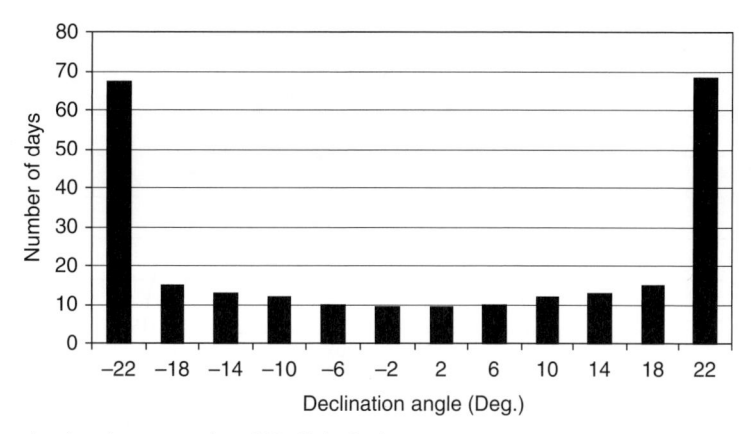

Figure 12 Number of consecutive days the sun remains within 4° declination.

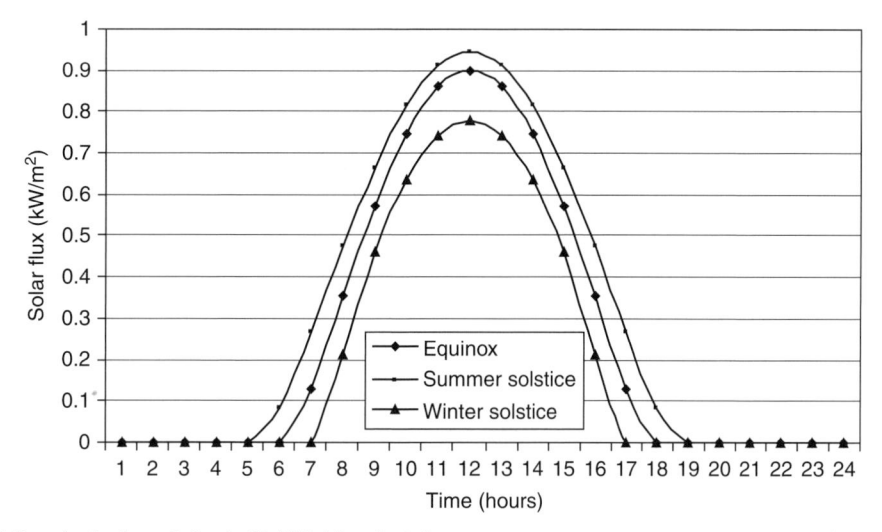

Figure 13 Daily variation of solar flux – N–S axis tilted/tilt daily adjusted.

solstices. The same comments about tilting of collector and shadowing effects applies here as in the previous configuration. The performance of this mount is shown in **Figure 14**.

The equinox and summer solstice performance, in terms of solar radiation collected, are essentially equal, that is, the smaller air mass for summer solstice offsets the small cosine projection effect. The winter noon value, however, is reduced because these two effects combine together. If it is desired to increase the winter performance, an inclination higher than the local latitude would be required, but the physical height of such configuration would be a potential penalty to be traded-off in cost-effectiveness with the structure of the polar mount. Another side effect of increased inclination is that of shadowing of the adjacent collectors, for multirow installations.

The slope of the surface varies continuously and is given by:

$$\tan(\beta) = \frac{\tan(L)}{\cos(z_s)} \qquad [25]$$

The surface azimuth angle is given by:

$$z_s = \tan^{-1}\frac{\sin(\Phi)\sin(z)}{\cos(\theta')\sin(L)} + 180 C_1 C_2 \qquad [26]$$

where $\cos(\theta') = \cos(\Phi)\cos(L) + \sin(\Phi)\sin(L)\cos(z)$ \qquad [27]

$$C_1 = \begin{cases} 0 & \text{if } \left(\tan^{-1}\frac{\sin(\Phi)\sin(z)}{\cos(\theta')\sin(L)}\right) z \geq 0 \\ 1 & \text{otherwise} \end{cases} \qquad [28]$$

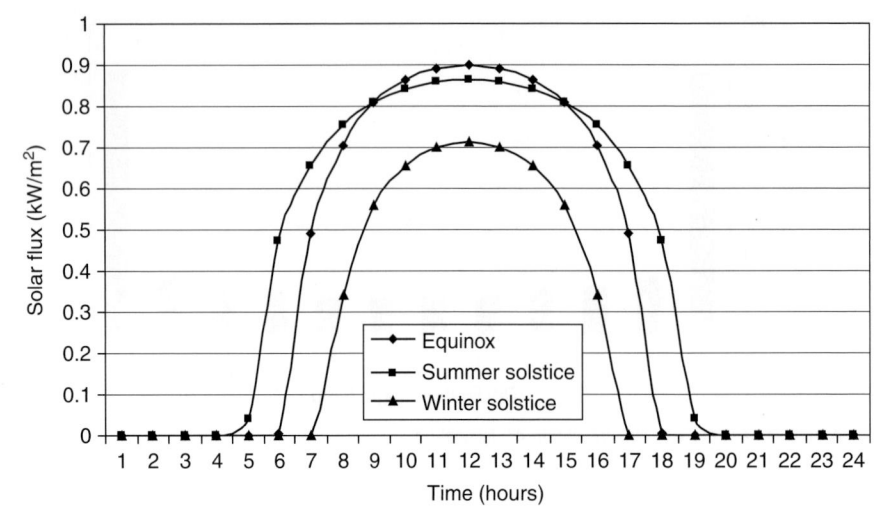

Figure 14 Daily variation of solar flux – N–S axis polar/E–W tracking.

$$C_2 = \begin{cases} 1 & \text{if } z \geq 0° \\ -1 & \text{if } z < 0° \end{cases} \quad [29]$$

3.01.3.4.4 E–W axis horizontal/N–S tracking

For a plane rotated about a horizontal east–west axis with continuous adjustment to minimize the angle of incidence, θ can be obtained from [16, 17]:

$$\cos(\theta) = \sqrt{1 - \cos^2(\delta)\sin^2(h)} \quad [30]$$

or from eqn [19]:

$$\cos(\theta) = \sqrt{\sin^2(\delta) + \cos^2(\delta)\cos^2(h)} \quad [31]$$

The basic geometry of this configuration is shown in **Figure 10(c)**. The shadowing effects of this arrangement are minimal. The principal shadowing is caused when the collector is tipped to a maximum degree south ($\delta = 23.5°$) at winter solstice. In this case, the sun casts a shadow toward the collector at the north. This assembly has an advantage in that it approximates the full tracking collector in summer (see **Figure 15**), but the cosine effect in winter greatly reduces its effectiveness. This mount yields a rather 'square' profile of solar radiation, ideal for leveling the variation during the day. The winter performance, however, is seriously depressed relative to the summer one.

The slope of this surface is given by:

$$\tan(\beta) = \tan(\Phi)|\cos(z)| \quad [32]$$

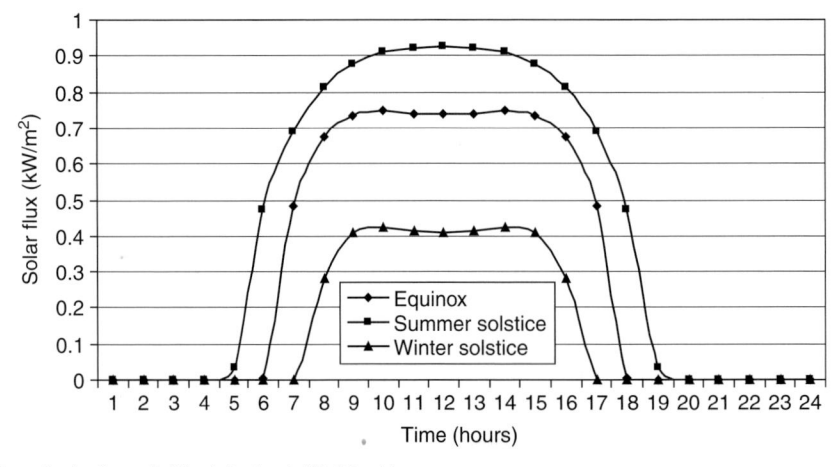

Figure 15 Daily variation of solar flux – E–W axis horizontal/N–S tracking.

The surface orientation for this mode of tracking changes between 0° and 180° if the solar azimuth angle passes through ±90°. For either hemisphere:

$$\text{If } |z| < 90°, \quad z_s = 0°$$
$$\text{If } |z| > 90°, \quad z_s = 180° \qquad [33]$$

3.01.3.4.5 N–S axis horizontal/E–W tracking

For a plane rotated about a horizontal north–south axis with continuous adjustment to minimize the angle of incidence, θ can be obtained from [16, 17]:

$$\cos(\theta) = \sqrt{\sin^2(\alpha) + \cos^2(\delta)\sin^2(h)} \qquad [34]$$

or from eqn [19]:

$$\cos(\theta) = \cos(\Phi)\cos(h) + \cos(\delta)\sin^2(h) \qquad [35]$$

The basic geometry of this configuration is shown in **Figure 10(d)**. The greatest advantage of this arrangement is that very small shadowing effects are encountered when more than one collector is used. These are present only at the first and last hours of the day. In this case, the curve of the solar energy collected during the day is closer to a cosine curve function (see **Figure 16**).

The slope of this surface is given by:

$$\tan(\beta) = \tan(\Phi)|\cos(z_s - z)| \qquad [36]$$

The surface azimuth angle (z_s) will be 90° or −90° depending on the solar azimuth angle as:

$$\text{If } z > 0°, \quad z_s = 90°$$
$$\text{If } z < 0°, \quad z_s = -90° \qquad [37]$$

3.01.3.4.5(i) Comparison

The mode of tracking affects the amount of incident radiation falling on the collector surface in proportion to the cosine of the incidence angle. The amount of energy falling on a surface per unit area for four modes of tracking for the summer and winter solstices and the equinoxes is shown in **Table 2**. This analysis has been performed with the same radiation model used to plot the solar flux figures in this section. Again, the type of the model used here is not important as it is used for comparison purposes only. The performance of the various modes of tracking are compared to the full tracking, which collects the maximum amount of solar energy shown as 100% in **Table 2**. From this table, it is obvious that the polar and the N–S horizontal modes are the most suitable for one-axis tracking as their performance is very close to the full tracking, provided that the low winter performance of the latter is not a problem.

3.01.3.5 Sun Path Diagrams

For practical purposes, it is convenient instead of using the proceeding equations to have the sun's path plotted on a horizontal plane, called the sun path diagram, and use the diagram to find the position of the sun on the sky at any time of the year. As can be

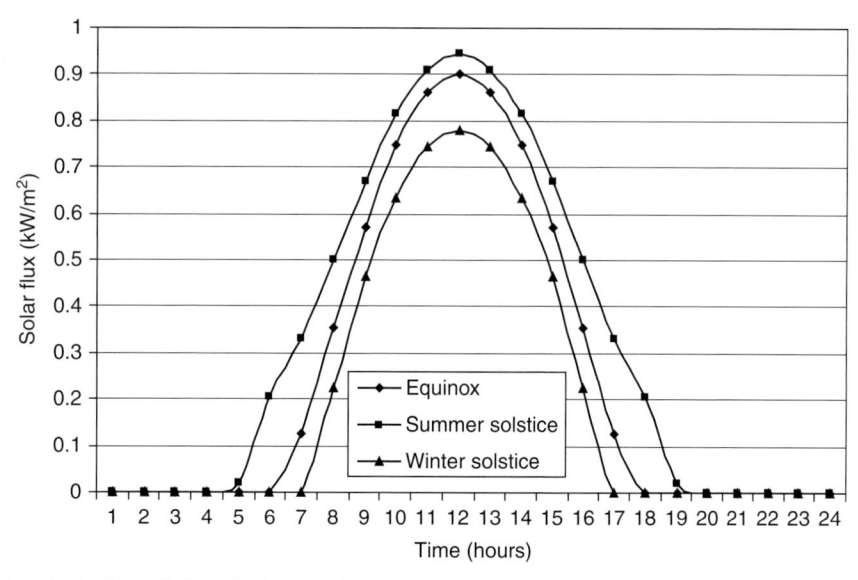

Figure 16 Daily variation of solar flux – N–S axis horizontal/E–W tracking.

Table 2 Comparison of energy received for various modes of tracking

Tracking mode	Solar energy received (kWh m^{-2}) E	SS	WS	Percentage to full tracking E	SS	WS
Full tracking	8.43	10.60	5.70	100	100	100
E–W polar	8.43	9.73	5.23	100	91.7	91.7
N–S horizontal	7.51	10.36	4.47	89.1	97.7	60.9
E–W horizontal	6.22	7.85	4.91	73.8	74.0	86.2

Notes: E, equinoxes; SS, summer solstice; WS, winter solstice.

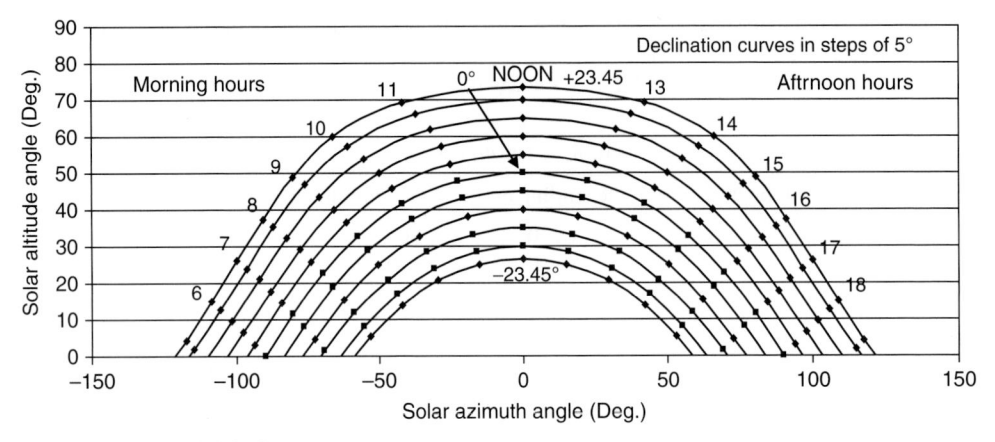

Figure 17 Sun path diagram for 35°N latitude.

seen from eqns [12] and [13], the solar altitude angle α and the solar azimuth angle z are functions of latitude L, hour angle h, and declination δ. In a two-dimensional plot, only two independent parameters can be used to correlate the other parameters; therefore, it is usual to plot different sun path diagrams for different latitudes. Such diagrams show the complete variations of hour angle and declination for a full year. **Figure 17** shows the sun path diagram for 40°N latitude. Lines of constant declination are labeled by the value of the angles. Points of constant hour angles are clearly indicated. This figure is used in combination with **Figure 7** or eqns [5]–[7], that is, for a day in a year **Figure 7** or the equations can be used to estimate declination which is then entered together with the time of day, converted to solar time using eqn [3], in **Figure 17** to estimate solar altitude and azimuth angles. It should be noted that **Figure 17** applies for the northern hemisphere. For the southern, the sign of the declination should be reversed.

3.01.4 Solar Radiation

All substances, solid bodies as well as liquids and gasses above the absolute zero temperature, emit energy in the form of electromagnetic waves.

The radiation which is important to solar energy applications is that emitted by the sun which lies within the ultraviolet, visible, and infrared regions. Thus, the radiation wavelength which is important to solar energy application is between 0.15 and 3.0 μm. The wavelengths in the visible region lie between 0.38 and 0.72 μm.

3.01.4.1 Thermal Radiation

Thermal radiation is a form of energy emission and transmission that depends entirely on the temperature characteristics of the emissive surface. There is no intervening carrier as in the other modes of heat transmission, that is, conduction and convection. Thermal radiation is in fact an electromagnetic wave that travels at the speed of light (C = 300 000 km s^{-1} in vacuum). This speed is related to the wavelength (λ) and frequency (v) of the radiation as given by the equation:

$$C = \lambda v \qquad [38]$$

When a beam of thermal radiation is incident on the surface of a body, part of it is reflected away from the surface, part is absorbed by the body, and part is transmitted through the body. The various properties associated with this phenomenon are the fraction of radiation

Table 3 Angular variation of absorptance for black pant [20]

Angle of incidence (°)	Absorptance
0–30	0.96
30–40	0.95
40–50	0.93
50–60	0.91
60–70	0.88
70–80	0.81
80–90	0.66

reflected, called 'reflectivity' (ρ); fraction of radiation absorbed, called 'absorptivity' (α); and fraction of radiation transmitted, called 'transmissivity' (τ). The three quantities are related by the following equation, which derives from the first law of thermodynamics:

$$\rho + \alpha + \tau = 1 \quad [39]$$

It should be noted that the radiation properties defined above are not only functions of the surface itself but also of the direction and wavelength of the incident radiation. Therefore, eqn [39] is valid for the average properties over the entire wavelength spectrum. The following equation is used to express the dependence of these properties on the wavelength:

$$\rho_\lambda + \alpha_\lambda + \tau_\lambda = 1 \quad [40]$$

where ρ_λ is spectral reflectivity, α_λ is spectral absorptivity, and τ_λ is spectral transmissivity.

The angular variation of absorptance for black paint is illustrated in **Table 3** for incidence angles of 0–90°. The absorptance for diffuse radiation is approximately 0.90 [20].

Most solid bodies are opaque, so that $\tau = 0$ and $\rho + \alpha = 1$. If a body absorbs all the impinging thermal radiation such that $\tau = 0$, $\rho = 0$, and $\alpha = 1$, regardless of the spectral character or directional preference of the incident radiation, it is called 'blackbody'. This is a hypothetical idealization that does not exist in reality.

Blackbody is not only a perfect absorber, but also characterized by an upper limit to the emission of thermal radiation. The energy emitted by a blackbody is a function of its temperature and is not evenly distributed over all wavelengths. The rate of energy emission per unit area at a particular wavelength is termed the monochromatic emissive power. Max Planck was the first to derive a functional relation for the monochromatic emissive power of a blackbody in terms of temperature and wavelength. This was done by using the quantum theory and the resulting equation, called the Planck's equation for blackbody radiation is given by:

$$E_{b\lambda} = \frac{C_1}{\lambda^5 (e^{C_2/\lambda T} - 1)} \quad [41]$$

where $E_{b\lambda}$ is monochromatic emissive power of a blackbody (W m^{-2} µm), T is temperature of the body (K), λ is wavelength (µm), C_1 is a constant which is 3.74×10^8 W µm^4 m^{-2}, and C_2 is a constant which is 1.44×10^4 µm K.

By differentiating eqn [41] and equating to zero, the wavelength corresponding to the maximum of the distribution can be obtained and is equal to $\lambda_{max} T = 2897.8$ µm K. This is known as the Wien's displacement law. **Figure 18** shows the spectral radiation distribution for blackbody radiation at three different temperature sources. The curves have been obtained by using the Planck's equation.

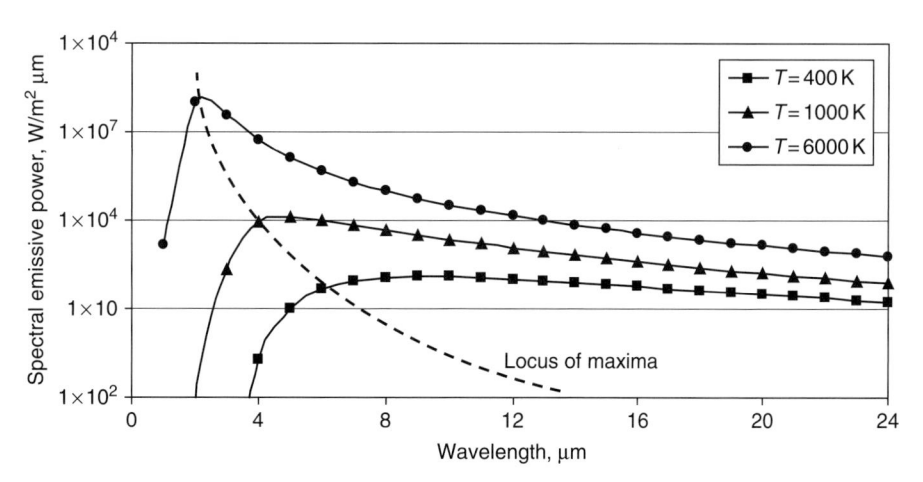

Figure 18 Spectral distribution of blackbody radiation.

The total emissive power E_b and the monochromatic emissive power $E_{b\lambda}$ of a blackbody are related by:

$$E_b = \int_0^\infty E_{b\lambda} d\lambda \qquad [42]$$

Substituting eqn [41] into eqn [42] and performing the integration result in the Stefan–Boltzmann law:

$$E_b = \sigma T^4 \qquad [43]$$

where σ is the Stefan–Boltzmann constant which is $5.669\,7 \times 10^{-8}\,\text{W}\,\text{m}^{-2}\,\text{K}^4$.

In many cases, it is necessary to know the amount of radiation emitted by a blackbody in a specific wavelength band $\lambda_1 \to \lambda_2$. This is done by modifying eqn [42] as $E_b(0 \to \lambda) = \int_0^\lambda E_{b\lambda} d\lambda$. Since the value of $E_{b\lambda}$ depends on both λ and T, it is better to use both variables as $E_b(0 \to \lambda T) = \int_0^{\lambda T} \frac{E_{b\lambda}}{T} d\lambda T$. Thus, for the wavelength band of $\lambda_1 \to \lambda_2$, we get $E_b(\lambda_1 T \to \lambda_2 T) = \int_{\lambda_1 T}^{\lambda_2 T} \frac{E_{b\lambda}}{T} d\lambda T$, which results in $E_b(0 \to \lambda_1 T) - E_b(0 \to \lambda_2 T)$. Values of $E_b(0 \to \lambda T)$ are usually given in tables as a fraction of the total emissive power $E_b = \sigma T^4$ for various values of λT. Such tables can be found in all heat transfer books.

A blackbody is also a perfect diffuse emitter, so its intensity of radiation, I_b, is a constant in all directions given by

$$E_b = \pi I_b \qquad [44]$$

Of course, real surfaces emit less energy than corresponding blackbodies. The ratio of the total emissive power E of a real surface to the total emissive power E_b of a blackbody, both at the same temperature, is called the emissivity (ε) of a real surface, that is,

$$\varepsilon = \frac{E}{E_b} \qquad [45]$$

The emissivity of a surface is not only a function of surface temperature, but depends also on wavelength and direction. In fact, the emissivity given by eqn [45] is the average value over the entire wavelength range in all directions and it is often referred as the total or hemispherical emissivity. Similarly to eqn [45], to express the dependence on wavelength, the monochromatic or spectral emissivity ε_λ is defined as the ratio of the monochromatic emissive power E_λ of a real surface to the monochromatic emissive power $E_{b\lambda}$ of a blackbody, both at the same wavelength and temperature, that is,

$$\varepsilon_\lambda = \frac{E_\lambda}{E_{b\lambda}} \qquad [46]$$

The Kirchoff's law of radiation states that for any surface in thermal equilibrium, monochromatic emissivity is equal to monochromatic absorptivity, that is,

$$\varepsilon_\lambda(T) = \alpha_\lambda(T) \qquad [47]$$

The temperature (T) is used in eqn [47] to emphasize that this equation applies only when the temperatures of the source of the incident radiation and of the body itself are the same. It should therefore be noted that the emissivity of a body on earth (at normal temperature) cannot be equal to solar radiation (emitted from the sun at $T = 5760\,\text{K}$). Equation [47] can be generalized as:

$$\varepsilon(T) = \alpha(T) \qquad [48]$$

Equation [48] relates the total emissivity and absorptivity over the entire wavelength. This generalization, however, is strictly valid only if the incident and emitted radiation have in addition to the temperature equilibrium at the surfaces, the same spectral distribution. Such conditions are rarely met in real life to simplify the analysis of radiation problems; however, the assumption that monochromatic properties are constant over all wavelengths is often made. Such a body with these characteristics is called a 'graybody'.

Similar to eqn [44] for a real surface, the radiant energy leaving the surface includes its original emission and any reflected rays. The rate of total radiant energy leaving a surface per unit surface area is called the 'radiosity' (J) and is given by:

$$J = \varepsilon E_b + \rho H \qquad [49]$$

where E_b is blackbody emissive power per unit surface area ($\text{W}\,\text{m}^{-2}$), H is irradiation incident on the surface per unit surface area ($\text{W}\,\text{m}^{-2}$), ε is emissivity of the surface, and ρ is reflectivity of the surface.

There are two idealized limiting cases of radiation reflection, the reflection is called 'specular' if the reflected ray leaves at an angle with the normal to the surface equal to the angle made by the incident ray and is called 'diffuse' if the incident ray is reflected uniformly in all directions. Real surfaces are neither perfectly specular nor perfectly diffuse. Rough industrial surfaces, however, are often considered as diffuse reflectors in engineering calculations.

A real surface is both a diffuse emitter and a diffuse reflector and thus it has a diffuse radiosity, that is, the intensity of radiation from this surface (I) would be constant in all directions. Therefore, the following equation is used for a real surface:

$$J = \pi \cdot I \qquad [50]$$

3.01.4.2 Transparent Plates

Glazing is often used in solar energy collectors to reduce thermal losses. When a beam of radiation strikes the surface of a transparent plate at an angle θ_1, called incidence angle, as shown in **Figure 19**, part of the incident radiation is reflected and the remainder is refracted or bent to an angle θ_2, called refraction angle, as it passes through the interface. Angle θ_1 is also equal to the angle at which the beam is specularly reflected from the surface. Angles θ_1 and θ_2 are not equal when the density of the plane is different from that of a medium through which the radiation is coming.

Additionally, refraction causes the transmitted beam to be bent toward the perpendicular to the surface of higher density. The two angles are related by the Snell's law:

$$n = \frac{n_2}{n_1} = \frac{\sin \theta_1}{\sin \theta_2} \qquad [51]$$

where n_1 and n_2 are the refraction indices and n is the ratio of refraction index for the two media forming the interface. The refraction index is the determinant factor for the reflection losses at the interface. A typical value of refraction index is 1.000 for air, 1.526 for glass, and 1.33 for water.

Expressions for perpendicular and parallel components of radiation for smooth surfaces were derived by Fresnel as:

$$r_\perp = \frac{\sin^2(\theta_2 - \theta_1)}{\sin^2(\theta_2 + \theta_1)} \qquad [52]$$

$$r_\parallel = \frac{\tan^2(\theta_2 - \theta_1)}{\tan^2(\theta_2 + \theta_1)} \qquad [53]$$

Equation [52] represents the perpendicular component of unpolarized radiation and eqn [53] represents the parallel one. It should be noted that parallel and perpendicular refer to the plane defined by the incident beam and the surface normal.

Properties are evaluated by calculating the average of the above two components as:

$$r = \frac{1}{2}(r_\perp + r_\parallel) \qquad [54]$$

For normal incidence, both angles are 0, and eqn [54] can be combined with eqn [51] to yield:

$$r_{(0)} = \left(\frac{n_1 - n_2}{n_1 + n_2}\right)^2 \qquad [55]$$

If one medium is air ($n = 1.0$), then eqn [55] becomes:

$$r_{(0)} = \left(\frac{n - 1}{n + 1}\right)^2 \qquad [56]$$

Similarly, the transmittance, τ_r (subscript r indicates that only reflection losses are considered), can be calculated from the average transmittance of the two components as follows:

$$\tau_r = \frac{1}{2}\left(\frac{1 - r_\parallel}{1 + r_\parallel} + \frac{1 - r_\perp}{1 + r_\perp}\right) \qquad [57]$$

For a glazing system of N covers of the same material, it can be proved that:

$$\tau_r = \frac{1}{2}\left(\frac{1 - r_\parallel}{1 + (2N - 1)r_\parallel} + \frac{1 - r_\perp}{1 + (2N - 1)r_\perp}\right) \qquad [58]$$

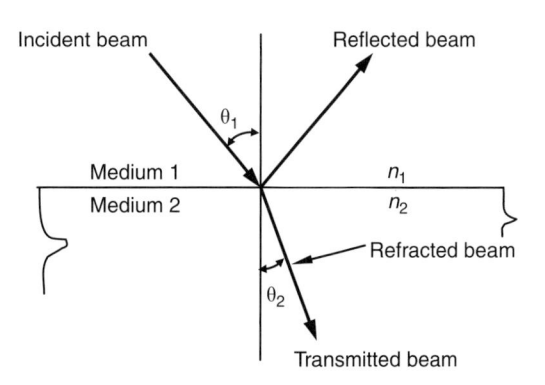

Figure 19 Incident and refraction angles for a beam passing from medium with refraction index n_1 to a medium with refraction index n_2.

The transmittance, τ_a (subscript a indicates that only absorption losses are considered), can be calculated from:

$$\tau_a = e^{\left(-\frac{KL}{\cos\theta_2}\right)} \quad [59]$$

where K is the extinction coefficient and can vary from 4 m^{-1} (for low-quality glass) to 32 m^{-1} (for high-quality glass) and L is the thickness of the glass cover.

The transmittance, reflectance, and absorptance of a single cover (by considering both reflection and absorption losses) are given by the following expressions. These expressions are for the perpendicular components of polarization, whereas the same relations can be used for the parallel components.

$$\tau_\perp = \frac{\tau_a(1-r_\perp)^2}{1-(r_\perp \tau_a)^2} = \tau_a \frac{1-r_\perp}{1+r_\perp}\left(\frac{1-r_\perp^2}{1-(r_\perp \tau_a)^2}\right) \quad [60]$$

$$\rho_\perp = r_\perp + \frac{(1-r_\perp)^2 \tau_a^2 r_\perp}{1-(r_\perp \tau_a)^2} = r_\perp(1+\tau_a \tau_\perp) \quad [61]$$

$$\alpha_\perp = (1-\tau_a)\left(\frac{1-r_\perp}{1-r_\perp \tau_a}\right) \quad [62]$$

Since for practical collector covers τ_a is seldom less than 0.9 and r is of the order of 0.1, the transmittance of a single cover becomes:

$$\tau \cong \tau_a \tau_r \quad [63]$$

The absorptance of a cover can be approximated by neglecting the last term of eqn [62]:

$$\alpha \cong 1 - \tau_a \quad [64]$$

and the reflectance of a single cover could be found by considering the fact that $\rho = 1 - \alpha - \tau$, as:

$$\rho \cong \tau_a(1-\tau_r) = \tau_a - \tau \quad [65]$$

For a two-cover system of not necessarily same materials, the following equation can be obtained (subscript 1 refers to outer cover and 2 to inner):

$$\tau = \frac{1}{2}\left[\left(\frac{\tau_1 \tau_2}{1-\rho_1 \rho_2}\right)_\perp + \left(\frac{\tau_1 \tau_2}{1-\rho_1 \rho_2}\right)_\parallel\right] = \frac{1}{2}(\tau_\perp + \tau_\parallel) \quad [66]$$

$$\rho = \frac{1}{2}\left[\left(\rho_1 + \frac{\tau \rho_2 \tau_1}{\tau_2}\right)_\perp + \left(\rho_1 + \frac{\tau \rho_2 \tau_1}{\tau_2}\right)_\parallel\right] = \frac{1}{2}(\rho_\perp + \rho_\parallel) \quad [67]$$

3.01.5 The Solar Resource

The operation of solar collectors and systems depends on the solar radiation input and the ambient air temperature and their sequences. One of the forms that solar radiation data are available is on maps. These give the general impression of the availability of solar radiation without details on the local meteorological conditions and for this reason must be used with care. One valuable source of such information is the Meteonorm [21].

For the local climate, usually data in the form of a typical meteorological year are required. This is a typical year, which is defined as a year which sums up all the climatic information characterizing a period as long as the mean life of a solar system. In this way, the long-term performance of a collector or a system can be calculated by running a computer program over the reference year.

3.01.5.1 Typical Meteorological Year

A representative data base of weather data for the 1-year duration is known as 'test reference year' (TRY) or 'typical meteorological year' (TMY). A TMY is a data set of hourly values of solar radiation and meteorological elements. It consists of months selected from individual years concatenated to form a complete year. The TMY contains values of solar radiation (global and direct), ambient temperature, relative humidity and wind speed, and direction for all hours of the year. The selection of typical weather conditions for a given location is very crucial in computer simulations for performance predictions of solar systems and thermal performance of buildings and has led various investigators either to run long periods of observational data or to select a particular year, which appears to be typical from several years of data. The use of a TMY is for computer simulations of solar energy conversion systems and building systems.

The adequacy of using an average or typical year of meteorological data with a simulation model to provide an estimate of the long-term system performance depends on the sensitivity of system performance to the hourly and daily weather sequences. Regardless of how it is selected, an 'average' year cannot be expected to have the same weather sequences as those occurring in the long term. However, the simulated performance of a system for an 'average year' may provide a good estimate of the long-term system performance if the weather sequences occurring in the average year are representative of those occurring in the long term or if the system performance is independent of the weather sequences [22]. Using this approach, the long-term integrated system performance can be evaluated and the dynamic system's behavior can be obtained.

In the past, many attempts have been made to generate such climatological data bases for different areas around the world using various methodologies. One of the most common methodologies for generating a TMY is the one proposed by Hall *et al.* [23] using the Filkenstein–Schafer (FS) statistical method [24].

The FS method algorithm is as follows: first, the cumulative distribution functions (CDFs) are calculated for each selected meteorological parameter and for each month, over the whole selected period as well as over each specific year of the period. In order to calculate the CDFs for each parameter, the data are grouped under a number of bins, and the CDFs are calculated by counting the cases under the same bin.

The next step is to compare the CDF of a meteorological parameter, for example, global horizontal radiation, for each month for each specific year with the respective CDF of the long-term composite of all years in the selected period.

The FS is the mean difference of the long-term CDF, CDF_{LT}, and the specific month's CDF, CDF_{SM}, calculated over the bins used for the estimation of the CDFs given by:

$$FS = \frac{1}{N} \sum_{i=1}^{N} \left| CDF_{LT}(z_i) - CDF_{SM}(z_i) \right| \quad [68]$$

where N is the number of bins (by default $N = 31$) and z_i is the value of the FS statistic for the particular month of the specific year and the meteorological parameter under consideration.

The next step is the application of the weighting factors, WF_j, to the FS statistics values, one for each of the considered meteorological parameters, FS_j, corresponding to each specific month in the selected period. In this way, a weighted sum or average value, WS, is derived and this value is assigned to the respective month, that is,

$$WS = \frac{1}{M} \sum_{j=1}^{M} WF_j FS_j \quad [69]$$

with

$$\sum_{j=1}^{M} WF_i = 1 \quad [70]$$

where M is the number of parameters in the data base.

The user can change the WF values by examining the relative importance of each meteorological parameter in the final result. The smaller the WS, the better the approximation to a 'typical meteorological month' (TMM).

Applying the above procedure for all months of the available period, a composite year can be formed consisting of the selected months with the smallest WS values.

The root mean standard deviation (RMSD) of the total daily values of the global solar irradiance distribution for each month of each year, with respect to the mean long-term hourly distribution and the FS statistics can then be estimated. The RMSD can be computed and, for each month, the year corresponding to the lowest value can be selected. The estimations are carried out according to the expressions:

$$RMSD = \sqrt{\frac{\sum_{i=1}^{N}(x_i - \bar{x})}{N}} \quad [71]$$

where $\bar{x}$ is the average value of its parameter over the number of bins ($N = 31$).

A total of 8760 rows are included in a TMY file, each corresponding to each hour of the year.

3.01.5.2 Typical Meteorological Year – Second Generation

A type-2 TMY format is completely different and consists of much more fields. Such a file can be used with detailed building analysis programs like DOE-2, BDA (Building Design Advisor), and Energy Plus. A TMY2 file also contains a complete year (8760 data) of hourly meteorological data. Each hourly record in the file contains values for solar radiation, dry bulb temperature, and meteorological elements such as illuminance, precipitation, visibility, and snowfall. Radiation and illumination data are becoming increasingly necessary in many simulation programs. A two-character source and uncertainty flag is attached to each data value to indicate whether the data value was measured, modeled, or missing, and to provide an estimate of the uncertainty of the data value. By including the uncertainty flags, users can evaluate the potential impact of weather variability on the performance of solar systems or buildings.

The first record of each file is the file header that describes the station. The file header contains a five-digit meteorological station number, city, state (optional), time zone, latitude, longitude, and elevation. The field positions and definitions of these header elements together with the values given for the TMY2 for Nicosia, Cyprus [25, 26], are shown in **Table 4**.

Table 4 Header elements in the TMY2 format [26]

Field position	Element	Definition	Value used
002–006	Five-digit number	Weather station's number	17 609
008–029	City	City where the station is located (maximum 22 characters)	Nicosia
031–032	State	State where the station is located (abbreviate to two letters)	
034–036	Time zone	Time zone is the number of hours by which the LST is ahead of Greenwich (+ve E, –ve W)	2
038–044	Latitude	Latitude of the station	
038		N = North of equator	N
040–041		Degrees	34
043–044		Minutes	53
046–053	Longitude	Longitude of the station	
046		W = West, E = East	E
048–050		Degrees	33
052–053		Minutes	38
056–059	Elevation	Elevation of station in meters above sea level	162

Bold values represent the main headings of the field positions.

Following the file header, 8760 hourly data records provide a 1-year of solar radiation, illuminance, and meteorological data, along with their source and uncertainty flags. Each hourly record begins with the year (field positions 2–3) from which the typical month was chosen, followed by the month, day, and hour information and the rest of the required data [27].

For solar radiation and illuminance elements, the data values represent the energy received during the 60 min proceeding the hour indicated. For meteorological elements (with a few exceptions), observations or measurements were made at the hour indicated. A few of the meteorological elements had observations, measurements, or estimates made at daily, instead of hourly, intervals. Consequently, the data values for broadband aerosol optical depth, snow depth, and days since last snowfall represent the values available for the day indicated.

With the exception of extraterrestrial horizontal and extraterrestrial direct radiation, the two field positions immediately following the data value provide source and uncertainty flags. Source and uncertainty flags for extraterrestrial horizontal and extraterrestrial direct radiation are not provided because these elements were calculated using equations considered to give exact values. Explanation of the uncertainty flags for the other quantities is given in Reference [27].

Recently, a third-generation TMY3 format is introduced. This is radically different from the TMY and TMY2 data. The older TMY data sets used columnar or positional formats, presumably as a method of optimizing data storage space. Such formats are difficult to read, and it is difficult to import specific fields into many software packages [28]. The comma separated value (CSV) format used in previous versions of TMY's is ubiquitous, and many existing programs and applications provide built-in functions to read or parse it. For that reason, the TMY3 data set is distributed in the CSV format.

Despite the format differences, the fields in the TMY3 are very similar to those in the TMY2 data set. Fundamental differences are the addition of three new fields for surface albedo and liquid precipitation and the removal of the fields for present weather, snow-depth, and days since last snowfall that were present in the TMY2 [28]. Presently, only US locations are given in TMY3 format.

References

[1] Kreith F and Kreider JF (1978) *Principles of Solar Engineering*. New York: McGraw-Hill Book Company.
[2] Anderson B (1977) *Solar Energy: Fundamentals in Building Design*. New York: McGraw-Hill Book Company.
[3] Dincer I (1998) Energy and environmental impacts: Present and future perspectives. *Energy Sources* 20(4/5): 427–453.
[4] Dincer I (1998) Renewable energy, environment and sustainable development. *Proceedings of the World Renewable Energy Congress V*. Florence, Italy, September 1998, pp. 2559–2562.
[5] Rosen MA (1996) The role of energy efficiency in sustainable development. *Technology and Society* 15(4): 21–26.
[6] Dincer I and Rosen MA (1998) A worldwide perspective on energy, environment and sustainable development. *International Journal of Energy Research* 22(15): 1305–1321.
[7] Worldwatch Institute (2007) www.worldwatch.org (last accessed September 2008).
[8] Dincer I (1999) Environmental impacts of energy. *Energy Policy* 27(14): 845–854.
[9] Colonbo U (1992) Development and the global environment. In: Hollander JM (ed.) *The Energy-Environment Connection*, pp. 3–14. Washington, DC: Island Press.
[10] IPCC (2007) Climate change 2007: The physical basis. *Contribution of Working Group I to the Fourth Assessment Report of the Intergovernmental Panel on Climate Change*. Cambridge, UK, and New York, US. www.ipcc.int (last accessed October 2008).
[11] Sayigh AAW (2001) Renewable energy: Global progress and examples. Renewable Energy 2001, WREN. pp. 15–17. London: Sovereign Publications.
[12] Johanson TB, Kelly H, Reddy AKN, Williams RH (eds.) (1993) Renewable fuels and electricity for a growing world economy. *Renewable Energy-Sources for Fuels and Electricity*, pp. 1–71. Washington, DC: Island Press.
[13] Abu-Zour A and Riffat S (2006) Environmental and economic impact of a new type of solar louver thermal collector. *International Journal of Low Carbon Technologies* 1(3): 217–227.
[14] Garg HP (1982) *Treatise on Solar Energy, Vol. 1: Fundamentals of Solar Energy Research*. New York: Wiley.
[15] Spenser JW (1971) Fourier series representation of the position of the sun. *Search* 2(5): 172.

[16] Kreith F and Kreider JF (1978) *Principles of Solar Engineering.* New York: McGraw-Hill Book Company.
[17] Duffie JA and Beckman WA (1991) *Solar Engineering of Thermal Processes.* Wiley.
[18] ASHRAE (1975) *Procedure for Determining Heating and Cooling Loads for Computerizing Energy Calculations.* Atlanta, GA: ASHRAE.
[19] Meinel AB and Meinel MP (1976) *Applied Solar Energy: An Introduction.* Reading, MA: Addison-Wesley Publishing Company.
[20] Löf GOG and Tybout RA (1972) Model for optimizing solar heating design. *ASME Paper*, 72-WA/SOL-8.
[21] Meteonorm (2007) Maps. http://www.meteonorm.com (last accessed August 2011).
[22] Klein SA, Beckman WA, and Duffie JA (1976) A design procedure for solar heating systems. *Solar Energy* 18: 113–127.
[23] Hall IJ, Prairie RR, Anderson HE, and Boes EC (1978) Generation of typical meteorological years for 26 SOLMET stations. Sandia Laboratories Report, SAND 78-1601. Albuquerque, New Mexico.
[24] Filkenstein JM and Schafer RE (1971) Improved goodness of fit tests. *Biometrica* 58: 641–645.
[25] Kalogirou SA (2003) Generation of typical meteorological year (TMY-2) for Nicosia, Cyprus. *Renewable Energy* 28(15): 2317–2334.
[26] Kalogirou SA (2009) *Solar Energy Engineering: Processes and Systems.* Academic Press. Amsterdam: Elsevier Science. ISBN: 978-0-12-374501-9
[27] Marion W and Urban K (1996) *User's Manual for TMY2s Typical Meteorological Years.* Colorado: National Renewable Energy Laboratory.
[28] Wilcox S and Marion W (2008) *Users Manual for TMY3 Data Sets.* Colorado: National Renewable Energy Laboratory.

3.02 The Solar Resource

HD Kambezidis, Institute of Environmental Research and Sustainable Development, Athens, Greece

© 2012 Elsevier Ltd. All rights reserved.

3.02.1	Introduction	28
3.02.2	Sun–Earth Astronomical Relations	29
3.02.3	Solar Constant	32
3.02.4	Solar Spectrum	33
3.02.4.1	Planck's Law	33
3.02.4.2	Wien's Displacement Law	33
3.02.4.3	Stefan–Boltzmann Law	34
3.02.5	Interference of Solar Radiation with the Earth's Atmosphere	34
3.02.5.1	The Earth's Atmosphere	34
3.02.5.2	Optical Air Mass	35
3.02.5.3	Attenuation of Solar Direct Radiation	36
3.02.5.4	Rayleigh and Mie Scattering, Reflection, and Absorption	36
3.02.6	Models of Broadband Solar Radiation on Horizontal and Tilted Surfaces	39
3.02.6.1	Calculation of Solar Radiation on a Horizontal Plane	40
3.02.6.2	The Meteorological Radiation Model	43
3.02.6.3	Calculation of Solar Radiation on a Tilted Surface	45
3.02.6.4	Quality Control of Solar Radiation Values	49
3.02.7	Evaluation of Models	49
3.02.7.1	The Standard Deviation	50
3.02.7.2	The Root Mean Square Error	50
3.02.7.3	The Mean Bias Error	51
3.02.7.4	The Mean Absolute Bias Error	51
3.02.7.5	The t-test	51
3.02.7.6	The Index of Agreement (d)	52
3.02.7.7	The Coefficient of Determination (R^2)	52
3.02.8	Models of Solar Spectral Radiation	54
3.02.9	Net Solar Radiation	54
3.02.10	Networks of Solar Radiation Stations – Solar Atlases	58
3.02.11	Utility Tools for Solar Radiation Calculations	62
3.02.12	Instruments for Measuring Solar Radiation	64
3.02.12.1	Solar Radiometers	64
3.02.12.2	The World Radiometric Reference	67
3.02.12.3	Calibration of Solar Radiometers	67
3.02.12.4	Uncertainty of Solar Radiometers	67
3.02.12.5	Correction of Common Solar Radiometer Errors	67
Appendix A:	Spectral Distribution of Solar Radiation	67
Appendix B:	Radiometric Terminology	78
Appendix C:	The Sun as a Blackbody	79
Appendix D:	Physical Constants and Conversion Factors	80
References		80

Glossary

Absorption Transfer of some of the solar radiation power (power of electromagnetic waves) to air molecules during collision of solar radiation with constituents in the atmosphere.
ACR Active-cavity radiometer (a reference radiometer for calibrating others).
Aphelion The longer distance between Earth and Sun (occurring around 3–8 April).
Attenuation Depletion of solar radiation (power of electromagnetic waves) due to absorption and scattering by the constituents (molecules) of the atmosphere of the Earth.
DNI Direct normal irradiance.
DU Dobson Unit (or atm-cm) A measure of the columnar height of ozone in the atmosphere.
Ecliptic plane The plane on which the Earth orbits around the Sun (heliocentric system) or the Sun around the Earth (geocentric system).
Equinox The positions of the Earth around the Sun on the ecliptic with (solar) declination equal to 0; this occurs twice a year, around 20–21 March

(vernal equinox) and 22–23 September (autumn equinox).
FOV Field-of-view (aperture of pyrheliometer).
Mie scattering Scattering of the solar radiation (electromagnetic waves) by molecules comparable in size with the wavelength.
Net solar radiation The difference between incoming (short-wave) and outgoing (long-wave) radiation.
Perihelion The shortest distance between Earth and Sun (occurring around 2–4 January).
Pyranometer A solar radiation instrument capable of measuring solar radiation in the range 0.29–2.8 µm.
Pyrheliometer A solar radiation instrument capable of measuring solar radiation at a point (usually the Sun).
Radiometer An instrument to measure solar radiation flux (or power).
Rayleigh scattering Scattering of the solar radiation (electromagnetic waves) by molecules of bigger dimensions than the wavelength.
TOA Top-of-the-atmosphere, referring to an altitude of 100 km from the surface of the Earth.

Scattering Re-distribution of the solar radiation power (power of electromagnetic waves) during collision of solar radiation with constituents in the atmosphere.
Solar atlas Map of an area showing the distribution of solar radiation (solar energy) over it.
Solar constant The solar radiation received at TOA on a plane normal to the solar rays at the mean Sun-Earth distance.
Solar declination The angle formed by the lines joining the centers of the Sun and Earth and the line towards the south of the observer on the Earth along the ecliptic plane.
Solar geometry The position of the Sun in the sky of any place on earth and any day of the year.
Solar (radiation) spectrum The electromagnetic waves emitted by the photosphere of the Sun.
Solstice The apparent position of the Sun in the sky reaching its northernmost or southernmost extremes in the sky; the first is called *summer solstice* (on 20–21 June) and the second *winter solstice* (on 21–22 December).
Spectrometer A radiometer capable to measure solar radiation at various wavelengths.
Statistic Statistical estimator.

3.02.1 Introduction

The Sun emits a tremendous amount of energy, in the form of electromagnetic (EM) radiation, into space. Most of the Sun's energy flows out of our solar system into interstellar space without ever colliding with anything. However, a very small fraction of that energy collides with planets, including the Earth, before it can escape into the interstellar void. A part of the fraction that the Earth intercepts is sufficient to warm our planet and drive its climate system.

The Sun emits about 1366 W of power in the form of EM radiation fall normally on an area of 1 m^2 at the top of the Earth's atmosphere (100 km from its surface). Thus, the average surface temperature of the Earth (including the effects of its atmosphere) is about 15 °C (http://encarta.msn.com/encyclopedia_761567022/Global_Warming.html). If, though, the Earth were displaced closer to the Sun, where, for example, the planet Mercury is, the number of watts per square meter (W m^{-2}) would be greater, giving an average temperature of about 179 °C (http://www.solarviews.com/eng/mercury.htm). If the Earth were further from the Sun, as, for example, the planet Jupiter is, the number of W m^{-2} would be lesser, giving an average temperature of about −145 °C (http://www.universetoday.com/guide-to-space/jupiter/temperature-of-jupiter). This is so because the surface area of a sphere varies as the square of the radius of the sphere, so the energy per unit area received varies inversely as the square of the distance from the Sun. A planet situated half as far from the Sun as is the Earth would be scorched by four times as much power from the Sun (5472 W m^{-2}). A planet twice as far from the Sun as is the Earth would be warmed by just one-fourth as much radiation (342 W m^{-2}). So our planet's distance from the Sun is the first key factor influencing the energy we receive, and thus the behavior of our climate.

Solar radiation refers to the energy coming from the Sun in the wavelength range 0.3–3 µm; it constitutes the principal source of energy for the global Earth–atmosphere system. Detailed knowledge of the solar radiation transmission through the atmosphere (under both clear and cloudy conditions) is crucial in determining any possible change in the Earth's radiation budget in a changing climate. For this reason, various solar radiation models have been developed to calculate solar fluxes at the surface either in the whole spectrum (0.3–3 µm) (broadband models) or in a part of it (spectral models). The basis of such models is the so-called radiative transfer models (RTMs), which are complex computer codes taking into account the interaction of solar radiation with the Earth's atmosphere.

Each location on the Earth's surface receives different amounts of solar energy throughout the year. This is due to many factors. Some of them relate to the geometry of the Earth's orbit around the Sun and others to the absorption and scattering of solar radiation by its atmosphere. In the first set, the eccentricity of the Earth's orbit, the solar declination, and the geographical coordinates of a location on the surface of the Earth and the position of the Sun in the sky play important roles. In the second set, the scattering and absorption of solar energy by the molecules in the atmosphere play important roles. In this context, one can distinguish between the direct solar radiation (or beam solar radiation) coming directly from the Sun's disk and the diffuse solar radiation coming from all parts of the sky (except the Sun's disk) as a result of scattering (including reflection) of solar rays by the molecules in the atmosphere. The sum of direct and diffuse components makes the global (or total) solar radiation. Usually, the measurements of solar radiation refer to the global and diffuse components on a horizontal plane, and so do most of the (broadband or spectral) models. Nevertheless, due to various applications of solar energy, such as solar thermal and photovoltaic (PV) systems, there is a need for measuring or calculating the incident solar energy on an inclined plane. This need is rarely met by measuring equipment (the so-called radiometers) worldwide. Therefore, this gap has been the target of various models.

A solar radiation model is a computer code that tries to simulate the solar radiation received on a (horizontal or inclined) surface with an area of 1 m^2. These models simulate solar radiation in either a statistical or a physical way. In the first case, a statistical model uses past (or historical) solar radiation data and tries to forecast future values at the same location. Such models use the autoregressive and moving average (ARMA) or neuronal technology. In the second case, the models take into account the interference between solar radiation and atmospheric molecules; that way they are simple or complicated RTMs. Whatever the category of the model is, there is a great need to evaluate simulation results against measurements. Several statistical indicators play an important role in this evaluation.

The need for the knowledge of solar energy received at a place is high, especially at places where no measuring (actinometric) stations exist, and the development of satellites oriented to providing the scientific community with the solar radiation received at regional scale aided this effort. Such satellite images are being verified by measurements performed at actinometric stations over Europe and the United States, Canada, and Japan in order for the satellite data to be used with certainty. The comparison shows that the satellite data up to now are reliable enough for solar energy engineering purposes; however, they are not ready for use in solar radiation research. The outcome of this exercise together with the use of solar radiation models has triggered interest in forming regional maps of solar availability. Therefore, such maps (also called solar atlases) exist nowadays covering several regions of the world, for example, the United States, Canada, Japan, the European Union, and India. These solar atlases give information about the expected mean levels of solar radiation received on horizontal (and in some cases inclined) surfaces throughout the year as well as seasonally. They are used for assessing the available solar energy at the scale of a region in a country or bigger; they are intended for use at specific locations as the satellite image pixels have dimensions of a few kilometers.

Nevertheless, the most accurate way of knowing the subhourly, hourly, daily, monthly, and annual levels of the various solar radiation components at a location is by performing measurements at the actinometric stations. The actinometers are sensors specially designed to measure solar radiation either in the broadband or in the spectral sense. The solar instruments that measure the global or the diffuse component in the whole solar spectrum (0.3–3 μm) are called pyranometers. If they are used to measure a part of the spectrum, they are called spectroradiometers. The instruments that measure the direct solar radiation are called pyrheliometers. Various spectral regions are possible with optical filters, for example, 0.525–2.8 μm (OG530 filter, ex OG1), 0.630–2.8 μm (RG630 filter, ex RG2), and 0.695–2.8 μm (RG695 filter, ex RG8). Those radiometers that measure the ultraviolet (UV) spectrum (0.295–0.385 μm) are called UV radiometers. Finally, the sensors for measuring the infrared (IR) band (0.750–100 μm) are called pyrgeometers. Several radiometer manufacturers exist worldwide. A solar radiation terminology is given in Appendix B.

3.02.2 Sun–Earth Astronomical Relations

The Earth moves around the Sun in an elliptical orbit, making a complete revolution in a year (365.24 days). **Figure 1** shows the orbit of the Earth together with the two equinoxes, the two solstices, the aphelion, and the perihelion, and the positions of the smallest distance between the Sun and the Earth. Equinox is the position of the Earth on its orbit when the length of the day is equal to that of the night. This occurs on 20–21 March (vernal equinox) and 22–23 September (autumnal equinox) each year. Solstice is the point on the Earth's orbit when the day has the longest (summer solstice, 20–21 June) or shortest (winter solstice, 21–22 December) length.

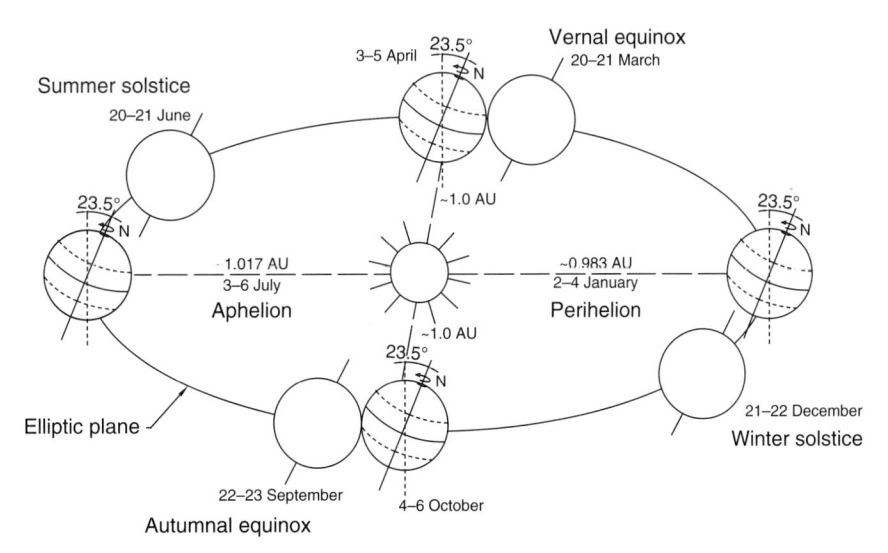

Figure 1 The motion of the Earth around the Sun counterclockwise on its ecliptic plane (heliocentric system). The aphelion is approximately on 4 July, the perihelion on about 3 January, while the Earth is at 1 AU distance from the Sun on 4 April and 5 October on average.

The aphelion and perihelion are those points of the orbit when the distance of the Earth from the Sun is greatest (152.1 million km) and smallest (147.3 million km) and occurs on 3–6 July and 2–4 January, respectively. The mean distance between the two planets occurs on 3–5 April and 4–6 October and is equal to 149.6 million km (more accurately 149.597 890 million km). This distance is called an astronomical unit (AU) and is used in astronomy exclusively. The aphelion distance is equal to 1.017 AU and the perihelion distance is equal to 0.983 AU.

The eccentricity correction factor of the Earth's orbit, S, is equal to the squared ratio of the mean distance Earth–Sun, r_0, to the distance at any instance of the year, r. An exact formula giving S according to [1] is

$$S = \left(\frac{r_0}{r}\right)^2 = 1.000\,110\,0 + 0.034\,221\cos M + 0.001\,280 \sin M + 0.000\,719 \cos 2M + 0.000\,077 \sin 2M \quad [1]$$

where M (in radians) is called the day angle and is given by [2]

$$M = \frac{2\pi D}{365} \quad [2]$$

D is the day number of the year. $D = 1$ on 1 January and 365 on 31 December. On leap years, D takes the value of 366 for the last day of December. Nevertheless, a more simple formula for S can be employed for engineering and technological applications according to [3]

$$S = 1 + 0.033 \cos\left(\frac{2\pi D}{365}\right) \quad [3]$$

Example 3.02.1. Consider 16 October ($D = 289$) in a non-leap year. Then $M = 284.16°$. The eccentricity of the Earth's orbit is found from eqns [1] and [2] as 1.0064 and 1.0091, respectively.

In order to better understand the paths of the Sun in the sky, one can imagine a celestial sphere with the Earth at its center and the Sun revolving around it (**Figure 2**). In the celestial sphere, the celestial poles are the points at which the Earth's polar axis intercepts with the celestial sphere. Similarly, the celestial equator is a projection of the Earth's equatorial plane on the celestial sphere. The plane on which the Earth revolves around the Sun is called the ecliptic plane. On the other hand, the Earth spins around its axis (polar axis). The angle between the polar axis and the normal to the ecliptic plane remains unchanged throughout the year. However, the angle between the lines joining the centers of the Sun and the Earth to the equatorial plane changes every day (every instant indeed). This angle is called solar declination, δ, and takes values between $+23.5°$ and $-23.5°$. These values are achieved during the summer and winter solstices, respectively. Note that when the northern hemisphere experiences summer, the southern hemisphere has winter, and vice versa.

An accurate formula for calculating δ, in degrees, is given by [1]

$$\delta = (0.006\,918 - 0.399\,912 \cos M + 0.070\,257 \sin M - 0.006\,758 \cos 2M + 0.000\,907 \sin 2M - 0.002\,697 \cos 3M \\ + 0.001\,48 \sin 3M)\left(\frac{180}{\pi}\right) \quad [4a]$$

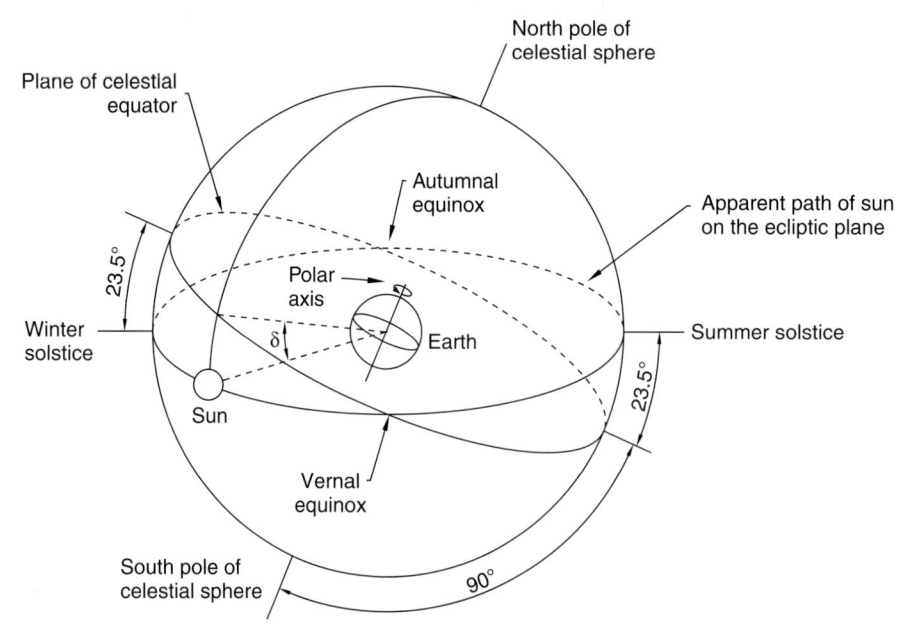

Figure 2 The celestial sphere, the apparent path of the Sun (geocentric system), and the Sun's declination angle. From http://devconsultancygroup.blogspot.com/2010/08/will-la-ninas-year-long-cooling-make.html.

Simpler formulas but not so accurate are given by

$$\delta = \sin^{-1}\left\{0.4 \sin\left[\left(\frac{360}{365}\right)(D-82)\right]\right\}, \text{ in degrees [3]} \quad \text{[4b]}$$

$$\delta = 23.45 \sin\left[\left(\frac{360}{365}\right)(D+284)\right], \text{ in degrees [4]} \quad \text{[4c]}$$

$$\delta = 23.45 \sin\left[2\pi \frac{(D+284)}{365}\right], \text{ in degrees [5]} \quad \text{[4d]}$$

Example 3.02.2. Consider 16 October ($D = 289$) in a non-leap year. Then $M = 4.975$ rad $= 284.16°$. The solar declinations resulting from eqns [4a]–[4d] give the values of $-8.67°$, $-9.42°$, $-9.97°$, and $-9.97°$. The last two equations give identical results.

To describe the Sun's path across the sky, one needs to know the angle of the Sun relative to a line perpendicular to the Earth's surface, the so-called zenith angle, θ_z, and the Sun's position relative to the observer's north–south axis, the azimuthal angle or azimuth, ψ. The angle of the position of the Sun on the plane of the Sun's path in the sky to the observer's horizon is called solar altitude, γ. The hour angle, ω, is easier to use than the azimuthal angle because the hour angle is measured in the plane of the 'apparent' orbit of the Sun as it moves across the sky (**Figure 3**). The position of the Sun in the sky is identified by the values of θ_z and ψ. Since the Earth rotates approximately once every 24 h, the hour angle changes by 15° per hour and moves through 360° over the day. Typically, the hour angle is defined to be zero at solar noon, when the Sun is highest in the sky (**Figure 3**).

$$\cos\theta_z = \sin\delta\sin\phi + \cos\delta\cos\phi\cos\omega = \sin\gamma \quad \text{[5]}$$

$$\cos\varphi = \frac{\sin\gamma\sin\phi - \sin\delta}{\cos\gamma\cos\phi} \quad \text{[6]}$$

where φ is the geographical latitude of the observer's location on the surface of the Earth. In the above equations, the refraction of the Earth's atmosphere has not been taken into account. Kambezidis and Papanikolaou [6] give corrections for this effect. The trigonometric parameters given above obey the following conditions:

$$\gamma = 90° - \theta_z \quad (0° < \theta_z < 90°, 90° > \alpha > 0°) \quad \text{[7a]}$$

$\omega = 0°$ at solar noon, positive in the morning, negative in the afternoon, $-90° \leq \omega \leq 90°$ [7b]

$\varphi > 0$ in the northern hemisphere, $\varphi < 0$ in the southern hemisphere, $-90° \leq \phi \leq 90°$ [7c]

$\psi = 0°$ at observe's south, $\psi > 0°$ to the east, $\psi < 0°$ to the west, $0° \leq \psi \leq 90°$ with $\cos\psi \geq 0°$ and
$$90° \leq \psi \leq 180° \text{ with } \cos\psi \leq 0° \quad \text{[7d]}$$

At sunrise, $\theta_z = 90°$. From eqn [5] the sunrise hour angle, ω_s, is found to be

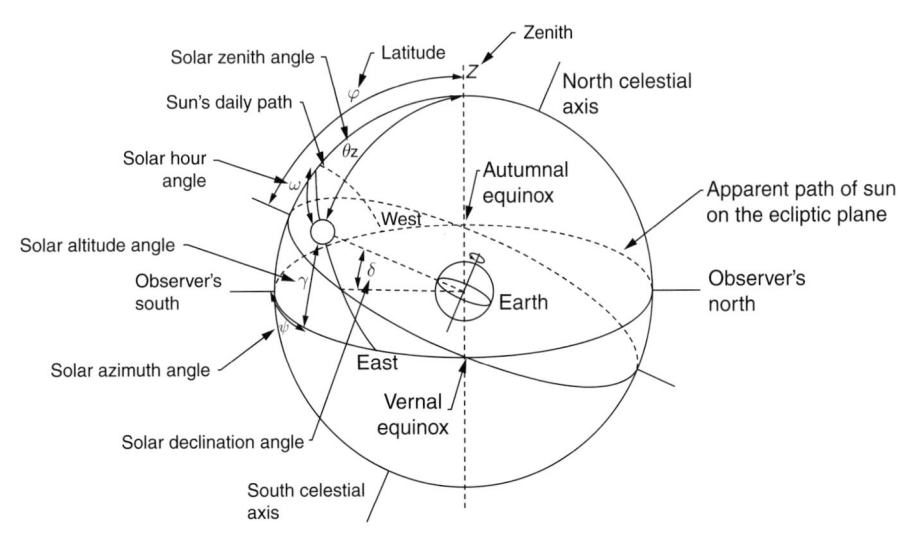

$$\omega_s = \cos^{-1}(-\tan\phi\tan\delta) \quad \text{[8]}$$

Figure 3 The apparent daily path of the Sun in the sky for a place on the Earth (geocentric system) specified by its geographical latitude. The coordinates of the Sun are given by the zenith angle and azimuth angle (or equivalently altitude angle).

It must be noted that the sunrise hour angle is equal to the sunset one apart from the difference in sign. Then the length of the day, L_{dt}, is $2\omega_s$:

$$L_{dt} = \left(\frac{2}{15}\right)\cos^{-1}(-\tan\phi\tan\delta), \quad \text{in hours} \qquad [9]$$

where 15 refers to the arc of 15° per hour that the Sun travels in the sky. Equations [8] and [9] refer to a flat terrain. If obstacles exist at the location of the observer obstructing solar rays during either sunrise or sunset, then other relationships for the hour angles of sunrise and sunset can be given [7] taking into account the height of the obstacle and its distance from the observer.

3.02.3 Solar Constant

The solar constant, H_{ex}, is the amount of the total solar energy at all wavelengths incident on an area of 1 m² exposed normally to the rays of the Sun at 1 AU. Because of the effects of the Earth's atmosphere on the transmission of the solar rays through it, the definition of the solar constant is implied at the top of the atmosphere (TOA); TOA is placed at the altitude of 100 km from the surface of the Earth where the density of the atmosphere is null. H_{ex} varies along the year due to varying distances of the Earth from the Sun by ~3.4% of its mean value. The first estimated mean value of H_{ex} was 1353 W m^{-2} [8]. This value was updated in 1977 to 1377 W m^{-2} [9] and later modified to 1367 W m^{-2} [10, 11]. The latest value of the solar constant is 1366.1 W m^{-2} [12]. The spectral distribution of the solar constant at TOA is given in Appendix A.

The calculation of the solar constant is an arduous process since it involves a series of solar radiation measurements. The first measurements were made with ground-based instrumentation. These were spectral observations of solar radiation extrapolated to their predicted values at TOA by taking into account the various attenuation effects produced by the molecules in the atmosphere. The spectral integration of these values yielded the solar constant. However, the ground-based measurements were subject to errors because of the uncertainties involved in estimating the attenuation effects of the atmospheric constituents on solar radiation. The second step was to perform these measurements at high-altitude observatories, flying aircraft, balloons, and space probes onboard rockets or satellites lately. The solar constant derived from the ground measurements was found to be consistently higher than its estimation at high-altitude platforms. Another issue causing uncertainty in the estimation of the solar constant was the intrinsic errors in the radiometers used in such measurements. To overcome the problem, the scientists had to intercompare all these devices to ensure that they work within certain limits of uncertainty. Furthermore, cavity-type absolute radiometers (see Section 3.02.12.1) started being used giving measurements of the solar irradiance with minimum error. For this reason, the World Meteorological Organization (WMO) adopted a new scale, the so-called World Radiometric Reference (WRR), as the basis of all actinometric measurements (see Section 3.02.12.2). Using this reference, Fröhlich and co-workers [10, 11] reexamined all sets of solar constant measurements in the period 1969–80 and recommended the revised value of 1367 W m^{-2}. With the use of satellites equipped with active cavity radiometers (ACRs), the measurement of the solar irradiance at TOA for long periods was possible. Such missions were the Nimbus 7 (Earth Radiation Budget) (1978–93), the Solar Maximum Mission (SMM) equipped with the Active Cavity Radiometer Irradiance Monitor I (ACRIM I) (1980–89), the Earth Radiation Budget Satellite (ERBS) Solar Monitor Measurements (1984–2003), and the Upper Atmosphere Research Satellite (UARS) ACRIM II Measurements (1991–97). These missions gave more accurate measurements of the solar constant with the current mean value at 1366.1 W m^{-2}. **Figure 4** shows the evolution of all measurements for the solar constant made from airborne sensors onboard satellites. Data and further information related to these satellites are available through the NASA Goddard Space Flight Center, Data Archive Center.

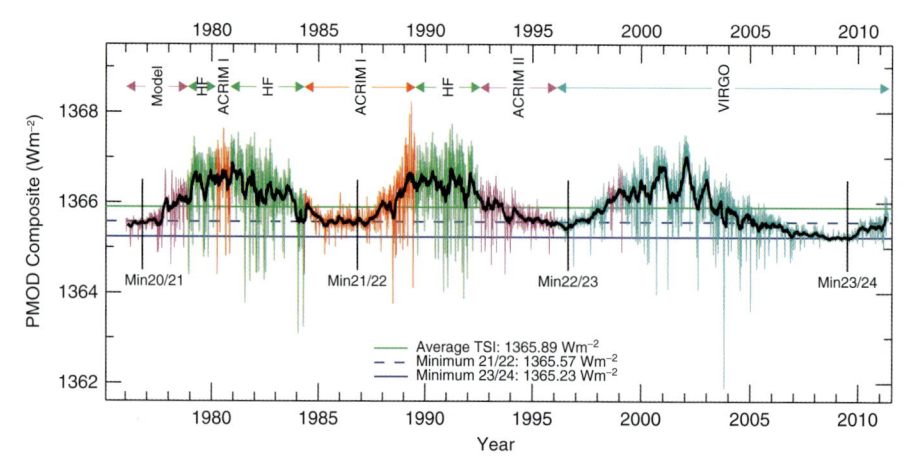

Figure 4 Solar irradiance measurements at TOA from airborne sensors onboard satellites in the period 1976–2008. The fluctuation of the measurements is due to the 22-year Sun spot cycle. The various sensors are shown at the top of the figure. Updated from Fröhlich (2011).

The composite in **Figure 4**, compiled by the VIRGO team at the Physikalisch Meteorologisches Observatorium, World Radiation Center (PMOD/WRC), Davos, Switzerland, shows the total solar irradiance as daily values plotted in different colors for the various experiments performed. The difference between the values at the minima is indicated together with the amplitudes of the three Sun spot cycles.

3.02.4 Solar Spectrum

The radiant solar energy comes from nuclear fusion happening in the Sun; the Sun has a surface temperature of 5777 K. The spectrum of the solar radiation received at TOA (see **Figure A.1** in Appendix A) can be well approximated by the spectrum of a blackbody having a surface temperature of 5777 K. Thus the Sun may be considered as a blackbody. A body is called a blackbody if, at a given temperature, it emits the maximum amount of energy at each wavelength and in all directions and it also absorbs all identical radiation at each wavelength and in all directions. The emission from a blackbody obeys the following laws.

3.02.4.1 Planck's Law

The power, $E_{b\lambda}$, emitted by a blackbody (or the emissive power) at a given wavelength and temperature is given by the following formula:

$$E_{b\lambda} = \frac{R_1}{\lambda^5 \left[\exp\left(\frac{R_2}{\lambda T_K}\right) - 1 \right]} \qquad [10]$$

where R_1 and R_2 are the radiation constants (3.7427×10^8 W μm m^{-2} and 1.4388×10^4 μm K, respectively), λ the wavelength (in μm), and T_K the blackbody temperature (K). $E_{b\lambda}$ is plotted for various temperatures in **Figure 5**.

It is seen from the diagram that the maximum of each curve is displaced toward longer wavelengths as the temperature decreases. This is known as the Wien's displacement law. The spectral distribution of the solar constant (the most recently measured extraterrestrial radiation at TOA) is given in Appendix A.

3.02.4.2 Wien's Displacement Law

By dividing both sides of eqn [10] by T_K^5, a function of the variable λT_K is obtained, that is,

$$\frac{E_{b\lambda}}{T_K^5} = \frac{R_1}{(\lambda T_K)^5 \left[\exp\left(\frac{R_2}{\lambda T_K}\right) - 1 \right]} \qquad [11]$$

From eqn [12] the locus of maximum λT_K, called $\lambda_{\max} T_K$, is 2897.8 μm K. The relation

$$\lambda_{\max} T_K = 2897.8 \text{ μm K} \qquad [12]$$

is called the Wien's displacement law. Assuming the Sun as a blackbody with a surface temperature of 5777 K, eqn [12] gives $\lambda_{\max} = 0.5016$ μm, which lies in the green region of the visible spectrum.

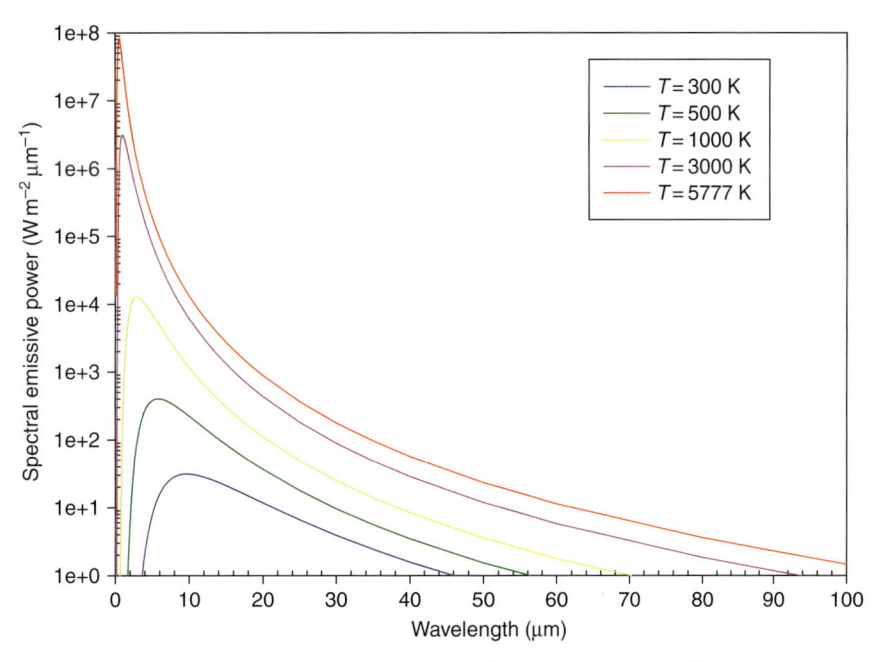

Figure 5 Spectral emissive power from a blackbody at various temperatures in the wavelength range 0–100 μm.

3.02.4.3 Stefan–Boltzmann Law

By integrating eqn [10] in all wavelengths, one gets the total power emitted from a blackbody at the temperature T_K:

$$E_b = \sigma T_K^4 \qquad [13]$$

where σ is called the Stefan–Boltzmann constant and is equal to $5.6697 \times 10^{-8}\,\mathrm{W\,m^{-2}\,K^{-4}}$. This is the theoretical value coming from the integration of eqn [10]. Its measured value is $5.6866 \times 10^{-8}\,\mathrm{W\,m^{-2}\,K^{-4}}$ [13].

Example 3.02.3. Determine (1) the surface temperature of a blackbody radiating with a total emissive power of $7.25 \times 10^{-4}\,\mathrm{W\,m^{-2}}$ and (2) the wavelength of maximum emissive power. (1) From eqn [13] the temperature $T_K = (E_b/\sigma)^{1/4} = (7.25 \times 10^4 / 5.6697 \times 10^{-8}) = 1063.4\,\mathrm{K}$. (2) From eqn [12], $\lambda_{\max} = 2.73\,\mu\mathrm{m}$.

3.02.5 Interference of Solar Radiation with the Earth's Atmosphere

When solar radiation enters the Earth's atmosphere, a part of the incident energy is attenuated by scattering and another part by absorption from the atmospheric constituents. The scattered radiation is called solar diffuse radiation or just diffuse radiation. A part of the diffuse radiation goes back to space and a part reaches the ground. The radiation that arrives at the surface of the Earth directly from the Sun is called solar direct or solar beam radiation (or just direct or beam radiation). The knowledge of the spectral irradiance (direct and diffuse) arriving at the surface of the Earth is important for the design of certain solar energy applications such as PVs. The integration of both diffuse and direct radiation over all wavelengths is called broadband; this is important in calculations concerning heating and cooling loads in architecture, the design of flat-plate collectors (e.g., Reference 14), or the study of radiation climate (e.g., References 15–17).

3.02.5.1 The Earth's Atmosphere

The actual composition of the constituents of the clean dry atmosphere (an atmosphere consisting of its natural chemical elements and no clouds) varies with geographical location, altitude, and season. Generally, the vertical structure of the Earth's atmosphere has been described by the so-called standard atmospheres. The standard atmosphere used so far is the US Standard Atmosphere of 1976 (USSA 1976) [18]. **Figure 6** shows the vertical temperature and pressure profiles indicating the layers of the lower (0–11 km) atmosphere, called the troposphere, the lower-middle (20–50 km) atmosphere, called the stratosphere, the upper-middle (56–80 km) atmosphere, called the mesosphere, and the upper (90–100 km) atmosphere, called the thermosphere. The turning points of the temperature profile are formed by intermediate layers, the tropopause (11–20 km), the stratopause (50–56 km), and the mesopause (80–90 km).

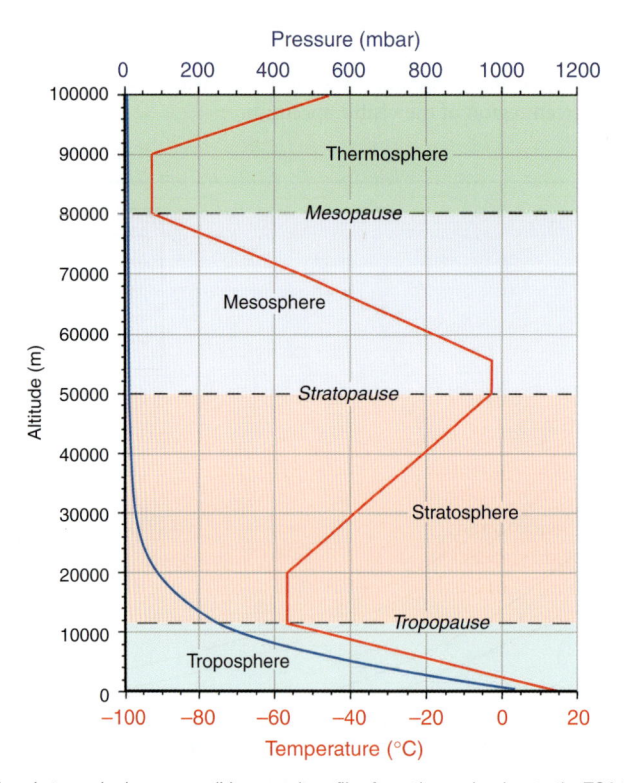

Figure 6 Air temperature (red curve) and atmospheric pressure (blue curve) profiles from the sea level up to the TOA (100 km) according to the USSA 1976. From http://www.physicalgeography.net/fundamentals/7b.html.

Table 1 The main chemical elements comprising the Earth's clean dry atmosphere (USSA 1976)

Name	Formula	Concentration (% by volume)
Nitrogen	N_2	78.084
Oxygen	O_2	20.948
Argon	Ar	0.934
Carbon dioxide	CO_2	0.333
Neon	Ne	0.001 818
Ozone	O_3	0–0.0012
Helium	He	0.000 524
Methane	CH_4	0.000 15
Krypton	Kr	0.000 114
Hydrogen	H_2	0.000 05
Nitrous oxide	N_2O	0.000 027
Xenon	Xe	0.000 008 9
Water vapor	H_2O	0–0.000 004
Nitric acid vapor		Traces

Table 1 shows the composition of the Earth's clean dry atmosphere. From this table, it is seen that more than three-quarters of the atmosphere is made up of nitrogen and most of the rest is oxygen. However it is the remaining 1%, a mixture of carbon dioxide, water vapor, and ozone, that not only produces important weather features, such as cloud and rain, but also has considerable influence on the overall climate of the Earth, through mechanisms such as the greenhouse effect and global warming. Ozone is concentrated in the stratosphere, while water vapor and nitrous oxide in the lower atmosphere. The main greenhouse gases are those of carbon dioxide and methane. Since methane, carbon dioxide, and ozone are also produced by anthropogenic activities on the surface of the Earth, their concentration is highly variable. These gases do not exhibit a homogeneous temporal or spatial distribution throughout the atmosphere over a certain location on the surface of the Earth.

All molecules of air deplete solar radiation by scattering, absorption, and reflection. Further details about these mechanisms are given in Section 3.02.5.4.

3.02.5.2 Optical Air Mass

Besides the chemical elements of a natural atmosphere (Table 1) the Earth's atmosphere contains aerosols. An aerosol is a small solid or liquid particle that remains suspended in the air and follows the motion of the airstream. All suspended particles that show variation in size, distribution, form, and material composition are aerosols. Suspended water and ice particles in fog and clouds are considered aerosol particles. Aerosols have diameters that range between 0.001 and 100 μm.

The attenuation of solar energy by molecules and aerosols in the atmosphere is a function of the number and type of molecules and aerosols in the path of the solar rays. The density of the molecules (or aerosols) multiplied by the path length traversed by a solar ray in the Earth's atmosphere implies the mass of a substance in a column in the atmosphere with unit area (cross section). This quantity is called actual optical air mass or simply air mass, m. The ratio of m in a slant path in the atmosphere to that to the zenith of a location is called relative air mass, m_r. This is given by Kasten and Young [19]:

$$m_r = [\sin\gamma + 0.505\,72\,(\gamma + 6.079\,95)^{-1.6364}]^{-1} \quad [14]$$

This expression for m_r is 99.6% accurate for zenith angles up to 89° (or γ as low as 1°) and refers to a standard pressure of 1013.25 hPa at sea level. For other pressures (or altitudes), m_r is corrected as

$$m' = m_r \left(\frac{P}{1013.25}\right) \quad [15]$$

where P is the atmospheric pressure (hPa). If P is not known but the altitude (z) is known, then an approximate formula for P is given by Lunde [20]:

$$P = P_0 \exp(-0.000\,118\,4z) \quad [16]$$

where P_0 is the reference pressure at sea level (1013.25 hPa or sometimes taken as 1000 hPa) and z the altitude in meters above sea level.

The air mass m_r (or simply m from now on) refers to a column in the clean dry atmosphere that contains all atmospheric constituents. Gueymard [21] has proposed a united formula for m according to the atmospheric constituent:

$$m_i = \left[\cos\theta_z + ai1\,\theta_z^{ai2}\,(ai3 - \theta_z)^{ai4}\right]^{-1} \quad [17]$$

where m_i stands for m_r (Rayleigh), m_a (aerosols), m_n (NO_2), m_o (O_3), m_g (mixed gases), or m_w (water vapor); the coefficients aij are given in **Table 2**.

Table 2 Coefficients for the optical masses of eqn [17]

Extinction process	ai1	ai2	ai3	ai4
Rayleigh	0.456 650	0.07	96.4836	−1.6970
O_3	268.450 000	0.50	115.4200	−3.2922
NO_2	602.300 000	0.50	117.9600	−3.4536
Mixed gases	0.456 650	0.07	96.4836	−1.6970
H_2O	0.031 141	0.10	92.4710	−1.3814
Aerosols	0.031 141	0.10	92.4710	−1.3814

3.02.5.3 Attenuation of Solar Direct Radiation

When solar radiation enters the Earth's atmosphere, it undergoes attenuation due to energy loss because of the scattering and absorption mechanisms [22–25]. According to the Bouguer–Lambert law, the attenuation of light through a medium is proportional to the distance traveled in it and the local flux of radiation. This law can be expressed as follows:

$$H_b = SH_{ex} \exp(-km) \quad [18]$$

where H_b is the direct (or beam) irradiance on a plane normal to solar rays, S the correction factor for the Sun–Earth distance, H_{ex} the solar constant, m the air mass, and k the total attenuation coefficient (or else extinction coefficient or optical thickness or optical depth). For H_b to be estimated on a horizontal plane, the right-hand side of the above equation must be multiplied by $\sin \gamma$. Also, $SH_{ex} \sin \gamma$ is the extraterrestrial radiation on a horizontal surface, denoted by H_0. The previous equation can also be written as

$$H_b = SH_{ex}T \quad [19]$$

where T is called the total transmittance and is equal to $\exp(-km)$.

3.02.5.4 Rayleigh and Mie Scattering, Reflection, and Absorption

When an EM wave hits a particle, part of its energy is scattered in all directions (**Figure 7**). This process causes the diffuse radiation. When the scattering particles are spheres, then the scattered energy can be obtained by solving the Maxwell's EM wave equation in spherical polar coordinates. All particles in nature scatter the EM waves, no matter whether these are electrons or planets. The first solution of the Maxwell's equation in the case of spherical particles with size much smaller than the wavelength of the incident energy was obtained late in the nineteenth century by Lord Rayleigh by means of Rayleigh's theory. This theory is useful in studying scattering of solar radiation by air molecules. Rayleigh, through his theory, explained the blue color of the sky in clear conditions.

On the other hand, when the particle size becomes comparable with the wavelength of the incident radiation, then the solution of the Maxwell's equation becomes extremely difficult. The solution was first successfully attempted by Gustav Mie at the beginning of the twentieth century through the known Mie's theory. Rayleigh's theory is a special case of Mie's theory. **Figure 8** shows the cases of Rayleigh (left) and Mie (middle and right) scattering in the atmosphere. The smaller the particle in comparison with the wavelength of the incident radiation, the more homogeneous the scattering in all directions. The bigger the particle is, the more directional the scattering becomes.

When solar radiation enters a medium (such as a cloud), then the process in the atmosphere that modifies the incoming radiation is called reflection (**Figure 9**). Reflection is a process where sunlight is redirected by 180° after it strikes an atmospheric particle. This redirection causes a 100% loss of the insolation. Most of the reflection in our atmosphere occurs in clouds when light is intercepted by particles of liquid and frozen water. The reflectivity of a cloud can range from 40% to 90%.

If intercepted, some gases and particles in the atmosphere have the ability to absorb incoming insolation (**Figure 10**). Absorption is defined as a process in which solar radiation is retained by a substance and converted into heat energy. The creation of heat energy also causes the substance to emit its own radiation. In general, the absorption of solar radiation by substances in the Earth's atmosphere results in temperatures that get no higher than 1800 °C. According to Wien's law, bodies with temperatures at

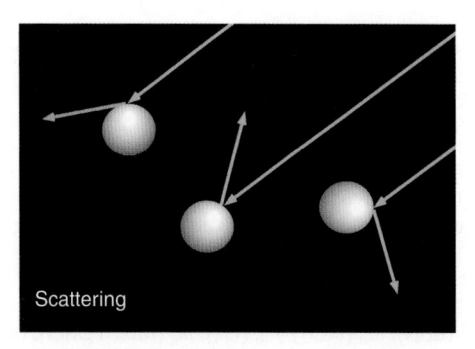

Figure 7 Scattering of incident radiation onto (spherical) particles. From http://www.physicalgeography.net/fundamentals/7f.html.

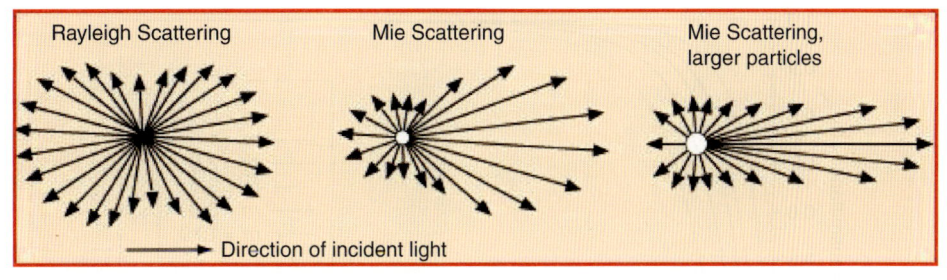

Figure 8 Rayleigh scattering (left) and Mie scattering (middle and right) of incident radiation onto (spherical) particles. The first case occurs when the particle size is much smaller than the wavelength of the incident radiation, the second when the particle size is comparable, and the third when the particle size is larger than the wavelength.

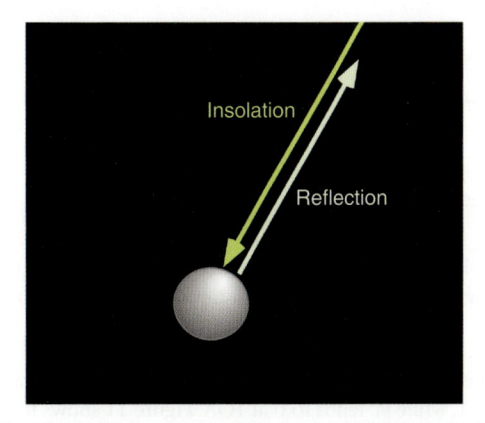

Figure 9 The process of atmospheric reflection. From http://www.physicalgeography.net/fundamentals/7f.html.

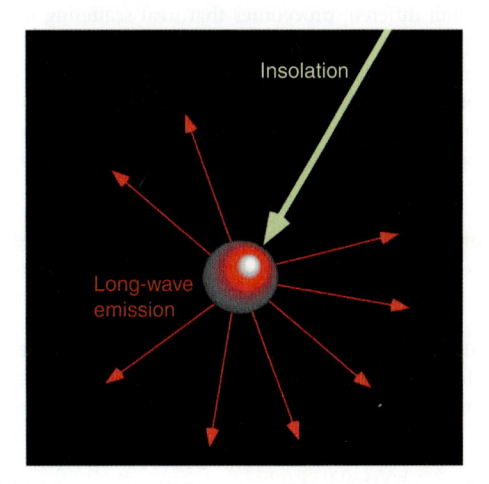

Figure 10 The process of absorption of incident (short-wave) radiation onto particles and emission of thermal (long-wave) radiation. From http://www.physicalgeometry.net/fundamentals/7f.html.

this level or lower would emit their radiation in the long-wave band. Furthermore, this emission of radiation is in all directions, so a sizable proportion of this energy is lost to space.

Scattering by air molecules described by Rayleigh's theory is based on the assumption that the scattering particles are spherical with a size less than about 0.2λ and that they scatter independently of one another. The essence of the Rayleigh's theory is that the monochromatic extinction coefficient varies approximately as λ^{-4}; this has been verified experimentally. As air density and composition vary with altitude, so does the value of attenuation extinction. On the basis of Penndorf's [22] theoretical formulation of molecular scattering, Leckner [23] has presented the following approximate formula for the scattering coefficient of dry air at standard conditions (sea level pressure and 0 °C):

$$k_{r\lambda} = 0.008\ 735 \lambda^{-4.08} \qquad [20]$$

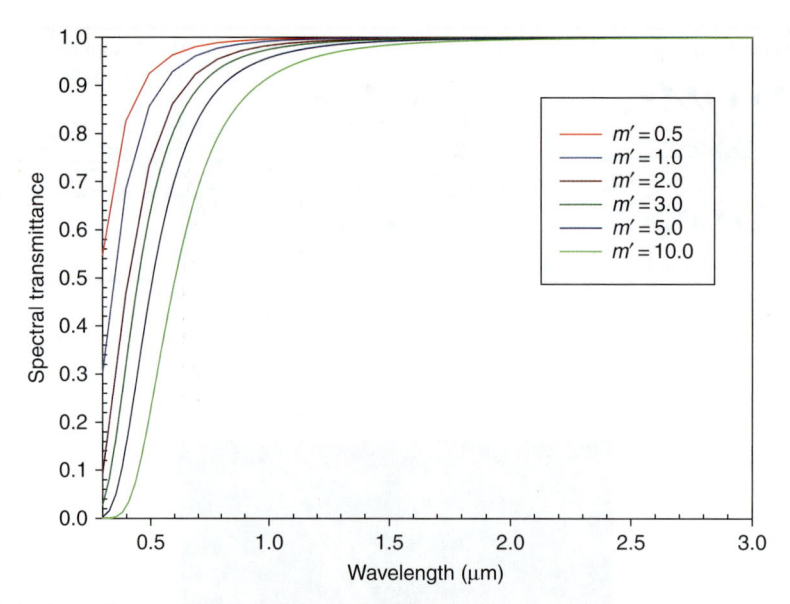

Figure 11 Rayleigh scattering transmittance as a function of wavelength and air mass.

Because of the variation of the Rayleigh scattering coefficient with λ^{-4}, the spectral transmittance rapidly increases with wavelength and decreases with increasing m. The spectral Rayleigh transmittance, $T_{r\lambda}$, is, therefore, written as

$$T_{r\lambda} = \exp\left(-m'\, 0.008\ 735\lambda\right)^{-4.08} \quad [21]$$

Multiplication by m', the relative air mass at the site's atmospheric pressure, is needed because $k_{r\lambda}$ in eqn [20] is estimated at standard pressure and $m' = 1$. At high altitudes, $m' < 1$, while m' tends to 0 at TOA. **Figure 11** shows the influence of wavelength and air mass on transmittance. At wavelengths greater than 1 μm, scattering is negligible. At $\lambda = 0.5$ μm and $m' = 1$, the atmosphere is more than 85% clear to solar radiation. It may therefore be concluded that Rayleigh (molecular) scattering is limited to shortwave radiation only.

In the literature, there are two simple but different procedures that treat scattering of radiation by particles other than dry air molecules. One was presented by Moon [24] and the other by Ångström [25, 26]. Moon presented the attenuation coefficients for particles in 1940, when the attenuation was believed to be caused by scattering effects only. However, particles absorb as well as scatter EM radiation. Various theoretical and experimental studies give good evidence for supposing that, in general, extinction by aerosols due to scattering or absorption or a combination of them is a continuous function of wavelength. In general, scattering is much greater than absorption. Ångström suggested a single formula that involves the combination of both mechanisms (scattering and absorption):

$$k_{a\lambda} = \beta\lambda^{-\alpha} \quad [22]$$

This relationship is known as the Ångström's turbidity formula. In this equation, β is called the Ångström turbidity coefficient and α the wavelength exponent; λ is in μm. According to eqn [22], the aerosol spectral transmittance function is written as

$$T_{a\lambda} = \exp\left(-m'\beta\lambda^{-\alpha}\right) \quad [23]$$

Routine measurements of β and α with a dual-wavelength sunphotometer have been carried out manually at a number of sites. Now some aerosol networks exist at global level and such measurements are performed automatically. From such measurements, McClatchey et al. [27] developed an expression for calculating β from visibility, Vis, at a site for visibility ranges greater than 5 km:

$$\beta = 0.55^{\alpha}\left(\frac{3.912}{\text{Vis}-0.011\ 62}\left[0.024\ 72(\text{Vis}-5) + 1.132\right]\right) \quad [24]$$

In order to predict β, it is necessary to guess a value for α. Therefore, the above relation gives only a gross estimate of β.

Apart from the Ångström turbidity coefficient there are other factors in the international literature expressing atmospheric turbidity. These are the Schüepp turbidity coefficient [28], B, the Linke turbidity parameter [29, 30], T_L, and the Unsworth–Monteith turbidity coefficient [31], T_{UM}. The first is strictly related to Ångström's α and β via the relation

$$B = 0.4343\beta(2^{-\alpha}) \quad [25a]$$

The main difference between B and β is that their reference wavelength does not coincide: $\lambda = 0.5$ μm (visible) for Schüepp's turbidity coefficient and $\lambda = 1$ μm (near IR (NIR)) for the Ångström's coefficient. Furthermore, Schüepp's B refers to the decadic logarithmic scale, rather than the natural logarithmic scale in more general use. This might explain why this turbidity coefficient is not in much use anymore.

The Linke turbidity parameter is defined as

$$T_L = Q(m')(\ln H_{ex} - \ln H_b + \ln S) \quad [25b]$$

and denotes the number of dry atmospheres necessary to produce attenuation of the extraterrestrial radiation to the same as that produced by the real atmosphere. $Q(m')$ is a function of the air mass and e the correction factor for the Sun–Earth distance (eqn [3]):

$$Q(m') = \frac{1}{0.4343\bar{k}_r m'} \qquad [25c]$$

where $\bar{k}_r$ is the mean attenuation due to Rayleigh and is given by $\bar{k}_r = (6.5567 + 1.7513\,m' - 0.1212\,m'^2 + 0.0065\,m'^3 - 0.00013\,m'^4)^{-1}$.

The Unsworth–Monteith turbidity coefficient expresses the number of clean dry atmospheres, which would produce the same attenuation as the actual atmosphere containing aerosols and water vapor. It is expressed as

$$T_{UM} = \frac{-(\ln H_b - \ln H_b^* - \ln S)}{m} \qquad [25d]$$

where H_b^* is the direct solar component at the bottom of a dust-free atmosphere.

Example 3.02.4. Considering the wavelengths of 0.38 and 0.50 μm, the corresponding aerosol attenuation coefficients are 0.3538 and 0.2661, respectively (according to USSA 1976). This is because

$$k_{a\lambda=0.38} = \beta(0.38)^{-\alpha} = 0.3538$$

$$k_{a\lambda=0.50} = \beta(0.50)^{-\alpha} = 0.2661$$

From the above two equations, we have

$$\alpha = \frac{\ln\left(\dfrac{0.3538}{0.2661}\right)}{\ln\left(\dfrac{0.50}{0.38}\right)} = 1.038$$

Now β can be computed by either of the wavelengths, that is, $\beta = 0.1296$ at $\lambda = 0.38$ μm, or $\beta = 0.1296$ at $\lambda = 0.50$ μm. Therefore, Vis can be estimated from eqn [24] as Vis = 24.18 km. For these conditions, the USSA gives Vis = 23 km.

Gueymard [21] has developed analytical expressions for the Rayleigh and aerosol transmittances as well as for the other extinction processes in the atmosphere (O_3, NO_2, mixed gases, and H_2O), which are not given here for the sake of saving space.

3.02.6 Models of Broadband Solar Radiation on Horizontal and Tilted Surfaces

This section is devoted to the modeling of solar radiation received on the surface of the Earth on either a horizontal plane or a tilted surface with arbitrary (azimuthal) orientation. Here the most common models that appear in the international literature are used. Their analytical formulations are deployed.

The solar radiation models available nowadays in the international literature can be categorized according to their specific requirements or characteristics. These groups of models have the following characteristics according to Gueymard and Myers [32]. (1) *Input data*. The input data for a solar radiation model may consist of meteorological and/or climatological parameters, or even irradiance components. These data may come from ground observations or from airborne/space-borne sensors [33, 34]. (2) *Output data*. The outputs from solar radiation models contain information about the direct, diffuse, and global irradiance components. In addition, many models try to compute the direct and/or diffuse component from global irradiance, which is used as input to the model [35–37]. (3) *Spatial resolution*. Some solar radiation models provide predictions of the location where the input data come from, while others give gridded results, especially when satellite observations are used as inputs. It is a matter of course that the former models provide greater spatial resolution and the latter greater spatial coverage [37]. (4) *Time resolution*. The irradiance results from any solar radiation model can vary in time resolution. They can be of high (minute), standard (hourly), average (daily), low (mean hourly or mean daily for a specific month), or climatological (mean hourly or daily over a long period, say 10–30 years) resolution. Generally, high-resolution data are used in solar radiation applications, while standard resolution data are used for solar system or building energy simulations, average resolution data are used in agricultural meteorology, and climatological resolution data are used in system design and climatology. Some models provide mean hourly data from mean daily data [38, 39]. (5) *Spectral resolution*. Most models work as broadband models, that is, they evaluate the short-wave radiation transmitted by the atmosphere in the spectrum 300–4000 nm. Others, however, consider two or more distinct bands for better resolution. For instance, there are models limited to the UV (below 400 nm) or the photosynthetic wavelengths (400–700 nm). For specific applications though (atmospheric physics, remote-sensing applications, or prediction of the performance of solar radiation devices, such as PV panels or coated glazings) spectral models are preferred. Such models are commented elsewhere [40]. (6) *Methodology*. The methodology followed by a model can be of deterministic or stochastic (statistical) nature. The first category tries to compute irradiance at a specific moment, in the past, the present, or the future. A short review of the stochastic models is given in Reference [41]. Lately, a third category of models combining deterministic and statistical features has appeared, although models in this category are rare; an example is METSTAT [35]. (7) *Algorithm*. Another classification of the solar radiation models can be made with respect to the physical or semiphysical parameterizations (e.g., Reference 42) and empirical methods used in their calculations (e.g., Reference 43). (8) *Surface geometry*. In many applications of solar energy, the solar receiver is fixed on an inclined plane or is tracking the Sun for better efficiency. Other applications involve modeling of topographic solar radiation over complex terrain (e.g., Reference 44). Therefore, any of the above-mentioned models (deterministic, statistical, empirical, physical) has to provide irradiance outputs for horizontal planes, tilted surfaces, or tracking surfaces pointing to the Sun. Solar radiation models for tilted surfaces can be based on horizontal radiation data by using the so-called transposition method [45–48]. (9) *Sky conditions*. The effect of clouds in solar radiation modeling is of high importance. There are, however, applications (e.g., energy loads in building, solar concentrator efficiency) that do not need irradiance predictions under any type of sky, but tailored to clear-sky conditions only; then an appropriate model from the literature is selected [42, 49–53]. It is obvious that if one wants to derive a solar radiation model, he/she can 'mix' any of the above nine characteristics, depending on the accuracy of the predictions. In practice, all nine characteristics are not taken into account in the development of a model. Contrarily, a usual practice is the use of cascaded models, which are interconnected. Each of these models serves a specific purpose in the overall application. Suppose that the irradiance on a tilted plane is to be computed from hourly meteorological and daily sunshine data. First, a model is invoked to 'break' the daily sunshine duration value into hourly ones. Then, a semiphysical model can be applied to give estimations of the hourly global horizontal irradiance. A third model predicts the global tilted irradiance from the outputs of the second model. A pack of the first and the second model is described in Section 3.02.6.2. Finally, it must be said that the above procedure can be reversed. When solar radiation is actually available, the model can be used to evaluate one or more atmospheric characteristic, usually the aerosol turbidity (e.g., References 54 and 55).

3.02.6.1 Calculation of Solar Radiation on a Horizontal Plane

The global (or total) solar radiation, H_g, is equal to the sum of the direct (or beam), H_b, and the diffuse, H_d, components, that is,

$$H_g = H_b + H_d \quad [26]$$

Therefore, if H_b and H_d are measured, or can be modeled, then H_g is known. H_b can be easily calculated from the analytical expression [18] or [19]; for this, the values of the parameters S and m must be estimated from eqn [1] or [3] for S and eqn [14] or [15] for m. Contrary to this, the estimation of k (or equivalently of T) requires explicit calculations, which are not given in this section. Nevertheless, this tedious procedure has to be performed for the estimation of H_b.

It should be mentioned here that H_g can be computed on any time basis (instantly, hourly, daily, monthly, annual); this depends on the corresponding values of H_b and H_d. As for H_b, the instantaneous value of the parameters S, H_{ex}, and m should be computed, when instant estimations are needed, or, alternatively, their average (hourly, daily, monthly, annual) values should be calculated. One should remember that the unit of solar radiation in these cases is W m^{-2}. If energy is to be used for H_g (in MJ m^{-2}), then the values of H_b, H_d, and H_{ex} must also be in MJ m^{-2}, and, furthermore, the values of S and m should be calculated as averages for the time interval considered.

The estimation of H_d is not as straightforward as of H_b. This is because diffuse radiation is caused not only by the atmosphere, but also by clouds in the sky on a partly cloudy or overcast day. Sophisticated algorithms can derive the diffuse component of solar radiation by performing calculations of the solar radiation received from every patch of the sky (usually the sky vault is divided into 150 patches) using RTMs. Nevertheless, such a task is time and computer memory consuming and it is used only in pure research situations. For ordinary applications, about 250 models based on empirical expressions have been developed over the last few decades. The main driving force for such developments has been the need to calculate H_g received on a plane for engineering applications. Nevertheless, here the most usable models are briefly described. These models can be used for any time basis, for example, for hourly, daily, or monthly calculations.

1. The daily diffuse fraction $f_d = H_{dd}/H_{gd}$ is calculated according to Bartoli *et al.*'s model [56]:

$$f_d = p + (1-p)\exp\left[\frac{-qK_d^s}{1-K_d}\right] \quad [27]$$

where $p = 0.154$, $q = 1.062$, and $s = 0.861$. K_d is called the daily clearness index and is equal to H_{gd}/SH_{exd}. The subscript d in the parameters H_{dd} and H_{gd} refers to their daily values; SH_{exd} is the daily horizontal extraterrestrial radiation.

2. The Hollands and Crha model [57] estimates the hourly diffuse radiation values. It considers the scattering of radiation between two atmospheric layers and the ground in a simplified manner. Its formulation is

$$\frac{H_{dh}}{H_{gh}} = \frac{a - \sqrt{\left[a^2 - 4x(1-x)(1-\rho_g^2 x^2)\right]}}{2x(1-\rho_g x)} \quad [28a]$$

$$x = \frac{K}{T_u} \quad [28b]$$

$$a = 1.03 + \rho_g x(1-2x) \quad [28c]$$

where ρ_g is the ground albedo, K here is the hourly global clearness index, and T_u is the transmittance of the upper layer of the atmosphere. The model does not take into account multiple reflections between the ground and the atmosphere. The subscript h in H_{dh} and H_{gh} refers to the hourly values.

3. The Maxwell model [33] predicts the hourly normal beam irradiation, H_{bh}, from hourly global radiation values. The maximum value for the cloudless-sky value of the normal beam clearness index value, $k' = H_{bh}/H_{exh}$, with H_{exh} the hourly normal extraterrestrial radiation, is first obtained:

$$\max[k'] = 0.886 - 0.122m + 0.0121m^2 - 0.000\,653m^3 + 0.000\,014m^4 \qquad [29a]$$

Then a reduction of k' is computed as a function of the air mass, m, and hourly global clearness index, that is, $k = H_{gh}/H_{exh}$:

$$k' = \max[k'(m)] - \Delta k'(m, k) \qquad [29b]$$

$$\Delta k' = a(k) + b(k)\exp[c(k)m] \qquad [29c]$$

$$a(k) = -5.74 + 21.77k - 27.49k^2 + 11.56k^3 \qquad [29d]$$

$$b(k) = 41.40 - 118.50k + 66.05k^2 + 31.90k^3 \qquad [39e]$$

$$c(k) = -47.01 + 184.2k - 222k^2 + 73.81k^3 \qquad [29f]$$

Finally, the normal beam hourly radiation is computed as the difference between global and diffuse values:

$$H_{dh} = H_{gh} - \sin\gamma\, H_{bh} \qquad [29g]$$

During the practical implementation of radiation models, the mid-hour value of the solar altitude is often used. However, for the above as well as with other similar models, this technique is not recommended, especially when handling the near-sunrise and near-sunset hourly values.

4. Another model by Macagnan *et al.* [58] proposed various empirical correlations along the same lines as those discussed for the daily timescale, namely for the overcast, partly cloudy, and clear sky. A version is shown here, which includes dependence on solar elevation and uses polynomials:

$$f_h = 0.995 + 2.3979k - 0.7033\sin\gamma^2, \quad \text{if } k \le 0.18 \qquad [30a]$$

$$f_h = 1.123 - 1.220k - 0.000\,273\sin\gamma, \quad \text{if } 0.18 < k \le 0.81 \qquad [30b]$$

$$f_h = 1.479 - 1.466k - 0.0810\sin\gamma, \quad \text{if } k > 0.81 \qquad [30c]$$

5. The original Liu and Jordan model [59] relates the ratio of the monthly average hourly to the daily diffuse horizontal values, H_{dh}/H_{dd}, to the corresponding ratio of the monthly average hourly to daily extraterrestrial radiation values, H_{0h}/H_{0d}. This model can be easily adapted to the daily timescale:

$$H_{dh}(t) = H_d\left[\frac{H_{0h}(t)}{H_{0d}}\right] \qquad [31]$$

where t is the solar hour. Here again, the hourly values should be treated with caution near sunrise and sunset. It should be noted that this model has a known problem. It has been observed, and there is supporting theoretical evidence (e.g., Reference 60), that daily mean trends of solar radiation present somewhat 'flatter' shapes near the central hours of the day than the monthly average daily profile. However, the Liu and Jordan model features no empirical coefficients and has shown considerable success at the monthly timescale.

6. The original Jain and Ratto model [61] is based on the β distribution. As in the case of the Liu and Jordan model, this was also developed for monthly average diffuse radiation values, but it can again be adapted to work on the daily level:

$$H_{dh}(t) = H_{dd}\, g(t, a, b) \qquad [32a]$$

$$g(t, a, b) = \left\{\frac{\Gamma(a+b)}{\Gamma(a)\Gamma(b)L_d^{a+b-1}}\right\} \times \left[(t-12) + \left(\frac{L_d}{2}\right)\right]^{a-1} \times [-(t-12) + L_d]^{b-1} \qquad [32b]$$

where Γ is the gamma function, L_d is the day length, and $a = b = 2.61 + 0.0385L_d$ are constants given by the authors.

7. Bivona *et al.* [62] proposed an exponential shape for the mean daily trend of H_{dh}:

$$H_{dh}(t) = H_d F(t, u1, u2) \qquad [33a]$$

$$F(t, u1, u2) = A(u1, u2)\exp\left\{\frac{u2(12-t-u1)^2}{\left[-(t-12)^2 + \left(\frac{L_d^2}{4}\right)\right]}\right\} \qquad [33b]$$

where $u1$ and $u2$ are two adjustable parameters giving the asymmetry of the curve and its width, respectively. $A(u1, u2)$ is a normalization constant given by the authors.

Apart from the above diffuse models, there are other models that specialize in estimating the total or direct radiation components. These are described below.

8. *The ASHRAE model.* This is a clear-sky model commonly used as a basic tool for calculating solar heat gains and cooling loads in buildings. It was introduced in 1972. The current version is 90.1 with new monthly coefficients [63]. The recent model does not depend on atmospheric data.

9. *The Bird model.* This is the original Bird model [64, 65]. Since the time of its development, the aerosol optical depth (AOD) was measured by sunphotometers at two wavelengths, that is, 380 and 500 nm; therefore, the model requires the estimation of the AOD at these two wavelengths. Nevertheless, networks of sunphotometers with typically 5–7 aerosol channels were developed in the 1990s worldwide and have expanded since (see, e.g., http://aeronet.gsfc.nasa.gov). Because of that, it is now easier to obtain the turbidity coefficients α and β by fitting the measured AOD at various wavelengths, $k_{a\lambda}$, to the Ångström's expression:

$$k_{a\lambda} = \beta \left(\frac{\lambda}{\lambda_o}\right)^{-\alpha}$$

where $\lambda_o = 1000$ nm. With α and β known, the AOD$_{380}$ and AOD$_{500}$ (the AOD at 380 and 500 nm) required by the model can be calculated by the expressions $\beta(0.38^{-\alpha})$ and $\beta(0.5^{-\alpha})$, respectively. The model computes clear-sky direct, diffuse, and global irradiances on a horizontal plane.

10. *The cloud layer-sunshine (CLS) model.* The model [66, 67] is based on the original works by Houghton [68] and Monteith [69]. Through the IEA Task 9 (Solar radiation and pyranometry studies) under the 'Solar Heating and Cooling Program', the model was evaluated by many researchers for almost all-sky conditions. The model uses the expression $T_a = 0.95^m$ for the aerosol transmittance, where m is the air mass.

11. *The CPCR2 model.* This is a two-band (290–700 and 700–4000 nm) model [49], which has been tested extensively in various studies [52, 70–74]. It normally requires input values of α and β for each of the two wavebands considered in the form of pairs (α_1, β_1) and (α_2, β_2) under the restriction of $\beta_1 = \beta_2(0.7^{\alpha_1-\alpha_2})$. Such data can be provided by contemporary sunphotometers by applying the equation of the Bird model deployed above. If data from sunphotometers are not available, the model can be satisfied with the assumptions $\alpha_1 = \alpha_2 = \alpha$ and $\beta_1 = \beta_2 = \beta$, with a slightly worse model performance.

12. *The ESRA model.* The original version of this model [75] initiated the second (and most recent) edition of the European Solar Radiation Atlas (ESRA) [76]. The Linke turbidity factor, T_L, was then a favorable way to assess the effect of aerosols. However, its drawback was that it could not be measured directly; to overcome the difficulty, T_L had to be evaluated by inversion of an appropriate irradiance model, using experimental clear-sky direct irradiance as the input. Even this solution created a headache in the sense that the measured direct irradiance values were used both to test the model's predictions and to derive its inputs (see Reason 1 in Section 3.02.7.7). The problem was finally solved in the new version of the model, which calculates T_L from air mass, precipitable water, and β [77].

13. *Iqbal's parameterization models A, B, and C.* These models are fully described in the original publication [78], and have been tested previously to a certain extent [71, 72].

14. *The Kasten model.* This is considered a classic model [79–81] that provides direct and global irradiance as a function of T_L [82]. To overcome the difficulty in using T_L (as in the case of the ESRA model), a simple linear function between T_L and β was developed in the form

$$T_L = 2.1331 + 19.0204\beta$$

where the numerical coefficients have been obtained by combining the empirical determinations of $\beta = f(T_L)$ proposed by various authors [83–86].

15. *The METSTAT model.* This model was developed specifically to support the production of the National Solar Radiation Data Base for the United States. The input parameters for METSTAT include total and opaque cloud cover, AOD, precipitable water vapor, ozone, surface albedo, snow depth, days-since-last-snowfall, atmospheric pressure, and present weather [35]. The model uses the broadband AOD (BAOD) to evaluate the aerosol transmittance. Like T_L, BAOD can only be obtained indirectly from an inverted model and irradiance measurements, a process that poses a problem. To overcome the difficulty, a convenient methodology [87] was, therefore, developed to derive BAOD from α and β through the relationship

$$\text{BAOD} = \beta[0.695 + (0.0160 + 0.066\beta(0.7^{-\alpha}))m]^{-\alpha}$$

16. *The McMaster (MAC) model.* This model is the evolution between its original development [88] and the latest performance assessment results [82]. If there is no information on the appropriate aerosol transmittance function to be used, the same formula for T_a as in the case of the CLS model [88, 89] is selected.

17. *The REST2 model*. This is a two-band model [42] based on CPCR2, but it incorporates completely revised parameterizations, which have been derived from the SMARTS spectral model [90, 91]. REST2 uses the same inputs as CPCR2, with the addition of the amount of nitrogen dioxide in a vertical atmospheric column, which is given if it is unknown.
18. *The Santamouris model*. The radiative code of the model [92] is quite similar to that of the Bird model, apart from the use of a fixed turbidity value.
19. *The Yang model*. The direct irradiance predictions of the model [93, 94] have shown a very good performance [70, 73] despite its diffuse irradiance, which has not yet been evaluated.
20. *The artificial neural network (ANN) models*. ANN models are modern statistical methodologies developed to serve various fields of research. The ANNs accumulate knowledge during training process, while their effectiveness depends on the quality of the training procedure. The goal of the training procedure is minimal deviations between the target and calculated outputs. ANNs constitute an appropriate tool for solving real problems in the cases where classical methods are insufficient. Therefore, ANNs have also been used in the prediction of solar radiation components at various timescales. In these models, the meteorological parameters are important for indicating the amount of available solar irradiation. There exist many works where ANNs are applied to predict average daily solar irradiation [95–99]. Only a few of them (e.g., References 100–102) are focused on solar irradiation at timescales of 1 h. Later developments of ANNs are the adaptive neuro-fuzzy interference systems (ANFIS; e.g., Reference 103) and the combination of the wavelet theory with ANNs (e.g., References 100 and 104).

3.02.6.2 The Meteorological Radiation Model

A specific reference to the meteorological radiation model (MRM) is given here since this broadband model has been developed for all-sky conditions by the Atmospheric Research Team (ART) of the National Observatory of Athens, Greece. MRM is a semiphysical model, that is, it is based on empirical radiation transmittance equations and, therefore, it has the credibility of the RTMs; on the other hand, it is a simple code in the sense that its input data are the parameters of air temperature, relative humidity, atmospheric pressure, and sunshine duration widely measured in every meteorological station. MRM is now in its version 5 and very much improved over its predecessors as far as the transmittance expressions and the solar geometry are concerned. Another fact that has come out from the improvement process of MRM v5 is the inappropriateness of the Van Heuklon's formula [105] for estimating the total ozone atmospheric column by comparing its effectiveness with Total Ozone Mapping Spectrometer (TOMS) satellite data over Athens and Jerusalem in the period 1996–2004. This outcome dictates the necessity of deriving new analytical expressions for the O_3 atmospheric column for the whole world, a heavy research endeavor under way by ART. A description of the model is given below.

The general transmittance function, T_i, for seven atmospheric gases (H_2O, O_3, CO_2, CO, N_2O, CH_4, and O_2) is [106–112]

$$T_i = 1 - \left\{ \frac{A'ml_i}{[(1 + B'ml_i)^{C'} + D'ml_i]} \right\} \quad [34]$$

where l_i is the vertical column for each of the above gases and A', B', C', and D' are coefficients. The l_i values are used in the analytical expressions of the corresponding transmittance functions (see below). The values of the coefficients are given in **Table 3**.

From eqn [34] the analytical expressions for the transmittance functions of O_3, H_2O, and mixed gases, T_o, T_w, and T_g, respectively, can be formulated from **Table 3**. This means that the transmittance function T_i, of any gas of **Table 3** is given by eqn [34] where the corresponding values of the coefficients A', B', C', and D' are taken from **Table 3**. Specifically, the transmittance function of mixed gases is

$$T_g = T_{CO_2} T_{CO} T_{N_2O} T_{CH_4} T_{O_2} \quad [35]$$

where all T's in the right-hand side of eqn [35] are the transmittance functions of the specific gases; the values of the corresponding l_i's have been considered to be 330, 0.075, 0.28, 1.6, and 2.095×10^5 atm-cm [108, 111], respectively. It should be noticed that for the estimation of T_o, if l_o, in atm-cm or Dobson unit (DU), is not available from *in situ* measurements, the Van Heuklon [105]

Table 3 Values of the coefficients in eqn [34]

Gas	A'	B'	C'	D'
H_2O	3.014	119.3	0.644	5.814
O_3	0.2554	6107.26	0.204	0.471
CO_2	0.721	377.89	0.5855	3.1709
CO	0.0062	243.67	0.4246	1.7222
N_2O	0.0326	107.413	0.5501	0.9093
CH_4	0.0192	166.095	0.4221	0.7186
O_2	0.0003	476.934	0.4892	0.1261

approximation may be used for the northern hemisphere with the caution mentioned above. Also, for the estimation of T_w, the following expressions must be taken into account:

$$l_w = 0.493 e_m T_d \left(\frac{P}{P_o}\right)^{0.75} \left(\frac{273.15}{T_d}\right)^{0.5} \quad [36a]$$

$$e_m = e_s \frac{RH}{100 T_d} \quad [36b]$$

$$e_s = \exp\left(22.329\,699 - 49.140\,396 T_{do}^{-1} - 10.921\,853 T_{do}^{-2} - 0.390\,151\,56 T_{do}\right) \quad [36c]$$

$$T_{do} = \frac{T_d}{100} \quad [36d]$$

where e_s is the saturation water vapor pressure, in hPa, given by Gueymard [113], RH is the relative humidity at the station's height, in %, T_d is the air temperature at the station's height, in K, and l_w is the precipitable water, in cm. Then, T_w is estimated through eqn [34]:

$$T_w = 1 - 3.014 m l_w \left[(1 + 119.3 m l_w)^{0.644} + 5.814 m l_w\right]^{-1} \quad [36e]$$

The Rayleigh scattering transmittance function is [109]

$$T_r = \exp\left[-0.1128 m'^{0.8346}\left(0.9341 - m'^{0.9868} 0.9391 m'\right)\right] \quad [37]$$

The Mie scattering transmittance function is [93]

$$T_a = \exp\left\{-m\beta\left[0.6777 + 0.1464 m\beta - 0.006\,26\,(m\beta)^2\right]^{-1.3}\right\} \quad [38]$$

where the Ångström's turbidity parameter, β, is in the range 0.05–0.4 for low-to-high aerosol concentrations. Some indicative values of β are given in **Table 4** [78].

Another way of estimating β, if it is not known from measurements, is by using Yang et al.'s expression [93], which relates β to the geographical latitude, φ, and the altitude of the station, z. This expression is

$$\beta = \beta' + \Delta\beta \quad [39a]$$

$$\beta' = (0.025 + 0.1 \cos\phi) \exp\left(\frac{-0.7 z}{1000}\right) \quad [39b]$$

$$\Delta\beta = \pm(0.02 \sim 0.06) \quad [39c]$$

where β' represents the annual mean value of the turbidity and $\Delta\beta$ the seasonal deviation from the mean, that is, low values in winter and high values in summer.

The aerosol transmittance function is $T_a = T_{aa} T_{as}$, where the aerosol absorption function, T_{aa}, is [64, 65, 114]

$$T_{aa} = 1 - 0.15\left(1 - m + m^{1.06}\right)(1 - T_a) \quad [40a]$$

and the aerosol scattering function, T_{as}, is

$$T_{as} = \frac{T_a}{T_{aa}} \quad [40b]$$

For clear-sky calculations (clear-sky MRM), H_b is estimated from eqn [19] with $T = T_a T_r T_o T_w T_g$. As for calculating H_d, this is taken by the expressions [111, 115]

$$H_{ds} = H_0 T_{aa} T_o T_w T_g 0.5 (1 - T_{as} T_r) \quad [41a]$$

Table 4 Indicative values of β representing various atmospheric conditions for different Vis values

Atmospheric condition	β	Vis (km)
Clean	0.0	340
Clear	0.1	28
Turbid	0.2	11
Very turbid	0.4–0.5	<5

$$H_{dm} = (H_b + H_{ds}) \left[\frac{\rho_g \rho_a}{(1 - \rho_g \rho_a)} \right] \qquad [41b]$$

$$H_d = H_{ds} + H_{dm} \qquad [41c]$$

where H_{ds} is the circumsolar diffuse radiation produced by a single-scattering mode of molecules and aerosols, H_{dm} the diffuse component reflected by the ground and backscattered by the atmosphere, ρ_g the ground albedo (usually given the value of 0.2), and ρ_a the albedo of the cloudless sky:

$$\rho_a = 0.0685 + 0.17(1 - T_{a1.66}) \qquad [41d]$$

where $T_{a1.66}$ implies the value of T_a at $m = 1.66$ (or $\theta_z = 53°$). The global horizontal solar radiation is then given by eqn [26].

For the cloudy-sky calculations (cloudy-sky MRM) the direct beam component is given by

$$H'_b = H_b T_c \qquad [42a]$$

$$T_c = k_p \left(\frac{L_{dm}}{L_{dt}} \right) \qquad [42b]$$

where k_p is a coefficient taking values in the range 0.75–1.0, L_{dm} is the actual (or measured) day length, in hours, and L_{dt} is the theoretical day length given by eqn [9]. The diffuse component is [111]

$$H'_{ds} = H_{ds} T_c + W[1 - T_c](H_b + H_{ds}) \qquad [43a]$$

$$H'_{dm} = (H'_b + H'_{ds}) \left[\frac{\rho_g \rho_a}{(1 - \rho_g \rho_a)} \right] \qquad [43b]$$

$$H'_d = H'_{ds} + H'_{dm} \qquad [43c]$$

$$H'_g = H'_b + H'_d \qquad [43d]$$

$$\rho'_a = 0.0685 + 0.17(1 - T_{a1.66}) + 0.4 \left(1 - \frac{L_{dm}}{L_{dt}} \right) \qquad [43e]$$

where ρ'_a is the albedo of the cloudy sky and W an empirical coefficient given in **Table 5**.

Figure 12 shows a comparison of the estimated hourly MRM horizontal global (total) radiation values with those measured in Athens, Greece, and Bed-Dagan, Israel, in a period of 8 years. By visual inspection, the agreement seems extremely good.

Example 3.02.5. Recapitulate the pros and cons of the above broadband global radiation models (numbers 8–19) including the MRM according to the work of Gueymard and Myers [117]. **Table 6** gives the number and kind of input data that each of the models needs to run. Those models with minimum input data are the most favorable, that is, ASHRAE, CLS, ESRA2, and Kasten.

As for performance of the models with respect to their estimation of the global radiation using some statistical estimators (discussed in Section 3.02.7), Gueymard and Myers [117] showed that the top five are the ASHRAE, REST2, CPCR2, Iqbal C, and METSTAT.

3.02.6.3 Calculation of Solar Radiation on a Tilted Surface

The total solar radiation on a tilted plane at an angle β, in degrees, with respect to the local horizon, $H_{g\beta}$, is equal to the sum of the direct, $H_{b\beta}$, the diffuse, $H_{d\beta}$, and the ground-reflected, $H_{r\beta}$, components, that is,

$$H_{g\beta} = H_{b\beta} + H_{d\beta} + H_{r\beta} \qquad [44a]$$

$$H_{r\beta} = \rho_g R_r H_g \qquad [44b]$$

$$R_r = \frac{(1 - \cos \beta)}{2} \qquad [44c]$$

Table 5 Typical values of *W* for various latitudes, φ, in the northern hemisphere

W	φ (degrees)
0.32	30
0.32	35
0.33	40
0.34	45

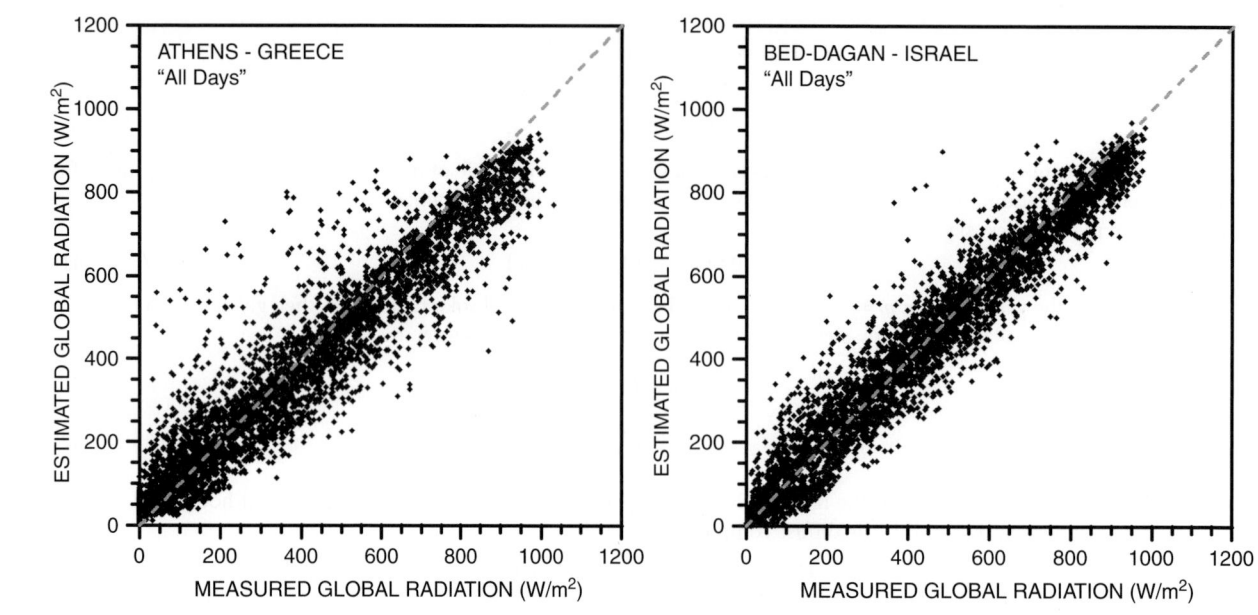

Figure 12 MRM-estimated vs. measured global horizontal radiation hourly values for Athens, Greece, and Bed-Dagan, Israel, for all-sky conditions in the period July 1996–September 2004. The line $y = x$ indicates complete agreement between estimated and measured values. From Muneer T (ed.) (1997) *Solar Radiation and Daylight Models for the Energy Efficient Design of Building*. Architectural Press [116].

Table 6 Inputs required by 15 broadband models for predicting global solar radiation

Model/#INP	m	e	ρ_g	P	T_d	I_o	I_n	I_w	T_L	k_a	α	β	SSA
1. ASHRAE/0													
2. Bird/8	X	X	X	X		X		X			X	X	
3. CLS/5	X	X	X	X				X					
4. CPCR2/9	X	X	X	X		X		X			X	X	X
5. ESRA2/5	X	X		X				X				X	
6. Iqbal A/9	X	X	X	X	X	X		X			X	X	
7. Iqbal B/8	X	X	X	X	X	X		X				X	
8. Iqbal C/9	X	X	X	X	X	X		X			X	X	
9. Kasten/4	X	X		X					X				
10. METSTAT/7	X	X	X	X		X		X		X			
11. MAC/6	X	X	X	X	X			X					
12. MRM/7	X	X	X	X	X	X		X					
13. REST2/10	X	X	X	X		X	X	X			X	X	X
14. Santamouris/6	X	X	X	X		X		X					
15. Yang/7	X	X	X	X		X		X				X	

#INP, Number of input data; SSA, single-scattering albedo.

where R_r is a configuration factor between the ground and the receiving surface. In the above equations, the direct radiation on the inclined surface is given by

$$H_{b\beta} = R_\beta H_b \quad [45a]$$

$$R_\beta = \frac{\cos \theta}{\cos \theta_z} \quad [45b]$$

where θ is the incidence angle, the angle between the normal to the surface and the direction to the Sun.

From the above, it is seen that the only parameters that need specific calculations are $H_{d\beta}$ and ρ_g, as the other three components, $H_{b\beta}$, $H_{r\beta}$, and H_b, can easily be computed from analytical expressions. Furthermore, $H_{b\beta}$ can also be the difference between the measured total and diffuse radiations on a sloped plane. Therefore, attention is paid to calculating the diffuse radiation on the inclined plane as well as the ground albedo. As far as the first issue is concerned, 12 sky diffuse submodels are selected from the international literature as the most promising for this study, based on published results for other locations. These models are listed in alphabetical order.

1. *The Bugler model* [118]:

$$H_{d\beta} = \frac{[H_d - 0.05H_{b\beta}]}{[\cos\theta_z]} R_{r1} + 0.05H_{b\beta}\cos\theta \qquad [46a]$$

$$R_{r1} = \frac{(1+\cos\beta)}{2} \qquad [46b]$$

2. *The Gueymard model* [119–121]:

$$H_{d\beta} = H_d\left[(1-N_{pt})R_{do} + N_{pt}R_{d1}\right] \qquad [47a]$$

where R_{do} and R_{d1} are expressions describing the effect of radiance patterns from the clear and overcast skies, respectively [121]; N_{pt} is a nebulosity weighting term. Because hourly cloud observations are not available, N_{pt} is estimated from radiation data using an approximate function that was originally proposed by Gueymard [121] for situations in which no coincident cloud opacity information is available:

$$N_{pt} = \max[\min(Y, 1), 0] \qquad [47b]$$

$$Y = 6.6667\left(\frac{H_d}{H_g}\right) - 1.4167, \quad \text{if } \frac{H_d}{H_g} \le 0.227 \qquad [47c]$$

$$Y = 1.2121\left(\frac{H_d}{H_t}\right) - 0.1758, \text{ otherwise} \qquad [47d]$$

3. *The Hay model* [122]:

$$H_{d\beta} = H_d[K_bR_b + (1-K_b)R_{r1}] \qquad [48a]$$

$$K_b = \min\left(\frac{H_b}{H_0}, 1\right) \qquad [48b]$$

$$R_b = \max\left(\frac{\cos\theta}{\cos\theta_z}, 0\right) \qquad [48c]$$

4. *The Hay–Willmott model* [123]:

$$H_{d\beta} = H_d\left[\frac{K_i}{\cos\theta_z} + C_\beta\left\{1 - \left(\frac{K_h}{\cos\theta_z}\right)\right\}\right] \qquad [49]$$

where C_β, K_h, and K_i are expressions given by Willmott [123].

5. *The isotropic model* [59]:

$$H_{d\beta} = H_dR_{r1} \qquad [50]$$

6. *The Klucher model* [124]:

$$H_{d\beta} = H_dR_{r1}M_1M_2 \qquad [51]$$

where M_1 and M_2 are expressions given by Klucher [124].

7. *The Muneer model* [125]:

$$H_{d\beta} = H_dT \qquad [52a]$$

for surfaces in shade and sunlit surfaces under overcast skies, and

$$H_{d\beta} = H_d[T(1-F) + FR_b] \qquad [52b]$$

for surfaces under clear or partly cloudy skies, where

$$T = R_{r1} + N_1N_2 \qquad [52c]$$

$$N_1 = 0.00263 - 0.7120F - 0.6883F^2 \qquad [52d]$$

$$N_2 = \sin\beta - \beta\cos\beta - \pi\sin^2\left(\frac{\beta}{2}\right) \qquad [52e]$$

$$F = \frac{H_b\cos\theta_z}{H_0} \qquad [52f]$$

8. *The Perez model* [45]:

$$H_{d\beta} = H_d \left[R_{r1}(1-F'_1) + F'_2 \left(\frac{\cos\theta}{\cos\theta_z}\right) + F'_2 \sin\beta \right] \quad [53]$$

where F'_1 and F'_2 are expressions for the circumsolar and horizon brightening effects as empirically determined by Perez et al. [45].

9. *The Reindl model* [126]:

$$H_{d\beta} = H_d \left[(1-K_b)R_{r1}\left\{1 + f\sin^2\left(\frac{\beta}{2}\right)\right\} + K_b R_b \right] \quad [54]$$

where K_b is defined as in eqn [48b].

10. *The Skartveit–Olseth model* [127]:

$$H_{d\beta} = H_d[K_b R_b + B\cos\beta + (1-K_b-B)R_{r1} - S(\omega_i, \theta_i)] \quad [55a]$$

$$B = \max\{(0.3 - 2K_b), 0\} \quad [55b]$$

where $S(\omega_i, \theta_i)$ evaluates the diffuse irradiation screened by obstacles on the horizon, and ω_i and θ_i are the solid and incidence angles for the ith sector of the actual horizon according to Skartveit and Olseth [127].

11. *The Temps–Coulson model* [128]:

$$H_{d\beta} = H_d R_{r1} P_1 P_2 \quad [56]$$

where P_1 and P_2 are expressions given by Temps and Coulson [128].

12. *The Willmott model* [123]. The expression for the sky diffuse component is the same as the one used in Hay–Willmott model, eqn [49]. The only difference between the two is that in the present model, the reflected radiation (see eqn [44b]) is multiplied by a coefficient K_r given in Reference [123].

For calculating ρ_g, four possible expressions are considered in this work.

1. *The isotropic constant model.* This is the most simple and commonly used ground albedo estimation with a constant value:

$$\rho_{g1} = 0.2 \quad [57]$$

2. *The isotropic seasonal model.* This is a function of the geographical latitude and the month of the year; it is fully described in Reference [129]. It was originally developed to estimate the monthly zonal albedo in North America. The zonal albedo refers to the average ground albedo over a large land area. Therefore, the zonal albedo is the space average of a myriad of individual local ground albedos. Although strictly speaking this model should not be used for the evaluation of a local ground albedo, it has already been used in such an extrapolated way [130] and has shown an accuracy comparable to the constant trivial 0.2 value in predicting the local albedo of six mid-latitude radiation stations. The isotropic seasonal model for northern geographical latitudes, φ, between 20° and 60° is given by

$$\rho_{g1} = r_0 + r_1\phi + r_2\phi_2 + r_3\phi^3 \quad [58]$$

where the geographical latitude is in degrees; the monthly values of the coefficients r_i are given in Reference [129]. From unpublished works, ρ_{g2} in the area of Athens varies between 0.141 in June and 0.288 in February with an annual value of 0.18. Although the existing coefficients r_i are not site-specific, they could be recalculated for various environments from *ad hoc* basic information, if available (e.g., maps of land use, maps of seasonal zonal albedo obtained from satellites). Furthermore, daily ground albedo values can easily be obtained from their monthly counterparts by interpolation.

3. *The climatological anisotropic model.* This was developed by Nkemdirim [131] and Arnfield [132]. This model expresses the ground albedo as a function of the solar zenith angle:

$$\rho_{g3} = g_1 \exp(g_2 \theta_z) \quad [59]$$

where $g_1 = 0.244$ and $g_2 = 0.005\,26$ deg^{-1} for morning hours, and $g_1 = 0.212$ and $g_2 = 0.008\,91$ deg^{-1} for afternoon hours, for any day of the year. The corresponding typical values of ρ_{g3} are 0.264 (morning) and 0.242 (afternoon) at a low zenith angle ($\theta_z = 15°$, the extreme value at the summer's solstice for Athens's latitude), and 0.382 (morning) and 0.452 (afternoon) at a high zenith angle ($\theta_z = 85°$). This model, therefore, predicts a large hourly albedo fluctuation and an average albedo significantly larger than ρ_{g1} and ρ_{g2}.

4. *The semiphysical anisotropic model.* It has been shown by Ineichen [133] that the apparent ground albedo may be significantly dependent on the direct radiation incident on it, H_b. Therefore, it makes sense to consider separate albedos for the direct and diffuse

components on the horizontal plane. In this respect, a model developed by Ångström [26] has been selected because it distinguishes between the reflectance for the direct and diffuse radiations. The resulting average ground albedo for global radiation is

$$\rho_{g4} = f_{bs}\, \rho_b k_b + \rho_d (1 - k_b) \qquad [60a]$$

where

$$\rho_b = \rho_n + F(f_{ab}, f_{af}) \times l \cos wl \exp(-1.77 - 1.53\gamma' - 3.61\gamma'^2) \qquad [60b]$$

$$\rho_d = \rho_n + 0.023(f_{ab} + f_{af}) \qquad [60c]$$

where ρ_b is the reflectance for the direct radiation, ρ_d is the reflectance for the diffuse component, ρ_n is the ground albedo for purely isotropic reflection, f_{ab} and f_{af} are the coefficients describing the backward and forward increase of the reflectance, respectively, $F(f_{ab}, f_{af})$ is a function defined in Reference [121], f_{bs} is the shadow factor for the direct radiation, $k_b = H_b/H_g$, w is the solar azimuth relative to the receiving surface, and $\gamma' = 0.01\gamma$. The values of the parameters f_{ab}, f_{af}, and f_{bs} for the area surrounding the Actinometric Station of the National Observatory of Athens (ASNOA), for instance, are estimated to be 0.5, 0.5, and 1.0, respectively. These coefficients are for pasture land, no beam shading, with reference to the guidelines provided [121]. (The area around ASNOA is quite dry in summer, with a few trees; 'pasture land' is the closest available description of this type of vegetation.) Accordingly, ρ_n is estimated to be constant at 0.16, so that ρ_d becomes 0.183. When modeling of ρ_g is done through the semiphysical anisotropic model (eqns [60]), the albedo of a particular ground surface is a function of the time of the day (through γ and θ) and of the atmospheric conditions (through k_b). For example, on a typical early morning or late afternoon in Athens around the winter solstice, γ and θ would be about 5° and 55°, respectively. At such a low solar elevation, k_b is about 0.5 for clear conditions (low turbidity, 1 cm precipitable water) according to a two-band solar irradiance model [49]. This would yield $\rho_b = 0.205$ and $\rho_{g4} = 0.194$. For typical noon conditions (cloudless but turbid sky) around the summer solstice, one would similarly obtain $\rho_b = 0.164$ and $\rho_{g4} = 0.170$. For overcast conditions at any time, $k_b = 0$, so that $\rho_{g4} = \rho_d = 0.183$. Thus it appears that, for the extreme conditions examined, eqns [60] predict relatively low variations of albedo from one hour to the other (i.e., nearly isotropic reflection, compared to the predictions of eqn [59]). Because the calculation of the irradiations by most of the aforementioned sky and albedo models requires the knowledge of the solar position in the sky, the SUNAE algorithm [134] can be used with all modifications suggested by Wilkinson [135], Muir [136], Kambezidis and Papanikolaou [6], and Kambezidis and Tsangrassoulis [137].

3.02.6.4 Quality Control of Solar Radiation Values

Before any manipulation of the gathered (measured or estimated) solar radiation values, these have to pass some quality control tests (QCTs) to become error free. These tests are the following:

QCT 1: Reject all diffuse horizontal values that are greater than 1.1 times the corresponding total horizontal ones. [61a]

QCT 2: Reject all global horizontal values that are greater than 1.2 times the solar constant on the horizontal plane. [61b]

QCT 3: Reject all diffuse horizontal values that are greater than 0.8 times the solar constant on the horizontal plane. [61c]

QCT 4: Reject all direct horizontal values that are greater than the solar constant on the horizontal plane. [61d]

QCT 5: Reject all global horizontal values equal to or less than 5 Wm^{-2}.
This value is associated with the sensitivity of the actinometers. [61e]

QCT 6: Reject all radiation values that correspond to solar elevation angles equal to or less than 5°.
This low value of the solar altitude is adopted to discard the cosine effect of the actinometer, that is, the high uncertainty of the instrument in registering the correct radiation value at solar positions near the horizon. [61f]

QCT 7: All diffuse radiation values are corrected for the shade ring effect.
The procedures of Littlefair [138] or Drummond [139] may be adopted. [61g]

3.02.7 Evaluation of Models

A perfect model, not only in the solar radiation sector, but also in any scientific field, never exists. This statement is valid, since the 'true' solar radiation value cannot be determined theoretically or measured experimentally with absolute certainty. For this reason, the various sources of uncertainty in experimental radiation measurements are described in Section 3.02.12. These rules must always be taken into account when the performance of a model is to be tested against measured data [117]. For a new model to be accepted by the solar radiation community, it needs to be tested against measured data from at least one location. If the model appears to perform equally well at many locations on the Earth, it then becomes 'universal'. It usually takes a relatively long time until a 'universal' model becomes acceptable in the international literature. On the other hand, any changes in the calibration of radiometers and measurement procedures (as described in Section 3.02.12) can alter the performance of a model or classification of the models according to their performance [117]. As said above, the usual way of assessing the validity and performance of a solar radiation model is by comparing its predictions with corresponding measurements; the derived uncertainty between the two should be reported as part of the validation process. Another way of validating a model under certain circumstances is by comparing its predictions to 'reference' (or trusted) predictions from a validated and more sophisticated solar radiation code. As has been demonstrated in Reference [70], such an approach has the advantage that there is no constraint in terms of particular atmospheric or climatological conditions of a specific experimental site, or the quality of the data. A counterpart of the 'reference' predictions is the availability of experimental data of exceptional quality. Such data must have documented uncertainties, so that various models can be tested with confidence. Such data can be grouped into a benchmark data set [42].

There are several ways for testing the agreement between measured and simulated values. Generally, the test of any model can be accomplished in two ways. One is its qualitative assessment. This is done in the form of scatter plots, which visually indicate the bias (systematic error) and scatter (random error) of the estimated against the measured values. Results from a perfect model align along the $y = x$ line. However, in most cases, a performance assessment study requires thousands of data points to be depicted in a diagram, particularly when short-term data and long periods are considered. This makes things more difficult in the sense that the so-derived scatter plots are becoming 'bulky' in terms of the number of data points to appear on them. In the above, one must bear in mind that both estimated and experimental values of the solar radiation component must refer to the same time basis (e.g., hourly, daily, or monthly values), and the two sets should be of equal length, that is, equal number of data points. In the ideal case that the predictions of a model agree completely with the measurements would deploy all data points (i.e., the pairs of the estimated and measured values) along the $y = x$ line. Since this is not the case, a dispersion of the pairs around the $y = x$ line is seen. The more the dispersion of the data points around the 'equality line', the lesser the efficiency of the model. Therefore, a (statistical) quantitative assessment is needed. Each of these statistical estimators tries to give a measure of this dispersion its own way. An adoption of some of them in the process of evaluating a model secures its efficiency since the combination of several such statistical estimators gives credibility to the final selection of the model as the best-performing. Measurements always provide the reference basis for evaluation of a model (e.g., the estimated values). Therefore, the estimators deployed below refer to the measurements.

3.02.7.1 The Standard Deviation

The standard deviation (SD) of the estimated solar radiation values is given by

$$\mathrm{SD}_{N-1} = \sqrt{\left[\frac{1}{N-1}\sum_{i=1}^{N}\left[(H_\mathrm{m} - H_\mathrm{e})\right]^2\right]} \qquad [62]$$

where H_m and H_e are the individual values of the measured and estimated solar radiation component values, respectively. SD provides significant information on the distribution of the data around the mean, approximating normality. The mean $\pm 1\mathrm{SD}$ contains approximately 68% of the measurements in the series. The mean $\pm 2\mathrm{SDs}$ contains approximately 95% of the measurements in the series. The mean $\pm 3\mathrm{SDs}$ contains approximately 99.7% of the measurements in the series. **Table 7** describes the abnormality of a data value, in general, by how many SDs it is located away from the mean. The probabilities in the third column assume that the data are normally distributed.

3.02.7.2 The Root Mean Square Error

The root mean square error (RMSE) is also known as the root mean square deviation (RMSD); its analytical expression is very similar to SD in the sense that RMSE refers to N data points instead of N^{-1}:

$$\mathrm{RMSE\ (units)} = \sqrt{\left[\frac{1}{N}\sum_{i=1}^{N}(H_{\mathrm{m}i} - H_{\mathrm{e}i})^2\right]} \qquad [63a]$$

Table 7 Abnormality of data points

SDs away from mean	Abnormality	Probability of occurrence (%)
Beyond −3 SD	Extremely subnormal	0.15
−3 SD to −2 SD	Greatly subnormal	2.35
−2 SD to −1 SD	Subnormal	13.5
−1 SD to +1 SD	Normal	68.0
+1 SD to +2 SD	Above normal	13.5
+2 SD to +3 SD	Greatly above normal	2.35
Beyond +3 SD	Extremely above normal	0.15

where the RMSE is in the same units as H_m and H_e. The subscript i denotes the corresponding individual values of the same pair of measured and estimated solar radiation component. Sometimes RMSE is expressed in %:

$$\text{RMSE} (\%) = \frac{\sqrt{\left[\frac{1}{N}\sum_{i=1}^{N}(H_{mi} - H_{ei})^2\right]}}{\frac{1}{N}\sum_{i=1}^{N}H_{mi}} \times 100 \qquad [63b]$$

The RMSE statistic provides information about the short-term performance of a model by allowing a term-by-term comparison of the actual difference between the estimated and the measured value [140]. The smaller the value, the better the model's performance. A drawback of this test is that few large errors in the sum may produce a significant increase in RMSE. In addition, the test does not differentiate between underestimation and overestimation [141].

3.02.7.3 The Mean Bias Error

The mean bias error (MBE) is given by

$$\text{MBE (units)} = \sum_{i=1}^{N}(H_{mi} - H_{ei}) \qquad [64a]$$

$$\text{MBE} (\%) = \frac{\sum_{i=1}^{N}(H_{mi} - H_{ei})}{\sum_{i=1}^{N}H_{mi}} \times 100 \qquad [64b]$$

The MBE statistic provides information about the long-term performance of a model. A positive value implies underestimation in the calculated values, while a negative value means overestimation [140]. The smaller the absolute value, the better the model's performance. A drawback of this test is that an overestimation in one observation can be cancelled by an underestimation in another [141].

3.02.7.4 The Mean Absolute Bias Error

The mean absolute bias error (MABE) statistic is defined as

$$\text{MABE (units)} = \sum_{i=1}^{N}|H_{mi} - H_{ei}| \qquad [65a]$$

$$\text{MABE} (\%) = \frac{\sum_{i=1}^{N}|H_{mi} - H_{ei}|}{\sum_{i=1}^{N}H_{mi}} \times 100 \qquad [65b]$$

MABE is more rarely used than the RMSE and MBE statistics. It is worth noting that a part of the apparent cumulative error described by MBE, RMSE, or MABE is actually the result of the measurement uncertainty. Another part is introduced by the uncertainties in the inputs to the model. For these reasons, some authors rather use the nomenclature MBD, RMSD, and MABD, where D stands for difference.

3.02.7.5 The *t*-test

To overcome the drawbacks of the RMSE and MBE statistics, the *t*-test can be used [141, 142] to illustrate the overestimation or underestimation of the data at a certain significance level, usually 95%. The *t*-test is calculated as the ratio of TT1 and TT2:

$$t = \frac{\text{TT1}}{\text{TT2}} \qquad [66a]$$

$$\text{TT1 (units)} = \frac{\sum_{i=1}^{N}(H_{mi} - H_{ei})}{N} \qquad [66b]$$

where TT1 is the average of the differences between the measured, H_{mi}, and the estimated, H_{ei}, radiation values, and

$$\text{TT2 (units)} = \sqrt{\frac{\sum_{i=1}^{N}\left[(H_{mi} - H_{ei}) - \text{TT1}\right]^2}{N-1}} \quad [66c]$$

For a population of $N > 120$ and the absolute value of t being less than or equal to 1.96, there is no statistically significant difference between the measured and calculated data at the confidence level of 95%. Values of t close to zero indicate a higher accuracy. When the t-test value is positive, then the measured value is not statistically greater than the estimated one at the confidence level of 95%. On the other hand, when the t-test value is negative, the calculated value is not significantly greater than the measured value at the confidence level of 95%.

3.02.7.6 The Index of Agreement (*d*)

The index of agreement (*d*) is a relative and bounded measure that can make cross-comparisons between models and measurements and is limited to the range of 0–1. A value of $d = 0$ denotes no agreement between the two samples, while $d = 1$ implies complete agreement. It is given by [143]

$$d = 1 - \frac{\sum_{i=1}^{N}(H_{ei} - H_{mi})^2}{\sum_{i=1}^{N}(|H'_{ei}| + |H'_{mi}|)^2} \quad [67]$$

where $H'_{ei} = H_{ei} - \bar{H}^m$ and $H'_{mi} = H_{mi} - \bar{H}^m$, and $\bar{H}^m$ is the mean of the measured solar radiation values.

3.02.7.7 The Coefficient of Determination (R^2)

A measured solar data set has values H_{mi} each of which has an associated modeled value H_{ei}. If each of the data sets has N data points, then different sums of squares can de defined [144]:

$$S_t = \sum_{i=1}^{N}(H_{mi} - \bar{H}_m)^2 \quad [68a]$$

the total sum of squares (proportional to the sample variance),

$$S_r = \sum_{i=1}^{N}(H_{ei} - \bar{H}_e)^2 \quad [68b]$$

the regression sum of squares, also called the explained sum of squares,

$$S_e = \sum_{i=1}^{N}(H_{mi} - H_{ei})^2 \quad [68c]$$

the sum of squared errors, also called the residual sum of squares. Then the definition of the coefficient of determination, R^2, is

$$R^2 = 1 - \frac{S_e}{S_t} \quad [68d]$$

R^2 can be seen to be related to the unexplained variance, since the second term compares the unexplained variance (variance of the model's errors) with the total variance of the data. In the special case that $S_e + S_r = S_t$:

$$R^2 = \frac{S_r}{S_t} \quad [68e]$$

R^2 is a statistic that gives some information about the goodness of fit of a model. In regression, the coefficient of determination is a statistical measure of how well the regression line approximates the real data points. An R^2 of 1 indicates that the regression line perfectly fits the data. Nevertheless, in cases that an agreement between measured and modeled values is sought through the R^2 statistic, this statistic can take values outside the range 0–1; this particularly occurs when the modeled values have not been obtained by linear expression. If eqn [68d] is used, values can never be greater than 1. If eqn [68e] is used, there are no constraints on the values obtainable.

Example 3.02.6. Recapitulate the findings from the work of Kambezidis et al. [145] about investigating which is the most suitable diffuse submodel combined with the most appropriate ground albedo submodel for Athens.

For this the authors collected 11 414 hourly values of tilted global solar radiation from the ASNOA in the period 19 January 1990 to 20 May 1991. Then, these measurements passed the QCTs dictated by eqns [61] from which $N = 5228$ remained. The tilted surface had a slope $\beta = 50°$ and an azimuth $\psi = 0°$, that is, it was south oriented. Afterward, the RMSE and MBE estimators were employed through eqns [63a] and [64a], respectively. In these expressions, H_m and H_e are $H_{g\beta m}$, the measured tilted total solar radiation, and $H_{g\beta e}$, the estimated tilted total solar radiation, respectively.

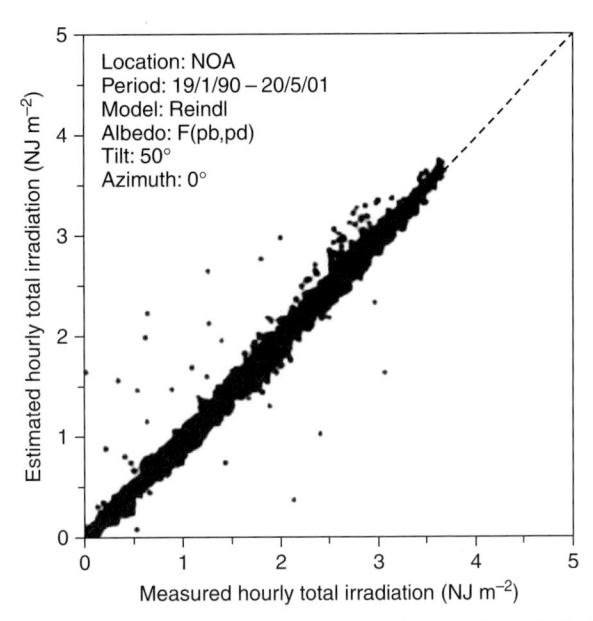

Figure 13 Estimated vs. measured global horizontal radiation hourly values for Athens, Greece, using the Reindl diffuse submodel and the semiphysical anisotropic ground albedo submodel for the period January 1990 to May 1991. The line $y = x$ indicates complete agreement between estimated and measured values. From Kambezidis HD, Psiloglou BE, and Gueymard C (1994) Measurements and models for total solar irradiance on inclined surface in Athens, Greece. *Solar Energy* 53(2): 177–185 [145].

The final conclusion of the study was that 4 of the 12 selected sky diffuse submodels (those of Gueymard, Hay, Reindl, and Skartveit–Olseth) perform equally when combined with either one of the three ground albedo submodels (1, 2, or 4) and, therefore they may be used to obtain accurate radiation estimates in Athens. The conclusion was based on the lowest possible values of the statistical estimators MBE and RMSE. **Figure 13** gives an indication of the good fit between the measured and estimated hourly values of the total solar radiation using the Reindl and the three semiphysical anisotropic submodels. The fit is visually seen as all data points lie around the $y = x$ line.

All solar radiation models must go through a verification and validation process against measurements in order to be able to 'stand decently' in the international literature. Nevertheless, solar radiation models are not always validated or verified convincingly because of a number of reasons [32], which are discussed briefly below.

Reason 1: Independence of the data set. The data set used to validate a model should be different from that used to derive it. This can be generally done by selecting two subsets, one for the development of the model and the other for its validation. The random selection of two subsets of solar radiation measurements, one for the derivation and the other for the evaluation of the model, is a more appropriate procedure.

Reason 2: Analysis of the uncertainty. Uncertainty analysis of the data set is important. A sensitivity analysis must also be carried out on the model's input parameters to determine how they affect the predictions of the model and to which extent they lead to prediction errors in comparison to the experimental uncertainty.

Reason 3: Filtering of the data. All available measured data points are not necessarily appropriate for validating a model. They need to be tested first for inconsistencies, gaps, inhomogeneities, and so on. Solar radiation data from actinometric stations, such as ASNOA, are generally well quality-controlled, but spurious data can still exist. QCTs, as those reported in Section 3.02.6.4, must apply to the reference data points in order to exclude all possible errors related to the measurements themselves [146–149].

Reason 4: Time and space. As already said in the beginning of Section 3.02.7, the model inputs and the validation data should have the same time resolution and come from the same site. Nevertheless, this is not always possible. Some inputs are not measured on-site at the proper sampling frequency; therefore, they must be extrapolated, interpolated, or averaged. When such imperfect data are used for a highly sensitive input, the performance of the model can be seriously influenced. This has been demonstrated in the literature [52, 71, 74]. This condition cannot be respected in the case that the model uses input data from a grid, such as cloud information, or 'ground truth'. This problem introduces significant random errors [37] and should be avoided.

Reason 5: Ancillary data. If there is a need for ancillary data to be used for the model to run, these should be of good quality. Such an action is often critical for the performance of a model. The use of low-quality ancillary data may result in biased or meaningless performance reports [52].

Reason 6: Radiative closure. All inputs to a model must be measured independently. For this reason, the measurements must come from co-located instruments at the required sampling frequency and with an uncertainty as low as possible. If the estimated uncertainty is higher than the uncertainty in the measurements to a significant extent, then the model can be considered validated. In the opposite case, the intrinsic performance of the model is inferior, or the input data are of low quality and do not meet the requirements of Reason 5.

Reason 7: Validity. In many cases, only particular atmospheric or climatic conditions are considered for a model's validation (see Reason 4). The solar radiation modeler must specify the limits of validity of his/her model to avoid extra work from the users. On the other hand, it is utopia to determine empirical equations from high-order polynomial fits and use them outside of their intended limits; such a process may lead to divergence. Therefore, more efficient mathematical modeling is required. Another factor to take care of is the clear identification of the timescale of the input data to avoid misinterpretations. As an example, Gueymard [21] showed the catastrophic effect of a global radiation model with empirical coefficients exclusively developed for estimating the annual mean sunshine when applied to compute the monthly mean sunshine.

3.02.8 Models of Solar Spectral Radiation

It is known that various biological, chemical, and physical processes are enhanced at some wavelengths than at others. Because of prohibitive costs associated with spectral measurements and technical difficulties, normally these processes cannot be monitored experimentally. For this reason, it is often desired to evaluate or predict the performance of such systems at an early phase, long before they are eventually 'launched'. Such predictions can be made through the use of mathematical models, which must include a description of the spectral features of the incident radiation. This spectral information can be provided for different spectral radiation models or RTMs of varied complexity and accuracy. As a matter of fact, atmospheric processes are selective by nature; it is, therefore, wise to model such processes on a spectral basis rather than on a broadband one. As an indirect consequence, the use of these RTMs as reference to test the performance of broadband radiation models is quite interesting.

Plenty of spectral models exist in the international literature. Most of them have been developed for specific applications. A detailed catalogue of spectral models, mostly for atmospheric applications, is given in **Table 8**. Atmospheric RTMs are generally the most complex of all spectral models; this is because they solve the equations of radiative transfer on a wavelength-by-wavelength practice and a layer-by-layer basis in the atmosphere. In addition, the scattering processes from which diffuse radiation is formed (under clear or cloudy skies) demand advanced modeling and arduous numerical solutions. A typical application of such models is the analysis of signals from sensors onboard satellites. Examples of this type of RTMs include the Santa Barbara DISORT Atmospheric Radiative Transfer (SBDART) and the moderate transmission MODTRAN. The SBDART [174] was developed at the University of California, Santa Barbara, and has a relatively simpler use than MODTRAN; it is freely accessible, and provides a convenient user interface online (http://arm.mrcsb.com/sbdart). The MODTRAN [161] was developed at the Air Force Geophysical Laboratory, and has a higher resolution; it is now considered a standard in atmospheric applications. MODTRAN is sold as a commercial product available from the Ontar Corporation (http://www.ontar.com). See **Table 8** for more details. The SBDART and MODTRAN models are, however, not appropriate for any solar energy application or other engineering project. Other models are recommended instead, for example, the Spectral Model of the Atmospheric Radiative Transfer of Sunshine (SMARTS) and the Bird simple spectral model (SPCTRAL2). Even though these models are restricted to perform under clear-sky conditions, they can also be empirically modified to derive spectra under cloudy conditions, at least partially [175, 176]. SMARTS was initially developed to investigate the effect of varying atmospheric conditions on the performance of spectrally selective glazings, but the model evolved into a versatile RTM appropriate for a variety of applications [177]. The derivation of previous versions is described elsewhere [21, 90]. The model has received considerable improvements and has undergone extensive testing. Its version 2.9.2 has been selected to define reference direct and global irradiance spectra at air mass 1.5 [178], which have now been standardized [179]. The model is able to predict clear-sky direct, diffuse, and global irradiance incident on any horizontal or tilted surface in a span of 2002 wavelengths, namely from 280 to 4000 nm, as well as illuminances, luminous efficacy, UV-action spectra, circumsolar irradiance, and broadband irradiances. The FORTRAN code and relevant documentation are available at http://rredc.nrel.gov/solar/models/SMARTS. The latest SMARTS version is 2.9.5. The SPCTRAL2 model was developed initially in the early 1980s [171, 180]; it has undergone no further improvement since. Therefore, its accuracy appears now relatively limited compared to SMARTS. Nevertheless, SPCTRAL2 is still a useful tool for very rapid estimates of the clear-sky direct, diffuse, and global irradiance on horizontal or tilted surfaces for a range of 122 wavelengths, that is, from 300 to 4000 nm. The SPCTRAL2 code exists in FORTRAN and C, and also as an electronic spreadsheet. These versions are available at http://rredc.nrel.gov/solar/models/spectral.

3.02.9 Net Solar Radiation

The radiation balance of the Earth system is the algebraic sum of the incoming and outgoing components of radiation. These components are balanced over long-time periods and over the Earth as whole. If they were not, the Earth would be continually cooling or warming. However, over a short period of time, radiant energy is unequally distributed over the Earth. The radiation balance of the Earth system is depicted in **Figure 14**. The short-wave radiation from the Sun penetrates through space to the outer edge of the atmosphere unimpeded by the vacuum of outer space. Once solar radiation begins to penetrate through the atmosphere, this amount begins to decrease due to absorption and scattering/reflection, mechanisms discussed in Section 3.02.5. Equation [26]

Table 8 Available RTMs

Name	Reference	Characteristics	Remarks
6S	[150]	Single scattering	6S is one of the best codes for satellite spectral radiation simulations with good documentation. Available at ftp://kratmos.gsfc.nasa.gov/pub/6S
BIRD	[65]		The code and its documentation are available at http://rredc.nrel.gov/solar/models/clearsky
CliRad SW and LW	[151]	2-stream, 1D	It is an RTM developed at Goddard, NASA, for use in global circulation and mesoscale models
CRM	NCAR		Available at http://www.cgd.ucar.edu/cms/crm. CRM is a stand-alone radiation code used in NCAR Community Climate Model
DISORT	[152]	1D, solver only	Available at ftp://climate.gsfc.nasa.gov/pub/wiscombe/Disc_Ord
DOM	[153]	Discrete-ordinate method (DOM)	
DOORS	[154]	DOM	DOORS uses aerosol data from LOWTRAN and gaseous absorption data from 6S
FASCODE	[155]	Line-by-line	Description of the code is found at http://www.kirtland.af.mil/library/factsheets/factsheet.asp?id=7913. The code can be downloaded free of charge from http://www.kirtland.af.mil/library/factsheets/factsheet.asp?id=7903, but a nondisclosure agreement (NDA) must first be signed and sent; a CD with the code is received afterward
FluxNet	[156]	Neural networks	FluxNet is a neural network version of STREAMER (see below). Given a set of input data consisting of surface, cloud, and atmospheric characteristics, FluxNet calculates upwelling and downwelling surface flux in either short wave or long wave. While it is not as flexible as STREAMER, FluxNet is faster by 2–4 orders of magnitude, making it ideal for large batch jobs and image processing
Fu-Liu v. 200503	[157]		The code was popular in the past. It is low-stream solver with good molecular package. Available from http://snowdog.larc.nasa.gov/cgi-bin/rose/flp200503/flp200503.cgi for online calculations. Poor documentation is provided at http://snowdog.larc.nasa.gov/rose/fu200503/flp200503_web.htm
GENSPECT	Commercial product	Line-by-line	GENSPECT is an RTM under MATLAB to calculate gas absorption and atmospheric physics emissivity, emission, and transmission for a wide range of atmospheric gases from near-UV to NIR. For information, see http://www.genspect.com
LBLRTM v8.1	[158]	Commercial product	Documentation and download of LBLRTM from http://www.rtweb.aer.com/lblrtm_frame.html. The code needs some input data, which can be taken from the output of the LNFL code (http://www.rtweb.aer.com)
libRadtran	[159]		libRadtran is a collection of C and FORTRAN functions and programs for calculation of solar and thermal radiation in the Earth's atmosphere. Free download from http://www.libradtran.org/doku.php?id=download
LidarPC			Download is available from http://www.cas.usf.edu/lidarlab/lidar_pc_intro.html
LOWTRAN7 v4.2	[27]	Line-by-line	LOWTRAN is a lower resolution code than its successor, MODTRAN. One should prefer to use MODTRAN instead. LOWTRAN source code is freely available from http://www1.ncdc.noaa.gov/pub/software/lowtran
MCML	[160]	Monte-Carlo technique	MCML is a steady-state Monte-Carlo simulation program intended for multilayered turbid media. Each layer has its own optical properties of absorption, scattering,

(Continued)

			anisotropy, and multilayer refractive index. MCML code and documentation can be found at http://omlc.ogi.edu/pubs/wang95c.html
MODTRAN4 v3.1	[161]	Line-by-line, DOM	MODTRAN is considered as one of the best codes because its molecular package (based on HITRAN) is often updated. A description of the code is given at http://www.kirtland.af.mil/library/factsheets/factsheet.asp?id=7915. Free download of the software package can be done through http://www.kirtland.af.mil/library/factsheets/factsheet.asp?id=7903, but an NDA must first be signed and sent; a CD with the code is received afterward. The MODTRAN5 (the most recent version of the model) is distributed on a commercial basis by Ontar Corp. (http://www.ontar.com/Software/ProductDetails.aspx?item=modtran)
MOSART v1.7			MOSART is a unified and seamless computer code for calculating atmospheric transmission and radiance at low altitudes for line-of-sight paths within the atmosphere and for paths that intersect the Earth's surface. A description of the RTM can be found at http://www.kirtland.af.mil/library/factsheets/factsheet.asp?id=7916. Free download of the code can be done through http://www.kirtland.af.mil/library/factsheets/factsheet.asp?id=7903. An NDA must first be signed and sent; a CD with the code is received afterward
mc-layer OPAC	[162] [163]	Monte-Carlo technique	An RTM for multiple scattering in vertically inhomogeneous atmospheres Description and availability of the code at http://www.lrz-muenchen.de/~uh234an/www/radaer/opac.html
PLEXUS v3.2	AFRL		A description of the code is given at http://www.kirtland.af.mil/library/factsheets/factsheet.asp?id=7917. Free download of the code can be done through http://www.kirtland.af.mil/library/factsheets/factsheet.asp?id=7903. An NDA must first be signed and sent; a CD with the code is received afterward
PolRadTran	[164, 165]		PolRadTran is a plane-parallel fully polarized atmospheric RTM. There are two related models: rt3 for solar or thermal radiation in a medium of randomly oriented particles, and rt4 for thermal radiation in a medium of azimuthally symmetrically oriented particles. Description and free download are available at http://nit.colorado.edu/polrad.html
SAMM	[166]		The code provides a seamless integration of the SHARC and MODTRAN atmospheric RTMs, extending the modeling capabilities down to ground level. The more recent SAMM2 code includes a kinetic model and a radiative-transfer model in a unified manner; the code can operate under thermal equilibrium or nonequilibrium. The new A3RTSS (All Altitude Atmospheric Radiation Transport for Scene Simulation) code is a completely restructured and modernized version of SAMM2 that incorporates new radiation transport algorithms of varying degrees of fidelity, increased efficiency for multiple line-of-sight scene computations, and the ability to readily integrate additional physical models
SBDART	[167]	1D code using DOM	SBDART is a FORTRAN computer code for the analysis of a wide variety of radiative transfer problems in satellite remote sensing and atmospheric energy budget studies. The source code can be downloaded from http://arm.mrcsb.com/sbdart, while a description of SBDART can be found at http://www.crseo.ucsb.edu/esrg/papers/SBDART.96/sbdart_96.html

(*Continued*)

Table 8 *(Continued)*

Name	Reference	Characteristics	Remarks
SCIATRAN v2.2.2	SCIATRAN working group, Institute of Remote Sensing/Institute of Environmental Physics (IRS/IUP), University of Bremen (UoB)	Line-by-line, plane-parallel mode	SCIATRAN is a software package incorporating an RTMI and a retrieval algorithm, which can easily be adjusted to solve a wide range of scientific tasks. The program has been developed at the IRS/IUP, UoB, Germany. Description of the code is given at http://www.iup.uni-bremen.de/sciatran, while a free download is available at http://www.iup.uni-bremen.de/sciatran/download/index.html after a license agreement
SHARC	[168]		The code was developed by SSI for the USAF as a nonequilibrium high-altitude (up to 300 km) IR emission model for quiescent and aurorally disturbed atmospheres. The SHARC 3D model solves the chemical kinetic equations pertinent above 30 km altitude to determine nonequilibrium distributions of molecular vibrational states, which are incorporated into line-of-sight calculations to determine path radiances and transmittances from 30 to 300 km. SHARC has been validated against measurements, and includes the effects of atmospheric structure, auroral enhancements, and solar terminator physics
SHDOM	[169]	3D DOM	This code computes unpolarized monochromatic or spectral-band radiative transfer in a 1D, 2D, and or harmonics 3D medium for collimated solar and/or thermal emission sources of radiation. It is one of the best 3D DOM codes available. Description and free download of the code are available at http://nit.colorado.edu/~evans/shdom.html
SIG			The source code is available from http://www2.bc.edu/_sullivab/soft/NDA_SIG.txt. An NDA must be signed first
SMAC	[170]		SMAC works over the whole solar spectrum. Free download is available from ftp://www.cesbio.ups-tlse.fr
SMARTS	[21, 90]	Transmittance parameterizations	The code calculates total as well as partial atmospheric transmittances, irradiances, and illuminances. Documentation of SMARTS and free download are available from http://www.nrel.gov/solar/models/SMARTS, after a password is given to download the code and an agreement is signed
SPCTRAL2	[171]	Transmittance parameterizations	The code is freely available from http://rredc.nrel.gov/solar/models/spectral/spectral and is available in different versions (C, FORTRAN, or spreadsheet)
STAR	[172]		The code, as a Java application, is available from http://www.meteo.physik.uni-muenchen.de/strahlung/uvrad/Star/STARneuro.html
STREAMER	[173]	N-stream approximation	STREAMER is an RTM that can be used for computing either radiances (intensities) or irradiances (fluxes) for a wide variety of atmospheric and surface conditions. The code uses N-stream approximation to the radiative transfer equations [152], and allows for flexible choice of bands. The code can be used for both satellite-radiance applications and estimates of heating rates in both cloudy and noncloudy atmosphere. One can specify surface reflectivity. STREAMER is a FORTRAN code A list with available links about many of the above-cited codes can be found at http://www.geocities.jp/null2unity/research/related_sites.html. Access to HITRAN is done through http://www.cfa.harvard.edu/hitran

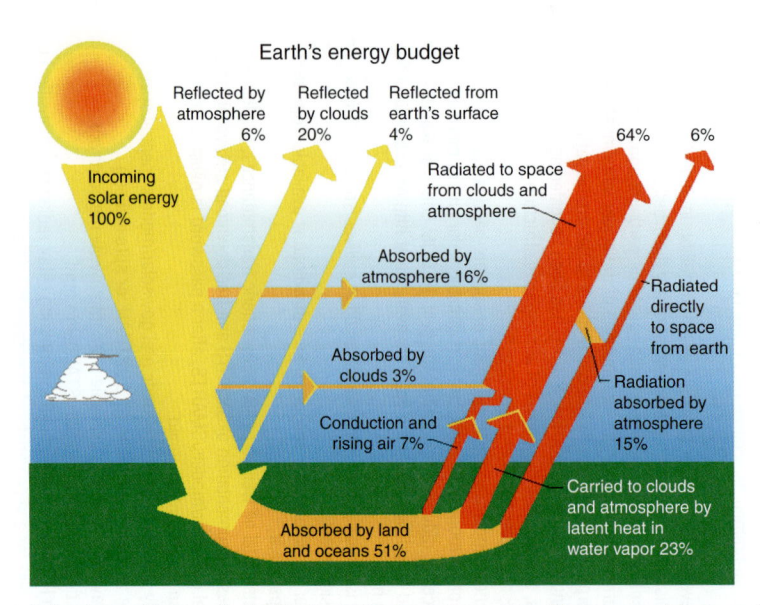

Figure 14 Schematic of the radiation (energy) balance (budget) in the Earth–atmosphere system. The incoming (short-wave) solar radiation is shown in yellow and the outgoing (long-wave or thermal) radiation in red. The various solar radiation depletion mechanisms are shown. From http://www.steir.aug.au/global-warming/.

describes the received incoming short-wave solar radiation at the surface on the Earth on a horizontal plane. If ρ_g is the surface albedo, then the portion of the incoming solar radiation reflected to space is

$$H_{gr} = (H_b + H_d)\rho_g \qquad [69a]$$

where H_{gr} is the reflected part of H_g. Then the net short-wave radiation, H_g^*, is

$$H_g^* = (H_b + H_d) - (H_b + H_d)\rho_g \qquad [69b]$$

The energy absorbed at the surface is radiated by the Earth as terrestrial long-wave radiation, $L\uparrow$. The amount of energy emitted is primarily dependent on the temperature of the surface. The hotter the surface, the more the radiant energy it emits. The gases of the atmosphere are relatively good absorbers of long-wave radiation and thus absorb the energy emitted by the Earth's surface. The absorbed radiation is emitted downward toward the surface as long-wave atmospheric counter-radiation, $L\downarrow$, keeping near-surface temperatures warmer than they would be without this blanket of gases. This is known as the greenhouse effect. The difference between incoming and outgoing long-wave radiation is the net long-wave radiation, L^*, expressed as

$$L^* = (L\downarrow - L\uparrow) \qquad [69c]$$

The combination of H_g^* and L^* gives the net radiation, Q^*:

$$Q^* = H_g^* - L^* = \left[(H_b + H_d) - (H_b + H_d)\rho_g\right] - (L\downarrow - L\uparrow) \qquad [69d]$$

Being consistent with the notation for the downward and upward long-wave radiations, the short-wave radiations can be written as $S\downarrow = H_b + H_d$, and $S\uparrow = (H_b + H_d)\rho_g$. Therefore, eqn [69d] can be rewritten as

$$Q^* = (S\downarrow - S\uparrow) - (L\downarrow - L\uparrow) \qquad [69e]$$

Net radiation can be positive, negative, or even zero. Net radiation is a positive value when there is more incoming radiation than outgoing radiation. This typically occurs during the daytime when the Sun is in the sky and the air temperature is the warmest. At night, net radiation is usually a negative value as there is no incoming solar radiation and net long-wave radiation is dominated by the outgoing terrestrial long-wave flux. Net radiation is zero when the incoming and outgoing components are in perfect balance, which does not occur too often. Between 40° N and 40° S, the Earth possesses a net gain of energy. Poleward of 40° N and 40° S, there is a net loss of radiation. Redistribution of heat is accomplished by ocean currents and the global circulation of the atmosphere. **Figure 15** shows the gain and loss of Q^* over the globe, while **Figure 16** gives its annual distribution.

3.02.10 Networks of Solar Radiation Stations – Solar Atlases

The renewable energy sources (RESs), such as wind and solar, are one of the most abundant energy sources available on the Earth. They are also renewable since they never end. For these reasons, man started exploiting them systematically since the first post-war economic crisis of 1973. As fossil fuel reservoirs have limited capacity and, therefore, limited 'life' and because of the fluctuating oil barrel price

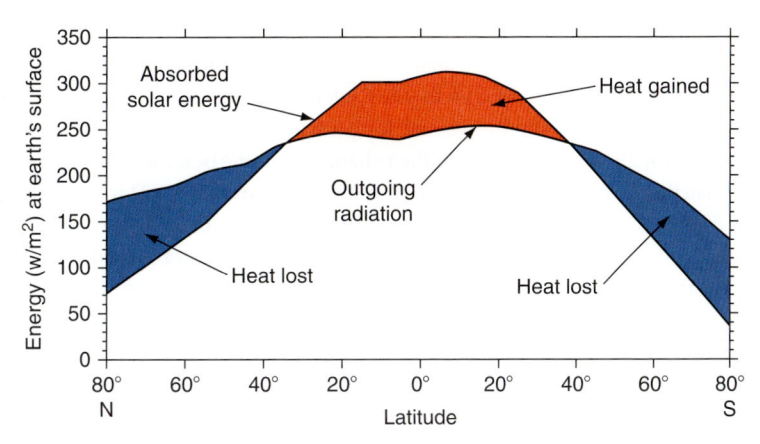

Figure 15 Gain (red) and loss (blue) of net radiation over the globe, from http://www.rst.gsfc.nasa.gov/Sect14/Sect14_1a.html. The unit of ly min^{-1} is equal to 698 W m^{-2}.

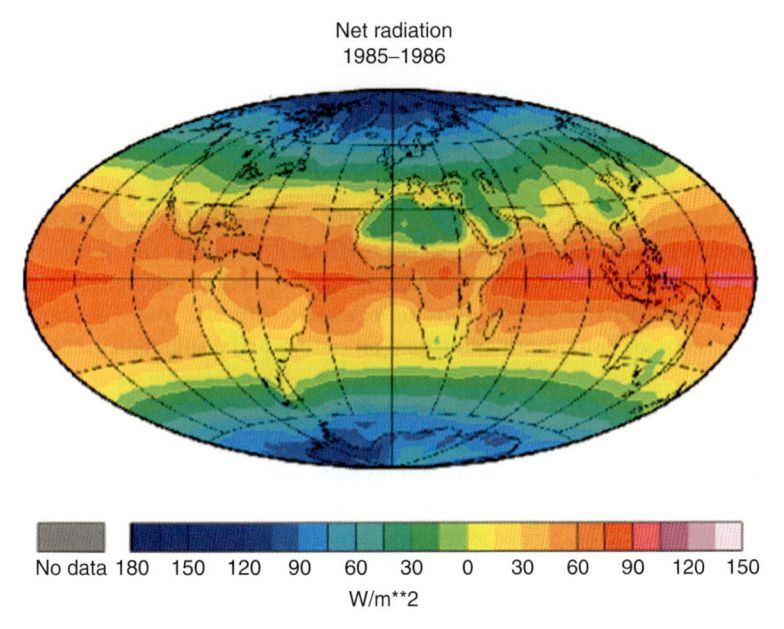

Figure 16 Annual distribution of Q^* over the globe, from Sellers WD (1965) *Physical Climatology*, 272p. Chicago: University of Chicago Press and http://knowledgedrift.wordpress.com/2010/01/20/poles-regulate-earth-temperature-data-suggests/.

due to various reasons, RESs seem to be the only alternative way (together with nuclear power) today to drive mankind out of the possible deadlock of facing an energy crisis in the future when all oil reserves will come to an end. On the other hand, the increasing threat of the greenhouse effect dictates the use of carbon-free energy sources. One of the main RESs is solar energy.

The very first application of solar radiation was the solar thermosyphon, a device to exploit solar radiation for heating water for domestic use at first place. Therefore, the first solar radiation models in the literature were driven by the fact that the manufacturers of such devices, inclined to the south at an angle approximately equal to the latitude of the location, should know the available solar energy at a place in order to design them as effective as possible. All models described in Section 3.02.6 serve this purpose. Of course, another important reason for the development of solar radiation models was and still is the scarcity of the solar/actinometric stations around the world. Such stations are considerably fewer than meteorological stations because of the relatively high purchase and maintenance costs of the radiometers as well as their arduous task of calibration. Therefore, networks of existing solar radiation stations to serve specific aims have been introduced. Such networks are the following.

1. *The Baseline Solar Radiation Network (BSRN)*. Because of the important role that solar radiation plays in the climate system, BSRN was established to provide a worldwide network to continuously measure radiative fluxes at the Earth's surface. Many of these stations began operation in 1992 and each year more stations are added to the network. These stations provide data for the calibration of the Surface Radiation Budget (SRB) Project and other satellite-based measurements of radiative fluxes. BSRN data are also used to validate radiative flux models. As of June 2008, there are 43 stations providing data to the BSRN archive

(http://www.bsrn.awi.de/en/home) at the World Radiation Monitoring Center (WRMC) operated by the Alfred Wegener Institute, Bremerhaven, Germany. In 2004, the Joint Planning Staff (JPS) for the World Climate Research Program (WCRP) endorsed BSRN as the global surface radiation network for the Global Climate Observing System (GCOS). The objectives of the BSRN are (1) to monitor the background short-wave and long-wave radiative components (least influenced by immediate human activities which are regionally concentrated) and their changes with the best methods currently available, (2) to provide data for the calibration of satellite-based estimates of the surface radiative fluxes, and (3) to produce high-quality observational data to be used for validating the theoretical computations of radiative fluxes by models. The parameters being monitored at the BSRN stations are (1) direct, diffuse, and global irradiances, (2) downward long-wave irradiance, (3) upward short-wave and long-wave irradiances, (4) narrowband direct irradiance (for AOD estimations), (5) narrowband diffuse and global irradiances, (6) UV-A/-B irradiances, (7) sky temperature, (8) total sky images, and (9) sunshine duration.

2. *The Atmospheric Radiation Measurement (ARM) Climate Research Facility.* This network covers the United States. It consists of 10 stations now within the United States and outside, all equipped with the same instrumentation, following the same setup, calibration, and data analysis procedures. More than 20 years after the dedication of the first research site of the US Department of Energy's (DoE) Climate Research Facility (http://www.arm.gov), ARM's primary tenet has remained unchanged: to improve the performance of the general circulation models used for climate research and predication by improving how those models deal with radiative energy transfer and the impact of clouds. To this end, ARM has made a significant contribution in improving climate prediction models: radiative heat transfer, radiation absorption, and cirrus cloud properties. ARM scientists use data gathered from ARM's fixed, mobile, and aerial facilities worldwide to address these issues and compare the observations to their models. Users worldwide propose and conduct field campaigns that target specific science questions as well as test and validate new instruments. This worldwide interest bodes well for the ARM program and for the future of ground-based remote sensing for climate modeling and weather forecasting. The parameters monitored by ARM are (1) aerosol characteristics, (2) meteorological variables, (3) cloud properties, and (4) short-wave and long-wave radiations.

3. *The Aerosol Robotic Network (AERONET).* The AERONET program is a federation of ground-based remote-sensing aerosol networks established by NASA and PHOTONS (University of Lille 1, CNES, and CNRS-INSU) and is greatly expanded by collaborators from national agencies, institutes, universities, individual scientists, and partners. The program provides a long-term, continuous, and readily accessible public domain database of optical, microphysical, and radiative properties of aerosols for aerosol research and characterization, validation of satellite retrievals, and synergism with other databases. The network imposes standardization of instruments, calibration, processing, and distribution. AERONET collaboration provides globally distributed observations of spectral AOD, inversion products, and precipitable water in diverse aerosol regimes. AOD data are computed for three data quality levels: Level 1.0 (unscreened), Level 1.5 (cloud-screened), and Level 2.0 (cloud-screened and quality-assured). Inversions, precipitable water, and other AOD-dependent products are derived from these levels and may implement additional quality checks. The processing algorithms have evolved from Version 1 to Version 2.0 (fully released in July 2006) and are available from the AERONET and PHOTONS web sites. Version 1 data may be downloaded from the web site through 2006. AERONET products will be released as new measurement techniques and algorithms are adopted and validated by the AERONET research community. The AERONET web site (http://aeronet.gsfc.nasa.gov) also provides AERONET-related news, a description of research and operational activities, related Earth Science links, and an AERONET staff directory. Currently, there are 398 AERONET stations worldwide.

4. *The Solar Radiation Network (SolRad-Net).* SolRad-Net is an established network of ground-based sensors providing high-frequency solar flux measurements in quasi-real time to the scientific community and various other end users. This network was implemented as a companion to AERONET and its instrumentation is invariably collocated with AERONET sites. The Brazilian core of the present network was developed within the scientific framework of the LBA-ECO component of the Large-Scale Biosphere–Atmosphere Experiment in Amazonia. Historically, SolRad-Net has preferentially selected sites that routinely experience intervals of biomass burning, such as Amazonia and Sub-Saharan Africa, for its long-term monitoring. All flux data are transmitted from the field on an hourly or half-hourly basis, and are accessible to the public shortly thereafter via the network's web site as Level 1.0 data (http://solrad-net.gsfc.nasa.gov/data_menu.html). Data quality for all sites is evaluated within a week and qualifying data are designated as Level 1.5 and also made available for download. Integration of these flux data with atmospheric aerosol data from Cimel sunphotometers provides a valuable tool for examining the effects of aerosols on flux attenuation. Similarly, the year-round, multiyear flux data sets (including records of total solar, 305–2800 nm), photosynthetically active radiation (PAR, 400–700 nm), and UV plus visible (305–695 nm) provide an opportunity to investigate the long-term influence of biomass-burning aerosols on solar fluxes and the resulting effects on vegetation productivity and regional meteorological processes. More recently, there are also continuous flux records for Kanpur (India) and Nairobi (Kenya) and the Goddard Space Flight Center (Greenbelt, Maryland) as well as contributed data from collaborators in Sede Boker (Israel), Kishinev (Moldova), and Crete. As with AERONET, this network's instrumentation is functional with minimal power and infrastructure requirements and thus has been well suited to venture into remote and underdeveloped regions and provide valuable, unprecedented data sets in climatically critical ecosystems. SolRad-Net,

like its associated network, AERONET, maintains a fundamentally open data policy and encourages collaborative and multi-disciplinary integrative analyses.

5. *The Canadian Sunphotometer Network (AeroCAN)*. The main component of the AeroCAN is the CIMEL sunphotometer CE-318. This last automatic sun/sky CIMEL radiometer measures atmospheric spectral transmission and sky radiance in the almucantar and principal plane. AeroCAN possesses 19 stations throughout Canada.

6. *The Surface Radiation Budget Network (SURFRAD)*. SURFRAD was established in 1993 through the support of NOAA's Office of Global Programs. The SURFRAD mission is clear; its primary objective is to support climate research with accurate, continuous, long-term measurements of the surface radiation budget over the United States. This differs from DoE's ARM program, where surface radiation budget measurements are also being made, in that ARM uses clustered measurements over a limited area for process-oriented studies. Currently, seven SURFRAD stations are operating in climatologically diverse regions: Montana, Colorado, Illinois, Mississippi, Pennsylvania, Nevada, and South Dakota. This represents the first time that a full surface radiation budget network has operated across the United States. Independent measures of upwelling and downwelling solar and IR radiations are the primary measurements; ancillary observations include direct and diffuse solar, PAR, UV-B, spectral solar, and meteorological parameters. Data are downloaded, quality controlled, and processed into daily files that are distributed in near-real time by anonymous FTP and the World Wide Web (http://www.srrb.noaa.gov). Observations from SURFRAD have been used for evaluating satellite-based estimates of surface radiation, and for validating hydrologic, weather prediction, and climate models. Quality assurance built into the design and operation of the network and good data quality control ensure that a continuous, high-quality product is released. AOD calculations for the SURFRAD network have been completed for 2008. For some stations, the AOD calculations go a few months into 2009.

7. *The Saudi Arabia Solar Radiation Network*. From 1993 to 2000, King Abdulaziz City for Science and Technology (KACST) in Riyadh, Saudi Arabia, and the US NREL conducted a joint solar radiation resource assessment project to upgrade the solar resource assessment capability of the Kingdom of Saudi Arabia. KACST deployed a high-quality 12-station network in Saudi Arabia for monitoring horizontal, direct beam, and diffuse total solar radiation. One- and 5-min network data were collected and assessed for quality. Eighty percent or more of the network data fall within the quality limits of $\pm 5\%$ for correct partitioning between the three radiation components.

8. *The NOAA-EPA Brewer Spectrophotometer UV and Ozone Network (NEUBrew)*. This network provides additional instrumentation to six of the SURFRAD stations in the United States. The NEUBrew network started operation in 2006. Its aim is to provide daily UV radiation and total column O_3 measurements (http://www.esrl.noaa.gov/gmd/grad/neubrew). For this reason, many Brewer spectrophotometers are co-located at NOAA SURFRAD stations.

Lately, the interest in solar radiation applications has shifted to PV applications. For these reasons, efforts have been made to achieve the solar radiation availability on horizontal or inclined surfaces over large areas, such as countries and continents. Nowadays, several solar radiation/energy maps or solar radiation atlases (SRAs) have been derived through funded projects. The most important SRAs are described below.

1. *The ESRA*. This is the product of a European project [182] and is the latest version of a previous edition. It has been published by Les Presses de l'Ecole des Mines de Paris on behalf of the European Commission. This atlas, in two volumes, is an instrument dedicated to providing knowledge and aiding exploitation of the solar resources across a wide sweep of Europe, from the Urals to the Azores and from northern Africa to the Polar Circle. It is a powerful tool for architects, engineers, meteorologists, agronomists, local authorities, and tourism professionals, as well as for researchers and students. The input data are based on the period 1981–90. The first volume provides a broad overview with supporting maps. It starts by describing the course of the Sun across the sky as it varies along the year with geographical location. Then the interactions of solar radiation with the atmosphere and its components (haze, turbidity, clouds, etc.) and the separation of solar radiation into direct and diffuse parts are discussed. The outline structures of the database and the ESRA software package are described. Sixteen colored maps provide data on the monthly mean global, beam, and diffuse irradiation on the horizontal surface and the clearness index for March, June, September, and December. The mapped values are averages over the 10-year period 1981–90. Additionally, there are four annual maps, also a country-based relief map, and a map of the ground-observing stations used. There are two special maps giving zones of similar irradiation and zones of similar biomass productivity.

2. *The US SRA (USSRA)*. The online N. American Solar Radiation Atlas (http://www.nrel.gov/gis/solar.html) displays solar collector performance at any location in the United States. The atlas has been developed at the National Renewable Energy Laboratory (NREL, Golden, CO). The new USSRA uses an interactive electronic map on the World Wide Web as an interface to multiple databases of solar collector performance and solar radiation data. The data delivered include estimated performance of various collector types, such as tilted flat-plate surfaces, one- and two-axis tracking flat-plate collectors, and concentrating collectors. The new World Wide Web user interface allows users to interact with maps of geographical features (terrain) and political features (state lines, county lines, cities, and roads) to select the location for which solar performance estimates are desired. Eventually, the USSRA is a comprehensive electronic database of measured, modeled, and satellite-derived solar resource estimates, along

with uncertainty statistics for the estimates at any location in the United States. The principal data source for the first prototype version of the atlas is the Climatological Solar Radiation (CSR) model, developed by NREL to estimate climatological averages of daily total solar radiation at a 40 km spatial resolution [183]. The model uses, as input, monthly climatological mean values of cloud cover, precipitable water vapor, AOD, surface albedo, and total column ozone. These input parameters are available from various sources, such as the National Aeronautics and Space Administration (NASA) and the National Climatic Data Center (NCDC). The model allows calculation of the output for the various collector types, such as tilted flat-plate surfaces, one- and two-axis tracking flat-plate collectors, and concentrating collectors.

3. *The Canadian SRA (CSRA)*. This is a part of the fifth edition of the *National Atlas of Canada* comprising 93 separate, stand-alone maps that were published between 1978 and 1995 (http://atlas.nrcan.gc.ca/site/english/maps/archives/5thedition/environment/climate/mcr4076). The maps cover a wide range of subjects, but there is a slight emphasis on environmental issues. Although the map sheets vary considerably in their overall size, the format of nearly all the maps consists of a central map at scale 1:7 500 000, accompanied by a legend, a source list, and extensive notes. The CSRA is given on an annual and monthly basis.

4. *The African SRA (ASRA)*. This product is a fine example of international cooperation wisely supported by the Commission of the European Communities [184]. A later study about the radiation climate in this continent has been presented in the international literature [185]. The ASRA contains information about the daily sums of global and diffuse radiation, maps of the ratio of diffuse-to-global radiation and maps of the atmospheric transmittance, annual and seasonal maps, monthly averages of the hourly values of global radiation, monthly averages of global radiation for western Africa and the Sahel zone, as well as isoline plots of the global radiation for the continent.

5. *The Mongolian SRA (MSRA)*. This was developed in 2007 by Batdelger Davaa at the Institute of Physics and Technology, Mongolian Academy of Sciences (www.mas.ac.mn/en/index.php). It is based on his 20 years of research work. The MSRA contains images in two sections: SRA under clear-sky and SRA under cloudy-sky conditions. Each section consists of 68 images that correspond to monthly, seasonal, and annual solar radiation distributions in the form of normal-incidence direct and horizontal direct, diffuse, and global radiation components.

6. *The Japanese SRA*. It is astonishing that Japan has not developed an updated version of its first solar atlas from 1957 [186].

7. *The Australian SRA (AusSRA)*. The Bureau of Meteorology in Australia provides daily maps of the global solar irradiation (http://www.bom.gov.au/sat/solrad.shtml). The Bureau currently runs a computer model [187], which produces estimates of the total amount of solar radiation that reaches the Earth's surface on a day. For each location on the surface of the Earth, an energy budget calculation is made using hourly visible radiation information from the Geostationary Meteorological Satellite, MTSAT-1R. This process involves calculation of instantaneous downward irradiance (radiative fluxes) at the ground every hour in real time over Australia using the hourly MTSAT-1R visible data, as well as hourly cloud albedos. The hourly irradiances are then integrated during each evening to give daily insolation totals in MJ m^{-2}, that is, the daily global solar exposure. The model's horizontal resolution is set at values appropriate for the natural variability of insolation and population density in different parts of Australia. The gridded data covering Australia (for which the color map is a graphical representation) have resolution intervals at 6 km. The accuracy of the model's daily estimates of insolation is estimated by comparison with independent measurements by the Bureau's ground-based instruments. These solar exposure values, derived from images from the MTSAT-1R satellite, are of slightly lower quality than those that were available prior to 22 May 2003, which were derived from the GMS-5 satellite. This is due to the difference in the characteristics of the MTSAT-1R imager as compared to those of GMS-5.

8. *The Indian SRA*. A handbook was presented online (http://mnes.nic.in/sec/srd-sec.pdf) in 2008. This gives mean monthly horizontal total and diffuse irradiation values over India, in MJ m^{-2}, covering the period 1986–2000.

3.02.11 Utility Tools for Solar Radiation Calculations

Since PV systems are the only ones to exploit solar energy for electricity production nowadays, the tools described in this section are merely devoted to them. In a PV (solar) module, light energy is converted into electricity. A PV module is the basic element of each PV system. It consists of many jointly connected solar cells. According to the solar cell technology, these cells are distinguished in monocrystalline, polycrystalline, and amorphous solar modules. Most commercial crystalline modules consist of 36 or 72 cells. Solar cells are connected and placed between a tedlar plate on the bottom and a tempered glass on the top. Between the solar cells and the glass, there is a thin usually ethylene vinyl-acetate (EVA) foil. Solar cells are interconnected with thin contacts on the upper side of the semiconductor material, which can be seen as a metal net on the solar cells. The net must be as thin as possible allowing a disturbance-free incidence photon stream. Usually a module is framed with an aluminum frame, occasionally with a stainless-steel or a plastic frame. Special flexible modules are designed for use on boats that can be walked upon without causing any damage to the modules. The typical crystalline modules power ranges from several watts to up to 200 W per module. Some manufacturers produce preassembled panels with several 100 Watt-panels (Wp). Over its estimated life a PV module may produce much more electricity than used in its production; a 100 W module can prevent the emission of over 2 tons of CO_2.

Prior to installing a PV system at a place, a survey of the solar availability at that location must be conducted or known from recent measurements or solar maps specific for the area. The choice of a proper location is the first and the very essential step in solar system design procedure. Even the most carefully planned solar system does not work satisfactorily if the location is not properly chosen. It is critical that the PV modules are exposed to sunlight without shadowing at least from 9 a.m. to 3 p.m.; therefore, the properties and values of solar insolation should be studied. The PV modules have to be fixed with proper tilt angle allowing the system efficient operation. For the estimation of the electricity to be generated for a predefined location (country or city), a PV potential estimation utility (http://re.jrc.ec.europa.eu/pvgis/apps/pvreg.php) is available on the web pages of the Institute of Environment and Sustainability (IES, http://ies.jrc.ec.europa.eu), Joint Research Centre (JRC, http://ec.europa.eu/dgs/jrc/index.cfm). Calculations for Europe, Africa, and the Mediterranean Sea are possible. The tool offers many different calculation options: (1) PV potential with given inclination and orientation, (2) calculation of optimal inclination for given orientation, and (3) calculation of optimal inclination and orientation. Figure 17 shows the optimal angle of tilt for a south-oriented PV module for various geographical latitudes in the northern hemisphere within a year.

Software and devices for site analysis are as follows:

1. *The Solar Pathfinder*. The Solar Pathfinder (http://www.solarpathfinder.com) has been the standard in the solar industry for solar site analysis for decades. Its panoramic reflection of the site instantly provides a full year of accurate solar/shade data, making it the instrument of choice.
2. *The SunEye*. The Solmetric SunEye (http://www.solmetric.com) is a handheld electronic device that allows users to instantly assess total potential solar energy given the shading of a particular site. Identifying the shading pattern early in the process reduces the expense of system and home design and improves the efficiency of the final system or house.
3. *The SunTracker*. It is an iPhone-based site evaluation tool (http://www.imeasuresystems.com), providing full solar site analysis in an affordable handheld package.
4. *The HORIcatcher*. It is an easy and fast tool for taking outdoor pictures of the horizon (http://www.meteotest.ch/en/horicatcher?w=ber). The pictures can be used to determine the solar energy input, sunshine duration, and sun exposure reduced by obstacles like trees, houses, or mountains.
5. *The PanoramaMaster*. With this device one can make exact matched sets of photos for panorama pictures (http://www.energieburo.ch/web/produkte/panoramamaster).
6. *The HorizON*. This software simulates Sun path diagrams for arbitrary latitude (http://www.energieburo.ch/web/produkte/horizon).
7. *The Pilkington Sun Angle Calculator*. This handy tool (http://www.pilkington.com/the+americas/usa/english/building+products/tools+and+calculators/sun+angle+calculator.htm) provides a relatively simple method of determining solar geometry variables for architectural design, such as designing shading devices or locating the position of the Sun relative to a particular latitude and time.
8. *The Sun path chart*. This program (http://solardat.uoregon.edu/SunChartProgram.html) creates Sun path charts in Cartesian or polar coordinates for 'typical' dates of each month (i.e., days receiving about the mean amount of solar radiation for a day in the given month).

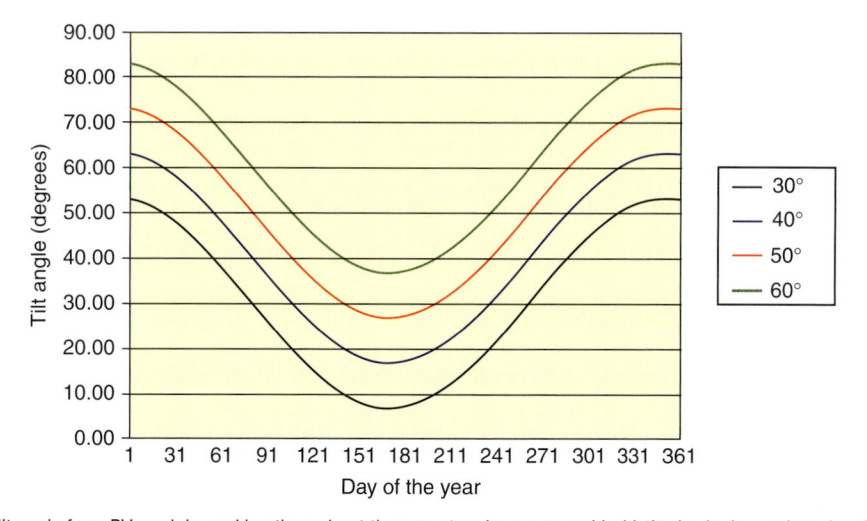

Figure 17 Optimal tilt angle for a PV module working throughout the year at various geographical latitudes in the northern hemisphere. From http://www.pvresources.com/en/location.php

9. *The Shadow Analyser*. This is an advanced parametric CAD tool (http://www.drbaumresearch.com/prod38.htm) for professionals in the area of solar energy engineering and architecture.
10. *The ECOTECT*. It is an industry-leading building analysis program (http://ecotect.com/) that allows designers to work easily in 3D and apply all the tools necessary for an energy-efficient and sustainable future.
11. *The Sombrero*. It is a PC-tool for calculating shadows on arbitrarily oriented surfaces (http://nesa1.uni-siegen.de). For active use of solar energy (domestic hot water, PVs) as well as for passive solar architecture, shading or lighting of planes plays an important role. Sombrero provides quantitative results for the shading of collectors or windows by buildings, trees, overhangs, or the horizon.
12. *The Renewable Resource Data Center (RReDC)*. The RReDC (http://www.nrel.gov/rredc) provides information on several types of RESs in the United States, in the form of publications, data, and maps. An extensive dictionary of renewable energy-related terms is also provided.
13. *The Logiciel CalSol*. This provides an estimation of the available solar energy for energy applications. The software is available in the French language only (http://ines.solaire.free.fr) and may be downloaded free of charge.
14. *The GIS Assessment of Solar Energy Resource in Europe*. Freely available information from JRC (http://re.jrc.ec.europa.eu/pvgis/index.htm) on GIS-based inventory of solar energy resource and estimations of the potential PV electricity generation in Europe.
15. *The Sun Position Calculator*. Online application by Volker Quaschning (http://www.volker-quaschning.de/datserv/sunpos/index_e.php) enabling calculation of the Sun position, sunrise, and sunset at any part of the world.

3.02.12 Instruments for Measuring Solar Radiation

This section gives a short introduction to modern solar radiometric devices and solar radiation measurements. Discussion is made about the instrumentation used to measure the solar radiation components, and the accuracy of these measurements depending on the sensitivity of the instruments and their calibration, the reference scale used, and the quality control adopted. The sources of errors in solar radiation measurements are presented in this section; also, a brief description of the contemporary radiometric devices is given. Existing measurement networks and data sources were described in Section 3.02.10, while the data quality tests were mentioned in Section 3.02.6.4. These measuring networks and associated quality tests are closely linked to solar radiation instruments.

3.02.12.1 Solar Radiometers

As mentioned in the Introduction (Section 3.02.1) a pyrheliometer measures the direct radiation. All pyrheliometers have a narrow aperture (generally between 5° and 6° total solid angle). Within this field of view (FOV), the instruments receive beam radiation with some circumsolar contribution from the solar disk, but they exclude all diffuse sky radiation [188]. Pyrheliometers are mounted on solar trackers to aim the Sun throughout the day. Their sensor is placed on a plane normal to the direct beam; therefore, the direct beam is also called direct normal irradiance (DNI).

A pyranometer measures the global total hemispherical or the diffuse sky hemispherical radiation. Pyranometers have FOV = 180° (2π steradians). The measurement of diffuse radiation is made by blocking out the Sun's beam radiation with a disk or ball placed over the instrument. This requires a steady or a moving mechanism, which accommodates the blocking device. The steady device is a low-cost one as it uses a fixed band or ring of opaque material to shadow the pyranometer throughout the day. This shading band/ring mechanism is not without incorporating errors into the measurement of diffuse radiation, since part of the sky radiation is blocked by the shading apparatus. This error varies with the geometry of the shading device, the time, and the atmospheric conditions. This error is usually corrected by applying a geometric correction or an empirical function to the data (e.g., References 138, 139, and 189); the result is, however, far from ideal. **Figure 18** shows radiometers used to measure global, direct, and diffuse radiation components. If the broadband glass dome of a pyranometer is replaced by another having response into a window of the solar radiation spectrum, then integrated (total) radiation values over these spectral bands can be measured.

The above instruments all have thermopile detectors. These detectors respond to the whole short-wave spectrum, in contrast with the solid-state detectors that are wavelength-selective. Nearly all radiometers have a glass window (also called glass dome) for protection. This limits the spectral response of the thermopile detectors inside them to either 290–2800 nm for glass domes (pyranometers) or 290–4000 nm for quartz windows (pyrheliometers). The principle of operation is based on the heating of the black surface of the thermopile detector by the incident solar radiation. The detector consists of a number of thermo junctions between dissimilar metals (typically type-T thermocouples made of copper and constantan) being in contact with the black absorbing surface. A voltage proportional to the difference in temperature between the heated (hot) junctions and a similar pair of unheated (cold) junctions is produced by the thermal flux on the hot junctions caused by radiation. Typically, 20–40 junctions make a thermopile, while the temperature difference between hot and cold junctions is 5 °C for a 1000 W m^{-2} incident radiation; the resulting signal ranges from 4 to 8 mV. The black absorbing surfaces of the detectors are not perfect isotropic (or Lambertian) surfaces, a fact that produces nonlinearities in the thermal response of the thermocouples. Apart from that, there occur IR radiation exchanges between the radiometer detectors and the sky, all of which contribute to the uncertainty in the calibration of the radiometer and the measurements [190]. The above

Figure 18 (a) An Eppley pyranometer (right) for measuring global horizontal radiation and a Kipp-Zonen UV-B sensor (left) at ASNOA, (b) an Eppley pyranometer with a shadow band for measuring diffuse horizontal radiation at ASNOA, and (c) a pyrheliometer mounted on a Sun-tracking mechanism for measuring direct solar radiation.

problems are avoided when using solid-state silicon photodiodes mounted beneath diffusers; they generate a photocurrent, which is proportional to the incident radiation. However, these radiometers have narrow spectral response (typically between 350 and 1000 nm) and do not produce a signal proportional to the entire spectrum of the incident radiation. A drawback of the photodiode radiometers is their inability to capture the varying IR spectral content of the solar radiation. This makes them less accurate than thermopile detectors.

The first sunshine recorders were invented by John Francis Campbell in 1853; they were later modified by Sir George Gabriel Stokes in 1879. The original device was a glass sphere filled with water, and later a solid glass sphere was used. The modified device, known as the Campbell–Stokes (CS) sunshine recorder (**Figure 19**), is still manufactured and used today,

Figure 19 The original Campbell–Stokes (CS) of 1899. Courtesy: Science Museum, London.

Figure 20 A contemporary electronic sunshine duration sensor (manufactured by EKO Instruments Co., Ltd., model MS-093) at ASNOA.

and is the oldest solar radiation instrument still in operation. Modern applications need the estimation of the sunshine fraction in 1 min; this is done by comparing the duration of time that a pyrheliometer signal is above the threshold of 120 W m^{-2} [188]. Nowadays, there exist specially designed electronic sunshine recorders (using photodiodes) to serve this purpose (**Figure 20**). These modern, automated devices have many advantages. They present a higher time resolution and a more precise threshold, and eliminate the daily tedious task of replacing the special card used by the CS instruments and of analyzing the burnt trace to estimate the daily hours of sunshine. These advantages have made the electronic sunshine recorders very attractive for application in meteorological/actinometric stations. Nevertheless, a comparison of sunshine duration measurements by the electronic recorders and the classical CS recorders has shown significant and nonsystematic differences. This prevents replacement of the old CS recorders with electronic recorders at many sites with long records, due to the undesired discontinuity in climatological sunshine trends that such a change may produce. The enhanced value of the solar radiation data in comparison to the sunshine data has made the measurement of the latter less important. For this reason, some countries (such as the United States) have already stopped the routine measurements of the sunshine duration.

The ACRs are used for accurate solar radiation measurements. ACRs are sophisticated pyrheliometers that absorb incoming radiation, and are electrically self-calibrated [191]. They are used to determine the solar constant and provide the reference for the calibration of other radiometers. **Figure 21** shows an ACR. ACRs make the temperature rise caused by absorption of sunlight by a cavity having a precision aperture equal to the temperature rise caused by an electrical current passing through the cavity walls, while the cavity is not 'seen' by the Sun. The aperture of an ACR is not protected by a (glass) window, and, therefore, is sensitive to incident radiation of all wavelengths. This temperature rise is measured as the potential difference between the hot and cold thermocouple junctions in the cavity. All ACR elements (area of the aperture, heating current, thermocouple voltages) are absolute values; these elements are used to compute precisely the generated electrical current, which is then transformed to solar flux [192].

Figure 21 An absolute cavity radiometer (ACR) pointing to the Sun. From http://solardat.uoregon.edu/AbsoluteCavityRadiometerPhoto.html#TopOfPage

3.02.12.2 The World Radiometric Reference

As the words imply, the WRR is the reference standard of solar insolation in solar radiometry. The WRR was originally established as the weighted average of measurements from a set of 15 ACRs. It was introduced to ensure homogeneous measurements of solar radiation worldwide. It has an accuracy of 0.3%, precision of 0.1%, and a temporal stability of better than 0.01% per year [193]. This determination has established a radiometric scale, which fully agrees with the absolute definition of the irradiance units in the International System (SI) [194, 195]. The WMO started the use of the WRR in 1979 as a successor of the older International Pyrheliometric Scale of 1956 (IPS56). Every 5 years, an International Pyrheliometer Comparison (IPC) takes place at the PMOD/WRC among the participating national reference instruments to obtain the WRR.

3.02.12.3 Calibration of Solar Radiometers

As mentioned above, the WRR is the only reference for solar radiometer calibrations. Therefore, reference pyrheliometers are calibrated by co-located measurements with an ACR referenced to the WRR. The calibration procedure for working pyrheliometers is accomplished with reference ACRs in operation [196].

3.02.12.4 Uncertainty of Solar Radiometers

The uncertainty in the measurement of a pyranometer depends upon the zenith angle, the voltage generated by the radiometer, and the intensity of the solar flux. With an error in the direct beam, zenith angle, and diffuse irradiance of ~4.0, ~0.06°, and ~2.0 W m^{-2}, respectively (representative for a black-and-white sensor), this uncertainty ranges from about 1.0% at small zenith angles to >10% for zenith angles >85° [32]. Various research studies on solar radiation instruments, such as those made by the BSRN, have taken into account the thermal effects in pyranometers with all-black sensors measuring global or diffuse radiation (http://www.gewex.org/bsrn.html). These thermal effects produce negative voltages at night and, therefore, lower clear-sky global or diffuse irradiances during daytime. To the contrary, the black-and-white sensors in radiometers produce more accurate diffuse sky measurements than all-black ones without appropriate corrections to the measurements or special care during their construction, such as the inclusion of compensating thermopiles.

The direct radiation has significant energy in the short-wave NIR region (1000–2800 nm), while the diffuse sky radiation has little. Therefore, a shaded pyranometer to measure the diffuse sky radiation is not affected by any atmospheric constituent, such as atmospheric water vapor, in the NIR region. This consequently dictates that the same measurement from a shaded pyranometer may be obtained for different water vapor concentrations and direct irradiances. It has been found [197] that a total precipitable water vapor in the range of 0.5–3.5 cm may result in differences of about 0.5% in the calibration of the pyranometer.

Other factors contributing to the uncertainty of radiometers are temperature coefficients, linearity, thermal electromotive forces, and EM interference. In addition, the FOV of many pyrheliometers is not comparable with that of the reference ACR. For pyranometers, inaccuracies in the zenith angle and the cosine response of the sensor must be taken into account. The cosine-response issue is significant, particularly when measuring global irradiance under clear skies, because of the predominance of the beam component. A last but not least issue concerns the accuracy and performance of the data-logging system, which must not be overlooked.

3.02.12.5 Correction of Common Solar Radiometer Errors

During the last decade, the results from high-quality research in radiometry have considerably improved our understanding of solar radiometer errors and have provided ways to correct them or avoid them altogether. As shown above, the cosine error problem is associated with the direct irradiance falling on the sensor of the pyranometer under clear skies. On the other hand, it was shown that the direct irradiance measurements have higher accuracy than the global ones. Therefore, it is wise to calculate global irradiance as the sum of the measured diffuse and direct irradiances. Nevertheless, an unshaded pyranometer is still useful. This methodology requires proper diffuse irradiance measurements. The use of a ventilated instrument is recommended to homogenize temperatures and avoid condensation or frost on the dome. Furthermore, the thermal effects have to be minimized (<~2 W m^{-2}), with the use of a pyranometer with a black-and-white sensor or an all-black sensor with proper correction.

Appendix A: Spectral Distribution of Solar Radiation

The spectral distribution of the solar constant at TOA is given in **Figure A.1**. The visible light in the spectrum of **Figure A.1** is confined to the range 400–700 nm, as shown in **Figure A.2**. Solar radiation is defined in the wavelength range 0.1–1000 μm, that is, from the beginning of the UV (~100 nm) to the end of the IR (~1 mm) bands. Nevertheless, 98% of the solar energy is contained in the region 0.3–3.0 μm, as can visually be seen from **Figure A.1**. This is the reason that all pyranometers measure in this spectral range.

In terms of absolute values, the solar extraterrestrial radiation spectrum is given in **Table A.1**.

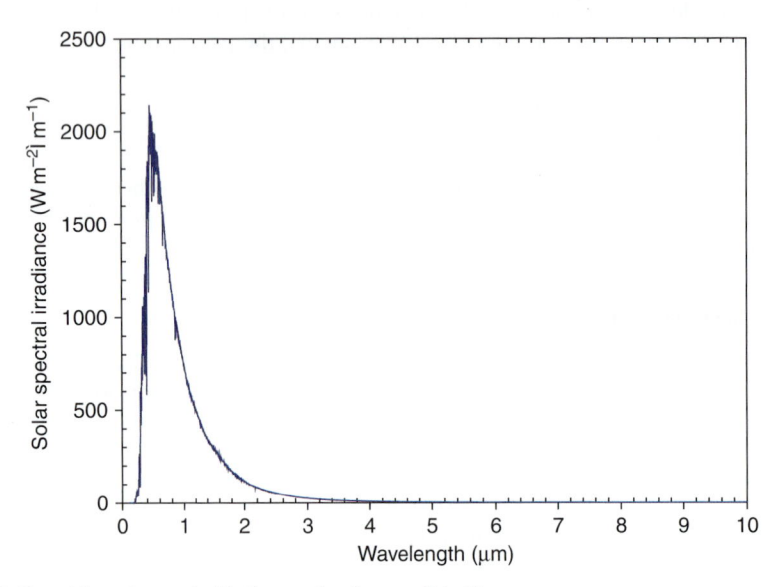

Figure A.1 Spectral distribution of the solar constant in the wavelength range 0.1–10 μm.

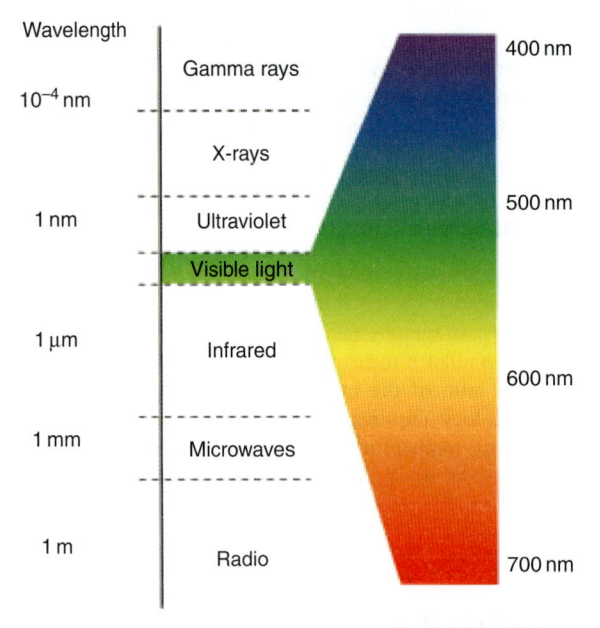

Figure A.2 The radiation emitted from the Sun extends from the radio waves down to the gamma rays. The solar radiation is confined in the region between the UV and IR bands. The visible spectrum is shown in color from violet to red. From http://themoderngreen.com/2008/10/new-material-able-to-absorb-full-light-spectrum, and Suehrcke H and McCormick PG (1987) The frequency distribution of instantaneous insolation values. *Solar Energy* 40(5): 413–422 [60].

Table A.1 Spectral distribution of the recent solar constant in the wavelength range 0.1195–10 μm

WL (μm)	SI (W m^{-2} μm^{-1})	WL (μm)	SI (W m^{-2} μm^{-1})	WL (μm)	SI (W m^{-2} μm^{-1})
0.1195	0.0619	0.1775	1.403	0.2355	51.42
0.1205	0.5614	0.1785	1.538	0.2365	48.59
0.1215	4.901	0.1795	1.576	0.2375	48.44
0.1225	1.184	0.1805	1.831	0.2385	41.96
0.1235	0.0477	0.1815	2.233	0.2395	44.12
0.1245	0.0343	0.1825	1.243	0.2405	39.56
0.1255	0.0288	0.1835	2.244	0.2415	51.48
0.1265	0.0352	0.1845	2.066	0.2425	70.6
0.1275	0.0213	0.1855	2.311	0.2435	66.53
0.1285	0.0173	0.1865	2.7	0.2445	60.97
0.1295	0.0399	0.1875	3.009	0.2455	49.39
0.1305	0.1206	0.1885	3.291	0.2465	50.4
0.1315	0.0398	0.1895	3.569	0.2475	55.5
0.1325	0.0413	0.1905	3.764	0.2485	45.65
0.1335	0.168	0.1915	4.165	0.2495	56.38
0.1345	0.0457	0.1925	4.113	0.2505	60.1
0.1355	0.038	0.1935	3.808	0.2515	46.01
0.1365	0.0309	0.1945	5.21	0.2525	41.55
0.1375	0.0292	0.1955	5.427	0.2535	51.55
0.1385	0.0397	0.1965	6.008	0.2545	59.57
0.1395	0.0756	0.1975	6.191	0.2555	79.3
0.1405	0.0608	0.1985	6.187	0.2565	101.8
0.1415	0.0421	0.1995	6.664	0.2575	125.4
0.1425	0.0468	0.2005	7.326	0.2585	125.1
0.1435	0.0511	0.2015	8.023	0.2595	104
0.1445	0.0509	0.2025	8.261	0.2605	85.51
0.1455	0.0554	0.2035	9.217	0.2615	89.8
0.1465	0.0709	0.2045	10.25	0.2625	103.6
0.1475	0.0849	0.2055	10.54	0.2635	165.8
0.1485	0.082	0.2065	11.08	0.2645	249.7
0.1495	0.0796	0.2075	12.65	0.2655	252.7
0.1505	0.087	0.2085	15.05	0.2665	249.4
0.1515	0.0927	0.2095	21.38	0.2675	250.8
0.1525	0.1163	0.2105	27.92	0.2685	243.8
0.1535	0.1299	0.2115	33.54	0.2695	238.9
0.1545	0.2059	0.2125	31.3	0.2705	267.3
0.1555	0.2144	0.2135	33.15	0.2715	224.4
0.1565	0.1847	0.2145	40.03	0.2725	197.4
0.1575	0.1717	0.2155	36.15	0.2735	196.5
0.1585	0.1675	0.2165	32.27	0.2745	132.6
0.1595	0.1754	0.2175	35.29	0.2755	175.1
0.1605	0.1934	0.2185	44.37	0.2765	242.8
0.1615	0.2228	0.2195	46.92	0.2775	233.8
0.1625	0.2519	0.2205	47.33	0.2785	259.3
0.1635	0.2841	0.2215	39.58	0.2795	85.55
0.1645	0.2973	0.2225	49.65	0.2805	94.63
0.1655	0.4302	0.2235	63.01	0.2815	208.3
0.1665	0.3989	0.2245	58.97	0.2825	294.1
0.1675	0.3875	0.2255	52.29	0.2835	313.5
0.1685	0.4556	0.2265	39.4	0.2845	235.3
0.1695	0.5877	0.2275	39.32	0.2855	163.1
0.1705	0.6616	0.2285	51.95	0.2865	332.7
0.1715	0.688	0.2295	47.71	0.2875	336.3
0.1725	0.7252	0.2305	52.12	0.2885	322.2
0.1735	0.7645	0.2315	50.97	0.2895	472.7
0.1745	0.9067	0.2325	53.97	0.2905	601.3
0.1755	1.079	0.2335	44.74	0.2915	580.8
0.1765	1.22	0.2345	38.97	0.2925	521.9

(Continued)

Table A.1 (Continued)

WL (μm)	SI (W m^{-2} μm^{-1})	WL (μm)	SI (W m^{-2} μm^{-1})	WL (μm)	SI (W m^{-2} μm^{-1})
0.2935	535.5	0.3525	907.9	0.4115	1817
0.2945	508.8	0.3535	1033	0.4125	1789
0.2955	553.2	0.3545	1111	0.4135	1756
0.2965	509.6	0.3555	1045	0.4145	1737
0.2975	507.3	0.3565	912.3	0.4155	1734
0.2985	465.5	0.3575	796	0.4165	1842
0.2995	484	0.3585	693.6	0.4175	1665
0.3005	420	0.3595	991.1	0.4185	1684
0.3015	455.5	0.3605	970.8	0.4195	1701
0.3025	489	0.3615	878.1	0.4205	1757
0.3035	620.6	0.3625	997.8	0.4215	1797
0.3045	602.5	0.3635	996.9	0.4225	1582
0.3055	594.8	0.3645	1013	0.4235	1711
0.3065	555.7	0.3655	1152	0.4245	1767
0.3075	615	0.3665	1233	0.4255	1695
0.3085	611.4	0.3675	1180	0.4265	1698
0.3095	496.5	0.3685	1101	0.4275	1569
0.3105	622.4	0.3695	1226	0.4285	1587
0.3115	729.2	0.3705	1139	0.4295	1475
0.3125	655.9	0.3715	1175	0.4305	1135
0.3135	699.9	0.3725	1054	0.4315	1686
0.3145	662.9	0.3735	920.2	0.4325	1646
0.3155	633	0.3745	900.4	0.4335	1731
0.3165	633.2	0.3755	1062	0.4345	1670
0.3175	773.9	0.3765	1085	0.4355	1723
0.3185	664.9	0.3775	1282	0.4365	1929
0.3195	710.5	0.3785	1327	0.4375	1806
0.3205	805.1	0.3795	1066	0.4385	1567
0.3215	699.5	0.3805	1202	0.4395	1825
0.3225	688.6	0.3815	1082	0.4405	1713
0.3235	661.3	0.3825	791.3	0.4415	1931
0.3245	760.8	0.3835	684.1	0.4425	1980
0.3255	875.8	0.3845	959.7	0.4435	1909
0.3265	979.5	0.3855	1008	0.4445	1973
0.3275	952.7	0.3865	1007	0.4455	1821
0.3285	917.6	0.3875	1004	0.4465	1891
0.3295	1061	0.3885	984.3	0.4475	2077
0.3305	1016	0.3895	1174	0.4485	1973
0.3315	965.7	0.3905	1247	0.4495	2027
0.3325	954.9	0.3915	1342	0.4505	2144
0.3335	921.6	0.3925	1019	0.4515	2109
0.3345	958.9	0.3935	582.3	0.4525	1941
0.3355	943.4	0.3945	1026	0.4535	1970
0.3365	809.5	0.3955	1314	0.4545	1979
0.3375	841.8	0.3965	854.5	0.4555	2034
0.3385	921.5	0.3975	928.8	0.4565	2077
0.3395	958.1	0.3985	1522	0.4575	2100
0.3405	1007	0.3995	1663	0.4585	1971
0.3415	923.8	0.4005	1682	0.4595	2009
0.3425	993	0.4015	1746	0.4605	2040
0.3435	950.6	0.4025	1759	0.4615	2055
0.3445	795.7	0.4035	1684	0.4625	2104
0.3455	939.2	0.4045	1674	0.4635	2040
0.3465	926.4	0.4055	1667	0.4645	1976
0.3475	901.7	0.4065	1589	0.4655	2042
0.3485	897.2	0.4075	1628	0.4665	1921
0.3495	889.8	0.4085	1735	0.4675	2015
0.3505	1050	0.4095	1715	0.4685	1994
0.3515	979.5	0.4105	1532	0.4695	1990

(Continued)

Table A.1 (Continued)

WL (μm)	SI (Wm^{-2}μm^{-1})	WL (μm)	SI (Wm^{-2}μm^{-1})	WL (μm)	SI (Wm^{-2}μm^{-1})
0.4705	1877	0.5295	1918	0.5885	1750
0.4715	2018	0.5305	1952	0.5895	1612
0.4725	2041	0.5315	1963	0.5905	1813
0.4735	1991	0.5325	1770	0.5915	1787
0.4745	2051	0.5335	1923	0.5925	1808
0.4755	2016	0.5345	1858	0.5935	1796
0.4765	1956	0.5355	1990	0.5945	1773
0.4775	2075	0.5365	1871	0.5955	1782
0.4785	2009	0.5375	1882	0.5965	1805
0.4795	2076	0.5385	1904	0.5975	1780
0.4805	2035	0.5395	1832	0.5985	1757
0.4815	2090	0.5405	1769	0.5995	1774
0.4825	2023	0.5415	1881	0.6005	1746
0.4835	2019	0.5425	1825	0.6015	1751
0.4845	1969	0.5435	1879	0.6025	1719
0.4855	1830	0.5445	1879	0.6035	1787
0.4865	1625	0.5455	1901	0.6045	1776
0.4875	1830	0.5465	1879	0.6055	1763
0.4885	1914	0.5475	1833	0.6065	1759
0.4895	1960	0.5485	1863	0.6075	1757
0.4905	2007	0.5495	1895	0.6085	1743
0.4915	1896	0.5505	1862	0.6095	1744
0.4925	1896	0.5515	1871	0.6105	1703
0.4935	1888	0.5525	1846	0.6115	1746
0.4945	2058	0.5535	1882	0.6125	1705
0.4955	1926	0.5545	1898	0.6135	1683
0.4965	2017	0.5555	1897	0.6145	1713
0.4975	2018	0.5565	1821	0.6155	1713
0.4985	1866	0.5575	1846	0.6165	1609
0.4995	1970	0.5585	1787	0.6175	1707
0.5005	1857	0.5595	1808	0.6185	1724
0.5015	1812	0.5605	1843	0.6195	1707
0.5025	1894	0.5615	1824	0.6205	1734
0.5035	1934	0.5625	1850	0.6215	1690
0.5045	1869	0.5635	1861	0.6225	1713
0.5055	1993	0.5645	1854	0.6235	1666
0.5065	1961	0.5655	1798	0.6245	1656
0.5075	1906	0.5665	1829	0.6255	1632
0.5085	1919	0.5675	1887	0.6265	1697
0.5095	1916	0.5685	1810	0.6275	1697
0.5105	1947	0.5695	1860	0.6285	1697
0.5115	1997	0.5705	1769	0.6295	1677
0.5125	1867	0.5715	1823	0.631	1639
0.5135	1861	0.5725	1892	0.633	1651
0.5145	1874	0.5735	1876	0.635	1656
0.5155	1900	0.5745	1867	0.637	1654
0.5165	1669	0.5755	1830	0.639	1651
0.5175	1726	0.5765	1846	0.641	1614
0.5185	1654	0.5775	1857	0.643	1621
0.5195	1828	0.5785	1783	0.645	1627
0.5205	1831	0.5795	1828	0.647	1603
0.5215	1906	0.5805	1838	0.649	1558
0.5225	1823	0.5815	1853	0.651	1606
0.5235	1894	0.5825	1873	0.653	1599
0.5245	1958	0.5835	1857	0.655	1532
0.5255	1930	0.5845	1860	0.657	1384
0.5265	1674	0.5855	1783	0.659	1549
0.5275	1828	0.5865	1830	0.661	1571
0.5285	1897	0.5875	1848	0.663	1555

(Continued)

Table A.1 (Continued)

WL (μm)	SI (W m^{-2} μm^{-1})	WL (μm)	SI (W m^{-2} μm^{-1})	WL (μm)	SI (W m^{-2} μm^{-1})
0.665	1560	0.783	1176	0.9	915.8
0.667	1535	0.785	1180	0.902	891.6
0.669	1546	0.787	1177	0.904	928.5
0.671	1516	0.789	1174	0.906	917.6
0.673	1521	0.791	1158	0.908	902.5
0.675	1510	0.793	1143	0.91	891.6
0.677	1508	0.795	1134	0.912	896.7
0.679	1498	0.797	1152	0.914	907.1
0.681	1492	0.799	1135	0.916	900.4
0.683	1479	0.801	1142	0.918	895.1
0.685	1455	0.803	1129	0.92	890.8
0.687	1467	0.805	1115	0.922	863
0.689	1461	0.807	1120	0.924	858.5
0.691	1448	0.809	1095	0.926	861.2
0.693	1448	0.811	1114	0.928	876.9
0.695	1436	0.813	1115	0.93	867.7
0.697	1416	0.815	1107	0.932	865.1
0.699	1425	0.817	1104	0.934	864.1
0.701	1386	0.819	1063	0.936	854.7
0.703	1388	0.821	1080	0.938	858
0.705	1415	0.823	1073	0.94	843.8
0.707	1400	0.825	1075	0.942	825
0.709	1384	0.826	1080	0.944	832.4
0.711	1385	0.828	1081	0.946	837.5
0.713	1373	0.83	1063	0.948	840.7
0.715	1366	0.832	1051	0.95	836.9
0.717	1354	0.834	1041	0.952	831.7
0.719	1328	0.836	1052	0.954	808
0.721	1331	0.838	1044	0.956	808.2
0.723	1348	0.84	1040	0.958	818.8
0.725	1350	0.842	1036	0.96	815.1
0.727	1346	0.844	1024	0.962	808.9
0.729	1319	0.846	1028	0.964	801.3
0.731	1326	0.848	1023	0.966	794.7
0.733	1318	0.85	966	0.968	796.9
0.735	1309	0.852	996.1	0.97	795.9
0.737	1307	0.854	878	0.972	793.6
0.739	1278	0.856	975.5	0.974	781.5
0.741	1258	0.858	1005	0.976	782.5
0.743	1286	0.86	996.9	0.978	777.9
0.745	1279	0.862	994.9	0.98	774.6
0.747	1283	0.864	999.3	0.982	776.4
0.749	1270	0.866	886.2	0.984	769.8
0.751	1262	0.868	939.5	0.986	766.1
0.753	1259	0.87	974.7	0.988	761.5
0.755	1255	0.872	983.3	0.99	754.1
0.757	1248	0.874	971.3	0.992	756.7
0.759	1240	0.876	964	0.994	755.6
0.761	1237	0.878	974.9	0.996	752.5
0.763	1241	0.88	955.4	0.998	751
0.765	1221	0.882	951.1	1	747.9
0.767	1185	0.884	957.9	1.002	746.9
0.769	1203	0.886	938.3	1.004	726.1
0.771	1204	0.888	944.3	1.006	713.6
0.773	1208	0.89	953	1.008	733.5
0.775	1188	0.892	939.4	1.01	731.3
0.777	1196	0.894	933.2	1.012	726.2
0.779	1187	0.896	938.7	1.014	721
0.781	1187	0.898	933.9	1.016	713.9

(Continued)

Table A.1 (Continued)

WL (μm)	SI (W m^{-2} μm^{-1})	WL (μm)	SI (W m^{-2} μm^{-1})	WL (μm)	SI (W m^{-2} μm^{-1})
1.018	710.7	1.136	565.8	1.254	457.4
1.02	704.1	1.138	556.9	1.256	455.1
1.022	702.1	1.14	553	1.258	453.3
1.024	705.4	1.142	553.1	1.26	453
1.026	702.7	1.144	551.4	1.262	449.7
1.028	698.9	1.146	554.8	1.264	447.8
1.03	693.7	1.148	552.5	1.266	446.7
1.032	690.5	1.15	548.9	1.268	441.7
1.034	681.7	1.152	545.8	1.27	445.3
1.036	684	1.154	547.9	1.272	445.2
1.038	677.2	1.156	545.5	1.274	443.1
1.04	676.1	1.158	543.5	1.276	445.1
1.042	674.6	1.16	532	1.278	444
1.044	671.4	1.162	532.5	1.28	435.6
1.046	660	1.164	533.2	1.282	401.4
1.048	664.4	1.166	530.3	1.284	425.9
1.05	662.2	1.168	531.2	1.286	432.8
1.052	658.6	1.17	527.6	1.288	431.4
1.054	654.9	1.172	531.5	1.29	425.5
1.056	655.7	1.174	527.3	1.292	425.4
1.058	645.1	1.176	518.4	1.294	422.3
1.06	641.5	1.178	519	1.296	422.4
1.062	643.8	1.18	523.9	1.298	418.4
1.064	645.9	1.182	515.9	1.3	418.6
1.066	639.5	1.184	510.3	1.302	413.9
1.068	631.7	1.186	518.7	1.304	411.1
1.07	624.1	1.188	507.5	1.306	413.6
1.072	632.6	1.19	508.5	1.308	412.3
1.074	627.6	1.192	516.1	1.31	410.6
1.076	628	1.194	514.5	1.312	403.3
1.078	627.2	1.196	508.4	1.314	402.2
1.08	624.7	1.198	494.3	1.316	397.9
1.082	609.9	1.2	500.3	1.318	401.7
1.084	618	1.202	506.8	1.32	401.6
1.086	620.8	1.204	494.8	1.322	398.6
1.088	610.3	1.206	503.9	1.324	398.1
1.09	619.9	1.208	489	1.326	394.9
1.092	615.9	1.21	488.2	1.328	390.8
1.094	584.9	1.212	493.3	1.33	387.8
1.096	598.3	1.214	494.2	1.332	386.3
1.098	596.1	1.216	493	1.334	389.2
1.1	604.2	1.218	489.7	1.336	386.6
1.102	593.2	1.22	487.5	1.338	383.2
1.104	597.4	1.222	485.4	1.34	379
1.106	594.5	1.224	484.6	1.342	380.5
1.108	591.6	1.226	481.7	1.344	379.8
1.11	590.6	1.228	477.1	1.346	377.2
1.112	584.3	1.23	479.2	1.348	376.6
1.114	584.4	1.232	475	1.35	372.4
1.116	583.1	1.234	472.9	1.352	374.2
1.118	581.5	1.236	471.9	1.354	372.2
1.12	574.1	1.238	470.3	1.356	367.5
1.122	579.6	1.24	465.3	1.358	368.8
1.124	576.9	1.242	464.2	1.36	367.3
1.126	565.5	1.244	461.9	1.362	367.7
1.128	570	1.246	463.5	1.364	365.7
1.13	565.3	1.248	463.3	1.366	365.7
1.132	567.8	1.25	462.4	1.368	362.8
1.134	563.8	1.252	457.1	1.37	359.9

(Continued)

Table A.1 (Continued)

WL (μm)	SI ($Wm^{-2}\mu m^{-1}$)	WL (μm)	SI ($Wm^{-2}\mu m^{-1}$)	WL (μm)	SI ($Wm^{-2}\mu m^{-1}$)
1.372	362.1	1.49	301.5	1.608	249.1
1.374	361.1	1.492	301.8	1.61	240
1.376	356.1	1.494	303.3	1.612	243
1.378	358	1.496	297.2	1.614	244.9
1.38	357.9	1.498	299.4	1.616	237.4
1.382	354.5	1.5	301.1	1.618	242.3
1.384	354.7	1.502	292.4	1.62	236.9
1.386	353.2	1.504	279.9	1.622	238.3
1.388	353	1.506	284.8	1.624	241.6
1.39	350.6	1.508	291.9	1.626	240.2
1.392	351.3	1.51	294.7	1.628	241.8
1.394	348.8	1.512	291.3	1.63	239.3
1.396	348.7	1.514	288.3	1.632	238.7
1.398	349.2	1.516	288.2	1.634	235.9
1.4	342.7	1.518	288.4	1.636	235.7
1.402	343.9	1.52	286.6	1.638	227.4
1.404	342.8	1.522	282.4	1.64	226.2
1.406	343.1	1.524	283.5	1.642	226.6
1.408	342.7	1.526	284.6	1.644	227.8
1.41	341.8	1.528	284.6	1.646	229.4
1.412	334.8	1.53	276.5	1.648	229.2
1.414	337.7	1.532	282.3	1.65	227.2
1.416	338.5	1.534	278.4	1.652	226.8
1.418	338.6	1.536	280.6	1.654	226.2
1.42	335.7	1.538	277.3	1.656	226
1.422	331.5	1.54	273	1.658	225.2
1.424	331.1	1.542	275.3	1.66	224.5
1.426	328.1	1.544	277.8	1.662	224.6
1.428	328.5	1.546	277.2	1.664	222.7
1.43	325.7	1.548	271.1	1.666	221.2
1.432	330	1.55	271.3	1.668	219.3
1.434	328.4	1.552	273.1	1.67	222.5
1.436	328.5	1.554	267.6	1.672	217.3
1.438	328.3	1.556	267.1	1.674	219.3
1.44	318.8	1.558	268.9	1.676	216.1
1.442	318.6	1.56	268.3	1.678	216.8
1.444	319.7	1.562	269.7	1.68	208
1.446	321.6	1.564	266.9	1.682	205.4
1.448	321.6	1.566	265.4	1.684	212.9
1.45	318.7	1.568	263.3	1.686	213.1
1.452	315.4	1.57	264.5	1.688	212
1.454	314.3	1.572	267.3	1.69	210.5
1.456	313.1	1.574	261	1.692	212.3
1.458	316.7	1.576	253.6	1.694	211.2
1.46	315.6	1.578	254.7	1.696	210
1.462	312.1	1.58	265	1.698	208.9
1.464	310.5	1.582	259	1.7	206.3
1.466	310.8	1.584	259.1	1.702	204.7
1.468	311.4	1.586	259.9	1.704	205.2
1.47	310.2	1.588	249	1.706	205
1.472	307.3	1.59	240.5	1.708	201.7
1.474	303.4	1.592	252.6	1.71	201.3
1.476	304.8	1.594	258.3	1.712	198.2
1.478	304.4	1.596	250.6	1.714	203.7
1.48	306.8	1.598	254.5	1.716	202.2
1.482	304.4	1.6	251.2	1.718	201
1.484	303.9	1.602	248.9	1.72	199.3
1.486	303.3	1.604	249.7	1.722	197.5
1.488	285.5	1.606	247.7	1.724	195.4

(Continued)

Table A.1 (Continued)

WL (μm)	SI (Wm^{-2}μm^{-1})	WL (μm)	SI (Wm^{-2}μm^{-1})	WL (μm)	SI (Wm^{-2}μm^{-1})
1.726	198.2	1.844	154.1	1.962	124
1.728	197.1	1.846	153.5	1.964	122.2
1.73	198.4	1.848	151	1.966	123.1
1.732	193.6	1.85	154.6	1.968	124
1.734	187.4	1.852	153.4	1.97	123.9
1.736	182.7	1.854	152.5	1.972	121.3
1.738	186.3	1.856	150.9	1.974	120.8
1.74	190.5	1.858	152.5	1.976	122.4
1.742	190.2	1.86	150.3	1.978	119.4
1.744	190.7	1.862	150.4	1.98	119.6
1.746	186.7	1.864	150.9	1.982	120.5
1.748	187.2	1.866	149.4	1.984	119.7
1.75	185.8	1.868	149.2	1.986	117.8
1.752	185	1.87	150.8	1.988	119.5
1.754	185.6	1.872	147.3	1.99	119.8
1.756	184.9	1.874	140.1	1.992	118
1.758	184.3	1.876	129.9	1.994	116.2
1.76	183.1	1.878	144.1	1.996	117.3
1.762	179.3	1.88	146.2	1.998	115.9
1.764	180.7	1.882	147.4	2	117
1.766	181.7	1.884	146.4	2.002	116.1
1.768	180.2	1.886	143.9	2.004	114.8
1.77	179.1	1.888	145.3	2.006	114.7
1.772	179.4	1.89	142.4	2.008	115.4
1.774	179.2	1.892	140.8	2.01	114.9
1.776	176.3	1.894	139.6	2.012	114.5
1.778	174.7	1.896	137.3	2.014	113.8
1.78	175.6	1.898	139	2.016	113.7
1.782	174.7	1.9	139.7	2.018	113.4
1.784	173.5	1.902	140.9	2.02	111.6
1.786	173.9	1.904	138.6	2.022	110.7
1.788	174.7	1.906	139	2.024	111.6
1.79	173.3	1.908	137.7	2.026	111.5
1.792	172.1	1.91	137.8	2.028	110.7
1.794	170.9	1.912	135.4	2.03	108.6
1.796	170.6	1.914	137	2.032	109.8
1.798	170.3	1.916	136	2.034	109.2
1.8	169.9	1.918	135.3	2.036	108.3
1.802	167.2	1.92	133.3	2.038	106.4
1.804	168.8	1.922	135	2.04	107.8
1.806	168.8	1.924	134.1	2.042	107.6
1.808	168.5	1.926	134.4	2.044	107.6
1.81	168.6	1.928	132.2	2.046	107.1
1.812	167.5	1.93	131.3	2.048	106.3
1.814	165.8	1.932	130.8	2.05	105.9
1.816	160.5	1.934	132	2.052	104.7
1.818	152	1.936	132.8	2.054	104.6
1.82	159.6	1.938	132.1	2.056	104.6
1.822	159.8	1.94	129.9	2.058	104
1.824	162.4	1.942	129.4	2.06	102.8
1.826	162.8	1.944	120.3	2.062	102.3
1.828	161.1	1.946	119.2	2.064	100.5
1.83	160.6	1.948	127.1	2.066	102.5
1.832	159.3	1.95	126.1	2.068	101.9
1.834	158.5	1.952	125.5	2.07	100.3
1.836	158.1	1.954	128.6	2.072	100.4
1.838	156.2	1.956	127.6	2.074	100.9
1.84	156.2	1.958	127.1	2.076	100.6
1.842	154	1.96	126.1	2.078	100

(Continued)

Table A.1 (Continued)

WL (μm)	SI (W m^{-2} μm^{-1})	WL (μm)	SI (W m^{-2} μm^{-1})	WL (μm)	SI (W m^{-2} μm^{-1})
2.08	98.78	2.198	82.99	2.316	67.79
2.082	98.64	2.2	82.65	2.318	67.45
2.084	97.72	2.202	82.3	2.32	67.68
2.086	98.52	2.204	82.11	2.322	66.75
2.088	98.35	2.206	79.66	2.324	65.36
2.09	97.88	2.208	79.66	2.326	65.59
2.092	95.67	2.21	80.8	2.328	66.29
2.094	95.93	2.212	81.05	2.33	66.16
2.096	95.8	2.214	80.72	2.332	65.84
2.098	96.2	2.216	79.94	2.334	65.71
2.1	96.06	2.218	79.7	2.336	65.36
2.102	95.77	2.22	79.97	2.338	64.96
2.104	95.59	2.222	79.62	2.34	65.2
2.106	95.74	2.224	79.26	2.342	65.39
2.108	95.13	2.226	78.11	2.344	65.09
2.11	93.96	2.228	78.26	2.346	64.86
2.112	94.52	2.23	78.31	2.348	64.72
2.114	94.36	2.232	78.15	2.35	64.53
2.116	93.31	2.234	78.02	2.352	62.89
2.118	93.11	2.236	77.58	2.354	62.39
2.12	92.75	2.238	76.48	2.356	62.82
2.122	92.75	2.24	76.39	2.358	62.66
2.124	91.89	2.242	76.42	2.36	63.08
2.126	92.08	2.244	76.24	2.362	63.05
2.128	92.25	2.246	76.12	2.364	62.95
2.13	92.09	2.248	75.2	2.366	62.84
2.132	92.1	2.25	75.41	2.368	62.63
2.134	91.55	2.252	75.12	2.37	62.11
2.136	90.12	2.254	74.02	2.372	62.07
2.138	91.1	2.256	74.22	2.374	60.66
2.14	90.83	2.258	74.41	2.376	61.64
2.142	90.64	2.26	74.21	2.378	61.92
2.144	90.06	2.262	72.99	2.38	61.72
2.146	89.39	2.264	73.29	2.382	60.98
2.148	89.79	2.266	73.15	2.384	58.85
2.15	89.57	2.268	73.27	2.386	59.08
2.152	89.13	2.27	72.97	2.388	60.04
2.154	88.78	2.272	72.77	2.39	60.29
2.156	88.74	2.274	72.52	2.392	60.08
2.158	88.42	2.276	72.39	2.394	60.03
2.16	87.81	2.278	72.42	2.396	59.96
2.162	86.86	2.28	71.65	2.398	59.89
2.164	84.56	2.282	70.07	2.4	59.44
2.166	78.49	2.284	71.25	2.402	59.65
2.168	83	2.286	71.24	2.404	59.45
2.17	85.57	2.288	71.27	2.406	59.19
2.172	85.91	2.29	71.1	2.408	59.15
2.174	85.92	2.292	70.67	2.41	59.02
2.176	85.32	2.294	69.2	2.412	58.94
2.178	84.25	2.296	69.08	2.414	57.34
2.18	84.97	2.298	69.19	2.416	55.99
2.182	84.25	2.3	69.53	2.418	57.48
2.184	84.57	2.302	69.55	2.42	57.7
2.186	84.65	2.304	69.31	2.422	57.67
2.188	82.77	2.306	69.23	2.424	57.26
2.19	83.04	2.308	69.01	2.426	57.17
2.192	83.77	2.31	68.7	2.428	57.12
2.194	83.49	2.312	68.67	2.43	57.12
2.196	83.18	2.314	68.26	2.432	57.02

(Continued)

Table A.1 (*Continued*)

WL (μm)	SI (W m^{-2} μm^{-1})	WL (μm)	SI (W m^{-2} μm^{-1})	WL (μm)	SI (W m^{-2} μm^{-1})
2.434	56.41	3.02	25.47	4.2	7.153
2.436	56.18	3.04	24.65	4.22	7.015
2.438	55.99	3.06	24.22	4.24	6.881
2.44	56.39	3.08	23.64	4.26	6.749
2.442	56.17	3.1	23.06	4.28	6.621
2.444	56.03	3.12	22.46	4.3	6.496
2.446	54.98	3.14	21.98	4.32	6.374
2.448	54.57	3.16	21.44	4.34	6.254
2.45	54.62	3.18	20.96	4.36	6.138
2.452	54.32	3.2	20.48	4.38	6.024
2.454	54.55	3.22	20	4.4	5.913
2.456	53.7	3.24	19.51	4.42	5.804
2.458	53.92	3.26	19.07	4.44	5.698
2.46	54.57	3.28	18.58	4.46	5.594
2.462	54.42	3.3	18.02	4.48	5.492
2.464	54.35	3.32	17.68	4.5	5.393
2.466	54.05	3.34	17.37	4.52	5.296
2.468	53.9	3.36	16.97	4.54	5.201
2.47	52.85	3.38	16.59	4.56	5.108
2.472	53.3	3.4	16.15	4.58	5.018
2.474	53.13	3.42	15.84	4.6	4.929
2.476	53.43	3.44	15.54	4.62	4.842
2.478	53.03	3.46	15.2	4.64	4.757
2.48	51.77	3.48	14.86	4.66	4.674
2.482	51.4	3.5	14.56	4.68	4.593
2.484	52.19	3.52	14.25	4.7	4.514
2.486	51.6	3.54	13.93	4.72	4.436
2.488	51.69	3.56	13.62	4.74	4.36
2.49	52.25	3.58	13.34	4.76	4.285
2.492	51.98	3.6	13.07	4.78	4.212
2.494	51.75	3.62	12.81	4.8	4.141
2.496	51.52	3.64	12.51	4.82	4.071
2.498	51.54	3.66	12.22	4.84	4.003
2.5	51.55	3.68	11.93	4.86	3.936
2.52	49.84	3.7	11.62	4.88	3.87
2.54	48.14	3.72	11.45	4.9	3.806
2.56	46.72	3.74	11.08	4.92	3.743
2.58	45.5	3.76	10.96	4.94	3.681
2.6	44.57	3.78	10.78	4.96	3.621
2.62	43.05	3.8	10.57	4.98	3.562
2.64	42.11	3.82	10.38	5	3.504
2.66	40.79	3.84	10.19	5.05	3.394
2.68	39.68	3.86	9.983	5.1	3.267
2.7	38.67	3.88	9.782	5.15	3.146
2.72	37.63	3.9	9.599	5.2	3.03
2.74	36.63	3.92	9.427	5.25	2.92
2.76	35.46	3.94	9.233	5.3	2.815
2.78	34.68	3.96	9.032	5.35	2.715
2.8	33.85	3.98	8.857	5.4	2.619
2.82	32.97	4	8.669	5.45	2.527
2.84	32.09	4.02	8.557	5.5	2.439
2.86	31.19	4.04	8.385	5.55	2.355
2.88	30.32	4.06	8.217	5.6	2.275
2.9	29.69	4.08	8.054	5.65	2.198
2.92	28.9	4.1	7.894	5.7	2.124
2.94	28.17	4.12	7.739	5.75	2.054
2.96	27.5	4.14	7.587	5.8	1.986
2.98	26.82	4.16	7.439	5.85	1.921
3	26.12	4.18	7.294	5.9	1.859

(*Continued*)

Table A.1 (Continued)

WL (μm)	SI (W m^{-2} μm^{-1})	WL (μm)	SI (W m^{-2} μm^{-1})	WL (μm)	SI (W m^{-2} μm^{-1})
5.95	1.799	7.35	0.7942	8.7	0.4135
6	1.742	7.4	0.7736	8.75	0.4044
6.05	1.687	7.45	0.7537	8.8	0.3956
6.1	1.634	7.5	0.7344	8.85	0.387
6.15	1.583	7.55	0.7158	8.9	0.3787
6.2	1.534	7.6	0.6977	8.95	0.3706
6.25	1.487	7.65	0.6802	9	0.3627
6.3	1.442	7.7	0.6633	9.05	0.355
6.35	1.399	7.75	0.6469	9.1	0.3475
6.4	1.357	7.8	0.631	9.15	0.3402
6.45	1.317	7.85	0.6156	9.2	0.3331
6.5	1.278	7.9	0.6006	9.25	0.3262
6.55	1.24	7.95	0.5862	9.3	0.3195
6.6	1.204	8	0.5721	9.35	0.3129
6.65	1.17	8.05	0.5585	9.4	0.3065
6.7	1.136	8.1	0.5453	9.45	0.3003
6.75	1.104	8.15	0.5324	9.5	0.2942
6.8	1.073	8.2	0.52	9.55	0.2883
6.85	1.043	8.25	0.5079	9.6	0.2825
6.9	1.014	8.3	0.4961	9.65	0.2769
6.95	0.9862	8.35	0.4847	9.7	0.2714
7	0.9592	8.4	0.4737	9.75	0.2661
7.05	0.9331	8.45	0.4629	9.8	0.2608
7.1	0.908	8.5	0.4525	9.85	0.2558
7.15	0.8836	8.55	0.4423	9.9	0.2508
7.2	0.8601	8.6	0.4324	9.95	0.246
7.25	0.8374	8.65	0.4228	10	0.2412
7.3	0.8154				

WL, Wavelength; SI, solar irradiance.

Appendix B: Radiometric Terminology

Table B.1 Radiometric terminology and units

Term	Description	Units
Absorptance	The fraction of the incident radiation flux by the Earth's surface	Dimensionless
Albedo	The ratio of reflected to the incident radiation component by the surface of the Earth	Dimensionless
Diffuse solar radiation	The downward scattered and reflected short-wave radiation coming from the whole sky vault with the exception of the solid angle subtended by the Sun's disk	W m^{-2} (instantaneous value) Wh m^{-2} (integrated value over 1 h)
Direct solar radiation	The short-wave radiation emitted from the solid angle of the Sun's disk, comprising mainly unscattered and unreflected solar radiation	W m^{-2} (instantaneous value) Wh m^{-2} (integrated value over 1 h)
Global (or total) solar radiation	The sum of diffuse and direct short-wave radiation components	W m^{-2} (instantaneous value) Wh m^{-2} (integrated value over 1 h)
IR (or terrestrial or long-wave or thermal) radiation	The radiation coming from the sky at wavelengths longer than about 4 μm	W m^{-2} (instantaneous value) Wh m^{-2} (integrated value over 1 h)
Irradiance	The radiant flux incident on a surface from all directions per unit area of this surface	W m^{-2} (instantaneous value) Wh m^{-2} (integrated value over 1 h)
Radiance	The radiant flux emitted by a unit solid angle of a source or scatterer incident on a unit area of a surface	W m^{-2} (instantaneous value) Wh m^{-2} (integrated value over 1 h)
Radiant flux	The amount of radiation coming from a source per unit time	W
Radiant intensity	The radiant flux leaving a source point per unit solid angle of space surrounding the point	W sr^{-1}
Reflectance/ transmittance	The fraction of radiant flux reflected by a surface or transmitted by a semitransparent medium	Dimensionless
Spectroradiometry	The radiant flux per unit wavelength	W m^{-2} nm^{-1} or W m^{-2} μm^{-1} (instantaneous value) Wh m^{-2} nm^{-1} or Wh m^{-2} μm^{-1} (integrated value over 1 h)

Appendix C: The Sun as a Blackbody

The curve of 5777 K corresponds to the temperature of the Sun. **Figure A.1** is redrawn (**Figure C.1**) to show the proximity of the Sun's spectral emissive power to the spectral distribution of the solar constant at TOA.

The red curve is computed via the following expression:

$$H_{ex\lambda} = E_{b\lambda}\left(\frac{r_s}{r_0}\right)^2 \quad [C.1]$$

where $H_{ex\lambda}$ describes the spectral variation of the solar constant (the extraterrestrial irradiance (red curve) received normally on a surface of 1 m^2 at the mean Sun–Earth distance $r_0 = 1$ AU) multiplied by the square of the ratio of the radius of the Sun ($r_s = 695\,980$ km) to the r_0. From **Figure C.1**, it is seen that the measured spectrum (that of the solar constant) does not strictly coincide with that of the blackbody curve. Also, the maximum of the observed spectrum lies at a wavelength shorter than that of the blackbody at 5777 K. This happens because the surface temperature of the Sun is not uniform; the solar disk appears hotter than its circumference.

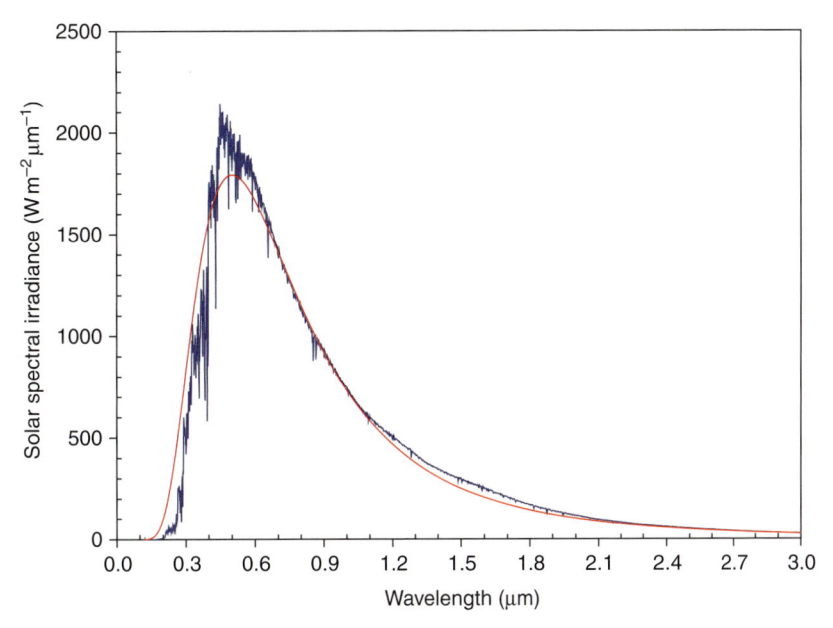

Figure C.1 Spectral distribution of the solar constant (blue line) and H_{ex} (red line) from eqn [C.1] at TOA in the wavelength range 0.3–3 µm.

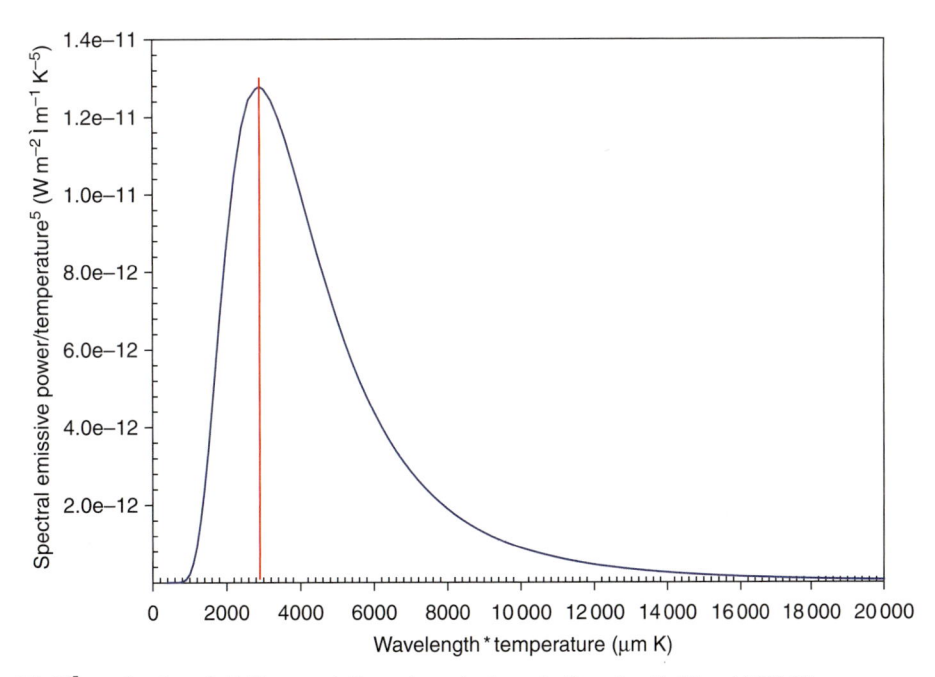

Figure C.2 Plot of $E_{b\lambda}/T^5$ as a function of λT (blue curve). Its maximum is shown by the red vertical line at 2897.8 K.

The shape of the curve expressed by eqn [11] in terms of the variable λT (denoted as $\lambda_{max}T$) is found at 2897.8 μm K (**Figure C.2**), that is,

$$\lambda_{max}T = 2897.8 \, \mu m \, K \qquad [C.2]$$

For the Sun as a blackbody of temperature of 5777 K, the above relationship gives $\lambda_{max} = 0.5016$ μm. From the blue curve in **Figure C.2**, λ_{max} is located at around 0.440 μm. The difference between the theoretical and experimental values of λ_{max} indicates that the Sun is not a real but a near-real blackbody.

Appendix D: Physical Constants and Conversion Factors

Table D.1 Basic physical constants

Constant	SI units
Astronomical unit (AU)	1.496×10^{11} m
Speed of light in vacuum	2.998×10^{8} m s^{-1}
Solar constant (H_{ex})	1366.1 W m^{-2} (instantaneous value)
	4.918 MJ m^{-2} h^{-1} (integrated value over 1 h)
Earth's radius (r_0)	6.37×10^{6} m
Sun's radius (r_s)	6.96×10^{8} m
Stefan–Boltzmann constant (σ)	5.6697×10^{-8} W m^{-2} K^{-4} (theoretical value)
	5.6866×10^{-8} W m^{-2} K^{-4} (experimental value)

Table D.2 Conversion factors of radiation per unit area

Unit	J m^{-2}	Wh m^{-2}	cal cm^{-2}
1 J m^{-2}	1	2.778×10^{-4}	2.39×10^{-5}
1 Wh m^{-2}	3.60×10^{3}	1	0.086
1 cal cm^{-2}	1.187×10^{4}	11.63	1

Table D.3 Conversion factors of radiant flux per unit area

Unit	W m^{-2}	cal m^{-2} min^{-1}
1 W m^{-2}	1	1.433×10^{-3}
1 cal cm^{-2} min^{-1}	698	1

References

[1] Spencer JW (1971) Fourier series representation of the position of the Sun. *Search* 2(5): 172.
[2] Partridge GW and Platt CMR (1976) *Radiative Processes in Meteorology and Climatology*. Amsterdam; New York: Elsevier Scientific Publishing Company.
[3] Perrin de Brichambaut Chr (1975) *Cahiers AFEDES*. Suplément au no. 1. Paris: Editions Européens Thermique et Industrie.
[4] Cooper PI (1969) The absorption of solar radiation in solar stills. *Solar Energy* 12(3): 333–346.
[5] Duffie JA and Beckman WA (1980) *Solar Engineering of Thermal Processes*. New York: Wiley.
[6] Kambezidis HD and Papanikolaou NS (1990) Solar position and atmospheric refraction. *Solar Energy* 44(3): 143–144.
[7] Kambezidis HD (1997) Estimation of sunrise and sunset hour angles for locations on flat and complex terrain: Review and advancement. *Renewable Energy* 11(4): 485–494.
[8] Drummond AJ and Thekaekara MP (eds.) (1974) *The Extraterrestrial Solar Spectrum*. Mount Prospect, IL: Institute of Environmental Sciences.
[9] Fröhlich C (1977) Contemporary measures of the solar constant. In: White OR (ed.) *The Solar Output and Its Variation*, pp. 93–109. Boulder, CO: Colorado Associated Press.
[10] Fröhlich C and Wehrli C (1981) Spectral distribution of solar irradiance from 25000 nm to 250 nm. World Radiation Center, Davos, Switzerland, Private Communication.
[11] Fröhlich C and Brusa RW (1981) Solar radiation and its variation in time. *Solar Physics* 74(1): 209–215.
[12] Gueymard C (2004) The sun's total and spectral irradiance for solar energy applications and solar radiation models. *Solar Energy* 76(4): 423–453.
[13] Kendall JM and Berdahl CM (1970) Two blackbody radiometers of high accuracy. *Applied Optics* 9(5): 1082–1091.
[14] De la Casinière A, Cabot T, and Benmansour S (1995) Measuring spectral diffuse solar irradiance with non-cosine flat-plate diffusers. *Solar Energy* 54(3): 173–182.
[15] Laue EG (1970) The measurement of solar spectral irradiance at different terrestrial elevations. *Solar Energy* 13(1): 43–50.
[16] Lorente J, Redaño A, and de Cabo X (1994) Influence of urban aerosol on spectral solar irradiance. *Journal of Applied Meteorology* 33(3): 406–415.
[17] Badarinath KVS, Kharol SK, Kaskaoutis DG, and Kambezidis HD (2007) Influence of atmospheric aerosols on solar spectral irradiance in an urban area. *Journal of Atmospheric Solar-Terrestrial Physics* 69(4–5): 589–599.
[18] US Standard Atmosphere (1976) US Government Printing Office, Washington, DC.
[19] Kasten F and Young AT (1989) Revised optical air mass tables and approximation formula. *Applied Optics* 28(15): 4735–4738.
[20] Lunde PJ (1980) *Solar Thermal Engineering*. New York: Wiley.
[21] Gueymard C (1995) SMARTS2, a simple model of the atmospheric radiative transfer of sunshine: Algorithms and performance assessment. *FSEC-PF-270-95*.

[22] Penndorf R (1957) Tables of the refractive index for standard air and the Rayleigh scattering coefficient for the spectral region between 0.2 and 20.0 μm and their application to atmospheric optics. *Journal of the Optical Society of America* 47(2): 176–182.
[23] Leckner B (1978) The spectral distribution of solar radiation at the earth's surface – elements of a model. *Solar Energy* 20(2): 143–150.
[24] Moon P (1940) Proposed standard solar radiation curves for engineering use. *Journal of the Franklin Institute* 230(5): 583–617.
[25] Ångström A (1929) On the atmospheric transmission of sun radiation and on dust in the air. *Geografiska Annaler* 2: 156–166.
[26] Ångström A (1930) On the atmospheric transmission of sun radiation. *Geografiska Annaler* 2–3: 130–159.
[27] McClatchey RA, Fenn RW, and Selby JE (1972) Atmospheric transmittance from 0.25 to 38.5 μm: Computer code LOWTRAN, Air force Cambridge research laboratories, AFCRL-72-0745. *Environmental Research Paper* 427.
[28] Schüepp W (1949) Die bestimmung der komponenten der atmosphärischen trübung aus aktinometer messungen. *Archiv fur Meteorologie, Geophysik und Bioklimatologie* B1: 257–346.
[29] Linke F (1922) Transmission koeffizient und trübungsfaktor. *Beitrage zur Physik der freien Atmosphäre* 10: 91–103.
[30] Linke F (1929) Messungen der sannenstrahlung bei vier freiballonfahren. *Beitrage zur Physik der freien Atmosphäre* 15: 176–185.
[31] Unsworth MH and Monteith JL (1972) Aerosol and solar radiation in Britain. *Quarterly Journal of the Royal Meteorological Society* 98(418): 778–797.
[32] Gueymard CA and Myers D (2008) Validation and ranking methodologies for solar radiation models. In: Badescu V (ed.) *Modeling Solar Radiation at the Earth's Surface*, pp. 479–509. Berlin: Springer.
[33] Maxwell EL (1987) A quasi-physical model for converting hourly global horizontal to direct normal insolation. *Report SERI/TR-215-3087*. Golden, CO: Solar Energy Research Institute.
[34] Perez R, Ineichen P, Maxwell EL, et al. (1992) Dynamic global-to-direct irradiance conversion models. *ASHRAE Transactions* 98(1): 354–369.
[35] Maxwell EL (1998) METSTAT – the solar radiation model used in the production of the National Solar Radiation Data Base (NSRDB). *Solar Energy* 62(4): 263–279.
[36] Muneer T, Gul MS, and Kubie J (2000) Models for estimating solar radiation and illuminance from meteorological parameters. *Transactions of the ASME, Journal of Solar Energy Engineering* 122(3): 146–153.
[37] Perez R, Ineichen P, Moore K, et al. (2002) A new operational model for satellite derived irradiances, description and validation. *Solar Energy* 73(5): 307–317.
[38] Collares-Pereira M and Rabl A (1979) The average distribution of solar radiation – correlations between diffuse and hemispherical and between daily and hourly insolation values. *Solar Energy* 22(2): 155–164.
[39] Gueymard C (2000) Prediction and performance assessment of mean hourly global radiation. *Solar Energy* 68(2): 285–303.
[40] Gueymard CA and Kambezidis HD (2004) Solar spectral radiation. In: Muneer T (ed.) *Solar Radiation and Daylight Models*, pp. 221–301. Oxford: Elsevier.
[41] Gordon J (ed.) (2001) *Solar Energy – the State of the Art, ISES Position Papers*. James & James; International Solar Energy Society.
[42] Gueymard CA (2008) REST2: High performance solar radiation model for cloudless-sky irradiance, illuminance and photosynthetically active radiation – validation with a benchmark dataset. *Solar Energy* 82(3): 272–285.
[43] Perez R, Seals R, Zelenka A, and Ineichen P (1990) Climatic evaluation of models that predict hourly direct irradiance from hourly global irradiance: Prospects for performance improvements. *Solar Energy* 44(2): 99–108.
[44] Wang Q, Tenhunen J, Schmidt M, et al. (2006) A model to estimate global radiation in complex terrain. *Boundary-Layer Meteorology* 119(2): 409–429.
[45] Perez R, Ineichen P, and Seals R (1990) Modelling daylight availability and irradiance components from direct and global irradiance. *Solar Energy* 44(5): 271–289.
[46] Gueymard CA (1987) An anisotropic solar irradiance model for tilted surfaces and its comparison with selected engineering algorithms. *Solar Energy* 38(5): 367–386.
[47] Hay JE (1993) Calculating solar radiation for inclined surfaces: Practical approaches. *Renewable Energy* 3(4–5): 373–380.
[48] Loutzenhiser PG, Manz H, Felsmann C, et al. (2007) Empirical validation of models to compute solar irradiance on inclined surfaces for building energy simulation. *Solar Energy* 81(2): 254–267.
[49] Gueymard C (1989) A two-band model for the calculation of clear sky solar irradiance, illuminance, and photosynthetically active radiation at the Earth's surface. *Solar Energy* 43(5): 253–265.
[50] Bird RE and Hulstrom RL (1981) Review, evaluation, and improvement of direct irradiance models. *Transactions of the ASME, Journal of Solar Energy Engineering* 103: 182–192.
[51] Ianetz A, Lyubansky V, Setter I, et al. (2007) Inter-comparison of different models for estimating clear sky solar global radiation for the Negev region of Israel. *Energy Conversion and Management* 48(1): 259–268.
[52] Ineichen P (2006) Comparison of eight clear sky broadband models against 16 independent data banks. *Solar Energy* 80(4): 468–478.
[53] Power HC (2001) Estimating clear-sky beam irradiation from sunshine duration. *Solar Energy* 71(4): 217–224.
[54] Gueymard CA (1998) Turbidity determination from broadband irradiance measurements: A detailed multi-coefficient approach. *Journal of Applied Meteorology* 37(4): 414–435.
[55] Louche A, Maurel M, Simonnot G, et al. (1987) Determination of Ångström's turbidity coefficient from direct total solar irradiance measurements. *Solar Energy* 38(2): 89–96.
[56] Bartoli B, Cuomo V, Amato U, et al. (1982) Diffuse and beam components of daily global radiation in Genoa and Macerata. *Solar Energy* 28(4): 307–311.
[57] Hollands KGT and Crha SJ (1987) An improved model for diffuse radiation correction for atmospheric back-scattering. *Solar Energy* 38(4): 233–236.
[58] Macagnan MH, Lorenzo E, and Jimenez C (1994) Solar radiation in Madrid. *International Journal of Solar Energy* 16(1): 1.
[59] Liu BYH and Jordan RC (1963) The long term average performance of flat plate solar energy collectors. *Solar Energy* 7(2): 53–74.
[60] Suehrcke H and McCormick PG (1987) The frequency distribution of instantaneous insolation values. *Solar Energy* 40(5): 413–422.
[61] Jain PC and Ratto CF (1988) A new model for obtaining horizontal instantaneous global and diffuse radiation from the daily values. *Solar Energy* 41(5): 397–404.
[62] Bivona S, Burlon R, and Leone C (1991) Instantaneous distribution of global and diffuse radiation on horizontal surfaces. *Solar Energy* 46(4): 249–254.
[63] ASHRAE (2005) *Handbook of Fundamentals, SI Edition*. Atlanta, GA: American Society of Heating, Refrigerating and Air-Conditioning Engineers.
[64] Bird RE and Hulstrom RL (1981) Review, evaluation and improvement of direct irradiance models. *Transactions of the ASME, Journal of Solar Energy Engineering* 103: 182–192.
[65] Bird RE and Hulstrom RL (1981) A simplified clear-sky model for the direct and diffuse insolation on horizontal surfaces. *US SERI Technical Report TR-642-761*. Solar Energy Research Institute, Golden, Colorado.
[66] Suckling PW and Hay JE (1976) Modelling direct, diffuse, and total solar radiation for cloudless days. *Atmosphere* 14: 298–308.
[67] Suckling PW and Hay JE (1977) A cloud layer-sunshine model for estimating direct, diffuse and total solar radiation. *Atmosphere* 15: 194–207.
[68] Houghton HG (1954) On the annual heat balance of the northern hemisphere. *Journal of Meteorology* 11(1): 1–9.
[69] Monteith JL (1962) Attenuation of solar radiation: A climatology study. *Quarterly Journal of the Royal Meteorological Society* 88(378): 508–521.
[70] Gueymard CA (2003) Direct solar transmittance and irradiance predictions with broadband models. Part 1: Detailed theoretical performance assessment. *Solar Energy* 74(5): 355–379; Corrigendum. *Solar Energy* 76(4): 513, 2004.
[71] Battles FJ, Olmo FJ, Tovar J, and Alados-Arboledas L (2000) Comparison of cloudless sky parameterizations of solar irradiance at various Spanish midlatitude locations. *Theoretical and Applied Climatology* 66(1–2): 81–93.
[72] Gueymard CA (1993) Critical analysis and performance assessment of clear sky solar irradiance models using theoretical and measured data. *Solar Energy* 51(2): 121–138.
[73] Gueymard CA (2003) Direct solar transmittance and irradiance predictions with broadband models. Part 2: Validation with high-quality measurements. *Solar Energy* 74(5): 381–395; Corrigendum. *Solar Energy* 76(4): 515, 2004.
[74] Olmo FJ, Vida J, Foyo-Moreno I, et al. (2001) Performance reduction of solar irradiance parametric models due to limitations in required aerosol data: Case of the CPCR2 model. *Theoretical and Applied Climatology* 69(3–4): 253–263.
[75] Rigollier C, Bauer O, and Wald L (2000) On the clear sky model of ESRA – European solar radiation Atlas – with respect to the Heliosat method. *Solar Energy* 68(1): 33–48.

[76] Scharmer K and Greif J (ed.) (2000) *The European Solar Radiation Atlas*, vol. 2. Paris: Presses de l' Ecole des Mines de Paris.
[77] Remund J, Wald L, Lefèvre M, *et al.* (2003) Worldwide Linke turbidity information. *Proceedings of the ISES Conference*. Gothenburg, Sweden: The International Solar Energy Society.
[78] Iqbal M (1983) *An Introduction to Solar Radiation*. New York: Academic Press.
[79] Kasten F (1980) A simple parameterization of the pyrheliometric formula for determining the Linke turbidity factor. *Meteorologische Rundschau* 33: 124–127.
[80] Kasten F (1983) Parametrisierung der Globalstrahlung durch Bedeckungsgrad und Trübungsfaktor. *Annalen der Meteorologie* 20: 49–50.
[81] Kasten F and Czeplak G (1980) Solar and terrestrial radiation dependent on the amount and type of cloud. *Solar Energy* 24(2): 177–189.
[82] Davies JA and McKay DC (1989) Evaluation of selected models for estimating solar radiation on horizontal surfaces. *Solar Energy* 43(3): 153–168.
[83] Abdelrahman MA, Said SA, and Shuaib AN (1988) Comparison between atmospheric turbidity coefficients of desert and temperate climates. *Solar Energy* 40(3): 219–225.
[84] Grenier JC, de la Casinière A, and Cabot T (1994) A spectral model of Linke's turbidity factor and its experimental implications. *Solar Energy* 52(4): 303–314.
[85] Hinzpeter H (1950) Über trübungsbestimmungen in Potsdam in dem Jahren 1946 und 1947. *Meteorologische Zeitschrift* 4: 1–8.
[86] Katz M, Baille A, and Mermier M (1982) Atmospheric turbidity in a semi-rural site – evaluation and comparison of different turbidity coefficients. *Solar Energy* 28(4): 323–327.
[87] Molineaux B, Ineichen P, and O'Neill N (1998) Equivalence of pyrheliometric and monochromatic aerosol optical depths at a single key wavelength. *Applied Optics* 37(30): 7008–7018.
[88] Davies JA, Schertzer W, and Nunez M (1975) Estimating global solar radiation. *Boundary-Layer Meteorology* 9(1): 33–52.
[89] Davies JA and Hay JE (1979) Calculation of the solar radiation incident on a horizontal surface. In: Hay JE and Thorne KW (eds) *Proceedings of the First Canadian Solar Radiation Data Workshop*, 17–19 April, 1978. Toronto Canada. Supply and Services Canada, Ottawa, Canada.
[90] Gueymard CA (2001) Parameterized transmittance model for direct beam and circumsolar spectral irradiance. *Solar Energy* 71(5): 325–346.
[91] Gueymard CA (2005) Interdisciplinary applications of a versatile spectral solar irradiance model: A review. *Energy* 30(9): 1551–1576.
[92] Santamouris M, Mihalakakou G, Psiloglou B, *et al.* (1999) Modeling the global solar radiation on the Earth's surface using atmospheric deterministic and intelligent data-driven techniques. *Journal of Climate* 12(10): 3105–3116.
[93] Yang K, Huang GW, and Tamai N (2001) A hybrid model for estimation of global solar radiation. *Solar Energy* 70(1): 13–22.
[94] Yang K and Koike T (2005) A general model to estimate hourly and daily solar radiation for hydrological studies. *Water Resources Research* 41: W10403. doi: 10.1029/2005WR003976.
[95] De Souza LJ, Nicacio RM, and Moura MA (2005) Global solar radiation measurements in Maceio, Brazil. *Renewable Energy* 30(8): 1203–1220.
[96] Cao JC and Cao SH (2006) Study of forecasting solar irradiance using neural networks with preprocessing sample data by wavelet analysis. *Energy* 31(15): 3435–3445.
[97] Pattanasethanon S, Lertsatitthanakorn C, Atthajariyakul S, and Soponronnarit S (2008) An accuracy assessment of empirical sine model, a novel sine model and an artificial neural network model for forecasting illuminance/irradiance on horizontal plane of all sky types at Mahasarakham, Thailand. *Energy Conversion and Management* 49(8): 1999–2005.
[98] Cao S and Cao J (2005) Forecast of solar irradiance using recurrent neural networks combined with wavelet analysis. *Applied Thermal Engineering* 25(2–3): 161–172.
[99] Jiang Y (2008) Prediction of monthly mean daily diffuse solar radiation using artificial neural networks and comparison with other empirical models. *Energy Policy* 36(10): 3833–3837.
[100] Cao J and Lin X (2008) Study of hourly and daily solar irradiation forecast using diagonal recurrent wavelet neural networks. *Energy Conversion and Management* 49(6): 1396–1406.
[101] Sfetsos A and Coonick AH (2000) Univariate and multivariate forecasting of hourly solar radiation with artificial intelligence techniques. *Solar Energy* 68(2): 169–178.
[102] Seme S, Štumberger G, and Pihler J (2009) Predicting daily distribution of solar irradiation by neural networks. *International Conference on Renewable Energies and Power Quality (ICREPQ'09)*, 15–17 April. Valencia. http://www.icrepq.com/papers-icrepq09.htm (accessed 28 June 2011).
[103] Mellit A, Kalogirou SA, Shaaric A, *et al.* (2008) Methodology for predicting sequences of mean monthly clearness index and daily solar radiation data in remote areas: Application for sizing a stand-alone PV system. *Renewable Energy* 33(7): 1570–1590.
[104] Mellit A, Benghanem M, and Kalogirou SA (2006) An adaptive wavelet-network model for forecasting daily total solar-radiation. *Applied Energy* 83(7): 705–722.
[105] Van Heuklon TK (1979) Estimating atmospheric ozone for solar radiation models. *Solar Energy* 22(1): 63–68.
[106] Kambezidis HD and Psiloglou BE (2008) The Meteorological Radiation Model (MRM): Advancements and applications. In: Badescu V (ed.) *Modeling Solar Radiation at the Earth's Surface*, pp. 357–392. Berlin: Springer.
[107] Psiloglou BE, Santamouris M, and Asimakopoulos DN (1994) On the atmospheric water-vapor transmission function for solar radiation models. *Solar Energy* 53(5): 445–453.
[108] Psiloglou BE, Santamouris M, and Asimakopoulos DN (1995) Predicting the broadband transmittance of the uniformly-mixed gases (CO2, CO, N2O, CH4 and O2) in the atmosphere for solar radiation models. *Renewable Energy* 6(1): 63–70.
[109] Psiloglou BE, Santamouris M, and Asimakopoulos DN (1995) On broadband Rayleigh scattering in the atmosphere for solar radiation modelling. *Renewable Energy* 6(4): 429–433.
[110] Psiloglou BE, Santamouris M, Varotsos C, and Asimakopoulos DN (1996) A new parameterisation of the integral ozone transmission. *Solar Energy* 56(6): 573–581.
[111] Psiloglou BE, Santamouris M, and Asimakopoulos DN (2000) Atmospheric broadband model for computation of solar radiation at the Earth's surface. Application to Mediterranean climate. *Pure and Applied Geophysics* 157(5): 829–860.
[112] Paltridge GW and Platt CMR (1976) *Radiative Processes in Meteorology and Climatology*. New York: American Elsevier.
[113] Gueymard C (1993) Assessment of the accuracy and computing speed of simplified saturation vapor equations using a new reference dataset. *Journal of Applied Meteorology* 32(7): 1294–1300.
[114] Bird RE and Hulstrom RL (1980) Direct insolation models. *US SERI Technical Report TR-335-344*. Solar Energy Research Institute, Golden, Colorado.
[115] Atwater MA and Brown PS (1974) Numerical computations of the latitudinal variations of solar radiation for an atmosphere of varying opacity. *Journal of Applied Meteorology* 13: 289–297.
[116] Muneer T (ed.) (1997) *Solar Radiation and Daylight Models for the Energy Efficient Design of Building*. Boston: Architectural Press.
[117] Gueymard CA and Myers D (2007) Performance assessment of routine solar radiation measurements for improved solar resource and radiative modelling. *Proceedings of the Solar 2007 Conference*. Cleveland, OH: American Solar Energy Society.
[118] Bugler JW (1977) The determination of hourly insolation on an inclined plane using a diffuse irradiance model based on hourly measured global horizontal insolation. *Solar Energy* 19(5): 477–491.
[119] Gueymard C (1984) Modelisation physique de l'irradiance diffuse recue par des surfaces inclinees en faction dc l'effet d'anisotropie des aerosols. *Colloquium Meteorologie et Energies Renouvelables*, pp. 303–314. Valbonne, France: AFME.
[120] Gueymard C (1986) Radiation on tilted planes: A physical model adaptable to any computational time-step. *Proceedings of the INTERSOL85*, pp. 2463–2467. Elmsford, NY: Pergamon Press.
[121] Gueymard C (1987) An anisotropic solar irradiance model for tilted surfaces and its comparison with selected engineering algorithms. *Solar Energy* 38(5): 367–386; Erratum. *Solar Energy* 40(2): 175, 1988.
[122] Hay JE (1979) Calculation of monthly mean solar radiation for horizontal and inclined surfaces. *Solar Energy* 23(4): 301–307.
[123] Willmott CJ (1982) On the climatic optimisation of the tilt and azimuth of flat-plate solar collectors. *Solar Energy* 28(3): 205–216.
[124] Klucher TM (1979) Evaluation of models to predict insolation on tilted surfaces. *Solar Energy* 23(2): 111–114.
[125] Muneer T (1990) Solar radiation model for Europe. *Building Services Engineering Research and Technology* 11(4): 153–163.
[126] Reindl DT, Beckmann WA, and Duffie JA (1990) Evaluation of hourly tilted surface radiation models. *Solar Energy* 45(1): 9–17.

[127] Skartveit A and Olseth JA (1986) Modelling slope irradiance at high latitudes. *Solar Energy* 36(4): 333–344.
[128] Temps RC and Coulson KL (1977) Solar radiation incident upon slopes of different orientation. *Solar Energy* 19(2): 179–184.
[129] Geuymard C (1993) Mathematically integrable parameterization of clear-sky beam and global irradiances and its use in daily irradiation applications. *Solar Energy* 50(5): 385–397.
[130] Ineichen P, Guisan O, and Perez R (1990) Ground-reflected radiation and albedo. *Solar Energy* 44(4): 207–214.
[131] Nkemdirim LC (1972) A note on the albedo of surfaces. *Journal of Applied Meteorology* 11(5): 867–874.
[132] Arnfield AJ (1975) Note on the diurnal, latitudinal and seasonal variation of the surface reflection coefficient. *Journal of Applied Meteorology* 14(8): 1603–1608.
[133] Ineichen P(1983) Quatre annees de mesures d'ensoleillement a Geneve. DSc Thesis, Universite de Geneve, Switzerland.
[134] Walraven R (1978) Calculating the position of the sun. *Solar Energy* 20(5): 393–397.
[135] Wilkinson BJ (1981) An improved FORTRAN program for the rapid calculation of the solar position. *Solar Energy* 27(1): 67–68.
[136] Muir LR (1983) Comments on 'The effect of atmospheric refraction on the solar azimuth'. *Solar Energy* 30(3): 295.
[137] Kambezidis HD and Tsangrassoulis AE (1993) Solar position and right ascension. *Solar Energy* 50(5): 415–416.
[138] Littlefair PJ (1989) Correcting for the shade ring used in diffuse daylight and radiation measurements. In: *Proceedings of the Daylight and Solar Radiation Measurement CIE Symposium*. Berlin. CIE x003-1989.
[139] Drummond AJ (1956) On the measurement of sky radiation. *Archiv fur Meteorologie, Geophysik und Bioklimatologie* A7: 413–437.
[140] Ma CCY and Iqbal M (1984) Statistical comparison of solar radiation correlations – monthly average global and diffuse radiation on horizontal surfaces. *Solar Energy* 33(2): 143–148.
[141] Stone RJ (1993) Improved statistical procedure for the evaluation of solar radiation estimation models. *Solar Energy* 51(4): 289–291.
[142] Grisollet H, Guilmet B, and Arhry R (1962) *Climatologie Methodes et Pratique*, pp. 152–153. Paris: Gauthier-Villars & Cie.
[143] Willmott CJ (1981) On the validation of models. *Physical Geography* 2: 184–194.
[144] Nagelkerke N (1991) A note on a general definition of the coefficient of determination. *Biometrika* 78(3): 691–692.
[145] Kambezidis HD, Psiloglou BE, and Gueymard C (1994) Measurements and models for total solar irradiance on inclined surface in Athens, Greece. *Solar Energy* 53(2): 177–185.
[146] Claywell R, Muneer T, and Asif M (2005) An efficient method for assessing the quality of large solar irradiance datasets. *Transactions of the ASME, Journal of Solar Energy Engineering* 127: 150–152.
[147] Hay JE (1993) Solar radiation data: Validation and quality control. *Renewable Energy* 3: 349–355.
[148] Muneer T and Fairooz F (2002) Quality control of solar radiation and sunshine measurements – lessons learnt from processing worldwide databases. *Building Services Engineering Research and Technology* 23: 151–166.
[149] Muneer T, Younes S, and Munawwar S (2007) Discourses on solar radiation modeling. *Renewable and Sustainable Energy Reviews* 11(4): 551–602.
[150] Vermote E, Tanré D, Deuzé JL, *et al* (1997) Second simulation of the satellite signal in the solar spectrum (6S). *User's manual v2*. Laboratoire d'Optique Atmospherique, University of Lille, France, pp. 1–54.
[151] Chou M-D and Suarez MJ (1999) A solar radiation parameterization (CLIRAD-SW) for atmospheric studies. *NASA Technical Memorandum 10460*, vol. 15, 48pp. Greenbelt, MD: NASA Goddard Space Flight Center.
[152] Stamnes K, Tsay SC, Wiscombe W, and Jayaweera K (1988) Numerically stable algorithm for discrete-ordinate-method radiative transfer in multiple scattering and emitting layered media. *Applied Optics* 27(15): 2502–2509.
[153] Haferman JL, Smith TF, and Krajewski WF (1996) A polarized multi-dimensional discrete-ordinates radiative transfer model for remote sensing applications. *IIHR Technical Report No. 382*. IIHR-Hydroscience & Engineering, Iowa City, Iowa.
[154] Godsalve C (1996) Simulation of ATR-2 optical data and estimates of land surface reflectance using atmospheric corrections. *IEEE Transactions on Geoscience and Remote Sensing* 34(5): 1204–1212.
[155] Anderson GP, Wang J, Hoke ML, *et al*. (1994) History of one family of atmospheric radiative transfer codes. *The European Symposium on Satellite Remote Sensing, Conference on Passive Infrared Remote Sensing of Clouds and Atmosphere II*. Rome, Italy.
[156] Key J and Schweiger AJ (1998) Tools for atmospheric radiative transfer: Streamer and FluxNet. *Computers & Geosciences* 24(5): 443–451.
[157] Fu Q and Liou K-N (1992) On the correlated k-distribution method for radiative transfer in nonhomogeneous atmospheres. *Journal of Atmospheric Science* 49: 2139–2156.
[158] Clough SA, Kneizys FX, Rothman LS, and Gallery WO (1981) Atmospheric spectral transmittance and radiance: FASCOD1B. *Proceedings of the Society of Photo-Optical Instrumentation Engineers* 277: 152–166.
[159] Mayer B and Kylling A (2005) Technical note: The libRadtran software package for radiative transfer calculations – description and examples of use. *Atmosphere Chemistry and Physics* 5(7): 1855–1877.
[160] Wang L, Jacques SL, and Zheng L(1995) MCML – Monte Carlo modeling of light transport in multi-layered tissues. *Computer Methods and Programs in Biomedicine* 47(2): 131–146.
[161] Berk A, Anderson GP, Bernstein LS, *et al*. (1999) MODTRAN4 radiative transfer modeling for atmospheric correction. *Proceedings of the Optical Spectroscopic Techniques and Instrumentation for Atmospheric and Space Research III, SPIE*, vol. 3756. Society of Photo-optical Instrumentation Engineers.
[162] Macke A (2000) Monte Carlo calculations of light scattering by large particles with multiple internal inclusions. In: Mishchenko MI, Hovenier JW, and Travis LD (eds.) *Light Scattering by Non-Spherical Particles*, vol. 10, pp. 309–322. San Diego, CA: Academic Press.
[163] Hess M, Koepke P, and Schult I (1998) Optical properties of aerosols and clouds: The software package OPAC. *Bulletin of the American Meteorological Society* 79(5): 831–844.
[164] Evans KF and Stephens GL (1991) A new polarized atmospheric radiative transfer model. *Journal of Quantitative Spectroscopy & Radiative Transfer* 46(5): 413–423.
[165] Evans KF and Stephens GL (1995) Microwave radiative transfer through clouds composed of realistically shaped ice crystals. Part II: Remote sensing of ice clouds. *Journal of Atmospheric Science* 52: 2058–2072.
[166] Dothe H, Duff JW, Gruninger JH, et al. (2004) Users' manual for SAMM-2, SHARC-4 and MODTRAN-4 MERGED, AFRL-VS-HA-TR-2004-1001.
[167] Ricchiazzi P, Yang S, Gautier C, and Sowle D (1998) SBDART: A research and teaching software tool for plane-parallel radiative transfer in the Earth's atmosphere. *Bulletin of the American Meteorological Society* 79(10): 2101–2114.
[168] Duff JW, Sundberg RL, Gruninger JH, et al. (1990) Description of the strategic high-altitude atmospheric radiation code (SHARC). *Scientific Report*, January 1989–October 1990. Burlington, MA: Spectral Sciences, Inc.
[169] Evans KF (1998) The spherical harmonic discrete ordinate method for three-dimensional atmospheric radiative transfer. *Journal of Atmospheric Science* 55(3): 429–446.
[170] Rahman H and Dedieu G (1994) SMAC: A simplified method for the atmospheric correction of satellite measurements in the solar spectrum. *International Journal of Remote Sensing* 15(1): 123–143.
[171] Bird RE (1984) A simple, solar spectral model for direct-normal and diffuse horizontal irradiance. *Solar Energy* 32(4): 461–471.
[172] Schwander H, Kaifel A, Ruggaber A, and Koepke P (2001) Spectral radiative transfer modeling with minimized computation time using neural network technique. *Applied Optics* 40(3): 331–335.
[173] Key J and Schweiger AJ (1998) Tools for atmospheric radiative transfer: Streamer and FluxNet. *Computers & Geosciences* 24(5): 443–451.
[174] Ricchiazzi P, Yang S, Gautier C, and Sowle D (1998) SBDART: A research and teaching software tool for plane-parallel radiative transfer in the earth's atmosphere. *Bulletin of the American Meteorological Society* 79(10): 2101–2114.
[175] Nann S and Riordan C (1991) Solar spectral irradiance under clear and cloudy skies: Measurements and a semi-empirical model. *Journal of Applied Meteorology* 30(4): 447–462.
[176] Bird RE, Riordan CJ, and Myers DR (1987) Investigation of a cloud-cover modification to SPCTRAL2, SERI's simple model for cloudless-sky. *Spectral Solar Irradiance, Report SERI/TR-215-3038*. Golden, CO: Solar Energy Research Institute (now NREL).

[177] Gueymard CA (2003) Interdisciplinary applications of a versatile spectral solar irradiance model: A review. *Proceedings of the International Expert Conference on Measurement and Modeling of Solar Radiation*. Edinburgh, Scotland.
[178] Gueymard C, Myers D, and Emery K (2002) Proposed reference irradiance spectra for solar energy systems testing. *Solar Energy* 73(6): 443–467.
[179] ASTM (2003) Standard tables for reference solar spectral irradiances: Direct normal and hemispherical on 37° tilted surface. *Standard G173-03, American Society for Testing and Materials*. http://www.astm.org (accessed 28 June 2011).
[180] Bird RE and Riordan C (1986) Simple solar spectral model for direct and diffuse irradiance on horizontal and tilted planes at the Earth's surface for cloudless atmospheres. *Journal of Climate and Applied Meteorology* 25: 87–97.
[181] Sellers WD (1965) *Physical Climatology*, 272p. Chicago: University of Chicago Press.
[182] Page JK, Albuisson M, and Wald L (2001) The European Solar Radiation Atlas: A valuable digital tool. *Solar Energy* 71(1): 81–83.
[183] Maxwell E, George R, and Wilcox S (1998) A climatological solar radiation model. *Proceedings of the 1998 Annual Conference*. Albuquerque, NM: ASES.
[184] Raschke E, Stuhlmann R, Palz W, and Steemers TC (1992) Solar radiation atlas of Africa, Published for the Commission of the European Communities by A. A. Balkema (Rotterdam), 1991. *Boundary-Layer Meteorology* 61(3): 315–316.
[185] Diabaté L, Blanc Ph, and Wald L (2004) Solar radiation climate in Africa. *Solar Energy* 76(3): 733–744.
[186] Sekihara K and Kano M (1957) On the distribution and variation of solar radiation in Japan. *Technical Report 551.521*, pp. 144–149. Tokyo: Japanese Meteorological Agency.
[187] Gautier C, Diak G, and Masse S (1980) A simple model to estimate the incident solar radiation at the surface from GOES satellite data. *Journal of Applied Meteorology* 19(8): 1005–1012.
[188] WMO (1983) Guide to meteorological instruments and methods of observation, 5th edn., OMM No. 8, Geneva, Switzerland: Secretariat of the World Meteorological Organization.
[189] Siren KE (1987) The shadow band correction for diffuse irradiation based on a two-component sky radiance model. *Solar Energy* 39(5): 433–438.
[190] Haeffelin M, Kato S, Smith M, *et al.* (2001) Determination of the thermal offset of the Eppley precision spectral pyranometer. *Applied Optics* 40(4): 472–484.
[191] Willson RC (1973) Active Cavity Radiometer. *Applied Optics* 12: 810–817.
[192] Kendall JM and Berdahl CM (1970) Two blackbody radiometers of high accuracy. *Applied Optics* 9(5): 1082–1091.
[193] Fröhlich C (1991) History of solar radiometry and the World Radiometric Reference. *Metrologia* 28(3): 111–115.
[194] Romero J, Fox NP, and Fröhlich C (1991) First comparison of the solar and SI radiometric scales. *Metrologia* 28(3): 125–128.
[195] Romero J, Fox NP, and Fröhlich C (1995) Improved intercomparison of the world radiometric reference and the SI scale. *Metrologia* 32(6): 523–524.
[196] ASTM (2005) *Standard Test Method for Calibration of Pyrheliometers by Comparison to Reference Pyrheliometers, Standard ASTM E816-05*. West Conshohocken, PA: American Society for Testing and Materials.
[197] Myers D, Reda I, Wilcox S, and Stoffel T (2004) Uncertainty analysis for broadband solar radiometric instrumentation calibrations and measurements: An update. In: Sayigh AAM (ed.) *World Renewable Energy Congress 2004*. Denver, CO: Elsevier.

3.03 History of Solar Energy

VG Belessiotis and E Papanicolaou, 'DEMOKRITOS' National Center for Scientific Research, Athens, Greece

© 2012 Elsevier Ltd. All rights reserved.

3.03.1	Introduction	85
3.03.1.1	The Sun	86
3.03.2	The Early Times	86
3.03.3	The Middle Ages	87
3.03.4	The Twentieth Century	91
3.03.4.1	Solar Engines – Solar Collectors	91
3.03.4.2	The Development of Flat-Plate Collectors	93
3.03.4.3	The Development of Selective Surfaces	93
3.03.4.4	Space Heating and Cooling with Solar Collectors	94
3.03.4.5	Concentrating System for Power Production	95
3.03.5	The First Scientific Solar Energy Meetings	96
3.03.6	Evacuated-Tube Collectors	96
3.03.7	Heat Pipes	97
3.03.8	Desalination with Solar Energy	97
3.03.8.1	Solar Distillation	97
3.03.8.2	Solar-Assisted Desalination	100
References		101
Further Reading		102

Glossary

Evacuated-tube solar collectors A device that transforms solar radiant energy into heat by means of suitably formed absorbing surfaces inside glass tubes and loss of heat to the surroundings is minimized by the use of vacuum.

Flat-plate solar collectors A device that transforms solar radiant energy into heat energy using flat absorbing surfaces and glass covers.

Heat pipe A very effective device for heat transmission at high rates and over considerable distances with extremely small temperature drops and with no external pumping power.

Selective surfaces Thin surface coating films designed to produce high solar radiation absorptivity.

Solar distillation Distillation of seawater or brackish water by direct use of incident solar radiation in devices called solar stills.

Solar-driven desalination Indirect use of solar energy by conversion to thermal energy or electricity, coupled with a conventional desalination technology such as reverse osmosis or conventional distillation.

Solar engines Engines, such as the Stirling engine, that are adapted to solar dish concentrators to transform solar energy into electricity.

Solar machines The first solar energy concentrating collectors used mainly to pump water.

3.03.1 Introduction

The era lost in the mists of prehistoric times has not, as expected, left behind any written manuscripts that would help us understand how the primeval mankind perceived energy. The mythology associated with that era is perhaps more illustrative, as myths, even though partially misquoted in their verbal impartment from one generation to the other until eventually established in the writings, were those that maintained the core of the chronicle.

Natural forces, such as the sun's heat and the power of wind and water streams, which we today refer to them as 'renewable energy sources', were known since the advent of mankind, either as useful or as destructive forces. The unsuspecting and frightened human race, not having any reasonable explanation for these big forces, regarded them as Gods. Before the availability of any written evidence whatsoever, different myths described how energy came into the hands of humans, such as the myth of Prometheus, which refers to the acquisition of fire, that is, of energy, some million years ago. The myth of Prometheus recounts how he has stolen fire from the Gods and carried it from the skies to Earth in order to contribute to the progress of early mankind.

For this act, he was punished by Gods with an inconceivable harshness. Maybe this was a signal myth, since fire, that is, energy, has ever since been associated by Gods with guilt or actually with the inappropriateness of its use by the immature human race. Humans ought to not yet become recipients of this divine stuff. This was the same as the dismissal of man from the Garden of Eden, the lost heaven, and something, which in our days manifests itself in the possession of the catastrophic nuclear energy.

From a practical viewpoint and rationally speaking, it can be claimed that the 'fire of Prometheus', that is, energy, has been known from the dawn of mankind, when humans realized the importance of fire, as this was accidentally lit by thunders. At first, they tended to preserve this valuable fire, until later they discovered the means of generating it themselves by friction. Many more millennia went by during which humans, being unable to explain by reason the elements of nature that impressed them, deified them instead. Later on, during antiquity, the big minds of the time, being able to explain the natural phenomena by reason, brought the Gods down from their pedestal, leaving only the colorful narration of the myths behind.

Solar energy is the oldest natural form of energy utilized by the human race from time immemorial. It was mainly used for drying of various materials, primarily food, as well as for their preservation. The first such documented application was discovered in Southern France, dated at 8000 BC, where during excavations, a bench which was used to dry agricultural products was found. At later times, during the period 5000–2000 BC, several sites were discovered, primarily in the Middle East, in which drying of different materials, such as animal skin and plates of clay intended for the construction of writing boards, took place; in those sites, it was discovered that Assyrians, for instance, used to dry writing boards made of clay initially in the sun, subsequently completing the process in the shade, by means of natural ventilation [1].

As of today, no device for heating water by means of solar energy has either been found or known. What is known, however, is that the palace of the Pharaoh was being heated by a system utilizing solar energy and hot air.

3.03.1.1 The Sun

The sun and its power has been and still is the most well-known form of energy, a life-creating force. The sun was the most beloved one among all Gods for the Greeks, the Egyptians, the Indians, the indigenous inhabitants of the American Continent, and many other peoples and religions.

The Greeks deified the sun (*Helios*), believing that he emerged from the river Ocean every morning on his float, traveled through the sky dome across the land of the Hyperboreans, and sank again into the river Ocean at sunset. They also regarded Apollo as the Sun God.

In India, it was *Surya*, the god of the sun (**Figure 1(a)**), the center of the world, and the source of heat, light, and life [5]. In the ancient manuscript of 'Brhad-Devata', it is cited [3]

> Of what is and has been and is to be, and what moves or remains still, the Sun alone is the source and the end
>
> भवद्भूतस्य भव्यस्य जङ्गमस्थावरस्य च ।
> अस्येके सर्यमेवैकं प्रभवं प्रलयं विदुः ॥

Almost all great civilizations that developed in the ancient times adored the sun as a deity.

The Incas in South America dedicated an entire city to the sun (*Inti*), not only as the source of light and life but also as the center of power and justice. The Toltec in their city of Teotihuacan dedicated the sun pyramid to the sun. In Egypt, it was Amun-Ra and Aten, the creator of the world adored during the era of Pharaoh Akhenaton (**Figure 1(b)**). During the historic era, sun descended from his pedestal and was since recognized as a natural celestial body.

3.03.2 The Early Times

The oldest practical application of solar energy known to us is the burning of the Roman fleet, in the bay of Syracuse, attributed to Archimedes, the Greek mathematician and philosopher (287–212 BC), who used flat reflecting surfaces to focus solar rays onto the Roman ships which were made of wood. This feat remained a subject of controversy and argument among scientists for centuries, which was later criticized as a myth because no technology existed at that time for manufacturing concave mirrors. In fact, Archimedes used well-polished brass military shields. Regardless of all relevant theories, it is well known that Archimedes was an expert in optics and is the author of the book called *On Mirrors or Constructing Spheres* (Περί κατόπτρων ή Σφαιροποιία) which was, unfortunately, not saved for posterity. The first traced reference on this event is given by Loukianos (AD 120–190). During the Byzantine time (AD 514), Proclus, the Bishop of Constantinople, repeated this feat by burning the enemy's fleet besieging Constantinople. Later on, once again during the Byzantine times, Ioannis Tzetsis (AD 1100–80), a Byzantine writer describes in his book *Chiliades*, Vol. 3, the burning of the Roman ships by Archimedes [2, 6]. Vitelion, a thirteenth-century Polish mathematician, describes Archimedes' experiment in detail in his book *Optics* [6]:

> The burning glass of Archimedes composed of 24 mirrors, which conveyed the rays of the sun into a common focus and produced an extra degree of heat

Later on, the experiment was repeated once again by the French naturalist and academician G. L. L. Buffon (1707–88) who experimented on solar energy applications and proved that Archimedes' experiment was realizable.

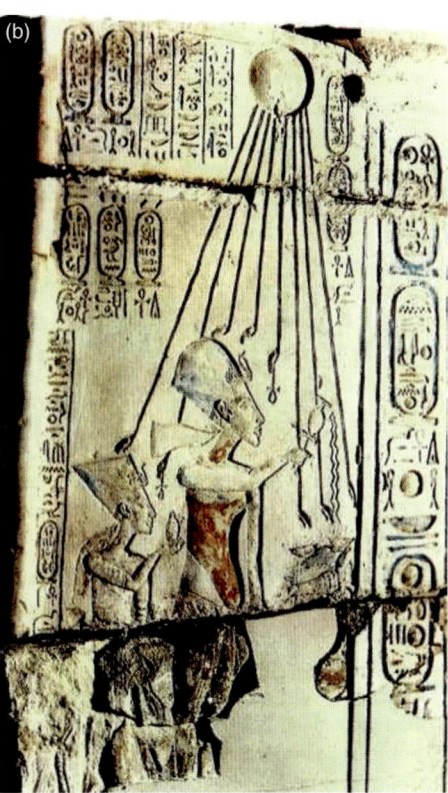

Figure 1 (a) Surya, the Sun God, surrounded by the Gods and Goddesses of the Indian pantheon. The figure was found in Konarak, India. It was built as a chariot on great wheels, which was drawn by rows of horses representing the seven steeds of the Sun in his journey across the heavens (National Museum, New Delhi, India [2]). (b) Pharaoh Akhenaton and his wife worshipping Aton, the Sun God (National Museum, Cairo, Egypt [5]).

It should be mentioned here that one of the most important descriptions on the sun's activities is that of the well-known Greek philosopher and scientist Aristotle (384–322 BC) who conceived the hydrologic water cycle [6, 7]:

> Now the Sun moving, as it does, sets up processes of change and becoming and decay and by its agency the finest and sweetest water is every day carried out and is dissolved into vapor and rises to the upper region, where it is condensed again by the cold and so returns to the earth. This, as we have said before, is the regular course of nature

As of today, no better explanation has been traced about the water hydrological cycle. Another evidence of solar heat utilization is the orientation of the houses. During antiquity, house builders oriented the house facades toward the south in order to best exploit the heat from sun rays (or 'warmth'). Socrates (469–399 BC), the Greek philosopher, describes that the optimum use of natural solar radiation is obtained by orienting the main rooms of a building southward.

China has also had its own share in solar energy applications. As reported by Kemper [8], during the Han Dynasty (220–201 BC), the Chinese used concave mirrors made of brass–tin alloy. The mirrors were used to light torches from the 'solar fire' for religious sacrificial rituals. All these applications are described in the book by Kircher (1671), where the different traces of the sun rays are outlined (**Figure 2**).

Kemper [8] also reports that Ibn Al-Haitan (about AD 1000), an Egyptian, described the burning of various materials from a distance by focusing the sun's rays on their surface, using mirrors.

3.03.3 The Middle Ages

For many centuries following these activities, no other important theoretical or practical works on the use of solar energy have been traced. Some minor experimental applications during the medieval times comprise solar distillation of plant extracts for medical purposes and production by solar distillation of various aromatic oils, wine, etc. [9].

During the early Renaissance, many studies and minor applications of solar energy were pursued, which were mainly dedicated to reflecting surfaces of concentrating collectors for steam production and/or high-temperature solar furnaces. Due to the rather cheap availability of fossil fuels at the dawn of the Industrial Revolution, solar energy found no practical applications, and the relevant experiments aimed rather at demonstrating the feasibility of solar energy applications by running pumps for water transportation. Leonardo da Vinci (1452–1519) is another famous scientist who experimented with solar energy. He performed

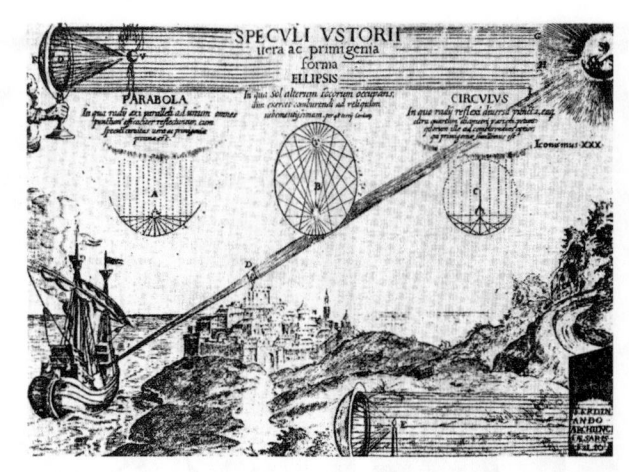

Figure 2 The paths of solar rays striking burning mirrors and reflectors, as shown in the book by Kircher, 1671 [8].

a series of experiments with a large parabolic mirror producing thermal energy for a dyeing industry. He left behind a notebook full of sketches illustrating his ideas, which included mirrors that were used in solar energy applications.

In 1615, in Heidelberg, Germany, the first solar pump was demonstrated by the French scientist, Salomon de Caux. Solar rays passing through the lenses heated up the water contained in a half-empty copper box. The air above the water surface was heated and its expansion was used to pump water from the lower to the upper level to feed a fountain (**Figure 3**). The solar works of de Caux are discussed by Ackerman, who also describes the achievements in the solar energy field by other inventors [10].

During that period, many researchers performed experiments on the potential applications of solar energy. Kircher was one such scientist, who, in 1671, published a book describing the various solar ray paths as illustrated in **Figure 2**. He also assembled various lenses for concentrating solar rays and constructed and used a solar radiation reflecting system consisting of five mirrors. In general, however, his inventions found no practical applications [8].

A scientist who was a contemporary of Kircher, von Tischirnhaus, constructed (c. 1781) various types of large concave lenses up to 1 m in diameter. He used these lenses to melt various materials by concentrating solar radiation on them. **Figure 4** presents a Tischirnhaus lens system, which is now exhibited at the Deutsche Museum in Munich, Germany [8].

In France, the well-known naturalist G. L. L. Buffon (1707–88) constructed and experimented with various solar devices such as polished metallic mirrors and/or lenses during the period 1747–48. He called his mirrors 'hot mirrors burning at long distance' [8]. Among his devices was a system consisting of 192 concave metallic mirrors having dimensions of $0.325 \times 0.325 \, \text{m}^2$. **Figure 5** presents some of Buffon's lenses and mirrors [8].

In Russia, Mikhail Vasilevich Lomonosov (1711–65) was the first to discuss the technological and economic difficulties that arise during the production of 'burning glasses' [11].

In 1774, Lavoisier (1743–94), the famous chemist and founder of modern chemistry, who discovered the role of oxygen in burning, constructed lenses to concentrate solar radiation. The lens system was assembled on a carriage and was used as a solar

Figure 3 The solar engine of Salomon de Caux (copper-plate engraving, 1615 (Frankfurt, Germany), Tl.1 Tafel 22 – Deutsches Museum Muenchen) [8].

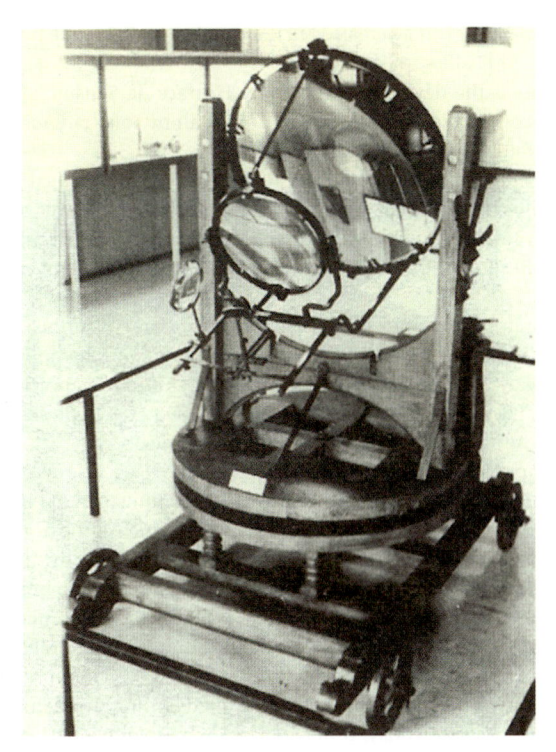

Figure 4 The burning lenses of Von Tschirnhause [8].

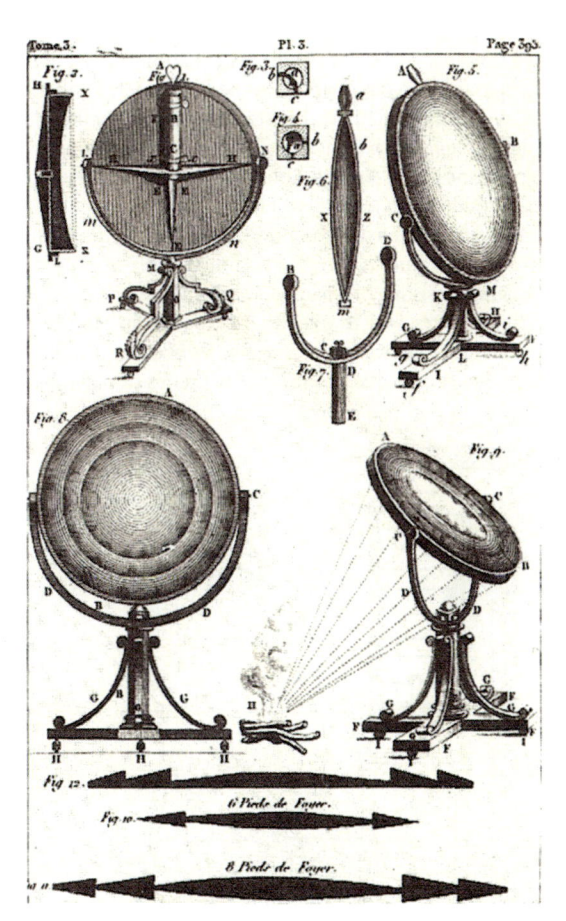

Figure 5 The hot mirrors of G.L.L. Buffon [8].

furnace. The lenses produced high temperatures and were used in melting and studying the properties of pure platinum. He attained temperatures of up to 1780 °C (3236 °F) [12].

An early ancestor of solar collectors is the device constructed by Horrace de Sausure. He called his invention a 'hot box'. It consisted of a wooden box lined with cork inside. Its purpose was to heat air by solar radiation and to measure the heat of incident solar radiation. He attained air temperatures of up to 160 °C.

In terms of technical evolution, the applications of solar energy essentially began during the Industrial Revolution and continued even after that. This period is essentially related to the nineteenth century, when the power of horses was replaced by the power of steam and engines. The steam engine, first developed by Thomas Newcomen (1663–1729), freed thousands of men and horses from hard physical labor. A wider application of the steam engine resulted with the improvements made to Newcomer's engine by James Watt (1736–1819).

The Industrial Revolution gave the opportunity to new scientists to experiment further on solar energy, as in the case of the French naturalist Becquerel (1820–91), who experimented with various lenses and a wooden box enclosed by a glass cover. The interior side of the box was painted black. This device may be considered as another ancestor of solar collectors. About the same period in Cape Town, South Africa, an engineer named J. F. W. Herschel (1792–1871) presented in 1837 a similar box constructed from mahogany. It was either used to heat air up to 120 °C or as a cooking device [8].

One of the most important developments of the new era, which became of great interest in recent years in conjunction with point-focusing concentrators, is the Stirling cycle. Robert Stirling, a Scottish minister and engineer, invented a solar steam engine patented in 1816 in Edinburgh. **Figure 6** presents the original Stirling engine, which at the beginning was used to pump water and to drive various devices, and printing machines among others, before being displaced by steam engines [13]. Around 1870, the Swedish engineer John Ericsson modified the Stirling engine and drove the Stirling cycle by using concentrated solar energy.

Today, the Ericsson engine is exhibited at the Philadelphia Museum. **Figure 7(a)** presents the operating principle of the Stirling cycle. The engine was commercialized in 1930 by the Philips Research Laboratories in Eindhoven, The Netherlands. Later, in 1960, Utz and Braun used a quartz transparent cover inside the engine to absorb solar radiation, as presented in **Figure 7(b)** [14]. Due to internal friction, the engine operation was problematic. In 1981, The United Stirling, Sweden, modified the engine again, in order to adapt it to tracking dish concentrating collectors. Today, it may be driven by solar energy, gas, or both.

The French mathematician Auguste Mouchot (1821–1911) is undoubtedly a pioneer of solar technology. He was the first to publish a book on solar energy in 1878, *La chaleur solaire et ses applications industrielles*, and he also presented many papers on the utilization of solar energy. He was also the first to express the possibility of fuel reserve depletion in the future, in an attempt thus to promote solar energy applications. In 1861, he presented his first solar steam engine, which he considered as not viable from the economic point of view, considering the very low coal prices. With his collaborator A. Pifre, he constructed and experimented on truncated conical mirrors installed in France and Algeria. In 1878, at the Paris International Exhibition, they presented a truncated parabolic mirror (**Figure 8 (a)**) of a total surface area of 20 m². The steam produced by the solar radiation drove a printing machine, used during the exhibition to print the *Sunshine Journal* in French [4]. In 1980, the above-mentioned book by Mouchot was reprinted by the Coopération Méditerrannéenne pour l' Énergie Solaire – Mediterranean Co-operation for Solar Energy (COMPLES) with a preface by Marcel Perrot [15, 16], President of COMPLES (**Figure 8(b)**).

John Ericsson (1803–89), who has already been referenced above in relation to the Stirling engine, constructed a steam engine driven directly by solar energy. He used water as the working fluid and claimed an efficiency of 72.5%. He also constructed various solar engines, for example, a system 3.3 m in length, consisting of a parabolic collector having 300 silver-coated mirrors [17]. He was the first to use nontarnishing, silver-coated reflecting surfaces, which were less expensive than Mouchot's metallic, silver-coated surfaces [18].

Around 1880, W. Calver applied for the first American patents on solar heaters (1882, 1883a, 1883b, 1884). During the same period, the first German patent on a solar device appeared, followed by a series of patents on domestic solar water heaters [3].

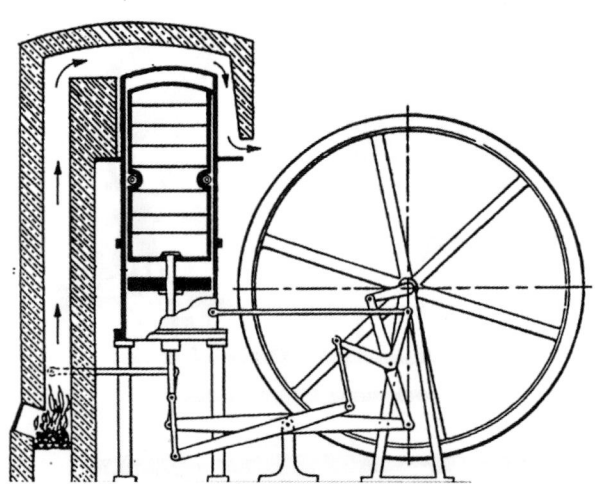

Figure 6 The original Stirling engine as presented in the patent application by Robert Stirling [13].

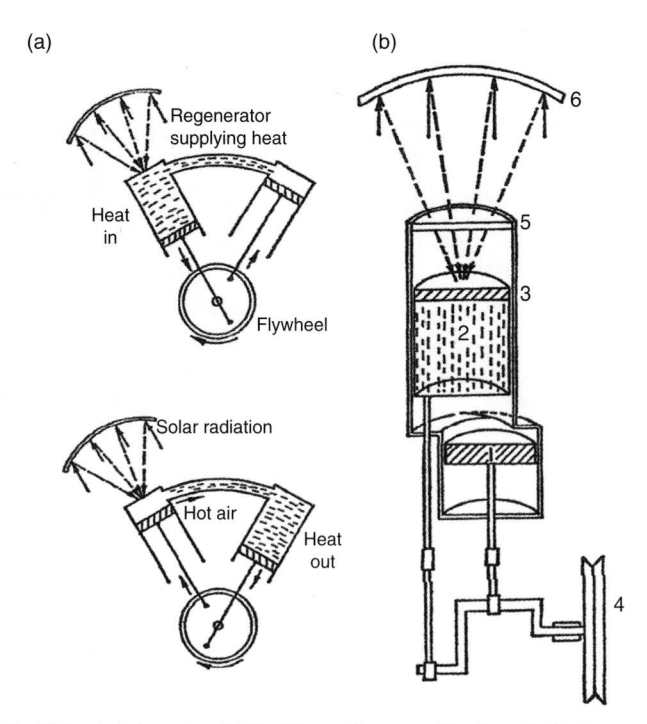

Figure 7 (a) Working principle of the Stirling hot air engine. (b) The Utz and Braun modification with the top cover made of transparent quartz [14]. 1, Piston moving in cylinder; 2, Displacer and generator; 3, Black porous absorber; 4, Flywheel with shaft and cams; 5, Transparent quartz window; 6, Focused solar radiation.

Figure 8 (a) The reflecting mirror presented at the International Exhibition of Paris, 1878, by Auguste Mouchot and his collaborator A. Pifre [19]. (b) The cover of Auguste Mouchot's book, reprinted in 1980 [15].

The first flat-plate collector, with a 20 m^2 surface area, was constructed by C. L. A. Tellier in France. A water–ammonia mixture was used as the working fluid. As the temperature increased, ammonia vapor was produced to drive a vertically oriented machine. Tellier is also regarded as the inventor of the refrigeration principles and the first engineer to install a domestic hot-water system [18].

It should be noted that scientists in Russia were studying utilization of solar energy as well. In 1890, V. A. Tsesarskii concentrated solar radiation for melting metals and other materials. He achieved a temperature of 3500 °C. Another Russian scientist, V. A. Mikhelson (1711–65), the founder of Russian sciences, organized the first scientific measurements of solar radiation in the Moscow area [11].

3.03.4 The Twentieth Century

3.03.4.1 Solar Engines – Solar Collectors

Toward the end of the nineteenth century, solar technology was carried over, primarily through the hands of French scientists, from Europe to engineers in the United States, where there was intense activity until 1913 in constructing and installing solar engines, with water pumping being the main application.

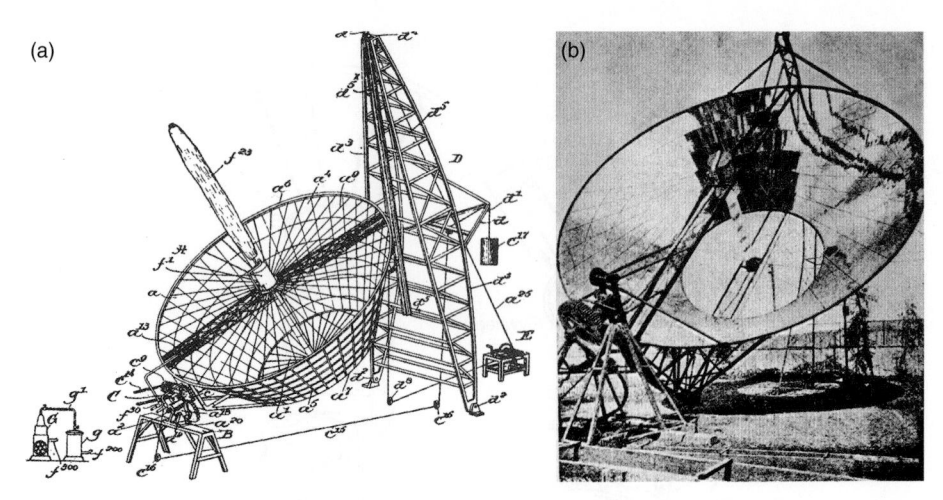

Figure 9 (a) Sketch of Enea's first conical solar concentrating collector (Smithsonian Institute [23]). (b) The solar engine erected at the Ostrich Farm, Pasadena, in 1901 (from the annual report of Smithsonian Institute, 1915 [17]).

Among the most prominent pioneers in the United States, was C. G. Abbot (1872–1973), the head of the Smithsonian Institute, Washington, DC. In 1897, he reported on a 'heat box' consisting of two concentric wooden boxes and a black metallic sheet covered by four glass sheets [20]. He promoted solar energy through a series of publications and patents (1931, 1934, 1938, 1941, 1949, etc.) [21]. During the International Power Conference in Washington, DC, and later in Florida, he exhibited a parabolic trough claiming 60% efficiency [22]. In 1972, when he was already 100 years old, he was granted another patent on 'the conversion of useful solar energy to electricity'. The following year, after his death, the International Solar Energy Society (ISES), in order to honor his work, established the 'Abbot Award'. Many solar energy pioneers, such as Maria Telkes, W. H. Klein, J. A. Duffie, W. Beckman, and E. Howe, etc., have received the Abbot award.

At the beginning of the twentieth century, in 1901, Aubrey G. Eneas installed the first large truncating conical solar concentrating system in Pasadena, California (**Figure 9(a)**). The collector's surface was 70 m^2. In 1903 and 1904, he erected two more truncated conical concentrators in Mesa and Willcox, Arizona, respectively. The working fluid was water [8, 18].

In 1902, the US Weather Bureau commenced systematic measurements of solar radiation in the United States. Total global radiation measurements began later, in 1909, in Washington, DC. In the beginning, the weather network comprised only a few measuring stations. In 1973, the interconnected network comprised 90 stations in various places [10]. Around 1915, Arthur Shurtleff, an American architect, constructed a device to estimate the direction of solar rays, which was applicable to all latitudes and all seasons. He called his device *Prodigal Sun*. Today, this device is exhibited at the Harvard University School of Design.

Around 1901, a group of researchers, the so-called 'Party of Boston Inventors', installed a solar truncated concentrator, the so-called 'Pasadena Sun Power Plant', in the 'Pasadena Ostrich Farm', a farm in Pasadena, California (**Figure 9(b)**). Its internal surface consisted of 1788 mirrors having a concentration ratio of 13.4. The system produced solar steam of 1.035×10^5 Pa (150 psi) and it was used to pump 5.3 m^3 min^{-1} of water to meet the requirement of the Ostrich farm [18].

Between 1902 and 1908, the American engineers H. E. Wilsie and J. Boyle, Jr., installed several solar engines, flat collectors, and tubular heaters all over the US territory. They used mixtures of water with ammonia, carbon dioxide, sulfur dioxide, etc., as working fluids. They claimed efficiencies ranging from 50% to 85%. In 1907, Frank Shuman, another American engineer, erected a horizontal water box consisting of black tubes covered by glass at Tacony, a suburb of Philadelphia, Pennsylvania. The absorbing surface of the box was 83.3 m^3. Later, in 1911, he installed, also in Tacony, a parabolic collector of 956.5 m^2 absorbing surface area with a concentration ratio of 2. **Figure 10(a)** presents a photograph of Shuman's flat-plate collector, as published in the *Engineering News Journal* in May 1909. One shallower-basin, glass-covered collector was installed in Needles, California. In this system, solar energy was transferred to a storage tank to be stored as sensible heat by the working fluid. This is the first reference on solar energy storage ever. Shallow solar ponds were used to run the engine in order to pump water [18, 23].

Frank Shuman extended his activities outside the United States as well. In 1913, in collaboration with C. V. Boys, another American engineer, he constructed and installed in Maadi, Egypt, an improved system of parabolic troughs to pump water from the river Nile (**Figure 10(b)**). The surface area of the parabolic trough was covered by reflecting mirrors. Steam was used as the working fluid. For a total collecting surface area of 1232.69 m^2 (13 369 ft^2) with a concentration ratio of 4.5, the power produced was 37.5 kW (50 hp). Although the system operated successfully, no further similar systems were installed. The reasons were the outbreak of World War I and the death of Frank Shuman in 1916. Meanwhile, the discovery of large oil reserves delayed solar energy activities, as fuel prices became very low. The story is described in detail by Butti and Perlin [24].

In general, most of the early solar engines of that time did not find wider application and were characterized as 'curiosities', being a way ahead of their time.

For a long time period thereafter, and up until the end of World War II, no references to large-scale solar energy applications are available. Nevertheless, research and development continued. Many patents were granted during that time, in particular, on solar

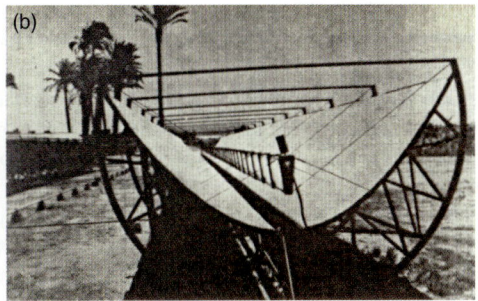

Figure 10 (a) The Shuman's flat-plate collector sun power system for pumping water erected at Tacony (*The Engineering News*, May 1909). (b) The Shuman–Boys solar power plant erected at Maadi, Egypt (Smithsonian Institute Report, 1915 [18]).

heaters and solar collectors, first to American and then to Japanese inventors. At the same time, a large number of solar heaters were installed all over the world [3].

3.03.4.2 The Development of Flat-Plate Collectors

The first collectors were originally made of iron tubes, which were later (around 1914) replaced by copper tubes. Relevant scientific publications have kept on appearing in various countries, while Japan and Israel developed and applied the first solar water heater installations on a massive scale; these still remain the most economical solar devices. In the 1920s, a large number of solar water heaters were installed in the United States and in many other countries as well.

Flat-plate collectors have an improved technology over that of the first water heaters. In the early years, all collectors and water heaters were constructed and operated based on empirical practice. Their commercialization started in 1930, although still based on technical experience. A detailed description of the early collector production is presented in Reference [24]. Morse [25] presents a short description of the Australian activities of the Commonwealth Scientific and Industrial Research Organization (CSIRO) and the industrialization of solar heaters, the commercialization of which started in 1957.

The first theoretical description of the flat-plate collector characteristics was briefly presented in 1936 by Fred Brooks. Excerpts of his work are presented in *SunWorld* [26]. However, a detailed mathematical analysis of the collected solar radiation in terms of transmissivity and absorptivity is presented in the works of Hottel and Woertz [27].

Although the analysis of the above authors was almost complete, after World War II, a series of similar studies appeared, as collectors were used in large-scale applications for domestic hot water and space heating. The use of plastic transparent covers and selective absorbing coatings started later, around 1960.

Reference should also be made here to 'solar ponds', which are considered as simple solar collectors. Kalecsinsky, in 1902, was the first to describe solar ponds after studying the natural heated lakes in Transylvania. The salinity at the bottom of the lake was 26‰. In Israel, in 1948, salt gradient ponds were proposed by Rudolf Bloch, who suggested that an effective solar collector could be created by suppressing convection in a stratified salt solution, that is, by creating a stable density gradient pond. He conceived this idea for practical use of solar ponds upon studying the works of Kalecsinsky on the natural lakes in Transylvania. Research in solar ponds initially was performed in Israel, and the first solar pond was proposed and constructed by Tabor [28] and Tabor and Matz [29]. Solar ponds were also been studied in Chile, the USSR, India, and the United States [10].

Shallow solar ponds were developed in the early 1900s by H. E. Wilsie and J. Boyle, Jr., the American engineers, mentioned previously. They used a shallow wooden basin coated with asphalt and divided by strips into a number of troughs. Frank Shuman also designed a shallow pond in order to run his solar steam engine [10].

3.03.4.3 The Development of Selective Surfaces

Selective surfaces constitute the most important part of flat-plate solar collectors, as they determine the efficiency of the absorption of solar radiation. Their application started by the end of the first 50 years of the twentieth century. Selective surfaces were initially studied by Ferry [30], without proceeding though to any practical application, and later on by Hottel and Woertz [27], who have simply noted their potential use in solar collectors [14]. H. Tabor commenced on the applications of selective surfaces around 1957. By 1948, Harris and his collaborators observed that the surfaces of smoked gold dust exhibit high transmission of infrared radiation and low transmission of visible light. Later on, Tabor [31] and, around the same time, Gier and Dunkle [32], described the potential of using these specialized surfaces in collectors. Furthermore, Tabor proceeded to the development and practical application of the first selective surfaces.

It should be noted that in the first scientific analysis of the selective flat-plate solar collectors, Hottel and Woertz [27] reported that one of their equations was not accurate due to the low emissivity of the absorption surface they used. They remarked that "it would be quite interesting if it was feasible to trace a surface with similar, ideal behavior as regards the absorptivity of the solar light as well." Later on, during the Symposium of Space Solar Heating at the University of Wisconsin (1953), Drake claimed that "There does not exist any known surface with the above mentioned properties," as reported by Tabor [33, 34].

Tabor observed that there is an increase in the efficiency of solar collectors with the application of selective surfaces, and presented the general calculation principles. The first selective surfaces, which the researcher prepared, included the superposition of black sulfide nickel and zinc into a galvanized iron surface. The researcher coated, through electroplating, metallic surfaces with black sulfide or black chrome. This selective surface presented absorptivity $\alpha = 0.92$ and emissivity $\varepsilon = 0.1$. Detailed calculations and the literature on the issue are provided by Tabor *et al.* [35].

Around roughly the same period, Hottel and Unger [36] developed a method for the deposition of thin particles of copper oxide onto an aluminum foil. Selective surface deposition of cobalt oxide onto foils of polished nickel, which presented stability in temperatures up to 621 °C, was studied by Gillette [37]. Black chrome, a synthetic material constituted by metallic chrome and dielectric chromium oxide, is considered the best and most widely used material. The first publication on the use of black chrome in solar energy is the one by McDonald [38].

Selective surfaces do not concern flat-plate collectors only, but concentrating systems as well. Descriptions of conical concentrating collectors, by the nineteenth and early twentieth centuries, do not include any analysis of their reflection and absorption properties for the improvement of their performance.

In the case of mirrors, and with regard to the use of selective surfaces, interest lies in the deposition, under vacuum, of glass foils with silver or gold, with the proper specification of the deposition thickness being such that a reflectivity of ~95% at a temperature of 300 °C is achieved for the final product. Tabor [33, 34] provides an analysis and the respective results for both plate and cylindrical receivers.

3.03.4.4 Space Heating and Cooling with Solar Collectors

The passive heating of houses has been a practice implemented ever since the ancient times, whereby the main rooms were oriented toward the south for achieving natural heating, while for cooling purposes, internal courtyards were built with peristyles for the circulation of air.

Following the development of flat-plate collectors in the twentieth century, the first research efforts on the heating and cooling of small dwellings were set off initially on an experimental basis. The development of selective surfaces led to the improvement of the performance of solar collectors and to their rapidly increasing application.

The first house to be heated by solar energy was built in 1939. The installation was granted to MIT by G. L. Cabot Funds for research purposes (**Figure 11(a)**). It was a simple dwelling, but it was not possible to investigate it in detail, due to the outbreak of World War II. Until 1948, a total of three dwellings were installed and investigated at MIT (**Figure 11(b)**). By 1953, the knowledge gained by the research performed in these three dwellings was discussed by a group of MIT researchers, leading to a study for the space heating of a two-floor house in the area of Boston.

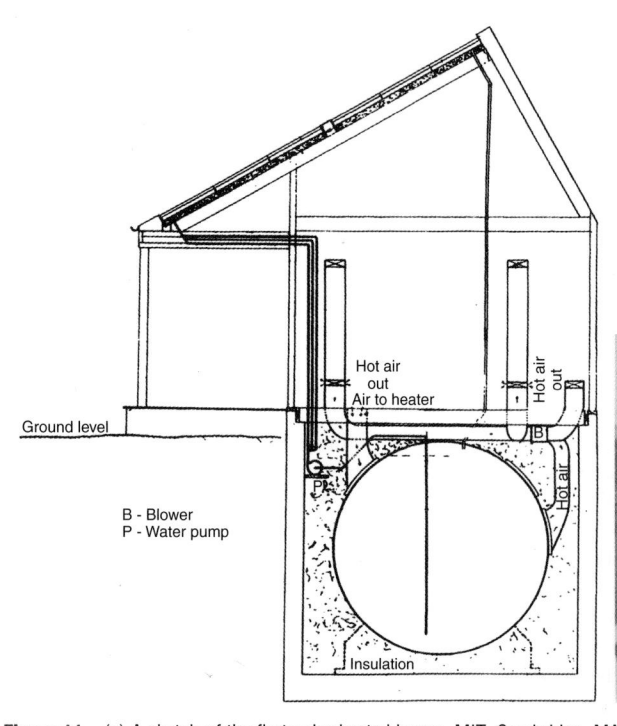

Figure 11 (a) A sketch of the first solar-heated house, MIT, Cambridge, MA, 1939 [39]. (b) A photograph of the third solar-heated house at MIT [11].

The work performed at MIT in 1950, in the field of space heating, under the guidance of Prof. Hottel [39], is considered as pioneering. By the same year, the first conference on solar space heating was held in Cambridge, Massachusetts, an event which contributed to the rapid dissemination of this area of research within the solar energy field. Austin Whillier [40], a South African, made a detailed presentation on the issue of designing space heating applications to the respective panel during the First World Congress in Tucson, Arizona, in 1955. Relevant works on three other residences were also presented to the same panel. The solar house by G. O. G. Löf [41] in Denver, Colorado, is of great interest, due to the fact that besides being the largest one, it was also the first application of air collectors on such a scale. In fact, the first application at this scale is the one developed in Boulder, Colorado, for the heating of a bungalow. The collectors, with a surface area of $43.10\,m^2$ (463 sqft), were installed on the roof, at an inclination of $27°$, and the heat storage system, which consisted of gravel, was installed in the basement of the dwelling, as shown in **Figure 11(a)** [39]. In the panel, the cases of two more residences heated by the sun were discussed by Telkes [42] and Bliss, Jr. [43]. The thermal needs of the dwelling described by Bliss, Jr., were covered 100% by solar energy, without the use of any backup heat. During the same period, the case of two dwellings in Tokyo [44] and of a laboratory in Nagoya may also be cited here [45]. The dwellings in Tokyo included heating, cooling, and a heat pump. One of the dwellings included hot water as well. The collectors were placed on a nearly horizontal roof. A description of the first dwellings utilizing solar energy for space heating is provided by Holtz [46].

Among the first references to space heating through the use of flat-plate solar collectors are those in the publication of Löf [47], who reviewed the contributions at the Conference of the United Nations on *New Energy Sources* in Rome, in 1961. In this work, he presented and critically evaluated nine totally different residences that were built in latitudes $35-42°$. All the residences included heat storage and backup systems, the contribution of which was in the range 5–75%.

Even though solar energy is generally considered as a heating source, in the so-called 'sunny zones' with high levels of solar radiation, the surroundings are hot, thus it is cooling rather than heating that is mainly required. For this reason, the studies so far performed on space heating were extended to solar cooling also, particularly, solar air-conditioning.

The first studies on solar cooling were performed in the Soviet Union in Tashkent, Uzbekistan, and are related to the production of ice and cooling for the conservation of food [48]. The solar cooling system used a rather large concentrating parabolic mirror, equipped with a boiler at the focal point. The production was 250 kg of ice on a daily basis.

Around 1880, François Carré developed the first cooling device, albeit a nonsolar one, using a water–ammonia mixture. In the early twentieth century, various engineers worked and experimented further on Carré's cooling machine and their work resulted in the development of a cooling machine which was later commercially introduced as the absorption cooling machine by Electrolux [49]. The use of lithium bromide–water was implemented later on, around 1940, as a result of studies performed by refrigeration equipment industries.

The use of solar energy for air-conditioning was initially proposed by Prof. Altenkirch (1936). In the 1930s, two solar residences had apparently been built in Germany, which were destroyed during World War II, and there are no written references existing on their operation. This was initially reported by Danniers, a collaborator of Prof. Altenkirch, and described in detail by him, later on in 1959. The same design was adopted for a dwelling at the Negev Institute for Arid Zone Research in Beersheba, Israel. The results from the operation of this residence were, however, not encouraging [50, 51].

3.03.4.5 Concentrating System for Power Production

The first concentrating mirrors, which rotated about two axes, were manufactured in Germany, sometime in the early 1920s, by W. Maier, in Aachen, and A. Remshardts, in Stuttgart [23]. In Germany, the first heliostat was also presented, *c.*1912, as shown in **Figure 12** [52].

Figure 12 The first known heliostat presented in 1912 [52].

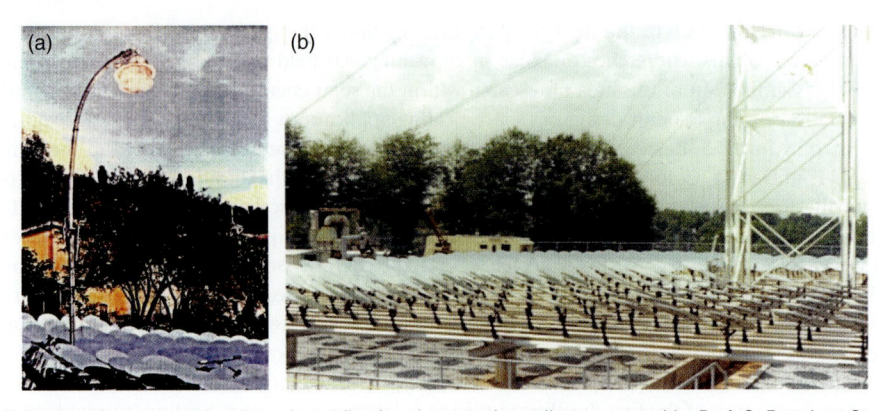

Figure 13 (a) The first solar-driven power plant (experimental) using concentrating collectors erected by Prof. G. Francia at St. Illario. (b) The solar power plant at Georgia Tech. (private photograph).

The oil crisis of 1973 accelerated the industrial production of concentrating collectors, initially of parabolic troughs, which were combined with the Rankine cycle for power production. Through the evolution of the technology, the first parabolic dishes including the use of Stirling engines came along. The Dish–Stirling technology was developed through the collaboration between two teams, one American and the other German, and the first system was installed in 1977 at the Edwards Air Force Base, California.

The system of central receivers, or the tower system, was proposed by Vicky Baum of Phisico Technological Institute, Turkmenian Academy of Science, Ashkabad, Turkmen SSR, in 1957. Baum had already worked on a tower system, where the mirrors were placed in coaches rotating around the solar energy collection tower, and he also proposed the first relevant theoretical equations [53].

The tower system was investigated on an actual central-receiver, pilot-plant installation by Prof. Francia [54] of the University of Genoa in 1965 (**Figure 13**(**a**)). The system was installed in St. Ilario-Nervi, near Genoa. It consisted of 270 cyclic heliostats of 1.1 m diameter. The steam reached a temperature of 500 °C and 15 MPa pressure. The cyclic reflectors rotated and concentrated the radiation in a boiler installed 10 m above the ground level. It had a power of 50 kW. In 1977, a pilot installation of similar type came into operation, through the supervision of Prof. Francia, at Georgia Tech., Atlanta, Georgia, USA. The installation consisted of 559 octagonal-shaped mirrors. Its power was 400 kW and the temperature in the boiler was ~1900 °C (**Figure 13**(**b**)).

Following these experimental installations, a series of large commercial plants, both of the parabolic-dish and of the central-receiver type, were developed in Europe, in the United States, and in the Soviet Union, starting in the year 1981, while large fields of parabolic troughs had also been installed earlier [55].

3.03.5 The First Scientific Solar Energy Meetings

Unlike the formal setup of scientific conventions that take place today, in the ancient times, and also for many centuries thereafter, discussions used to take place unofficially, in various gatherings; such events were obviously not reported or recorded.

With respect to solar energy, in particular, the first symposium took place at MIT, Cambridge, Massachusetts, in 1950, and concerned 'Space Heating with Solar Energy'. It was organized by the American Academy of Arts and Science, and 20 announcements were presented [56]. The chairman of the Congress was H. C. Hottel.

This was followed in 1953 by a meeting on 'The Utilization of Solar Energy' in which the chairman was Farington Daniels. It was a meeting of 40 invited participants at the University of Wisconsin under the auspices of the National Science Foundation. The proceedings were published by F. Daniels and J. A. Duffie in 1955. Duffie added a chapter reviewing all patents related to solar energy up to that time [56]. The next solar congress was held in New Delhi, India, in 1954, under the auspices of UNESCO, and included wind energy as well.

The large boost though was provided by the *World Symposium on Applied Solar Energy*, in 1955, in Phoenix, Arizona, and the subsequent one was held also in the same city in 1958 on the *Use of Solar Energy: The Scientific Basis*. These two conferences were organized by the Association of Applied Solar Energy, which was later renamed as the well-known International Solar Energy Society (ISES). ISES continues to organize international and local conferences on solar energy. In 2005, Böer edited the 50-year-history of ISES in two volumes [11].

3.03.6 Evacuated-Tube Collectors

The vacuum tube collectors constitute an achievement of the beginning of the twentieth century. Emmet was the first to introduce this technology, and in 1911, he was granted a patent in which the various types developed for solar energy collection are described in detail. Emmet did not, however, succeed in the practical implementation of his invention. It was not until 1965, after quite a significant time period, that E. Speyer was able to promote this kind of collectors on a practical level and proceeded to their commercialization. Two of the design suggestions of Emmet are still available on the market.

3.03.7 Heat Pipes

Heat pipes constitute a relatively recent achievement, developed by the middle of the twentieth century, even though they are considered descendants of the Perkin (1836) tube, the first thermosiphon system.

The idea of heat pipes was initially introduced by R. S. Gaugler of General Motors Corporation, Ohio, in 1942, and was published in 1944 as a patent. Nevertheless, it was not until later on, by 1960, that G. M. Grover, independent of Gaugler, pushed heat pipes into practical application. Grover's patent describes a device that is almost identical to that of Gaugler. Grover had initially worked on the development of high-temperature heat pipes, and experimented with liquid metals, under the supervision of Grover [55].

Studies continued with other liquids, such as water, acetone, ammonia, and alcohol, as well as gases, such as helium and nitrogen. Starting in 1963, an extended research program on heat pipes was initiated at the Los Alamos National Laboratory, New Mexico. Within the framework of this program, Cotter published a work on the theoretical investigation of heat pipes, thus allowing a better understanding of their operation, while research on experimental basis was widely pursued [57]. Experiments continued in Harwell, United Kingdom, and Ispra, Italy, as well as in other research centers and industries in Europe and America. By the 1970s, a wide variety of commercial heat pipes from several manufacturing companies were already available on the market.

3.03.8 Desalination with Solar Energy

3.03.8.1 Solar Distillation

Desalination with solar energy is perhaps the most ancient of all natural methods, as it takes place in nature through an open cycle known as the 'water cycle', referred to earlier. The implementation of this cycle inside a confined and enclosed space gives rise to the solar distillation process. Thus, this process may be considered as the oldest method of solar energy utilization for potable water production.

The first person to observe this phenomenon was Aristotle (348–322 BC), who provided a detailed description of it in his *Meteorologica* [6, 7]. Below is another description of water evaporation:

> Sun and air are evaporating water from the sea, which is moving up because fresh and potable water is light. When heat has left the vapors, they are transformed into freshwater, which falls on earth. Once evaporated, seawater does not become salty again. Salinity is concentrated in the remaining seawater, because salty is heavy. Evaporation velocity depends on the magnitude of the surface.
>
> Cold brackish water is not potable, but it becomes fresh after boiling and cooling. Salts contained in brackish water are precipitated during boiling.
>
> Salt water when it turns into vapor becomes sweet, and the vapor does not form salt water when it condenses again. This is known by experiment.

Aristotle also describes in a stunningly precise manner the origin of brackish and saline water, as well as of seawater, according to reports by Von Lippman [58, 59] and Briegel [60] two commentators of Aristotle's work.

From the times following antiquity, even though many references on desalination of seawater have been available, these concern mainly distillation using conventional fuels. The first known reference on solar distillation is in the book of Giovanni B. Della Porta (1535–1615), *De Distillatione, Libri IX*, issued in Rome (1608). It refers to the potential of using solar energy as the heating source for the distillation of seawater and presents a solar desalination device with the description of the process being provided in Latin [61]. This description was translated into English by the Department of Education, McGill University, as follows [62]:

> … insert these into wide earthen pots full of water so that the vapors may thicken more quickly into water. Turn all this apparatus, when it has been very carefully prepared, to the most intense heat of the sun's rays. For immediately they dissolved into vapors, and will fall drop by drop into the vases which have been placed underneath. In the evening, after sunset, remove them and fill with new herbs. Knot-grass, also commonly called 'sparrow's tongue', when it has been cut up and distilled is very good for inflammation of the eyes and other afflictions. From the ground-pine is produced a liquid which will end all convulsions if the sick man washes his limbs with it. And there are other examples too numerous to mentioned. The picture demonstrates the method of distilling.

In 1717, Jean Gautier (1679–1743), a physicist from Nantes, France, developed a distiller that was used in a French battleship for the production of freshwater. Gautier also experimented with a solar still, which he describes [61]:

> … mit de l' eau de la mer dans un cucurbite de verre assez haute et couverte de son chapiteil l' exposa aux soleil, de sorte que cet astre échaufoit la curcubite, sans fraper sur le chapiteau. Lorsque tout fut distillé, jusque à siccité, il trouva de l' eau très bonne et très saine dans le récipient, et du sel dans la cucurbite. – … place seawater into a glass vessel, enough hot and cover with his cover. Expose the vessel in the sun in such a manner that the star will heat the vessel without sticking its cover until all will be distilled up to dryness, in the receptacle there is very good and healthy water.

The first book concerning the sea and seawater was published in 1725 by Comnte de Marsilli (*Histoire Physique de la Mer – Physical History of the Sea*, Amsterdam, 1725) which included four parts. The first part concerned the sea, the second one the physical and chemical properties of seawater, while the last two parts described the sea streams and sea flora and fauna [61].

By 1739, another book was published, which included an extensive analysis of all relevant technical problems, state-of-the-art and literature reviews on desalination technology and methods of that era. The first specific reference to the production of freshwater from the sea through the use of solar energy is provided by Nicolo Ghenzi (1742) [63]:

> Pottebbe adoparsi un vaso a guisa di storts, sù cui battesse il sole, (che anche ne' climi, e ne' giorni temperati ha non picola attivitá per alzar del' vapori) di modo però, che il cappello del vaso forse difeso sall' azzione solare. Con che verrebbe ad aversi più lunga uscita di acqua dolce. – Perhaps placing a cast iron vase containing water in such a manner that the sun's rays will strike it (and during the mild days and seasons not a insignificant amount of vapor will formed) and if the spot of the vase is shaded from the sun it will result a more copious and more extended flow of fresh water.

During the period from the Middle Ages to the Renaissance, solar energy was used to fire alembics for the condensation of various dilute or alcohol solutions for the production of wine and plant infusions for medicinal use. Adam Loncier in his book *L' Histoire Naturelle – History of Nature*, published in 1551, reports on the distillation of essential oils from flowers; there was a similar report presented by Mouchot (1878) also. In the same book, Mouchot reports that Arabs used concave mirrors [61]:

> se servaient de vase de verre pour opérer certaines distillations au soleil, se servaient de miroirs concave, polis, fabriquée à Damas – they used glass vessels to functions some solar distillations with convave polished mirors which were constructed in Damscus.

From the time of Della Porta and until roughly the middle of the nineteenth century, there are no references on any worthwhile applications of desalination with solar energy.

Around 1870, the first American patent for solar distillation was awarded, based on experimental data by Wheeler and Evans [64]. The patent includes extensive reference to all issues related to solar desalination, such as the black absorber surface, the greenhouse effect, the condensation of vapor on the glass surface, and the corrosion phenomena. The inventors state that "This invention is based upon well known physical laws." It presents the first thorough and accurate description of a solar collector. By the end of 1872, the first large-scale installation of a solar distillation unit was set up in the mines of Las Salinas, Chile (**Table 1**). The stills and the whole plant were designed and constructed by the Swedish engineer Carlos Wilson. The plant used brine as the supply medium, with a concentration of $140\,g\,kg^{-1}$, which is three times more denser than normal seawater, and provided freshwater to the miners [61]. The installation was operated for 36 years, continuously [65, 66].

Following the installation in Chile, no manufacturing of other large-scale solar distillation systems was reported for a long period. The interest in solar desalination was rekindled by the mid-1920s when the French army established an award for the design of portable solar stills for its troops in the African colonies. Boutari provided the relevant information in 1930 [67]. Many publications and bibliographical data are available for this period; a detailed discussion of which is, however, beyond the scope of this review.

In 1935, Trofimov, from the Soviet Union, proposed the design of an inclined wick-type distiller, while Tekuchev in 1935, also from the Soviet Union, investigated a wetted evaporation surface with fins [68]. In general, from 1930 onward, until toward the late 1970s, there had been intense activity worldwide, concerning either just studies or studies accompanied by construction of singular or low-capacity solar desalination units for remote or small communities.

During World War II, Maria Telkes [69] developed at MIT the inflatable solar stills for use on life rafts. Approximately, 200 000 pieces saved the lives of many castaways during the war (**Figure 14**). After the war, she continued experimental research on solar stills, proposing different designs for these devices [70].

In the following years, a rush of experimental research and development of different types of solar still installations took place worldwide. Extensive studies were performed at the University of Bologna by Giorgio Nebbia; at the CSIRO, Australia, by Roger Morse; at the Technical University of Athens by Prof. Delyannis; in Bhavnagar, India, by Dr. Datta; and later in

Table 1 The characteristics of the first large solar distillation plant erected at La Salinas, Chile [71]

Number of bays	64
Bay's width	1143 m (3.75″)
Surface area	4450 m^2 (48 000 sqft)
Glass cover area	4757 m^2 (51 000 sqft)
Total land surface	7896 m^2 (85 000 sqft)
Glass panels, sloped 9°, 13 min	$0.3048 \times 0.3048\,m^2$ (2″×2″)
Brine depth	5–7.5 cm, 2.5 cm slope at 6.0 m (2″ to 3″, slope. 200″)
Freshwater productivity (peak)	$22.70\,m^3\,d^{-1}$, $5.10 \times 10^{-3}\,m^3\,m^{-2}\,d^{-1}$ (6000 gpd, 0.12 gpd sqft^{-1})

Figure 14 The life raft stills developed by M. Telkes.

New Delhi, India, by Prof. K. Tiwari; in Turkmen, the USSR, by Prof. V. Baun; in the United States by G. O. G. Löf; at the McGill University in Canada by T. Lawand; and by many others. These experimental works led to the construction of the solar distillation plants, referred to in **Table 2**. This table presents only the large-capacity installations; it should also be noted that these are no more in operation.

In 1950, the Office of Saline Water was established by the US State Department, aiming at developing and promoting desalination in general. A station was set up in Daytona Beach for the installation and study of solar stills, where various researchers from around the world worked on several still designs. Around the same time, in various parts of the world, studies concerning solar distillation plants were being carried out and installations were being developed. It is, not possible to describe, in this text, the vast amount of activities of that period. For the installations until the year 1965, detailed information is provided by the Research Report of Battelle Memorial Institute in Columbus [71].

Table 2 The larger solar distillation plants built, worldwide, up to about the 1970 decade (they are not any more in operation) [62]

Construction year	Place	Country	Cover material	Basin surface area (m^2)	Mean daily productivity (m^3)
1872	Las Salinas	Chile	Glass	4450	22.7, peak
1959	Daytona Beach	USA	Glass	227	0.53
1959	Daytona Beach	USA	Glass	246	0.58
1963	Daytona Beach	USA	Inf. plastic	215.4	0.38
1963	Muresk I	Australia	Glass	372	0.84
1964	Island of Symi	Greece	Plastic	2692	7.6
1965	Island of Aegina	Greece	Plastic	1490	4.3
1965	St. Maria do Sal	Cabo Verde	Plastic	743	2.2
1965	Bhavnagar	India	Glass	377	0.84
1966	Coober Pedy	Australia	Glass	3158	6.36
1966	Hamelin Pool	Australia		557.4	1.21
1966	Las Marinas	Spain	Glass	868.6	2.58
1967	Griffin	Australia	Glass	423.4	0.91
1967	Patmos Island	Greece	Glass	8639	26.6
1967	Petit St. Vincent	West Indies	Plastic	1709	4.92
1968	Kimolos Island	Greece	Glass	2508	7.5
1968	Mahdia	Tunisia	Glass	1300	4.2
1969		Pakistan	Glass		
1969	Natividad Island	Mexico	Glass	95	0.34
1969	Nisyros Island	Greece	Glass	2044	6.1
1969	Bakharden	Turkmenia	Glass	599.5	1.63

Figure 15 The plastic-cover-inflated still designed by Edlin and erected at the island of Symi, Greece.

In the year 1968, UN panel was formed, comprising V. A. Baum, Turkmenia Academy of Science, Turkmen, the USSR; A. A. Delyannis, Technical University of Athens, Greece; J. A. Duffie, University of Wisconsin, United States; E. D. Howe, University of California, Berkeley, United States; G. O. G. Löf, Denver, Colorado, United States; R. N. Morse, CSIRO, Melbourne, Australia; and H. Tabor, National Physical Laboratory, Jerusalem, Israel [72]. The United Nations published the report of the panel, with the intention of defining conditions under which solar distillation may provide an economic solution to the problems of freshwater shortage in small communities.

The first solar stills had a glass cover. The use of transparent plastic cover in solar stills was developed later. These materials are resistant to solar radiation, and wettable through the treatment of their internal surface, with the most commercial products encompassing Mylar and Tedlar. The first installations with inflated plastic covers were those installed in the island of Symi, Greece (**Figure 15**), by the Church World Service, and in Cabo Verde, designed by Edlin [73].

In the field of solar energy utilization, many pioneers have experimented and made the use of solar heat in a variety of fields possible. As Carl Sagan said "the remarkable assertions need remarkable proofs," and those pioneers did prove indeed that solar energy is a practical, applicable energy source.

3.03.8.2 Solar-Assisted Desalination

Solar-assisted desalination (indirect or solar-driven) presents a technique that was essentially developed after 1980, a time when concentrating collectors became commercialized. At earlier times, flat-plate collectors had been used for supplying the heat required to the solar stills. Pilot plants of this type have been developed within the framework of the project of United States–Saudi Arabian Joint Program in the field of Solar Energy called 'SOLERAS', such as those in Coober Pedy, Australia (**Figure 16(a)**), and in Kimolos Island, Greece (**Figure 16 (b)**).

In **Figure 17**, the first solar-driven desalination unit for private use, developed in 1979, is presented. The plant that was developed by Agip Gas in Rome, Italy, has a water production capability of $7\,m^3\,day^{-1}$ and makes use of evacuated-tube collectors combined with the multistage flash (MSF) desalination technology.

Figure 16 (a) The Coober Pedy, Australia, solar distillation, glass-covered, plant. (b) The distillation plant on the island of Kimolos, with Thomas Lawand of McGill University walking between the solar stills (private photographs).

Figure 17 The first MSF evacuated-tube solar-driven desalination plant developed by Agip Gas, Rome, Italy.

References

[1] Kröll K and Kast W (1989) *Trocknungstechnik (Drying Technology)*, vol. 3. Berlin: Springer Verlag.
[2] Kapur J (1984) Surya, maker of the seasons, giver of life, Lord of planets. *SunWorld* 8(1): 2–4.
[3] Delyannis A and Piperoglou E (1967) *Handbook of Saline Water Conversion Bibliography, Vol. 1, Antiquity to 1940*. Athens: Technical University of Athens.
[4] Delyannis E and Belessiotis V (2000) The history of renewable energies for water desalination. *Desalination* 128: 357–366.
[5] Anonymous (1981) *SunWorld*, Vol. 5, No. 5. Cover.
[6] Aristotle (1956) *Meteorologica*, Book II, ch. 1, 254b, 20–Book II, ch. 3, 356, 15. Cambridge, MA: Harvard University Press.
[7] Aristotle (1956) *Encyclopedia Britannica: The Works of Aristotle*, vol. 1. London: William Benton, Publisher.
[8] Kemper JP (1977) Pictorial history of solar energy use. *SunWorld* 5: 17–32.
[9] Singer C, Holmyard EJ, Hall AE, and Williams II (1969) *A History of Technology, Vol. 2, the Mediterranean Civilization and the Middle Ages (700 BC to 1500 AD)*. Oxford: Calderon Press.
[10] Dickinson WC and Cheremisinoff PN (1980) *Solar Energy Technology Book, Part A: Engineering Fundamentals*. Butterworths, New York: Marcel Dekker, Inc.
[11] Böer KW (ed.) (2005) *The Fifty Years History of ISES and Its National Sections*, vol. 1, ch. 17. Boulder, CO: American Solar Energy Society, Inc.
[12] Delyannis E (2003) Historic background of desalination and renewable energy. *Solar Energy* 75: 357–366.
[13] Goswami YD, Kreith F, and Kereider JF (1999) *Principles of Solar Engineering*. Philadelphia, PA: Taylor & Francis.
[14] Daniels F (1964) *Direct Use of the Sun's Energy*. New Haven; London: Yale University Press.
[15] Perrot M (1979) Extrait de l'allocution du Professeur Perrot, *Revue Internationale d' Heliotechnique*, 2e Semestre, 1–6.
[16] Perrot M (1978) 20 ans: Le premier Institut universitaire Français de l'énergie solaire. *Revue Internationale d' Heliotechnique*, 2e Semestre, 1–8.
[17] Jordan RC and Ibele WE (1956) Mechanical energy from solar energy. *Proceedings of the World Symposium on Applied Solar Energy*. pp. 81–101. Phoenix, AZ, USA, 1–5 November 1955. Menlo Park, CA, USA: Stanford Research Institute.
[18] Mills DR (2001) Solar thermal electricity. In: Gordon J (ed.) *Solar Energy, the State of the Art*, 706pp. Chicago, IL: ISES.
[19] Teller E (1979) *Energy from Heaven and Earth*. San Francisco: W. H. Freeman & Co.
[20] Abbot CG On Solar Heaters. US Patent 1,801,710, 21 April 1931; US Patent 1,946,184, 6 February 1934; US Patent 2m 247 830, 1 July 1941. Solar Heat Collectors. US Patent 2,460,482, 1 January 1949 (In [14], Daniels F., Direct Use of Solar Energy, 1964).
[21] Abbot CG (1943) Solar radiation as a power source. *Journal of the American Society of Naval Engineers* 55: 381–388.
[22] Abbot CG (1931) 25 Years study of solar radiation. *Smithsonian Institute Report*, pp. 175–198.
[23] Robinson N (1956) Solar machines. *Proceedings of the World Symposium on Applied Solar Energy*, pp. 43–46. Phoenix, AZ, USA, 1–5 November 1955. Menlo Park, CA: Stanford Research Institute.
[24] Butti K and Perlin J (1977) Solar heaters in California, 1890–1930. *Coevolution Quarterly Issue 15*, 4–13.
[25] Morse R (1990) The Australian solar manufacture in industry in review. *SunWorld* 14(2): 39–4.
[26] Brooks FA (1988) Solar energy and its uses for heating water in California. *SunWorld* 12(3): 88–92.
[27] Hottel HC and Woertz BB (1942) The performance of flat-plate solar heat collectors. *Mechanical Engineering* 64: 91–104.
[28] Tabor H (1963) Solar Ponds. *Solar Energy* 7(4): 189–194; Selected reprints of papers by H. Tabor, *Solar Energy Pioneer*, Balaban Publisher, ISES, 252pp, 122–131, 1999.
[29] Tabor H and Matz R (1965) Solar ponds status report. *Solar Energy* 9(4): 177–182.
[30] Ferry C (1909) Propriétés selectives des corps noirs employés comme recepteur dans la mésure de l' énergie rayonnante et consequences qui en decoulent (Selective properties of blacks used as receivers of radiant energy). *Journal de Physique* 8: 758–770.
[31] Tabor H (1958) Selective radiation. I. Wavelength discrimination. *Transactions Conference on the Use of Solar Energy* 2(1A), pp. 24–33. Tucson: The Scientific Basis University of Arizona Press.
[32] Gier JT and Dunkle RV (1958) Selective spectral characteristics as an important factor in the efficiency of solar collectors. *Transactions Conference on the Use of Solar Energy* 2(1A), pp. 41–56. Tucson: The Scientific Basis University of Arizona Press.
[33] Tabor H (1955) Solar energy collector design. *Bulletin of the Research Council of Israel* 5C(1): 5–27.
[34] Tabor H (1999) Selected reprints of papers by H. Tabor, *Solar Energy Pioneer*, Balaban Publisher, ISES, 252pp, 17–39, 1999.
[35] Tabor H, Harris J, Weinberger H, and Doron B (1964) Further studies on selective black coatings. *Proceedings of the UN Conference on New Energy Sources*, Rome, Italy, 1961, Paper E-35, S16, United Nations/Nations Unies.
[36] Hottel HC and Unger TA (1959) The properties of copper-oxide-aluminium selective black surface absorber of solar energy. *Solar Energy* 3(2): 10–15.
[37] Gillette RB (1954) Selective emissive materials for solar absorber. *Solar Energy* 4(4): 24–32.
[38] McDonald GF (1975) Spectral reflectance properties of black chrome for use as a solar selective coating. *Solar Energy* 17(2): 119–122.
[39] Hottel HC (1956) Residential uses of solar energy. *Proceedings of the World Symposium on Applied Solar Energy*, pp. 103–112. Phoenix, AZ, USA, 1–5 November 1955. Menlo Park, CA: Stanford Research Institute.
[40] Whillier A (1956) Solar house heating – A panel. *World Symposium on Applied Solar Energy*, pp. 115–130. Phoenix, AZ, USA, 1–5 November 1955. Menlo Park, CA: Stanford Research Institute.

[41] Löf GOG (1956) Cooling with solar energy. *Proceedings of the World Symposium on Applied Solar Energy*, pp. 171–189. Phoenix, AZ, USA, 1–5 November 1955. Menlo Park, CA: Stanford Research Institute.
[42] Telkes M (1956) Solar house heating – A panel. *Proceedings of the World Symposium on Applied Solar Energy*, pp. 147–150. Phoenix, AZ, USA. 1–5 November 1955. Menlo Park, CA: Stanford Research Institute.
[43] Bliss RW (1956) Panel in solar heating IV. *Proceedings of the World Symposium on Applied Solar Energy*, pp. 151–158. Phoenix, AZ, USA, 1–5 November 1955. Menlo Park, CA: Stanford Research Institute.
[44] Yanagimachi M (1964) Report on two year's and half experimental living in Yanagimachi solar house. *Proceedings of the UN Conference on New Sources of Energy*, Rome, Italy, 1961, vol. 5, *Solar Energy* II.D.2, pp. 235–247. United Nations/Nations Unies.
[45] Ishibashi T (1979) Solar heating and cooling in Japan. *SunWorld* 3(6): 154–159.
[46] Holtz MJ (1975) Design concept for solar dwellings. *Proceedings on Solar Energy Storage for Heating and Cooling of Building*, Charlottesville, VA, 16–18 April. ASHRAE, 16-158, ASHRAE No. NSF-RA-75-041.
[47] Löf GOG (1964) The use of solar energy for space heating. *Proceedings of the UN Conference on New Sources of Energy*, Rome, Italy, 1961, Paper E35-Gr-S14, United Nations/Nations Unies.
[48] Kirpichev MV and Baum VA (1954) Exploitation of sun's rays, Priroda. *Nature* 43: 45–53.
[49] Oniga T (1964) Absorption cooling unit with fixed conoidal reflector. *Proceedings of the UN Conference on New Sources of Energy*, vol. 6, pp. 31–40. Rome, Italy, 21–31 August 1961 United Nations/Nations Unies.
[50] Adler S, Levite G, and Tabor H (1964) The Altenkirch solar-cooled house. *Proceedings of the UN Conference on New Sources of Energy*, Rome, Italy, 21–31 August 1961, vol. 6, pp. 60–65.
[51] Adler S, Levite G, and Tabor H (1999) United Nations/Nations Unies; Ibid, Selected reprints of papers by H. Tabor, *Solar Energy Pioneer*, Balaban Publisher, ISES, 252pp, 75–88.
[52] Palz W (1978) *Solar Electricity: An Economic Approach to Solar Energy*. Paris-Butterworths, London-Boston: UNESCO.
[53] Baum VA, Aparasi RR, and Garf BA (1956) High power solar installations. *Teploenerghetica (Thermal Energy)* 3(6): 31–39.
[54] Francia G (1968) Pilot plants of solar steam generating stations. *Solar Energy* 12: 51–59.
[55] Skinrood A (1982) Recent developments in central receivers. *SunWorld* 6(4): 98–105.
[56] The association for applied solar energy (AASE) (1959) In: Burda EJ (ed.) *Applied Solar Energy Research: A Directory of World Activity and Bibliography of Significant Literature*, 268pp. Stanford, CA: Stanford Research Institute.
[57] Faghri A (1995) *Heat Pipe Science and Technology*, 858pp. Washington, DC, London: Taylor & Francis.
[58] Von Lippman E (1910) Chemisches and Alchemisches aus Aristoteles (Chemistry and alchemistry from Aristotle). *Chemiker Zeitung* 2: 233–300.
[59] Von Lippman E (1911) Die Entzalzung des Meerwassers bei Aristoteles (The desalination of seawater from Aristotle). *Chemiker Zeitung* 35: 629–639.
[60] Briegel Z (1918) Zur Entsalzung des Meerwassers bei Aristoteles (The desalination of seawater by Aristotle). *Chemiker Zeitung* 42: 302–310.
[61] Nebbia G and Nebia-Menozzi G (1967) A short history of water desalination. *Proceedings of the International Symposium, Acqua Dolce dal Mare*, Milano, April 1966, 129–172, Consiglio Nazionale delle Richerche.
[62] Lawand TA (1968) Engineering and economic evaluation of solar distillation for small communities. *Technical Report No. MT–6*. Quebec, Canada: Brace Research Institute of McGill University.
[63] Lawand T (1975) Systems for solar distillation. *Proceedings of the International Conference on Appropriate Technologies for Semiarid Areas: Wind and Solar Energy for Water Supply*, 15–20 September, Berlin, pp. 201–250, Germany: German Foundation for International Development.
[64] Wheeler NW and Evans WW (1870) US Patent 102,633, A short history of water desalination. *Proceedings of the International Symposium Aqua Dolce dal Mare*, pp. 129–172.
[65] Telkes M (1956) Solar stills. *Proceedings of the World Symposium on Applied Solar Energy*, pp. 73–79. Phoenix, AZ, USA. 1–5 November 1955. Menlo Park, CA: Stanford Research Institute.
[66] Hirschmann JR (1964) Evaporateur et deistaillateur solaires (Solar evaporators and distillators in Chile). *Proceedings of the UN Conference on New Sources of Energy*, vol. 6, pp.224–236. Rome, Italy, 21–31 August 1961. United Nations/Nations Unies.
[67] Nebbia G (1964) Present status and future of the solar stills. *Proceedings of UN Conference on New Sources of Energy*, vol. 6, pp. 276–281. Rome, Italy, 21–31 August 1961. United Nations/Nations Unies.
[68] Baum V (1964) Solar distillers. *Proceedings of UN Conference on New Sources of Energy*, vol. 6, pp. 178–18. Rome, 21–31 August 1961. United Nations/Nations Unies.
[69] Telkes M (1945) Solar distillers for life rats. *US Office of Science Report No. 5225*, P. B. 21120, 24pp.
[70] Telkes M (1953) Fresh water from seawater by solar distillation. *Industrial and Engineering Chemistry* 45: 1108–1114.
[71] Talbert SG, Eibling JA, and Loef GOG (1970) Manual on solar distillation of saline water. *Research Report*, 124pp. Columbus, OH: Battelle Memorial Institute.
[72] United Nations (1970) *Solar Distillation, as Means of Meeting Small-Scale Water Demands*, 86pp. New York: United Nations.
[73] Edlin FE (1965) Air Supported Solar Still. US Patent 3,174,915, 23 March 1965.

Further Reading

[1] Calver W Method for Utilizing the Rays of the Sun. US Patent 260,657, 4 July 1882; Apparatus for Storing and Distributing Solar Heat. US Patent 290,851, 25 December 1883; Water Lens for Solar Heaters. US Patent 290,852, 25 December 1883; Method and Means for Compensating Solar Rays. US Patent 294,117, 26 February 1884.
[2] Delyannis E and Belessiotis V (1996) A historical overview on renewable energies. *Proceedings of the Mediterranean Conference on Renewable Energy Sources for Water Production*, pp. 13–19.
[3] Kirby RS, Withington S, Darling AB, and Kilgour FG (1990) *Engineering in History*, 530pp. New York: Dover Publications.
[4] Löf GOG (1961) Solar house heating – A panel. *Proceedings of the World Symposium on Applied Solar Energy*, pp. 131–145. Phoenix, AZ, USA. 1–5 November 1955.
[5] Scott JE (1976) The solar water heater industry in South Florida: History and projections. *Solar Energy* 18(5): 387–393.
[6] Shurcliff WA (1992) The rediscovered Arthur A. Shurtleff sun angle indicator. *Sun World* 16(4), 20–21. *History of Technology, Vol. 2, The Mediterranean Civilization and the Middle Ages (700 BC to 1500 AD)*. Oxford: Calderon Press.
[7] Speyer E (1965) Solar energy with evacuated tubes. *Transactions of the ASME, Journal of Engineering for Power* 86: 270.
[8] Telkes M (1943) Distilling water with solar energy. *Report to Solar Energy Conversion Committee*, MIT, January 1943.

3.04 Low Temperature Stationary Collectors

YG Caouris, University of Patras, Patras, Greece

© 2012 Elsevier Ltd. All rights reserved.

3.04.1	**Introduction**	103
3.04.1.1	Flat-Plate Collectors	103
3.04.1.2	Absorbers for Liquid FPCs	104
3.04.1.2.1	Stamped absorbers	104
3.04.1.2.2	Tube absorbers	104
3.04.1.2.3	Roll-bond absorbers	106
3.04.1.2.4	Organic absorbers	107
3.04.1.3	Absorbers for Air FPCs	108
3.04.1.4	Absorber Coating	108
3.04.1.5	Cover Material for FPCs	111
3.04.1.6	Back and Side Insulation for FPCs	113
3.04.1.7	Enclosure or Casing for FPCs	113
3.04.1.8	Evacuated Tube Collectors	116
3.04.2	**Optical Analysis**	120
3.04.2.1	Reflection and Transmission of Radiation	120
3.04.2.2	Antireflective Coatings	125
3.04.2.3	Absorption of Solar Radiation	126
3.04.2.4	Transmittance–Absorptance Product	127
3.04.2.5	Absorbed Solar Energy	128
3.04.3	**Thermal Analysis**	129
3.04.3.1	Steady-State Energy Balance of FPC	129
3.04.3.1.1	Radiation exchange between glazing and sky h_r^{c-a}	130
3.04.3.1.2	Convection exchange between glazing and ambient h_c^{c-a}	131
3.04.3.1.3	Radiation exchange between absorber and glazing h_r^{p-c}	132
3.04.3.1.4	Convection exchange between absorber and cover h_c^{p-c}	132
3.04.3.1.5	Conduction back and edge exchange between absorber and ambient	132
3.04.3.1.6	Overall thermal loss determination q_{loss}	133
3.04.3.2	Solar Collector Top Heat Loss Coefficient U_t	134
3.04.3.3	Useful Energy Transferred to the Working Fluid	134
3.04.3.4	Collector Heat-Removal Factor	138
3.04.4	**Collector Performance Determination**	141
3.04.4.1	Collector Efficiency	141
3.04.4.2	Incident Angle Modifier	143
3.04.4.3	Determination of Effective Thermal Capacity	145
References		146

3.04.1 Introduction

The main part of a solar system is the solar collector, a device that absorbs solar radiation and converts it into heat. Low-temperature stationary collectors are the most commonly used solar collectors. They can supply heat at temperatures up to about 90 °C above ambient. The advantages of these collectors include the lack of moving parts and the capability of collecting both direct and diffuse radiation. They can be divided into two main categories: flat-plate collectors (FPCs) and vacuum tube collectors.

3.04.1.1 Flat-Plate Collectors

Partial components of flat-plate solar collectors, shown in **Figures 1** and **2**, are as follows:

- *Absorbing plate*

    It is suitably treated or painted to absorb as much as possible the incident solar radiation.

- *Heat transfer area*

    The area (tubes or channels) through which the absorbed energy is transferred to a fluid (liquid or air).

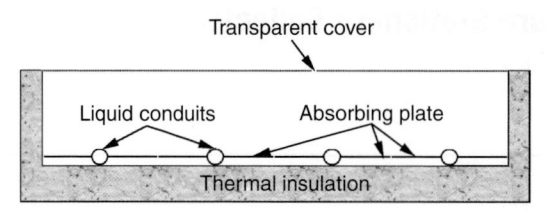

Figure 1 Cross section of a simple liquid flat-plate solar collector.

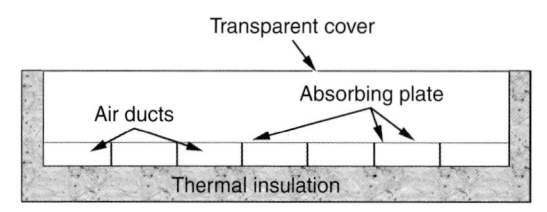

Figure 2 Cross section of a simple air flat-plate solar collector.

- *Top cover(s) that are transparent to solar spectrum*

  They are placed over the solar absorber surface to reduce convection and radiation losses to the atmosphere.

- *Back and edge insulation*

  It substantially reduces back and edge thermal losses.

- *Enclosure or casing*

A supportive structure where the absorber is mounted on, together with the top cover and the back and edge insulation, thus forming an enclosure or casing.

The heart of any solar collector is the absorber, which usually consists of a plate with channels for the flow of the heat-removal fluid. It is fabricated from metals (copper, aluminum, steel) or organic material. A portion of incident solar radiation is absorbed, and the net produced heat (minus heat losses to ambient) is transferred to a gaseous or liquid heat transfer fluid. Thermal insulation is placed on the back surface (not facing the sky) and edges of the absorber. The front surface (facing the sky) is covered by sheet(s) that are transparent to solar radiation, placed at close distance. Absorber, cover(s), and insulation are assembled into a supportive structure, thus forming an enclosure or casing.

3.04.1.2 Absorbers for Liquid FPCs

In liquid solar heaters, the liquid usually flows either in passages formed by tubes or in passages formed in metal sheets by stamping. Almost all commercially available liquid heating solar collectors use parallel flow through the absorber. The individual channels connect into headers at each end. Wide spacing of channels reduces absorber cost, while close spacing increases cost, but improves efficiency. Fin efficiency drops rather fast as the tube spacing is increased to >15 cm, depending on the thickness and thermal conductivity of the fin and effectiveness of the thermal contact. The highest quality, most cost-effective absorbers have sufficient spacing typically no more than 15 cm. According to the way of manufacturing, flat-plate absorbers can be classified as stamped, tube, roll bond, and organic ones.

3.04.1.2.1 Stamped absorbers

In large-scale industrial production, the most popular and cheapest way of absorber fabrication is to bond two metal sheets, usually steel, together. The absorbers are formed by expensive machinery, and they are quite heavy and thermally inert. Channels for the liquid flow are formed, usually on one sheet, by pressure. A suitable pattern is pressed on the sheet so that all necessary flow passages are formed. The two sheets are placed one over the other and are bonded across the channels, usually by in-line spot welding. Furthermore, the two sheets are welded peripherally with electrical current. During the process, a peripheral continuous seam is applied, as shown in **Figure 3**. Stamped absorbers of a popular form are shown in **Figure 4**, ready for further treatment.

3.04.1.2.2 Tube absorbers

Another type of flat-plate solar absorber is the tube absorber. It is widely fabricated by small and medium size industries, because for its fabrication there is no need of heavy machinery. It consists of tubes attached or soldered to a fin or sheet. Copper is the most popular material for the tubes and fins, because of its good thermal conductivity and corrosion resistance.

Figure 3 Fabrication of stamped steel absorbers.

Figure 4 Stamped steel absorbers.

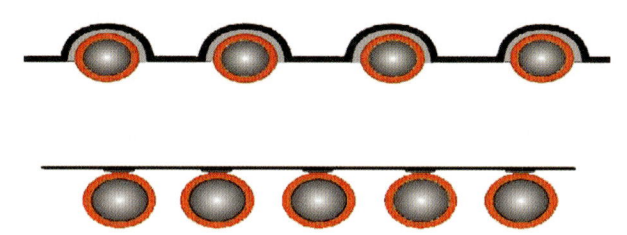

Figure 5 Typical forms of tube absorbers.

The bonded-tube absorber is one of the earliest designs. Liquid tubes are fastened to the sheet metal absorber by soldering, wiring, or other methods. Tubes must be continuously bonded to the plate for adequate heat transfer. However, an aluminum absorber with copper tubes attached by a forced fit combines the desirable features of copper with the economy of aluminum. Copper tubes are usually welded, soldered, or clamped to copper or aluminum plates, as shown schematically in **Figure 5**. The methods commonly used include the tube-in-strip method, tubes welded into headers, and finned tubes. The most popular fabrication technique is the tube-in-strip method (**Figure 6**). Prefabricated parts of single tube-in-strip absorbers are commonly supplied in an overlapping fashion to enable small operators to make up solar collectors of their own designs. The method of joining tubes to headers, finned or otherwise, is widely favored and may well be carried out in a small workshop without much expenditure. It is best to set out the tubes on a frame to ensure correct alignment and grading of the headers. A simple swage tool may be used to provide an overlapping joint, finished with high-grade silver solder. Butt welds are prone to damage in transit and to leakage.

Often, a pipe is simply bent into a serpentine shape and welded onto the back of a flat sheet of metal. **Figure 7** depicts two possible arrangements of serpentine tube collectors. This design reduces slightly heat transfer efficiency but eliminates the possibility of header leaks and ensures uniform flow. However, it also increases the pressure drop, and it is not suitable for a system using drain-down protection, because the curved flow passages cannot always be drained completely.

Figure 6 Tube-in-strip absorbers.

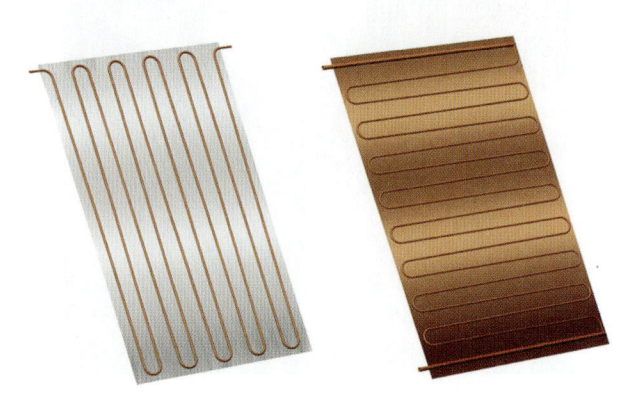

Figure 7 Serpentine tube absorbers.

The technique of mechanical bonding (the absorber is crimped around the tubes) can be an effective means to attach the tubes to the sheet but there is a risk of poor mechanical sealing and then the thermal performance of the collector is greatly diminished. Sometimes, it is used for the application of copper fins to copper tubes, but it must be applied with care. A simple sheet metal folding machine may be used for this purpose. This technique is widely used with hardened aluminum fins, but suitable protection must be applied at the interface between dissimilar metals. The application of aluminum fins to copper tubing is best carried out by purpose-made and expensive machinery.

Lately, the use of laser and ultrasonic welding machines has been introduced by the industry, which improves both the speed and the quality of welds. Fins or sheets are welded on risers, in order to improve heat conduction. The greatest advantage of the ultrasonic technique is that the welding is performed at room temperature. Therefore, deformation of the welded parts is avoided and the quality of the weld can readily be seen. However, this technique leaves a line down the absorber, which diminishes slightly the blackened collecting area. **Figure 8** illustrates a tube absorber welded by ultrasonic technique. Laser welding provides a good seal between the absorber and the tubes without having the weak line associated with ultrasonic welding. **Figure 9** shows the result of laser welding underneath the absorbing plate.

3.04.1.2.3 Roll-bond absorbers

The roll-bond technique, depicted schematically in **Figure 10**, lends itself to the production of low-cost absorbers. This technique has been applied for many years to produce heat exchangers for refrigerators. It is a well-developed application of mass production methods in the solar hardware field. The majority of roll-bond manufacturers produce aluminum absorbers, while the same technique is applicable to copper and steel sheet metals. The roll-bond process requires very thin sheet metals. The production process starts with two sheets of metal that are thoroughly cleaned to remove the surface oxide film. A silk screen process is applied to print the desired pattern of the cooling liquid channels onto the plate. A special stop-weld ink is used to prevent bonding in the patterned area. Next, the two sheets of metal are bonded together by a heating and pressure process. After the adhesion, air pressure is applied to separate the metal sheets by inflation where they have not been bonded because of the stop-weld ink pattern. Thus, the channels for the heat transfer liquid are produced in the absorber. It follows from this manufacturing procedure that, during operation, roll-bond absorbers cannot withstand high working pressure, which might lead to leakage of the absorber. Roll-bond absorbers also deserve particular attention with respect to corrosion.

Figure 8 Tube absorber welded by ultrasonic technique.

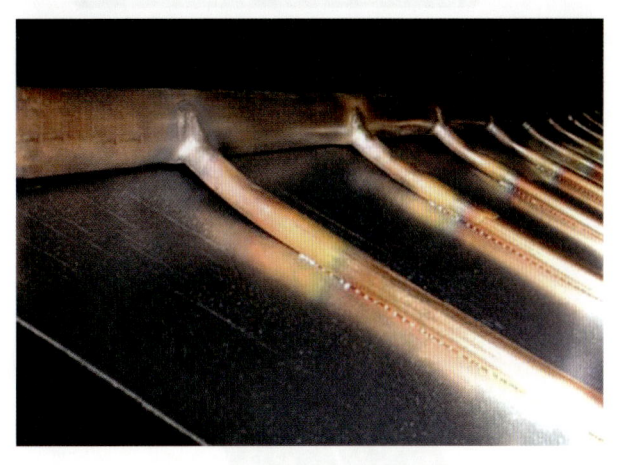

Figure 9 Tube absorber welded by laser technique.

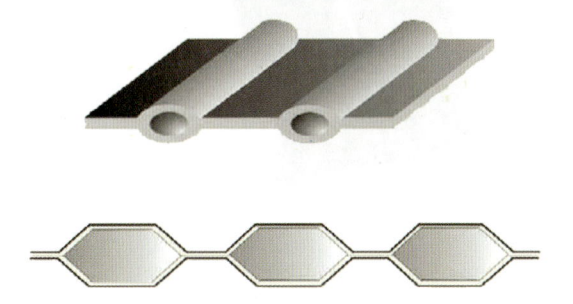

Figure 10 Roll-bond absorbers.

3.04.1.2.4 Organic absorbers

In many low-temperature applications, such as pool and basin heating, unglazed and uninsulated flat-plate organic collectors are used. Their main advantage is the much lower cost (about 10 times lower than common metal glazed collectors). In industrial production, a molten organic substance is molded in the form of channeled sheets, as shown in **Figure 11**. The substances used are colored black, so there is no need of painting. However, for aesthetic reasons, many manufacturers produce sheets in a variety of colors, as shown in **Figure 12**. Sheets are produced in various lengthwise sizes, for example, 400 × 30 cm. They are assembled by the

Figure 11 Organic absorber.

Figure 12 Colored organic absorbers.

Figure 13 Module of unglazed collectors.

use of suitable fittings, which are bonded at the edges. They are easily installed on roofs or terrains in a way of module assembling, as shown in **Figure 13**. The major components of liquid flat-plate unglazed collectors are the absorber plate and the water passages. Since no insulation or glazing is needed, there is no need for an enclosure. They require closely spaced thin-walled water passages because of the low thermal conductivity of plastics. Their composition makes them susceptible to damage by abrasions and punctures. Organic collectors are easier to install because of their lighter weight and flexibility, compared to metal collectors. Some manufacturers also produce glazed collectors with organic roll-bond absorbers. If they are intended to be used at higher temperatures, they must be constructed by more expensive organic material with improved properties.

3.04.1.3 Absorbers for Air FPCs

Solar FPCs can be used to heat air or other gases, with satisfactory performance. Because of the low heat transfer coefficients between absorber and air, some type of extended surface geometry is needed to counteract this problem. **Figure 14** shows a number of absorber designs for FPC solar air heaters that have been used with various accomplishments [1]. Metal plates or thin corrugated metal sheets or fabric matrices may be used, in combination with selective or flat black surfaces. Therefore, the principal requirement of a large contact area between the absorbing surface and the air applies for all types of absorbers.

3.04.1.4 Absorber Coating

The upper surface of the absorber that faces the sun must be suitably coated. The type of coating plays a significant role in the performance of solar collectors and determines the absorbed fraction of incident solar energy. Coatings must have high absorptance for radiation in the solar energy spectrum and long-wave emittance as low as possible, to reduce infrared (IR) thermal radiation losses. Coatings are classified as flat black (nonselective) and selective. Flat black paints consist of a pigment material (an organic binder that polymerizes during drying) and solvents that permit easy application of the paint film. In drying, the solvent evaporates

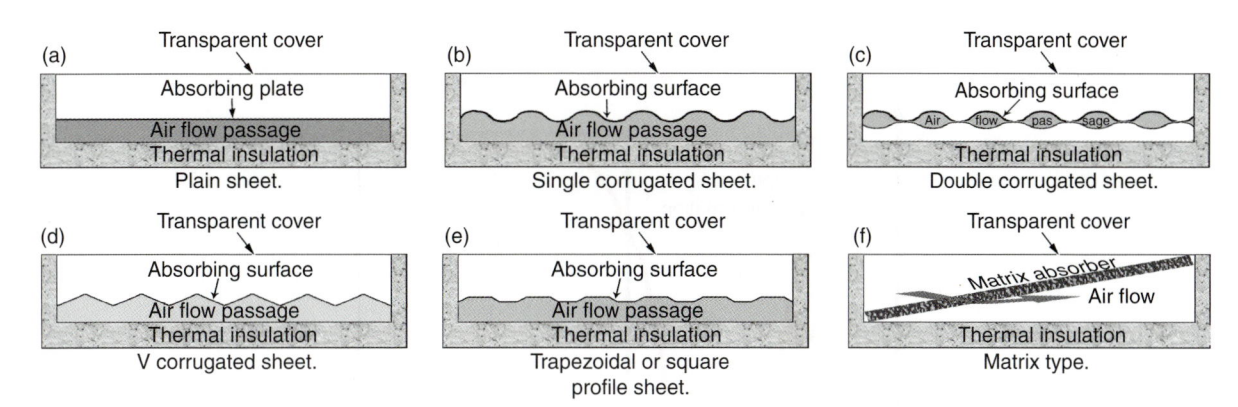

Figure 14 Flat-plate solar air heater designs.
(a) Plain sheet. (b) Single corrugated sheet. (c) Double corrugated sheet. (d) V corrugated sheet. (e) Trapezoidal or square profile sheet. (f) Matrix type.

Figure 15 Flat black painting process in isolated space.

and the pigment and binder form a film of 1–3 mils thick. Flat black coatings are applied as a common color painting. The typical method of application is by spray gun, and all the work is done in chambers that are well ventilated or isolated, as in **Figure 15**. A flat black paint is a good absorber, but since the paint film is not selective at all, it has absorptance and emittance of 0.95–0.98. Until a few years ago, flat black paint was the most commonly used coating, because it is cheap and quite durable. Lately, the mass production of good-quality, not expensive selective surfaces tends to dominate the solar thermal market.

The temperature of the absorbing surface in most stationary collectors is <100 °C (373 K), while the equivalent temperature of the sun is ~6000 K. The great portion (98%) of the extraterrestrial solar radiation lies in the range of 0.2–3.0 μm, while 99% of the long-wave radiation of a blackbody at 200 °C lies at wavelengths <3.0 μm. So a perfect coating for solar absorber surface should have absorptance $\alpha = 1$ for solar spectrum and emittance $\varepsilon = 0$ for long-wave radiation. The characteristics desired for an ideal coating surface are as follows: $\alpha = \varepsilon = 1$ for wavelengths <4 μm and $\alpha = \varepsilon = 0$ for wavelengths >4 μm. A surface with these ideal properties is called 'selective', because of its selective behavior for those two discrete radiation wavelength ranges. Unfortunately, materials with these properties do not exist in nature. Virtually, all black materials have high solar absorptance and also high IR emittance. Thus, it is necessary to manufacture selective materials with ideal or very close to ideal properties. Selective coatings should have the following physical properties [2]:

- They must have high absorptance for solar spectrum in the range of 0.2–2.5 μm and low emittance for spectrum >2.0 μm.
- The spectral transition between the region of high absorptance and low emittance must be as sharp as possible.
- The opto-physical properties of the coating must remain stable under long-term operation at elevated temperatures, repeated thermal cycling, air exposure, ultraviolet radiation, and other conditions.
- Adherence of coating to substrate must be good.
- Coating should be easily applicable and must be economical.

Figure 16 illustrates the reflectance ρ (with absorptance $\alpha = 1-\rho$) and emittance ε of an ideal and a real selective coating.

The most commonly used selective surfaces are thin layers of metal oxides that are deposited by electrolysis or in vacuum on the polished metal absorber plate. Typical selective surfaces consist of a thin upper layer, which is highly absorbent to solar radiation but relatively transparent to long-wave thermal radiation, deposited on a surface that has high reflectance and low emittance for long-wave radiation. Lately, low-cost mechanically manufactured selective solar absorber surfaces have been developed.

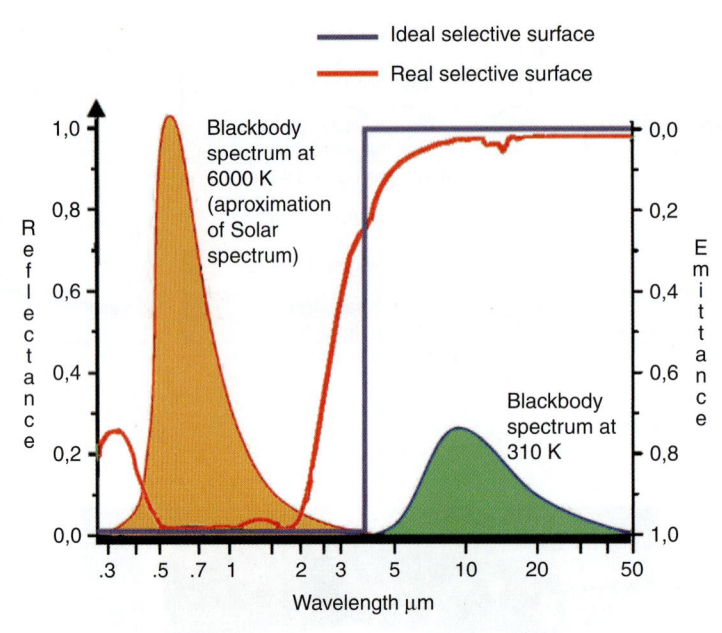

Figure 16 Reflectance and emittance of selective surfaces.

Selective coatings can be categorized into six distinct types [3]: (1) intrinsic, (2) semiconductor–metal tandems, (3) multilayer absorbers, (4) metal–dielectric composite coatings, (5) textured surfaces, and (6) selectively solar-transmitting coating on a blackbody-like absorber. Intrinsic coatings use substances having intrinsic properties that lead to the desired spectral relevance. Semiconductor–metal tandems are highly absorbing for solar radiation because of the semiconductor band gap and have low long-wave emittance as a result of the metal layer. Multilayer absorbers use multiple reflections between layers to absorb light. Metal–dielectric composites (cermets) consist of fine metal particles in a dielectric or ceramic host material. Textured surfaces present high solar absorptance because of multiple reflections among porous dendritic, or needle-like, microstructure. For low-temperature applications, solar-transmitting and high-IR-reflecting coatings on a blackbody-like absorber are also used. Solar selective surfaces can be fabricated by the following major techniques [1]: (1) vacuum evaporation, (2) vacuum sputtering, (3) ion exchange, (4) chemical vapor disposition, (5) chemical oxidation, (6) dipping in chemical baths, (7) electroplating, (8) spraying, (9) screen printing, and (10) brush painting method. During recent years, much of the progress has been based on the implementation of vacuum techniques for the production of fin- and sheet-type absorbers. The chemical and electrochemical processes were readily taken over from the metal finishing industry. The vacuum techniques are, nowadays, mature, characterized by low cost and have the advantage of being less environmentally polluting than the wet processes. A typical structure of commercial tandem selective absorber is shown in **Figure 17**. The substrate could be any material used in solar energy collection, usually metal or glass. The second layer is an IR-reflecting low-emittance layer, usually a copper-deposited layer, which reflects back the long-wave radiation of the substrate. There is no need of this layer if the substrate is metal. The third layer is the selective absorbing surface, usually made of nickel, chrome, or copper oxides. Finally, the fourth antireflective layer improves the optical performance as it decreases reflectance losses of the absorbing layer. It also has the function of a protective film and is made typically of dielectrics with a graded refractive index.

In **Table 1**, solar absorptance and long-wave emittance values for some common selective surfaces are given [2, 3].

Today, technology produces selective surfaces in large ribbon rolls, as shown in **Figure 18**, ready for further elaboration, that is, welding on tubes. Furthermore, selective thin surfaces are offered in ribbon rolls of self-adhesive thin-film metal sheets, as shown in **Figure 19**, which are tightly pasted to the absorber surface.

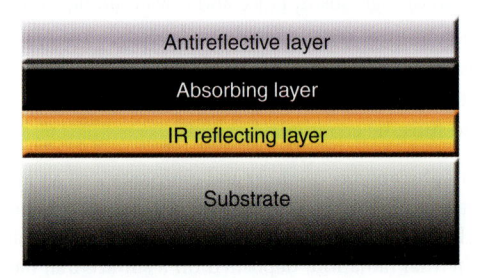

Figure 17 Typical selective absorber structure.

Table 1 Absorptance and emittance of selective surfaces

Coating/substrate	Absorptance	Emittance
Copper, aluminum, or nickel plate with CuO coating	0.8–0.93	0.09–0.21
Black nickel on Zn/Fe substrate	0.94	0.09
Black copper (BlCu-Cu$_2$O:Cu) on Cu substrate	0.97–0.98	0.02
Metal, plated black chrome	0.87	0.09
Metal, plated nickel oxide	0.92	0.08

Figure 18 Commercial selective metal roll sheet.

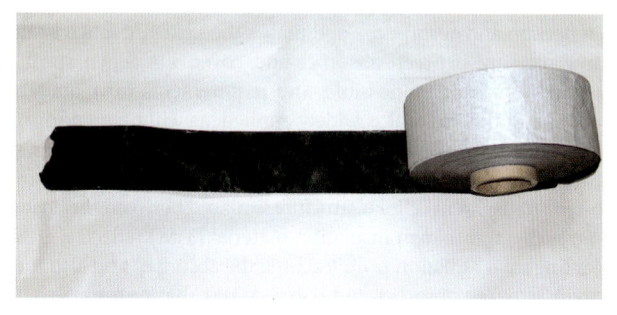

Figure 19 Self-adhesive selective thin metal roll sheet.

3.04.1.5 Cover Material for FPCs

Covering or glazing is essential for the prevention of absorber thermal losses to ambient. The glazing should allow as much as possible incident solar irradiation to arrive at the absorber and reduce as much as possible the upward heat losses. As upward heat losses occur by convection and long-wave radiation, covering must reduce both of them. The presence of cover(s) prevents convection losses by shielding the absorber from ambient air. The perfect shielding for long-wave radiation happens when a reflective cover is used. However, a thermally opaque material acts in the same way. Absorber thermal losses cause an increase in the cover temperature and subsequently a loss of heat to ambient by radiation and convection.

Glass has been widely used to glaze solar collectors because it can transmit as much as 92% of the incoming solar irradiation [1]. Also, being thermally opaque it absorbs around 88% of the absorber long-wave radiation and reflects back the rest. Glass has very good mechanical and physical properties, and withstands perfectly time aging under ambient conditions. Some drawbacks of common glass are that it is usually heavy and vulnerable to breaking by hail or stones. However, the use of tempered glass surpasses the last disadvantage. Tempered or toughened glass is glass that has been processed by controlled thermal or chemical treatments, which create balanced internal stresses, to increase its strength compared with normal glass. Of the various grades of tempered plate glass, low-iron glass has the highest transmission and lowest reflection for solar radiation. These properties result in significant increase in collector efficiency, so the cost premium for low-iron glass is smaller than the increase in efficiency. Coatings that are antireflective to solar spectrum, and surface texture (e.g., prismatic), can also improve transmission significantly. In **Figure 20**, a prismatic textured (at the internal surface only) tempered glass cover of a commercial collector is shown. Also, coatings that are reflective to thermal radiation reduce thermal radiation losses when applied to the internal glass surface (absorber side).

Figure 20 Internally prismatic tempered glass, at work.

Polymeric materials also indicate high solar transmittance, but because almost all of them have transmission bands in the thermal radiation spectrum, they may allow a substantial portion (as high as 40%) of the absorber long-wave radiation to pass through. Furthermore, polymers can sustain smaller temperature limits and deteriorate easily. Only a few types of polymers can withstand the sun's ultraviolet radiation for long periods. Polymers inside a well-sealed collector may deteriorate rapidly and will outgas, depositing a haze of condensed oily liquid on the inside surface of the glazing. Such haze may seriously reduce the collector efficiency. However, they are not broken by hail or stones, have increased strength, less weight than glass, and in the form of thin films, they are completely flexible. In some double-glazing designs, one layer of glass is used along with a layer of thin polymer underneath.

The effect of dirt and dust on collector glazing must be quite small, and the cleansing effect of an occasional rainfall is usually adequate to maintain the transmittance within 96–98% of its maximum value [1].

The presence of one transparent cover reduces absorber thermal losses by convection and radiation. As radiation loss is almost eliminated with the use of selective coatings, the cover contributes almost exclusively to the suppression of convective loss. Further suppression could be achieved if two or more covers are placed. However, the presence of more covers decreases essentially the transmitted solar radiation, due to reflection and absorption, and makes the structure much heavier. An alternative solution would be to maintain vacuum or very low pressure between absorber and cover, but when speaking for FPC designs, insuperable difficulties appear. Vacuum maintenance is almost impossible, and requirements for material strength are very high. However, for other collector designs (evacuated tube), this concept is widely applied, as will be mentioned later.

Convection loss could be as well inhibited if the air between absorber and cover remains stagnant. For free convection, this means that buoyant forces must be less than friction forces. This is the case of enclosed air in narrow cavities. Thus, convection loss could be prevented if a honeycomb-type transparent cellular structure is placed between the absorber and the outer cover, as shown schematically in **Figure 21**. However, such a transparent insulation material (TIM) reflects a greater part of the incoming radiation than a simple glass cover, thus preventing solar radiation from reaching the absorber, and also increases the cost. A cellular structure also increases the thermal conductivity between absorber and cover. A TIM that transmits well solar radiation, is opaque in the thermal radiation, and has low thermal conductivity could be ideal for a solar collector. Solar transmittance and heat loss coefficient are the two parameters used for the characterization of a TIM. Various prototypes of transparently insulated FPCs have been fabricated and tested in the last decade [4, 5]. **Figure 22** shows a cutout of TIM used in a collector. Low-cost and high-temperature-resistant TIMs have been developed so that the commercialization of these collectors becomes feasible. A comparative study of TIM cover systems shows that honeycomb systems excel over other systems [6]. TIM covers presently available (e.g., small-celled

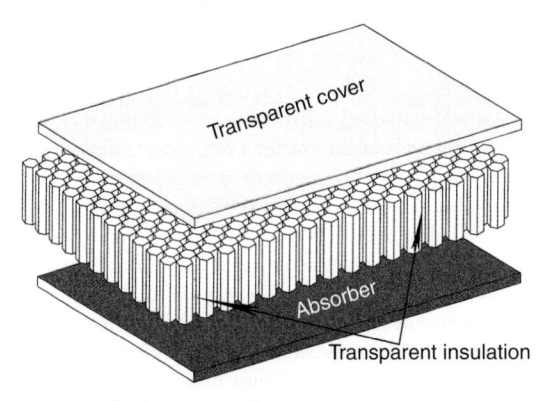

Figure 21 Honeycomb structure for absorber convective loss suppression.

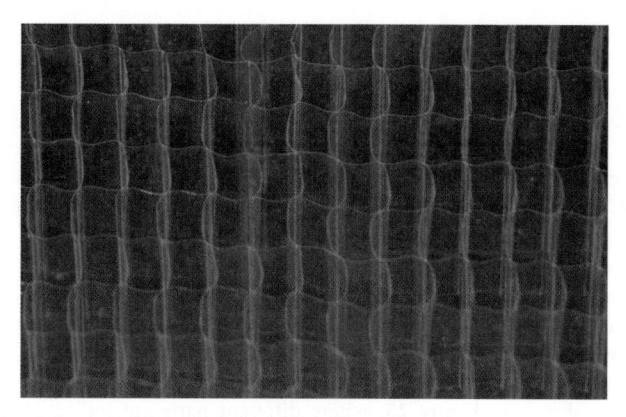

Figure 22 Commercial transparent insulation material over collector's absorbing surface.

polycarbonate honeycomb TIM covers) offer good possibilities for their application where the typical working temperatures are between 50 and 80 °C. Recently, the cost of optimized honeycomb covers made of Mylar and Lexan runs into $9 and $7 m^{-2}, respectively [6, 7].

3.04.1.6 Back and Side Insulation for FPCs

Insulation plays a significant role in curbing heat loss due to conduction in a solar collector. Various types of insulation can be used in collectors. Polyurethane chlorofluorocarbon (CFC)-free case insulation has become popular for solar collectors because it has a higher insulation value than any other practical insulation material and does not deteriorate with humidity. However, it must be used in solar collectors with great care. An otherwise well-designed solar collector will experience stagnation temperatures that will cause the insulation of this type to outgas and rapidly destroy the efficiency of the collector. Another solution is the use of hardened glass wool or mineral wool, which are temperature and fire resistant, although they are very sensitive to humidity. Insulation must be kept dry or else it loses all or most of its insulating value. When the collector is assembled, the air trapped inside will contain moisture, which eventually will condense and become soaked into the insulation. To prevent it, quality collectors contain porous bags of silica gel desiccant to absorb the moisture. Typically, the desiccant is contained in the hollow spacers separating the glazing and the absorber, and small holes on the surface of the spacers facing the space between the panes permit the trapped air to contact the desiccant. If desiccant is not used, it will become apparent through condensation of drops of water on the inner surface of the glass. A cheaper solution is to create small holes at the bottom (base) frame, so that rain water is very difficult to enter and any formed condensation can come out by evaporation. Usually, a thin reflective aluminum foil is adhered at the absorber side of the back insulation. The absorber must not touch the foil. It must be mounted in suitable sockets keeping a distance of 0.5–1.5 cm away from the foil, so that the foil acts as a reflector (radiation shield) to thermal radiation emitted by the absorber.

Case insulation is not the only important insulation task in a quality collector. The absorber plate and connecting tubing penetrating the enclosure must be thermally insulated from the case at every point of the support. Heat paths from the warm sections of the collector to the basic structure must be eliminated. The supports for the cover, for instance, must be insulated not only from the absorber surface but also from glass and the air spaces. Heat losses can be severe if either the absorber or tubing touches the case or is supported through heat-conducting materials to the case.

Vacuum insulation materials, which are recently developed for other applications such as building insulation or insulation for stoves and boilers, could also be used. With vacuum insulation materials, it should be possible to reach thermal conductivity values between 5 and 10 times lower than for ordinary insulation materials, depending on the temperature range. Vacuum insulation panels consist in general of a base material that is placed in a volume surrounded by gastight foils [8]. The vacuum inside these panels has a key function due to the fact that the thermal conductivity of an insulation material depends mainly on the heat conduction of the gas inside the material. By evacuation, the conductivity of the composite structure will be reduced. The base material is a kind of silicon acid with a very small pore size. It is produced under low pressure and packed in panels, covered with a gastight foil [8]. However, this material is still expensive and its use in solar collectors is not yet cost-effective.

3.04.1.7 Enclosure or Casing for FPCs

The absorber, the top cover, and the back and edge insulation must be mounted together on a supportive structure, forming thus an enclosure or casing. The enclosure serves to contain insulation, provides support for the absorber and glazing, and protects the collector from heat loss to ambient. Furthermore, it has the important function of keeping moisture from rain and dew out of the insulation. Enclosures are made of a variety of materials and designs but are usually made of galvanized steel (bonded or formed) or of aluminum profiles with a back aluminum thinner sheet. Whatever the case material and construction, it must be weather resistant, fireproof, durable, dimensionally stable, strong, and completely sealed permanently against moisture intrusion. As a general rule, the joints and seams should be minimized and completely sealed. Aluminum should be used with caution in areas exposed to salt air, industrial pollution, or smog in the air. Most top-quality collectors use enclosures of anodized aluminum similar to those for exterior windows. Adequate clearance (e.g., around the glass cover) and proper gaskets must be provided for the expansion of various collector components. Provision must be made for expansion and contraction of the cover plate material, because its expansion coefficient is quite different from that of the framework. These requirements are generally met by using a U-shaped, extruded rubber gasket held in place within a metal trim strip. A silicone rubber is an excellent choice because this material is very weather resistant. The frame should be designed to cast almost no shadow on the absorber plate, and the aperture area should be at least 85% of the gross area. Sealing compounds and gaskets should be capable of withstanding thermal cycling and stagnation temperatures without outgassing.

An enclosure made of anodized aluminum profiles, with a polyurethane back and side insulation, is shown in **Figure 23**. The adhered reflective aluminum foil (malformed) is also shown. The sockets for the absorber support are made from hard rubber. They are incorporated into the insulation and are shown as knobs (indicated by arrows). **Figure 24** shows, on the left side, enclosures made of formed galvanized steel plates and, on the right side, the glass wool insulation, covered by thin aluminum foil.

An entire collector structure is shown in **Figure 25**, where different parts are indicated separately. Flat Plate Collectors dominate today's solar thermal market, with higher quality issue the full face absorber type, which has reduced thermal losses and greatest absorber to enclosure ratio. Some other collector types must also be mentioned, such as the transpired air collectors and multipass types.

Transpired air collectors are quite simple structures for heating purposes in buildings. A perforated blackened metal sheet is placed at close distance, in front and across a building wall. A fan sorbs ambient air, which passes through the perforation holes, and is heated and distributed inside the building, as shown in **Figure 26**.

Multipass solar collectors are another type, dedicated for different applications [9–11]. In **Figure 27**, a two-pass solar air heater is shown schematically. This design doubles the heat transfer area and improves the performance for elevated air temperatures. Another two-pass liquid collector is shown schematically in **Figure 28**. The first liquid layer (2) is made of transparent material with ducts where a transparent heat transfer liquid passes through and functions as a preheater, absorbing the heat loss of the absorber (3). It has been shown that this collector type outperforms when inlet temperature is kept low (near ambient temperature) [12, 13]. Therefore, it is suitable for once-through systems.

Typical flow rate for liquid FPC is 0.01–0.05 kg s^{-1} m^{-2} and for air FPC it is 0.01 m^3 s^{-1} m^{-2}.

Figure 23 Enclosure made by aluminum profiles and plastic joins.

Figure 24 Galvanized steel enclosures (in stock) and fiber glass wool insulation plates.

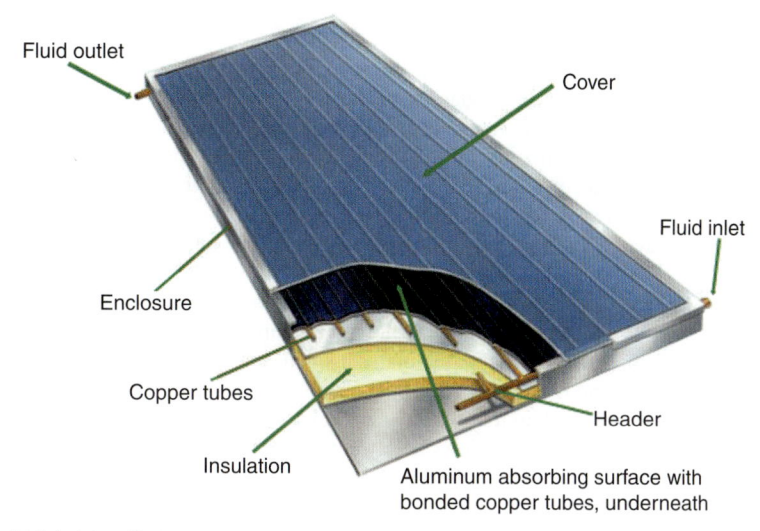

Figure 25 Typical commercial flat-plate collector.

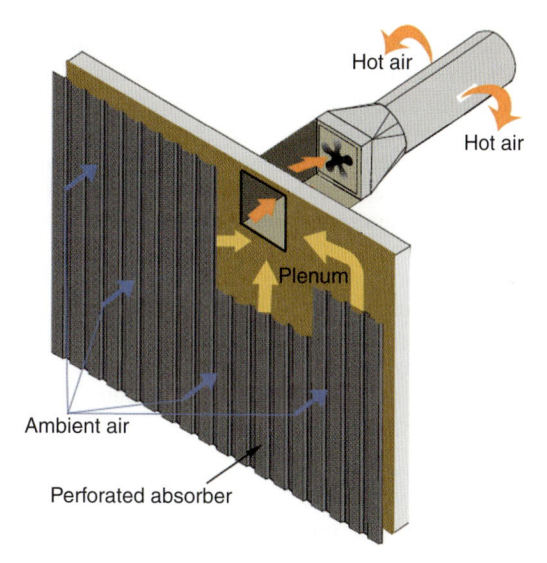

Figure 26 Transpired air heating collector.

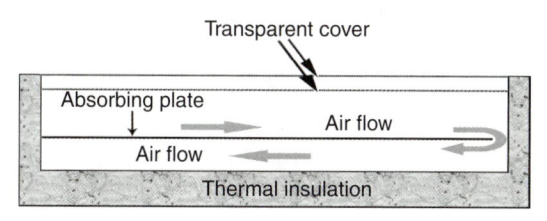

Figure 27 Schematic diagram of a two-pass air heater.

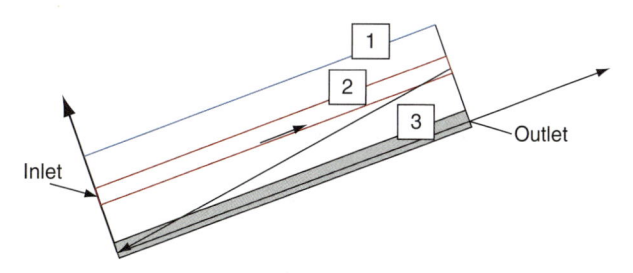

Figure 28 Schematic diagram of a two-pass once-through liquid solar collector. 1, glazing; 2, preheating transparent layer; 3, absorber.

3.04.1.8 Evacuated Tube Collectors

The previously mentioned concept, that is, the evacuation of the space between the absorber and the outer cover, can be easily applied on tubular collector designs. The vacuum glass tube technology is extremely mature, from the well-established production of fluorescent lamps, special scientific apparatus, and other products. Thereby, a collector with evacuated space between absorber and cover could be created, if an absorbing finned tube is placed inside a glass tube, which is then welded at its edges to the glass and finally the tube is evacuated and sealed. Because of differential expansion of glass and finned tube, it is essential to have only a single welding area, or withstanding bellows; otherwise, the glass tube will be broken. This vulnerability has been surpassed by mainly two types of configurations: the single-glass type and the twin-glass type (also called Dewar or Sydney type).

The 'single-glass type' consists of a glass vacuum tube with an inside mounted flat absorber. The absorber tube may have U-shaped forms or concentric forms, as in **Figure 29**. The type shown in **Figure 29(a)** has a heat pipe absorber with a single glass-to-metal seal. Heat pipe is a hermetically sealed tube that contains a small amount of vaporizable fluid (e.g., methanol). When the tube is heated, the liquid evaporates and condenses at a colder chamber (condenser, heat sink section), transferring heat with great effectiveness (thousands of times greater than that of the best solid heat conductor of the same dimensions), because of the latent heat of condensation. To ensure that the liquid flows back to the heated tube, the heat pipe contains a wick or is tilted (or both). With a proper tilt, gravity returns the condensed fluid back to the evaporating region, so there is no need of capillary wick and thereby it functions only in one direction. In an evacuated tube collector (ETC), a sealed copper pipe (heat pipe) is bonded to a copper absorbing fin, usually selective, that is mounted inside the evacuated glass space. A small condenser is attached to the top of the heat pipe and is inserted into a thermally insulated heat exchanger duct, at the top of the solar collector system. As the absorber is heated, the heat pipe liquid boils and hot vapor rises toward the condenser. A heat transfer liquid (usually water or water–glycol mixture) flows through the duct and cools the condenser. This heat transfer liquid delivers its heat to storage and/or to load through a heat exchanger. The whole process is shown schematically in **Figure 30**. The maximum operating temperature of a heat pipe is the critical temperature of the vaporizable fluid used. Since no evaporation/condensation above the critical temperature is possible, the thermodynamic cycle interrupts when the temperature of the evaporator exceeds this critical temperature. Thus, the heat pipe offers inherent protection from overheating and freezing. This self-limiting temperature control is a unique feature of the heat pipe collector. Also, heat pipes have lower heat capacity than ordinary liquid-filled absorber tubes, thus collecting solar energy more efficiently by minimizing warm-up and cool-down losses. A heat pipe ETC unit is shown in **Figure 31**.

In the second configuration (**Figure 29(b)**), liquid flow is 'down and back' through a U-shaped tube. Two glass-to-metal seals are formed at the same edge of the tube, so attention must be given to the edge geometry to allow absorption of differential expansions. Also the two flow streams must be thermally decoupled as much as possible and the solution is to split the fin into two parts [14].

The third configuration (**Figure 29(c)**) has a single glass-to-metal seal and heat is extracted through concentric tube geometry. The heat transfer fluid enters the inner tube (inlet) and turns back through the outer tube (outlet). In a multi-glass-tube collector configuration, inlets and outlets are connected to separate top headers.

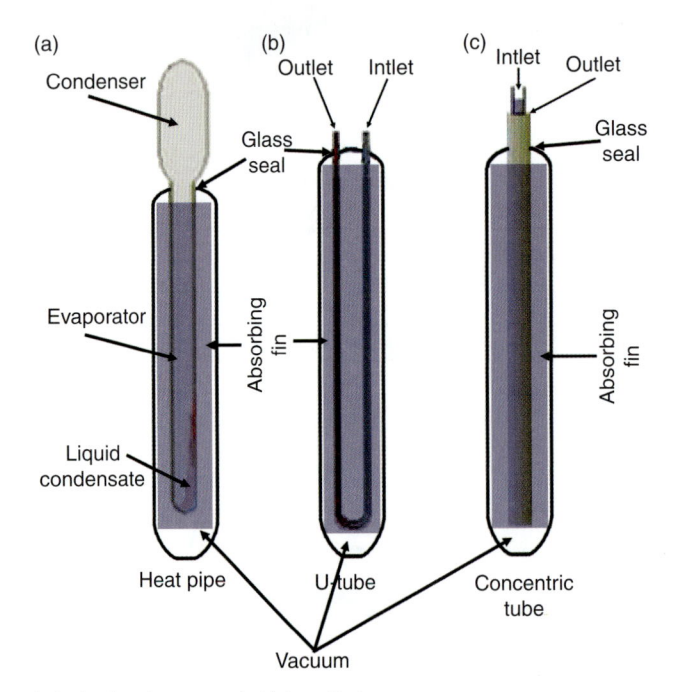

Figure 29 Various configurations of single-glass-type evacuated tube collectors.

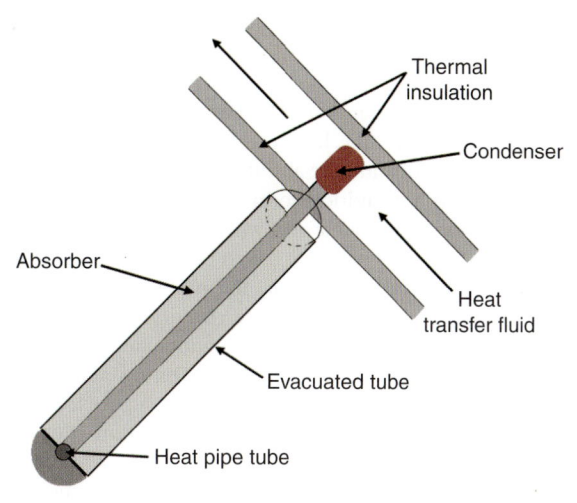

Figure 30 Schematic diagram of heat pipe operation process.

Figure 31 Heat pipe evacuated tube collector.

The 'twin-glass ETC' (Dewar) type consists of two glass tubes, usually made of borosilicate glass (commercially known as SCHOTT or PYREX), as shown schematically in **Figure 32**. The outer tube is transparent allowing solar radiation to pass through with minimal reflection. The two tubes are fused together at the top, and the air contained in the space between the tubes is pumped

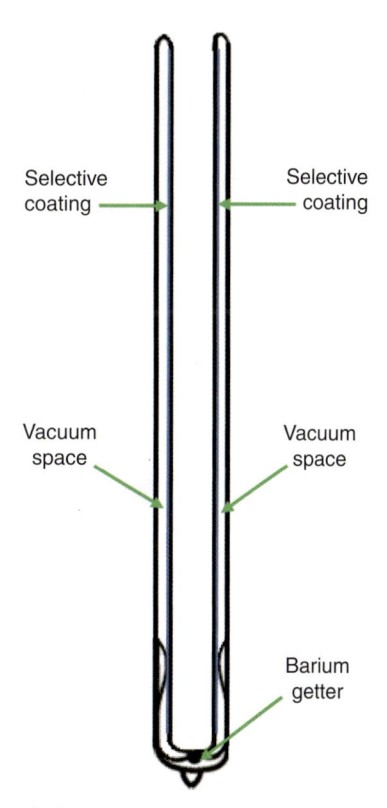

Figure 32 Schematic diagram of twin-glass evacuated tube.

out, thus creating a vacuum jacket. The inner tube is coated outside (vacuum-side surface) with a selective absorbing coating. The advantage of this design is that it is made entirely of glass, thus leakage losses are avoided. Another big advantage of the twin-glass ETC is its ability to passively track the sun. This feature gives a more consistent output than any other collector over the whole day. It is also less expensive compared to the single-glass configuration [15]. Heat can be extracted if a heat transfer fluid fills directly the inside Dewar space and turns back through a concentric tube, but a breakage of glass tube will result in loss of fluid and failure of an entire collector array. A safer solution is to insert a fin-and-tube absorber inside the Dewar space, in good thermal contact with the inner glass; for this, the fin must be rolled into a cylindrical form to provide a 'spring' fit when inserted. In **Figure 33**, two configurations of twin-glass ETC with fin-and-tube absorber are shown: a U-tube type (a) and a heat pipe type (b).

The vacuum (10^{-5} torr) of a tubular evacuated solar collector has to be maintained during the 25+ years life of the device. It has been found that a number of evacuated solar collectors face the problem of vacuum degradation due to poor sealing techniques. Therefore, highly reliable vacuum seals are key quality criterion as the seals withstand the thermal stress and temperature shocks. To absorb material outgassing due to the high operational temperature, the vacuum is maintained through a barium getter (as in old radio tubes) inserted in the collector tube. During manufacture, this getter is exposed to high temperature, which causes the bottom of the evacuated tube to be coated with a pure layer of barium. This barium layer actively absorbs any CO, CO_2, N_2, O_2, H_2O, and H_2 outgassed during storage and operation, thus helping to maintain the vacuum. The barium layer also provides a clear visual indicator of the vacuum status. The silver-colored barium layer will turn white if the vacuum is lost. The dose of barium must be calculated for the targeted life cycle of the system. A final remark is that system stagnation reduces the life expectancy of tubes.

A complete collector panel consists of a large number of individual tubes positioned in parallel rows and connected to separate header pipes (U-tube or concentric tube type) or to a manifold header (heat pipe type). The headers are mounted in a well-insulated box that reduces the heat loss. The number of tubes depends on the heating needs of every individual application. A typical ETC panel used for hot water production is shown in **Figure 34**. Several manufacturers produce ETC panels with an added diffuse or compound parabolic reflector (CPR) of low concentration ratio, underneath the tubes. CPRs are nonimaging concentrators. They are capable of reflecting the incident solar radiation to the absorber, within the wide limits of the acceptance angle. They are trough-shaped with two sections of a truncated parabola facing each other. They can accept incoming radiation over a relatively wide range of incident angles [1]. By multiple reflections, any radiation that is entering the aperture, within the collector acceptance angle, strikes the absorber surface at the bottom of the structure, as shown schematically in **Figure 35**. For stationary collectors mounted in CPR, big acceptance angles are used to enable the collection of diffuse radiation, at the expense of a lower concentration ratio. A CPR with low concentration ratio (e.g., $C = 1.5$) collects two-thirds of the available diffuse solar radiation [16]. An ETC commercial panel with CPRs is shown in **Figure 36**.

One of the principal advantages of conventional vacuum tube collectors is that the wind can pass between the tubes; however with a reflector, increased wind loading is inevitable. It is also very important to verify that the reflectors are very tightly connected to minimize rattles.

Like FPCs, ETCs collect both direct and diffuse radiation. However, their efficiency is higher at low incidence angles. This effect tends to give ETC an advantage over FPC in day-long performance. ETCs are more breakable by hailstones, although some manufacturers construct the outer tube of extremely strong transparent borosilicate glass that is able to resist impact from hailstones of up to 25 mm in diameter [17]. Another disadvantage is their difficulty of snow rejection. If snow is accumulated over and between glass tubes, it does not melt easily, because of their negligible heat loss and the collector will not be able to capture solar energy.

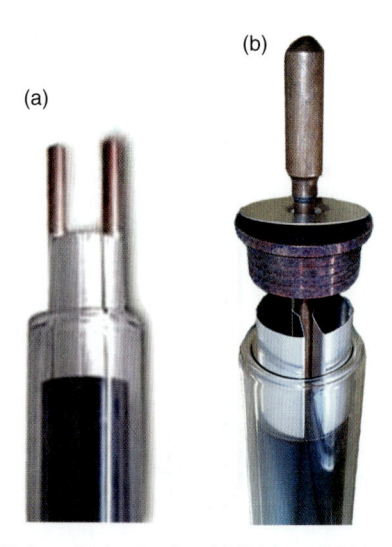

Figure 33 Twin-glass evacuated tube collector with fin-and-tube absorber: (a) U-tube and (b) heat pipe.

Figure 34 Typical evacuated tube collector panel.

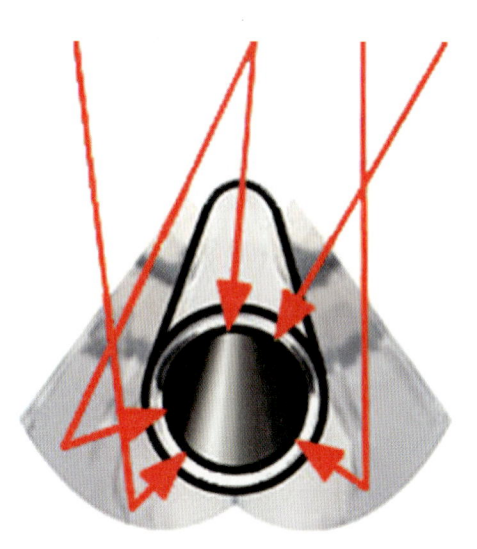

Figure 35 Light trapping by evacuated tube collector with compound parabolic reflector to the back.

Figure 36 Typical evacuated tube collector panel with a low-concentration compound parabolic reflector.

3.04.2 Optical Analysis

Generally, the term 'optical' refers to how visible electromagnetic radiation (light) is propagated through various mediums. Hereafter, it will be used for the description of how various parts of a solar collector behave to solar radiation spectrum (0.2–4 μm). This behavior in the transmission, reflection, and absorption of solar radiation is important for the determination of collector performance. The transmittance, reflectance, and absorptance of transparent materials depend on the thickness, extinction coefficient k, and refractive index n of the material. The refractive index of a medium is specified as the ratio of the radiation velocity in vacuum to that in the medium. The extinction coefficient is a proportionality constant related with the per unit distance absorption of radiation through a medium. Physically, k and n depend on the wavelength of the radiation. However, for common glazing materials (glass and plastics), they are assumed to be independent of the wavelength, considering their mean values for the solar spectrum. Of significant importance is the effect of radiation polarization. Polarization describes the orientation of wave oscillations in space. Transverse electromagnetic waves such as solar radiation exhibit polarization. In a uniform isotropic medium, solar radiation waves may be described as a superposition of sinusoidally varying electric $\vec{E}$ and magnetic $\vec{B}$ field plane waves, aligned perpendicular to one another and to the direction of propagation. For polarization description, it is sufficient to specify the behavior of the electric field $\vec{E}$ only, while the magnetic field $\vec{B}$ can be always determined from $\vec{E}$. The electric field may be oriented in a single direction (linear polarization) or it may rotate as the wave travels (circular or elliptical polarization). The most common situation is the linear polarization relative to a plane. It is illustrated in **Figure 37**, where the radiation propagates in the z-direction and its electric field $\vec{E}$ oscillates in a plane A, forming angle θ with an arbitrarily sketched plane B. Thus, $\vec{E}$ can be analyzed in two components $\vec{E}_x$ and $\vec{E}_y$, parallel and perpendicular to plane B, respectively. Components $\vec{E}_x$ and $\vec{E}_y$ are called the parallel and perpendicular component, respectively, relative to plane B.

When radiation of intensity I contacts a transparent (or translucent) medium, a part I_r of it is reflected, a part I_α is absorbed, and a part I_τ is transmitted. Reflectance r, absorptance α, and transmittance τ are defined as the ratios $r = I_r/I$, $\alpha = I_\alpha/I$, $\tau = I_\tau/I$, and according to the first law of thermodynamics $r + \alpha + \tau = 1$.

3.04.2.1 Reflection and Transmission of Radiation

Fresnel, Snell, and Stokes have established the principles governing the radiation transmission through smooth, homogeneous transparent mediums with no internal scattering. When a radiation beam is passing from a medium 1 with refractive index n_1 to another medium 2 with refractive index n_2, then at the interface of the two mediums a part is reflected and the rest passes into medium 2, subjected to direction change. The ratio of the intensity of reflected radiation I_r to the intensity of incident radiation I_i is defined as surface reflectance $r = I_r/I_i$.

Considering the case of a plane interface as in **Figure 38**, if the incident radiation forms angle ϕ_1 with the normal to the plane, called angle of incidence, then the reflected radiation forms an equal angle at the same incident plane, defined by the incident beam and the surface normal. The following relationships apply for the parallel $r_\parallel$ and perpendicular $r_\perp$ reflectance components, relative to the plane of incidence:

$$r_\perp = \frac{\sin^2(\phi_2 - \phi_1)}{\sin^2(\phi_1 + \phi_2)} \qquad [1]$$

$$r_\parallel = \frac{\tan^2(\phi_2 - \phi_1)}{\tan^2(\phi_1 + \phi_2)} \qquad [2]$$

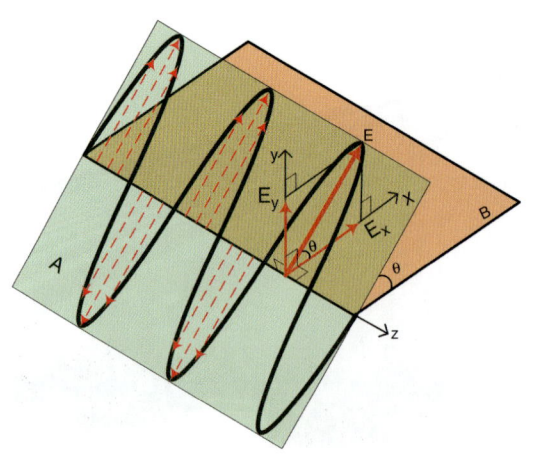

Figure 37 Linear polarization of transverse radiation wave.

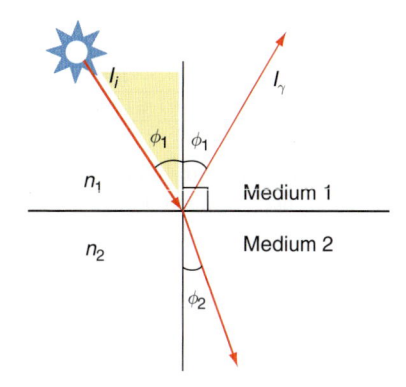

Figure 38 Reflection and refraction of smooth surfaces.

For unpolarized radiation, which is the case of natural solar radiation, the total reflectance is equal to the average of the two components:

$$r = \frac{I_r}{I_i} = \frac{r_\perp + r_\parallel}{2} \qquad [3]$$

The transmitted radiation is deflected by an angle ϕ_2 on the same plane of incidence and is related to ϕ_1, n_1, and n_2 by the relation

$$\frac{n_1}{n_2} = \frac{\sin \phi_2}{\sin \phi_1} \qquad [4]$$

For normal incidence, $\phi_1 = \phi_2 = 0$ and the reflectance is

$$r(0) = \left(\frac{n_1 - n_2}{n_1 + n_2}\right)^2 \qquad [5]$$

In collector glazing, the transmission of radiation takes place through a slab of transparent material and there are thus two interfaces per cover to cause reflection. Same rules apply for the beam at the second surface as at the first, assuming that there is air on both sides of the sheet. At each interface and for off-normal incidence, the reflected and transmitted radiation is partially polarized, and each polarization component is treated separately. Neglecting absorption of the material and considering unit intensity of the incident solar beam, the resulting transmittance for the parallel polarization component $\tau_{\parallel,r}$, as explicitly illustrated in **Figure 39**, is expressed by the following series of terms:

$$\tau_{\parallel,r} = (1 - r_\parallel)^2 + (1 - r_\parallel)^2 r_\parallel^2 + (1 - r_\parallel)^2 r_\parallel^4 + \cdots = (1 - r_\parallel)^2 (1 + r_\parallel^2 + r_\parallel^4 + \cdots) = (1 - r_\parallel)^2 \sum_{i=0}^{\infty} r_\parallel^{2i} \qquad [6]$$

where series $\sum_{i=0}^{\infty} r_\parallel^{2i}$ tends to $1/(1 - r_\parallel^2)$, so

$$\tau_{\parallel,r} = \frac{(1 - r_\parallel)^2}{1 - r_\parallel^2} = \frac{1 - r_\parallel}{1 + r_\parallel} \qquad [7]$$

In the same way, the perpendicular transmittance component is $\tau_{\perp,r} = (1 - r_\perp)/(1 + r_\perp)$. The two components $r_\parallel$ and $r_\perp$ have in general different values, so the total transmittance τ_r (without absorption) is the average of the components $\tau_{\parallel,r}$ and $\tau_{\perp,r}$:

$$\tau_r = \frac{\tau_{\parallel,r} + \tau_{\perp,r}}{2} = \frac{\left[\dfrac{1 - r_\perp}{1 + r_\perp} + \dfrac{1 - r_\parallel}{1 + r_\parallel}\right]}{2} \qquad [8]$$

The transmitted radiation becomes thus partially polarized, because of the different values of $\tau_{\parallel,r}$ and $\tau_{\perp,r}$:

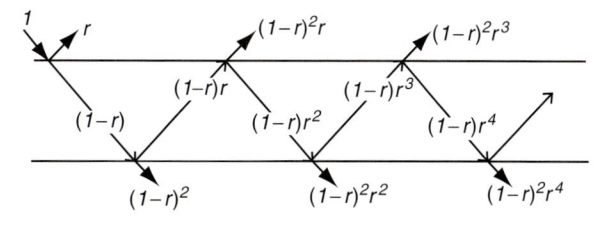

Figure 39 Ray trace for transmission and reflection of one nonabsorbing cover.

In a similar manner, for a system of n covers of the same material, the transmittance due to reflection only is

$$\tau_{r,n} = \frac{\left[\dfrac{1-r_\perp}{1+(2n-1)r_\perp} + \dfrac{1-r_\parallel}{1+(2n-1)r_\parallel}\right]}{2} \qquad [9]$$

Until now, no absorption of radiation by the transparent medium has been considered. In a partially transparent (translucent) medium, the absorption of radiation is expressed by the Beer–Lambert–Bouguer law, which assumes that absorption of radiation in an infinitesimal path dx, at a point inside a medium, is proportional to the intensity of radiation I at that point and the path length:

$$dI = -Ik\,dx \rightarrow \frac{dI}{I} = -k\,dx \qquad [10]$$

where dI is the infinitesimal absorption or the incremental decrease of the radiation intensity, k is a proportionality coefficient, the absorption or extinction coefficient, which is assumed to be constant in the solar spectrum, and x is the distance that radiation travels. Because there are fewer photons that pass through the path than those that are entering it, the intensity change is actually negative. The solution of the differential equation [10], for an overall traveled distance X, is obtained by integrating both sides.

$$\int_{I_0}^{I_X} \frac{dI}{I} = \int_0^X -k\,dx \rightarrow \ln(I_X) - \ln(I_0) = -kX$$

and because $\ln(I_X) - \ln(I_0) = \ln\dfrac{I_X}{I_0}$ then $\dfrac{I_X}{I_0} = e^{-kx}$ $\qquad [11]$

where I_0 is the entering radiation and I_X the transmitted radiation after traveling the distance X. The transmittance τ_a due to absorption in a path length X is by definition $\tau_a = I_X/I_0$. For a cover with thickness L, any traveled distance X can be expressed as $X = L/\cos(\phi_2)$, where ϕ_2 is the beam deflection angle, as in Figure 38. Then from eqn [11],

$$\tau_a = e^{\left(\dfrac{-kL}{\cos(\phi_2)}\right)} \qquad [12]$$

For glass, the extinction coefficient k takes values from $4\,\text{m}^{-1}$ (water white glass) to $34\,\text{m}^{-1}$ (high-iron glass).

Taking into account the transmittances due to reflection and absorption, a similar analysis, as previously for the combined transmittance τ, reflectance ρ, and absorptance α, for each polarization component yields the following relations (perpendicular polarization component):

$$\tau_\perp = \frac{\tau_a(1-r_\perp)^2}{1-(r_\perp \tau_a)^2} = \tau_a \frac{1-r_\perp}{1+r_\perp}\frac{1-r_\perp^2}{1-(r_\perp \tau_a)^2} \qquad [13]$$

$$\rho_\perp = r_\perp + \frac{\tau_a^2 r_\perp(1-r_\perp)^2}{1-(r_\perp \tau_a)^2} = r_\perp(1-\tau_a \tau_\perp) \qquad [14]$$

$$\alpha_\perp = (1-\tau_a)\left(\frac{1-r_\perp}{1-r_\perp \tau_a}\right) \qquad [15]$$

Similar relations are also extracted for the parallel polarization component. Thus, the total transmittance τ, reflectance ρ, and absorptance α are

$$\tau = \frac{\tau_\perp + \tau_\parallel}{2},\quad \rho = \frac{\rho_\perp + \rho_\parallel}{2},\quad a = \frac{a_\perp + a_\parallel}{2} \qquad [16]$$

From eqn [13], it is easily concluded that the last term $(1-r_\perp^2)/(1-(r_\perp \tau_a)^2)$ is approximately unity, because τ_a is usually >0.9 and $r<0.1$ for common collector covers. The same happens also for the parallel polarization component, and taking into account relation [8], the total transmittance can be written as

$$\tau \cong \tau_a \tau_r \qquad [17]$$

In a similar way, it can be seen that

$$\rho \cong \tau_a - \tau \quad \text{and} \quad a \cong 1 - \tau_a \qquad [18]$$

For a multicover system, ray-tracing technique and net radiation method [18] can be used to derive appropriate relations. For a two-cover system, the following equations apply for transmittance and reflectance:

$$\tau = \frac{\left(\dfrac{\tau_1 \tau_2}{1-\rho_1 \rho_2}\right)_\perp + \left(\dfrac{\tau_1 \tau_2}{1-\rho_1 \rho_2}\right)_\parallel}{2} \qquad [19]$$

$$\rho = \frac{\left(\rho_1 + \frac{\tau_1 \tau \rho_2}{\tau_2}\right)_\perp + \left(\rho_1 + \frac{\tau_1 \tau \rho_2}{\tau_2}\right)_\parallel}{2} \qquad [20]$$

where subscripts 1 and 2 refer to the external and internal cover, respectively. Using eqns [16] and [19], diagrams are extracted for the angular dependence of the transmittance, as shown in **Figures 40** and **41**. **Figure 40** refers to single-glass or double-glass, with same glasses, cover systems (refraction index $n = 1.526$, $kL = 0.05$), while **Figure 41** illustrates similar dependence for polycarbonate cover systems (refraction index $n = 1.6$, $kL = 0.03$). In each figure, three curves are plotted: one for the transmittance of a single nonabsorbing cover (due to reflection only), one for the combined (total) transmittance due to reflection and absorption for a single cover, and finally, one for the combined transmittance of a double cover system. Generally, the transmittance can be expressed as normalized quantity $\tau(\phi)/\tau(0)$, where $\tau(\phi)$ is the transmittance for incidence angle ϕ and $\tau(0)$ at normal incidence, otherwise denoted as τ_n. It can be expressed by a polynomial in cosine of incidence angle:

$$\frac{\tau}{\tau_n} = \sum_{i=0}^{I} a_i \cos^i(\phi) \qquad [21]$$

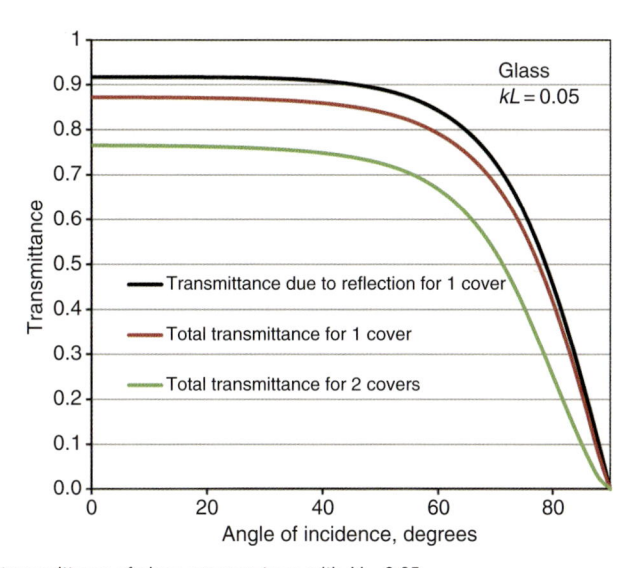

Figure 40 Angular dependence of transmittance of glass cover systems with $kL = 0.05$.

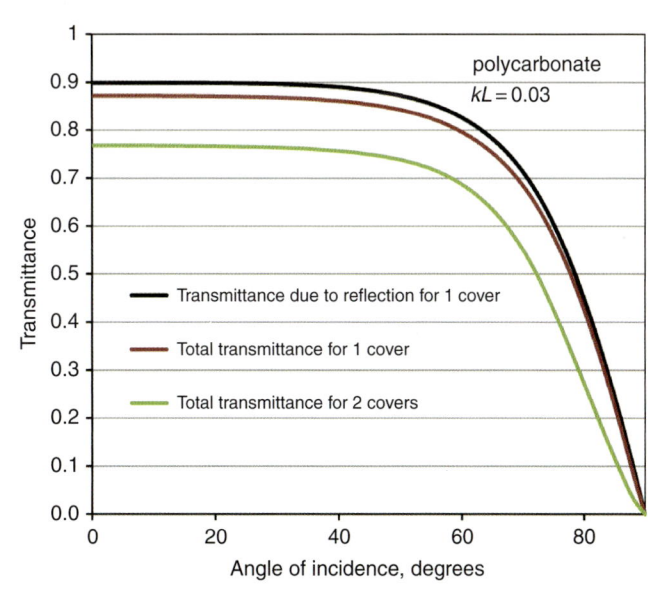

Figure 41 Angular dependence of transmittance of polycarbonate cover systems with $kL = 0.03$.

Table 2 Correlation coefficients for single and double glazing

Coefficient	Single glazing	Double glazing
A_0	−0.014 58	−0.017 91
A_1	3.371 57	1.548 39
A_2	−3.868 84	2.991 74
A_3	1.511 85	−7.155 28
A_4	–	3.633 05

Table 2 lists the coefficients a_i for single- and double-glass covers made of 4 mm-thick common float glass, whose refractive index is 1.517 and extinction coefficient is 28 m^{-1} [19].

Figure 42 illustrates the angular dependence of normalized transmittance τ/τ_n for common glazings, of single- and double-glass cover systems.

The previous analysis applies only to the beam component of solar radiation. However, the radiation incident on a collector consists also of diffuse sky radiation and radiation diffusely reflected from the ground. While the preceding analysis can be applied directly to beam contribution, the transmittance cover systems for diffuse and ground-reflected radiation must be calculated by integrating the transmittance over the appropriate incidence angles with an assumed sky model. In general, the angular distribution of sky and ground-reflected radiation is unknown. The calculation can be simplified by defining equivalent angles that give the same transmittance as the result of integration for diffuse and ground-reflected radiation [20]. The integration of the transmittance over the appropriate incident angle, with an isotropic diffuse radiation model, leads to an equivalent angle of incidence θ_{sky} for diffuse sky radiation:

$$\theta_{sky} = 59.68 - 0.138\,8\beta + 0.001\,497\beta^2 \qquad [22]$$

where β is the tilt angle of solar collector. For ground-reflected radiation, the equivalent angle of incidence θ_{gnd} is given by

$$\theta_{gnd} = 90 - 0.578\,8\beta + 0.002\,693\beta^2 \qquad [23]$$

For a collector tilt angle of 45°, $\theta_{sky} = 56.5°$ and $\theta_{gnd} = 69.4°$. Note that even when the beam radiation is at near-normal incidence, the equivalent incidence angles for the diffuse components are large.

For a stationary compound parabolic concentrator (CPC) collector with half-acceptance angle ψ, the equivalent angle of incidence for diffuse sky radiation is given by

$$\theta_{sky} = 44.86 - 0.071\,6\psi + 0.005\,12\psi^2 - 0.000\,027\,98\psi^3 \qquad [24]$$

All angles in relations [22]–[24] are expressed in degrees.

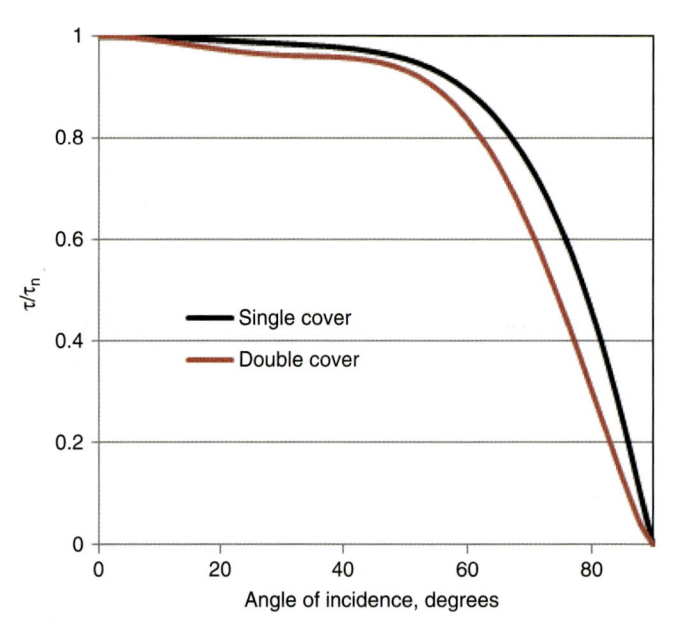

Figure 42 Angular dependence of normalized transmittance of common cover systems.

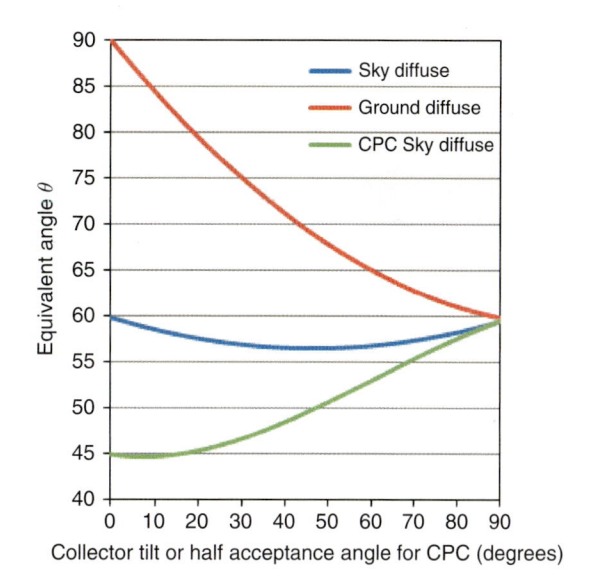

Figure 43 Equivalent angles of incidence versus collector tilt angle or half-acceptance angle (for compound parabolic concentrator collectors).

East–west orientations of CPC collectors accept very little diffuse ground radiation. North–south orientations see, however, the ground. In this case, the equivalent angles for diffuse ground and diffuse sky radiation can be assumed to be equal [14]. Diagrams of equivalent angles according to relations [22]–[24] are shown in **Figure 43**.

3.04.2.2 Antireflective Coatings

The total solar near-normal transmittance for common glass containing 0.01–0.1% iron oxide is 80–85%. For a low-iron glass, the near-normal total solar transmittance is approximately 90%. This is the upper limit for the transmittance of glass. It is, however, possible to further increase the transmittance by applying an optically thin film. As shown in **Figure 40**, the overall reflectance of one glass cover is ~8% (transmittance due to reflection-only curve) for normal incidence. This loss is even greater for greater angles of incidence. If a thin-film coating of a second transparent material, with refractive index n_2, is applied on one surface of a glass cover, at a thickness δ of several micrometers, the reflectivity is reduced and can be calculated from previous relevant relations, for normal incidence, as

$$\rho = 1 - \frac{4n_1 n_2}{(n_2^2 + n_1)(n_1 + 1)} \qquad [25]$$

It can be shown that eqn [25] has a minimum when $n_2 = \sqrt{n_1}$ and thus for glass (n_1 = 1.526) $n_2 = \sqrt{1.526} = 1.235$ leading to a minimum reflectance of 2.2%, and concerning also the reflectance at the second interface, the overall value amounts to around 4.1%, which is about half of this for uncoated glass. Unfortunately, there is no material with such an index that has good physical properties for an optical coating. The closest 'good' materials available are magnesium fluoride (MgF$_2$) (with an index of 1.38) and fluoropolymers (which can have indices as low as 1.30, but are more difficult to apply). for n_2 = 1.38 and from eqn [25], ρ = 2.8%, leading to a single sheet reflectance of 5.2%, instead of 8% for uncoated glass.

Furthermore, if the layer thickness δ is controlled precisely, so as to be exactly one-quarter of the radiation's wavelength ($\delta = \lambda/4$), then the layer is called a quarter-wave coating. For this type of coating, the incident beam I, when reflected from the second interface, will travel exactly half its own wavelength further than the beam reflected from the first surface. As shown in **Figure 44**, if the intensities of the two beams I_{R_1} and I_{R_2} are exactly equal, they will destructively interfere and cancel each other since they are exactly out of phase. Therefore, there is no reflection from the surface, and all the energy of the beam is added to the transmitted ray. However, the layer thickness will be ideal for only one distinct wavelength of radiation. This means it gives zero reflectance only at the specified wavelength and decreased reflectance for a broad wavelength interval around it.

Further reduction is possible by using multiple coating layers, designed such that reflections from the surfaces undergo maximum destructive interference. One way to do this is to add a second quarter-wave-thick higher index layer between the low-index layer and the substrate. The reflection from all three interfaces produces destructive interference and antireflection. Many coatings consist of transparent thin-film structures with alternating layers of contrasting refractive index. Layer thicknesses are chosen to produce destructive interference in the beams reflected from the interfaces and constructive interference in the corresponding transmitted beams. This makes the structure's performance changeable with wavelength and incident angle, so that color effects often appear at oblique angles. Common coatings on eyeglasses and photographic lenses often look somewhat bluish, since they reflect slightly more blue light than other visible wavelengths. Multilayer films have higher transmittance in a narrow wavelength interval. For wavelengths outside this design interval, the transmittance is lower than that of the bare substrate.

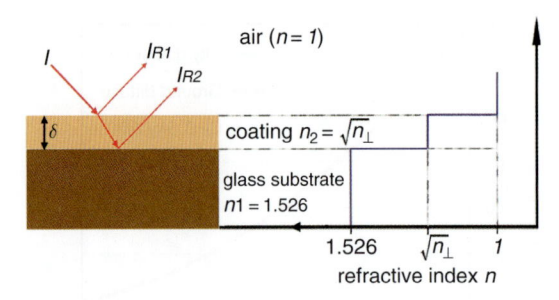

Figure 44 Antireflective thin-film coating, applied to glass substrate.

As solar collectors operate in a very broad wavelength interval, it is not easy to obtain high transmittance throughout this entire wavelength interval with a multilayer stack. However, coatings that give very low reflectivity over a broad band can be fabricated, although these are complex and expensive.

Multilayer thin-film coatings have durability problems. They can be destroyed if exposed to ambient conditions, as their scratch resistance is very poor. Fortunately, a proper thin film can be etched on the surface of glass by immersion in a silica supersaturated fluorosilicic acid bath. The acid attacks the glass surface, leaving a skeletonized porous silica layer with a near-optimum refractive index. In this way, the overall reflection loss can be reduced from 8% to 2%. It has been shown that antireflective films made with the etching process are long-term stable in outdoor conditions for at least 7 years [21]. Also, a further tempering treatment (which is usual for collector glazing) enhances durability properties of the antireflection layer. A disadvantage with this method is that glass containing boron is not etchable, and glazing of ETCs usually contains boron.

All glazings for solar collectors will probably have an antireflective coating in the future, as low-cost antireflection-treated glazings are now available in the market. The overall solar transmittance of one cover glazing is at maximum 90% and becomes easily 95% after treatment. This increment in the solar transmittance would lead to an increment of 10% in the annually collected energy.

3.04.2.3 Absorption of Solar Radiation

The absorption of electromagnetic radiation is a property of matter, associated with energy excitation bands in nuclear, atomic, or molecular level. A material can absorb an incident photon if it has an energy excitation gap equal to the energy of the photon. The energy E of a photon is given by the relation $E = h\nu = hc/\lambda$, where h is the Plank's constant ($6.625\,6 \times 10^{-34}$ J s), ν is the photon's frequency, c is the velocity of light in vacuum, and λ is the photon's wavelength. So, the absorption of radiation depends on the photon's wavelength, and it is essential to speak of wavelength-dependent or monochromatic absorptance. Also, the degree of absorption depends on the angle of incidence, and furthermore, a monochromatic directional absorptance $a_\lambda(\mu,\phi)$ is defined as the fraction of the incident radiation from the direction μ,ϕ at the wavelength λ that is absorbed, given by

$$a_\lambda(\mu,\phi) = \frac{I_{\lambda,a}(\mu,\phi)}{I_{\lambda,i}(\mu,\phi)} \qquad [26]$$

where μ is the cosine of the polar angle, ϕ the azimuth angle, and $I_{\lambda,a}(\mu,\phi)$ and $I_{\lambda,i}(\mu,\phi)$ the absorbed and incident radiation, respectively.

A directional absorptance $a(\mu,\phi)$ is defined as the fraction of radiation all over the wavelengths from the direction μ,ϕ that is absorbed by a surface:

$$a(\mu,\phi) = \frac{\int_0^\infty a_\lambda(\mu,\phi) I_{\lambda,i}(\mu,\phi)}{\int_0^\infty I_{\lambda,i}(\mu,\phi)} \qquad [27]$$

As concluded from the previous relation, the directional absorptance is also a function of the wavelength distribution of the incident radiation. The directional absorptance for solar absorbing surfaces can be considered as a function of only the angle of incidence. **Figure 45** demonstrates the angular dependence of solar absorptance for a typical selective surface [22]. However, it is convenient to express this dependence in a normalized form as the ratio a/a_n of angular absorptance and absorptance at normal incidence, as shown in **Figure 46** for a typical selective surface. Flat black and selective surfaces behave quite the same. A polynomial fit of a/a_n is developed for flat blackened surfaces, versus incidence angle θ (degrees), which can also be applied for selective surfaces [14],

$$\frac{a}{a_n} = 1 - 1.587\,9 \times 10^{-3}\theta + 2.731\,4 \times 10^{-4}\theta^2 - 2.302\,6 \times 10^{-5}\theta^3 + 9.024\,4 \times 10^{-7}\theta^4 - 1.8 \times 10^{-8}\theta^5$$
$$+ 1.773\,4 \times 10^{-10}\theta^6 - 6.993\,7 \times 10^{-13}\theta^7 \qquad [28]$$

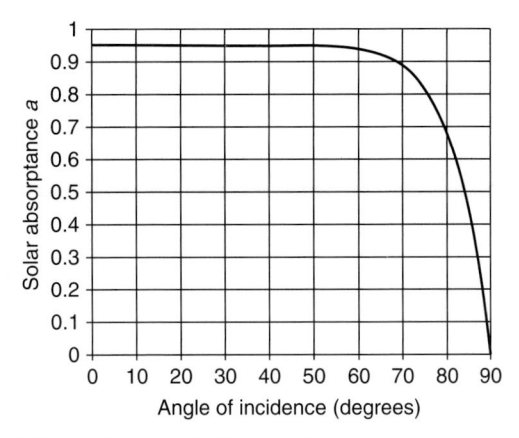

Figure 45 Solar absorptance of a typical selective surface versus incidence angle.

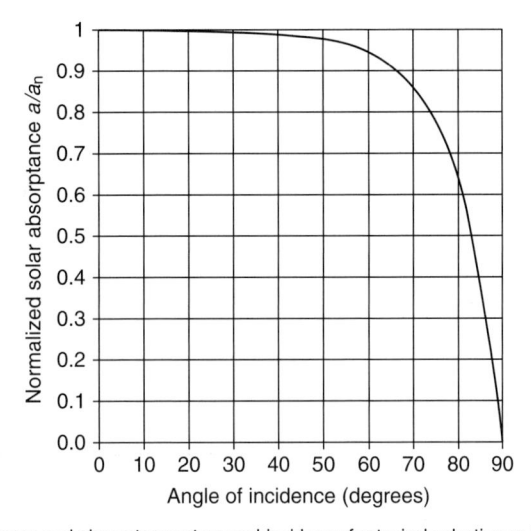

Figure 46 Ratio of solar angular absorptance and absorptance at normal incidence for typical selective or flat black surfaces.

or in polynomial form versus $\cos(\theta)$ as

$$\frac{a}{a_n} = 0.003\,38 + 5.751\,84\cos(\theta) - 15.741\,39\cos^2(\theta) + 23.586\,81\cos^3(\theta) \\ - 18.257\,56\cos^4(\theta) + 5.656\,58\cos^5(\theta)$$
[29]

Also, the curve of **Figure 46** can be correlated with the following polynomial fit versus $\cos(\theta)$:

$$\frac{a}{a_n} = 0.003\,54 + 5.421\,14\cos(\theta) - 13.222\,42\cos^2(\theta) + 17.516\,21\cos^3(\theta) \\ - 12.183\,44\cos^4(\theta) + 3.460\,29\cos^5(\theta)$$
[30]

3.04.2.4 Transmittance–Absorptance Product

For the performance calculation of solar collectors and systems, it is necessary to know the absorbed fraction of incident solar radiation. The net radiation transmitted through the cover system, calculated from eqn [13], [16], or [19], contacts the absorber. A great amount is absorbed, while a small portion is diffusively reflected and then a portion of this is reflected back to the absorber and so on. An infinite series of reflections–absorptions occur as illustrated in **Figure 47**. The energy absorbed by the absorber is then the sum of terms

$$(\tau a) = \tau a \sum_{i=0}^{\infty} \{(1-a)\rho_d\}^i = \frac{\tau a}{1-(1-a)\rho_d}$$
[31]

where τ is the transmittance of the cover at a certain incident angle, a the absorptance of the absorber, and ρ_d the reflectance of the cover system for diffuse radiation coming from the absorber. The reflectance ρ_d can be calculated from eqn [14] or [16] or in approximation from eqn [18], for an equivalent incident angle of 60°, as it is easily concluded from **Figure 43**. For a single untreated glass cover, $\rho_d \approx 0.15$. Note that (τa) is slightly greater than the product $\tau \times a$.

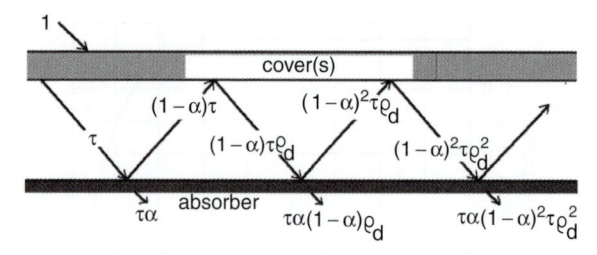

Figure 47 Ray tracing of absorption of solar radiation by absorber.

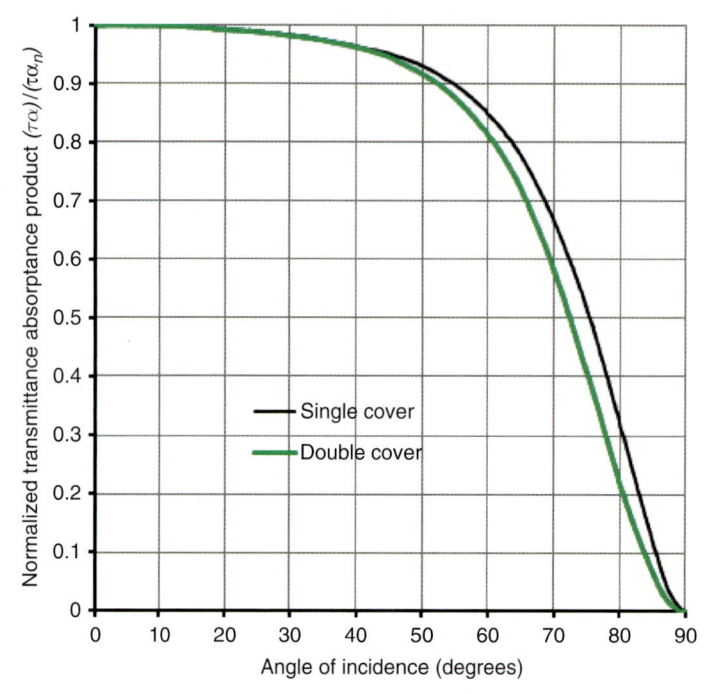

Figure 48 Normalized transmittance–absorptance product versus incidence angle.

As previously shown, the cover(s) transmittance and collector absorptance are functions of angle of incidence of the incident solar radiation. It is more convenient to express this dependence in normalized form $(\tau a)/(\tau a_n)$, as previously for τ/τ_n and a/a_n. Using previous relevant equations [13]–[31], diagrams of single- and double-glass ($n = 1.526$) cover systems with $kL = 0.04$ are drawn for FPCs, as shown in **Figure 48**. The plots are nearly independent of the value of kL within the range 0.01–0.06 but are sensitive to the refractive index of the cover material, so **Figure 48** is applicable only for glass or other glazing materials that have a refractive index similar to that of glass [23]. ETCs, with or without back reflectors, behave generally differently, depending on their orientation.

According to ISO, EN, and ASHRAE standardizations for solar collector performance, the angular dependence of $(\tau a)/(\tau a_n)$ is expressed by a measurable factor, the incident angle modifier K_θ, which is determined experimentally, as a characteristic property of every collector and it will be discussed later.

3.04.2.5 Absorbed Solar Energy

The solar radiation incident on the collector plane includes three components: beam, sky diffuse, and diffusely reflected from the ground. Each component must be treated separately, as differently originated. So the absorbed solar energy q_s, per square meter of collector area, will be the sum of three terms, each comprising the product of the respective radiation component I and transmittance–absorptance product (τa). If I_b and I_d are the beam and sky diffuse solar radiation intensity on horizontal plane and $(\tau a)_b$, $(\tau a)_d$, and $(\tau a)_g$ are the transmittance–absorptance product for beam, sky diffuse, and ground-reflected radiation, respectively, then

$$q_s = I(\tau a) = I_b R_b (\tau a)_b + I_d R_d (\tau a)_d + \rho_g (I_b + I_d) R_g (\tau a)_g \qquad [32]$$

where R_b, R_d, and R_g are the ratios of beam, sky diffuse, and ground-reflected radiation on the collector surface to that on the horizontal plane, respectively, and ρ_g is the ground reflectance. The ratio R_b is a complicated function of angles of incidence on the collector plane and on the horizontal plane, as defined in the previous section. The ratios R_d and R_g depend on the diffuse radiation model. If the isotropic model is considered, then the two ratios are equal to the thermal radiation view factors between collector and sky and collector and ground [24], that is, $R_d = (1 + \cos \beta)/2$, $R_g = (1 - \cos \beta)/2$, where β is the collector tilt. Therefore, eqn [32] is modified as

$$q_s = I_b R_b (\tau\alpha)_b + I_d \frac{1 + \cos\beta}{2} (\tau\alpha)_d + \rho_g (I_b + I_d) \frac{1 - \cos\beta}{2} (\tau\alpha)_g \qquad [33]$$

The transmittance–absorptance products $(\tau\alpha)_b$, $(\tau\alpha)_d$, and $(\tau\alpha)_g$ are determined for the relative angles of incidence, as described previously.

3.04.3 Thermal Analysis

Well-known heat transfer laws are applied for the description of solar collector thermal behavior and the definition of energy gains. The examination of FPCs will be first accomplished and where necessary it will be extended to ETCs, which in general behave quite the same. Basic heat transfer knowledge will be considered acquainted in what follows.

3.04.3.1 Steady-State Energy Balance of FPC

An FPC with one cover is considered, as in **Figure 49**. The absorbed portion $q_s = I(\tau\alpha)$ of the incident radiation I heats up the absorber and then a fraction of q_s is transferred as useful energy q_u to the working fluid, while the rest is lost to ambient. Heat loss occurs through the mechanisms of convection, radiation, and conduction between absorber–cover and absorber–casing. Then, heat is lost to ambient by convection and radiation from the top cover and the outside surface of the casing (back and edge). In the case of a non-IR-opaque cover (semitransparent), such as one made from organic materials, a part of the absorber IR radiation is exchanged directly with the ambient. Absorber, cover, and external casing surface can be considered at first approach as isothermal nodes, provided there is adequate fluid flow rate to keep temperature gradients on the absorber plate (across the fluid flow) small. This assumption is intensified by the high thermal conductivity of the absorber material (metal sheets in majority), which results in temperature gradient smoothing. Also, because the cover plate is very thin, there is no practical temperature drop across its thickness. Under these assumptions, the energy balance is written in terms of power exchanged per square meter of collector area A_c, which might be the absorber area, the aperture area, or the gross area (including casing):

$$q_c^{c-a} = h_c^{c-a}(T_c - T_a), \quad q_r^{c-a} = h_r^{c-a}(T_c - T_{sk}), \quad q^{c-a} = q_c^{c-a} + q_r^{c-a} \qquad [34]$$

$$q_c^{p-c} = h_c^{p-c}(T_p - T_c), \quad q_r^{p-c} = h_r^{p-c}(T_p - T_c), \quad q^{p-c} = (h_c^{p-c} + h_r^{p-c})(T_p - T_c) \qquad [35]$$

$$q_r^{p-a} = \tau_{c,r} h_r^{p-a}(T_p - T_{sk}), \quad q_{cd}^{p-b} = \frac{k_b}{d_b}(T_p - T_b) \qquad [36]$$

$$q_c^{b-a} = h_c^{b-a}(T_b - T_a), \quad q_r^{b-a} = h_r^{b-a}(T_b - T_a) \qquad [37]$$

where superscripts p, c, a, and b denote absorber plate, cover, ambient, and back plate, respectively. Subscripts c, r, and cd denote heat transfer by convection, radiation, and conduction, respectively. Symbols T_c, T_p, T_b, T_a, and T_{sk} are the cover, absorber plate, back plate, ambient, and sky equivalent temperature, respectively, while $\tau_{c,r}$ is the cover transmittance for thermal radiation and k_b and d_b the

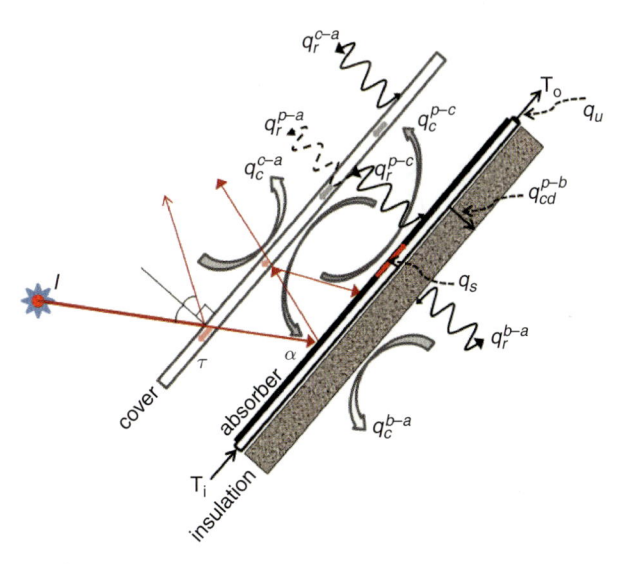

Figure 49 Energy balance in a flat-plate collector.

thermal conductivity and thickness of the back insulation, respectively. Various heat transfer coefficients are denoted by letter h. Heat loss from the edges of the casing must also be calculated. The evaluation of edge loss is a complicated task, because the absorber to edge insulation contact area is not exactly known. However, edge loss is very small, so it is not necessary to predict it precisely. Because the edge area is much smaller than the collector area, edge heat loss must be referenced to the collector area. It is more convenient to consider an overall edge loss coefficient area product $(UA)_{\text{edge}}$, so the edge loss, based on the collector area A_c, becomes

$$q_{cd}^{p-e} = \frac{(UA_e)}{A_c}(T_p - T_e) \qquad [38]$$

$$q_c^{e-a} = h_c^{e-a}(T_e - T_a)\frac{A_e}{A_c}, \quad q_r^{e-a} = h_r^{e-a}(T_e - T_a)\frac{A_e}{A_c} \qquad [39]$$

where superscript and subscript 'e' denotes edge. Edge external surface temperature T_e can be considered equal to T_b, because edge insulation is usually similar to back insulation.

The sky temperature T_{sk} is a function of T_a. Then the top and back-edge loss can be calculated as

$$q_{\text{top}} = q^{c-a} + q_r^{p-a} = q^{p-c} + q_r^{p-a} \qquad [40]$$

$$q_{\text{back-edge}} = q_{cd}^{p-b} + q_{cd}^{p-e} = q_c^{b-a} + q_r^{b-a} + q_c^{e-a} + q_r^{e-a} \qquad [41]$$

Defining various heat transfer coefficients h, thermal conductivities k, thicknesses d, areas A, and $\tau_{c,r}$, then for fixed values of T_p, T_a, and T_{sk}, the above system of equations [34]–[41] can be solved for the determination of T_c, T_b, T_e, q_{top}, and $q_{\text{back-edge}}$ and thus the energy gain obtained is calculated. A simpler schematic representation (electrical analog) of the energy balance configuration is given in **Figure 50**, and the individual terms will be described below. However, further assumptions can be made. The back and edge loss can be considered to occur directly to the ambient, because the back and edge insulation is strong enough such that $T_b \approx T_e \approx T_a$. Thus, R_4 can be neglected:

$$q_{cd}^{p-b} = \frac{k_b}{d_b}(T_p - T_a) \quad \text{and} \quad q_{cd}^{p-e} = \frac{(UA_e)}{A_c}(T_p - T_a) \qquad [42]$$

Furthermore, if the cover is considered as IR-opaque material, then the term q_r^{p-a} is 0 and the terms that remain to be defined are h_r^{c-a}, h_c^{c-a}, h_r^{p-c}, and h_c^{p-c}.

3.04.3.1.1 Radiation exchange between glazing and sky h_r^{c-a}

The exchange of thermal radiation between two diffuse surfaces 1 and 2, with areas A_1, A_2 and emittances ε_1, ε_2, is expressed by the following equation:

$$Q_1 = -Q_2 = \frac{\sigma(T_2^4 - T_1^4)}{\frac{1-\varepsilon_1}{\varepsilon_1 A_1} + \frac{1}{A_1 F_{12}} + \frac{1-\varepsilon_2}{\varepsilon_2 A_2}} \qquad [43]$$

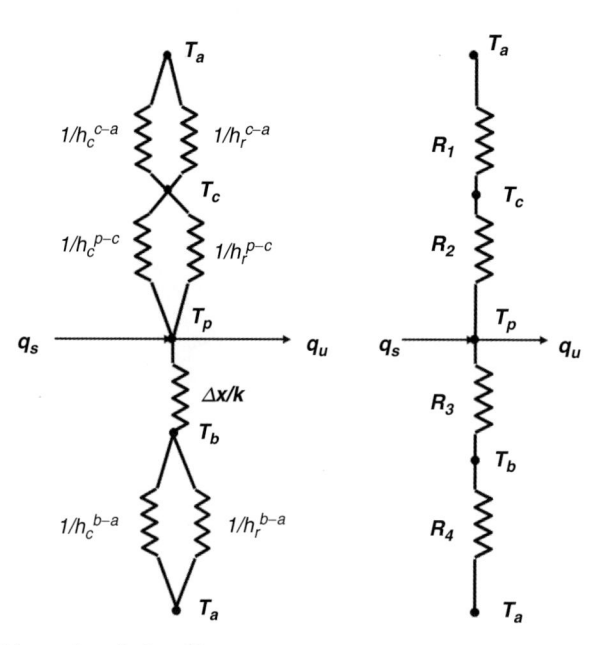

Figure 50 Equivalent heat flow circuit for a solar collector with one cover.

where σ is the Stefan–Boltzmann constant equal to 5.6697×10^{-8} W m^{-2} K^{-4} and F_{12} is a geometric configuration factor, called shape factor or view factor, which determines the fraction of emitted radiation from surface 1, which is incident on surface 2.

A special case is when a small surface 1 is surrounded by a large surface 2. So $A_1/A_2 \approx 0$ and $F_{12} = 1$; then dividing both sides of eqn [43] by A_1 yields

$$\frac{Q_1}{A_1} = \frac{\dfrac{\sigma(T_2^4 - T_1^4)}{\dfrac{1-\varepsilon_1}{\varepsilon_1 A_1} + \dfrac{1}{A_1 F_{12}} + \dfrac{1-\varepsilon_2}{\varepsilon_2 A_2}}}{A_1} = \frac{\sigma(T_2^4 - T_1^4)}{\dfrac{1-\varepsilon_1}{\varepsilon_1} + \dfrac{1}{F_{12}} + \dfrac{A_1}{A_2}\dfrac{1-\varepsilon_2}{\varepsilon_2}} = \frac{\sigma(T_2^4 - T_1^4)}{\dfrac{1}{\varepsilon_1} - 1 + 1 + 0} = \varepsilon_1 \sigma(T_2^4 - T_1^4)$$

$$Q_1 = \varepsilon_1 A_1 \sigma(T_2^4 - T_1^4) \qquad [44]$$

This result is independent of the large surface properties, since very little of the radiation leaving the small surface is reflected back from the large enclosure. Therefore, the large enclosure acts like a blackbody. The sky can be considered as a blackbody at an equivalent temperature T_{sk}, so the net radiation exchange between a horizontal surface and the sky is calculated from eqn [44], that is, the net radiation from a surface, with area A, emittance ε, and temperature T, to the sky is

$$Q = \varepsilon A \sigma(T^4 - T_{sk}^4) \qquad [45]$$

A radiation heat transfer coefficient h_r^{c-a} must be defined for the calculation of q_r^{c-a}:

$$h_r^{c-a} = \varepsilon_c \sigma(T_c + T_{sk})(T_c^2 + T_{sk}^2) \qquad [46]$$

which multiplied by $(T_c - T_{sk})$ gives q_r^{c-a}.

The atmosphere does not have a uniform temperature. It radiates selectively at certain wavelengths and is essentially transparent in the wavelength range from 8 to 14 μm, while outside this range it has absorbing bands covering much of the far-IR spectrum. Several relations have been proposed to associate T_{sk} with measured meteorological variables. The most important are summarized in **Table 3**. Different correlations are suitable for different conditions. If calculations should be compared to solar collector experimental results at clear sky conditions, it is recommended to use the correlation according to reference [25], while if ambient relative humidity ϕ_a is measured, the correlation of reference [26] is more suitable. For whole-year simulations, based on climatic and operation conditions, the correlation of reference [27] incorporating the influence of humidity and sky cloudiness is more adequate. Climatic databases usually contain information on relative humidity ϕ_a and sky clearness index K_T, which is the ratio between global solar horizontal radiation at the earth's surface and solar horizontal extraterrestrial radiation. Temperatures of **Table 3** represent ambient temperature as T_a and dew point temperature as T_{dp}. The variable p_d in the correlation of reference [27] represents the partial water vapor pressure in Pa, which is equal to $\phi_a \, p_d''$, where p_d'' is the partial saturated water vapor pressure, which can be calculated from the following relation [27]:

$$p_d'' = 611 e^{17.27 \frac{T_a - 273}{T_a - 36}} \qquad [47]$$

Dew point temperature T_{dp} (K) can be calculated according to the following equation, with p_d in Pa [28]:

$$T_{dp} = \frac{5179.25}{20.519 - \ln\left(\dfrac{760 p_d}{101\,325}\right)} \qquad [48]$$

3.04.3.1.2 Convection exchange between glazing and ambient h_c^{c-a}

The determination of heat transfer by convection from the collector glazing to ambient is a quite difficult task. The convection heat transfer coefficient h_c^{c-a} is influenced by collector dimensions, its slope, airflow yaw angle, turbulence intensity, and the ratio of free to forced convection. A large number of relationships and correlations can be found in the literature. All are derived from experiments, having more or less relation with the operational conditions of solar collector installations. Correlations obtained from experiments in wind tunnels with low turbulence levels [29, 30] will produce lower values for h_c^{c-a} than correlations obtained from outdoor experiments [31–34]. More complicated expressions are those relating the heat transfer coefficient with Nusselt number. The majority of relative works tend to produce simple correlations in the form of linear functions $h_c^{c-a} = a + bw$, where w is

Table 3 Relations for equivalent sky temperature, T_{sk} (K)

Reference	Relation – description
[25]	$T_{sk} = 0.0552 T_a^{1.5} - T_{sk}$ and T_a in kelvin, clear sky
[26]	$T_{sk} = T_a (0.711 + 0.0056 T_{dp} + 0.00073 T_{dp}^2 + 0.013 \cos(15t))^{\frac{1}{4}} - T_{sk}$ and T_a in kelvin, T_{dp} in °C, t in hours from midnight, clear sky
[27]	$T_{sk} = 94 + 12.6 \ln(p_d) - 13 K_T + 0.341 T_a - T_{sk}$ and T_a in kelvin, p_d in Pa

Table 4 Relations for glazing to ambient heat transfer coefficient, h_c^{c-a} (W m^{-2} K^{-1})

Reference	Relation – description
[35]	$h_c^{c-a} = 5.7 + 3.8w$ for $w < 5$ m s^{-1}
	$h_c^{c-a} = 6.47 w^{0.78}$ for $w > 5$ m s^{-1}
[31], [32]	$h_c^{c-a} = 8.55 + 2.56w$ for $0 < w < 5$ m s^{-1}
[33]	$h_c^{c-a} = 10.03 + 4.687w$ for $0 < w < 4$ m s^{-1}
[34]	$h_c^{c-a} = 8.3 + 2.2w$ for $0.8 < w < 6.5$ m s^{-1} and yaw 0°
	$h_c^{c-a} = 6.5 + 3.3w$ for $0.8 < w < 6.5$ m s^{-1} and yaw 90°
[36]	$h_c^{c-a} = 2.3 + 3.0w$ for $0 < w < 7$ m s^{-1}

the wind velocity in m s^{-1}. These relations have been chosen to be mentioned here, as easier to use relations, and are presented in Table 4. In solar collector calculations, the most used correlation is that of reference [35], as it gives results that are closer to experimental values confirmed by many other authors.

3.04.3.1.3 Radiation exchange between absorber and glazing h_r^{p-c}

The radiation heat transfer between absorber and cover can be described as a special case of eqn [43]. The absorber and cover areas are equal and the absorber plate lies very close to the cover, so $A_1 = A_2 = A_c$ and $F_{12} = 1$ and eqn [43] reduces to

$$q_r^{p-c} = \frac{Q_r^{p-c}}{A_c} = \frac{\sigma(T_p^4 - T_c^4)}{\frac{1}{\varepsilon_p} + \frac{1}{\varepsilon_c} - 1} \qquad [49]$$

Therefore, the radiation heat transfer coefficient h_r^{p-c} is defined as

$$h_r^{p-c} = \frac{\sigma}{\frac{1}{\varepsilon_p} + \frac{1}{\varepsilon_c} - 1} (T_p^2 + T_c^2)(T_p + T_c) \qquad [50]$$

such as eqn [49] becomes

$$q_r^{p-c} = h_r^{p-c}(T_p - T_c) \qquad [51]$$

3.04.3.1.4 Convection exchange between absorber and cover h_c^{p-c}

Heat transfer between absorber and cover takes place by natural circulation of the gas (air) enclosed in the space between absorber and cover. Heat transfer by natural convection in the enclosed gas layer is characterized by Nusselt number Nu_L related to characteristic dimension of the layer, that is, its thickness L (the spacing between absorber and cover). Nusselt number definition leads to the calculation of heat transfer coefficient h_c^{p-c}:

$$h_c^{p-c} = \frac{Nu_L \, k_a}{L} \qquad [52]$$

where k_a is the thermal conductivity of the enclosed gas evaluated at the mean absorber–cover temperature $\bar{T}_{p-c}$, in W m^{-1} K^{-1}, and L the length in meters. The Nusselt number for natural convection in enclosures is dependent on Rayleigh number Ra_L, that is, the product of Grashof number Gr_L and Prandtl number Pr:

$$Ra_L = Gr_L \, Pr, \quad Gr_L = \frac{\beta g L^3 \, \Delta T^2}{\nu} = \frac{1}{\bar{T}_{p-c}} \frac{gL^3 (T_p - T_c)}{\nu^2}, \quad Pr = \frac{\nu}{a} = \frac{\nu \rho c}{k_a} = \frac{\mu c}{k_a} \qquad [53]$$

where ν is the gas kinematic viscosity (m^2 s^{-1}), a the gas thermal diffusivity (m^2 s^{-1}), ρ the gas density (kg m^{-3}), c the gas specific heat capacity (J kg^{-1} K^{-1}), β the gas volumetric thermal expansion coefficient (K^{-1}), equal to $1/T$ for ideal gases, and g the acceleration due to gravity (m s^{-2}).

A great number of relations exist in the literature for natural convection heat transfer in gas enclosures with upward heat flow. They are all correlations developed from experimental data, for various validity ranges of Raleigh Ra_L or Grashof Gr_L number, inclination angles ψ, and aspect ratios H/L (where H is the length of the enclosure). Selected equations are presented in Table 5, accompanied by their experimental limits. The last correlation represents an overall mean value of many models, valid for high values of H/L (>20) on which Nusselt number does not show any practical dependence.

3.04.3.1.5 Conduction back and edge exchange between absorber and ambient

Absorber back thermal loss was previously simplified as conduction heat loss to ambient temperature:

$$q_{cd}^{p-b} = \frac{k_b}{d_b}(T_p - T_a)$$

Table 5 Relations for convection heat transfer between absorber and cover (for h_c^{p-c} calculation)

Reference	Relation – description
[37]	$Nu_L = 1 + 1.44 \left[1 - \dfrac{1708}{Ra_L \cos\psi}\right]^+ \left(1 - \dfrac{(\sin 1.8\psi)^{1.6} 1708}{Ra_L \cos\psi}\right) + \left[\left(\dfrac{Ra_L \cos\psi}{5830}\right)^{1/3} - 1\right]^+$ for $0 < Ra_L < 10^5$ and $0° < \psi < 75°$, where $[X]^+ = (|X| + X)/2$
[38]	$Nu_L = 0.118[Ra_L \cos^2(\psi - 45)]^{0.29}$ for $2.8 \times 10^3 < Ra_L < 2.2 \times 10^5$, $45° < \psi < 90°$, and $9 < H/L < 36$
[39]	$Nu_L = 0.210 Gr_L^{0.269}(H/L)^{-0.131}$ for $1.5 \times 10^3 < Gr_L < 7 \times 10^6$, $\psi = 90°$, and $5 < H/L < 79$
[40]	$Nu_L = a(\psi) Ra_L^{1/3}$ for $10^5 < Ra_L < 4 \times 10^6$, $0° < \psi < 90°$, and $6 < H/L < 27$

ψ	$a(\psi)$	ψ	$a(\psi)$	ψ	$a(\psi)$	ψ	$a(\psi)$	ψ	$a(\psi)$	ψ	$a(\psi)$	ψ	$a(\psi)$	ψ	$a(\psi)$	ψ	$a(\psi)$	ψ	$a(\psi)$
0	0.080	10	0.079	20	0.075	30	0.074	40	0.074	50	0.074	60	0.072	70	0.069	80	0.068	90	0.062

[41]	$Nu_L = (0.1464 - 2.602 \times 10^{-4}\psi - 2.046 \times 10^{-6}\psi^2) Ra_L^{0.29}$ for $10^4 < Ra_L < 2 \times 10^6$ and $0° < \psi < 90°$

and edge loss as

$$q_{cd}^{p-e} = \frac{(UA_e)}{A_c}(T_p - T_a)$$

So, the only task is to determine the thermal conductivity k_b and thickness d_b of back insulation and an overall product of edge loss coefficient and edge area (UA_e). For usual insulating materials (polyurethane, mineral wool, glass wool, etc.), k_b takes values between 0.032 and 0.035 W m^{-1} K^{-1} and usual thicknesses are 0.03–0.05 m. For a well-insulated collector, $(UA_e)/A_c$ usually has a value lower than 0.10 W m^{-2} K^{-1}.

3.04.3.1.6 Overall thermal loss determination q_{loss}

The overall heat loss of a solar collector can be determined by analyzing it as three components: top loss, back loss, and edge loss. According to **Figure 50**, the following relationships could be written:

$$q_{loss,top} = (h_c^{p-c} + h_r^{p-c})(T_p - T_c) \qquad [54]$$

$$q_{loss,top} = h_c^{c-a}(T_c - T_a) + h_r^{c-a}(T_c - T_{sk}) \qquad [55]$$

The above system of nonlinear equations [54] and [55] can be solved for given values of T_p, T_a, and T_{sk}, so that T_c and $q_{loss,top}$ are determined.

The back and edge losses are already determined as

$$q_{loss,back} = \frac{k_b}{d_b}(T_p - T_a) \qquad [56]$$

$$q_{loss,edge} = \frac{(UA_e)}{A_c}(T_p - T_a) \qquad [57]$$

so they are easily calculated for given values of T_p and T_a. The overall loss q_{loss} is then calculated as the sum of all three losses:

$$q_{loss} = q_{loss,top} + q_{loss,back} + q_{loss,edge} \qquad [58]$$

For ETCs, the term h_c^{p-c} is 0, and for Dewar-type absorber (concentric tubes), the term h_r^{p-c} becomes [42]

$$h_r^{p-c} = \frac{\sigma(T_p + T_c)(T_p^2 + T_c^2)}{\dfrac{1}{\varepsilon_p} + \dfrac{D_p}{D_c}\left(\dfrac{1}{\varepsilon_c} - 1\right)} \qquad [59]$$

where ε_p and ε_c are the absorber and cover emittance, respectively, and D_p and D_c are the inner (absorber) and outer (cover) glass diameters, respectively.

If a second cover is used, then one more isothermal node must be added and one more equation is to be solved for the unknown temperature of the second cover.

It is, however, convenient to define an overall thermal loss coefficient U_L as the sum of three individual loss coefficients, the top U_t, back U_b, and edge U_e:

$$U_L = U_t + U_b + U_e \quad [60]$$

According to **Figure 50**

$$U_t = \frac{1}{R_1 + R_2}, \quad U_b = \frac{1}{R_3} = \frac{k_b}{d_b}, \quad U_e = \frac{(UA)_e}{A_c} \quad [61]$$

with

$$R_1 = \frac{1}{h_c^{c-a} + h_r^{c-a}}, \quad R_2 = \frac{1}{h_c^{p-c} + h_r^{p-c}} \quad [62]$$

3.04.3.2 Solar Collector Top Heat Loss Coefficient U_t

The evaluation of top heat loss coefficient U_t from eqn [61] involves an iterative process for the determination of the cover temperature as an intermediate step. The elimination of the cover temperature would greatly facilitate the evaluation of U_t. Efforts in this direction have been made yielding relations of semiempirical nature. Thus, the top heat loss coefficient may be written as

$$U_t = \left[\frac{N}{\frac{C}{T_p}\left[\frac{T_p - T_a}{(N+f)}\right]^e} + \frac{1}{h_w} \right]^{-1} + \frac{\sigma(T_p^2 + T_a^2)(T_p + T_a)}{\frac{1}{d} + \frac{2N + f - 1}{\varepsilon_g} + g - N} \quad [63]$$

For the three most popular relations, expressions of the various parameters are presented in **Table 6**, where N is the number of glass covers, β the collector tilt (degrees), ε_g the emittance of glass cover, ε_p the absorber emittance, T_p the absorber temperature (K), T_a the ambient temperature (K), h_w the wind heat transfer coefficient h_c^{c-a} (W m^{-2} K^{-1}), and L the air gap spacing between absorber and cover (m).

Comparative diagrams of U_t for the three relations as a function of absorber temperature are presented in **Figure 51**, where numbering corresponds to the tabulation of **Table 6**.

For the evaluation of heat loss coefficient of ETCs, an algorithm has been proposed as described in reference [45].

3.04.3.3 Useful Energy Transferred to the Working Fluid

Heat transfer from the absorber surface to the working fluid can be described by considering an internal energy balance. In steady-state condition, the rate of heat transfer to the fluid flowing through the collector depends on the temperature of the collector surface, the temperature of the fluid, and the heat transfer coefficient between collector and fluid. A liquid FPC of bonded-tube type will be initially analyzed, as it has a more complicated geometry. Theoretical elaboration will be based on defining the temperature distribution on the absorber fin, as shown schematically in **Figure 52**.

Solar radiation is absorbed on the upper surface of the collector plate. A part is absorbed on the surface directly above the bonded tubes, while another part is absorbed on the plate connecting any two adjacent tubes. The latter part is conducted in a transverse direction toward the tubes. The temperature of the plate has a maximum at any midpoint between adjacent tubes, and the collector plate acts as a fin bonded to the walls of the flow tubes. The distance between adjacent tubes is indicated as W, the tube external diameter as D, and the plate thickness as δ. The temperature gradient in the flow direction is considered negligible, and because the plate material is a good heat conductor, the temperature gradient through the fin thickness is also considered negligible. Therefore, the region between a midpoint and the tube base can be considered as fin with length $(W - D)/2$. If an elemental area of width Δx and unit length in the direction of flow is considered, as in **Figure 53**, then from Fourier's law an energy balance on this element yields

Table 6 Parameters for expressions of top heat loss coefficient, U_t

Reference	C	d	e	f	g
[14]	$520(1-0.000\,051\,\beta^2)$ for $0° < \beta < 70°$, if $70° < \beta < 90°$ then $\beta = 70°$	$\varepsilon_p + 0.00591Nh_w$	$0.43\left(1 - \dfrac{100}{T_p}\right)$	$(1 + 0.089h_w - 0.1166h_w\varepsilon_p)$ $(1 + 0.078\,66\,N)$	$\dfrac{0.133\varepsilon_p}{\varepsilon_g}$
[43]	$250[1 - 0.004\,4(\beta - 90)]$	$\varepsilon_p + 0.05N(1 - \varepsilon_p)$	0.33	$(1 - 0.04h_w + 0.000\,5\,h_w^2)$ $(1 + 0.091N)$	0
[44]	$\dfrac{204.429(\cos\beta)^{0.252}}{L^{0.24}}$	$\varepsilon_p + 0.425N(1-\varepsilon_p)$	0.252	$\left(\dfrac{9}{h_w} - \dfrac{30}{h_w^2}\right)\dfrac{T_a}{316.9}(1 + 0.091N)$	0

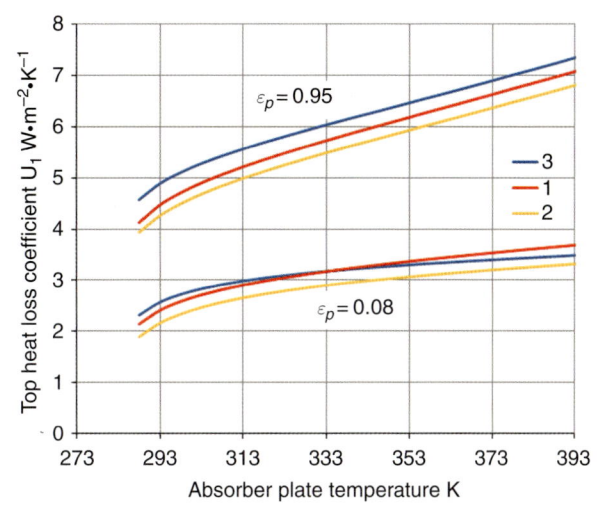

Figure 51 Top loss coefficient as a function of absorber temperature, for one glass cover, $h_w = 10\,W\,m^{-2}\,K^{-1}$, $T_a = 283\,K$, $\beta = 45°$, and for two absorbing surfaces, flat black ($\varepsilon_p = 0.95$) and selective ($\varepsilon_p = 0.08$).

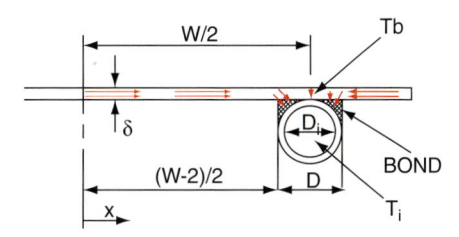

Figure 52 Schematic of a bonded-tube absorber.

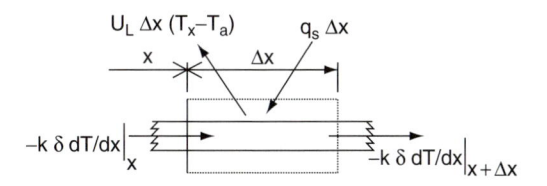

Figure 53 Fin elemental energy balance.

$$q_s\,\Delta x - U_L\,\Delta x(T_{av} - T_a) + \left(-k_p\delta\frac{dT}{dx}\right)\bigg|_x - \left(-k_p\delta\frac{dT}{dx}\right)\bigg|_{x+\Delta x} = 0 \qquad [64]$$

where q_s is the absorbed solar energy per unit area, U_L the overall heat loss coefficient, k_p the plate thermal conductivity, T_a the ambient temperature, and T_{av} the average temperature of the element.

Making a Taylor's expansion of the temperature gradient $\frac{dT}{dx}\big|_{x+\Delta x}$ at $x+\Delta x$ in terms of that at x, one finds that

$$\frac{dT}{dx}\bigg|_{x+\Delta x} = \frac{dT}{dx}\bigg|_x + \frac{d}{dx}\left(\frac{dT}{dx}\right)\bigg|_x \Delta x + \frac{d^2}{dx^2}\left(\frac{dT}{dx}\right)\bigg|_x \frac{(\Delta x)^2}{2!} + \cdots \qquad [65]$$

Then considering that the plate thickness δ is uniform and the thermal conductivity k_p is independent of the temperature and dividing by Δx, eqn [64] becomes

$$q_s - U_L(T_{av} - T_a) - k_p\delta\frac{dT}{dx}\bigg|_x + k_p\delta\frac{dT}{dx}\bigg|_x + k_p\delta\frac{d^2T}{dx^2}\bigg|_x + \frac{d^3T}{dx^3}\bigg|_x \frac{(\Delta x)}{2!} + \cdots = 0 \qquad [66]$$

This conservation of energy must be satisfied for all elements of the fin, so upon allowing $\Delta x \to 0$ also $T_{av} \to T_x$, and the following differential equation is obtained:

$$q_s - U_L(T_x - T_a) + k_p\delta\frac{d^2T}{dx^2} = 0 \to \frac{d^2T}{dx^2} = \frac{U_L}{k_p\delta}\left(T_x - T_a - \frac{q_s}{U_L}\right) \qquad [67]$$

This second-order differential equation has two boundary conditions:

- $dT/dx|_{x=0} = 0$, because of the symmetry at the midpoint, and
- $T|_{x=(W-D)/2} = T_b$, as it was assumed.

For convenience, two auxiliary variables are defined:

$$\Psi = T_x - T_a - \frac{q_s}{U_L}, \quad m = \sqrt{\frac{U_L}{k_p \delta}} \quad [68]$$

Thus, eqn [67] is transformed to

$$\frac{d^2\Psi}{dx^2} - m^2\Psi = 0 \quad [69]$$

with boundary conditions

$$\left.\frac{d\Psi}{dx}\right|_{x=0} = 0, \quad \Psi|_{x=(W-D)/2} = T_b - T_a - \frac{q_s}{U_L} \quad [70]$$

For the solution of the differential equation [69], U_L is considered constant, so the resulting second-order homogeneous differential equation [69] has the characteristic (algebraic) equation

$$\lambda^2 - m^2 = 0, \text{ thus } \lambda = \pm m \text{ and } \lambda_2 = -\lambda_1$$

The general solution in this case is

$$\Psi = c_1 e^{\lambda_1 x} + c_2 e^{\lambda_2 x}, \quad \Psi = C_1 \sinh mx + C_2 \cosh mx \quad [71]$$

with $C_1 = c_1 + c_2$, $C_2 = c_1 - c_2$ and $\sinh mx = \frac{1}{2}(e^{mx} - e^{-mx})$, $\cosh mx = \frac{1}{2}(e^{mx} + e^{-mx})$.

The constants C_1 and C_2 are determined by satisfying the boundary conditions:

- At $x = \frac{(W-D)}{2}$, $\Psi = T_b - T_a - \frac{q_s}{U_L}$, thus,

$$T_b - T_a - \frac{q_s}{U_L} = C_1 \sinh m\left(\frac{W-D}{2}\right) + C_2 \cosh m\left(\frac{W-D}{2}\right) \quad [72]$$

- At $x = 0$, $\left.\frac{d\Psi}{dx}\right|_{x=0} = 0$, thus, $C_1 m \cosh 0 + C_2 m \sinh 0 = 0 \rightarrow C_1 m = 0 \rightarrow C_1 = 0$ [73]

Substituting C_1 in eqn [72]:

$$T_b - T_a - \frac{q_s}{U_L} = C_2 \cosh m\left(\frac{W-D}{2}\right) \rightarrow C_2 = \frac{T_b - T_a - \frac{q_s}{U_L}}{\cosh m\left(\frac{W-D}{2}\right)} \quad [74]$$

Substituting C_1 and C_2 in eqn [71], the expression for T_x results:

$$T_x = T_a + \frac{q_s}{U_L} + \frac{T_b - T_a - \frac{q_s}{U_L}}{\cosh m\left(\frac{W-D}{2}\right)} \cosh mx \quad [75]$$

and

$$\frac{dT_x}{dx} = m \frac{T_b - T_a - \frac{q_s}{U_L}}{\cosh m\left(\frac{W-D}{2}\right)} \sinh mx \quad [76]$$

Applying Fourier's law at the fin base, the energy q_f transferred to the bond area of the tube, per unit length in the direction of the flow, is then $q_f = -k_p \delta dT_x/dx|_{x=(W-D)/2}$, and therefore, eqn [76] is written as

$$q_{\rm f} = -k_{\rm p}\delta m \frac{T_{\rm b}-T_{\rm a}-\dfrac{q_{\rm s}}{U_{\rm L}}}{\cosh m\left(\dfrac{W-D}{2}\right)} \sinh m\left(\frac{W-D}{2}\right) = -k_{\rm p}\delta m \tanh m\left(\frac{W-D}{2}\right)\left(T_{\rm b}-T_{\rm a}-\frac{q_{\rm s}}{U_{\rm L}}\right) \quad [77]$$

Multiplying and dividing eqn [77] by $U_{\rm L}$ one gets

$$q_{\rm f} = -k_{\rm p}\delta m \tanh m\left(\frac{W-D}{2}\right)\left(T_{\rm b}-T_{\rm a}-\frac{q_{\rm s}}{U_{\rm L}}\right)\frac{U_{\rm L}}{U_{\rm L}} = -\frac{k_{\rm p}\delta m}{U_{\rm L}} \tanh m\left(\frac{W-D}{2}\right)((T_{\rm b}-T_{\rm a})U_{\rm L}-q_{\rm s})$$

Observing that $\dfrac{k_{\rm p}\delta m}{U_{\rm L}} = \dfrac{k_{\rm p}\delta}{U_{\rm L}}\sqrt{\dfrac{U_{\rm L}}{k_{\rm p}\delta}} = \sqrt{\dfrac{U_{\rm L}}{k_{\rm p}\delta}}\sqrt{\dfrac{k_{\rm p}\delta}{U_{\rm L}}}\sqrt{\dfrac{k_{\rm p}\delta}{U_{\rm L}}} = \dfrac{1}{m}$, eqn [77] becomes

$$q_{\rm f} = \frac{1}{m}[q_{\rm s}-U_{\rm L}(T_{\rm b}-T_{\rm a})]\tanh m\left(\frac{W-D}{2}\right) \quad [78]$$

Equation [78] expresses the energy transferred to the tube area from only one side of the fin. Then, from both sides this quantity is simply doubled:

$$q_{\rm f} = \frac{2}{m}[q_{\rm s}-U_{\rm L}(T_{\rm b}-T_{\rm a})]\tanh m\left(\frac{W-D}{2}\right) \quad [79]$$

Multiplying and dividing eqn [79] by $(W-D)$, a final expression for $q_{\rm f}$ is obtained:

$$q_{\rm f} = (W-D)[q_{\rm s}-U_{\rm L}(T_{\rm b}-T_{\rm a})]\frac{\tanh[m(W-D)/2]}{m(W-D)/2} \quad [80]$$

The maximum energy $q_{\rm f,max}$ that would be transferred by the fin is obtained if the entire fin had been at uniform temperature equal to $T_{\rm b}$. Then

$$q_{\rm f,max} = (W-D)[q_{\rm s}-U_{\rm L}(T_{\rm b}-T_{\rm a})] \quad [81]$$

If the transferred energy $q_{\rm f}$ is written using the concept of fin efficiency F, then $q_{\rm f} = Fq_{\rm f,max}$, so from eqns [80] and [81]

$$F = \frac{\tanh[m(W-D)/2]}{m(W-D)/2} \quad [82]$$

which expresses the standard fin efficiency for straight fins with a rectangular profile.

Equation [80] gives the energy flow to the tube area through the fin. In order to express the total energy gain, the energy $q_{\rm t}$ collected above the tube region must be added. The energy gain for this region is

$$q_{\rm t} = D[q_{\rm s}-U_{\rm L}(T_{\rm b}-T_{\rm a})] \quad [83]$$

and the total useful energy gain $q_{\rm u}$ is the sum of $q_{\rm t}$ and $q_{\rm f}$:

$$q_{\rm u} = [D+(W-D)F][q_{\rm s}-U_{\rm L}(T_{\rm b}-T_{\rm a})] \quad [84]$$

This useful energy gain is transferred to the flowing fluid inside the tube. This energy transfer takes place through the bond by conduction with resistance $1/C_{\rm b}$ and through the inner tube surface by convection with resistance $1/h_{\rm f}\pi D_{\rm i}$, where $h_{\rm f}$ is the heat transfer coefficient between the tube wall and the fluid (W m^{-2} K^{-1}), $D_{\rm i}$ the internal tube diameter (m), and $C_{\rm b}$ the bond conductance (W m^{-1} K^{-1}).

The bond conductance has a significant effect on the collector efficiency and must be well estimated. It can be determined by the relation $C_{\rm b} = k_{\rm b}d_{\rm b}/\delta_{\rm b}$, where $k_{\rm b}$ is the bond thermal conductivity, $d_{\rm b}$ the bond width, and $\delta_{\rm b}$ the average bond thickness.

The useful energy gain $q_{\rm u}$ per unit length in the flow direction is expressed as

$$q_{\rm u} = \frac{T_{\rm b}-T_{\rm f}}{\dfrac{1}{h_{\rm f}\pi D_{\rm i}} + \dfrac{1}{C_{\rm b}}} \quad [85]$$

where $T_{\rm f}$ is the fluid temperature.

Equations [84] and [85] include the bond temperature $T_{\rm b}$, which, in general, is unknown. It is therefore more useful to express $q_{\rm u}$ in terms of $T_{\rm f}$, by introducing a collector efficiency factor F', in the form

$$q_{\rm u} = WF'[q_{\rm s}-U_{\rm L}(T_{\rm f}-T_{\rm a})] \quad [86]$$

By combining eqns [84] and [85] $T_{\rm b}$ is eliminated and the collector efficiency factor is expressed as

$$F' = \frac{1/U_L}{W\left[\dfrac{1}{U_L[D+(W-D)F]} + \dfrac{1}{h_f \pi D_i} + \dfrac{1}{C_b}\right]} \qquad [87]$$

Physically, F' represents the ratio of the actual useful energy gain to the useful gain that would result if the absorbing surface of the collector had been at the fluid temperature. In eqn [87], the parameters U_L, h_f, and F are functions of temperature. As U_L and h_f are not strong functions of temperature, it means that F is also not a strong function of temperature, as can be seen from eqns [68] and [82]. Therefore, for any specific collector design and fluid flow rate, the collector efficiency factor F' is essentially a characteristic property.

Many relations for the calculation of the heat transfer coefficient h_f exist in heat transfer literature. For fully developed turbulent liquid flow inside tubes, one widely used relation [46], valid for $2300 < Re = \rho v D/\mu < 5 \times 10^6$ and $0.5 < Pr < 2000$, is

$$Nu = \frac{(f/8)(Re - 1000)Pr}{1 + 12.7\sqrt{f/8}(Pr^{2/3} - 1)} \qquad [88]$$

where the friction factor for smooth pipes is given by

$$f = (0.79 \ln Re - 1.64)^{-2} \qquad [89]$$

For laminar forced convection heat transfer in circular pipes, the case of constant heat flux shows higher applicability than for the constant temperature case, because the riser pipe is uniformly irradiated. Other boundary conditions can also be taken into account as developing profiles of temperature or velocity. One useful relation [47] is

$$Nu = 3.66 + \frac{0.066\,8(D/L)Re\,Pr}{1 + 0.04[(D/L)Re\,Pr]^{2/3}} \qquad [90]$$

where in eqns [88]–[90], D and L are the inside diameter and the length of the pipe.

For noncircular tubes, the hydraulic diameter $D_h = 4 \times$ (flow area)/(wetted perimeter) is used for the characteristic length, in the preceding equations.

For solar air collectors, a useful relation [48] for the calculation of the heat transfer coefficient, in the case of fully developed turbulent flow, with one side heated and the other side insulated, is the following:

$$Nu = 0.0158\,Re^{0.8} \qquad [91]$$

For other collector designs, the same methodology as mentioned above can be applied and similar relations for F and F' are extracted. In **Table 7**, expressions for F' are presented for some typical liquid and air collector cases. Similar expressions can be extracted for ETCs. For example, for the ETC shown in **Figure 29(b)**, the same analysis as mentioned above applies, if the two streams of the U-type tube are well thermally decoupled.

3.04.3.4 Collector Heat-Removal Factor

Considering an FPC with n risers in parallel flow, the useful energy q_u is transferred to the fluid resulting in an increase in its temperature. An energy balance for a section of flow duct Δy, as in **Figure 54**, can be written as

$$(\dot{m}/n)c_p T_f|_{y+\Delta y} - (\dot{m}/n)c_p T_f|_y - q_u \Delta y = 0 \qquad [92]$$

where c_p is the fluid specific heat and $\dot{m}$ is the overall collector flow rate. As $\Delta y \to 0$ and substituting q_u from eqn [86], the following differential equation is obtained:

$$\dot{m} c_p \frac{dT_f}{dy} - nW F'[q_s - U_L(T_f - T_a)] = 0 \qquad [93]$$

If F' and U_L are considered independent of temperature and position and if $T_{f,in}$ is the inlet fluid temperature, then the solution to eqn [93] is

$$\frac{T_f - T_a - \dfrac{q_s}{U_L}}{T_{f,in} - T_a - \dfrac{q_s}{U_L}} = e^{-\left(\dfrac{U_L nWF'y}{\dot{m}c_p}\right)} \qquad [94]$$

For $y = L$, where L is the total length of the collector, then $T_f = T_{f,out}$, where $T_{f,out}$ is the fluid outlet temperature, and eqn [94] becomes

$$\frac{T_{f,out} - T_a - \dfrac{q_s}{U_L}}{T_{f,in} - T_a - \dfrac{q_s}{U_L}} = e^{-\left(\dfrac{U_L nWF'L}{\dot{m}c_p}\right)}$$

and observing that $nWL = A_c$, where A_c is the collector area, then

Table 7 Collector efficiency factors for various collector designs

Reference	Collector design
	Liquid solar collectors

[49]

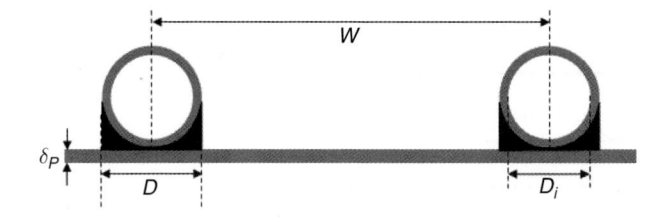

$$F' = \cfrac{1}{\cfrac{WU_L}{\pi D_i h_f} + \cfrac{D}{W} + \cfrac{1}{\cfrac{WU_L}{C_b} + \cfrac{W}{(W-D)F}}}, \quad F \text{ the same as in eqn [82]}$$

[49]

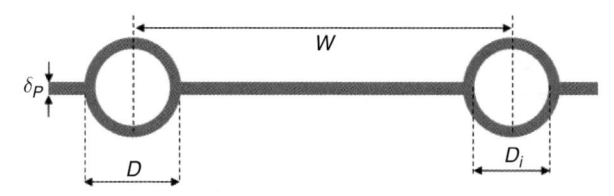

$$F' = \cfrac{1}{\cfrac{WU_L}{\pi D_i h_f} + \cfrac{W}{D + (W-D)F}}, \quad F \text{ the same as in eqn [82]}$$

[50]

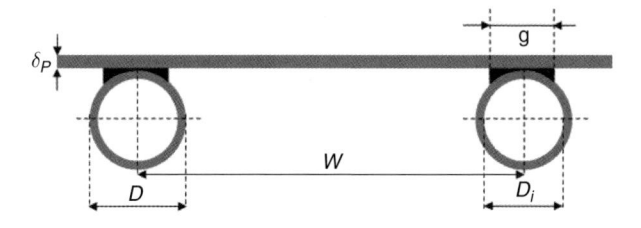

$$F = \cfrac{\tanh\left[\sqrt{\cfrac{U_L}{k_p \delta_p}}(W-g)/2\right]}{\sqrt{\cfrac{U_L}{k_p \delta_p}}(W-g)/2}, \quad F' = \left[W\left(\cfrac{1}{(W-g)F+g} + \cfrac{U_L}{k_{gF}\pi D_i}\right)\right]^{-1},$$

$$k_{gF} = \left(\cfrac{1}{c} + \cfrac{1}{S_\infty}\right)^{-1} \cfrac{k_F\, Nu}{\pi D_i/2}, \quad c = \cfrac{k_{gd}\, g/2}{k_F\, Nu}$$

$$S_\infty = \cfrac{\pi \eta_d}{2} + \cfrac{(1+\eta_d)g/2}{D_i}, \quad \eta_d = \cfrac{\tanh \mu_d}{\mu_d}, \quad \mu_d = \cfrac{1}{2}(\pi D_i - g)\sqrt{\cfrac{Nu\, k_F}{D_i k_t \delta_t}}$$

where k_{gd} is the heat transfer coefficient between fin base and tube or the bond conductance (W m^{-2} K^{-1}), k_F the fluid thermal conductivity (W m^{-1} K^{-1}), k_t the tube thermal conductivity (W m^{-1} K^{-1}), δ_t the tube wall thickness (m), and Nu the Nusselt number for the tube flow

(Continued)

140 Components

Table 7	(Continued)	
Reference	Collector design	
	Air solar collectors	
[14]	flow → ε_1, h_1, T_1 → ← ε_2, h_2, T_2 flow → $$F' = \cfrac{1}{1 + \cfrac{U_L}{h_1 + \cfrac{1}{\cfrac{1}{h_2}+\cfrac{1}{h_r}}}} , \quad h_r = \cfrac{\sigma(T_1^2 + T_2^2)(T_1 + T_2)}{\cfrac{1}{\varepsilon_1}+\cfrac{1}{\varepsilon_2}-1}$$	
[14]	flow normal to view, ε_1, h_1, T_1, ε_2, h_2, T_2, ψ $$F' = \cfrac{1}{1 + \cfrac{U_L}{\cfrac{h_1}{\sin(\psi/2)} + \cfrac{1}{\cfrac{1}{h_2}+\cfrac{1}{h_r}}}}, \quad h_r = \sigma(T_1^2 + T_2^2)(T_1 + T_2)$$ $$\cfrac{1}{\varepsilon_1}+\cfrac{1}{\varepsilon_2}-1$$	

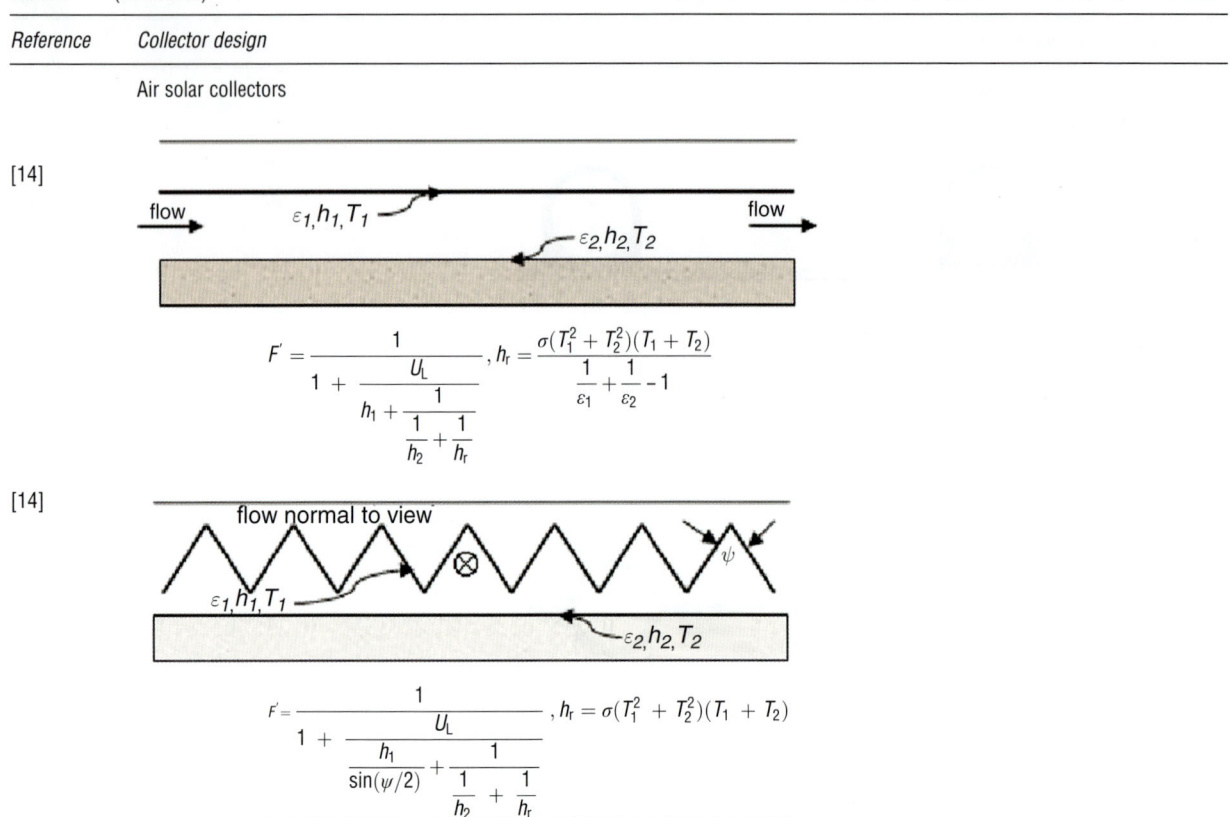

$$\frac{T_{f,\text{out}} - T_a - \dfrac{q_s}{U_L}}{T_{f,\text{in}} - T_a - \dfrac{q_s}{U_L}} = e^{-\left(\frac{U_L A_c F'}{\dot{m} c_p}\right)} \qquad [95]$$

The thermodynamic optimum of a collector occurs when the working fluid remains at the inlet temperature throughout the whole collector (this could be approached when the fluid flow is very high). To compare the performance of a real collector with its thermodynamic optimum, it is convenient to introduce a heat-removal factor F_R as the ratio of the actual heat gain to the maximum heat gain (thermodynamic optimum):

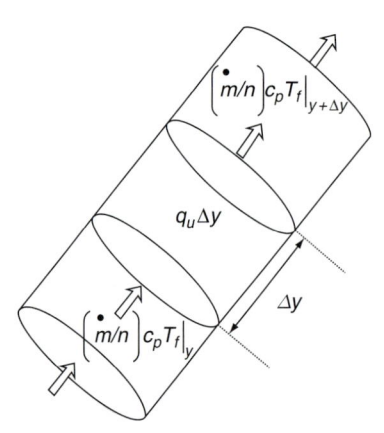

Figure 54 Energy balance in the fluid flow direction.

$$F_R = \frac{\dot{m}c_p(T_{f,out} - T_{f,in})}{A_c[q_s - U_L(T_{f,in} - T_a)]} = \frac{\dot{m}c_p}{A_cU_L}\left[\frac{T_{f,out} - T_{f,in}}{\frac{q_s}{U_L} - (T_{f,in} - T_a)}\right] = \frac{\dot{m}c_p}{A_cU_L}\left[\frac{\left(T_{f,out} - T_a - \frac{q_s}{U_L}\right) - \left(T_{f,in} - T_a - \frac{q_s}{U_L}\right)}{\frac{q_s}{U_L} - (T_{f,in} - T_a)}\right] \quad [96]$$

which combined with eqn [95] is written as

$$F_R = \frac{\dot{m}c_p}{A_cU_L}\left[1 - \frac{\frac{q_s}{U_L} - (T_{f,out} - T_a)}{\frac{q_s}{U_L} - (T_{f,in} - T_a)}\right] = \frac{\dot{m}c_p}{A_cU_L}\left[1 - e^{-\left(\frac{A_cU_LF'}{\dot{m}c_p}\right)}\right] \quad [97]$$

From eqn [97], it is evident that F_R increases with increasing flow rate and approaches F', the collector efficiency factor, as an upper limit. Thus, it is convenient to define the collector flow factor F'' as the ratio of F_R to F', which is a function of the dimensionless collector capacitance rate $A_cU_LF'/\dot{m}c_p$

$$F'' = \frac{F_R}{F'} = \frac{\dot{m}c_p}{A_cU_LF'}\left[1 - e^{-\left(\frac{A_cU_LF'}{\dot{m}c_p}\right)}\right] \quad [98]$$

Since the numerator $\dot{m}c_p(T_{f,out} - T_{f,in})$ of eqn [96] represents Q_u, the useful energy transferred to the fluid, it can now be expressed in terms of the fluid inlet temperature as

$$Q_u = A_cF_R[q_s - U_L(T_{f,in} - T_a)] \quad [99]$$

By substituting q_s from eqn [32], eqn [99] becomes

$$Q_u = A_cF_R[I_T(\tau\alpha) - U_L(T_{f,in} - T_a)] \quad [100]$$

where I_T is the intensity of solar radiation on the collector plane. This is a very convenient expression for Q_u because the fluid inlet temperature is usually known or can be easily specified. Another useful expression is to write Q_u using the collector efficiency factor F' in place of F_R, which means that $T_{f,in}$ must also be replaced by the mean fluid temperature $T_{f,m}$, so that

$$Q_u = A_cF'[I_T(\tau\alpha) - U_L(T_{f,m} - T_a)] \quad [101]$$

3.04.4 Collector Performance Determination

There are a number of existing standards that specify procedures for testing the performance of stationary solar collectors. The most important are documented in ASHRAE 93-2003 [51], ISO 9806-1 [52], and EN12975-2 [53] editions. The ASHRAE 93 standard requires an experimental determination of the steady-state collector efficiency under prescribed environmental conditions for a range of collector fluid temperatures. The EN12975-2 and ISO 9806-1 standards include similar steady-state test procedures, while providing an alternative transient test method that can be conducted over a larger range of environmental conditions. All of them include the determination of (1) instantaneous efficiency (with beam radiation near normal to the absorber surface), (2) effects of angle of incidence of solar radiation, and (3) heat capacity effects.

3.04.4.1 Collector Efficiency

The useful gain Q_u of a solar collector can be determined by measuring the fluid flow rate $\dot{m}$, the inlet fluid temperature $T_{f,in}$, and the outlet fluid temperature $T_{f,out}$:

$$Q_u = \dot{m}c_p(T_{f,out} - T_{f,in}) \quad [102]$$

In steady-state conditions, the instantaneous efficiency η_i can be defined as

$$\eta_i = \frac{Q_u}{A_cI_T} = \frac{\dot{m}c_p(T_{f,out} - T_{f,in})}{A_cI_T} \quad [103]$$

If radiation I_T on the collector plane and the ambient temperature T_a are also monitored, then using eqn [100]

$$\eta_i = \frac{Q_u}{A_cI_T} = F_R(\tau\alpha) - \frac{F_RU_L(T_{f,in} - T_a)}{I_T} \quad [104]$$

It is also possible to express η_i versus the mean fluid temperature $T_{f,m} = (T_{f,out} + T_{f,in})/2$, as predicted by the EN12975-2 standard, so that

$$\eta_i = F_m(\tau\alpha) - \frac{F_m U_L (T_{f,m} - T_a)}{I_T} \qquad [105]$$

where F_m is equal to F' as concluded from eqn [86].

The instantaneous efficiency η_i can be calculated from eqn [103], using appropriate instrumentation for the measurement of temperature, flow rate, and solar radiation intensity. From eqns [104] and [105], it is obvious that the results for η_i can be plotted versus $(T_{f,in} - T_a)/I_T$ or $(T_{f,m} - T_a)/I_T$. Almost the same specifications, details, and means are provided in all three standards. Measurements may be carried out either outdoors or indoors. Indoor tests are made using a solar simulator and means to produce wind, resembling ambient conditions (incident solar radiation, wind, etc.). Outdoor steady-state tests are carried out in the midday hours on clear days (high beam radiation) with the beam radiation nearly normal to the collector plane. Thus, the value of the transmittance–absorptance product is approximately that at normal incidence and is written as $(\tau\alpha)_n$. ASHRAE 93-2003 standard specifies the plot of η_i versus $(T_{f,in} - T_a)/I_T$ and a linear expression for η_i according to eqn [104]. Thus, a straight line is produced with intercept $F_R(\tau\alpha)_n$ and slope $-F_R U_L$. Disregarding experimental errors, mainly because F_R and U_L are not constant, there is always data scattering. The EN12975-2 and ISO 9806-1 standards specify the plot of η_i versus $(T_{f,m} - T_a)/I_T$, and generally a second-order expression for η_i is obtained in the form

$$\eta_i = \eta_0 - a_1 \frac{T_{f,m} - T_a}{I_T} - a_2 I_T \left(\frac{T_{f,m} - T_a}{I_T} \right)^2 \qquad [106]$$

According to ISO 9806-1 standard, the choice between a first- or a second-order curve shall be based on the closeness of fit, which can be achieved by least squares regression. However, a second-order fit shall not be used if the value deduced for a_2 is negative, as suggested by both EN12975-2 and ISO 9806-1. The constant term η_0 is called zero-loss or optical efficiency and is equal to $F'(\tau\alpha)_n$. Also, from eqn [106] it is concluded that $F'U_L = a_1 + a_2 (T_{f,m} - T_a)$.

The collector area A_c in the denominator of eqn [103] may be determined in various ways as gross area, aperture area, or absorber area. Gross area is defined as the total area occupied by a collector module, that is, including external dimensions of casing and headers. Aperture area is the unobstructed cover area or the total area less the cover supports. The absorber area is simply the unobstructed area of the absorber. The differences between these areas are small for FPCs, while they may be large for ETCs. However, for design calculations, it does not matter which area is used if it is clearly specified. Only for impression purposes, some manufacturers use the more spectacular results, which usually are extracted based on the absorber area.

In **Figure 55**, instantaneous efficiencies, according to EN12975-2, are presented for three representative collector designs: a flat plate with selective paint ($a_p = 0.96$, $\varepsilon_p = 0.1$), another flat plate with ordinary flat black paint ($a_p = 0.97$, $\varepsilon_p = 0.95$), and one evacuated tube ($a_p = 0.96$, $\varepsilon_p = 0.08$) of twin glass type, with U-type finned tubes and CPC reflector. As shown, each collector design is suitable for different combinations of temperature differences ($T_{f,m} - T_a$) and insolation rates I_T. Finally, in **Figure 56**, the influence of the chosen collector area on the calculation of instantaneous efficiency is shown, where the efficiency curves correspond to a heat pipe ETC without back reflector.

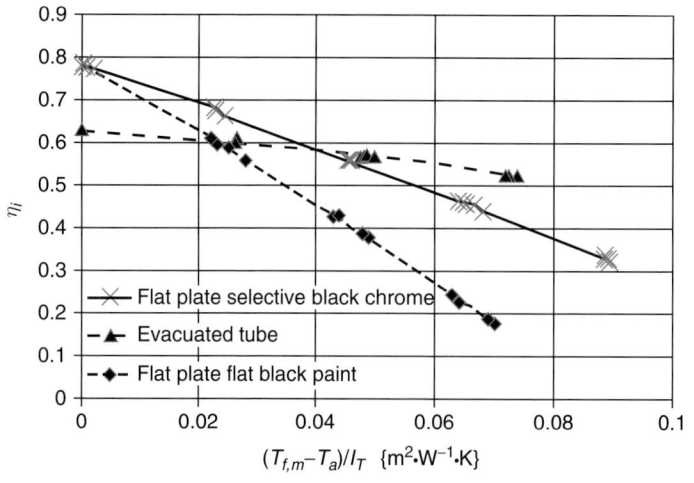

Figure 55 Instantaneous efficiency for typical collector designs based on aperture area.

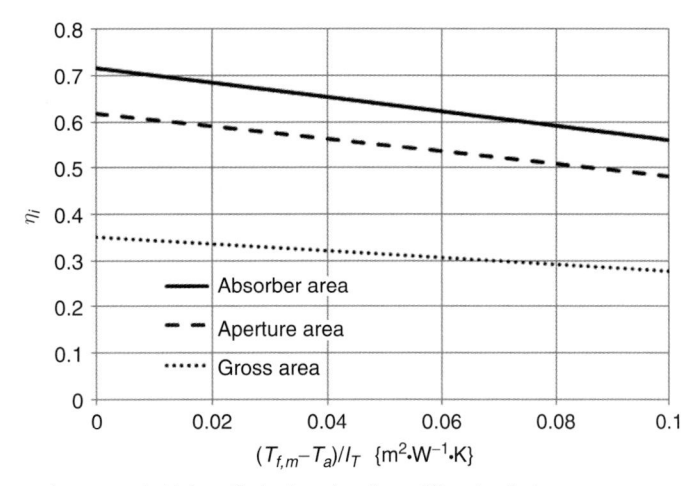

Figure 56 Instantaneous efficiency of an evacuated tube collector based on three different collector areas.

3.04.4.2 Incident Angle Modifier

The calculation of useful energy gain, Q_u, in any operative condition by eqns [100] and [101] requires the knowledge of transmittance–absorbance product $(\tau\alpha)$ in any arbitrary angle of incidence, which generally is a property of any individual collector design. If the term $F'(\tau\alpha)$ or $F_R(\tau\alpha)$ could be replaced by the terms $F'(\tau\alpha)_n$ and $F_R(\tau\alpha)_n$, as they are previously mentioned, then Q_u is calculated easily, provided that another measurable factor called the incidence angle modifier, K_θ, is introduced in eqns [100] and [101], so that

$$Q_u = A_c F_R \left[I_T K_\theta (\tau\alpha)_n - U_L (T_{f,in} - T_a) \right] \quad [107]$$

and

$$Q_u = A_c F' \left[I_T K_\theta (\tau\alpha)_n - U_L (T_{f,m} - T_a) \right] \quad [108]$$

where $K_\theta = (\tau a)/(\tau a)_n$. According to the methodology established in the standards mentioned above, the efficiency tests are carried out on clear days around midday. This means that the experimental value of (τa) is essentially the same for beam radiation $(\tau a)_b$, so the incidence angle modifier for beam radiation incident at angle θ_b is written as

$$K_\theta(\theta_b) = \frac{(\tau a)_b}{(\tau a)_n} \quad [109]$$

In ASHRAE 93-2003, EN12975-2, and ISO 9806-1 standards, procedures for the determination of K_θ are provided, and its dependence on the angle of incidence is expressed by the following relation:

$$K_\theta = 1 - b_o \left(\frac{1}{\cos\theta} - 1 \right) \quad [110]$$

where b_o is a constant called the incidence angle modifier coefficient, defined experimentally. A more accurate relation [54] may be written in the following form:

$$K_\theta = 1 - b_o \left(\frac{1}{\cos\theta} - 1 \right)^n \quad [111]$$

which, by determining b_o and n, significantly improves the fit and the range of validity.

Isotropic collectors are adequately described by a single incidence angle modifier, which depends only on the incidence angle θ between the incident beam solar radiation and the aperture normal. Isotropic collectors are called collectors that have optical characteristics essentially identical in all directions in the collector aperture plane, so the incidence angle modifier is independent of the solar azimuth angle in this plane. An example of this type is an FPC whose cover glazing, absorber surface, and housing have no obvious directional properties such as might be associated with the use of mirrors, heat transfer structures (e.g., fins or convective suppressors), and manufacturing process techniques.

Anisotropic collectors (e.g., ETCs with or without CPC reflectors) have optical characteristics that depend on the direction in the aperture plane, so the incidence angle modifier depends on both the solar azimuth in the aperture plane and the incidence angle θ. Collectors of this type require at least two incidence angle modifiers for the adequate description of their optical behavior. The complex individual incidence angle modifier can be estimated by considering it to be the product of the separate incidence angle modifiers, the longitudinal $K_{\theta L}$ and the transversal $K_{\theta T}$, for two perpendicular symmetry planes, respectively:

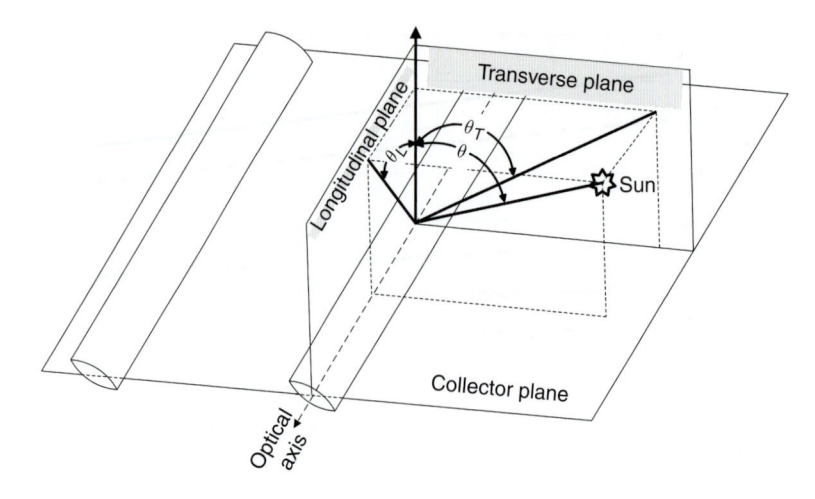

Figure 57 Graphical representation of the transverse and longitudinal planes for the determination of $K_{\theta L}$ and $K_{\theta T}$ incident angle modifiers.

$$K_\theta = K_{\theta L} K_{\theta T} \qquad [112]$$

A sketch of the two planes of an ETC is shown in **Figure 57**. The longitudinal plane runs parallel to the optical axis of the collector, and the transverse plane is perpendicular to the optical axis. The angles θ_L and θ_T are the projections of the incidence angle θ onto the longitudinal and transverse planes, respectively.

For the correlation between θ, θ_L, and θ_T, the following equation holds:

$$\tan^2\theta = \tan^2\theta_L + \tan^2\theta_T \qquad [113]$$

Figure 58 shows graphical interpretations of incident angle modifiers of two FPCs and one ETC with two independent modifiers separately defined.

According to eqn [33], the absorbed energy, per square meter of collector area, is

$$q_s = I_b R_b (\tau\alpha)_b + I_d \frac{1+\cos\beta}{2}(\tau\alpha)_d + \rho_g(I_b + I_d)\frac{1-\cos\beta}{2}(\tau\alpha)_g \qquad [114]$$

In terms of incident angle modifiers, this can be written as

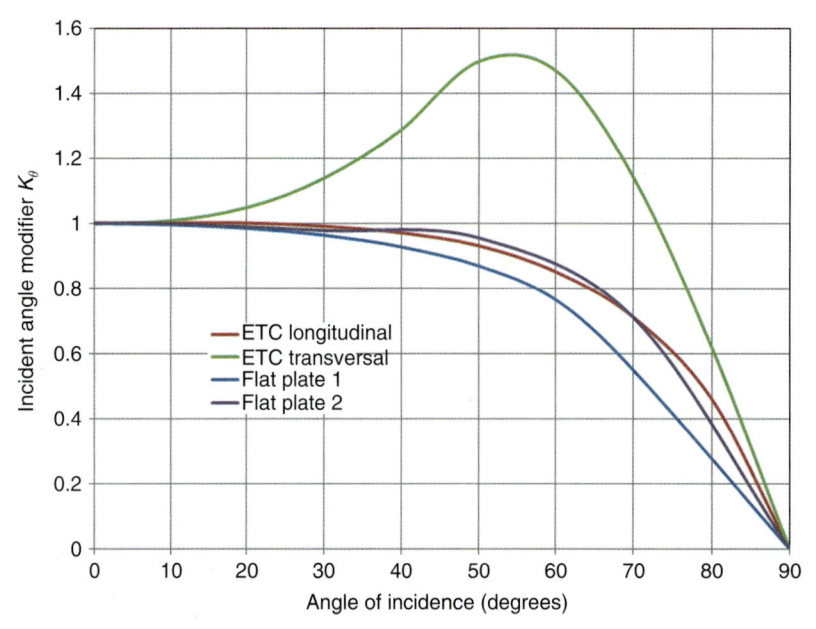

Figure 58 Incident angle modifiers for two flat-plate and one evacuated tube collectors.

$$q_s = I_b R_b K_\theta(\theta_b)(\tau\alpha)_n + I_d \frac{1+\cos\beta}{2} K_\theta(\theta_d)(\tau\alpha)_n + \rho_g(I_b + I_d)\frac{1-\cos\beta}{2} K_\theta(\theta_g)(\tau\alpha)_n \qquad [115]$$

where θ_b, θ_d, and θ_g are the incidence angles of beam, sky diffuse, and ground-reflected solar radiation. For isotropic diffuse sky radiation, θ_d and θ_g are determined from eqns [22] and [23]. If an overall incident angle modifier K_θ is to be considered, then

$$q_s = I_T K_\theta (\tau\alpha)_n \qquad [116]$$

where I_T is the total solar radiation on the collector plane and the overall K_θ is

$$K_\theta = \frac{I_b R_b K_\theta(\theta_b) + I_d \frac{1+\cos\beta}{2} K_\theta(\theta_d) + \rho_g(I_b + I_d)\frac{1-\cos\beta}{2} K_\theta(\theta_g)}{I_T} \qquad [117]$$

3.04.4.3 Determination of Effective Thermal Capacity

A collector can be considered as a device consisting of masses, each at a different temperature. Each component of an operating collector responds differently to any change in operating conditions, so it is useful to consider an effective thermal capacity for the whole collector. The effective thermal capacity and the time constant are important parameters for the determination of collector transient performance. The determination of collector effective thermal capacity C (J K^{-1}) is provided by EN12975-2 and ISO 9806-1 standards. Two procedures are provided: one in direct relevance with mass and heat capacity of individual parts of a solar collector and another indirect, through elaboration of experimental indoor or outdoor test data. Both standards describe analytically the two procedures. According to the first procedure, the effective collector thermal capacity is calculated as the sum, for each constituent element of the collector (glass, absorber, liquid contained, insulation), of the product of its mass m_i (kg), its specific heat c_i (J kg^{-1} K^{-1}), and a weighting factor p_i:

$$C = \sum_i p_i m_i c_i \qquad [118]$$

The weighting factor p_i (between 0 and 1) allows for the fact that certain elements are only partially involved in collector thermal inertia. The values of p_i are given in **Table 8**, where a_1 is taken from eqn [106].

Another magnitude, representative of the heat capacity, is the time constant τ_c. Physically, the time constant represents the time it takes for a system's step response to reach $(1 - 1/e) = 0.632$ (63.2%) of its final (asymptotic) value. For a collector, subjected to a step change in incident solar radiation level or inlet fluid temperature, the time constant is defined as the time required to reach a level of $(1 - 1/e) = 0.632$ (63.2%) of its final steady-state condition. It can be expressed as the time required for the exit temperature of a fluid leaving the collector to change by 63.2% of the total change from its initial to its final steady-state value, after a step change in incident solar radiation or inlet fluid temperature. All three standards provide procedures for the determination of τ_c. The difference between the temperature of the fluid at the collector outlet and that of the surrounding air $(T_e - T_a)$ is plotted against time, beginning with the initial steady-state condition $(T_e - T_a)_{initial}$ and continuing until the final steady state has been achieved at a higher temperature $(T_e - T_a)_{final}$, as shown in **Figure 59** (for an FPC with $\tau_c = 43$ s).

Unfortunately, the effective thermal capacity depends on the operating conditions and is not a collector parameter with a unique value. For most collectors, the dominant influence on the response time is the fluid transit time, and hence the first-order response varies with the fluid flow rate. Other collector components respond with different times to give an effective overall time constant, which depends on the operating conditions. Thus, the value of this quantity provides an estimation of the heat capacity influence on the system and therefore of the time required to reach steady efficiency values. The lower the time constant, the faster the collector response to solar insolation and inlet temperature fluctuations, so more energy is collected by minimizing warm-up and cool-down losses.

Table 8 Weighting factors for collector heat capacity determination

Elements	p_i
Absorber	1
Insulation	0.5
Heat transfer liquid	1
External glazing	$0.01a_1$
Second glazing	$0.2a_1$
Third glazing	$0.35a_1$

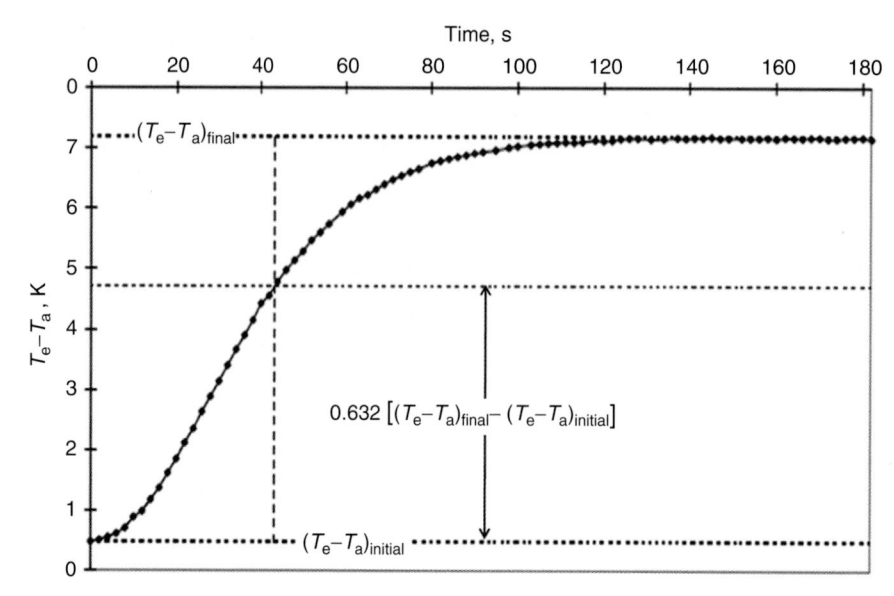

Figure 59 Experimental determination of collector time constant.

References

[1] Kalogirou SA (2004) Solar thermal collectors and applications. *Progress in Energy and Combustion Science* 30: 231–295.
[2] Garg HP and Prakash J (1997) *Solar Energy, Fundamentals and Applications*. New Delhi: Tata McGraw-Hill Publishing Co. Ltd.
[3] Kennedy CE (2002) Review of mid- to high-temperature solar selective absorber materials. July, NREL/TP-520-31267 National Renewable Energy Laboratory, 1617 Cole Boulevard, Golden, CO 80401-33, USA.
[4] Spate F, Hafner B, and Schwarzer K (1999) A system for solar process heat for decentralized applications in developing countries. *Proceedings of ISES Solar World Congress*, CD-ROM. Jerusalem, Israel.
[5] Schweiger H (1997) Optimization of Solar Thermal Absorber Elements with Transparent Insulation. Thesis, Universita Politecnica de Catalunya, Terrassa, Barcelona, Spain.
[6] Kaushika ND and Sumathy K (2003) Solar transparent insulation materials: A review. *Renewable and Sustainable Energy Reviews* 7: 317–351.
[7] Schaefer R and Lowrey P (1992) The optimum design of honeycomb solar ponds and a comparison with salt gradient solar ponds. *Solar Energy* 48: 69.
[8] Furbo S, Shah LJ, and Jordan U (2003) Solar Energy State of the art. *Internal Report BYG•DTU SR-03-14*, ISSN 1601-8605.
[9] Wijeysundera NE, Ah LL, and Tjioe LE (1982) Thermal performance study of two-pass solar air heaters. *Solar Energy* 28: 363–370.
[10] Ezeike GOI (1986) Development and performance of a triple-pass solar collector and dryer system. *Energy in Agriculture* 5: 1–20.
[11] Jain D (2005) Modeling the system performance of multi-tray crop drying using an inclined multi-pass solar air heater with in-built thermal storage. *Journal of Food Engineering* 71: 44–54.
[12] Caouris YG and Lefas CC (1984) A two layer thermal trap collector. *International Journal of Energy Systems* 4: 20–22.
[13] Caouris YG, Syrimbeis N, and Gertzos KP (2009) Construction and experimental evaluation of a prototype once through two pass solar collector. *Proceedings of National Congress for Renewable Energies*, pp. 457–463. Cyprus, 26–28 March 2009. ISSN 1108-3603 (in Greek).
[14] Duffie JA and Beckman WA (2006) *Solar Engineering of Thermal Processes*, 3rd edn. New York: John Wiley & Sons. ISBN-13 978-0-471-69867-8, ISBN-10 0-471-69867-9.
[15] Morrison GL (2001) Solar Collectors, Solar Energy: The State of the Art, pp. 145–221. Germany: ISES.
[16] Lunde PJ (1980) *Solar Thermal Engineering*. New York: John Wiley.
[17] Alghoul MA, Sulaiman MY, Azmi BZ, and Wahab MA (2005) Review of materials for solar thermal collectors. *Anti-Corrosion Methods and Materials* 52: 199–206.
[18] Siegel R and Howell JR (2002) *Thermal Radiation Heat Transfer*, 4th edn. New York: Taylor & Francis.
[19] British Standards Institution Draft for Development (1982) Methods of test for the thermal performance of solar collectors. BSI, DD 77.
[20] Brandemuehl MJ and Beckman WA (1980) Transmission of diffuse radiation through CPC and flat-plate collector glazings. *Solar Energy* 24: 511–513.
[21] Chinyama GK, Roos A, and Karlsson B (1993) Stability of antireflection coatings for large area glazings. *Solar Energy* 50(2): 105–111.
[22] Tesfamichael T and Wackelgård E (1999) Angular solar absorptance of absorbers used in solar thermal collectors. *Applied Optics* 38: 4189–4197.
[23] Klein SA (1979) Calculation of the monthly-average transmittance–absorptance product. *Solar Energy* 23: 547–551.
[24] Liu BYH and Jordan RC (1963) The long-term average performance of flat-plate solar energy collectors. *Solar Energy* 7: 53–74.
[25] Swinbank WC (1963) Long-wave radiation from clear skies. *Quarterly Journal of Royal Meteorological Society* 89: 339–348.
[26] Berdahl P and Martin M (1984) Emittance of clear skies. *Solar Energy* 32: 663–664.
[27] Aubinet M (1994) Longwave sky radiation parameterizations. *Solar Energy* 53: 147–154.
[28] Berger X, Buriot D, and Garnier F (1984) About the equivalent radiative temperature for clear skies. *Solar Energy* 32: 725–733.
[29] Sparrow EM, Ramsey JW, and Mass EA (1979) Effect of finite width on heat transfer and fluid flow about an inclined rectangular plate. *Transactions of ASME Journal of Heat Transfer* 101: 199–204.
[30] Sparrow EM and Lau SC (1981) Effect of adiabatic co-planar extension surfaces on wind-related solar-collector heat transfer coefficient. *Transactions of ASME Journal of Heat Transfer* 103: 268–271.
[31] Test FL and Lessmann RC (1980) An experimental study of heat transfer during forced convection over a rectangular body. *Transactions of ASME Journal of Heat Transfer* 102: 146–151.
[32] Test FL, Lessmann RC, and Johary A (1981) Heat transfer during wind flow over rectangular bodies in the natural environment. *Transactions of ASME Journal of Heat Transfer* 103: 262–267.
[33] Kumar S, Sharma VB, Kandpal TC, and Mullick SC (1997) Wind induced heat losses from outer cover of solar collector. *Renewable Energy* 10: 613–616.
[34] Sharples S and Charlesworth PS (1998) Full-scale measurements of wind-induced convective heat transfer from a roof-mounted FPC. *Solar Energy* 62: 69–77.

[35] McAdams WH (1954) *Heat Transmission*, 3rd edn. New York: McGraw-Hill.
[36] Watmuff JH, Charters WWW, and Proctor D (1977) Solar and wind induced external coefficients for solar collectors. *Revue Internationale d'Heliotechnique* 2: 56.
[37] Hollands KGT, Unny TE, Raithby GD, and Konicek L (1976) Free convective heat transfer across inclined air layers. *Transactions of ASME Journal of Heat Transfer* 98: 189–193.
[38] Randall KR, Mitchell JW, and El-Wakii MM (1979) Natural convection heat transfer characteristics of flat-plate enclosures. *Transactions of ASME Journal of Heat Transfer* 101: 120–125.
[39] Yin SH, Wung TY, and Chen K (1977) Natural convection in an air layer enclosed within rectangular cavities. *International Journal of Heat and Mass Transfer* 21: 307–315.
[40] Schinkel WMM (1980) *Natural Convection in Inclined Air-Filled Enclosures*. Pijnacker: Dutch Efficiency Bureau. ISBN 90-6231-079-6.
[41] Matuska T and Zmrhal V (2009) *A Mathematical Model and Design Tool KOLEKTOR 2.2 Reference Handbook* (3rd draft, 01-2009). Department of Environmental Engineering, Faculty of Mechanical Engineering, Czech Technical University in Prague, Technicka 4, 166 07 Prague 6, Czechoslovakia.
[42] Mullick SC and Nanda SK (1989) An improved technique for computing the heat loss factor of a tubular absorber. *Solar Energy* 42: 1–7.
[43] Agarwal VK and Larson DC (1981) Calculation of top heat loss coefficient of a flat-plate solar collector. *Solar Energy* 27: 69–71.
[44] Malhotra A, Garg HP, and Palit A (1981) Heat loss calculation of flat-plate solar collectors. *Journal of Thermal Engineering (Journal of the Indian Society of Mechanical Engineers)* 2(2): 59–62.
[45] Mazumder RK, Bhowmik NC, Hussain M, and Huq MS (1986) Heat loss factor of evacuated tubular receivers. *Energy Conversion and Management* 26: 313–316.
[46] Gnielinski V (1976) New equations for heat and mass transfer in turbulent pipe and channel flow. *International Chemical Engineering* 16: 359–368.
[47] Hausen CH (1934) Zeitschrift des Vereins Deutscher Ingenieure *Beih. Verfahrenstech* 91(4).
[48] Kays WM and Crawford ME (1980) *Convective Heat and Mass Transfer*, 2nd edn. New York: McGraw-Hill.
[49] Bliss RW (1959) The derivations of several 'plate-efficiency factors' useful in the design of flat-plate solar heat collectors. *Solar Energy* 3: 55–64.
[50] Eisenmann W, Vajen K, and Ackermann H (2004) On the correlations between collector efficiency factor and material content of parallel flow flat-plate solar collectors. *Solar Energy* 76: 381–387.
[51] ANSI/ASHRAE Standard 93-2003 (2003) Methods of testing to determine thermal performance of solar collectors. ASHRAE, 1791 Tullie Circle, Ne, Atlanta, GA 30329, USA. ISSN: 1041-2336.
[52] ISO Standard 9806-1:1994(E) (1994) Test methods for solar collectors – Part 1: Thermal performance of glazed liquid heating collectors including pressure drop. ISO, Case Postale 56, CH-1211 Genève 20, Switzerland.
[53] European Standard EN12975-2:2006 (2006) Thermal solar systems and components – solar collectors – Part 2: test methods, CEN, Rue de Stasart, 36, B-1050. Brussels, Belgium.
[54] Tesfamichael T and Wäckelgård E (2000) Angular solar absorptance and incident angle modifier of selective absorbers for solar thermal collectors. *Solar Energy* 68: 335–341.

3.05 Low Concentration Ratio Solar Collectors

SA Kalogirou, Cyprus University of Technology, Limassol, Cyprus

© 2012 Elsevier Ltd. All rights reserved.

3.05.1	Introduction	150
3.05.1.1	Maximum Concentration Ratio	150
3.05.2	Flat-Plate Collectors with Diffuse Reflectors	151
3.05.3	Reverse Flat-Plate Collectors	152
3.05.4	Compound Parabolic Collectors (CPC)	153
3.05.4.1	Optical and Thermal Analysis of CPCs	154
3.05.5	Concentrating Evacuated Tube Collectors	158
3.05.6	Integrated Collector Storage Systems	159
References		162

Nomenclature

A_a absorber area (m^2)
A_c total collector aperture area (m^2)
A_r receiver area (m^2)
C collector concentration ratio (=A_a/A_r) (–)
D sun–earth distance (m)
F view factor (–)
F_R heat removal factor (–)
G incident radiation (kJ m^{-2})
n average number of reflections (–)
Q radiated energy (kJ)

Q_s radiation emitted by the sun (kJ)
Q_u useful energy collected (kJ)
R sun radius, receiver radius (m)
S absorbed solar radiation per unit area (kJ m^{-2})
T_a ambient temperature (°C)
T_i collector inlet temperature (°C)
T_r receiver temperature (°C)
T_s apparent black body temperature of the sun (~6000 K)
U_L solar collector heat transfer loss coefficient (W m^{-2} °C)

Greek

α absorptivity (–)
β collector slope (degrees)
γ correction factor for diffuse radiation (–)
θ angle of incidence (degrees)
θ_c collector acceptance half-angle for CPC collectors (degrees)
θ_e effective incidence angle (degrees)

θ_s sun half-acceptance angle (degrees)
η efficiency (–)
ρ specular reflectivity (–), distance in **Figure 17**
σ Stefan–Boltzmann constant (=5.67 × 10^{-8} W m^{-2} K^{-4})
τ_c transmittance of CPC cover (–)
τ_{CPC} transmissivity of the CPC to account for reflection loss

Subscripts

a aperture
B beam
c cover
D diffuse
G ground reflected
max maximum

n normal
r receiver
R reflector
s sun
t total
T truncated
u useful

Glossary

Collector Any device which can be used to gather the sun's radiation and convert it to a useful form of energy.
Concentration ratio Ratio of aperture to receiver area of a solar collector.

Concentrating collector A solar collector that uses reflectors or lenses to redirect and concentrate the solar radiation passing through the aperture onto an observer.
CPC collector Compound parabolic concentrator. It is a non-imaging collector consisting of two parabolas one facing the other.

Evacuated tube collector A collector employing a glass tube with an excavated space between the tube and the absorber and using a heat pipe for energy collection.
Heat pipe A passive heat exchanger employing principles of evaporation and condensation to transfer heat at high levels of effectiveness.

Insolation A term applying specifically to solar energy irradiation (J/m^2)
Integrated collector storage A solar heating system in which the solar collector also functions as the storage device.

3.05.1 Introduction

This chapter deals with low concentration solar collectors. These are collectors that apply some form of concentration but their concentration ratio (C), defined as the ratio of the aperture area to the absorber area, is not more than about 10. According to the concentration ratio, these collectors are usually steady (C < 2), or if tracking is applied (for the higher concentration ones), this is intermittent and not very accurate. Fixed concentrators are very important because of the practical advantages enjoyed by fixed solar systems. By increasing the concentration ratio, the frequency of tracking increases. Thus a collector with C = 3 needs only biannual adjustment, whereas a collector with C = 10 requires almost daily adjustment [1]. Generally speaking, the higher the concentration ratio, the higher the temperature a collector can attain but the higher the tracking requirements. Because of the low concentration ratio, these collectors usually collect both direct and diffuse solar radiation as opposed to the high concentration ones that collect only direct solar radiation.

Generally, concentrating collectors can be classified into nonimaging and imaging depending on whether the image of the sun is focused on the receiver or not. The representative types of concentrators belonging to the first category are the reverse flat-plate collector and the compound parabolic collector (CPC).

3.05.1.1 Maximum Concentration Ratio

In equation form, the concentration ratio (C), defined as the ratio of the aperture area to the receiver/absorber area, is given by:

$$C = \frac{A_a}{A_r} \qquad [1]$$

For flat-plate collectors with no reflectors, C = 1. For concentrators, C is always greater than 1. It is required to define the maximum possible concentration ratio that a concentrator can achieve based on the limitations of the laws of thermodynamics. In this analysis, a circular (three-dimensional) concentrator with aperture A_a and receiver area A_r located at a distance D from the center of the sun is considered, as shown in **Figure 1**. The sun is a sphere of radius R; therefore, as seen from the earth, the sun has a half-angle θ_s, which is called the sun acceptance half-angle, and this angle is used for the calculation of the maximum concentration. If both the sun and the receiver are considered to be black bodies at temperatures T_s and T_r, respectively, the amount of radiation emitted by the sun is given by [1]:

$$Q_s = (4\pi R^2)\sigma T_s^4 \qquad [2]$$

The fraction of radiation intercepted by the collector is given by:

$$F_{s-r} = \frac{A_a}{4\pi D^2} \qquad [3]$$

Thus the energy radiated from the sun and received by the concentrator is [1]:

$$Q_{s-r} = A_a \frac{4\pi R^2}{4\pi D^2} \sigma T_s^4 = A_a \frac{R^2}{D^2} \sigma T_s^4 \qquad [4]$$

A black body receiver, which is considered a perfect radiator and absorber, radiates energy equal to $A_r T_r^4$ and a fraction of this reaches the sun, given by:

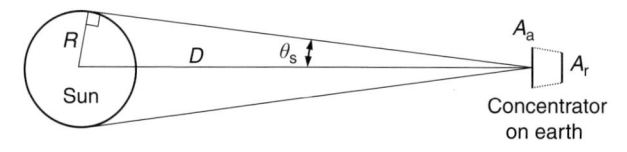

$$Q_{r-s} = A_r F_{r-s} \sigma T_r^4 \qquad [5]$$

Figure 1 Schematic of the sun and a concentrator on earth.

Under this idealized condition, the maximum temperature of the receiver is equal to that of the sun. According to the second law of thermodynamics, this is true only when $Q_{r-s} = Q_{s-r}$. Therefore, from eqns [4] and [5]:

$$\frac{A_a}{A_r} = \frac{D^2}{R^2} F_{r-s} \qquad [6]$$

Since the maximum value of F_{r-s} is equal to 1, the maximum concentration ratio for three-dimensional concentrators, and considering that $\sin(\theta_s) = R/D$, is:

$$C_{max} = \frac{1}{\sin^2(\theta_s)} \qquad [7]$$

A similar analysis for linear or two-dimensional concentrators gives:

$$C_{max} = \frac{1}{\sin(\theta_s)} \qquad [8]$$

As seen from the earth, the angle $2\theta_s$ of the sun is equal to $0.53°$ (or $32'$), so θ_s, the sun half-acceptance angle, is equal to $0.27°$ (or $16'$). The sun half-acceptance angle denotes the coverage of one-half of the angular zone within which radiation is accepted by the concentrator's receiver. Radiation is accepted over an angle of $2\theta_s$ because radiation incident within this angle reaches the receiver after passing through the aperture. This angle describes the angular field within which radiation can be collected by the receiver without having to track the concentrator [1].

Equations [7] and [8] define the upper limit of concentration that may be obtained for a given collector viewing angle. For a stationary CPC, the angle θ_s depends on the motion of the sun in the sky. For example, for a CPC having its axis in a north–south direction and tilted from the horizontal such that the plane of the sun's motion is normal to the aperture, the acceptance angle is related to the range of hours over which sunshine collection is required, for example, for 6 h of useful sunshine collection, and as the sun travels $15° \text{ h}^{-1}$, $2\theta_s = 90°$. In this case, $C_{max} = 1/\sin(45°) = 1.41$.

For a tracking collector, θ_s is limited by the size of the sun's disk, small-scale errors, irregularities of the reflector surface, and tracking errors. For a perfect collector and tracking system, C_{max} depends only on the sun's half-acceptance angle. Therefore,

$$\text{For single-axis tracking}: C_{max} = \frac{1}{\sin(16')} = 216$$

$$\text{For full tracking}: C_{max} = \frac{1}{\sin^2(16')} = 46\,747$$

It can therefore be concluded that the maximum concentration ratio for two-axes tracking collectors is much higher. However, high tracking accuracy and careful construction of the collector are required with increased concentration ratio as θ_s is very small and a possible small error will focus the sun beam away from the receiver. In practice, due to various errors, much lower values than the above maximum ones are employed [1].

In this chapter, only low concentration ratio collectors are considered with $C \leq 10$. These are two-dimensional concentrators and the relation considered for C_{max} is eqn [8].

3.05.2 Flat-Plate Collectors with Diffuse Reflectors

The first type of a solar concentrator examined in this chapter, shown in **Figure 2**, is effectively a flat-plate collector fitted with simple flat diffuse reflectors. This can markedly increase the amount of direct radiation reaching the collector. This is in fact a concentrator because the aperture is bigger than the absorber but the system is stationary. This simple enhancement of flat-plate collectors was initially suggested by Tabor [2]. A comprehensive analysis and a model of such a system are presented by Garg and Hrishikesan [3].

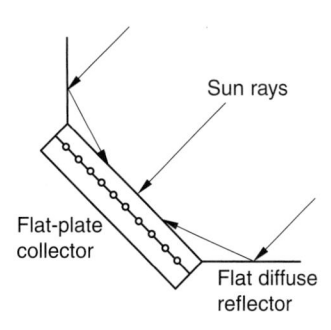

Figure 2 Flat-plate collector with flat diffuse reflectors.

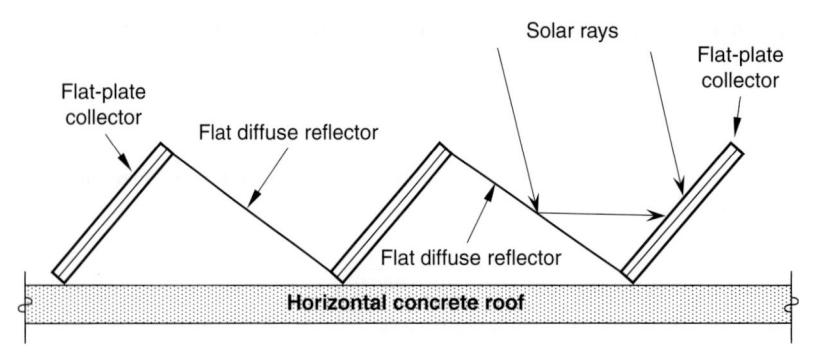

Figure 3 Flat-plate collectors with sawtooth reflectors.

The model facilitates the prediction of the total energy absorbed by the collector at any hour of the day for any latitude for random tilt angles and azimuth angles of the collector and reflectors.

Individual flat-plate collectors can be equipped with flat reflectors in the way shown in **Figure 2**; however, for multirow collector installations, a sawtooth arrangement shown in **Figure 3** can be used. In both cases, the use of simple flat diffuse reflectors can significantly increase the amount of direct radiation reaching the collector.

The expression 'diffuse reflector' denotes a material which is not a mirror, thus avoiding forming an image of the sun on the absorber, which will create uneven radiation distribution and thermal stresses. Diffuse reflectors are usually made from galvanized or stainless steel sheets, and their cost is usually a fraction of the cost of the collector. This is the reason why this type of enhancement is considered as one of the most effective. Extensive, mostly experimental, studies on this type of systems are presented by Tripanagnostopoulos *et al.* as part of their studies with collectors employing color absorbers [4] and hybrid PV/T systems [5, 6].

3.05.3 Reverse Flat-Plate Collectors

In an attempt to extend the operation of flat-plate collectors to medium temperatures, many researchers investigated a type of system called reversed or upside down absorber plate configuration. Kienzlen *et al.* [7] were the first who investigated this type of system. On these systems, radiation is directed on the underside of the plate by a stationary concentrator of the shape shown in **Figure 4**. The shape of this type of collector is like a CPC described in more detail in the next section. Heat losses from the absorber are significantly reduced as the upper side of the plate is well insulated, and as the plate is upside down, there is little convective motion in the air layer just below the plate. Another type is the inclined design shown in **Figure 5**. Compared with a normal flat-plate collector, the reverse plate design has lower optical efficiency (maximum efficiency the collector can attain at inlet fluid temperature equal to ambient temperature) due to the scattering losses in the reflector.

An extension of the concept is the double-sided flat-plate collector investigated by Goetzberger *et al.* [8] and Tripanagnostopoulos *et al.* [9]. These are called bifacially irradiated solar flat-plate collectors because the absorber is a flat plate and they have the advantage that they are illuminated at both sides of the absorber. In the design presented by Goetzberger *et al.* [8], the absorber is 'insulated' at all sides with a transparent insulation (TI), whereas in the design presented by Tripanagnostopoulos

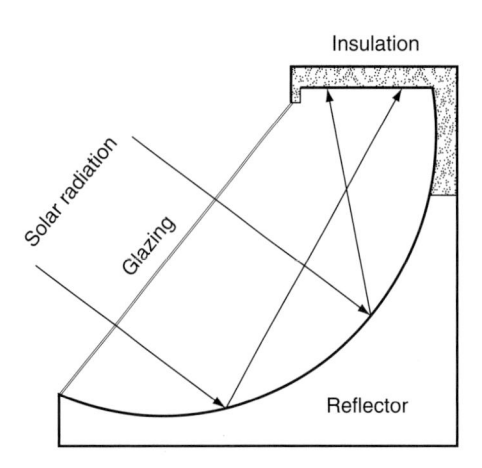

Figure 4 Inverted flat-plate collector.

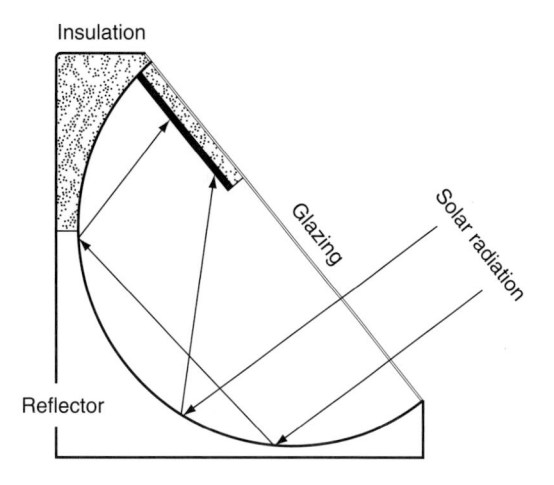

Figure 5 Inclined flat-plate collector.

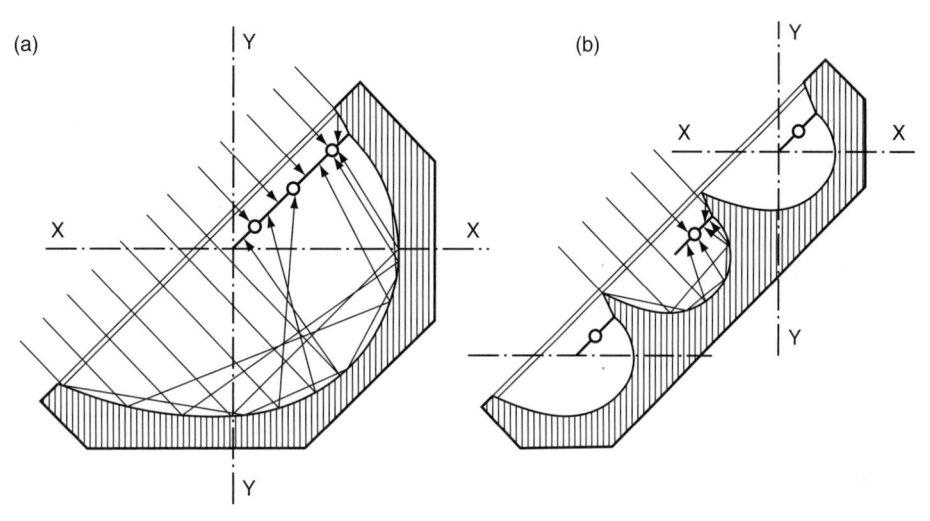

Figure 6 Cross section of a (a) CPC collector with one mirror–absorber unit and (b) CPC collector with three mirror–absorber units. Modified from Tripanagnostopoulos Y, Yianoulis P, Papaefthimiou S, and Zafeiratos S (2000) CPC solar collectors with flat bifacial absorbers. *Solar Energy* 69(3): 191–203.

et al. [9], a simple glazing is used either in one mirror–absorber unit or in three mirror–absorber units as shown in **Figures 6(a)** and **6(b)**, respectively, which are adapted from Reference [9] with many design details removed from the original figures for clarity.

3.05.4 Compound Parabolic Collectors (CPC)

CPCs are nonimaging concentrators. These have the capability of reflecting to the absorber all of the incident radiation within wide limits. Their potential as collectors of solar energy was pointed out by Winston [10]. The necessity of moving the concentrator to accommodate the changing solar orientation can be reduced by using a trough with two sections of a parabola facing each other, as shown in **Figure 7**.

Compound parabolic concentrators can accept incoming radiation over a relatively wide range of angles. By using multiple internal reflections, any radiation that is entering the aperture, within the collector acceptance angle, finds its way to the absorber surface located at the bottom of the collector. Generally, CPCs are characterized by a relatively high average number of reflections, ranging in most of the cases between 1.1 and 1.6, determined by ray tracing, so that if the reflectivity of the concentrating surface is not high, optical losses may be significant [11]. The absorber of a CPC can take a variety of configurations. As can be seen in **Figure 7**, it can be flat, bifacial, wedge, or cylindrical.

Two basic types of CPC collectors have been designed: the symmetric, shown in **Figure 7**, and the asymmetric, which have shapes similar to the ones shown in the figures of the previous section. CPCs usually employ two main types of absorbers: fin type with pipe and tubular absorbers. The fin type can be flat, bifacial, or wedge as shown in **Figure 7** for the symmetric type and can be single channel or multichannel.

CPCs should have a gap between the receiver and the reflector to prevent the reflector from acting as a fin conducting heat away from the absorber and this is more important for flat receivers. As the gap results in a loss of reflector area with a corresponding loss of performance, it should be kept small.

Depending on the acceptance angle of the CPC, the collector can be stationary or tracking. When tracking is used, this is very rough or intermittent as concentration ratio is usually small and radiation can be collected and concentrated by one or more reflections on the parabolic surfaces. For higher temperature applications, a tracking CPC can be used.

CPCs can be manufactured either as one unit with one opening and one receiver (see **Figure 7**) or as a panel as shown in **Figure 8(a)**. When constructed as a panel, the collector looks like a flat-plate collector as shown in **Figure 8(b)**.

In the following section, the optical and thermal analysis of CPCs is presented.

3.05.4.1 Optical and Thermal Analysis of CPCs

The optical analysis of CPC collectors concerns mainly the way to construct the collector shape. A CPC of the Winston design [12] is shown in **Figure 9**. It is a linear two-dimensional concentrator consisting of two distinct parabolas A and B, the axes of which are inclined at angles $\pm\theta_c$ with respect to the optical axis of the collector. The angle θ_c is called the collector half-acceptance angle and is defined as the angle through which a source of light can be moved and still converge at the absorber. CPCs have a constant acceptance angle over the entire aperture area [11].

The Winston-type collector is a nonimaging concentrator with a concentration ratio approaching the upper limit permitted by the second law of thermodynamics as explained in Section 3.05.1.1.

The receiver of the CPC does not have to be flat and parallel but as shown in **Figure 7** can be bifacial, wedge, or cylindrical. In **Figure 10**, a cylindrical receiver collector is shown. In this collector, the lower portion of the reflector (AB and AC) is circular while the upper portions (BD and CE) are parabolic. In this design, the requirement for the parabolic portion of the collector is that at any point P, the normal to the collector must bisect the angle between the tangent line PG to the receiver and the incident ray at point P at angle θ_c with respect to the collector axis. The side wall profile of fully developed CPCs terminates when it is parallel to the optical axis so that very little concentration is lost by truncating these devices by some fraction, usually about 0.6–0.9 of their full height [11]. Therefore, as the upper part of a CPC contributes little to the radiation reaching the absorber, it is usually truncated, thus forming a shorter version of the CPC. Truncation affects little the acceptance angle but results in considerable material saving and changes the height-to-aperture ratio, the concentration ratio, and the average number of reflections. CPCs are usually covered with glass to avoid dust and other materials from entering the collector, thus reducing the reflectivity of its walls.

These collectors are more useful as linear or trough-type concentrators. The orientation of a CPC collector is related to its acceptance angle ($2\theta_c$, in **Figures 9** and **10**). The two-dimensional CPC is an ideal concentrator, that is, it works perfectly for all rays within the acceptance angle $2\theta_c$. Also depending on the collector acceptance angle, the collector can be stationary or tracking. A CPC concentrator can be orientated with its long axis along either the north–south or the east–west direction, and its aperture is tilted

Flat absorber   Bifacial absorber

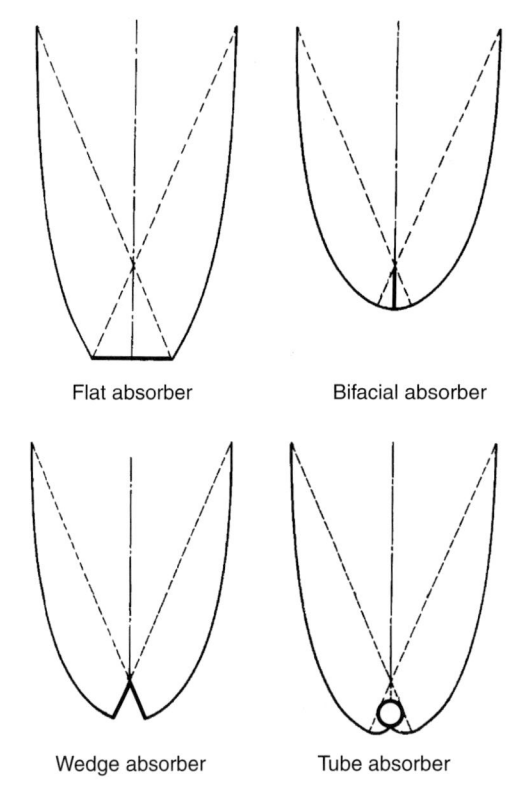

Wedge absorber   Tube absorber

Figure 7 Various absorber types for CPCs.

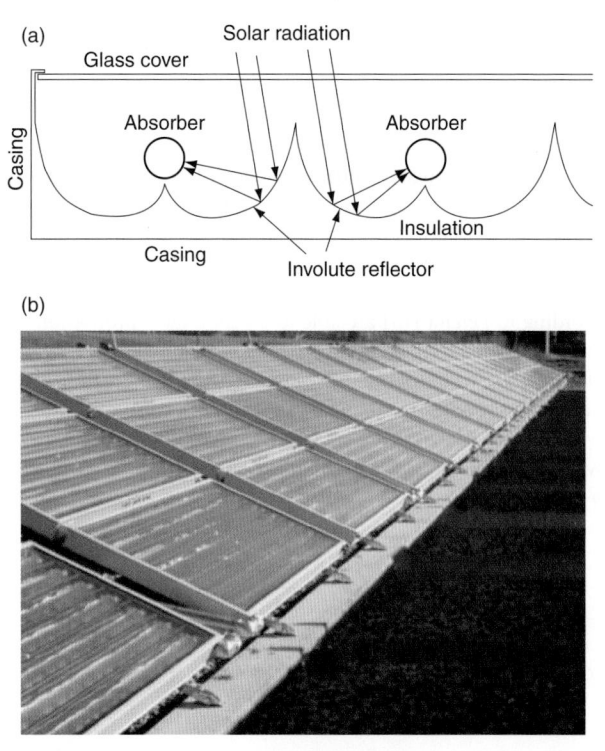

Figure 8 Panel CPC collector with cylindrical absorbers. (a) Schematic diagram. (b) Photo of a CPC panel collector installation.

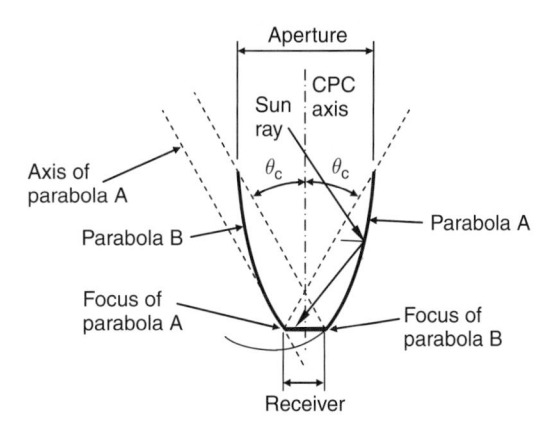

Figure 9 Construction of a flat receiver CPC.

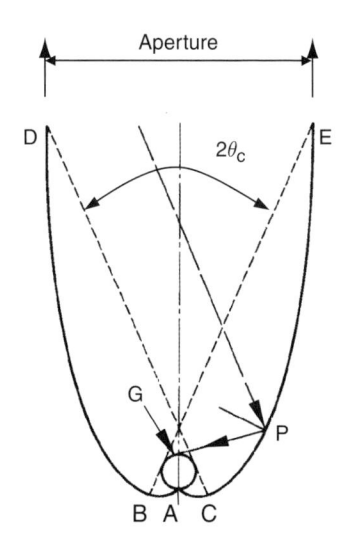

Figure 10 Schematic diagram of a CPC collector.

directly toward the equator at an angle equal to the local latitude. When orientated along the north–south direction, the collector must track the sun by turning its axis so as to face the sun. As the acceptance angle of the concentrator along its long axis is wide, seasonal tilt adjustment is not necessary. It can also be stationary but radiation will only be received during the hours when the sun is within the collector acceptance angle [1].

When the concentrator is orientated with its long axis along the east–west direction, with a little seasonal adjustment in tilt angle, the collector is able to catch the sun's rays effectively through its wide acceptance angle along its long axis. The minimum acceptance angle in this case should be equal to the maximum incidence angle projected in a north–south vertical plane during the times when output is needed from the collector. For stationary CPC collectors mounted in this mode, the minimum acceptance angle is equal to 47°. This angle covers the declination of the sun from summer to winter solstices ($2 \times 23.5°$). In practice, bigger angles are used to enable the collector to collect diffuse radiation at the expense of a lower concentration ratio. Smaller (less than 3) concentration ratio CPCs are of greatest practical interest. These according to Pereira [13] are able to accept a large proportion of diffuse radiation incident on their apertures and concentrate it without the need of tracking the sun. Finally, the required frequency of collector adjustment is related to the collector concentration ratio. Thus for $C \leq 2$, the collector can be steady, whereas for $C = 3$, the collector needs only biannual adjustment, while for C close to 10, it requires almost daily adjustment and these systems are also called quasi-static [1].

Concentrators of the type shown in **Figure 7** have an area concentration ratio, which is a function of the acceptance half-angle θ_c. For an ideal linear concentrator system, this is given by eqn [8] by replacing θ_s with θ_c.

The instantaneous efficiency η of a CPC is defined as the useful energy gain divided by the incident radiation on the aperture plane, that is,

$$\eta = \frac{Q_u}{A_a G_t} \qquad [9]$$

In eqn [9], G_t is the total incident radiation on the aperture plane. The useful energy Q_u is given by an equation similar to that of a flat-plate collector, by using the concept of absorbed radiation, as [1]:

$$Q_u = F_R[SA_a - A_r U_L(T_i - T_a)] \qquad [10]$$

The absorbed radiation S is obtained from [14]:

$$S = G_{B,CPC}\tau_{c,B}\tau_{CPC,B}\alpha_B + G_{D,CPC}\tau_{c,D}\tau_{CPC,D}\alpha_D + G_{G,CPC}\tau_{c,G}\tau_{CPC,G}\alpha_G \qquad [11]$$

where τ_c is the transmittance of the CPC cover and τ_{CPC} is the transmissivity of the CPC to account for reflection loss.

The various radiation components in eqn [11] refer to radiation falling on the aperture within the acceptance angle of the CPC and are given from the following relations:

$$G_{B,CPC} = G_{Bn}\cos(\theta) \quad \text{if} (\beta - \theta_c) \leq \tan^{-1}[\tan(\Phi)\cos(z)] \leq (\beta + \theta_c) \qquad [12a]$$

$$G_{D,CPC} = \begin{cases} \dfrac{G_D}{C} & \text{if} (\beta + \theta_c) < 90° \\ \dfrac{G_D}{2}\left(\dfrac{1}{C} + \cos(\beta)\right) & \text{if} (\beta + \theta_c) > 90° \end{cases} \qquad [12b]$$

$$G_{G,CPC} = \begin{cases} 0 & \text{if} (\beta + \theta_c) < 90° \\ \dfrac{G_G}{2}\left(\dfrac{1}{C} - \cos(\beta)\right) & \text{if} (\beta + \theta_c) > 90° \end{cases} \qquad [12c]$$

In eqns [12a]–[12c], β is the collector aperture inclination angle with respect to the horizontal. In eqn [12c], the ground-reflected radiation is only effective if the collector receiver 'sees' the ground, that is, $(\beta + \theta_c) > 90°$.

It has been shown by Rabl et al. [15] that the insolation G_{CPC} of a collector with a concentration C can be approximated very well from:

$$G_{CPC} = G_B + \frac{1}{C}G_D = (G_t - G_D) + \frac{1}{C}G_D = G_t - \left(1 - \frac{1}{C}\right)G_D \qquad [13]$$

It is convenient to express the absorbed solar radiation S in terms of G_{CPC} in the following way:

$$S = G_{CPC}\tau_c\tau_{CPC}\alpha_r = \left[G_t - \left(1 - \frac{1}{C}\right)G_D\right]\tau_c\tau_{CPC}\alpha_r = G_t\tau_c\tau_{CPC}\alpha_r\left[1 - \left(1 - \frac{1}{C}\right)\frac{G_D}{G_t}\right] \qquad [14]$$

or

$$S = G_t\tau_c\tau_{CPC}\alpha_r\gamma \qquad [15]$$

where α_r is the absorptivity of the receiver and γ is the correction factor for diffuse radiation given by:

$$\gamma = 1 - \left(1 - \frac{1}{C}\right)\frac{G_D}{G_t} \qquad [16]$$

The factor γ given by eqn [16] accounts for the loss of diffuse radiation, which is outside of the acceptance angle of the CPC with a concentration C. The ratio G_D/G_t varies from about 0.11 on very clear sunny days to about 0.23 on hazy days.

It should be noted that only part of the diffuse radiation effectively enters the CPC and this is a function of the acceptance angle. For isotropic diffuse radiation, the relationship between the effective incidence angle and the acceptance half-angle is given by [16]:

$$\theta_e = 44.86 - 0.0716\theta_c + 0.00512\theta_c^2 - 0.000\,02798\theta_c^3 \qquad [17]$$

The effective transmissivity τ_{CPC} of the CPC accounts for reflection loss inside the collector. The fraction of the radiation passing through the collector aperture and eventually reaching the absorber depends on the specular reflectivity, ρ, of the CPC walls and the average number of reflections, n, expressed approximately by:

$$\tau_{CPC} = \rho^n \qquad [18]$$

This equation can also be used to estimate $\tau_{CPC,B}$, $\tau_{CPC,D}$, and $\tau_{CPC,G}$ for use in eqn [11], which are usually treated as the same. Values of the average number of reflections, n, for full and truncated CPCs can be obtained from [17] (the subscript T is for the truncated CPC design):

$$n = \max\left[C\frac{A_{RT}}{4a_T} - \frac{x^2 - \cos^2(\theta)}{2(1+\sin(\theta))},\; 1 - \frac{1}{C}\right] \qquad [19]$$

where:

$$x = \left(\frac{1+\sin(\theta)}{\cos(\theta)}\right)\left(-\sin(\theta) + \left[1 + \frac{h_T}{h}\cot^2(\theta)\right]^{1/2}\right) \qquad [20]$$

A_{RT} is the reflector area for the truncated CPC (m^2).

As noted before, the upper ends of CPCs contribute little to the radiation reaching the receiver and usually CPCs are truncated for economic reasons. As can be seen from eqn [19], the average number of reflections is a function of concentration ratio C and the collector acceptance half-angle θ_c. For a truncated concentrator, the value $(1 - 1/C)$ can be taken as the lower bound for the number of reflections for radiation within the acceptance angle.

The following equations can be used to design a CPC. The various symbols used in the following equations are shown in **Figure 11**.

The following equations apply for a full and truncated (subscript T) CPC [18]:

$$f = a'(1 + \cos(\theta_c)) \qquad [21]$$

$$a = \frac{a'}{\sin(\theta_c)} \qquad [22]$$

$$h = \frac{f\cos(\theta_c)}{\sin^2(\theta_c)} \qquad [23]$$

$$a_T = \frac{f\sin(\Phi_T - \theta_c)}{\sin^2(\Phi_T/2)} - a' \qquad [24]$$

$$h_T = \frac{f\cos(\Phi_T - \theta_c)}{\sin^2(\Phi_T/2)} \qquad [25]$$

$$\text{For a truncated CPC:}\quad C = \frac{a_T}{a'} \qquad [26]$$

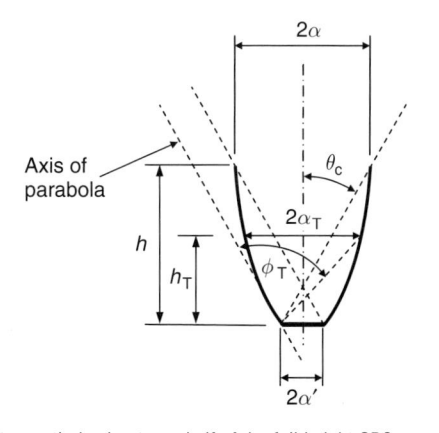

$$\text{For a full CPC:}\quad C = \frac{a}{a'} \qquad [27]$$

Figure 11 A truncated CPC – its height-to-aperture ratio is about one-half of the full height CPC.

By replacing α from eqn [22]

$$C = \frac{1}{\sin(\theta_c)} \qquad [28]$$

which is the same as eqn [8] with the use of θ_c instead of θ_s. The reflector area per unit depth of a truncated CPC is given by:

$$\frac{A_{RT}}{2\alpha_T} = \frac{f}{2}\left[\frac{\cos(\Phi/2)}{\sin^2(\Phi/2)} + \ln\cot\left(\frac{\Phi}{4}\right)\right]\bigg|_{\theta_c + \pi/2}^{\Phi_T} \qquad [29]$$

For eqn [29] if $\Phi_T = 2\theta_c$, then $A_{RT} = A_R$.

It should be noted that the above equations can be replaced by graphs, which can be found from the original paper of Rabl [19].

Eames and Norton [20] presented a detailed parametric analysis of heat transfer in CPC solar energy collectors, whereas in a second paper [21] they presented the thermal and optical consequences of the introduction of baffles into compound parabolic concentrating solar collector cavities, used to reduce the internal convection, thereby reducing thermal losses, with a consequent small reduction in the optical efficiency.

3.05.5 Concentrating Evacuated Tube Collectors

The benefits of the simple flat-plate solar collectors that are developed for use in sunny and warm climates reduce greatly when conditions become unfavorable during cold, cloudy, and windy days. Evacuated tube solar collectors operate differently, usually consisting of a heat pipe inside a vacuum-sealed tube, as shown in **Figure 12**. To increase the heat collection area, many tubes are connected to the same manifold as shown in the figure.

Evacuated tube collectors (ETCs) have demonstrated that the combination of selective surface and the effective convection suppressor can result in good performance at high temperatures. The vacuum envelope reduces convection and conduction losses, so the collectors can operate at higher temperatures than flat-plate collectors. Like flat-plate collectors, they collect both direct and diffuse radiation, but their efficiency is higher at low incidence angles. This effect tends to give ETCs an advantage over flat-plate collectors in day-long performance [1].

ETCs use liquid–vapor phase change materials to transfer heat at high efficiency. These collectors usually feature a heat pipe placed inside a vacuum-sealed tube. The pipe, which is a sealed copper pipe, is then attached to a black copper fin that fills the tube (absorber plate). Protruding from the top of each tube is a metal tip attached to the sealed pipe, which acts as a condenser. The heat pipe contains a small amount of volatile fluid that undergoes an evaporating–condensing cycle. Solar heat evaporates the liquid, and the vapor due to lower density rises to the heat sink region where it condenses and releases its latent heat. The

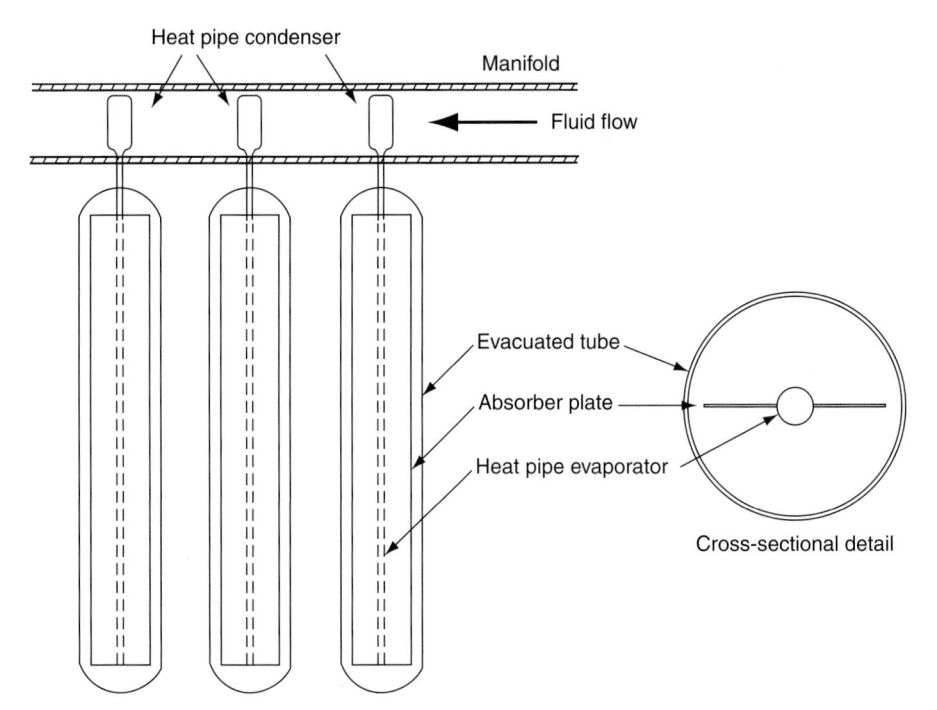

Figure 12 Schematic diagram of an ETC.

condensed fluid due to gravity returns back to the solar collector and the process is repeated. When these tubes are mounted, the metal tips up into a manifold as shown in **Figure 12**. Water, or water–glycol mixture, flows through the manifold and picks up the heat from the tubes. The heated liquid circulates through a heat exchanger and gives off its heat to a process or to water that is stored in a storage tank.

Because no evaporation or condensation above the phase change temperature is possible, the heat pipe offers inherent protection from freezing and overheating. This self-limiting temperature control is a unique feature of the evacuated heat pipe collector [1].

A large number of absorber shape variations of ETCs exist in the market. One such design consists of an all-glass Dewar-type ETC. In this, two concentric glass tubes are used and the space between the tubes is evacuated creating a vacuum jacket. In this type of ETC, the selective coating is deposited onto the outside surface of a glass tube domed at one end. This tube is then inserted into a second larger diameter domed glass tube and the tubes are joined at the open end. The advantage of this design is that it is made entirely of glass and it is not necessary to penetrate the glass envelope in order to extract the heat from the tube; thus, leakage losses are eliminated and it is cheaper than the single-envelope system [1]. This type is also called a wet-tube ETC. A variation of the wet-tube ETC is a normal single-glass ETC in which water (or any other fluid) flows through the collector in either a U-tube or a coaxial pipe.

Evacuated tubes with external or internal (inside the glass tube) reflectors are also commercialized by several manufacturers. A diffuse reflector (reflectivity, $\rho = 0.6$) mounted behind the tubes spaced one tube diameter apart, as shown in **Figure 13**, increases the absorbed energy in each tube by more than 25% for normal incidence. This system presents also a 10% increase in energy collection over a full day because of incidence angle effects.

CPC reflectors can also be used either externally or internally, which increases the effectiveness of ETCs. A better enhancement per tube can be achieved by using CPC-type reflectors as shown in **Figure 14**. In this design, the number of tubes is decreased and they use reflectors to concentrate the solar radiation onto the tubes. Evacuated tube arrays with stationary concentrators may have stagnation temperatures exceeding 300 °C.

When the reflector is installed inside the tube, the system is called integrated compound parabolic collector (ICPC). This is an ETC in which at the bottom part of the glass tube, a reflective material is fixed [22]. In this case, either a CPC reflector, shown in **Figure 15(a)**, or a cylindrical reflector, shown in **Figure 15(b)**, is used. The latter does not achieve the concentration of the shaped reflector but has a very low manufacturing cost. In this way, the collector combines into a single unit the advantages of vacuum insulation and nonimaging stationary concentration. In another design, a tracking ICPC is developed, which is suitable for high-temperature applications [23].

ETCs are produced in a variety of sizes with outer diameters ranging from 30 mm to about 100 mm. The usual length of these collectors is about 2 m.

3.05.6 Integrated Collector Storage Systems

Integrated collector storage (ICS) system is a water heating method that uses the hot water storage as part of the collector, that is, the storage tank is used also as the collector absorber. As in all other systems, to improve stratification, the hot water is drawn from the top of the tank and cold make-up water enters the bottom of the tank on the opposite side. Usually, the coating of the storage tank surface is selective to minimize heat loss.

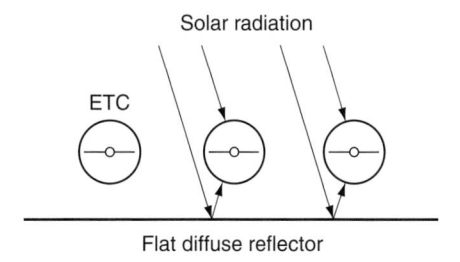

Figure 13 ETCs with external flat diffuse reflector.

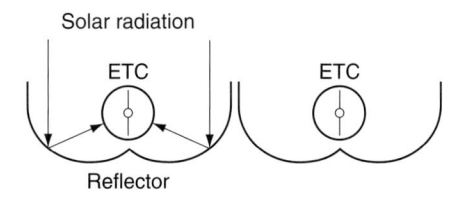

Figure 14 ETCs with external CPC-type reflectors.

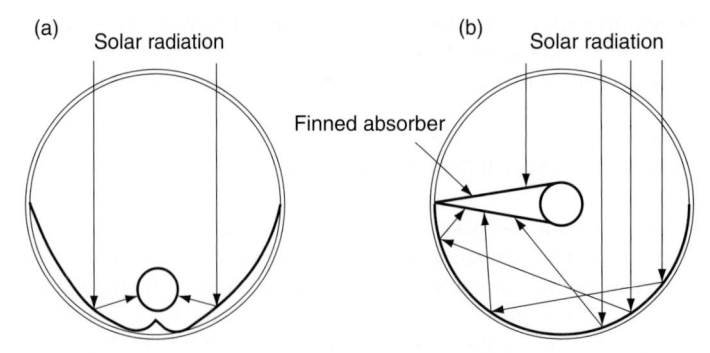

Figure 15 Integrated CPC tubes. (a) Internal compound parabolic. (b) Circular reflector with finned absorber.

Details of an ICS unit developed by the author are presented here [24]. The system employs a nonimaging CPC cusp-type collector. A fully developed cusp concentrator for a cylindrical receiver is shown in **Figure 16**. The particular curve illustrated has an acceptance half-angle, θ_c, of 60° or a full acceptance angle, $2\theta_c$, of 120°. Each side of the cusp has two mathematically distinct segments smoothly joined at a point P related to θ_c. The first segment, from the bottom of the receiver to point P, is the involute of the receiver's circular cross section. The second segment is from point P to the top of the curve, where the curve becomes parallel to the y-axis [25].

With reference to **Figure 17**, for a cylindrical receiver with radius R and acceptance half-angle, θ_c, the distance, ρ, along a tangent from the receiver to the curve is related to the angle θ between the radius to the bottom of the receiver and the radius to the point of tangency, T, by the following expressions for the two sections of the curve [25]:

$$\rho(\theta) = R\theta, \quad |\theta| \leq \theta_c + \frac{\pi}{2} \quad \text{(the involute part of the curve)}$$

$$\rho(\theta) = R\left\{\frac{\left[\theta + \theta_c + \frac{\pi}{2} - \cos(\theta - \theta_c)\right]}{1 + \sin(\theta - \theta_c)}\right\}, \quad \theta_c + \frac{\pi}{2} \leq \theta \leq \frac{3\pi}{2} - \theta_c \quad [30]$$

The two expressions for $\rho(\theta)$ are equivalent for the point P in **Figure 16**, where $\theta = \theta_c + \pi/2$. The curve is generated by incrementing θ in radians, calculating ρ, and then calculating the coordinates, X and Y, by:

$$X = R\sin\theta - \rho\cos\theta$$
$$Y = -R\cos\theta - \rho\sin\theta \quad [31]$$

Figure 16 shows a full untruncated curve, which is the mathematical solution for a reflector shape with the maximum possible concentration ratio. The reflector shape shown in **Figure 16** is not the most practical design for a cost-effective concentrator, because

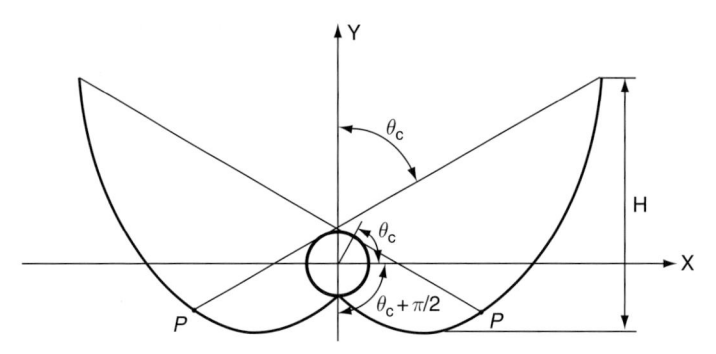

Figure 16 Fully developed cusp.

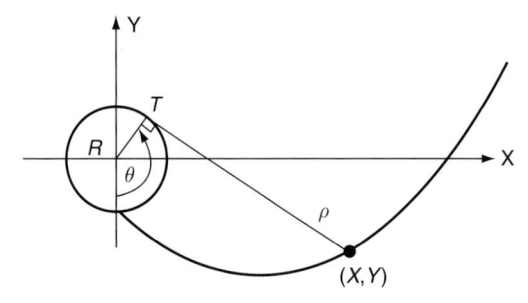

Figure 17 Mirror coordinates for ideal nonimaging cusp concentrator.

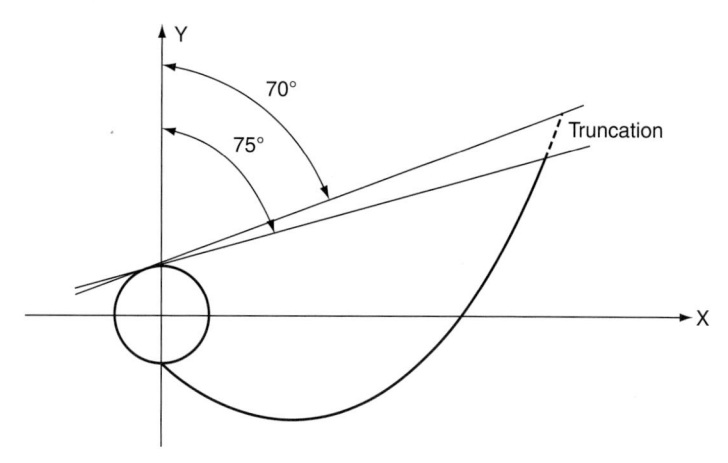

Figure 18 Truncation of nonimaging concentrator.

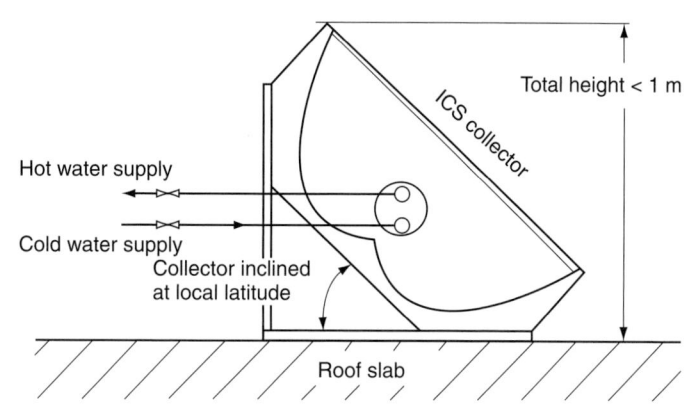

Figure 19 The complete solar ICS hot water system.

reflective material is not effectively used in the upper portion of the concentrator. As in the case of the CPC, a theoretical cusp curve should be truncated to a lower height and slightly smaller concentration ratio. Graphically, this is done by drawing a horizontal line across the cusp at a selected height and discarding the part of the curve above the line. Mathematically, the curve is defined to a maximum angle θ of value less than $3\pi/2 - \theta_c$. The shape of the curve below the cut-off line is not changed by truncation, so the acceptance angle used for the construction of the curve (using eqn [30]) of a truncated cusp is equal to the acceptance angle of the fully developed cusp from which it was truncated.

A large acceptance angle of 75° is used in this design so that the collector would be able to collect as much diffuse radiation as possible [24]. The fully developed cusp together with the truncated one is shown in **Figure 18**. The receiver radius considered in the construction of the cusp is 0.24 m. The actual cylinder used is only 0.20 m. This is done in order to create a gap at the underside of the receiver and the edge of the cusp in order to minimize the optical and conduction losses.

The final design is shown in **Figure 19**. The collector aperture is 1.77 m^2, which in combination with the absorber diameter used gives a concentration ratio of 1.47 [24]. It should be noted that the collector axis is east–west and as shown in **Figure 19**, the system is inclined at the local latitude in order to work effectively.

The main disadvantage of ICS systems is the high thermal losses from the storage tank to the surroundings since most of the surface area of the storage tank cannot be thermally insulated as it is intentionally exposed so as to be able to absorb solar radiation. In particular, the thermal losses are greatest during the night and overcast days with low ambient temperature. Due to these losses, the water temperature drops substantially during night time especially during the winter. Various techniques have been used to avoid this from happening. Tripanagnostopoulos et al. [26] presented a number of experimental units in which the reduction of thermal losses was achieved by considering single and double cylindrical horizontal tanks properly placed in truncated symmetric and asymmetric CPC reflector troughs. Two such designs are shown in **Figure 20** adapted from [26], with many design details removed from the original figures for clarity.

Another possibility considered in the design shown in **Figure 19**, in view of the findings of Eames and Norton [21] on the use of baffles to reduce the thermal losses, is the insertion of a second cylinder of smaller diameter in the space between the main cylinder and the glass cover and using a small piece of insulation at the point of contact between the two cylinders and between the secondary cylinder and the glass cover as shown in **Figure 21**. This modification offers a number of advantages: storage capacity increased by 30%, top cylinder provides some sort of insulation (for radiation heat loss) as the main cylinder does not see the sky

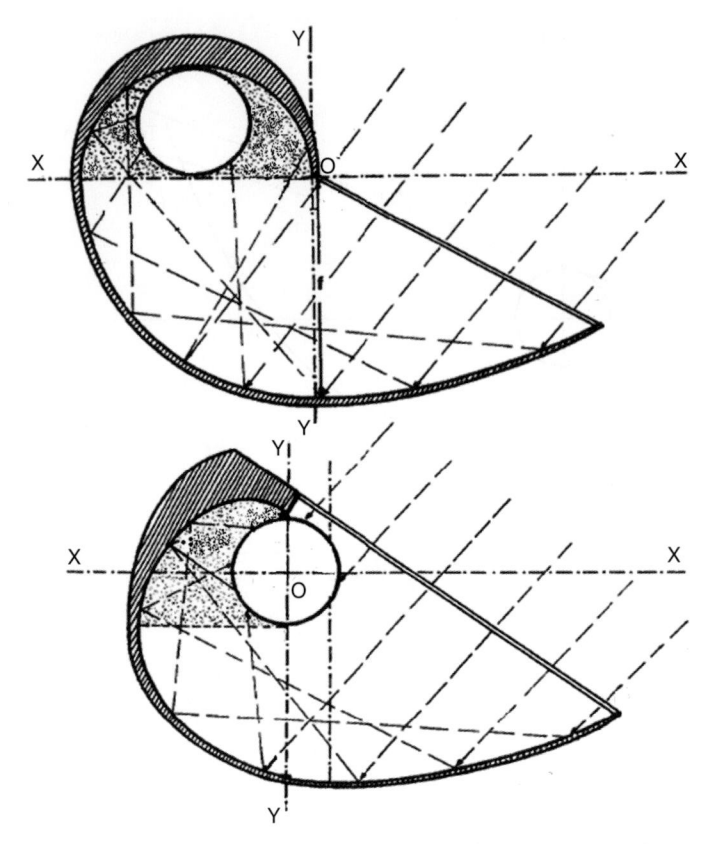

Figure 20 Cross section of two ICS unit designs with a partial protection of the storage tank. Modified from Tripanagnostopoulos Y, Souliotis M, and Nousia Th (2002) CPC type integrated collector storage systems. *Solar Energy* 72(4): 327–350.

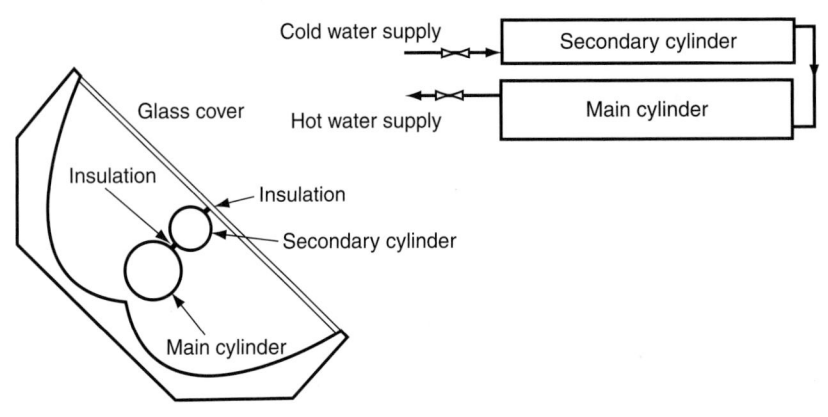

Figure 21 Basic system modification.

directly, the top cylinder creates a restriction to the flow of the convection currents (just like the baffle does), and finally, the secondary cylinder is used as a preheating for the main one and thus the draw-off characteristics of the whole unit improved considerably, as the cold make-up water does not enter into the main cylinder directly. The extra cylinder increased the cost of the ICS system by 8%, whereas the performance of the system increased by about 7% [27].

Alternatively, if a 24-h hot water supply is required, these systems can be used only for preheating and in such a case must be connected in series with a conventional water heater [1].

References

[1] Kalogirou SA (2009) *Solar Energy Engineering: Processes and Systems*. New York: Elsevier Science; Academic Press. ISBN: 978-0-12-374501-9.
[2] Tabor H (1966) Mirror boosters for solar collectors. *Solar Energy* 10(3): 111–118.

[3] Garg HP and Hrishikesan DS (1998) Enhancement of solar energy on flat-plate collector by plane booster mirrors. *Solar Energy* 40(4): 295–307.
[4] Tripanagnostopoulos Y, Souliotis M, and Nousia Th (2000) Solar collectors with colored absorbers. *Solar Energy* 68(4): 343–356.
[5] Tripanagnostopoulos Y (2007) Aspects and improvements of hybrid photovoltaic/thermal solar energy systems. *Solar Energy* 81(9): 1117–1131.
[6] Tripanagnostopoulos Y, Nousia Th, Souliotis M, and Yianoulis P (2002) Hybrid photovoltaic/thermal solar systems. *Solar Energy* 72(3): 217–234.
[7] Kienzlen V, Gordon JM, and Kreider JF (1988) The reverse flat-plate collector: A stationary non-evacuated, low technology, medium temperature solar collector. *ASME Journal of Solar Energy Engineering* 110: 23–30.
[8] Goetzberger A, Dengler J, Rommel M, *et al.* (1992) New transparently insulated, bifacially irradiated solar flat-plate collector. *Solar Energy* 49(5): 403–411.
[9] Tripanagnostopoulos Y, Yianoulis P, Papaefthimiou S, and Zafeiratos S (2000) CPC solar collectors with flat bifacial absorbers. *Solar Energy* 69(3): 191–203.
[10] Winston R (1974) Solar concentrators of novel design. *Solar Energy* 16: 89–95.
[11] Winston R (2001) Solar concentrators. In: Gordon J (ed.) *Solar Energy: The State of the Art*, ISES, pp. 357–436. London: James & James.
[12] Winston R and Hinterberger H (1975) Principles of cylindrical concentrators for solar energy. *Solar Energy* 17(4): 255–258.
[13] Pereira M (1985) Design and performance of a novel non-evacuated 1.2x CPC type concentrator. In: *Proceedings of Intersol Biennial Congress of ISES*, vol. 2, pp. 1199–1204. Montreal, Canada.
[14] Duffie JA and Beckman WA (1991) *Solar Engineering of Thermal Processes*. New York: John Wiley & Sons.
[15] Rabl A, O'Gallagher J, and Winston R (1980) Design and test of non-evacuated solar collectors with compound parabolic concentrators. *Solar Energy* 25(4): 335–351.
[16] Brandemuehl MJ and Beckman WA (1980) Transmission of diffuse radiation through CPC and flat-plate collector glazings. *Solar Energy* 24(5): 511–513.
[17] Rabl A (1976) Optical and thermal properties of compound parabolic concentrators. *Solar Energy* 18(6): 497–511.
[18] Welford WT and Winston R (1978) *The Optics of Non-Imaging Concentrators*. New York: Academic.
[19] Rabl A (1976) Comparison of solar concentrators. *Solar Energy* 18(2): 93–111.
[20] Eames PC and Norton B (1993) Detailed parametric analysis of heat transfer in CPC solar energy collectors. *Solar Energy* 50(4): 321–338.
[21] Eames PC and Norton B (1995) Thermal and optical consequences of the introduction of baffles into compound parabolic concentrating solar collector cavities. *Solar Energy* 55(2): 129–150.
[22] Winston R, O'Gallagher J, Muschaweck J, *et al.* (1999) Comparison of predicted and measured performance of an integrated compound parabolic concentrator (ICPC). In: *Proceedings of the ISES Solar World Congress on CD ROM*. Jerusalem, Israel.
[23] Grass C, Benz N, Hacker Z, and Timinger A (2000) Tube collector with integrated tracking parabolic concentrator. In: *Proceedings of the Eurosun'2000 Conference on CD ROM*. Copenhagen, Denmark.
[24] Kalogirou SA (1997) Design, construction, performance evaluation, and economic analysis of an integrated collector storage system. *Renewable Energy* 12(2): 179–192.
[25] McIntire WR (1979) Truncation of nonimaging cusp concentrators. *Solar Energy* 23(4): 351–355.
[26] Tripanagnostopoulos Y, Souliotis M, and Nousia Th (2002) CPC type integrated collector storage systems. *Solar Energy* 72(4): 327–350.
[27] Kalogirou SA (1998) Performance enhancement of an integrated collector storage hot water system. In: *Proceedings of the World Renewable Energy Congress V*, pp. 652–655. Florence, Italy.

3.06 High Concentration Solar Collectors

B Hoffschmidt, S Alexopoulos, J Göttsche, M Sauerborn, and O Kaufhold, Aachen University of Applied Sciences, Jülich, Germany

© 2012 Elsevier Ltd. All rights reserved.

3.06.1	Introduction	167
3.06.2	General Considerations of High-Concentration Solar Collectors	167
3.06.2.1	Basic Characteristics	167
3.06.2.1.1	Components	167
3.06.2.1.2	Characteristics	167
3.06.2.2	Types	168
3.06.2.2.1	Application	168
3.06.2.2.2	Control	168
3.06.2.3	System Determination of Performance	168
3.06.2.3.1	Definition of efficiencies	168
3.06.2.3.2	Sunshape	168
3.06.2.4	Optical and Thermal Analysis of High-Concentration Solar Collector Systems	169
3.06.2.4.1	Structure	169
3.06.2.4.2	Reflector	169
3.06.2.4.3	Linear receiver	172
3.06.2.4.4	Area receiver	173
3.06.2.5	Operation and Maintenance	174
3.06.2.5.1	Cleaning	174
3.06.3	**Parabolic Trough Collectors**	174
3.06.3.1	Introduction	174
3.06.3.2	Basic Characteristics	174
3.06.3.2.1	Structure	174
3.06.3.2.2	Components	175
3.06.3.2.3	Specific characteristics	175
3.06.3.3	Types	176
3.06.3.3.1	Size	176
3.06.3.3.2	Material	176
3.06.3.3.3	Heat transfer fluid	176
3.06.3.3.4	Specific control components	177
3.06.3.3.5	Drives	177
3.06.3.3.6	Tracking system	177
3.06.3.3.7	Diverse	177
3.06.3.4	Construction and Installation	178
3.06.3.4.1	Prefabrication	178
3.06.3.4.2	*In situ* assembly	178
3.06.3.4.3	Adjustment	178
3.06.3.5	System-Specific Determination of Performance	178
3.06.3.5.1	Definition of efficiencies	178
3.06.3.5.2	Error sources	178
3.06.3.6	Models of Collectors and Their Construction Details	178
3.06.3.6.1	LS-1, LS-2, and LS-3	178
3.06.3.6.2	EuroTrough	179
3.06.3.6.3	Solargenix collector	180
3.06.3.6.4	HelioTrough	181
3.06.3.6.5	Ultimate Trough collector	181
3.06.3.6.6	PT-1	182
3.06.3.6.7	SkyTrough	182
3.06.3.6.8	SenerTrough	183
3.06.3.6.9	Research	183
3.06.3.7	Solar Absorbers for PTCs	183
3.06.3.7.1	The solar absorber of SCHOTT Solar	183
3.06.3.7.2	The solar absorber of Siemens	184
3.06.3.8	Operation and Maintenance	184

3.06.3.8.1	Cleaning techniques	184
3.06.3.8.2	Maintenance of HTF quality	185
3.06.3.8.3	Replacement of parts	185
3.06.3.8.4	Adjustment	185
3.06.4	**Central Receiver Systems**	185
3.06.4.1	Introduction	185
3.06.4.2	Basic Characteristics	185
3.06.4.2.1	Structure	185
3.06.4.2.2	Components	186
3.06.4.2.3	Specific characteristics	186
3.06.4.3	Types	186
3.06.4.3.1	Geometry of receiver aperture	186
3.06.4.3.2	Heat transfer medium	186
3.06.4.3.3	Receiver	187
3.06.4.3.4	Tower construction	187
3.06.4.3.5	Heliostat drives, kinematics, coupling, facets, mirror material, and foundation	187
3.06.4.3.6	Specific control components	187
3.06.4.3.7	Aim-point strategy	187
3.06.4.4	System-Specific Determination of Performance	187
3.06.4.4.1	Receiver efficiency and optical and thermal losses	187
3.06.4.4.2	Heliostat loss mechanisms, tracking accuracy, and beam error	188
3.06.4.5	Secondary Optics	189
3.06.4.5.1	Tower reflector	189
3.06.4.5.2	Secondary concentrators	189
3.06.4.6	Models of Heliostats and Their Construction Details	190
3.06.4.7	Receiver Types on the Market	192
3.06.4.8	Operation and Maintenance	195
3.06.4.8.1	Cleaning techniques	195
3.06.4.8.2	Replacement of parts	195
3.06.4.8.3	Adjustment	195
3.06.5	**Linear Fresnel Collectors**	195
3.06.5.1	Introduction	195
3.06.5.2	Basic Characteristics	195
3.06.5.2.1	Structure	195
3.06.5.2.2	Components	195
3.06.5.2.3	Specific characteristics	195
3.06.5.3	Types	196
3.06.5.3.1	Size	196
3.06.5.3.2	Material	196
3.06.5.3.3	Heat transfer fluid	196
3.06.5.3.4	Specific operation control components	196
3.06.5.3.5	Drives	196
3.06.5.3.6	Tracking system	196
3.06.5.4	System-Specific Determination of Performance	196
3.06.5.4.1	Definition of efficiencies	196
3.06.5.4.2	Error sources	197
3.06.5.5	Models of Collectors and Their Construction Details	197
3.06.5.5.1	Solar Power Group	197
3.06.5.5.2	Solarmundo	198
3.06.5.5.3	Ausra/Areva	198
3.06.5.5.4	NOVATEC BioSol	198
3.06.5.5.5	Mirroxx	199
3.06.5.5.6	Research	199
3.06.5.6	Operation and Maintenance	199
3.06.5.6.1	Cleaning techniques	199
3.06.5.6.2	Replacement of parts	199
3.06.6	**Solar Dish**	199
3.06.6.1	Introduction	199
3.06.6.2	Basic Characteristics	200

3.06.6.2.1	Structure	200
3.06.6.2.2	Components	200
3.06.6.2.3	Specific characteristics	200
3.06.6.3	Types	201
3.06.6.3.1	Geometry, material use, and surface characteristics of the concentrator	201
3.06.6.3.2	Geometry of receiver aperture with Stirling device	201
3.06.6.3.3	Characteristics of Stirling or Brayton engine	201
3.06.6.3.4	Working gas	202
3.06.6.4	System-Specific Determination of Performance	202
3.06.6.4.1	Definition of efficiencies	202
3.06.6.4.2	Error sources	203
3.06.6.5	Models of Solar Dishes and Their Construction Details	203
3.06.6.5.1	First models	203
3.06.6.5.2	EuroDish	203
3.06.6.5.3	Stirling Energy Systems	204
3.06.6.5.4	SAIC and STM	204
3.06.6.5.5	Infinia Solar System	204
3.06.6.5.6	Others	204
3.06.6.5.7	Research	204
3.06.6.6	Operation and Maintenance	205
3.06.6.6.1	Control system/diverse	205
3.06.7	**Criteria for the Choice of Technology**	205
3.06.7.1	Location	205
3.06.7.2	Grid Capacity and Net System	206
3.06.7.3	Local Cost Structure	206
3.06.7.4	Country-Specific Subsidies, Feed-in Tariffs, and Environmental Laws	206
References		207

3.06.1 Introduction

There are different types of high-concentration solar collectors such as the parabolic trough, the central receiver system (CRS), the Fresnel collector, and the solar dish.

3.06.2 General Considerations of High-Concentration Solar Collectors

3.06.2.1 Basic Characteristics

3.06.2.1.1 Components

The main components of a concentration solar collector are a foundation, a structure that holds the reflector (mirror), a solar concentrator, which reflects the solar radiation, and an absorber, to where the solar beams are directed.

3.06.2.1.2 Characteristics

The main optical characteristics of concentrating systems are the specular reflectivity and the shape accuracy of the reflecting surface.

3.06.2.1.2(i) Specular reflectivity
The fraction of reflected solar radiation that actually hits the absorbing surface of a concentrating solar system depends strongly on the specular reflectivity of radiation in the full solar spectrum. In contrast to lenses, the direction of specularly reflected light from smooth surfaces (e.g., no refraction grating) is independent of the wavelength of the radiation. This is one major reason why mirrors are preferred to lenses in solar systems. Nevertheless, the reflectivity may be a function of wavelength. Deviation from ideal reflection is a result of absorption and/or scattering of light.

Solar-weighted specular reflectivity should be at least 90%, measured in a cone that corresponds to the desired concentration ratio. As we are receiving the Sun's radiation in a ± 4 mrad cone, radiation should not be scattered into a much wider cone.

3.06.2.1.2(ii) Shape accuracy
The accuracy of the reflector's shape also determines the amount of radiation that hits the absorber. Any deviation from the ideal shape results in a widening of the cone of reflected sunlight. Shape quality can be determined by photogrammetry or deflectometry.

168   Components

3.06.2.2 Types

3.06.2.2.1 Application
The size of a collector differs according to the application. In this chapter, only medium- to large utility-scale applications, like power and steam generation, are considered.

3.06.2.2.2 Control
Solar sensors in order to send precise signals to the motors for the correct tracking of the Sun and a control via computer are essential in order to achieve concentration of a huge amount of sunlight in the receiver.

3.06.2.3 System Determination of Performance

3.06.2.3.1 Definition of efficiencies
The reflector of a solar thermal collector shows different optical loss mechanisms like shadow and blocking. The loss mechanisms differ for each collector type.

The receiver converts concentrated solar radiation to thermal energy. An ideal receiver may be characterized as a black body, which has only radiative losses. In reality, further losses occur due to convection, conduction, and thermal radiation.

3.06.2.3.2 Sunshape
Basic astronomic and atmospheric knowledge is required for optimizing the technique of concentrating solar radiation in creating a beam for energy recovery. This knowledge may influence the optical technique that is being employed in high-concentrating systems.

Due to the long distance between Sun and Earth, at the Earth's hemisphere the massive Sun appears as only a plane surface with a nearly ideal circular silhouette and is called sunshape. This highly perfect (at the 0.001% level) circular shape is because of its extremely strong gravity. This makes the Sun the smoothest natural object in the solar system [1]. On the other hand, the apparent angular diameter of the Sun on Earth is 31.45 arcmin when the Earth is at aphelion (the farthest point in its orbit), and grows about 3% to 32.53 arcmin when the Earth is at perihelion (the closest point in its orbit). During an astronomic year, the Sun has a mean geometric diameter of 31.98 arcmin or 9.3 mrad [2]. These data are valid only outside the atmosphere.

In space, the sunshape rim is sharply cut against the cold background space. On the way through the Earth's atmosphere, solar radiation scatters off fluid drops and different kinds of gases and solids. These atmospheric effects together lead to solar brightness distribution and create the circumsolar aureole. The sharp silhouette in space changes to a subaerial radially diminishing light. The two images shown in **Figure 1** are the same photo of the Sun, but are differently digitally prepared.

Both photos are gray-green filtered; however, in the right photo, the lighting rate is also colored and the maximum lighting level is totally reduced so that only an annular residual brightness – the circumsolar aureole – is left. The circumsolar ratio (CSR) quantifies these distribution effects and compares the energy contained in the solar aureole with the total energy. CSR is given by taking the integrated brightness or intensity over the solar disk as I_{Sun} and the integrated intensity of the aureole around the solar disk as I_{CS} (the circumsolar region) and is expressed as the following equation:

$$\text{CSR} = \frac{I_{CS}}{(I_{CS} + I_{Sun})} \qquad [1]$$

The results of CSR measurements at DLR (German Aerospace Center) are shown in **Figure 2**. They explain the strong statistical conjunction between CSR and the energy density of the sunshape ratio.

When CSR increases, the relative flux density of the Sun decreases, and vice versa. In addition to the derived characteristic sunshapes, Neumann *et al.* [3] developed frequency distributions of those sunshapes for different levels of solar radiation (see **Figure 2**, left).

The CSR has a supplementary influence on the performance of concentrating solar thermal systems – especially on high-concentration systems. The image size produced in the focal plane of the concentrator system depends on the sunshape diameter and solar brightness distribution. Due to this, when a solar concentrator system is projected, the effective size of the solar image at the absorber plane should be identified and accommodated in the design and optimization.

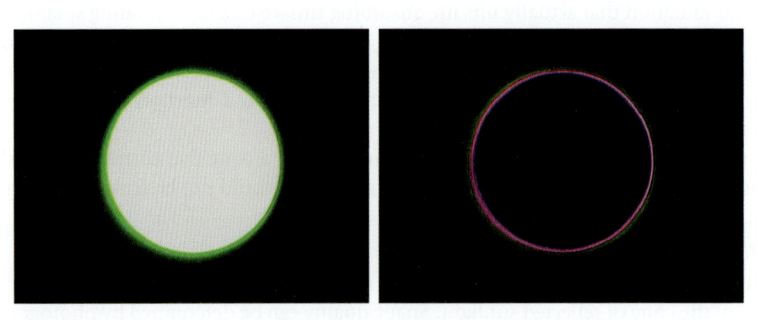

Figure 1 Filtered digital photo of the sunshape and the circumsolar ratio visualized by image processing.

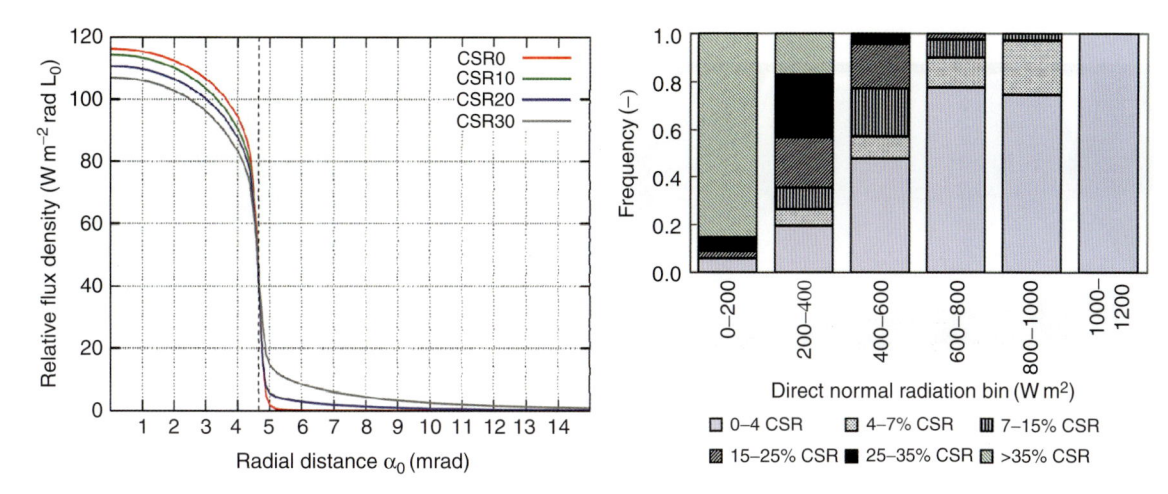

Figure 2 (left) Radial flux density distribution of the sunshape at different circumsolar ratios (CSRs). Reproduced from Neumann A, Witzke A, Scott J, and Schmitt G (2002) Representative terrestrial solar brightness profiles. *ASME Journal of Solar Energy Engineering* 124: S198–S204 [3]; Mertins M (2009) Technische und wirtschaftliche Analyse von horizontalen Fresnel-Kollektoren. Dissertation, Universität Karlsruhe (TH), Fakultät für Maschinenbau [4]. (right) Frequency distribution of circumsolar ratio scans for different solar radiation levels. Reproduced from Neumann A, Witzke A, Scott J, and Schmitt G (2002) Representative terrestrial solar brightness profiles. *ASME Journal of Solar Energy Engineering* 124: S198–S204 [3]; Chapman DJ and Arias DA (2009) Effect of solar brightness profiles on the performance of parabolic concentrating collectors. *Proceedings of the ASME 2009 3rd International Conference on Energy Sustainability, ES2009.* San Francisco, CA, USA, 19–23 July [5].

An example of the influence is given by measurements of Neumann *et al.* [3] at the high-flux solar furnace at DLR in Cologne. The laboratory furnace is a high flux concentrator with a two-stage off-axis system with a stationary focus. The test facility has over 100 spherical reflectors creating a combined focus in the laboratory building, with a concentrating factor of about 5000. The focus diameter for narrow sun conditions is less than 13 cm at low CSR (< 1%) but reaches more than 16 cm at high CSR (> 40%), thus resulting in an increase of 34% of the focus area and a reduction of the same level of the maximal flux density.

3.06.2.4 Optical and Thermal Analysis of High-Concentration Solar Collector Systems

3.06.2.4.1 *Structure*

3.06.2.4.1(i) *Geometry*

The structure of concentrators is designed to place the reflecting surface at the desired position and angle at any sunny moment. The main loads that the structures have to withstand are wind loads, which are usually much larger than the loads resulting from the weight of the concentrator. Therefore, lightweight constructions usually show no benefit unless they are cheaper without compromising the structure's stiffness. The structure must be designed in such a way that the angle of the reflecting surface is not affected by thermal expansion of the components involved.

3.06.2.4.1(ii) *Tracking accuracy*

Tracking accuracy is the key property of the mechanical concentrator components. It depends on the mechanical properties of the structure, the interface to the drives, and the drives and their control. A deviation in the orientation of the mirror surface results in twice the deviation of the reflected beam. While it is possible to adjust parabolic troughs based on sensors, this is not easily done with heliostats or Fresnel reflectors where multiple surfaces contribute radiation to a focal point or a focal line.

3.06.2.4.2 *Reflector*

The final performance of the power plant is strongly influenced by the optical quality of the solar trough collectors or heliostats on field. To qualify and reduce the problematic effect and optimize especially trough concentrators and heliostat mirror assemblies, several measurement techniques have been designed.

3.06.2.4.2(i) *Photogrammetry*

Photogrammetry can be used to measure local shape deviation of solar concentrators. Photogrammetry first started as a long-range measurement technique of landscape by analyzing analogue photographs. Development in digital camera chip technique with high megapixel level and improvement of software enabled high-accuracy 3D coordinates measuring all kinds and ranges of surfaces. During the last decade, digital photogrammetry as mentioned in Reference 6 has successfully progressed to an exact and efficient short-distance measurement system for analyzing the quality of optical components of solar concentrators. The analyzed surface data can be used to estimate slope errors and undertake ray-tracing studies to compute intercept factors and access concentrator qualities. Photogrammetry can also provide information for the analysis of curved shapes and surfaces, which are very difficult to

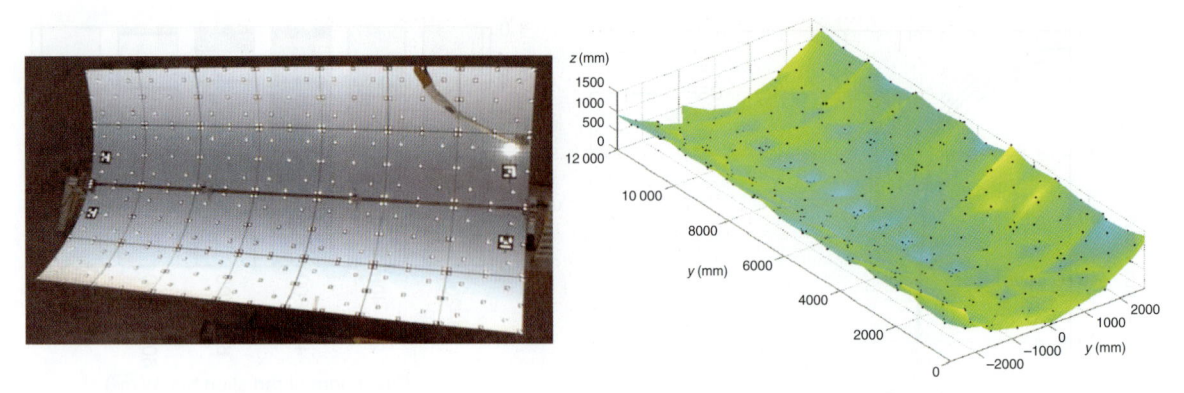

Figure 3 Analysis by photogrammetry of a common collector element (EuroTrough) measurement. Source: Pottler (2010) Information provided by K. Pottler, DLR [6].

measure by conventional measuring instruments [6]. High-sensitive photogrammetry even detects very small effects of elongation from thermal expansion and the force of gravitation on selected components.

Figure 3 (left) shows a common trough mirror during photogrammetry inspection with the target points.

On the measured surface, a large number of these markers have to be fixed in order to be used as individual surface measuring points and can be defined three-dimensionally (3D) by digital photogrammetry analysis. The measurement result of **Figure 3** (right) indicates deviations from the design heights (expanded scale).

Since this testing method is more time consuming, it is not practical for measuring large numbers of mirrors [7].

One of the published examples of measuring systems to analyze EuroTrough collector modules is described by Pottler [6]. Plain heliostat mirrors are analyzed with the same principle.

3.06.2.4.2(ii) Deflectometry

Deflectometry is an optical 3D measurement method (**Figure 4**) that uses projections of test cards to characterize reflecting surfaces. The range of application covers analysis of basic elements of optical instruments (lens, prism, mirrors, etc.), eyeglass lenses, microelectronic semiconductor surfaces such as wafer and solar cells, and varnished and polished components. Because of its interesting features, the measurement system was adapted for the inspection of mirrors in solar technology [8].

A homogeneously radiating projector radiates on a diffusing screen or white target an image with equal and equidistant dark bars. The reflected image of the inspected mirror surface is taken by a digital camera and an example is shown in **Figure 5**. An analysis of the picture of the distorted bars by specially programmed image processing software allows calculation of the observed surface structure and characterization of its irregularities.

Because deflectometry is an easy and very flexible concept, the aim was to develop a system that allows measurement of surface slopes with high resolution and high accuracy and one which is suitable for large surfaces and also rapid and easy to set up [7].

3.06.2.4.2(iii) Reflectivity measurement

The mirror of a solar thermal collector has to be measured at regular intervals at as much different points at the surface area as possible, in order to get an exact result of the average reflectivity. Outdoor measurements are performed with portable reflectometers.

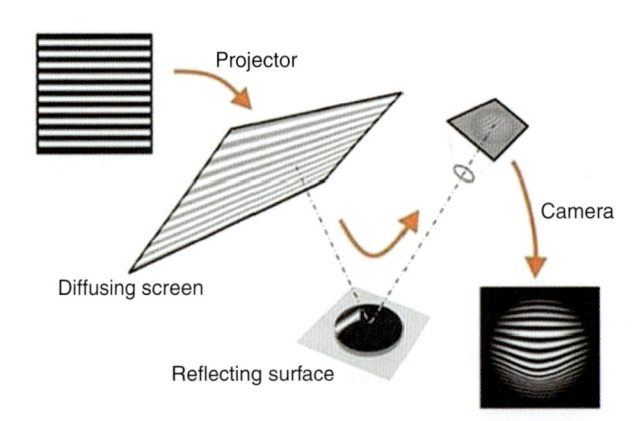

Figure 4 Measurement principle of deflectometry of a reflecting surface. Reproduced from Rahlves M and Seewig J (2009) *Optisches Messen Technischer Oberflächen: Messprinzipien und Begriffe*, p. 17. Berlin, Germany: Beuth Verlag [8].

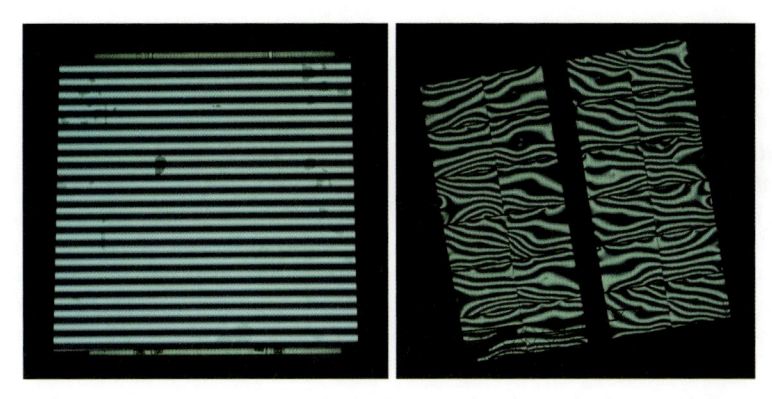

Figure 5 The bar projection field for the deflectometry and the reflecting image on the mirrors of an inspected heliostat. Reproduced from Ulmer S, März T, Prahl C, et al. (2009) *Automated High Resolution Measurement of Heliostat Slope Errors*. Berlin, Germany: SolarPACES [7].

A widely used reflectivity measurement device is the D&S Portable Specular Reflectometer Model 15R. Since the D&S device uses 660-nra-wavelength light as its light source, the measured reflectance values require an adjustment to estimate a solar average specular reflectivity value of the mirror over the solar spectrum [9].

Each specular reflectance value has to be obtained from many measurements at randomly selected points (clean or dirty) on the mirror modules on the bottom row of the heliostat [9].

As mentioned in Reference 10, also other special apertures are used such as the large aperture near specular imaging reflectometer (LANSIR) of the National Renewable Energy Laboratory (NREL) for material specularity testing.

3.06.2.4.2(iv) Laser
The optical reflecting quality of a mirror surface (plane, parabolic, spherical, trough, Fresnel formed, etc.), curved in whichever way, of low- or high-concentration systems can also be controlled by laser analysis. A laser scan concept has been developed by several institutes. Sandia and NREL developed the so-called V-shot measurement system, which is shown in **Figure 6** [11].

The local slopes of a mirror are scanned with a laser beam, finding the point of incidence of the reflected beam and calculating the resulting surface normal. Until now, this system was only able to measure dishes and parabolic troughs, with adequate precision.

Because of the extremely high pointing precision required of the laser and the required large distances, until now the system could not measure heliostats. A further problem is the large amount of time required for a high-resolution scan, and the scan is not applicable for different collector positions [11].

3.06.2.4.2(v) Abrasion test
Several companies are working toward improving the abrasion resistance of the reflector. Material degradation rates increase with temperature for absorber, receiver, and heat transfer fluid (HTF).

Research facilities provide data on performance losses as a function of outdoor exposure time at a number of locations that are attractive to utilities and industrial companies interested in concentrating solar power (CSP) generation. Complementary accelerated laboratory exposure testing is also performed [12].

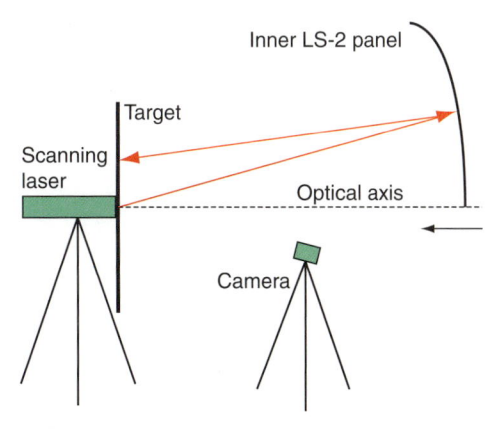

Figure 6 Sketch of the laser scanner VSHOT developed by Sandia National Laboratories and NREL. Reproduced from Jones SA, Neal DR, Gruetzner JK, et al. (1996) VSHOT: A tool for characterizing large, imprecise reflectors. *International Symposium on Optical Science Engineering and Instrumentation*. Denver, CO, USA [11].

As an example, Price *et al.* [13] describe the abrasion resistance measurement of an antireflective (AR) layer using a standard method developed by SCHOTT. A cylindrical standard eraser with a cross section of 5 mm is moved under pressure and the number of strokes needed to remove the layer is counted.

3.06.2.4.3 Linear receiver
3.06.2.4.3(i) Infrared light
Infrared radiation can be used to measure absorber temperatures. However, there are limitations due to the fact that the glass tube is not transparent to radiation with wavelengths greater than 4 µm. On the other hand, the infrared signal should not be affected by reflected solar radiation which extends to about 3 µm wavelength. In order to detect a signal that corresponds well to the absorber surface temperature, filters have to be used that transmit only a thin band of radiation. This spectral range is difficult to use as the emittance of the selective absorber surface drops sharply from shorter to longer wavelengths. Therefore, careful calibration is required to obtain meaningful results [6].

3.06.2.4.3(ii) Receiver reflection method
The receiver reflection method can be used to analyze the hit rate of a trough mirror on the absorber rod. An example is shown in **Figure 7**. In order to trace back the solar radiation path, a camera stands orthographic to the longitudinal plane of the open trough in order to take a high-resolution image of the absorber from a longer distance. To ease the position of the camera, the trough should stand totally vertical (−90° or 90°).

Only the incoming part of the image, which is orthographic to the trough longitudinal axis is approximate equal to the parallel radiation distribution of the Sun. This means, if a telephoto lens is used, only the central part of the image is taken in the solar radiation axis and shows if the absorber is straight. To analyze the complete trough, the camera has to be positioned parallel to the vertical standing trough. The parallel photos can be assembled to a large complete image. All parts of this photo that show the absorber are correct and the corresponding parts of the trough are correctly targeted. All other parts of the assembled photo that show the backgrounds are out of alignment.

3.06.2.4.3(iii) ParaScan
ParaScan is a measurement unit developed by DLR for analyzing trough systems (see **Figure 8**). It consists of two separate detectors that are installed on the absorber tube and which scan the reflected incoming sunlight by moving across the length of the tube by a moving arm.

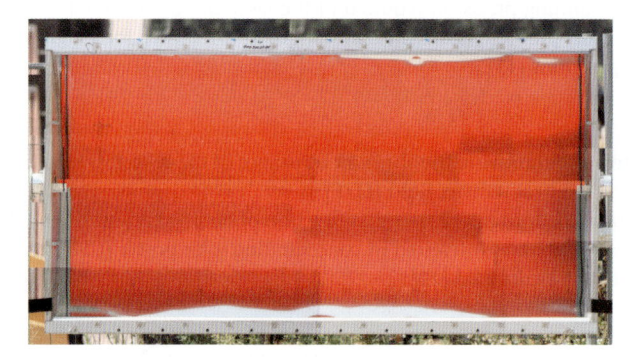

Figure 7 Receiver reflection analysis of the intercept factor of a small parabolic trough. The transparent absorber tube was filled with a red-colored fluid. At the assembled image, all out of alignment oriented mirror surfaces are white instead of red.

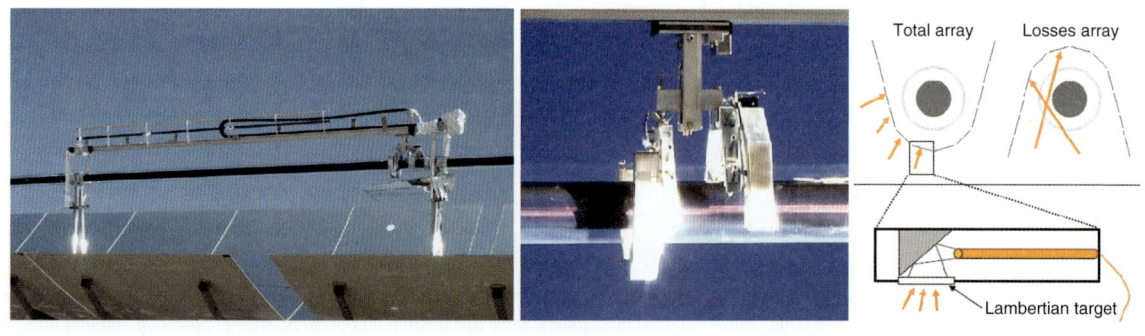

Figure 8 ParaScan with two light intensity detector arrays mounted on a moving arm.

Both detector systems are array systems, each with a transparent Lambertian area target that is analyzed by a calibrated light intensity detector. The first detector system measures all the light that is reflected in the direction of the absorber tube and the second detector system measures the light that misses the absorber tube. The combined data reveal unfocused and other problematic areas in the trough mirror.

3.06.2.4.3(iv) Vacuum hydrogen absorption

3.06.2.4.3(iv)(a) Thermocouples Thermocouples (TCs) use the thermoelectric effect (Seebeck effect) to measure the temperature difference between a measuring point and a reference junction with known temperature. The Seebeck effect induces a potential between two metal tips made of different material, twisted or welded together, and the reference junction. The measured potential could be translated to a temperature difference using specific tables or polynomial equations.

TCs have a wide measurement range and a fast response time and do not influence the measuring media (unlike resistance thermometers due to the measuring current). There are TCs for measuring different temperature ranges like type T for lower temperatures (−185 to 300 °C) and type S for higher temperatures (up to 1600 °C). The most common types in industrial applications are type K TCs, which are capable of measuring temperatures from 0 to 1100 °C in continuous operation. The accuracy depends on the type of the TC but usually does not exceed ± 3 K.

TCs are available with different kinds of insulation like ceramics or stainless steel. Different diameters (starting at 0.25 mm) and shapes of the coating make them applicable to a wide range of measuring tasks/media like hot exhaust gases, corrosive acids, and high-pressurized applications.

3.06.2.4.3(v) Mass flow measurements

In all solar thermal power plants, the mass flow is strictly connected with the absorber temperature reached and the thermal energy gained. Therefore, measurement of the flow is a very important input for regulation of the power plant. The techniques employed are standard industrial measuring systems. The mass flow of the air receiver, the heat accumulator, and the heat exchanger is typically defined by ultrasonic flow measuring systems and consists of several cross-installed detectors.

3.06.2.4.3(vi) Further thermal tests (heat transport, pressure)

Further measurements include pressure measurement and calculation of heat transport coefficients. Heat transport coefficient measurements are mainly done under set conditions. Another measuring method used for absorbers is the so-called 'Pizza board'.

3.06.2.4.4 Area receiver

3.06.2.4.4(i) Luminance

A solar radiation receiver absorbs most of the sunlight but a considerable part is reflected. Because of its high temperature, the receiver also emits thermal radiation. To measure the total radiation, which includes both reflection and emission of an area receiver, a photometric measure called the luminance is used (see **Figure 9**).

The luminance is the luminous intensity per unit area of light passing in a given direction. It quantifies the amount of light that radiates through or is emitted from a particular area under a defined angle. The SI unit of luminance is candela per square meter ($Cd\,m^{-2}$). The measured result of the emitting area is given by a special calibrated digital luminance camera which detects the local radiation values.

3.06.2.4.4(ii) Thermography

Of main interest for all high-concentrated solar thermal systems is monitoring of the temperature reached of the absorber material in order to avoid thermal damages. Infrared cameras offer a good way of comprehensive and real-time observation.

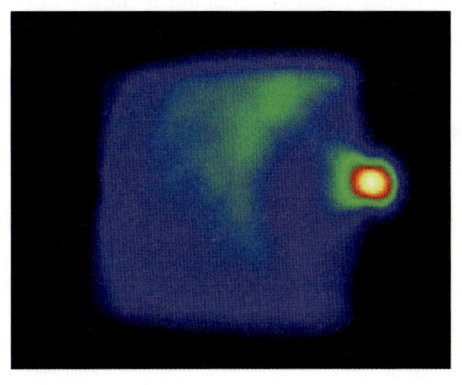

Figure 9 Spotlight beam on a white target analyzed by luminance camera.

Especially for the receivers of solar tower power plants working with large surfaces, where rapidly changing high temperatures and strong thermal gradients prevail, hundreds of feeler sensors have to be installed in the receiver field. The infrared detector on the camera measures the emitted thermal radiation, which depends on the emission factor ε and the temperature T to the power of 4:

$$I \approx \varepsilon(T)T^4 \qquad [2]$$

The emission factor depends on temperature and should be analyzed for example by laboratory tests to grade up the measured quality.

By measuring the temperature level, heat energy can be calculated and the heat exchanger can be run continuously and equally.

The exact temperature level is important, but another important task of an observing infrared camera is locating disruptive hot spots, where high temperature gradients occur. These problems can reduce significantly the lifetime of the absorber cups and lead to an early replacement.

3.06.2.4.4(iii) Infrared light
Nonglazed receivers can be analyzed using standard infrared cameras that are calibrated to high-temperature surfaces. As in the case of linear receivers, the emittance of the surface has to be considered when interpreting infrared camera images.

3.06.2.4.4(iv) Absorber tests
Absorber tests are carried out to specify the thermal efficiency, mechanical stability, and lifetime of an absorber cup. In a power plant environment, an absorber has to withstand 3500 heating cycles per year due to cloud transients. Each cycle is like a thermal shock to the absorber with high temperature gradients (cooling down as well as heating up).

The tests are done in special testing rigs that are capable of measuring or comparing the thermal efficiency of different absorber types or run cyclic tests to estimate the lifetime and thermal shock resistance. There are also some tests to evaluate the highest reachable outlet temperature or even overheat tests of the absorber until melting.

3.06.2.4.4(v) Moving bar, TCs
To evaluate the total efficiency of a complete receiver, the input power to the receiver has to be known. To minimize the influence of the measurement technique on the operation of the receiver and due to the high radiation flux (up to 1 MW m^{-2}) at the target area, the so-called moving bar is used. This is made of a bar with high diffuse reflection, and is placed directly in front of the receiver. To measure the radiation distribution in front of the receiver, the bar is panned over the receiver area in a short time (less than 5 s). A video camera records the brightness of the reflected light from the moving bar and some reference radiometers. The reference radiometers are placed near the receiver at some place with lower flux densities but within the panning area of the moving bar. The recorded brightness values and the known flux at the reference radiometers enable calculation of the flux distribution and total radiation flux at the panning area. With the flux distribution it is also possible to determine possible divergences in the targeting accuracy of the heliostat field.

3.06.2.4.4(vi) Mass flow measurements and thermal tests
Measurements of mass flow as well as of pressure and heat transport are done the same way as with linear receivers with the exception that the temperature is higher.

3.06.2.5 Operation and Maintenance
3.06.2.5.1 Cleaning
When cleaning the different optical components of CRS, it is important to minimize the amount of water used, the required time, the environmental impact, and the energy demand. Cleaning is mostly done at night, and water is used a cleaning medium.

3.06.3 Parabolic Trough Collectors

3.06.3.1 Introduction
Parabolic trough collector (PTC) is a line-focusing system that uses a moving parabolic reflector to concentrate direct solar radiation onto a linear receiver.

3.06.3.2 Basic Characteristics
3.06.3.2.1 Structure
The different parts of PTCs are shown in Figure 10.

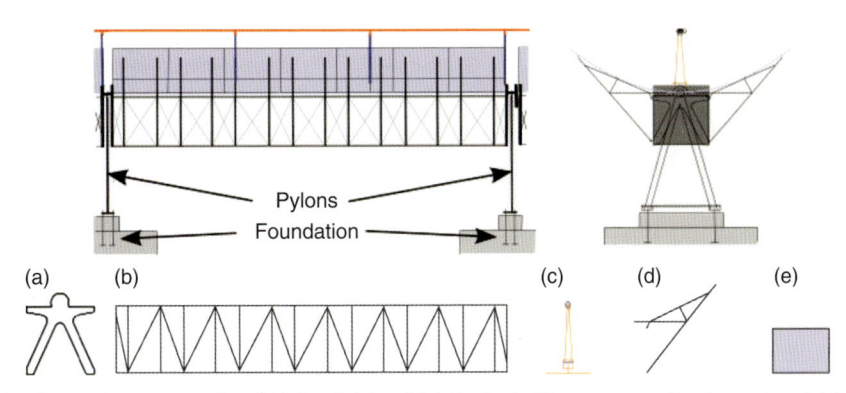

Figure 10 EuroTrough collector element consisting of (a) 2 end plates, (b) 4 simple steel frames screwed to a torque box, (c) 3 absorber tube supports, (d) 28 cantilever arms, and (e) 28 mirror facets [14].

The pylons are usually attached to some kind of foundation or rammed into the ground. The torque body, which could be made of some kind of framework (**Figure 10**) or a simple solid tube (SenerTrough Collector [15]), is mounted onto these pylons. Cantilever arms connected to the torque body hold the mirror facets, which concentrate the direct solar radiation onto the absorber tube at the focal line of the reflectors.

3.06.3.2.2 Components

In the position of the focal length of a parabolic trough stands the absorber tube. The absorber surface shows solar flux densities up to 100-fold of the incident solar radiation. The main function of the receiver is to absorb the concentrated sunlight and convert it with a high efficiency to heat.

The operating temperature of the heat medium is typically 400 °C. The heat transport medium may be water/steam, thermal oil, or molten salt [16].

The manufacturer aims at an optimum radiation absorption with low heat losses.

3.06.3.2.3 Specific characteristics

Absorption, reflection, and transmission may occur when electromagnetic radiation impacts with a solar absorber. **Figure 11** shows these different phenomena.

Absorption is the reception of solar radiation by the solar absorber. Absorption occurs inside the glass seal as well as in the absorber tube. Reflection is the amount of direct solar radiation that is reflected by the surface of the glass and from the surface of the absorber tube. Transmission is the transition of radiation through the glass. The higher the transmission is, the more solar energy reaches the surface of the absorber tube. Each body acts as an emitter of long-wave radiation. Further losses occur as convection and conduction losses of the absorber tube and the glass seal.

An absorber must show high solar absorptance as well as low thermal emittance. **Figure 12** shows the standard design of an absorber tube. In order to achieve high efficiencies, in addition to the selective coating, a vacuum is used between the inner absorber tube and the outer glass tube.

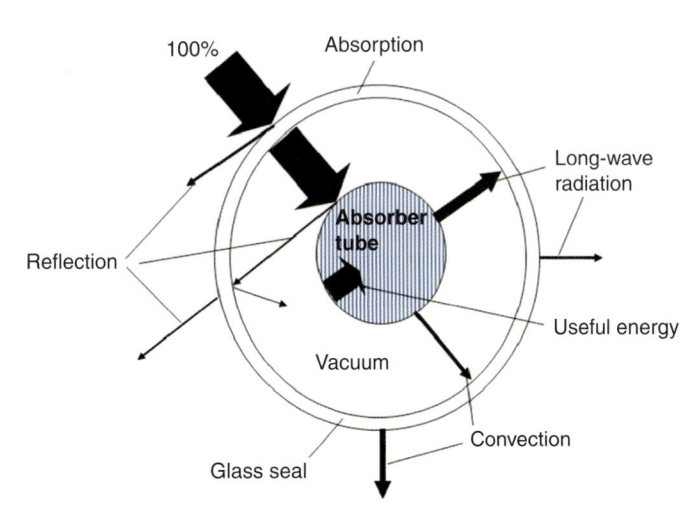

Figure 11 Energy balance of an absorber tube.

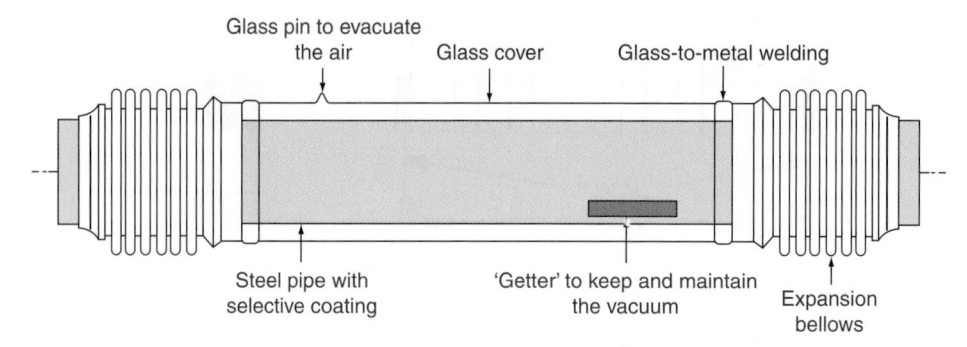

Figure 12 Absorber tube layout.

Metal bellows are used to accommodate thermal expansion difference between the steel tubing and the glass envelope. The glass tubes of the receivers are usually coated with AR films for improved solar transmittance. To minimize heat conduction losses, the absorber is insulated with vacuum enclosed by a glass tube. A getter keeps and maintains the vacuum.

3.06.3.3 Types

3.06.3.3.1 Size

The collector size was increased at the beginning of the technical development in the early 1980s from 34 m^2 for the Acurex to 128 m^2 for the LS-1 collector. The next generations of the Luz collector reached an aperture area of 525 m^2 (LS-3). Nowadays, sizes range from 817 m^2 as in the EuroTrough collector to about 1000 m^2 and higher and these may reach values of about 1700 m^2 or even exceed them in the near future.

3.06.3.3.2 Material

The pylons, torque body, and mirror support arms of PTCs are usually made of steel, which is protected against corrosion by paint or galvanization. For smaller applications (roof-mounted collectors for generation of process steam), deep-drawn troughs made of stainless steel or plastic are currently being examined [17]. A different approach used to build more rigid PTCs is to use concrete frames that are fabricated on-site [18].

3.06.3.3.3 Heat transfer fluid

The current HTF (Monsanto Therminol VP-1) is an aromatic hydrocarbon (biphenyl-diphenyl oxide). As HTF, thermal oil, suitable up to 300 °C, or synthetic oil, suitable up to 400 °C, is deployed. Winter et al. [19] mentioned one important advantage of oil, that is, a low vapor pressure; the disadvantage of oil is its low viscosity at low temperatures, which is critical in particular at start-up after the plant has cooled down.

As an alternate to the use of oil as HTF, water/steam is used in some applications. In direct steam generation technology, only water is used as a heat transport medium, replacing thermal oil in the solar cycle. In such a system, high-pressure steam is generated by concentrating solar radiation in a one-step process. **Table 1** shows the advantages and disadvantages of the direct steam generation technology, which are confirmed by Mohr and Svoboda [20]. The trough collectors require some modification due to the higher operating pressure and lower fluid flow rates [21].

Molten nitrate salt mixtures offer higher operating temperatures with a low vapor pressure, but their freezing points are typically too high to prevent freezing during off-sun periods. Ternary eutectic mixtures of nitrate salts have recently been discovered that have lower freezing points and may offer a path to a practical molten salt heat transport fluid for parabolic trough power plants [23].

Table 1 Advantages and disadvantages of direct steam generation

Advantages	Disadvantages
Decrease of heat losses through the elimination of thermal oil	Eventual instabilities at the two-phase flow
Increase of the annual efficiency of the water–steam cycle through better steam parameters	Need of development activities and experiments
Saving in the investment cost by the omission of the treatment system for the thermal oil and of the heat exchangers [22]	Extra costs for equipment components
Lower pressure drop resulting in lower pump work	

3.06.3.3.4 Specific control components

Tracking of parabolic trough mirrors is usually controlled by solar position algorithms assisted by sensors which can be used for fine-tuning the tilt angle in such a way that the optical axis is in line with the direction of sunlight. **Figure 13** shows a characteristic sensor for fine-tuning of mirror tilt angle.

On the other hand, the control system must be fail-safe in the case of an electricity failure. Either centralized or decentralized power backup systems must be installed in order to defocus the troughs or move the focus away from the receiver in the case of an emergency.

3.06.3.3.5 Drives

The parabolic trough systems that have been installed so far are using hydraulic drives, which are robust, do not have any slackness or play, and are able to provide strong forces with small-step movements (typically 1/10 mm). **Figure 14** shows a characteristic hydraulic drive for PTCs.

3.06.3.3.6 Tracking system

The collectors track the Sun automatically and continuously during the day. The tracking system might be of one or two dimensions. In order to start tracking, a sun sensor is located on the parabolic trough.

3.06.3.3.7 Diverse

Getters – metallic compounds designed to absorb gas molecules – are installed in the vacuum space to absorb hydrogen and other gases that permeate into the vacuum annulus over time. The receivers include an evaporable barium getter, which is used to monitor the vacuum in the receiver. The barium getter will have a silver appearance when the receiver has good vacuum, but will turn white if

Figure 13 Sensor for fine-tuning of mirror tilt angle. Source: Solar Millennium.

Figure 14 Acciona hydraulic drive. Source: NREL.

the receiver loses vacuum and is exposed to air. Because of the higher operating temperatures at the latest plants, substantial thermal decomposition of the HTF is expected, and as a result, hydrogen buildup in the vacuum becomes more of a concern. In addition to getters, a special hydrogen removal (HR) membrane made from a palladium alloy can help to remove excess hydrogen from the vacuum annulus [24].

3.06.3.4 Construction and Installation

3.06.3.4.1 Prefabrication

A large PTC usually consists of a holding structure, curved mirror facets, the absorber tube, and the foundation with pylons. The holding structure can generally be separated into a torque-resistant body and the cantilever arms, which carry the mirrors. These components are prefabricated at specialized facilities. The holding structure and the pylons are usually made of steel. The torque-resistant body can be a round tube or made of some kind of framework. The cantilever arms are made of a framework construction but can also be stamped similar to sheet form profiles of a car bodywork. These processes can be highly automated in order to produce at low cost and at a high level of quality. Because of the size of a larger PTC (span more than 5 m), these parts may be shipped separately to the construction site to minimize the transport volume.

3.06.3.4.2 In situ assembly

The entire steel structure of a parabolic trough consists of standard components that can be manufactured or sourced locally.

All the previously described elements are put together on-site. The pylons are put on the foundation to later incorporate the parabolic trough. The parabolic trough itself is assembled on the field or sometimes in temporary factory buildings. The cantilever arms are mounted to the torque body (welded, screwed, jig). Afterward, the mirror facets are assembled on the cantilever arms. To complete the PTC, the absorber tube is installed in the focal line of the parabola. The last step is to hoist each segment between two pylons and connect the absorbers and transmission elements to the next segment.

3.06.3.4.3 Adjustment

After the erection of the parabolic trough segments, the alignment of the mirrors is checked. There are several techniques available to verify that the mirrors are shaped as desired and to detect errors in the alignment. Some of these techniques are 'video scanning Hartmann optical test' (VSHOT) [25] or 'Sandia optical fringe analysis slope tool for mirror characterization' (SOFAST) [26]. Depending on the mirror support, it is possible to adjust the alignment of single mirror elements.

3.06.3.5 System-Specific Determination of Performance

3.06.3.5.1 Definition of efficiencies

For collectors the efficiency can be written according to Reference 27 as

$$\eta = F_R \eta_0 - \frac{c_1(T_i - T_a)}{CG_b} - \frac{c_2(T_i - T_a)^2}{CG_b} \qquad [3]$$

where T_i is the temperature of the fluid entering the PTC, T_a is the ambient temperature, C is the concentration ratio, G_b is the direct irradiation, c_1 and c_2 are the first- and second-order coefficients of the collector efficiency, and F_R is the heat removal factor.

Denoting $k_0 = F_R \eta_0$, $k_1 = c_1/C$, $k_2 = c_2/C$, and $\gamma = (T_i - T_a)/G_b$ leads to [27]

$$\eta = k_0 - k_1 \gamma - k_2 G_b \gamma^2 \qquad [4]$$

3.06.3.5.2 Error sources

Mirror surface waviness is an important factor for parabolic collector surfaces.

3.06.3.6 Models of Collectors and Their Construction Details

3.06.3.6.1 LS-1, LS-2, and LS-3

The company Luz developed the collectors LS-1, LS-2, and LS-3 (**Figure 15**). Luz first developed the LS-1 PTC with an aperture of 2.5 m and a concentration ratio of 61. According to Reference 22, the maximum operating temperature was 307 °C and the collector was installed in the first SEGS plant of approximately 14 MW.

Luz system collectors of the next generation are LS-2 and LS-3, which were used at most of the SEGS plants and represent the standard by which all other collectors are compared.

The LS-2 collector has a torque tube structure and has six torque tube collector modules, three on either side of the drive [28]. Each torque tube has two 4 m long receivers. The receiver consists of a steel tube with a black selective surface coating, surrounded by an evacuated glass tube. The LS-2 design accounted for about 65% of the collectors installed in the SEGS II–VII in California [29]. The mirror aperture was 5 m and the length 49 m. Luz managed to reach a maximum operation temperature of 390 °C [22].

Figure 15 Luz parabolic trough collectors as installed in the SEGS plants in the United States. Source: Sandia.

For reducing manufacturing costs, Luz designed the larger LS-3 to lower manufacturing tolerance and steel requirements. The new collector system uses a bridge truss structure in place of the torque tube. Luz's LS-3 collector has truss assemblies on either side of the drive and each of them has three 4 m long receivers. The LS-3 collector was the last design produced by Luz and it was primarily used at the larger 80 MW SEGS plants. The LS-3 reflectors are made from hot-formed, mirrored glass panels and the width of the parabolic reflectors is 5.76 m and the overall length is 95.2 m (net glass). The mirrors are made from a low-iron float glass with a transmissivity of 98%; they are silvered on the back and then covered with several protective coatings. Ceramic pads used for mounting the mirrors to the collector structure are attached with a special adhesive [30].

3.06.3.6.2 EuroTrough

The EuroTrough (ET, SKALET) PTC was developed by a European multinational consortium and financially supported by the European Commission, based on the LS-3 collector technology of Luz. It has been developed for the generation of solar steam for process heat applications and solar power generation.

Huge efforts were made by the manufacturers to achieve cost-efficient solar power generation [31]. Cost reduction is achieved, on the one hand, by simplification of the design due to less different profiles and parts, compact transportation, and efficient manufacture and assembly concept and, on the other hand, by weight reduction of the structure as well as by improvement of the optical performance.

The EuroTrough (**Figure 16**) consists of identical 12 m long collector modules. Each module comprises 28 parabolic mirror panels – 7 along the horizontal axis between pylons and 4 in a vertical cross section. Each mirror is supported on the structure at four points on its backside. This permits the glass to bend within the range of its flexibility without any effect on the focal point. The 100 m long parabolic trough is called ET100 and has 8 collector modules and an aperture area of 545 m^2; the 150 m long ET150 has 12 collector modules and an aperture area of 817.5 m^2 [12]. The reflectivity of the mirror is 0.94 and the optical concentration is 94.

Both parabolic troughs track the Sun during operation along their long axis with a hydraulic drive. The drive system consists of two hydraulic cylinders mounted on the central drive pylon. As mentioned in Reference 14, the control box is mounted on the drive pylon signal and power lines lead to the hydraulic unit, the rotational encoder, limit switches, and temperature sensors.

Figure 16 EuroTrough collector. Source: Schlaich Bergermann und Partner (SBP).

Figure 17 EuroTrough prototype installation at the PSA. Source: EuroTrough Final Report (2001)[32].

An HTF, usually synthetic oil heated to a temperature of nearly 400 °C, circulates through the absorber tube.

A prototype of the EuroTrough was tested successfully up to 390 °C, with an oil loop and furthermore with direct steam generation at the Plataforma Solar de Almería (PSA), Spain. **Figure 17** shows the four solar collector elements (SCEs) of the EuroTrough prototype that were manufactured and installed for testing at the PSA. Overall collector efficiency of 3–4% above LS-2 was claimed.

The outcome of the EuroTrough project was above all the prototype of a commercial product under testing, along with associated detailed background information. As mentioned in Reference 32, the design of the new trough collector support structure, including conceptual studies, wind tunnel measurements, and finite element method (FEM) calculations, resulted in a structure with a central box framework element. This torque box design showed lower weight and less deformation of the collector structure than the other design options considered.

The EuroTrough PTC design was further developed separately by the companies Abengoa and Flagsol. As absorber for the collector SCHOTT Solar or the absorber of Siemens may be used. The EuroTrough collector is used in the Andasol 1–3 power plants in Spain. Abengoa used the EuroTrough collector for the ISCC plant in Ain Béni Mathar in Morocco [33].

3.06.3.6.3 Solargenix collector

Under the US Department of Energy's USA Trough Initiative, Solargenix, now part of Acciona Energy, developed a new collector structure through a cost-shared R&D contract with NREL (**Figure 18**).

The Solargenix trough concentrator uses an all-aluminum space frame [34]. It uses a unique organic hubbing structure, which Gossamer Space Frames initially developed for buildings and bridges [28].

The 64 MW_e Nevada Solar One parabolic trough project features the Solargenix SGX-1 collector. The Solargenix SGX-1 collector uses an innovative new aluminum hubbing system developed in partnership with Gossamer Space Frames to create a structure that is 30% lighter, has 50% fewer pieces, and requires substantially fewer fasteners than earlier designs [35]. The aluminum structure provides better corrosion resistance and has been designed so that the mirrors are mounted directly to the structure and do not require any alignment in the field. The collector uses a new SCHOTT receiver featuring a number of improvements that increase

Figure 18 Solargenix collector as implemented in the Nevada Solar One plant. Source: Acciona Energy.

receiver lifetime and performance. The end result is a collector that increases performance by about 15%, decreases investment costs by about 15%, and improves component reliability of NREL researcher's advance solar technologies, such as this PTC [35, 36].

3.06.3.6.4 HelioTrough

In 2005, Flagsol GmbH jointly with Schlaich Bergermann und Partner (SBP), Fraunhofer Institute for Material Flow and Logistics (IML), and DLR started the development and design of the next generation PTC. A HelioTrough collector as shown in **Figure 19** has a length of 191 m and an aperture area of 1263 m^2.

Compared to the EuroTrough collector, this new approach has the same thermal output with 10% smaller solar field. It has shorter header pipelines and fewer drives, foundations, and wiring, resulting in less investment costs [37]. One LS-2 loop was removed and replaced by a HelioTrough demonstration loop at the commercial SEGS V solar power plant in the United States and has been in operation since the end of 2009.

3.06.3.6.5 Ultimate Trough collector

In 2010, SBP and Fraunhofer IML started the development of the next generation collector for parabolic trough power plants under the leadership of FLABEG Holding GmbH (FLABEG).

The new collector design of the Ultimate Trough was developed with an aperture area of 1689 m^2 and an aperture width of 7.5 m. A first prototype was erected and tested in Cologne, Germany. Due to its huge dimensions, the collector is suitable for large solar power plants in the range of 100–400 MW$_e$. As mentioned in Reference 38, the collector will be ready for projects after passing a demonstration loop phase starting construction after mid-2012 (**Figure 20**).

The Ultimate Trough drive system was designed to allow for two stow positions for wind protection, one in the east and one in the west. This reduces the time the collector needs to move to safe wind protection position. The number of collector-specific parts, for example, drive units, sensors, control units, pylon foundations, and loop-specific piping, will decrease by 50%. A huge cost reduction is related to the solar field assembly costs: as the number of SCEs is decreased by 60%, the labor cost is reduced by around 30%. As a further result of improved efficiency and specific cost reductions, the investment cost for the Ultimate Trough solar field is reduced by 25% [38].

Figure 19 HelioTrough. Source: Solar Millennium.

Figure 20 Ultimate Trough collector. Source: FLABEG.

3.06.3.6.6 PT-1

Abengoa Solar's PT-1 PTC system is shown in **Figure 21** and has a proven record of field operations as it has been operating since 1990.

Its latest version is the result of more than 20 years of continuous improvement aimed at increasing performance and durability while reducing costs and maintenance requirements. The concentrator of the PT-1 is built out of aluminum and steel according to a unique patented design that makes it very lightweight and exceedingly strong. The reflective surface is made out of silvered plastic film or reflective aluminum sheet.

The receiver is made of a steel absorber tube coated with a black chrome selective surface, and a surrounding envelope of Pyrex® glass to reduce heat loss. An AR coating on the glass increases light transmission [39]. The maximum operating temperature is 288 °C. Fully insulated stainless-steel hoses accommodate the motion of the receiver with respect to the fixed field piping and require no maintenance.

Local controllers regulate the collector tracking motors, while a single field controller monitors operation of the overall system. A unique multirow configuration drives two rows of troughs in unison, reducing the number of moving parts and increasing reliability. Each module is about 6.1 m and all eight collector modules together are about 50 m long. Each module has an area of about 14 m^2. Typical row-to-row collector spacing is 5.5–6.1 m.

The roof-mounted trough (RMT) presented in **Figure 22** is a compact, value-engineered version of the PT-1 with a surface of about 4 m^2. It employs the same unique patented space frame design, but its smaller profile reduces wind loads to allow roof-mounting. The collector performance is similar, although the delivered energy is estimated to be 5–10% less than the PT-1. The maximum operating temperature is 204 °C [39].

A further improvement is the development of the Solúcar TR system. Foundations to reduce costs and allow easier transportation and assembly are optimized. Galvanized steel is used for the structure and glass mirrors of 68 m^2 collector area.

3.06.3.6.7 SkyTrough

SkyFuel has developed a parabolic trough solar concentrator, the SkyTrough®, for utility-scale power generation. The collectors are deployed at the SEGS II (**Figure 23**) facility in Daggett, CA, USA.

Each mirror module in the SkyTrough single-axis linear parabolic concentrating collector has an aperture of 6 m (width) by 13.7 m (length). The standard Solar Collector Assembly (SCA) includes eight mirror modules for a total net aperture area of 656 m^2.

Figure 21 PT-1 parabolic trough collector. Source: http://www.abengoasolar.com [39].

Figure 22 RMT parabolic trough collector. Source: http://www.abengoasolar.com [39].

Figure 23 Collector module test at collector loop at SEGS II. Source: McMahan A, White D, Gee R, and Viljoen N (2010) Field performance validation of an advanced utility-scale parabolic trough concentrator. *SolarPACES Symposium*. Perpignan, France [40].

As described in Reference 40, the mirror panels are supported by an all-aluminum space frame made from extruded components that are shipped directly to the site and field assembled and the collector uses SCHOTT PTR®80 4.7 m receivers. The primary structure of each module is a space frame, an efficient truss structure made from aluminum tubing with joints enabling rapid assembly. Next, a series of ribs, which hold nine mirror panels, are attached, which provide parabolic guide rails for holding the mirror sheets [41]. The collector was also tested at the NREL Optical Efficiency Test Loop, and further information regarding performance calculations and test is provided in Reference 40.

3.06.3.6.8 SenerTrough

The SenerTrough (SNT-1) has a mirror aperture area of 817.5 m^2 and uses mirror panels from FLABEG and absorber tubes from SCHOTT. The main characteristic of the SNT-1 collector is that metallic structure integrates a torque tube and stamped cantilever arms: torque tube provides a high torsional stiffness and stamped arms assure an outstanding accuracy for mirror positioning.

SenerTrough-1 (SNT-1) collector was first installed at the PSA at prototype level: an SCE of 12 m length was constructed and tested at PSA facilities in 2005. In 2007, a complete commercial 600 m loop was constructed, tested, and later integrated into Andasol 1 solar field. The first commercial solar thermal power plant using SNT-1 design, Extresol-1 (Badajoz, Spain), was launched in 2007 as well [42] (**Figure 24**).

Sener collectors are installed or will be implemented in 16 plants in Spain and other countries around the world.

3.06.3.6.9 Research

Universities and industries have undertaken many research activities with the aim to develop, study, and optimize the first prototypes and introduce a new PTC in the market.

3.06.3.7 Solar Absorbers for PTCs

3.06.3.7.1 The solar absorber of SCHOTT Solar

The SCHOTT absorber tube is shown in **Figure 25**.

SCHOTT Solar has developed and patented a new absorber coating with remarkable optical values and long-term thermal stability. The emittance values are ≤ 10%, at a working temperature of 400 °C.

Figure 24 Senertrough-1 collector. Source: Relloso S, Calvo R, Cárcamo S, and Olábarri B (2011) SenerTrough-1 collector: Commercial operation experience, continuous loop monitoring. *SolarPACES Symposium*. Granada, Spain [42].

Durable glass-to-metal seal
Material combination with matching coefficients of thermal expansion

AR-coated glass tube
Ensures high transmittance and high abrasion resistance

New absorber coating
Achieves emittance ≤10% and absorptance ≥95%

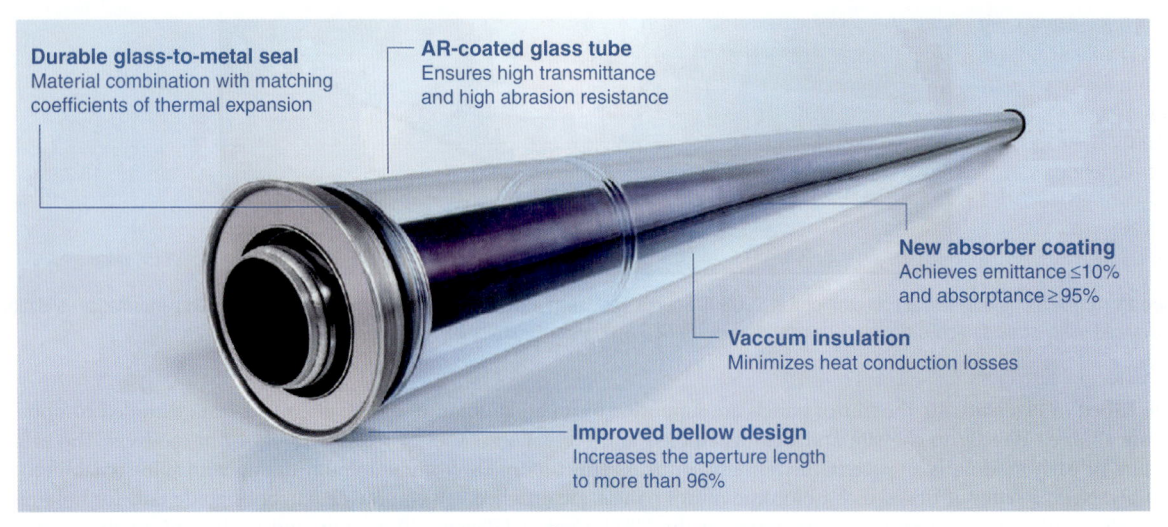

Vaccum insulation
Minimizes heat conduction losses

Improved bellow design
Increases the aperture length to more than 96%

Figure 25 The absorber tube of SCHOTT Solar. Source: SCHOTT PTR®70 Receiver The Next Generation, 2009 [43].

Due to the combination of materials with similar coefficients of thermal expansion, the glass-to-metal seal of the SCHOTT PTR®70 receiver can handle dramatic temperature changes and ensures vacuum stability [43].

Due to a patented production process, SCHOTT Solar has been able to introduce an AR layer with maximum adhesion and long-term abrasion resistance, achieving transmittance values of more than 96%.

To reduce shading of the absorber tube by the bellows, a new design where bellows and glass-to-metal seal are placed on top of each other was developed. Another advantage is the protection of the glass-to-metal seal from concentrated solar radiation [44].

The SCHOTT Solar absorber increases the active aperture area of the receiver to more than 96% of the total area, which is at least 2% more compared to other designs [43]. Furthermore, by integrating the getter material in the coolest position of the receiver, the full getter capacity can be utilized. This increases the lifetime of the receiver up to 30% in comparison to other designs where the getter is positioned on the absorber tube.

3.06.3.7.2 The solar absorber of Siemens

After acquiring Solel Solar Systems, Siemens got access to Solel's solar absorber [45]. Solel Solar Systems was one of the world's two leading suppliers of solar receivers for parabolic trough power plants.

The Siemens' UVAC (Universal Vacuum Air Collector) 2010 solar absorber includes the patented vacuum maintenance unit designed for up to 35 years and anti-'fluorescent phenomenon' coating, designed to provide stable performance over time even under extreme conditions. The absorber has a length of 4 m and consists of a stainless-steel tube with a selective coating and a borosilicate AR glass envelope. This selective surface has absorptivity higher than or equal to 96% for direct beam solar radiation and design emissivity of lower than 9% at 400 °C. The outer glass enclosure features an AR coating on both surfaces and transmissivity of 96.5% or more. The UVAC 2010 features glass-to-metal seals and metal bellows to achieve vacuum tightness of the enclosure. By preventing hydrogen permeation, which would otherwise diminish the vacuum and permit heat loss, Siemens' patented 'Getter Bridge' is designed to help keep the product performing well over many years [46].

3.06.3.8 Operation and Maintenance

3.06.3.8.1 Cleaning techniques

Less than 3% of total water consumption of solar thermal plants is used for the purpose of washing mirrors [47].

Development of an efficient and cost-effective program for monitoring mirror reflectivity and washing mirrors is critical. Differing seasonal soiling rates require flexible procedures. For example, high soiling rates of 0.5% day^{-1} have been experienced during summer periods. After considerable experience, operation and maintenance (O&M) procedures have settled on several methods, including deluge washing and direct and pulsating high-pressure sprays. All methods use demineralized water for good effectiveness. The periodic monitoring of mirror reflectivity can provide a valuable quality control tool for mirror washing and help optimize wash labor. As a general rule, the reflectivity of glass mirrors can be returned to design levels with good washing [22].

Experience has shown that demineralized water must be used for wet mirror cleaning. As revealed by Winter *et al.* [19], this is due to the fact that the reflectivity of collector surfaces washed with hard water was lower than the reflectivity of those left dirty.

Rain is very effective at washing the reflective surfaces to maintain performance. In drier climates, the collectors should be washed about every 2 months. A widespread method of washing, as described in Reference 39, is by spraying the collectors with deionized water using a truck-mounted pressure washer and water tank.

Research has been carried out in France on the characterization of self-cleaning glass, the properties of which arise from a thin TiO_2 coating which is activated when exposed to solar light [48].

3.06.3.8.2 Maintenance of HTF quality

In a parabolic trough solar power plant, a backup fuel has to be added to keep the HTF in the solar field above freezing point and to maintain its temperature in order to compensate for the lack of solar radiation, which could affect the established delivery of energy [49].

Parabolic trough plants currently in operation use an HTF in the collector field that is a mixture of the organic compounds diphenyl oxide and biphenyl oxide. This synthetic oil offers the best combination of low freezing point (14 °C) and upper temperature limit (393 °C) among available HTFs. However, the thermal stability of this HTF limits the efficiency of the Rankine cycle [50].

In addition to synthetic oil, melting salt can also be used as an HTF. But melting salt has limitation regarding low freezing point and upper temperature limit. Of particular interest are the chemical stability and physical properties of multicomponent mixtures that display significantly lower melting points than solar nitrate salt.

In general, the HTF is utilized in the liquid phase in a closed-loop configuration, which includes a surge or expansion tank from which low-boiling thermal degradation products may be vented for removal from the system. If the HTF contains impurities, then this can enhance its degradation.

Fluid life, as mentioned by Gamble and Schopf [51], is limited by the accumulation of high-boiling organic degradation products, which accumulate slowly, and is a function of the time the fluid spends at elevated operating temperatures. Proper design to ensure the fluid is maintained in the turbulent flow regime prevents overstressing the fluid at a given temperature in the solar energy collection field where fluid heating occurs. The early plants did not employ nighttime operation by fuel-fired boilers or thermal storage and generated power only during daytime hours. Plants designed for extended-service (e.g., nighttime) power generation will experience a rate of thermal degradation proportionally increased according to the time spent at operating temperatures.

In addition to the influence of impurities, thermal stability is another factor that has influence on the quality of an HTF. For example, standard methods for testing the thermal stability of organic HTFs include DIN 51528 and ASTM D-6743 [51].

In order to ensure long service life with acceptable thermal degradation, there exists a maximum recommended operating temperature for commonly used HTFs in parabolic troughs. For example, the maximum recommended operating temperature for Therminol VP-1 is 400 °C. Operating at higher temperatures increases the thermal degradation rate and reduces service life. When a fluid is thermally stressed, its activation energy decreases and degradation rate increases. Therefore, the high amount of the biphenyl and the diphenyl oxide used to produce HTFs for high-temperature operation is essential to minimize negative impacts on fluid life [51]. This is particularly important for parabolic trough plants, which require large amounts of fluid.

3.06.3.8.3 Replacement of parts

Most problems can be detected through off-site monitoring. Periodic site inspections, every 1 or 2 weeks, are generally adequate to monitor system operations and to perform routine maintenance. At different plants around the world such as SEGS or Andasol plants, a few old collectors have been replaced by new collector designs.

3.06.3.8.4 Adjustment

Nowadays, installing the mirror sheets of parabolic troughs is rapid as a single panel may be inserted and stiffeners attached in a few minutes.

A collector loop is very often equipped with different devices for volumetric flow measurements, temperature readings, monitoring the cleanliness factor (with the aid of a portable specular reflectometer), and monitoring of mirror and Heat Collector Element (HCE) tube conditions.

3.06.4 Central Receiver Systems

3.06.4.1 Introduction

CRS is a point-focusing system that uses individually tracked heliostat mirrors to concentrate direct solar radiation onto a stationary receiver located on top of a solar tower.

3.06.4.2 Basic Characteristics

3.06.4.2.1 Structure

Most of the current commercially operating CRS power plants (PS10, PS20, Gemasolar (**Figure 26(b)**), Solar-Tower Jülich (**Figure 26(a)**)) have a tower made of (reinforced) concrete. The shape of the tower depends on the configuration of the power plant. In the case of the Solar-Tower Jülich, all the components of the power plant (boiler, turbine, heat storage) are located inside the tower building, which has a rectangular outline. Other concepts are the use of a monopole tower similar to the towers used for wind turbines (Sierra SunTower (**Figure 26(c)**)) or steel framework constructions (Solar One and Two (**Figure 26(d)**)).

Figure 26 Several tower concepts.

3.06.4.2.2 Components
A CRS includes the heliostat field and the tower. The heliostat field is made up of individual heliostats. Each heliostat follows the Sun in two dimensions and concentrates the solar arrays onto a receiver area. The receiver is mostly located on top of a tower. Both tower and each heliostat normally have foundation for stabilization of the whole construction. In order to increase the concentrated sunlight reaching the receiver aperture, a secondary concentrator is used.

3.06.4.2.3 Specific characteristics
By concentrating the solar radiation and by absorbing that energy in a receiver, it is possible to provide high-temperature process heat to energy conversion devices. From a thermodynamic point of view, these processes should be operated at temperatures as high as possible because of the limitation imposed by the Carnot efficiency [52]. The highest temperature that can be achieved is dependent on the optics of the heliostats and on the ability and build of the solar receiver to absorb and to convert solar radiation into heat.

3.06.4.3 Types

3.06.4.3.1 Geometry of receiver aperture
The geometry of central receivers depends on the heliostat field layout and the HTF used. A flat (billboard) receiver is used only on north/south fields, while cylindrical/pyramidal receivers can be used on surround fields as well. Sometimes, the receiver area is inclined in the direction of the heliostat field. This is the case especially when secondary concentrators (compound parabolic concentrator (CPC)) or receivers with cavity are used because of their small acceptable angle of incidence.

All directly radiated flat area receivers have high thermal losses due to natural convection and thermal radiation to the environment. To minimize these losses, the receiver area could be surrounded by a cavity. This is in principal a box surrounding the absorber elements with a small hole. Radiation strikes the absorber through this hole while the reradiated energy is kept inside the box. The temperature of the outer wall of the box is close to ambient temperature, so heat losses through convection are almost eliminated. The opening of the cavity could even be covered with a quartz glass window to further minimize thermal losses. A disadvantage of cavities is that the aiming of the heliostats needs to be very precise. A small deviation in the orientation of the heliostat means that the reflected sunlight will miss the cavity opening.

3.06.4.3.2 Heat transfer medium
An HTF is a fluid or gas that has the ability to transport heat. In a CRS system, an HTF is used, on the one hand, to cool the absorber and, on the other hand, for the transport of the absorbed heat. Criteria for choosing an HTF are heat capacity, thermal conductivity, reached outlet temperature, and heat flux density.

Although sodium has high heat conductivity, it is not considered anymore as HTF in CRS due to high operational risks.

Water/steam has been used as HTF for a long time as it is used in conventional steam cycles [21]. Steam has a good specific heat capacity and a high thermal conductivity. Another important advantage is that no further heat exchanger is needed and the steam can be directly expanded in a steam turbine later. In the solar cycle, a problem is the storage, corrosion effect, and the transient behavior of water/steam at changing weather conditions. Additionally, in order to avoid thermal losses, water has to be cleaned of particles.

The choice of molten salt as HTF in both the receiver and heat storage yields high capacity factors [53]. According to Reference 54, the molten salt technology is the best-developed CRS today. Molten salt can be operated only in a closed cycle and has a low working pressure demand. Because of the solidification temperature, trace heating is required.

Air as HTF has the advantage of being environmentally benign and free. No trace heating is needed and the highest fluid outlet temperature can be achieved. Air can be operated in both open and closed solar power cycles.

3.06.4.3.3 Receiver

The design of the receiver depends on the HTF, the operation temperature, the material used, and the method of energy transfer. It is the most critical component of a CRS and its design and operation must be investigated very thoroughly.

Receivers are available in different shapes. The most commonly deployed are the tube receivers, the open and closed volumetric receivers, and the direct absorption receiver.

When applying the tube receiver concept, concentrated radiation is directed onto tubes configured as a vertical cylinder or a flat vertical plate, or arranged within a cavity [19]. The HTF is heated through either metal or ceramic tubes depending on the operation temperature and the required temperature gradients.

The volumetric receiver concept considers a system of structures arranged to fill a volume. The structures might be a wire grid made of ceramic fibers or metal, foil, foam, or another alternative system. In an open system, concentrated sunlight hits the volumetric receiver, which absorbs the incident solar radiation and convectively heats the ambient air passing by.

A special case of an open receiver technology is the film receiver concept. Another way to use a volumetric receiver is by inserting a quartz window at the entrance. Such a solution is requested if the receiver is operated under pressure at high temperatures above 1000 °C.

The direct absorption receiver concept uses direct absorption of highly concentrated sunlight, thus allowing immediate transfer of solar energy into a medium [19]. The HTF might be either a liquid suspension or a cloud of particles.

3.06.4.3.4 Tower construction

The choice of tower construction depends primarily on the required height of the tower. Towers are mainly constructed of steel or reinforced concrete. Steel towers are similar to guy wire-supported television transmission towers or free-standing microwave relay towers. Several central receiver design studies have considered guyed towers, but the presence of guy wires and their attachments to the tower in concentrated solar flux proved unworkable [55]. Concrete towers are similar to tall chimneys at conventional fossil power plants.

Factory-made towers which are commonly used for wind turbines may also be a possible solution for tower constructions. The shape of a tower differs from cylindrical to rectangular.

3.06.4.3.5 Heliostat drives, kinematics, coupling, facets, mirror material, and foundation

A heliostat, depending on the size, may be composed of several mirror module panels or may consist of a single large or small mirror. The thin glass mirrors are supported by a substrate backing to form a slightly concave mirror surface. Individual panels on the heliostat are also canted toward a point on the receiver.

For middle to large heliostats composed of panels, each mirror segment is concaved slightly and each mirror segment on a heliostat is canted toward a focal point. This produces a higher flux density at the aim point.

As a foundation of the heliostat, different solutions may be chosen. One main possibility is the use of a standard concrete foundation or a ring. Also firms offer a screw foundation for each heliostat.

3.06.4.3.6 Specific control components

Large heliostat fields require a great effort to control several hundred or thousands of single units. Presently, wire-based bus systems are used to identify heliostats, transmit individual signals from the central control unit to the heliostats, and transmit feedback signals about the position and status of each heliostat back to the central unit. Wire systems may lead to high lightning protection efforts. An interesting solution to this problem could be autonomous heliostats, which are controlled by a wireless system. In this concept, no induced voltages are transmitted and in case of lightning, each heliostat could float at its individual electric potential.

On the other hand, the control system must be fail-safe in the case of an electricity failure. Either centralized or decentralized power backup systems must be installed in order to defocus the heliostats or move the focus away from the receiver in case of emergency.

3.06.4.3.7 Aim-point strategy

Different aim-point strategies are used. A first approach is to aim the heliostats at different points on the receiver. Another commonly used method is a single aim-point strategy. All heliostats are pointed at the center (when viewed from the heliostat surface) of the receiver. This option produces maximum flux on the receiver.

A totally different approach is the following. Heliostat images are spread out along the 'height' of the receiver or aperture until the spillage starts to increase. This option reduces both the peak flux and the flux gradients on the receiver.

A single aim point at the lower part of the receiver is a further possibility. Heliostats are aimed as close to the bottom of the receiver as possible without increasing spillage significantly. Also many different aim-point strategies are possible and tested in solar tower facilities around the world.

3.06.4.4 System-Specific Determination of Performance

3.06.4.4.1 Receiver efficiency and optical and thermal losses

The heliostat field concentrates the solar beams onto the receiver. Not all of the radiation reaches the surface. Atmospheric attenuation and intercept appear on the way to the receiver as well as spillage losses. Spillage occurs due to dilution of light at the surface and is derived from the effects of a finite solar heliostat and various errors inherent in optical hardware and control of the

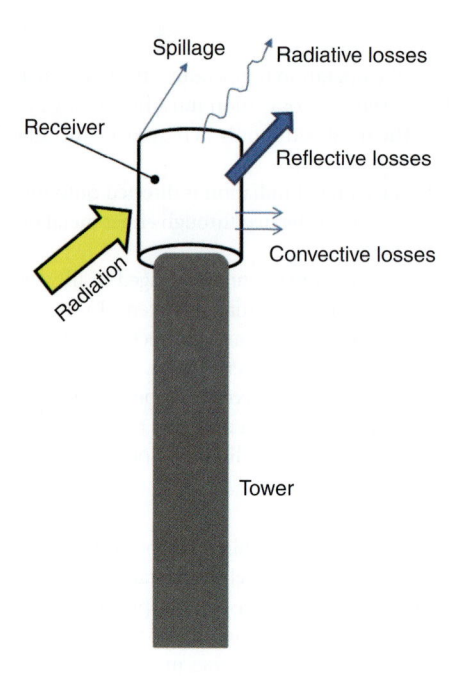

Figure 27 Energy balance of a solar receiver.

heliostat field. Further, not all of the radiation is absorbed due to the reflectivity ratio of the receiver material. **Figure 27** displays the different loss mechanisms at the receiver.

Wind velocity induces forced convection at the absorber surface. Also natural convection appears, which is dependent on the ambient temperature.

In addition to convection, radiation from the receiver to ambient contributes largely to thermal loss, according to Stefan–Boltzmann equation. The final heat loss term represents the heat conducted away from the receiver. Most of this heat is lost through the receiver-supporting components that connect the receiver to the tower structure.

Thermal losses also take place by heat transport of the HTF via pipes to the steam recovery heat generator.

Receiver efficiency η_{rec} may be defined as described in Reference 56 as the product of each loss mode efficiency:

$$\eta_{rec} = \eta_{sp}\eta_{abs}\eta_{rad}\eta_{conv}\eta_{cond} \qquad [5]$$

where η_{sp}, η_{abs}, η_{rad}, η_{conv}, and η_{cond} are efficiencies based on receiver spillage, absorption, radiation, convection, and conduction losses, respectively.

3.06.4.4.2 Heliostat loss mechanisms, tracking accuracy, and beam error

Different loss mechanisms have to be minimized in order to achieve an optimum layout of a heliostat field.

The major factor determining an optimum heliostat field layout is the cosine 'efficiency' of the heliostat. The effective reflection area of the heliostat may be reduced by the cosine depending on both the Sun's position and the location of the individual heliostat relative to the receiver.

Also reflectivity losses at the mirror surface are significant and make less than 10%.

A further loss mechanism is the shadowing and blocking by adjacent heliostats, which reduces the concentrated solar energy reaching the receiver. The amount of shadowing and blocking in a considered field layout is a function of the heliostat spacing, tower height, and sun angle. **Figure 28** shows diagrammatically the loss mechanism of shadowing and the cosinus effect.

One major limitation of placing the heliostat at a distance from the tower is the attenuation of the reflected beam as it travels from the heliostat to the receiver.

An ideal heliostat, if perfectly flat or slightly concaved, generates a flux distribution at the focus point. A number of factors tend to increase the image size from a particular heliostat. As mentioned in Reference 56, the gross curvature error of each mirror segment and the errors associated with accurate canting of each mirror segment on the heliostat frame further increase the image error. All these errors build the beam error, which is an indicator of the tracking quality of a heliostat.

The tracking accuracy, on the other hand, is also dependent on external influences. Positioning errors may be caused by vertical and horizontal errors in heliostat positioning or feedback mechanisms. In addition, changing wind loads can produce structural deflections, causing position errors.

Defining each of these losses in terms of efficiency, the field efficiency η_{hf} may be defined according to Reference 56 as

$$\eta_{hf} = \eta_{cos}\eta_{sh}\eta_{bl}\eta_{ref}\eta_{att} \qquad [6]$$

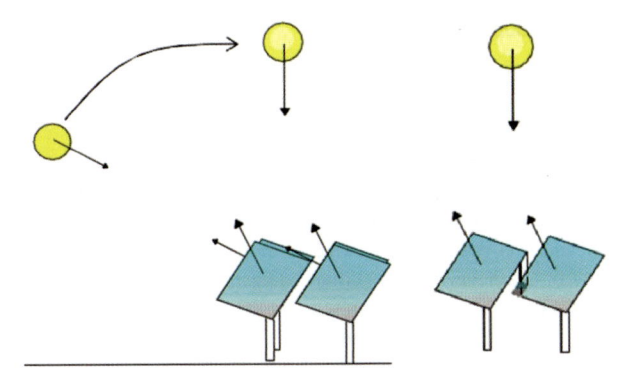

Figure 28 Illustration scheme of the cosinus losses (left) and shadowing losses (right).

where η_{cos}, η_{sh}, η_{bl}, η_{ref}, and η_{att} are efficiencies based on cosine, shadowing, blocking, mirror reflectance, and atmospheric attenuation losses, respectively.

3.06.4.5 Secondary Optics

3.06.4.5.1 Tower reflector

Tower reflectors (TRs) are used to reflect concentrated solar radiation from the heliostat field to a receiver placed on the ground. All heliostats are focusing to the focal point of a hyperboloidal mirror which is placed at the top of a tower (see **Figure 29**).

The fact that the receiver is placed on the ground makes this technique ideal for solar chemistry where solid reactants or gases are involved. These heavy equipment and maintenance-intensive processes can benefit from the easily accessible receiver configuration.

Because of economical considerations, the TR is usually cooled by natural convection, which leads to a limited radiation flux (30–35 kW m^{-2}) on the mirror [57]. In order to reach higher temperatures, it is necessary to use secondary concentrators in front of the receiver to achieve higher radiation fluxes.

3.06.4.5.2 Secondary concentrators

Secondary concentrators are used to distribute the radiation flux equally on the absorber tube of a linear (Fresnel) collector or to further concentrate the radiation flux entering an absorber.

Most common are the CPCs, which are designed to reach flux densities suitable for temperatures above 1200 °C. They usually have a hexagonal shape at the incoming side, which makes it possible to arrange several concentrators next to each other without any gaps. The mirrors are made of 1D curved facets with integrated cooling channels.

A metal construction groups the mirror facets and the cooling pipe work to a compact unit. Some of these units can be arranged together in a cluster.

CPCs have a small acceptable angle of incidence for the incoming radiation, which leads to a heliostat field with elongated shape if they are directly irradiated.

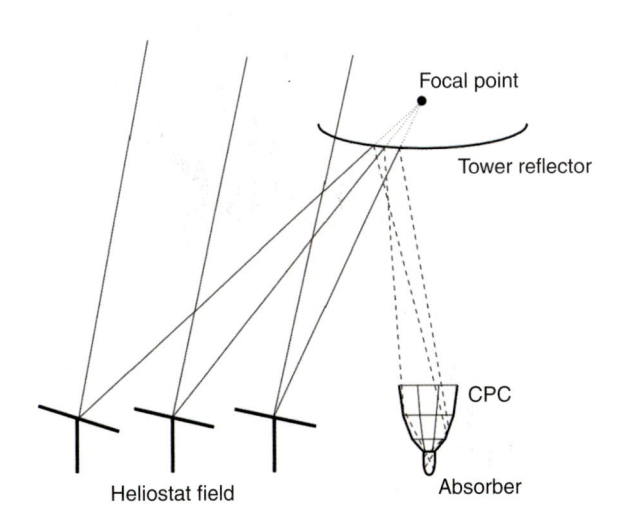

Figure 29 Configuration of a tower reflector and a secondary concentrator (compound parabolic concentrator (CPC)).

3.06.4.6 Models of Heliostats and Their Construction Details

The leading global supplier of heliostats is Inabensa in Spain (Instalaciones Abengoa, S.A.), a subsidiary of Abengoa. At present, Inabensa offers different types of heliostat design. Abengoa Solar New Technologies has developed two heliostats: Sanlúcar 90 and Sanlúcar 120.

The Sanlúcar 90 heliostat is composed of a flat reflective surface, a supporting structure, and a solar tracking mechanism in two axes and can be viewed in **Figure 30**. It is composed of 21 4.33-m^2 facets in 7 rows and 3 columns [12]. As listed in Reference 58, the heliostat has a weight of 3.5 tons and the mirror is fixed to a steel frame. It is held in place by four trusses, torque, and concrete pedestal. The slope error is estimated as lower than 2.8 mrad and the reflectivity is 0.92.

The structure is remarkably light with facets weighing less than 14 kg m^{-2}. Control is simplified and is based on the use of two microcontrollers with master/slave concept. This configuration reduces the complexity of the PCB design and the size of the control card while maintaining performance. As described in Reference 59, the new on-axis canting procedure incorporates theoretical correction of reflector surface deformation at typical tracking positions. The Sanlúcar 90 heliostat evolved from the experience in glass–metal technology accumulated at PSA in the last 20 years. Two prototypes of the Sanlúcar 90 heliostat have been developed and installed at the PSA for testing. The first prototype installed and tested had a Peerless-Winsmith worm-gear drive and the second a hydraulic mechanism [48].

The Sanlúcar 120 heliostat is a mirror technology to be used as part of a heliostat field, to concentrate solar power on a solar tower. It is large with a surface area of 120 m^2 and offers two-axis tracking. It is composed of 28 individual 3.21 m × 1.35 m facets arranged in 7 rows and 4 columns [12] as can be viewed in **Figure 31**.

Figure 30 Sanlúcar 90 heliostat. Source: http://www.abengoasolar.com [39].

Figure 31 Sanlúcar 120 heliostat. Source: http://www.abengoasolar.com [39].

Figure 32 Ausra heliostat.

Specific increase in the reflective surface per heliostat is 33% compared with the Sanlúcar 90 prototype, while stiffness and optical quality design criteria have remained unchanged. As mentioned in Reference 39, it is constructed out of galvanized steel. At wind speeds more than 36 km h^{-1}, the heliostat is set vertically to avoid structural damage [60]. It is installed at the world's first commercial CSP tower PS10 in Sevilla, Spain.

Another company from the United States also builds heliostats using prefabricated components. Each heliostat developed consists of a single facet with a surface area of 7.2 m^2 and has a reflectivity of 93%. It has a low-voltage electrical supply (24 V DC), which can be provided by a photovoltaic power system or batteries. The heliostat and its controlling computer can be connected by a cable or wireless connection. The heliostat is equipped with two actuators, allowing it to track the Sun in two axes. The mirror surface may be slightly curved, depending on the focal distance. **Figure 32** shows the heliostat of Ausra with a pedestal height of about 2.4 m. Such heliostats were installed at the CSIRO's test facility in Australia. An improved version of this heliostat was installed at the solar tower power plant of Jülich in Germany.

Further heliostats of middle size are constructed. A heliostat named HydroHelio™ with a mirror surface area of 30 m^2 was designed by Robert Lehle and CIRRIS Solutions GmbH at Jettingen, Germany, where also the necessary electronic and electromechanical control and test systems are developed. In 2007, a heliostat prototype was constructed and tested. It consists of four mirror frames. The mirrors are accommodated and fixed in a closed mirror frame.

The HydroHelio™ uses a hydraulic actuation system. The adoption of this solution follows the positive experience gained with the hydraulic actuators of the parabolic troughs for more than 20 years of uninterrupted operation. The operating fluid is natural or synthetic oil which is biologically safe, is rapidly degradable, and is also used without difficulty or harm in agriculture and forestry [61].

Once the target position is reached – a matter of milliseconds – the valves close the cylinder ports and the target position is maintained with absolute stability and with no backlash until the next adjustment. The hydraulic system also protects against overload. The special properties of the hydraulic actuation system enable anticipation of high precision and durability for HydroHelio™.

BrightSource's smaller, flat mirrors are efficient and simple to manufacture. The heliostats are highly accurate and have over 35 years of longevity with practically zero maintenance. The Luz Power Tower (LPT) 550 heliostats consist of two flat glass mirrors, a support structure, a pylon, and a tracking system. The mirrors are mounted onto the pylon and track the Sun in two dimensions, reflecting the sunlight onto a boiler atop a tower.

The ability to follow the Sun in two dimensions enables the power system to track a greater percentage of the Sun's energy and achieve a much higher efficiency than other solar thermal technologies. Each heliostat, with a reflecting area of 14.4 m^2, is individually installed and controlled with optimization software, resulting in greater flexibility in site configuration and requiring much less site preparation. The pylons are placed directly into the ground, eliminating the need for concrete pads used with other solar thermal technologies and reducing the system's environmental impact.

A further developer of heliostat fields, eSolar, USA, follows a different approach. A dual-axis heliostat, eSolar™, with a low wind profile design is the basic element of the eSolar solution. By having a small and mass-manufactured commercial mirror of 1.14 m^2, as can be seen in **Figure 33**, the developed heliostat minimizes a number of costs.

By leveraging established commercial suppliers to mass-manufacture thousands of heliostats, eSolar realizes economy-of-scale benefits at much smaller power plant sizes. Heliostats are designed for preassembly at the factory and to fit efficiently into shipping containers to reduce transportation costs and on-site labor. By employing a repeating structure and a revolutionary calibration

Figure 33 Heliostats developed by eSolar. Source: eSolar.

system, eSolar follows the ambitious goal of eliminating the need for high-precision surveying, delicate installation, and individual alignment of mirrors [62].

The heliostat includes a 1.42 m × 0.8 m reflector module which has motors and gears to point the reflected beam at the receiver. The reflector's aspect ratio was chosen to reduce blocking and shading by neighboring reflectors. As explained in Reference 63, eSolar™ heliostats are mounted approximately 1 m above the ground level to allow for simple installation and maintenance while minimizing dust accumulation and wind profile.

Furthermore, there are a number of manufacturers who are able to develop and construct different types of heliostats, which however have not yet reached commercialization.

3.06.4.7 Receiver Types on the Market

The development and production of solar receiver technology is concentrated in three countries worldwide: United States, Germany, and Spain.

CSP tower technology with molten salt as an HTF was demonstrated in California under a US Department of Energy-sponsored pilot project in the late 1990s. The 10 MW pilot facility utilized a molten salt receiver designed, engineered, and assembled by Boeing Rocketdyne, now a part of United Technologies Corporation [64]. Pratt & Whitney Rocketdyne has combined its liquid rocket engine heat transfer technology and molten salt handling expertise to develop a tower receiver technology with thermal storage capabilities [65]. United Technologies, one of the world's leading technology conglomerates, proved and demonstrated this technology. It was demonstrated successfully both at the Solar One and Solar Two power plants in Southern California. United Technologies has decades of experience in these technologies in land-based as well as space applications. Rocketdyne, the US Department of Energy, and others invested more than $100 million into the design and manufacture of these components [66].

United Technologies has granted SolarReserve the proprietary technology know-how. SolarReserve holds the exclusive worldwide license to build state-of-the-art solar thermal electricity generation (STEG) plants that use equipment manufactured and guaranteed by United Technology Corp. subsidiary Hamilton Sundstrand through its Rocketdyne division.

The Rocketdyne receiver is based on the deployed solar receiver in the Solar Two power tower plant. This high heat flux hardware represents a unique blend of liquid rocket engine heat transfer technology and molten salt handling expertise. The installed receiver comprises a series of panels (each made of 32 thin-walled, stainless-steel tubes) through which the molten salt flows in a serpentine path. The panels form a cylindrical shell surrounding piping, structural supports, and control equipment. The external surfaces of the tubes are coated with a black Pyromark™ paint that is robust, resistant to high temperatures and thermal cycling, and absorbs 95% of the incident sunlight. The receiver design has been optimized to absorb a maximum amount of solar energy while reducing the heat losses due to convection and radiation. The design, which includes laser-welding, sophisticated tube-nozzle-header connections, a tube clip design that facilitates tube expansion and contraction, and noncontact flux measurement devices, allows the receiver to rapidly change temperature without being damaged. For example, during a cloud passage, the receiver can safely change from 570 to 290 °C in less than 1 min [67].

SolarReserve, the exclusive license holder of this receiver technology, has assembled a development portfolio of more than 25 projects featuring its licensed solar power technology with potential output of more than 3000 MW in the United States and Europe, with early stage activities in Africa, the Middle East, Latin America, and Australia. SolarReserve has previously developed, and financed with more than $15.0 billion, renewable and conventional energy projects in more than a dozen countries around the world [68].

SolarReserve has activities in Italy and Greece and is also looking at proposals in Morocco and Algeria, South Africa, and the Middle East. India and China represent fairly long-term markets, but mainly the United States and Southern Europe are really the key focus at this stage [65].

Figure 34 Solar receiver system of eSolar. Source: eSolar.

A further developer of solar receiver in the United States is BrightSource Energy. Its proprietary LPT 550 energy system is based on proven power tower technology. The tower is a metal structure designed specifically to support the boiler and efficiently move high-quality steam to the power block at its base. The receiver is a traditional high-efficiency boiler positioned on top of the tower. The boiler converts the concentrated energy of the Sun reflected from the heliostats into superheated steam. It is supplied by conventional boiler manufacturers and complies with standard boiler design parameters. The boiler's tubes are coated with a material that maximizes energy absorbance. The boiler has steam generation, superheating, and reheating sections, and is designed to generate superheated steam at 550 °C temperature and 160 bar pressure [69].

Another supplier of solar receiver systems is eSolar. **Figure 34** shows a characteristic solar receiver system in operation.

eSolar provides a dual cavity as well as an external receiver. The manufacturer of the dual-cavity receiver system is Victory Energy Operations, LLC, and of the external receiver system the Babcock & Wilcox Power Generation Group.

Both receiver configurations are natural circulation type steam generators making use of evaporator panels, steam separation drum/vertical separator, and superheater panels, and are similar to those employed in fossil-fired power plants. The main difference between each receiver design is the configuration of the heat absorption panels [62].

Each receiver generates a nominal $3.8\,\text{kg}\,\text{s}^{-1}$ of superheated steam at 440 °C and 63 bar which is directed to the steam turbine/generator in a common steam line. As emphasized in Reference 63, the cavity receiver can produce steam conditions admissible to the turbine in 66 min from startup.

The principle of a solar thermal power plant with an open volumetric receiver was conceived by the Swiss company Sulzer AG in the 1980s and was tested on a small scale on the basis of metallic absorbers, in collaboration with the DLR, at the PSA test center in Almeria, Spain [70]. Due to the porosity of the material of the open volumetric receiver, the concentrated solar radiation is absorbed in part of the volume of the material. It is absorbed in the depth of the porous structure and the heat is transferred by convection to the airflow. When Sulzer AG ceased all activities in the power plant sector at the end of the 1980s, the technology was sold to the German firm Steinmüller.

In the early 1990s, in further cooperation with the DLR within the so-called TSA project funded by the German Federal Ministry of Education and Research, Steinmüller further developed a receiver prototype with a thermal power rating of 2.5 MW [71]. The German company Steinmüller demonstrated successfully the volumetric air receiver design in the 1990s in Spain. The design of the volumetric receiver as shown in **Figure 35** is based originally on the wire-mesh concept, since it was extensively investigated and documented at this TSA trial between 1993 and 1995 on the test area of the PSA in Spain [72].

After the takeover of Steinmüller by Babcock and its following bankruptcy, activity in this technological field came to end.

Starting in 1993, the DLR increasingly concentrated on absorber and material tests, in their solar oven in Cologne, for a new absorber concept using ceramic materials. The DLR managed to win over the industrial and power plant constructor Kraftanlagen München (KAM) for the further development of the technology.

Within the framework of various research projects, KAM, in the role of industry partner, played a decisive role in the further development of the tower technology [73]. Thus, at the end of 2003, the DLR and KAM entered into a wide-ranging license agreement for the implementation of the technology by KAM. KAM chose an especially heat-resistant ceramic material for the components that are directly exposed to the highly concentrated solar irradiation.

The receiver is made up of various modular components [74]:

- Ceramic absorber
- Metallic carrier structure
- Hot air collector
- Cool air recirculation system

Figure 35 Open volumetric receiver tests at the PSA.

The solar radiation is absorbed on the front side of the receiver and converted to high-temperature thermal energy. In the process, temperatures of up to 1000 °C are produced and the irradiation concentration reaches up to 1000 kW m^{-2} [75].

The carrier structure on the front side of the receiver is furnished with ceramic absorbers. It consists of a multitude of single square absorbers, made of a special porous ceramic material, which is heated up by the incident solar radiation. Ceramic has some important advantages as absorber material because it allows, on the one hand, higher flux densities and gradients and, on the other hand, enables reduction of receiver aperture [72].

The carrier structure is modular and made up of many similar units. As described analytically in Reference 76, the strictly modular concept consists of ceramic cups containing the porous absorber structure. The cups are supported in a steel structure that is cooled by recirculated air, which is fed to the receiver. The cool air recirculation serves to cool the metallic structure.

The air is drawn through the absorber, gets heated up, and exits from the rear side of the subreceiver modules. It is then accumulated by a hot air collector pipe and transported to the gas loop. Absorber modules as shown in **Figure 36** can be easily disassembled, allowing maintenance-friendly exchange of receiver.

Depending on the corresponding operating conditions, the maximum application temperature is 1350 °C. The absorption coefficient is higher than 95%. Absorbers of 140 mm × 140 mm size are used by KAM in the Solar Tower Power Plant of Jülich. The absorber material has very good thermal shock resistance, stability of shape up to maximum operating temperature, and very good thermal conductivity. Various forming processes are available depending on the different shape geometries required. The main process used is slip-casting, which enables production of complex shapes while at the same time keeping tight dimensional tolerances.

Abengoa Solar New Technologies has also developed a solar receiver that uses water/steam as an HTF. It is a 'cavity' receiver that is capable of operating at a thermal efficiency of 92% [60]. It is basically a forced-circulation radiant boiler with a low steam ratio at

Figure 36 Absorber module.

the panel outlet to ensure wet inner walls in the tubes. Special steel alloys are used in its construction in order to operate under high heat flux and temperatures [47].

The cavity concept receiver was designed to reduce radiation and convective losses as much as possible. The tube panels inside the receiver are independent and spaced to allow thermal expansion and mechanical deformation without causing breaks or leaks. The receiver was implemented in the PS10 solar tower power plant and produces saturated steam at 40 bar/250 °C, and feeds it into a drum that increases system thermal inertia [77]. The generated solar saturated or wet steam is then guided to a steam turbine in a highly conservative approach for electricity production.

3.06.4.8 Operation and Maintenance

3.06.4.8.1 Cleaning techniques

Different techniques are used for cleaning the mirror surfaces of heliostats. Cleaning is always performed when heliostats are not in use at night or on no operation days.

For example, in the Sierra power plant, the dense, linear arrangement of the heliostat field facilitates an automated washing system. At night, after the heliostats are brought to cleaning position, a maintenance technician positions a small cleaning robot at the end of an aisle. This robot travels unattended down the aisle and back, pressure-washing heliostats on either side as it travels. A single operator, as described in Reference 63, is able to control several robots, cleaning effectively a subfield of heliostats in 3 h. The system, as mentioned in this report, is highly efficient in both water usage and operator labor.

3.06.4.8.2 Replacement of parts

During the lifetime of a heliostat field of a solar tower power plant, it will be necessary to replace single mirrors or components. As described in Reference 63, at the Sierra power plant, whenever a heliostat or its reflector is serviced or replaced, maintenance personnel scan the barcodes of the hardware and the heliostat's location. These data are fed into a maintenance database and, if necessary, the heliostat is automatically scheduled for recalibration.

3.06.4.8.3 Adjustment

As the orientation of heliostat mirrors usually cannot be detected directly, calibration procedures have to be carried out at regular intervals in order to assure high tracking accuracy. In some cases, this can be done only under sunshine conditions. However, artificial fixed light sources and detectors can also be used to check the mirror orientation at selected positions.

3.06.5 Linear Fresnel Collectors

3.06.5.1 Introduction

A Fresnel collector is a line-focusing system that uses individually tracked reflector rows to concentrate direct solar radiation onto a stationary linear receiver.

3.06.5.2 Basic Characteristics

3.06.5.2.1 Structure

Currently, there exist two types of support structure designs: bench bar and ring design. In the bench bar design, the reflector is placed over a parallel bench bar structure. It is made of standard steel profiles or cold rolled steel and allows the use of space below the structure as it forms a very light structure. In the ring design, the reflector is supported by a metallic structure central to the rings. Mirrors are supported by only two contact points, which requires less raw materials (steel) but results in lower optical precision [78].

3.06.5.2.2 Components

The Fresnel collector consists of a receiver with its selectively coated absorber tube, concentrator, secondary reflector, cover plate, and thermal insulation.

A foundation is necessary to stabilize the system and to withstand high wind loads. One basic element of the Fresnel collector is the concentrator. It consists of small tracking mirrors which reflect the sunlight to a fixed receiver.

The receiver is based on a vacuum tube and a secondary reflector on top of it. The receiver serves as a radiation absorber and converts solar radiation into thermal energy. A heat medium carries the gained energy away.

The absorber tube is composed of two glass layers with vacuum in between. It is specially coated for good absorption properties of the sunlight and low thermal emission in the infrared spectrum. A secondary reflector has the real task not to concentrate, but to direct radiation that misses the entrance of the absorber aperture again to the absorber tube. It is a compound parabolic component (CPC) where two sections of parabolic trough are placed together. It is covered by an insulation to reduce thermal losses.

3.06.5.2.3 Specific characteristics

The optimal height of the receiver is related to the choice of the mirror field width and the number of mirrors [79].

A manufacturer of Fresnel collectors aims to catch Sun's rays from all Fresnel mirrors. The reflected light from central mirrors travels less distance before it reaches the absorber. Reflectors at the end points of the mirror field are further and the shift of the Sun's image is greater and they have high cosine losses.

Therefore, the receiver should be longer than the mirror field. However, the longer the receiver, the higher the thermal losses, so it is tempting to reduce the receiver length. This means that a manufacturer shall optimize the receiver length under thermodynamic and optical considerations.

Regarding the receiver width it has to match the focal image of the mirror field. The optimal width of the receiver depends on the time of the day and the day of the year [79]. If the width is chosen too small, spillage on the sides of the CPC will occur. On the other hand, a large width will mean also a large CPC, which will shade the mirrors, thus reducing the solar energy collection.

3.06.5.3 Types

3.06.5.3.1 Size

Principally, the Fresnel collector is not limited in aperture width; therefore, a wide range of free geometry parameters is possible. The width of mirrors has to be coordinated with their gaps, their number, and the height of the receiver [80]. Basic mirror modules are combined in a longitudinal direction to form collector rows. These rows can be arranged in parallel to form a solar array of any size.

Today's power plants with Fresnel collectors have a typical size of 50 MW gross electrical output. On the other hand, solar thermal power projects have a relatively high risk due to limited experience. This applies especially to the Fresnel collector, since this new technology has not yet been proven in full-scale size.

3.06.5.3.2 Material

A Fresnel collector uses standard materials such as metal sheets and flat glass mirrors and has a significant material reduction compared to parabolic trough technology.

3.06.5.3.3 Heat transfer fluid

Water, air, or oil is used as HTF. When using direct steam generation (DSG), no heat exchanger is required, but when using thermal oil, a heat exchanger is imperative.

3.06.5.3.4 Specific operation control components

There exist a variety of different operation concepts as well as different power plant integration concepts for Fresnel collectors. Examples of different operation modes are the use of a central steam separator (steam drum), decentral in-line steam separators, and even once-through superheating. Different kinds of desuperheaters/injection coolers can be realized with different kinds of controllers. In order to avoid interruption of operation at extreme conditions (e.g., high wind loads), the mirrors can be defocused stepwise.

An important variable that has to be controlled in a Fresnel collector system is the mass flow. By an inherent self-regulating mass flow control effect, it is possible to maintain, to a large extent, superheated steam temperature at the collector outlet, even at very unsteady solar conditions and even without water injection cooling if not integrated.

3.06.5.3.5 Drives

The mirror rows are driven individually. Mostly, mechanical drives are used in the market. As mentioned in Reference 78, another possibility is mechanical coupling. In this approach, rotational movement of the mirrors along their longitudinal axis is coupled, enabling one rotating motor to rotate several mirrors at once. Mechanical coupling can be done, for example, with a worm gear as realized by Solarmundo [81].

3.06.5.3.6 Tracking system

Linear Fresnel collectors (LFCs) are usually oriented along a polar north–south axis.

As in heliostat fields, it is not possible to use simple sensors in a control loop that would guarantee optimum tracking, but the mirrors and their drives must be calibrated and tracked according to solar position algorithms [82].

3.06.5.4 System-Specific Determination of Performance

3.06.5.4.1 Definition of efficiencies

Concentrated solar radiation reaches the absorber of the Fresnel collector and is converted to heat. **Figure 37** illustrates the different types of thermal losses at a typical Fresnel collector. The absorber surface has a reflectivity ratio and acts also as a radiation body, producing extra radiation losses.

In case the absorber pipe is not insulated by a vacuum, extra losses occur. Further convective losses occur at the surface of the secondary concentrator as well as at the cover glass. Losses are highest at the cover glass. A small fraction of thermal energy is dissipated by heat conduction via the carrying steel.

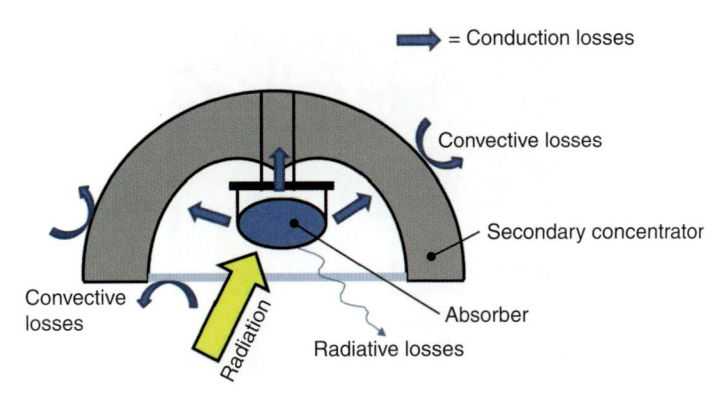

Figure 37 Energy balance of a Fresnel collector.

The efficiency η_{Fr} of an LFC depends on the operation temperature of the collector, the direct normal irradiation E_b, and the incidence angle θ_i of the solar radiation [83]. The efficiency is defined as the ratio of the thermal power, absorbed by the HTF, to the direct normal irradiation on the aperture area.

$$\eta_{Fr} = \frac{\dot{m}(h_{out} - h_{in})}{A_{col}E_b} \qquad [7]$$

The collector area A_{col} is defined as the cumulative area of the primary mirrors.

The determination of a thermal efficiency characteristic for all operation points of a Fresnel collector is also important. Similar to the definition for PTC as provided by Kalogirou [27], the thermal efficiency η_{therm} for a Fresnel collector is defined as the ratio of thermal power to the fluid $\dot{Q}_{therm}$ to the solar power incident on the net mirror area $\dot{Q}_{sol}$. From heat loss tests, optical efficiency tests, and thermal efficiency tests, the coefficients c_1 and c_2 of the efficiency characteristic are identified:

$$\eta_{therm} = \frac{\dot{Q}_{therm}}{\dot{Q}_{sol}} = \eta_{opt}^* - \frac{c_1 \Delta T}{DNI} - c_2 \, DNI \left(\frac{\Delta T}{DNI}\right)^2 \qquad [8]$$

The current optical efficiency η_{opt}^* indicates the maximum possible efficiency limited by all optical influences, for example, incidence angle modifier, reflectivity, and mirror precision. The operation point is further characterized by the direct normal irradiance (DNI) and the temperature difference ΔT between the fluid and ambient [84].

3.06.5.4.2 Error sources

A major difference in comparison to PTC is the additional use of secondary concentrator. Solar radiation that does not reach the absorber, due to optical errors of the collector surface, is collected by the secondary concentrator and directed to the absorber tube. As mentioned in Reference 85, Fresnel collectors suffer higher optical losses due to less favorable incidence angles, additional optical losses of the secondary reflector, and higher thermal losses.

3.06.5.5 Models of Collectors and Their Construction Details

Currently, there are a number of different Fresnel models, developed by different companies. These companies are Ausra/Areva (United States, France), MAN Ferrostaal/Solar Power Group (SPG) (Germany), Novatec BioSol (Germany), and Mirroxx (Germany) [86]. First commercial plants are in operation.

3.06.5.5.1 Solar Power Group

The SPG, working in partnership with the industrial services company MAN Ferrostaal, is planning a 15 MW hybrid plant in Libya, North Africa, in addition to other projects in Spain and North Africa. According to Clarke [87], the company has been testing a 1 MW prototype that produces superheated steam, at the PSA research center in Spain, since 2007.

Within the German R&D project FRESDEMO, partly funded by the German Federal Ministry for the Environment, Nature Conservation and Nuclear Safety (BMU), the first prototype of an LFC with a length of 100 m and a width of 21 m was erected at the PSA (Spain) [83].

As a first activity, the Fresnel demonstration plant FRESDEMO was planned and built by the company together with MAN Ferrostaal Power Industry and scientifically supported by the DLR, the Fraunhofer Institute for Solar Energy Systems (ISE), and PSE GmbH. **Figure 38** shows the Fresnel collector of SPG.

Within FRESDEMO, MAN Ferrostaal is responsible for the project coordination, the optimization of the collector structure, the operation and control of the test collector, and the economic analysis of the system. The SPG has worked on the design and engineering of the collector, supported the construction, and developed O&M procedures.

Figure 38 Fresnel collector of SPG. Source: SPG.

The design of the Fresnel collector in Almeria is based on a 2100 m² collector prototype, which has been constructed in 2001 in Liège (Belgium) by the company Solarmundo, predecessor of SPG. After having demonstrated the mechanical and optical feasibility of this demonstration collector, the construction of another demonstration collector was decided, in order to determine the efficiency of the entire system under real solar operating conditions. Ground for this construction was provided by Ciemat on the PSA, where the demonstration collector was connected to the existing DISS test facility 2 with water and steam supply, allowing tests in three different operation modes: preheating, evaporation, and superheating [83].

The LFC consists of a steel construction that contains primary mirrors and a receiver unit, containing secondary mirrors and the absorber tube.

The mirrors are commercially available flat glass mirrors with a reflectivity of 93%. For safety reasons, they are tempered, which also improves their mechanical properties for later bending operations. Drives fixed in the center of the module track 25 rows of mirrors individually. The steel structure of the prototype supports a fixed central absorber tube located in the center of a secondary reflector and 25 rows of slightly curved primary mirrors. The absorber tube contains water, which is converted in successive steps to superheated steam. The steam is then available and can be used to drive a turbine for electricity generation or for other applications. The Fresnel collector of SPG operates at a temperature of 450 °C and a pressure of 100 bar.

3.06.5.5.2 Solarmundo

In 1999, Solarmundo erected a 2500 m² prototype collector in Liège, Belgium. The collector consisted of 48 rows of mirrors, which led to a total collector width of 24 m. Each mirror had a width of 0.5 m and was not completely flat but had a very small curvature, which was achieved by mechanical bending [81]. The prototype collector was operated under real conditions and produced steam. Solarmundo uses a selectively coated steel absorber tube with a secondary reflector which is positioned above the absorber tube.

3.06.5.5.3 Ausra/Areva

In the United States, Ausra, a company that was recently taken over from Areva, is operating two small demonstration projects using its compact linear Fresnel reflector (CLFR) technology: the 5 MW Kimberlina plant in California and a 3 MW plant that substitutes a part of the coal consumption for the 2000 MW Liddell Power Station in New South Wales, Australia [87].

3.06.5.5.4 NOVATEC BioSol

The NOVATEC BioSol Corporation, a company mainly located in Germany, develops Fresnel collectors too. Their product is NOVA-1, a linear-focused solar power system based on the Fresnel collector principle for generating saturated steam at temperatures of up to 300 °C.

The main components of this Fresnel collector system are the foundations, supporting structure, primary reflectors, radiation receivers, as well as systems for controlling the primary reflector tracking and the output of the solar array.

Figure 39 shows the basic module of the NOVA-1. According to Reference 88, it consists of 128 primary reflector units with a total mirror surface area of 513.6 m² and 8 receiver units. The basic module can be arranged in a longitudinal direction to form a collector row. A row might range between 224 and 986 m. These rows oriented in a north–south axis with a longitudinal deviation of ± 20° can be arranged in parallel to form a solar array of any size.

Figure 39 NOVA-1 solar power system. Source: NOVATEC BioSol.

For NOVA-1, the company guarantees an optical efficiency after 25 years of at least 95% of the original value of the optical efficiency, provided that cleaning and care of the solar field components are carried out as per the producer's instruction and the setup is in noncorrosive, nonabrasive atmosphere.

As mentioned in Reference 87, NOVATEC BioSol is operating in Europe a 1.4 MW demonstration plant in Murcia, southern Spain, and is arranging financing for a 30 MW plant on an adjacent site.

3.06.5.5.5 Mirroxx

Mirroxx GmbH was founded in November 2008 as a spin-off of PSE AG. PSE itself was founded in 1999 as a spin-off of Fraunhofer ISE and since its founding was engaged in the field of concentrating technologies.

Each module of Mirroxx is 4 m long and 8 m wide, with 11 primary mirror rows. The structure is made of hot-dip galvanized and powder-coated steel and the secondary reflector of highly reflective aluminum [89]. Mirroxx uses an absorber tube of SCHOTT PTR®70. As an HTF, pressurized water at low temperature, as well as thermal oil, can be used. Also direct steam generation can be applied at saturated steam up to 40 bar and 250 °C.

Due to the high output temperatures of up to 400 °C, when using thermal oil, the Mirroxx collectors are perfectly suited to driving Organic Rankine Cycle (ORC) turbines or steam engines. Their combination with absorption chillers and other process heat applications in cogeneration or polygeneration systems is even more attractive.

3.06.5.5.6 Research

There are different studies and research activities in the field of LFCs in the world.

In the last years, for example, a study was carried out with the aim of optimizing an LFC geometry for a prototype being built in Sicily [90]. The focus of the study was on the optimization of the primary mirror field and tracking.

3.06.5.6 Operation and Maintenance

3.06.5.6.1 Cleaning techniques

Flat mirrors of Fresnel collectors can be cleaned easily in an automated process with low water consumption and low operational costs. After cleaning, the reflectivity of the surface is restored to its original high values.

3.06.5.6.2 Replacement of parts

The structure consists of standard components that can be manufactured, sourced as well as replaced if necessary locally. As outlined in Reference 91, small LFC mirror facets might break less frequently than PTC mirrors and are probably cheaper to replace than the expensive curved glass mirrors used in PTCs.

3.06.6 Solar Dish

3.06.6.1 Introduction

Solar dish is a point-focusing system that uses curved solar sun tracking mirrors to concentrate direct solar radiation onto a receiver. This technology is suitable for stand-alone installations, utility-scale projects, and off-grid and small grids, and can play a role in inland isolated areas and islands.

Solar dish systems are flexible in terms of size and scale of deployment. Owing to their modular design, they are capable of small-scale distributed power output and also suitable for large, utility-scale projects with thousands of dishes arranged in a solar park. Dish/engine systems produce relatively small amounts of electricity – typically in the range of 3–25 kW – compared with other CSP technologies. There is no typical size for a plant – it can meet any individual demand – and specific land requirements are negligible. The solar dish systems have decades of recorded operating history.

3.06.6.2 Basic Characteristics

3.06.6.2.1 Structure
The commonly used material in a solar dish is metal. In order to achieve a high optical precision, mainly large, lightweight, and nonrigid structures are applied. Some solar concentrators are supported with a truss structure in order to hold the mirrors of the concentrator. A foundation is essential in order to withstand high wind loads.

3.06.6.2.2 Components
The major parts of a system are the solar concentrator and the power conversion unit.

A parabolic concentrator gathers solar energy onto a receiver at its focal point. For this purpose, mirrors are distributed over the parabolic dish surface. The dish is mounted on a structure that tracks the Sun continuously throughout the day to reflect the highest percentage of sunlight possible onto the thermal receiver [92].

The power conversion unit includes the thermal receiver and the engine/generator.

The thermal receiver is the interface between the dish and the engine/generator. It absorbs the concentrated beams of solar energy, converts them to heat, and transfers the heat to the engine/generator. The thermal energy can be either transported to a central generator for conversion or converted directly into electricity at a local generator coupled to the receiver. A thermal receiver can be a bank of tubes with a cooling fluid– usually hydrogen or helium – that typically is the heat transfer medium and also the working fluid for an engine. Alternate thermal receivers are heat pipes, where boiling and condensing of an intermediate fluid transfers the heat to the engine [92].

The engine/generator system is the subsystem that takes the heat from the thermal receiver and uses it to produce electricity. A Stirling engine uses the heated fluid to move pistons and create mechanical power. The mechanical work, that is, rotation of the engine's crankshaft, drives a generator and produces electrical power [92].

3.06.6.2.3 Specific characteristics
The concentrator's optical design and accuracy determine the concentration ratio. Concentration ratio, defined as the average solar flux through the receiver aperture divided by the ambient direct normal solar insolation, is typically over 2000. Intercept fractions, defined as the fraction of the reflected solar flux that passes through the receiver aperture, are usually over 95%.

In general, the efficiency is not increased by an increase of the receiver diameter as there exists a limitation. Regarding the relationship between concentration factor and system efficiency, the efficiency increases with the increase in the concentration factor, but above a concentration factor of 1000 no further significant advantage results. Very high concentration is not necessarily advantageous and as depicted by Winter et al. [19] it has been shown that dish/Stirling annual energy performance is not improved much beyond a concentration of about 1500–2000.

A cavity absorber is very often used as a dish receiver, and the relevant energy fluxes in the cavity are shown in **Figure 40**. The incoming radiation is absorbed by the absorber and transformed to heat, but conduction, radiation, and convection losses occur.

As confirmed by Conde et al. [93], conduction losses are small compared to convection and radiation losses. Convection losses depend on the geometry and orientation of the cavity, air and cavity temperatures, wind speed, and wind direction. At solar noon, the cavity is facing downward and the convection is relatively stable. However, during the morning and the afternoon, the cavity

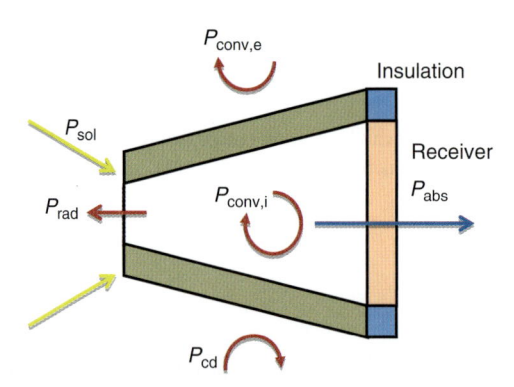

Figure 40 Energy fluxes in a cavity. P_{sol} is the radiant power entering the cavity, P_{rad} is the radiation loss, P_{cd} is the conduction loss through the cavity walls, P_{conv} is the convection loss, and P_{abs} is the power absorbed by the receiver.

aperture is closer to the vertical, making it easier for the airflow to enter in the cavity, increasing convection. Dish/Stirling systems operate at high temperatures and therefore radiation losses are expected to be the most significant fraction of thermal losses at the cavity-absorber ensemble.

3.06.6.3 Types

3.06.6.3.1 Geometry, material use, and surface characteristics of the concentrator

As mentioned in Reference 19, the key element of a solar dish is the paraboloidal shape of the concentrator which is formed by either individual reflector elements or a continuous surface.

Concentrators use a reflective surface of aluminum or silver, deposited on glass or plastic. Another possibility is the use of low-cost reflective polymer films, but they have had limited success. Because dish concentrators have short focal lengths, relatively thin glass mirrors are required to accommodate the required curvatures. Glass with a low iron content is desirable to improve reflectance. Depending on the thickness and iron content, silvered solar mirrors can have solar reflectance values of up to 94%.

The concave surface is covered by second-surface glass mirrors or by front-surface reflective films [19]. One way to approximate the shape of the solar concentrators is with the use of multiple, spherically shaped mirrors with a support structure.

A further solar concentrator design possibility is the use of stretched membranes in which a thin reflective membrane is stretched across a rim or hoop. A second membrane is used to close off the space behind. A partial vacuum is drawn in this space, bringing the reflective membrane into an approximately spherical shape [94].

3.06.6.3.2 Geometry of receiver aperture with Stirling device

The receiver of a solar dish absorbs energy reflected by the concentrator and transfers it to the engine's working fluid. The absorbing surface is usually placed behind the focus of the concentrator to reduce the flux intensity incident on it. An aperture is placed at the focus to reduce radiation and convection heat losses. The main function of the receiver is to transfer concentrated solar energy to a high-pressure oscillating gas with high efficiency. As outlined in Reference 94, two general types of Stirling receivers exist, direct illumination receivers (DIRs) and indirect receivers; the indirect receivers use an intermediate HTF.

Directly illuminated Stirling receivers adapt the heater tubes of the Stirling engine to absorb the concentrated solar flux. Because of the high heat transfer capability of high-velocity, high-pressure working gas, such receivers are capable of absorbing high levels of solar flux. In a heat-pipe receiver, liquid sodium metal is vaporized on the absorber surface of the receiver and condensed on the Stirling engine's heater tubes. This results in a uniform temperature distribution on the heater tubes, thereby enabling a higher engine working temperature for a given material and therefore higher engine efficiency. The heat-pipe receiver isothermally transfers heat by evaporation of sodium on the receiver/absorber and condensing it on the heater tubes of the engine. The sodium is passively returned to the absorber by gravity and distributed over the absorber by capillary forces in a wick.

There also exist solar receiver designs for dish/Brayton systems which use mainly volumetric absorption. In such a system, concentrated solar radiation passes through a fused silica quartz window and is absorbed by porous matrix material. This approach provides significantly greater heat transfer area than conventional heat exchangers that utilize conduction through a wall. Volumetric Brayton receivers may use honeycombs and reticulated open-cell ceramic foam structures.

As mentioned in Reference 94, Brayton receiver efficiency is typically over 80% and Stirling receivers are typically about 90% efficient in transferring energy delivered by the concentrator to the engine.

3.06.6.3.3 Characteristics of Stirling or Brayton engine

Stirling or Brayton cycle engines may be used in solar dish systems.

Stirling cycle engines used in solar dish/Stirling systems are high-temperature, high-pressure externally heated engines that use a working gas. In modern high-performance Stirling engines, typical working gas temperature is above 700 °C and pressure is as high as 20 MPa.

In the Stirling cycle, the working gas is alternately heated and cooled by constant-temperature and constant-volume processes. Stirling engines usually incorporate an efficiency-enhancing regenerator that captures heat during constant-volume cooling and replaces it when the gas is heated at constant volume. In order to reach constant-temperature and constant-volume processes, special pistons and cylinders are used. Some use a displacer to shuttle the working gas back and forth from the hot region to the cold region of the engine. For most engine designs, power is extracted kinematically by a rotating crankshaft. An exception is the free-piston configuration, where the pistons are not constrained by crankshafts or other mechanisms. They bounce back and forth on springs and the power is extracted from the power piston by a linear alternator or pump [94, 95].

In general, a Brayton engine is an internal combustion engine that produces power by the controlled burning of fuel. In the dish/Brayton engine system, air is compressed, solar heat is added, and the mixture is burned. The resulting hot gas expands rapidly and is used to produce power. In the gas turbine, the burning is continuous and the expanding gas is used to turn a turbine and alternator.

As mentioned in Reference 94, predicted thermal-to-electric efficiencies of Brayton engines for dish/Brayton applications are over 30% and for Stirling engines 40%. Although a Brayton engine has been tested on a solar dish [96], most companies use Stirling engines. As outlined in Reference 97, this is due to the fact that dish/Stirling engines have higher efficiency, high power density, potential for long-term, low-maintenance operation, and a modular function as each system may have a self-contained power generator allowing assembly even in a solar park of some megawatt size.

3.06.6.3.4 Working gas

In contrast to other CSP technologies that employ steam to create electricity via a turbine, a dish engine system uses a working fluid such as hydrogen or helium that is heated up to high temperatures above 600 °C and pressurized in the receiver to drive an engine, which could be a Stirling engine. When a Brayton engine is used in a solar dish, then air is used as the working fluid.

3.06.6.4 System-Specific Determination of Performance

3.06.6.4.1 Definition of efficiencies

Concentration ratios of more than 2000 can be reached. Dishes track the Sun on two axes, and thus they are the most efficient collector systems because they are always focused.

As analyzed in Reference 98, the optical efficiency of a solar concentrator collector can be obtained by the following equation:

$$\eta_o = \rho_c \tau \alpha_r S \qquad [9]$$

where ρ_c is the concentrator reflectance, τ is the receptor coating transmittance, α_r is the receptor absorptance, and S is the fraction of the concentrator aperture area that is not shadowed by the receptor.

The instantaneous efficiency of a solar concentrator η_c is defined as the ratio between the useful power delivered and the total solar power on the system, and is given by

$$\eta_c = \eta_o - \frac{U_L \alpha_r}{DNI\, A_a}(T_{rm} - T_{amb}) \qquad [10]$$

where DNI is the incident radiation flux on the collector, A_a is the collector aperture area, U_L is the total heat loss factor, T_{amb} is the ambient temperature, and T_{rm} is the receptor average temperature.

As shown in **Figure 41**, the energy conversion in a solar dish/Stirling system has a series of stages, each one with its own efficiency.

The global system efficiency η is defined as the product of the global efficiency of a solar collector η_c, the gear efficiency η_m, the electric generator efficiency η_g, and the inverter efficiency η_i:

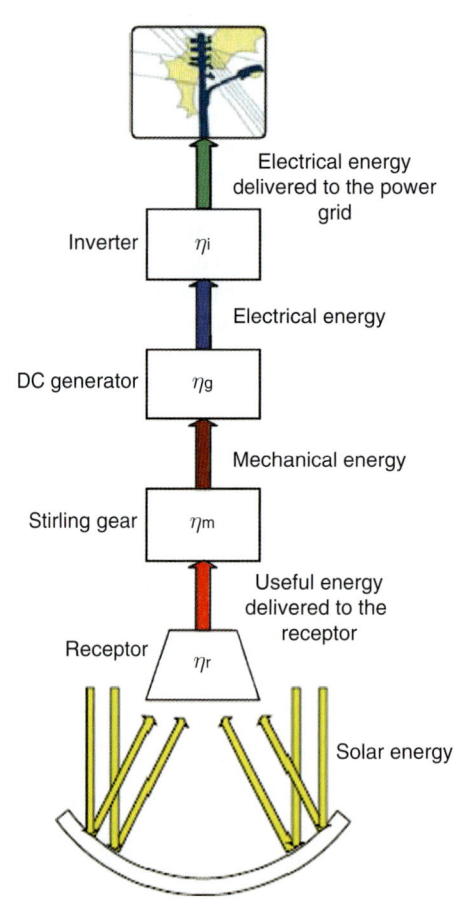

Figure 41 Efficiencies of dish/Stirling systems. Source: Macêdo WN, Pinho JT, Almeida MP, *et al.* (2009) Efficiency evaluation and economic feasibility of small dish-Stirling power systems in Brazil. *SolarPACES Symposium.* Berlin, Germany, 15–18 September [98].

$$\eta = \eta_c \eta_m \eta_g \eta_i \qquad [11]$$

The power generated by a solar dish/Stirling P_{el} is a linear function of the DNI and is equal to the product of the global system efficiency η, the concentrator aperture area A_a, and the DNI according to the equation

$$P_{el} = \eta A_a \, \text{DNI} \qquad [12]$$

3.06.6.4.2 Error sources

There are many potential sources of error in a concentrating solar dish system. When considering facet options, the surface waviness, characterized as a normally distributed slope error, has the greatest impact on the aperture size and therefore the thermal losses.

According to Reference 99, two primary impacts of optical imperfections appear: service life and performance reductions. Error sources that simply impact the aperture size will reduce performance. However, errors that can increase the peak flux on the receiver will impact the receiver's service lifetime. Further errors are observed in solar dishes like facet shape errors, alignment errors, structural deflections due to gravity and wind, and tracking system errors, and all shall be reduced by the manufacturer.

Another important loss mechanism is the occurrence of spillage, which is the quantity of energy reflected by the concentrator that for several reasons does not reach the receiver of a solar dish. It is a direct loss of energy and it is expressed as percent value with respect to the total amount of concentrated energy. As mentioned in Reference 100, it is closely related with the distribution of energy and the concentrated heat flux density obtained on the focal plane in such a way that it is to a large extent a consequence of the concentrator optical errors. Other causes may be misalignment or a bad design of the receiver of the solar dish, tracking errors, or shading produced by the support structure.

3.06.6.5 Models of Solar Dishes and Their Construction Details

Several different dish/Stirling systems have been built and operated over the last 25 years.

3.06.6.5.1 First models

Since 1970, several dish/Stirling systems ranging in size from 5 to 50 kW$_e$ were developed, installed, and tested in different regions of the world (United States, Spain, Germany, France, Italy, and Australia).

From all developments during that time, the 25 kW Vanguard system built by ADVANCO in the United States can be mentioned as it reached a solar-to-electric efficiency of about 30% [101]. Another system built by McDonnell Douglas Aerospace Corporation (MDAC) used stretched-membrane concentrators and was tested in the early 1980s [97].

3.06.6.5.2 EuroDish

The EuroDish project was a joint-venture project between the European Community and German/Spanish industries and research institutions. The developed EuroDish as shown in **Figure 42** is a dish/Stirling solar thermal generator with a nominal electrical

Figure 42 EuroDish installation in France.

power of $10\,kW_e$ at $1000\,W\,m^{-2}$ of direct normal irradiance (DNI). The concentrator of the EuroDish consists of a thin shell and is equipped with thin glass mirrors, supported on a rigid space frame ring truss. It has a diameter of 8.5 m and is suspended in a turntable with the azimuth bearing as a central king pin, rolling with six wheels on a ring-shaped foundation. Large drive arches are used in both axes, driven by servo motors that act via gear boxes and opinions on roller chains [102].

Heat is supplied to the receiver at temperatures in the range of 800–650 °C, where a gas (helium) drives a closed Stirling thermodynamic cycle inside the motor, producing mechanical work. This work is then converted into electricity by an asynchronous generator. A software-driven two-axis tracking system permits to maintain the dish pointed at the Sun during the day [103].

The EuroDish was tested in European counties like Italy and France and at the PSA in Spain.

3.06.6.5.3 Stirling Energy Systems

The Stirling Energy Systems (SES) company based in Phoenix, Arizona, developed a dish/Stirling system of 25 kW called SunCatcher. SES SunCatcher™ is 11.6 m tall and 12.2 m wide.

A field of six dish systems have been built at Sandia National Laboratories' National Solar Thermal Test Facility (NSTTF) in the last years. Further developments of the SunCatcher system have been made and four dish systems have been tested at NSTFF. As one of the next steps, Tessera Solar and Salt River Project will build a plant of 1.5 MW. The solar project, Maricopa Solar LLC, in Peoria, Arizona, located in the West Valley of the greater Phoenix area, will be the first commercial-scale plant consisting of 60 SunCatchers.

For over 20 years, the SES dish has held the world's efficiency record for converting solar energy into grid-quality electricity, and in January 2008, it achieved a new record of 31.25% efficiency rate.

3.06.6.5.4 SAIC and STM

Science Applications International Corp. (SAIC) and STM Power, Inc. had been developing a dish/Stirling power system since November 1993. SAIC mainly concentrated its efforts on the development of the stretched-membrane solar concentrator and STM on the kinematic Stirling engine.

The dish concentrator consisted of 16 round, stretched-membrane mirror facets mounted on a truss structure. As described in Reference 97, an engine support arm articulated at the hub to allow the system to move to a face-down stow position for maintenance.

The receiver consisted of a cavity containing a direct insolation heated head in the shape of a truncated cone. The heater head was divided into four spiral-shaped quadrants, each feeding one cylinder of the engine and composed of tubes.

As mentioned in Reference 97, the integrated engine used was an STM 4-120 four-cylinder, kinematic Stirling engine and the solar to net electric energy conversion efficiency of the system has been measured at 20%, the peak power output 22.9 kW, and the availability 88%. The solar dish was tested at different sites in the United States such as in Phoenix, Arizona.

3.06.6.5.5 Infinia Solar System

Infinia Solar System's (ISS) engine converts an externally applied temperature differential into electricity [104]. Each ISS has a peak power of 3 kW and avoids more than 5 tons of greenhouse gases annually per ISS (**Figure 43**).

The ISS is a self-contained system, which according to Reference 104 operates unattended and needs no plumbing and no cooling water.

3.06.6.5.6 Others

Further companies are developing solar dishes, but they have not yet brought their products to the market.

3.06.6.5.7 Research

A lot of different research activities were done in the last decades and new ones are progressing in the world.

Figure 43 Infinia solar dish system.

Figure 44 An early test involving venting of steam from the SG4 receiver.

For example, an SG4 500 m² dish system was completed on the Australian National University (ANU) campus in 2009 where the design and construction of the system followed on from earlier ANU big dish designs implemented in Canberra and was later installed at the Ben Gurion University in Israel. The average diameter is 25 m and the number of mirrors is 380. As mentioned in Reference 105, very high concentration levels have been achieved, with a peak of 14 100 suns and a geometric concentration ratio of 2240 for 95% capture.

The SG4 dish (**Figure 44**) is currently being operated with a direct steam generation cavity receiver, which consists of a winding of steel tube coiled to form a cavity with an approximately top hat-shaped cross section.

Feed water enters the receiver at the beginning of a conical front section and exits at the top of the cavity; the conical section serves to collect spillage outside of the cavity entrance. Experimental runs have been carried out at the receiver design conditions of 500 °C and 4.5 MPa, as well as at lower temperatures and pressures. Results to date indicate receiver thermal efficiencies in excess of 90% during quasi-steady-state periods [105].

In Korea, KIER (Korea Institute of Energy Research) had developed several types of dish concentrator since 1996 and demonstrated the 10 kW dish/Stirling system in 2007. According to the operation results, linear power generation trend could be observed with increasing DNI and the solar-to-electric efficiency reached more than 19% at a DNI value greater than $700 \, W \, m^{-2}$. Further information can be found in Reference 106.

3.06.6.6 Operation and Maintenance

The solar dish technology does not use water in the power conversion process (neither for steam generation nor for cooling), and water is used only for washing the mirrors, and this is the key differentiator that sets apart the solar dish technology from other solar thermal technologies. Scheduled maintenance can be done on individual units while the others continue to generate power.

3.06.6.6.1 Control system/diverse

A solar dish is mainly designed to operate autonomously without direct surveillance, following the sun path day by day with automatic switch off at sunset and restart at dawn. The solar dish system is mostly controlled by a microprocessor-based control system which enables also switching off from solar to fuel operation if a hybrid system is integrated. The control system may include data logging and temperature balance for concentrator tracking adjustment.

Direct solar radiation, ambient temperature, and wind velocity can affect the energy production of a solar dish. In general, daily parasitic consumption can vary up to 15% of the gross power produced according to the average solar radiation intensity and stability of the weather conditions.

3.06.7 Criteria for the Choice of Technology

3.06.7.1 Location

The potential of available locations for CSP plants is determined by using satellite data or by using meteorological data from weather stations. Suitable sites for solar thermal power are those that get a lot of direct sun – at least 2000 kilowatt hours (kWh) of sunlight radiation per square meter, annually. The best sites receive more than 2800 $kWh \, m^{-2} \, yr^{-1}$, in the world's Sunbelt. Additionally, these areas are also dry, which leads to less cloud coverage. Typical regions for CSP are those without large amounts of atmospheric humidity, dust, and fumes. They include steppes, bush, savannas, semideserts, and true deserts, ideally located within less than 40 degrees of latitude north or south. Therefore, the most promising areas of the world include the Southwestern United States, Central and South America, North and Southern Africa, the Mediterranean countries of Europe, the Near and Middle East, Iran and the desert plains of India, Pakistan, the former Soviet Union, China, and Australia [107].

Starting from this basis, exclusions are made to yield the possible locations where CSP plants could be built. These exclusions include locations with DNI less than $6 \text{ kWh m}^{-2} \text{ yr}^{-1}$, land exclusions due to culturally and environmentally sensitive lands, mountains, urban areas, lakes, and rivers. Also the topology is important when choosing a suitable location for the erection of a solar thermal power plant. Areas with average land slope greater than 1% and less than 1 km^2 do not match the requirements for a parabolic trough or Fresnel. A heliostat field on the contrary may be installed even in hilly regions.

Locations that exceed a maximum wind velocity over many time periods are not suitable because of the high risk of damage to the collector field. Hail is not a problem for the mirrors, nowadays, as they have to withstand such conditions. Places with high seismic activity, like earthquakes, have to fulfill extra requirements regarding stability of infrastructure and power station.

Furthermore, from the available areas and their solar resources, the electricity that could be generated by CSP plants can be calculated. Therefore, further assumptions have to be made. For instance, the capacity factor has to be chosen to estimate how much electricity correlates to a specific area. For typical parabolic trough plants, this value varies from 5 to 10 acres MW^{-1} [28], due to the fact that mainly heat storage is integrated with CSP then the value of 10 acres/MW is reached. Another assumption may be the capacity factor of the plant, which describes the relative amount of the average yearly peak power production. These values can be in the range of 25% in premium ($>7 \text{ kWh m}^{-2} \text{ yr}^{-1}$), 22.5% in excellent ($>6.5 \text{ kWh m}^{-2} \text{ yr}^{-1}$), and 20% in good ($>6 \text{ kWh m}^{-2} \text{ yr}^{-1}$) solar resource areas [108].

3.06.7.2 Grid Capacity and Net System

Solar thermal systems can be installed in island or off-grid systems, as well as to feed the existing grid. An important issue of a solar thermal power plant is to achieve the energy demand and to enable a smooth flow connection to the existing electricity net system. Special requirements also have to be considered, such as access to water for the cooling system or to a gas net in case a hybrid station is planned.

An advantage is to choose a location close to metropolitan cities where electricity consumption is at a high level. In such cases, the solar-generated electricity needs to be transmitted over only short distances.

Even electricity transport over long distances is possible. High-voltage DC (HVDC) transmission lines have been in commercial use for decades, and manufacturing capacity may be expanded as required. HVDC transmission can be used both with overhead lines and with underground cables. In contrast to AC technology, HVDC provides the possibility to use underground cables for the transmission of electrical energy, even over long distances [109].

3.06.7.3 Local Cost Structure

Many factors affect the CSP electricity cost as well as the costs for grid connection and local infrastructure, project development, and mass production. Such costs differ from country to country, but also different local structures exist, which have to be considered as well.

3.06.7.4 Country-Specific Subsidies, Feed-in Tariffs, and Environmental Laws

Revenues from CSP projects are needed to encourage private sector investment and provide a stable investment climate. This can be achieved by feed-in tariffs, production tax credits, or public benefit charges specific to CSP. Such supports shall be reduced over time, as the CSP technology becomes competitive in the power market.

Countries with feed-in tariffs are seeing the most progress in replacing fossil fuel-based power with renewable energy. Feed-in tariffs require utilities to purchase electricity from renewable energy producers at-market or above-market costs (or above the cost of using more traditional resources) [110]. They indirectly encourage manufacturers to increase design efficiency and to invest in R&D activities.

There are many different incentive mechanisms and tariff frameworks for solar power in each country, depending on the political and physical limitations of each country. Countries with feed-in tariffs or discussions about the tariffs include Algeria, Australia, China, Egypt, France, Germany, Greece, Israel, Morocco, Portugal, Spain, and the United States. Many of the feed-in tariffs are the result of climate change legislation.

In Europe, Directive 2001/77/EC of the European Parliament required the European member states to implement on a national basis incentives to expand renewable energy power.

Among the various incentives implemented by the different member states, the renewable feed-in tariffs chosen by Germany and Spain have been the most successful in Europe in creating additional renewable energy generation.

Since 1990, Germany has developed and politically supported feed-in tariffs. This has helped Germany maintain its position as one of the world leaders in renewable energy technologies.

In Spain, for example, consistent legislation in the form of feed-in tariffs since 1994 has led to the development of more than 60 new projects, making Spain the world's leader in CSP. Countries around the world are following Spain's example and are implementing legislation [110]. The Spanish Legal Foundation, which implements the law, offers renewable energy operators two options: the tariff model and the premium model. Under the tariff model, utilities get one fixed price for electricity. Under the premium model in Spain, producers offer their energy a day ahead, identifying hours of production, energy amount, and price. Regarding hybridization, Spanish producers should not mix the CSP plant output with more than 15% fossil fuels.

On the contrary, in Algeria, there are no restrictions for mixing CSP with fossil fuels. Algeria's feed-in law is the first of its kind outside of Europe. It allows producers to combine solar and fossil fuels with the goal of producing a cost-effective, cleaner overall energy mix.

The United States is also making legislative headway, especially in California. The California Public Utilities Commission (CPUC) in 2008 approved its own feed-in tariff. The tariffs provide a 10-, 15-, or 20-year fixed-price nonnegotiable contract to participating small renewable energy generators, that is, those with plants that produce up to 1.5 MW.

References

[1] Fivian M, Hudson H, Lin R, and Zahid J (2008) A large excess in apparent solar oblateness due to surface magnetism. *Science Express*, October, 2nd issue. http://science.nasa.gov/headlines/y2008/02oct_oblatesun.htm (accessed 10 February 2008).
[2] Williams DR (2004) Sun fact sheet. NASA. http://nssdc.gsfc.nasa.gov/planetary/factsheet/sunfact.html (accessed 21 December 2011).
[3] Neumann A, Witzke A, Scott J, and Schmitt G (2002) Representative terrestrial solar brightness profiles. *ASME Journal of Solar Energy Engineering* 124: S198–S204.
[4] Mertins M (2009) Technische und wirtschaftliche Analyse von horizontalen Fresnel-Kollektoren. Dissertation, Universität Karlsruhe (TH), Fakultät für Maschinenbau.
[5] Chapman DJ and Arias DA (2009) Effect of solar brightness profiles on the performance of parabolic concentrating collectors. *Proceedings of the ASME 2009 3rd International Conference on Energy Sustainability, ES2009*. San Francisco, CA, USA, 19–23 July.
[6] Pottler (2010) Information provided by K. Pottler, DLR.
[7] Ulmer S, März T, Prahl C, *et al.* (2009) *Automated High Resolution Measurement of Heliostat Slope Errors*. Berlin, Germany: SolarPACES.
[8] Rahlves M and Seewig J (2009) *Optisches Messen Technischer Oberflächen: Messprinzipien und Begriffe*, p. 17. Berlin, Germany: Beuth Verlag.
[9] Strachan JW and Houser RM (1993) Testing and evaluation of large-area heliostats for solar thermal applications. Sandia National Laboratories, SAND92-1381, Albuquerque, NM, USA, February.
[10] Stine WB and Diver RB (1994) A compendium of solar dish/Stirling technology. Sandia National Laboratories, SAND93-7026 UC-236, Albuquerque, NM, USA, January.
[11] Jones SA, Neal DR, Gruetzner JK, *et al.* (1996) VSHOT: A tool for characterizing large, imprecise reflectors. *International Symposium on Optical Science Engineering and Instrumentation*. Denver, CO, USA, 8-9 August.
[12] Geyer M, Quaschning V, Steinfeld A, and Romero M (2002) Solar power and chemical energy systems. Köln, Germany: SolarPaces, Annual Report.
[13] Price H, Hale MJ, Mahoney R, *et al.* (2004) Developments in high temperature parabolic trough receiver technology. *Proceedings of ISEC: Solar 2004*. Portland, OR, USA, 11–14 July.
[14] Geyer M, Lüpfert E, Osuna R, *et al.* (2002) EUROTROUGH – Parabolic trough collector developed for cost efficient solar power generation. *11th International Symposium on Concentrating Solar Power and Chemical Energy Technologies*. Zurich, Switzerland, 4–6 September.
[15] Castaneda N, Vazquez J, and Castaneda D (2009) First commercial application of Senertrough collector high performance at reduced cost. SolarPACES Conference Proceedings, Berlin.
[16] Goebel O, Geskes P, Geyer M, *et al.* Direkte Dampferzeugung in Parabolrinnen-Solarkraftwerken. Forschungsverbund Sonnenenergie, Themen 96/97. http://www.fvee.de/fileadmin/publikationen/Themenhefte/th1996/th1996_02_14.pdf (accessed 01 November 2011).
[17] Anthrakidis A, Kroker J, Rusack M, *et al.* (2009) *Technical Improvement of a Small Modular Parabolic Trough Collector*. Berlin, Germany: SolarPACES.
[18] Bader R, Haueter P, Pedretti A, and Steinfeld A (2009) *Optical Design of a Novel 2-Stage Solar Trough Concentrator Based on Pneumatic Polymeric Structures*. Berlin, Germany: SolarPACES.
[19] Winter C-J, Sizmann RL, and Vant-Hull LL (1991) *Solar Power Plants*. Berlin, Germany: Springer.
[20] Mohr M and Svoboda P (1999) *Praxis Solarthermischer Kraftwerke*. Berlin, Germany: Springer.
[21] SolarPaces (2010) Solar parabolic trough. http://www.solarpaces.org (accessed 21 December 2011).
[22] Eickhoff M and Zarza E (2007) *Solare Direktverdampfung in der Praxis*. Sonnenkolloquium, DLR, Köln.
[23] Glatzmaier GC (2009) Modeling hydrogen occurrence in parabolic trough power plants. *SolarPaces Conference*.15–18 September. Berlin, Germany.
[24] Price H, Forristall R, Wendelin T, *et al.* (2006) Field survey of parabolic trough receiver thermal performance. *Proceedings of ISEC2006, ASME International Solar Energy Conference*. Denver, CO, USA, 8–13 July.
[25] Wendelin T (2006) Video scanning Hartmann optical testing of state-of-the-art parabolic trough concentrators. *Proceedings of the ASME 2006 International Solar Energy Conference (ISEC2006)*. Denver, CO, USA, 8–13 July.
[26] Sandia Optical Frubge Analysis Slope Tool for Solar Mirror Characterization (SOFAST). Albuquerque, NM, USA: Sandia National Laboratories. https://ip.sandia.gov/technology.do/techID=48 (accessed 01 December 2011).
[27] Kalogirou SA (2004) Solar thermal collectors and applications. *Progress in Energy and Combustion Science* 30: 231–295.
[28] NREL (2010) TroughNet – Parabolic trough solar field technology. http://www.nrel.gov/csp/troughnet (accessed 28 January 2010).
[29] Dudley VE, Kolb GJ, Sioan M and Kearney D (1994) Test results: SEGS LS-2 Solar Collector. Sandia National Laboratories, Report SAND94-1884, December.
[30] NREL (2005) Concentrating solar power (CSP) potential for renewable energy in the San Diego region. August.
[31] Lupfert E, Geyer M, Schiel W, *et al.* (2000) Eurotrough: A new parabolic trough collector with advanced light weight structure. *Proceedings of the Solar Thermal 2000 International Conference*. 8–10 March. Sydney, NSW, Australia.
[32] EUROTrough (2001) Development of a low cost European parabolic trough collector. EUROTrough Final Report, Contract: JOR3-CT98-0231, European Commission.
[33] Brakmann G, Badaoui N-E, Dolejsi M, and Klingler R(2010) Construction of ISCC Ain Béni Mathar in Morocco. *SolarPACES Symposium*. 21–24 September. Perpignan, France.
[34] Price H, Lupfert E, Kearney D, *et al.* (2002) Advances in parabolic trough solar power technology. *ASME Journal of Solar Energy Engineering* 124: 109–125.
[35] Menand G (2006) NREL research helps deliver clean, solar electricity to thousands of homes in the southwest. *CSP Today*, June.
[36] Hurt R, Yim W, Boehm R, *et al.* (2006) Advanced parabolic trough field testing Real-time data collection, archiving, and analysis for the Solargenix advanced parabolic trough. *Proceedings of ISEC 2006, ASME International Solar Energy Conference*. Denver, CO, USA, 8–13 July.
[37] Riffelmann K-J, Kötter J, Nava P, *et al.* (2009) HELIOTROUGH – A new collector generation for parabolic trough power plants. *SolarPACES Symposium*. Berlin, Germany, 15–18 September.
[38] Schweitzer A, Schiel W, Abul-Ella Z, *et al.* (2010) ULTIMATE TROUGH® – The next generation collector for parabolic trough power plants. *SolarPACES Symposium*. 21–24 September. Perpignan, France.
[39] http://www.abengoasolar.com (accessed 01 October 2011).
[40] McMahan A, White D, Gee R, and Viljoen N (2010) Field performance validation of an advanced utility-scale parabolic trough concentrator. *SolarPACES Symposium*. 21–24 September. Perpignan, France.

[41] Brost R, Gray A, Burkholder F, *et al.* (2009) SkyTrough optical evaluation VSHOT measurement. *SolarPACES Symposium*. 15–18 September. Berlin, Germany.
[42] Relloso S, Calvo R, Cárcamo S, and Olábarri B (2011) SenerTrough-1 collector: Commercial operation experience, continuous loop monitoring. *SolarPACES Symposium*. 20–23 September. Granada, Spain.
[43] Schott PTR®70 Receiver The Next Generation, 2009.
[44] Using solar energy for solar thermal power plants. The Schott PTR®70 Receiver. May 2004.
[45] Siemens to decisively strengthen its position in the growth market solar thermal power. *Siemens Press Release*, 15 October, Munich, Germany, 2009.
[46] Information used from the internet home address of Siemens, 2010.
[47] Geyer M, Mehos M, Meier A, *et al.* (2006) Solar power and chemical energy systems. Köln, Germany: Annual Report, SolarPaces.
[48] Grasse W, Geyer M, Pitz-Paal R, *et al.* (2000) Solar power and chemical energy systems. Köln, Germany: Annual Report, SolarPaces.
[49] Gonzalvez CH, Bueno CH, Blazquez LM, and Baonza CY (2009) *Iberdrola Renewables and the Solar Thermal Technologies*. Berlin, Germany: Proceedings SolarPACES conference.
[50] Bradshaw RW and Siegel NP (2009) *Development of Molten Nitrate Salt Mixtures for Concentrating Solar Power Systems*. Berlin, Germany: Proceedings SolarPACES conference.
[51] Gamble C and Schopf M (2009) Optimization opportunities for Therminol® VP-1 heat transfer fluid in concentrating solar power facilities. Proceedings SolarPACES conference.
[52] Steinfeld A and Schubnell M (1993) Optimum aperture size and operating temperature of a solar cavity-receiver. *Solar Energy* 50(1): 19–25.
[53] Ortega JI, Burgaleta JI, and Tellez FM (2008) Central receiver system (CRS) solar power plant using molten salt as heat transfer fluid. *Journal of Solar Energy Engineering* 130(2): 24501.
[54] ECOSTAR European Concentrated Solar Thermal Road-Mapping. Final Report Summary, 2005. Köln, Germany: deutsche zentrum für luft- und raumfahrt e.V.
[55] Falcone PK (1986) A handbook for solar central receiver design. Report SAND 86-8009, Albuquerque, NM, USA, December.
[56] Stine WB and Geyer M (2001) Power from the sun.
[57] Segal A and Epstein M (2006) Practical considerations in designing large scale 'beam down'optical systems. *SolarPACES Conference*. 19–23 June. Sevilla, Spain.
[58] Mancini TR (2000) Catalog of solar heliostats. Köln, Germany: SolarPaces Technical Report, No. III – 1/00, June.
[59] Geyer M, Pitz-Paal R, Steinfeld A, and Tyner C (2001) Solar power and chemical energy systems. Köln, Germany: Annual Report, SolarPaces.
[60] Abengoa solar: Solutions to global climate change power tower plants. White Paper, 2010.
[61] Information about the HydroHelio™ heliostat, provided by Mr. Robert Lehle.
[62] Utility-scale solar power. Information brochure of the eSolar company, 2010.
[63] Sierra sun tower report on the first six months. eSolar, March 2010.
[64] SolarReserve signs power contract with PG&E for utility scale solar power project in California. Press Release, *SolarReserve*, 22 December 2009.
[65] Stancich R (2010) It's rocket science: How SolarReserve is conquering new frontiers. *CSP Today*, Paris, France, 15 January.
[66] Argonaut increases renewable energy interests with SolarReserve. Press Release, *SolarReserve*, 30 October 2008.
[67] SolarPaces (2010) Solar power tower. http://www.solarpaces.org (accessed 21 December 2011).
[68] SolarReserve and Preneal receive environmental permit for 50 MW solar energy project in Spain. Press Release, *SolarReserve*, 17 November 2009.
[69] Information used from the internet home address of the Brightsource Energy Coorporation, 2010.
[70] Fricker HW (1986) Tests with a small volumetric wire receiver. *Proceedings of the Solar Central Receiver Systems Workshop 1986*. Konstanz, Berlin, Germany: Springer.
[71] Pitz-Paal R, Hoffschmidt B, Böhmer M, and Becker M (1997) Experimental and numerical evaluation of performance and flow stability of different types of open volumetric absorbers under non-homogeneous irradiation. Aufsatz in Zeitschrift. *Solar Energy* 60: 135–150.
[72] Hoffschmidt B, Dibowski G, Beuter M, *et al.* (2003) Test results of a 3 MW solar open volumetric receiver, ISES Solar World Congress, Goteburg, 14–19 June.
[73] Hoffschmidt B, Schwarzbözl P, Koll G, and Fernández V (2003) Design of the PS10 solar tower power plant. *ISES Solar World Congress 2003*. Göteburg, Sweden, 14–19 June.
[74] Koll G and Hoffschmidt B (2005) Die Zukunft der Stromerzeugung. DLR Nachrichten. *Köln, Ausgabe* 109, pp.42–47.
[75] Solarturmkraftwerk. Information available by the company Kraftanlagen München 2010.
[76] Hoffschmidt B, Schwarzbözl P, Quero VF, and Koll G (2003) Design of the PS 10. Solar tower power plant, ISES Solar World Congress 2003, Göteburg, 14–19 June.
[77] Geyer M, Richter C, Steinfeld A, and Romero M (2003) Solar power and chemical energy systems. Köln, Germany: Annual Report, SolarPaces.
[78] World Bank (2010) Phase I (Part I): Review of CSP Technologies and Cost Drivers Overview. South Asia Energy Unit Sustainable Development Department, The World Bank.
[79] Veynandt F, De La Torre J, Bezian J-J, and Ghatuary A (2010) Design optimization of a solar power plant based on linear Fresnel reflector. *SolarPACES Symposium*. 21–24 September. Perpignan, France.
[80] Mertins M, Lerchenmüller H, and Häberle A (2004) Geometry optimization of Fresnel-collectors with economic assessment. *Proceedings EuroSun Conference*, Freiburg, Germany, 20–24 June..
[81] Häberle A, Zahler C, Lerchenmüller H, *et al.* (2002) The Solarmundo line focussing Fresnel collector. Optical and thermal performance and cost calculations. *SolarPACES Conference*. 9-10 September. Interlaken, Switzerland.
[82] Mills DR and Morrison GL (2000) Compact linear Fresnel reflector solar thermal power plants. *Solar Energy* 68(3): 263–283.
[83] Bernhard R, Hein S, de LaLaing J, *et al.* (2008) Linear Fresnel collector demonstration on the PSA PART I – Design, construction and quality control. *14th International Symposium on Concentrated Solar Power and Chemical Energy Technologies*. 3–7 March. Las Vegas, NV, USA.
[84] Bernhard R, de LaLaing J, Kistner R, *et al.* (2009) Linear Fresnel collector demonstration at the PSA – Operation and investigation. *SolarPACES Conference*. 15–18 September. Berlin, Germany.
[85] Hoyer M, Riffelmann K-J, Benitez D, and Nava P (2004) Performance and cost comparison of linear Fresnel and parabolic trough collectors. *SolarPACES Symposium*. Freiburg, Germany.
[86] Dersch J, Morin G, Eck M, and Häberle A (2009) Comparison of linear Fresnel and parabolic trough collector systems – System analysis to determine break even costs of linear Fresnel collectors. *SolarPACES Symposium*. Berlin, Germany, 15–18 September.
[87] Clarke E (2010) Industry insight, hovering in the wings: Linear Fresnel technology. *CSP Today*, 14 January.
[88] NOVATEC BioSol Technical Date NOVA-1. July 2008.
[89] Information used from the internet home address of the company Mirroxx, 2010.
[90] Barale G, Heimsath A, Nitz P, and Toro A (2010) Optical design of a linear Fresnel collector for Sicily. *SolarPACES Symposium*. 21–24 September. Perpignan, France.
[91] Morin G, Dersch J, Eck M, *et al.* (2009) Comparison of linear Fresnel and parabolic trough collector systems influence of linear Fresnel collector design variations on break even cost. *SolarPACES Symposium*. Berlin, Germany, 15–18 September.
[92] Kroposki B, Margolis R, and Ton D (2009) An overview of solar technologies. *IEEE Power & Energy Magazine* 7(3): 23–33.
[93] Conde JMG, Pérez MAS, and Bravo IL (2011) GTER-Dish: Development of a dish-Stirling system model. *SolarPACES Symposium*. Granada, Spain.
[94] SolarPaces (2011) Solar dish engine. http://www.solarpaces.org (accessed 21 December 2011).
[95] El Ouederni AR, Ben Salah M, Ben Nasrallah S, and Aloui F (2010) Potential of the dish-Stirling technology introduction in Tunisia. *SolarPACES Symposium*. 21–24 September. Perpignan, France.
[96] Jaffe LD (1988) A review of test results on solar thermal power modules with dish-mounted Stirling and Brayton cycle engines. *ASME Journal of Solar Energy Engineering* 110(4): 268–274.
[97] Mancini T, Heller P, Butler B, *et al.* (2003) Dish-Stirling systems: An overview of development and status. *Journal of Solar Energy Engineering* 12: 135–151.

[98] Macêdo WN, Pinho JT, Almeida MP, *et al.* (2009) Efficiency evaluation and economic feasibility of small dish-Stirling power systems in Brazil. *SolarPACES Symposium.* Berlin, Germany, 15–18 September.
[99] Andraka CE (2008) Cost/performance trade offs for reflectors used in solar concentrating dish systems. *Proceedings of ES2008 Energy Sustainability 2008*, ES2008-54048, Jacksonville, FL, USA, 10–14 August.
[100] Murillo M, Silva M, Ruiz V, and Gavilán A (2009) A proposal for reducing spillage of concentrated heat flux in a parabolic dish/Stirling. *SolarPACES Symposium.* Berlin, Germany, 15–18 September.
[101] EPRI Report (1986) Performance of the Vanguard solar dish-Stirling engine module. Electric Power Research Institute, AP 4608, Project 2003-5.
[102] Keck T, Schiel W, Heller P, *et al.* (2009) EURODISH – Continuous operation, system improvement and reference units. *SolarPACES Symposium.* Berlin, Germany, 15–18 September.
[103] Brignoli V and Bombelli D (2009) An easy software to estimate the production of the Eurodish solar generator in Italy. *SolarPACES Symposium.* Berlin, Germany, 15–18 September.
[104] Infinia Solar System Product Specification. Infinia Corporation, 2009.
[105] Burgess G, Lovegrove K, Mackie S, *et al.* (2011) Direct steam generation using the SG4 500 m^2 paraboloidal dish concentrator. *SolarPACES Symposium.* 20–23 September. Granada, Spain.
[106] Kim J-K, Lee S-N, and Kang Y-H (2010) 10 kW dish-Stirling system operation in Korea. *SolarPACES Symposium.* 21–24 September. Perpignan, France.
[107] What will the size of the market be? Information provided online from Greenpeace, 2010.
[108] Leitner A and Owens B (2003) Brighter than a hundred suns: Solar power for the Southwest. Platts Research and Consulting. Boulder, CO, USA: National Renewable Energy Laboratory, January.
[109] Desertec Foundation: Red Paper. An overview of the Desertec concept. Berlin, Germany, 2009.
[110] Cohn L and Smit R (2008) The future: Widespread use of CSP? *Sun & Wind Energy* 2/2008: 42–53.

3.07 Thermal Energy Storage

LF Cabeza, GREA Innovació Concurrent, Universitat de Lleida, Lleida, Spain

© 2012 Elsevier Ltd. All rights reserved.

3.07.1	Introduction	212
3.07.1.1	Definition of Thermal Energy Storage	212
3.07.1.2	TES and Solar Energy	213
3.07.1.3	Design of Storages	213
3.07.1.4	Integration of Storages into Systems	214
3.07.2	**Methods for TES**	214
3.07.2.1	Sensible Heat	214
3.07.2.1.1	Definition	214
3.07.2.1.2	Air	215
3.07.2.1.3	Water	216
3.07.2.1.4	Other materials	219
3.07.2.1.5	Underground thermal energy storage	219
3.07.2.2	Latent Heat	221
3.07.2.2.1	Definition	221
3.07.2.2.2	Exergy analysis of a latent storage system	222
3.07.2.3	Thermochemical Heat	224
3.07.2.3.1	Definition	224
3.07.2.3.2	Chemical reactions	224
3.07.2.3.3	Sorption systems	224
3.07.2.4	Comparison of Thermal Storage System Types	227
3.07.3	**Economics of TES**	227
3.07.3.1	TES and Energy Savings	227
3.07.3.2	Thermoeconomics of TES	228
3.07.4	**Case Studies**	232
3.07.4.1	Combisystems	232
3.07.4.2	BTES in a UK Office Building	237
3.07.4.3	Molten Salts in High-Temperature Solar Power Plants	239
3.07.4.4	Concrete and Other Solid Materials in High-Temperature Solar Power Plants	242
3.07.4.5	PCM in Buildings as Passive Energy System	243
3.07.4.6	PCM in Buildings as Active Energy System	247
3.07.4.7	Seasonal Storage of Solar Energy	248
3.07.4.8	Open Absorption Systems for Air Conditioning	250
References		253

Glossary

ATES In aquifer thermal energy storage (ATES) systems, groundwater is used to carry the thermal energy into and out of an aquifer. For connection to the aquifer, water wells are used.

BTES Borehole thermal energy storage (BTES) systems consist of a number of closely spaced boreholes, normally 50–200 m deep. Boreholes act as heat exchangers to the underground, usually the U-pipe borehole heat exchangers.

Latent energy storage When a material stores heat while phase transition, the heat is stored as latent heat.

Phase change material A phase change material (PCM) is a substance with a high heat of fusion that (melting and solidifying at a certain temperature) is capable of storing and releasing large amounts of energy. Heat is absorbed or released when the material changes from solid to liquid phase and vice versa.

Sensible energy storage In sensible thermal energy storage, energy is stored by changing the temperature of the storage medium, such as water, air, oil, rock beds, bricks, concrete, or sand.

Thermal energy storage Thermal energy storage (TES) allows the storage of heat and cold for later use. TES is also known as heat or cold storage.

Thermochemical energy storage Any chemical reaction with high heat of reaction can be used for TES if the products of the reaction can be stored and if the heat stored during the reaction can be released when the reversible reaction takes place.

UTES Underground thermal energy storage (UTES) uses underground reservoirs for storing heat and cold in different ways, depending on geological, hydrogeological, and other site conditions. The two most promising options are storage in aquifers (ATES) and storage through borehole heat exchangers (BTES) and cavern thermal energy storage (CTES) by way of underground cavities is a technology rarely applied commercially.

Nomenclature

A	area (m^2)
C	cost (€)
c_a	specific heat of the air (J kg^{-1} K^{-1})
c_b	specific heat of the bed material (J kg^{-1} K^{-1})
c_p	specific heat of the storage material (J kg^{-1} °C^{-1})
d	rock diameter (m)
G	air mass velocity per square meter of bed frontal area (kg s^{-1} m^{-2})
H	enthalpy (kJ kg^{-1})
h_v	volumetric heat transfer coefficient (W m^{-3} K^{-1})
L	bed length (m)
m	mass of storage material (kg)
m_{sorb}	mass of the adsorbent (kg)
$\dot{m}$	mass flow of the air (kg s^{-1})
$\dot{m}_c$	charging fluid flow rate (kg s^{-1})
NTU	number of transfer units (–)
Q_{bind}	binding energy (W)
Q_{cond}	condensation energy (W)
Q_u	rate of collected solar energy delivered to the storage tank (W)
Q_l	rate of energy removed from storage tank to load (W)
Q_{sens}	sensible heat (W)
Q_{tl}	rate of energy loss from the storage tank (W)
S	entropy (J K^{-1})
t	time (s)
T_o	reference (dead-state temperature) temperature (K)
T_a	temperature of the air (°C)
T_b	temperature of the bed material (°C)
T_{env}	environment where the storage tank is located (°C)
T_{s-n}	new storage tank temperature after the time interval Δt (°C)
U	overall heat transfer coefficient (W °C^{-1} m^{-2})
$(UA)_s$	storage tank loss coefficient and area product (W °C^{-1})
V	volume of storage material (m^3)
V_{sorb}	volume of the adsorbent (m^3)
W	work (W)
x	position along the bed in the flow direction (m)
ΔC	difference in water concentration of the adsorbent (kg$_{water}$/kg$_{ads}$)
Δh	phase change enthalpy, also called melting enthalpy or heat of fusion (kJ kg^{-1})
ΔH_{ads}	integrated differential heat of adsorption (kJ kg^{-1})
ΔT	temperature change (°C)
ΔT_{lm}	logarithmic mean temperature difference (°C)
Δx	humidity ratio difference (–)
ρ	density of the storage material (kg m^{-3})
ρ_a	density of the air (kg m^{-3})
ρ_b	density of the bed material (kg m^{-3})
ρ_{sorb}	density of the adsorbent (kg m^{-3})
ε	void fraction of the packing, that is, the void volume over the total volume of the bed (–)

3.07.1 Introduction

3.07.1.1 Definition of Thermal Energy Storage

Thermal energy storage (TES) allows the storage of heat and cold for later use. TES is also known as heat or cold storage [1].

TES can aid in the efficient use and provision of thermal energy whenever there is a mismatch between energy generation and use. This mismatch can be in terms of time, temperature, power, or site [2].

The potential advantages on the overall system performance are as follows [1]:

- Better economics – reducing investment and running costs
- Better efficiency – achieving a more efficient use of energy
- Less pollution of the environment and less CO$_2$ emissions
- Better system performance and reliability.

The basic principle is the same in all TES applications. Energy is supplied to a storage system for removal and use at a later time [2]. A complete process involves three steps (**Figure 1**): (1) charging, (2) storing, and (3) discharging. In practical systems, some of the steps may occur simultaneously, and each step can happen more than once in each storage cycle [3].

Several factors have to be taken into consideration when deciding on the type and the design of any thermal storage system, and a key issue is its thermal capacity. However, selection of an appropriate system depends on many factors, such as cost–benefit considerations, technical criteria, and environmental criteria [3].

The cost of a TES system mainly depends on the following items: the storage material itself, the heat exchanger for charging and discharging the system, and the cost of the space and/or enclosure for the TES.

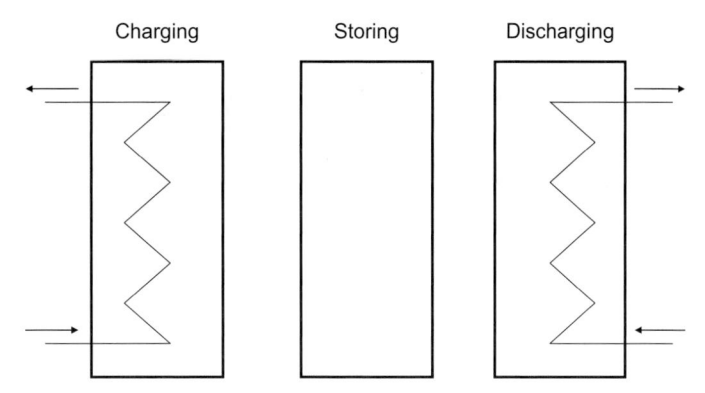

Figure 1 Steps involved in a complete TES system: charging, storing, and discharging.

From a technical point of view, the most important requirements are as follows:

- High energy density in the storage material (storage capacity)
- Good heat transfer between heat transfer fluid (HTF) and storage medium (efficiency)
- Mechanical and chemical stability of storage material (must support several charging–discharging cycles)
- Compatibility between HTF, heat exchanger, and/or storage medium (safety)
- Complete reversibility of a number of charging–discharging cycles (lifetime)
- Low thermal losses
- Easy control.

And the most important design criteria from the point of view of technology are

- Operation strategy
- Maximum load
- Nominal temperature and specific enthalpy drop in load
- Integration into the whole application system.

3.07.1.2 TES and Solar Energy

TES is important to the success of any intermittent energy source in meeting demand [2]. This problem is especially severe for solar energy because it is usually needed most when solar availability is lowest, that is, during winter. TES complicates solar energy systems in two main ways. First, a TES subsystem must be large enough to permit the system to operate over periods of inadequate sunshine. The alternative is to have a backup energy supply, which adds a capital cost and provides a unit that remains idle. The second major complication imposed by TES is that the primary collecting system must be sufficiently large to build the supply of stored energy during periods of adequate insolation. Thus, additional collecting area is needed.

Examinations of typical sunshine records show that even in the desert, the periods of cloudy and clear weather are about equally spaced; a few days of one followed by a few days of the other. Partly cloudy days can greatly affect performance and make the difference between practical and impractical energy storage. If the total energy of a partly cloudy day can be collected, then the periods requiring energy storage are greatly reduced.

Concentrating solar systems must cope with the intermittent nature of direct sunlight on a cloudy day. Consequently, absorbers and boilers must be designed with care to avoid problems of burnout when the sun suddenly returns with full brilliance. Nonconcentrating systems face the fundamental problem of trying to provide sufficiently high efficiency at medium temperatures to yield energy output at reasonable cost.

Most TES applications involve a diurnal storage cycle; however, weekly and/or seasonal storage is also used [2]. Solar energy applications require storage of thermal energy for periods ranging from very short duration to annual storage. Advantages of diurnal storage include low capital investments for storage and low energy losses, smaller devices, and not-so-critical sizing of storage systems. Advantages of seasonal storage are lower heat losses due to lower surface-to-volume ratios, and elimination of backup systems because periods of adverse weather have little effect on the long-term thermal energy availability.

3.07.1.3 Design of Storages

Figure 2 shows the basic working scheme of a heat storage: heat or cold supplied by a heat source is transferred to the heat storage, stored in the storage, and later transferred to a heat sink to cope with the demand [1].

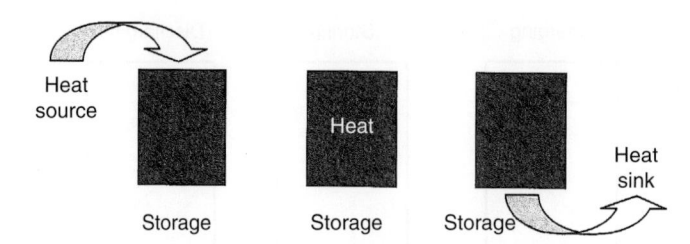

Figure 2 Basic working scheme of a storage: heat or cold from a source is transferred to the storage, stored in the storage, and later transferred to a sink [1].

Every application sets a number of boundary conditions, which must be looked into carefully:

- From the temperature point of view, the supply temperature at the source has to be higher or equal to the temperature of the storage, and the storage to the sink.
- From the power point of view, that is, the amount of heat transferred in a certain time must be the required in the charging and discharging.
- In some applications, the HTF and its movement by free or forced convection has to be considered.

There are three basic design options in storage systems [1]. The first one is when heat is exchanged by heat transfer on the surface of the storage. This becomes a typical heat transfer problem where heat transfer resistance on the surface of the storage tank is the main parameter. Conduction and free or forced convection mechanism are to be considered here.

Second, when a heat exchanger is used separating the HTF with the storage material, the surface of heat transfer increases significantly. This surface can be increased even further with the use of fins.

Finally, a third scheme is used when the heat storage medium is also the heat transfer medium. An example is when a water tank is discharged due to the demand of the shower, and cold water enters the tank replacing the hot one. In this case, heat transfer is basically by convection.

3.07.1.4 Integration of Storages into Systems

The main goal to integrate a heat or cold storage tank into a system is to supply heat or cold. However, the different supply and demand situations have a great influence on the integration concept [1].

The first case to consider is when there is no overlap in time between loading from the supply and unloading to the demand. In this case, the storage system can match different times of supply and demand; in many cases, the storage system can match different supply and demand power, and even supply and demand location, with transport of the storage medium.

If there is a partial or total overlap in time, it is possible to smooth out fluctuations of the supply and/or the demand. Thus, the typical goals of storage integration are temperature regulation and power matching.

The basic goals of the storage are to match supply and demand regarding the amount of heat and cold and the heating or cooling power at the right time. While the amount of heat or cold is determined by the size of the storage and the heating or cooling power, which depend mainly on the design of the storage, the integration concept has a large influence with respect to time.

3.07.2 Methods for TES

3.07.2.1 Sensible Heat

3.07.2.1.1 Definition

In sensible TES, energy is stored by changing the temperature of a storage medium such as water, air, oil, rock beds, bricks, concrete, or sand. The amount of energy introduced to the storage system is proportional to the temperature lift, the mass of the storage medium, and the heat capacity of the storage medium. Each medium or material has its own advantages and disadvantages, but usually its selection is based on the heat capacity and the available space for storage [2].

The amount of heat stored in a material, Q, can be expressed as

$$Q = m \times c_p \times \Delta T \qquad [1]$$

or

$$Q = \rho \times c_p \times V \times \Delta T \qquad [2]$$

where c_p is the specific heat of the storage material (J kg^{-1} °C^{-1}), ΔT the temperature change (°C), m the mass of storage material (kg), V the volume of storage material (m^3), and ρ the density of the storage material (kg m^{-3}).

Sensible storage is the most common method of heat and cold storage. Some common materials used in TES systems are presented in **Table 1** [2]. The material must be inexpensive and should have good thermal capacity ($\rho \times c_p$) to be useful in a storage

Table 1 Thermal capacity at 20 °C of some common materials used in sensible TES [2]

Material	Density (kg m^{-3})	Specific heat (J kg^{-1} K^{-1})	Volumetric thermal capacity ($\times 10^6$, J m^{-3} K^{-1})
Clay	1458	879	1.28
Brick	1800	837	1.51
Sandstone	2200	712	1.57
Wood	700	2390	1.67
Concrete	2000	880	1.76
Glass	2710	837	2.27
Aluminum	2710	896	2.43
Iron	7900	452	3.57
Steel	7840	465	3.68
Gravelly earth	2050	1840	3.77
Magnetite	5177	752	3.89
Water	988	4182	4.17

application. Besides the density and the specific heat of the storage material, other properties that are also important for sensible heat storage are operational temperatures, thermal conductivity and diffusivity, vapor pressure, compatibility among materials, stability, heat loss coefficient as a function of the surface areas-to-volume ratio, and cost [3].

A sensible TES system consists of a storage medium, a container (commonly, tank), and inlet–outlet devices. Tanks must retain the storage material and prevent losses of thermal energy. The existence of a thermal gradient across storage is desirable [3].

Sensible heat storage can be made from solid or liquid media. Solid media are usually used in packed beds, requiring a fluid to exchange heat. When the fluid is a liquid, the heat capacity of the solid in the packed bed is not negligible, and the system is called dual storage system.

3.07.2.1.2 Air

In solar heating systems that use air as heat transport fluid, the packed bed is a convenient and attractive storage device because it is generally formed from low-cost materials and exhibits a large heat transfer surface-to- occupancy volume ratio; typically 400 m^2 m^{-3} can be found in a bed of particles of 0.01 m diameter [4].

The packed or fixed bed is generally a random assemblage of solid particles, each in physical contact with its neighbors and held firm in a container as shown in **Figure 3**. In the charging mode, the hot air flowing in warms the storage material and leaves the bin cooler. The ideal storage process is achieved when all the solid materials are at the inlet temperature of the fluid. To withdraw energy from the storage, discharging mode, the direction of the flow is reversed and the incoming cool air is heated progressively along the matrix.

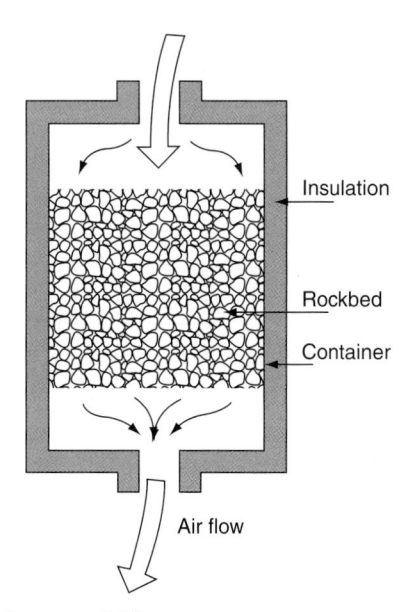

Figure 3 Schematic representation of packed bed storage unit [4].

In packed bed storage units, charge and discharge happen alternatively and cannot happen at the same time. In these storage units, stratification is easily maintained.

3.07.2.1.2.1 Thermal analysis of air systems

In air–pebbles storage units, both the air and the rocks change temperature in the direction of the airflow and there are temperature differentials between the rocks and the air. In the thermal analysis of these systems, the following assumptions are made [5]:

1. The forced airflow is one dimensional.
2. The system properties are constant.
3. The heat transfer conduction along the rocked bed is negligible.
4. There is no heat loss to the ambient.

The thermal behavior of the pebbles and air are described by

$$\rho_b c_b (1-\varepsilon) \frac{\partial T_b}{\partial t} = h_v (T_a - T_b) \qquad [3]$$

$$\rho_a c_a \varepsilon \frac{\partial T_a}{\partial t} = -\frac{\dot{m} c_a}{A} \frac{\partial T_a}{\partial x} - h_v (T_a - T_b) \qquad [4]$$

where A is the cross-sectional area of the storage tank (m^2); T_b the temperature of the bed material (°C); T_a the temperature of the air (°C); ρ_b the density of the bed material (kg m^{-3}); ρ_a the density of the air (kg m^{-3}); c_b the specific heat of the bed material (J kg^{-1} K^{-1}); c_a the specific heat of the air (J kg^{-1} K^{-1}); t the time (s); x the position along the bed in the flow direction (m); $\dot{m}$ the mass flow of the air (kg s^{-1}); ε the void fraction of the packing, that is the void volume over the total volume of the bed; and h_v the volumetric heat transfer coefficient (W m^{-3} K^{-1}).

An empirical equation for the determination of the volumetric heat transfer coefficient (h_v) is

$$h_v = 650 \left(\frac{G}{d} \right)^{0.7} \qquad [5]$$

where G is the air mass velocity per square meter of bed frontal area (kg s^{-1} m^{-2}) and d is the rock diameter (m).

If the energy storage capacity of the air within the bed is neglected, eqn [4] is reduced to

$$\dot{m} c_a \frac{\partial T_a}{\partial x} = -A h_v (T_a - T_b) \qquad [6]$$

Equations [3] and [6] can also be written in terms of number of transfer units (NTUs) as

$$\frac{\partial T_b}{\partial (\theta)} = \text{NTU}(T_a - T_b) \qquad [7]$$

$$\frac{\partial T_a}{\partial (x/L)} = \text{NTU}(T_b - T_a) \qquad [8]$$

where L is the bed length (m).

The dimensionless NTUs is given by

$$\text{NTU} = \frac{h_v A L}{\dot{m} c_a} \qquad [9]$$

The parameter θ, which is also dimensionless in eqn [7], is equal to

$$\theta = \frac{t \dot{m} c_a}{\rho_b c_b (1-\varepsilon) A L} \qquad [10]$$

3.07.2.1.3 Water

Water storage is the oldest and more developed storage technology. One can find water tanks for heating and cooling, and it is also possible to find tanks for short-term and seasonal storage. Recently, interest in water tanks has risen more and more due to their use in domestic solar systems.

For a water tank to be effective, stratification is a key issue. Water stratification occurs when water of high and low temperatures (thermocline) forms layers that act as barriers to water mixing (**Figure 4**). A thermally naturally stratified storage tank has no inside partitions. Warm water has low density and moves to the top of the tank, whereas cooler water with higher density sinks to the bottom.

A thin and tall water tank is desirable to improve thermal stratification. The water inlet and outlet should be installed in a manner so as to produce a uniform flow to avoid mixing. The surfaces that are in contact with the storage water should be minimized, and the insulation should be optimized. The velocity of the water flowing into and out of the tank should be low [2].

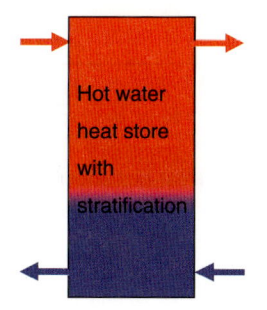

Figure 4 Stratified water tank.

Another type of water storage systems is solar ponds. A solar pond is simply a pool of saltwater that collects and stores solar thermal energy. The saltwater naturally forms a vertical salinity gradient, also known as a 'halocline', in which low-salinity water floats on top of high-salinity water, introducing water stratification due to the different salinity of the water. The layers of salt solutions increase in concentration (and therefore density) with depth. Below a certain depth, the solution has a uniform and high salt concentration [2, 6].

When solar energy is absorbed by the water, its temperature increases, causing thermal expansion and a reduction in density. If the water is fresh, the low-density warm water would float to the surface, causing a convection current. The temperature gradient alone causes a density gradient that decreases with depth. However, the salinity gradient forms a density gradient that increases with depth, and this counteracts the temperature gradient, thus preventing heat in the lower layers from moving upwards by convection and leaving the pond. This means that the temperature at the bottom of the pond will rise to over 90 °C, while the temperature at the top of the pond is usually around 30 °C. A natural example of these effects in a saline water body is the Solar Lake located in Sinai, Israel.

The heat trapped in the salty bottom layer can be used for many different purposes, such as heating of buildings, or for industrial hot water, or to drive an organic Rankine cycle turbine or Stirling engine for generating electricity.

One can use two types of water storage for water systems: pressurized and unpressurized [5]. Other differences include the use of an external or internal heat exchanger and single- or multiple-tank configurations. Water may be stored in copper, galvanized metal, or concrete tanks. Whatever storage vessel is selected, it should be well insulated, and large tanks should be provided with internal access for maintenance. Recommended U-value is about $0.16\,\mathrm{W\,m^{-2}\,K^{-1}}$.

Pressurized storage is preferred for small service water heating systems and the typical storage size is about $40–80\,\mathrm{l\,m^{-2}}$ of collector area. With pressurized storage, the heat exchanger is always located on the collector side of the tank. Either internal or external heat exchanger configurations can be used. The two principal types of internal heat exchanger are an immersed coil and a tube bundle (**Figure 5**).

Due to the required storage volume, more than one tank can be used instead of a large one. Additional tanks offer increased heat exchanger surface and reduced pressure drop in the collection loop. A multiple-tank configuration for pressurized storage is shown in **Figure 6**.

An external heat exchanger provides greater flexibility because the tank and the exchanger can be selected independently of other equipments (**Figure 7**). The disadvantage of this system is the parasitic energy consumption, in the form of electrical energy, due to the additional use of the pump.

For small systems, an internal heat exchanger–tank arrangement is usually used, which has the advantage of preventing the water side of the heat exchanger from freezing. However, the energy required to maintain the water temperature above freezing point is

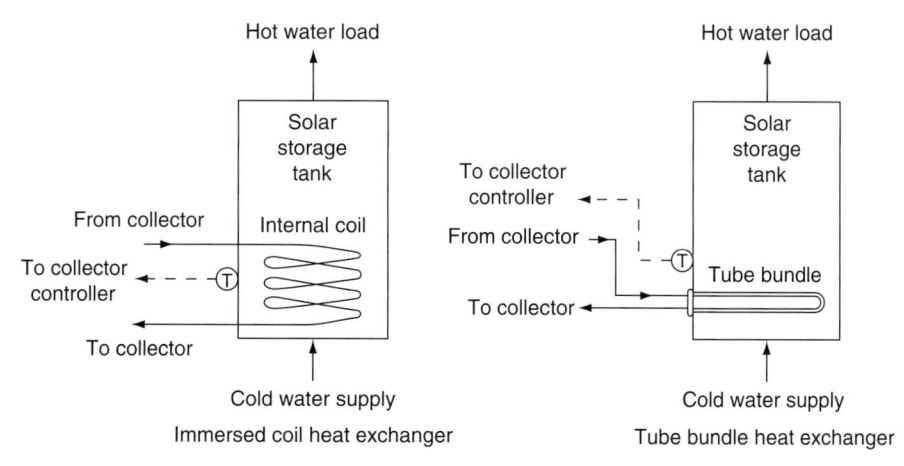

Figure 5 Pressurized storage water tank with internal heat exchanger [5].

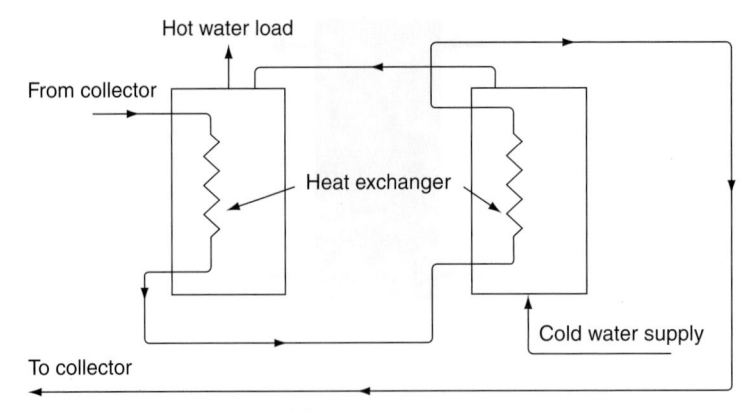

Figure 6 Multiple-tank storage arrangement with internal heat exchangers [5].

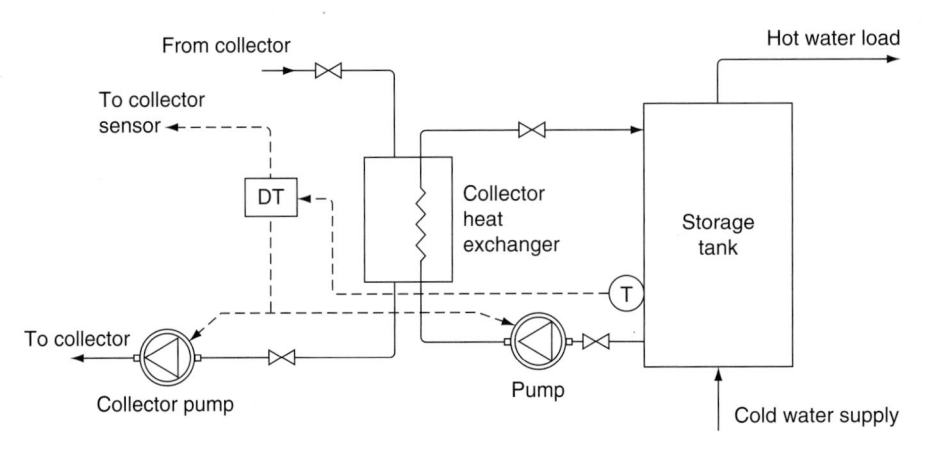

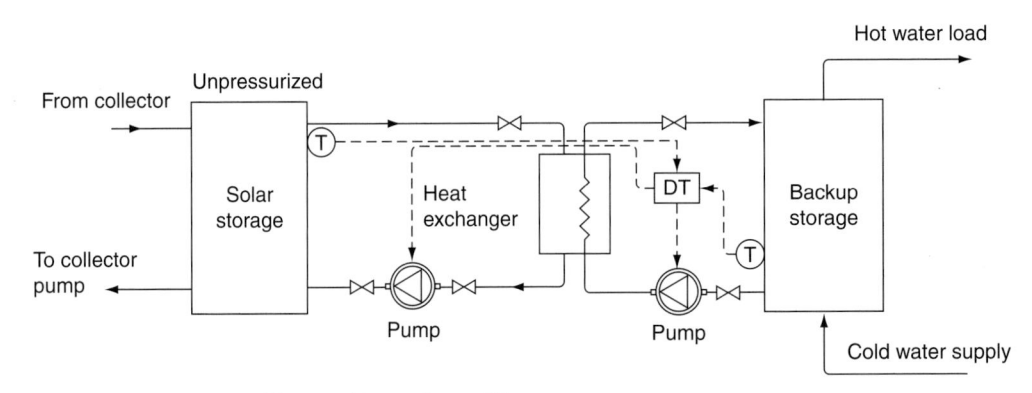

Figure 7 Pressurized storage system with external heat exchanger [5].

extracted from storage; thus, the overall system performance is decreased. With an external heat exchanger, a bypass can be used to divert the cold fluid around the heat exchanger until it has been heated to an acceptable level of about 25 °C. When the HTF is warmed to this level, it can enter the heat exchanger without causing freezing or extraction of heat from storage. If necessary, this arrangement can also be used with internal heat exchangers to improve performance [5].

For systems with sizes greater than about 30 m³, unpressurized storage is usually more cost-effective than the pressurized. This system, however, can also be employed in small domestic flat-plate collector systems, and in this case, the make-up system water is usually supplied from a cold water storage tank located on top of the hot water cylinder.

Unpressurized storage for water and space heating can be combined with the pressurized storage for city water supply. This implies the use of a heat exchanger on the load side of the tank to isolate the high-pressure mains' potable water loop from the low-pressure collector loop. An unpressurized storage system with an external heat exchanger is shown in **Figure 8**. In this

Figure 8 Unpressurized storage system with external heat exchanger [5].

configuration, heat is extracted from the top of the solar storage tank and the cooled water is returned to the bottom of the tank so as to not distract stratification. For the same reason, on the load side of the heat exchanger, the water to be heated flows from the bottom of the backup storage tank, where relatively cold water remains, and heated water returns to the top. Where an HTF is circulated in the collector loop, the heat exchanger may have a double-wall construction to protect the potable water supply from contamination. A differential temperature controller controls the two pumps on either side of the heat exchanger. When small pumps are used, both may be controlled by the same controller without overloading problems [5]. The external heat exchanger shown in **Figure 8** provides good system flexibility and freedom in component selection. In some cases, system cost and parasitic power consumption may be reduced by an internal heat exchanger.

3.07.2.1.3.1 Thermal analysis of water storage systems

For fully mixed or unstratified energy storage, the capacity (Q_s) of a liquid storage unit at uniform temperature, operating over a finite temperature difference (ΔT_s), is given by

$$Q_s = (mc_p)_s \Delta T_s \qquad [11]$$

where m is the mass of storage capacity (kg).

The temperature range over which such a unit operates is limited by the requirements of the process. The upper limit is also determined by the vapor pressure of the liquid.

An energy balance of the storage tank gives

$$(mc_p)_s \frac{dT_s}{dt} = Q_u - Q_l - Q_{tl} \qquad [12]$$

where Q_u is the rate of solar energy collected and delivered to the storage tank (W), Q_l the rate of energy removed from storage tank to load (W), and Q_{tl} the rate of energy loss from the storage tank (W).

The rate of energy loss from the storage tank is given by

$$Q_{tl} = (UA)_s (T_s - T_{env}) \qquad [13]$$

where $(UA)_s$ is the storage tank loss coefficient and area product (W °C^{-1}) and T_{env} is the environment where the storage tank is located (°C).

To determine the long-term performance of the storage tank, eqn [16] may be rewritten in finite difference form as [5]

$$(mc_p)_s \frac{T_{s-n} - T_s}{\Delta t} = Q_u - Q_l - Q_{tl} \qquad [14]$$

or

$$T_{s-n} = T_s + \frac{\Delta t}{(mc_p)_s} \left[Q_u - Q_l - (UA)_s (T_s - T_{env}) \right] \qquad [15]$$

where T_{s-n} is the new storage tank temperature after the time interval Δt (°C).

The above equation assumes that the heat losses are constant in the period Δt. The most common time period for this estimation is an hour, because the solar radiation data are also available on an hourly basis.

3.07.2.1.4 Other materials

Concrete is chosen because of its low cost, availability, and easy processing [2, 3]. Moreover, concrete is a material with high specific heat, good mechanical properties (e.g., compressive strength), thermal expansion coefficient similar to that of steel (pipe material), and high mechanical resistance to cyclic thermal loading.

When concrete is heated, a number of reactions and transformations take place, which influence its strength and other physical properties. Resistance to thermal cycling depends on the thermal expansion coefficients of the materials used in the concrete. To minimize such problems, a basalt concrete is sometimes used. Steel needles and reinforcements are sometimes added to the concrete to impede cracking. At the same time, by doing so, the thermal conductivity is increased by about 15% at 100 °C and 10% at 250 °C.

For high-temperature TES, liquid media is the preferred choice. Different materials that can be used as liquid media are molten salts (a eutectic of sodium and potassium nitrate), silicon and synthetic oils (very expensive materials), and nitrites in salts (with potential corrosion problems) [3].

3.07.2.1.5 Underground thermal energy storage

Underground thermal energy storage (UTES) uses underground reservoirs for storing heat and cold in different ways, depending on geological, hydrogeological, and other site conditions. The two most promising options are storage in aquifers (ATES) and storage through borehole heat exchangers (BTES) [7]. TES through underground cavities (CTES, cavern thermal energy storage) is a technology rarely applied commercially.

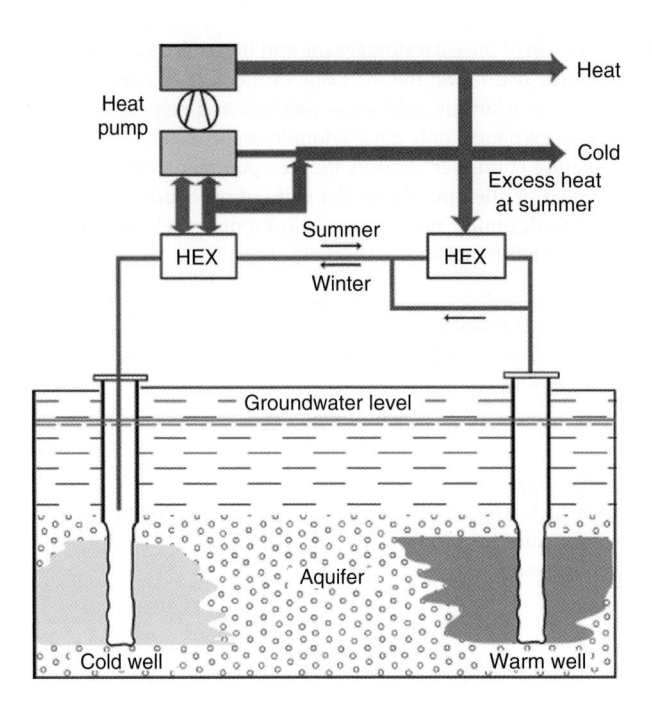

Figure 9 ATES configuration [7].

In ATES systems, groundwater is used to carry the thermal energy into and out of an aquifer [7]. For the connection to the aquifer, water wells are used (**Figure 9**).

In ATES systems, the energy is partly stored in the groundwater, and partly also in the solid mass which forms the aquifer. This will result in the development of a thermal front with different temperatures. This front will move in a radial direction from the well during charging of the store and then turn back while discharging.

There are several hundreds of these systems in operation, with the Netherlands and Sweden as dominating countries of implementation. Practically, all systems are designed for low-temperature applications where both heat and cold are seasonally stored, but they are sometimes used for short-term storage.

BTES systems consist of a number of closely spaced boreholes, normally 50–200 m deep (**Figure 10**). Boreholes act as heat exchangers to the underground, usually the U-pipe borehole heat exchangers [7].

In some countries, the boreholes are grouted after the installation of borehole heat exchangers; but in this case, the thermal efficiency will decrease even though the groundwater is protected.

The HTF flows through the U-pipe introducing or extracting heat from the underground. The storing process is mainly conductive, and the temperature change of the rock will be restricted to only a few meters around each of the individual boreholes.

These systems have been implemented in many countries with thousands of systems in operation. The numbers of plants are steadily growing and more new countries are gradually starting to use these systems. They are typically applied for combined heating and cooling, normally supported with heat pumps for a better use of the low temperature from the storage [7].

Any ATES realization is quite a complex procedure and has to follow a certain pattern to be properly developed [7]. Typical designing steps are as follows:

- Prefeasibility studies describing the principal issues
- Feasibility studies giving the technical and economical feasibility and environmental impact compared to one or several reference systems
- First permit applications to local authorities
- Definition of hydrogeological conditions by means of complementary site investigations and measurements of loads and temperatures on the user's side
- Evaluation of results and modeling used for technical, legal, and environmental purposes
- Final design used for tender documents
- Final permit applications for court procedures.

The technical issues are general, but the permit procedure may vary from country to country.

While designing borehole heat exchangers, accurate information on the soil thermal parameters, such as thermal conductivity, heat capacity, and temperature, is essential for an economically sized and well-functioning thermal energy store [8]. Especially, the soil thermal conductivity is critical as it affects both total length of heat exchanger needed as well as optimum interborehole distances.

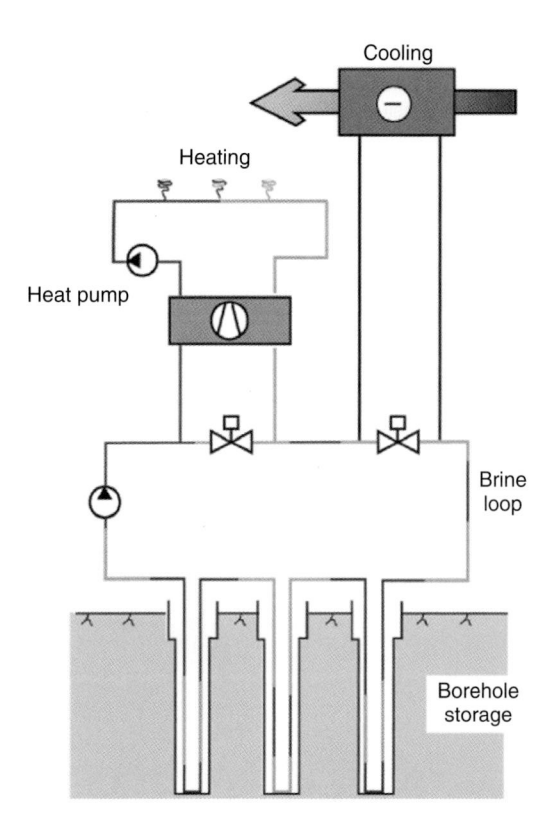

Figure 10 BTES configuration [7].

Due to the importance of ground thermal conductivity, several geothermal response test methods have been developed to measure the effective thermal conductivity of the ground and the local thermal resistance of the borehole heat exchanger installation.

All these tests operate under the assumption that the principal heat transport mechanism is conduction and therefore there is a relation between the thermal power applied to a heat exchanger, the temperature development with time, and the thermal conductivity of the material. Other mechanisms of heat transfer are not taken into account, which may invalidate the analysis of results.

Another UTES system used is energy piles. Energy piles use the building foundation as ground heat exchangers [9]. This technology allows great possibility of cost reduction in the construction of ground heat exchangers and nowadays attracts a lot of attention in some countries like Japan.

The types of foundation piles are classified broadly into three categories. First is the cast-in-place concrete pile. Second is the precasting concrete pile, which has a hole in the center. The final one is the steel foundation pile with a blade on the tip of the pile, which is screwed into the ground by a rotating burying machine.

The steel foundation can be easily utilized as the ground heat exchanger just after filling water and inserting several sets of U-tubes in the pile. There are two typical methods that enable the steel foundation pile to provide ground heat exchanging. One is direct water circulation method and the other one is indirect method using U-tubes filled with water. The latter one can take a closed circulating system, which is better in terms of maintenance for many years.

3.07.2.2 Latent Heat

3.07.2.2.1 Definition

When a material stores heat while at phase transition, the heat is stored as latent heat. Solid–liquid phase change process by melting and solidification can store large amounts of heat and cold if a suitable material is selected. Upon melting, while heat is transferred to the storage material, the material still keeps its temperature constant at the melting temperature, also called phase change temperature [1]. This is one of the main differences with sensible heat (**Figure 11**). Usually the solid–liquid phase change is studied, but some solid–solid phase changes are of interest in some applications.

The amount of heat stored can be calculated by

$$Q = m \times \Delta h \qquad [16]$$

where Δh is the phase change enthalpy, also called as melting enthalpy or heat of fusion, and m is the mass of storage material.

Figure 12 shows the typical range of melting enthalpy and temperature of common material classes used as phase change materials (PCMs) [1]. The best known and the mostly commonly used PCM is water, which has been used for cold storage since the

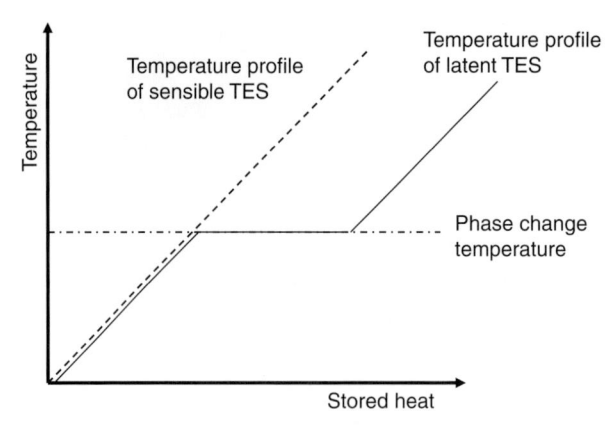

Figure 11 Heat storage as sensible and latent TES.

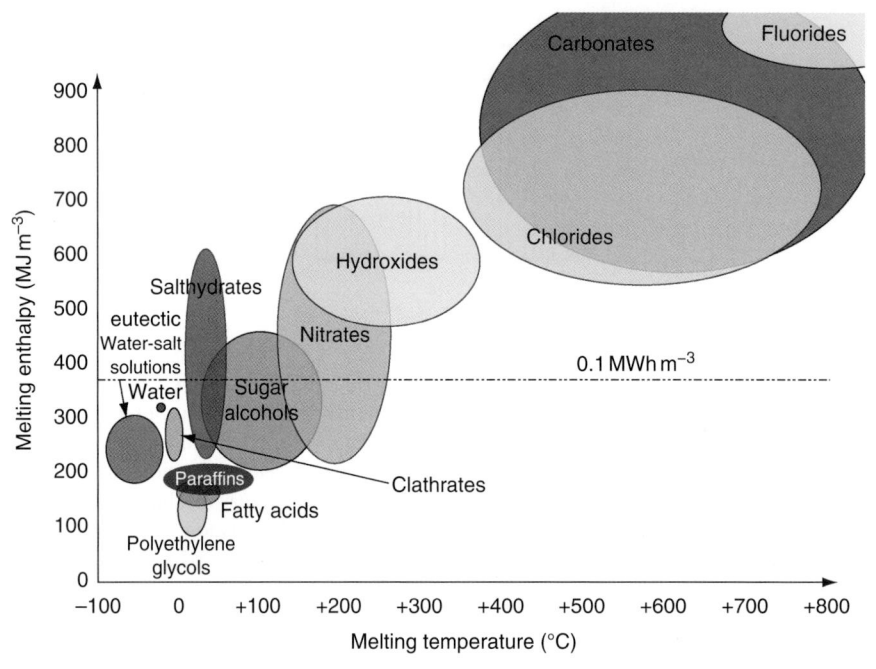

Figure 12 Classes of materials that can be used as PCM and their typical range of melting temperature and melting enthalpy [1].

early times. For temperatures below 0 °C, water salt solutions are the typically used materials. For temperatures between 0 and 130 °C, paraffins, salt hydrates, fatty acids, and sugar alcohols are used. For temperatures above 150 °C, salts and other inorganic materials are utilized.

Many substances have been studied as potential PCMs, but only a few of them are commercialized [1, 10, 11]. The selection of the material to be used in latent heat storage is not easy. Availability and cost are usually the main drawbacks for the selection of a technically suitable material. Still today, problems such as phase separation, subcooling, corrosion, long-term stability, and low heat conductivity have not been totally solved and are under research.

Recently, storage concepts have been classified as active or passive systems [3]. An active storage system is mainly characterized by forced convection heat transfer into the storage material. The storage medium itself circulates through a heat exchanger (the heat exchanger can also be a solar receiver or a steam generator). This system uses one or two tanks as storage media. Active systems are subdivided into direct and indirect systems. In a direct system, the HTF serves also as the storage medium, while in an indirect system, a second medium is used for storing the heat. Passive storage systems are generally dual-medium storage systems: the HTF passes through the storage only for charging and discharging a solid material.

3.07.2.2.2 Exergy analysis of a latent storage system

Accessible work potential is called the exergy, that is, the maximum amount of work that may be performed theoretically by bringing a resource into equilibrium with its surrounding through a reversible process [12]. Exergy analysis is essentially a thermodynamic analysis and utilizes the combined laws of thermodynamics to account the loss of available energy. Exergy is always destroyed by irreversibilities in a system and expressed by

$$X = H - T_0 S \quad [17]$$

where H is the enthalpy, T_0 the reference (dead-state temperature) temperature, and S the entropy. For an incompressible fluid initially at temperature T_i with constant heat capacity and negligible pressure change, the exergy is a simple function of temperatures:

$$X = \dot{m} C_p \left[(T_i - T_o) - T_o \ln\left(\frac{T_i}{T_o}\right) \right] \quad [18]$$

where T_o is the dead-state (environment) temperature and C_p is the specific heat.

The exergy balance and the lost work are given by

$$\sum_{\text{into system}} \left[\dot{m}X + \dot{Q}\left(1 - \frac{T_o}{T_s}\right) + \dot{W}_s \right] - \sum_{\text{out of system}} \left[\dot{m}X + \dot{Q}\left(1 - \frac{T_o}{T_s}\right) + \dot{W}_s \right] = \dot{W}_{\text{lost}} \quad [19]$$

where W is the work and the superimposed dot shows the change of variable in time. The terms in square brackets show the exergy accompanying mass, heat, and work, respectively. W_{lost} represents the destruction of exergy. If a system undergoes a spontaneous change to the dead state without a device to perform work, then exergy is completely destroyed. Therefore, exergy is a function of both the physical properties of a resource and its environment.

Figure 13 shows the charging and discharging operations with appropriate valves, and temperature profiles for countercurrent latent heat storage with subcooling and sensible heating. An optimum latent heat storage system performs exergy storage and recovery operations by destroying as little as possible the supplied exergy.

- Charging

  A charging fluid heats PCM, which may initially be at a subcooled temperature T_{sc} and may eventually reach to a temperature T_{sh} after sensible heating. Therefore, the latent heat storage system undergoes a temperature difference of $T_{sh} - T_{sc}$, as shown in **Figure 13**. The heat available for storage would be

$$Q_c = UA(\Delta T_{lm})_c = \dot{m}_c C_{pc}(T_{ci} - T_{co}) \quad [20]$$

where U is the overall heat transfer coefficient, A the heat transfer area, $\dot{m}_c$ the charging fluid flow rate, and ΔT_{lm} the logarithmic mean temperature difference expressed by

$$(\Delta T_{lm})_c = \frac{(T_{ci} - T_{cs}) - (T_{co} - T_{ch})}{\ln\left(\frac{T_{ci} - T_{cs}}{T_{co} - T_{ch}}\right)} = \frac{T_{ci} - T_{co}}{\text{NTU}_c} \quad [21]$$

where $\text{NTU}_c = UA/\dot{m}_c C_{pc} = T_{ci} - T_{co}/\Delta T_{lm}$ is the number of transfer units. Equation [21] relates the value of NTU with temperature. Heat lost by the charging fluid will be gained by the PCM

$$Q_c = Q_s = m_s \left[C_{ps}(T_l - T_{si}) + \Delta H_m + C_{pl}(T_{sh} - T_h) \right] \quad [22]$$

where ΔH_m is the heat of melting, T_l and T_h are the lowest and highest melting points of phase change, and C_{ps} and C_{pl} denote the specific heats of solid and liquid states of PCM, respectively.

The net exergy X change of the charging fluid would be

$$\Delta X_c = (X_{co} - X_{ci}) = \dot{m}_c C_{pc} \left[(T_{ci} - T_{co}) - T_o \ln\left(\frac{T_{ci}}{T_{co}}\right) \right] \quad [23]$$

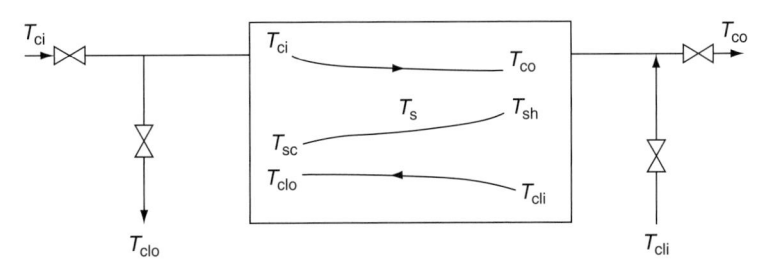

Figure 13 Typical temperature profiles of a latent heat storage system for charging and discharging operations [12].

The exergy stored by the PCM is

$$X_s = Q_s \left(1 - \frac{T_o}{T_s}\right) \quad [24]$$

where T_s is an average temperature of storage, which may be approximated by $.(T_{sc} - T_{sh})/2$.

The first and second law efficiencies are

$$\eta_I = \frac{\text{actual heat stored}}{\text{maximum energy gain}} = \frac{T_{ci} - T_{co}}{T_{ci} - T_s} \quad [25]$$

$$\eta_{II} = \frac{\text{exergy of PCM}}{\text{exergy of charge fluid}} = \frac{(T_{ci} - T_{co})\left(1 - \frac{T_o}{T_{sh}}\right)}{\left[(T_{ci} - T_{co}) - T_o \ln\left(\frac{T_{ci}}{T_{co}}\right)\right]} \quad [26]$$

- Discharging

It is assumed that the PCM is totally melted and heated to a temperature T_{sh} when discharging fluid starts recovering heat, which is estimated by

$$Q_d = UA(\Delta T_{lm})_d = \dot{m}_d C_{pd}(T_{di} - T_{do}) \quad [27]$$

The heat gained by the discharging fluid will be lost by the PCM and the net exergy change of the charging fluid would be

$$\Delta X_d = (X_{di} - X_{do}) = m_d C_{pd}\left[(T_{di} - T_{do}) - T_o \ln\left(\frac{T_{di}}{T_{do}}\right)\right] \quad [28]$$

The first and second law efficiencies are

$$\eta_I = \frac{T_{do} - T_{di}}{T_{di} - T_{sl}} \quad [29]$$

$$\eta_{II} = \frac{\text{exergy given to discharge fluid}}{\text{exergy of PCM}} = \frac{\left[(T_{do} - T_{di}) - T_o \ln\left(\frac{T_{do}}{T_{di}}\right)\right]}{(T_{do} - T_{cdi})\left(1 - \frac{T_o}{T_{sl}}\right)} \quad [30]$$

Overall efficiencies for a latent heat storage system become

$$\eta_{Io} = \eta_{Ic}\eta_{Id} \quad [31]$$

$$\eta_{IIo} = \eta_{IIc}\eta_{IId} \quad [32]$$

All the temperatures are time dependent, and the charging and discharging cycles need to be monitored over the time of operation.

3.07.2.3 Thermochemical Heat

3.07.2.3.1 Definition
Any chemical reaction with high heat of reaction can be used for TES if the products of the reaction can be stored and if the heat stored during the reaction can be released when the reverse reaction takes place [1].

A comparison of the energy storage densities achieved with different methods of storage are shown in **Table 2**.

3.07.2.3.2 Chemical reactions
Higher energy storage density and reversibility are required on the materials for thermal energy conversion and storage [13]. Energy density of chemical changes is relatively higher than one of physical changes. A merit of chemical energy conversion is the possession of efficient energy storage performance. Especially, the performance is advantageous for TES. Chemical storage can store energy as reactants with small loss.

It is important to find the appropriate reversible chemical reaction for the temperature range of subjected energy source.

3.07.2.3.3 Sorption systems
TES can be realized by utilizing reversible chemical reactions [32]. Here the process of adsorption on solid materials or absorption on liquids is explained. Adsorption means binding of a gaseous or liquid phase of a component on the inner surface of a porous

Table 2 Comparison of storage densities of different TES methods

Type of storage technology	Material	Energy stored (MJ m^{-3})	Energy stored (kJ kg^{-1})	Comments
Sensible heat	Granite	50	17	$\Delta T = 20\,°C$
	Water	84	84	$\Delta T = 20\,°C$
Latent heat	Water	306	330	$T_{melting} = 0\,°C$
	Paraffins	180	200	$T_{melting} = 5–130\,°C$
	Salt hydrates	300	200	$T_{melting} = 5–130\,°C$
	Salt	600–1 500	300–700	$T_{melting} = 300–800\,°C$
Chemical reactions	H$_2$ gas (oxidation)	11	120 000	300 K, 1 bar
	H$_2$ gas (oxidation)	2 160	120 000	300 K, 200 bar
	H$_2$ liquid (oxidation)	8 400	120 000	20 K, 1 bar
	Fossil gas	32		300 K, 1 bar
	Gasoline	33 000	43 000	
Electrical storage	Zn/Mn oxide battery		180	
	Pb battery		70–180	

Adapted from Mehling H and Cabeza LF (2008) *Heat and Cold Storage with PCM: An Up to Date Introduction into Basics and Applications*. Berlin, Heidelberg: Springer.

material. During the desorption step, heat is put into the sample. The adsorbed component is removed from the inner surface. As soon as the reverse reaction (adsorption) is started, the heat will be released. The adsorption step represents the discharging process.

There are two types of sorption systems, closed and open storage systems. In a 'closed sorption system', the heat is transferred to and from the adsorbent by a heat exchanger, usually called condenser/evaporator. The heat has to be transported to the absorber at the same time when it is extracted from the condenser to keep the HTF, usually water, flowing from the adsorber to the condenser. This flow of HTF is very important, because if the sorption process reaches equilibrium, the process stops.

The energy density expected is lower than an open sorption system because the adsorptive fluid is part of the storage system and also has to be stored. In the case of using zeolite or silica gel as adsorbent, this can be up to 30–40% of the weight of the storage material.

The advantages of closed systems are that they can reach higher output temperatures for heating operations compared to open systems. Furthermore, they can supply lower temperatures for cooling, and it is possible to produce ice in the evaporator.

In an 'open sorption storage system', air transports water vapor and heat in and out of the packed bed of solid or liquid adsorbents. In the desorption mode, hot air enters the packed bed, desorbs the water from the adsorbent, and leaves the bed cooler and saturated. In the adsorption mode, the humidified cool air enters the desorbed packed bed. The adsorbent adsorbs the water vapor and releases the heat of sorption. The air that exits is warm and dry.

If a solid adsorbent is used, very hot air can be obtained. If a liquid adsorbent is used, the process becomes absorption, and the humidification of the air is the main purpose.

TES is achieved by separating the desorption step (charging mode) from the adsorption step (discharging mode). After desorption, the adsorbent can theoretically stay in this desorbed state without any thermal losses until the adsorption or absorption process is activated.

The most common classes of solid absorbents are zeolites and silica gels. Zeolites have a crystalline structure and a certain pore size, while silica gels have a pore size distribution. The chemical composition of two typically used zeolites is shown in **Table 3**, and their properties are presented in **Table 4**. Silica gel is composed of 99% SiO$_2$, while the rest are OH groups together with changing amounts of integrated water. The properties of silica gel are presented in **Table 5**. Concerning the application of these adsorbents as TES, the amount of water that can be adsorbed is the most important property.

For the characterization of solid sorbents in thermal applications like heating, cooling, and TES, the criteria to be used are

- the possible temperature lift (and drop in humidity ratio),
- the breakthrough curves (responsible for the dynamics of the process),
- the thermal coefficient of performance, and
- the energy density referring to the volume of the adsorbent.

Table 3 Chemical composition of zeolite [32]

Zeolite	Composition	Pore diameter (Å)	SiO$_2$–Al$_2$O$_3$
Type A	Na$_{12}$[(AlO$_2$)$_{12}$(SiO$_2$)$_{12}$]·27H$_2$O	4.1	2.0–2.5
Type X	Na$_{86}$[(AlO$_2$)$_{86}$(SiO$_2$)$_{106}$]·264H$_2$O	7.4	2.0–3.0

Table 4 Properties of zeolites [32]

Property	Type A	Type X
Inner surface ($m^2\ g^{-1}$)	800–1000	800–1000
Specific heat ($kJ\ kg^{-1}\ K^{-1}$)	0.8–0.9	0.8–0.9
Heat conductivity ($W\ m^{-1}\ K^{-1}$)	0.58	0.58
Packed bed density ($kg\ m^{-3}$)	750	700

Table 5 Properties of silica gel [32]

Property	Wide	Narrow
Inner surface ($m^2\ g^{-1}$)	300–500	600–800
Pore diameter (Å)	25–50	10–15
Specific heat ($kJ\ kg^{-1}\ K^{-1}$)	0.92–1.0	0.92–1.0
Heat conductivity ($W\ m^{-1}\ K^{-1}$)	0.14–0.2	0.14–0.2
Packed bed density ($kg\ m^{-3}$)	450	700

For liquid absorbents, a similar theory could be explained.

The 'temperature lift' (ΔT) is defined as the temperature difference between the air outlet and the air inlet. The possible temperature lift is crucial for the design of sorption systems for heating applications. The temperature lift of each adsorbent can be very different under the same adsorption conditions. The temperature lift can be calculated from

$$\Delta T = \Delta x \frac{\Delta H_{ads}}{c_{p\ air} - (\Delta x/\Delta C) \times c_{sorb\ eff}} \quad [33]$$

where Δx is the humidity ratio difference

$$\Delta x = x_{in} - x_{out} \quad [34]$$

ΔH_{ads} is the integrated differential heat of adsorption ΔH_d between C_{ads} and C_{des}, and $C_{p\ air}$ is the heat capacity of air. ΔC is the difference in water concentration of the adsorbent

$$\Delta C = C_{ads} - C_{des} \quad [35]$$

$C_{sorb\ eff}$ is the effective heat capacity of the adsorbent

$$c_{sorb\ eff} = c_{sorb} + (C_{des} \times C_{H_2O}) \quad [36]$$

The time-dependent changes in the properties of the outlet air of an adsorber is called 'breakthrough curve'. In most applications, it is referring only to the changes in the water content, but for thermal applications, the temperature change is also important. The shape of the breakthrough curve depends on the behavior of the so-called mass transfer zone (MTZ). Within the MTZ, the properties of the incoming air change to the properties of the outlet air.

The dimension of the MTZ within a packed bed can be constant, expanding, or shrinking. The zeolite breakthrough curve is caused by a constant or slightly shrinking MTZ, whereas the silica gel curve is caused by an expanding MTZ. With the expanding MTZ cooler, more humid air is reached at the end of the bed, leading to a decrease in the outlet temperature and increase in the water content as shown in **Figure 14**.

The thermal 'coefficient of performance' (COP) in sorption systems is defined as

$$COP_{th} = \frac{Q_{cond} - Q_{ads}}{Q_{des}} \quad [37]$$

The energies are defined per mass of adsorbent, and they can be calculated from the adsorption equilibrium:

$$Q_{des} = Q_{cond} + Q_{bind} + Q_{sens} \quad [38]$$

where Q_{sens} is the amount of sensible heat brought into the system to heat up the packed bed of adsorbent pellets:

$$Q_{sens} = \Delta T_{sorb} \times c_{sorb\ eff} \quad [39]$$

Q_{cond} is the condensation energy:

$$Q_{cond} = (C_{ads} - C_{des}) \times L(T) \quad [40]$$

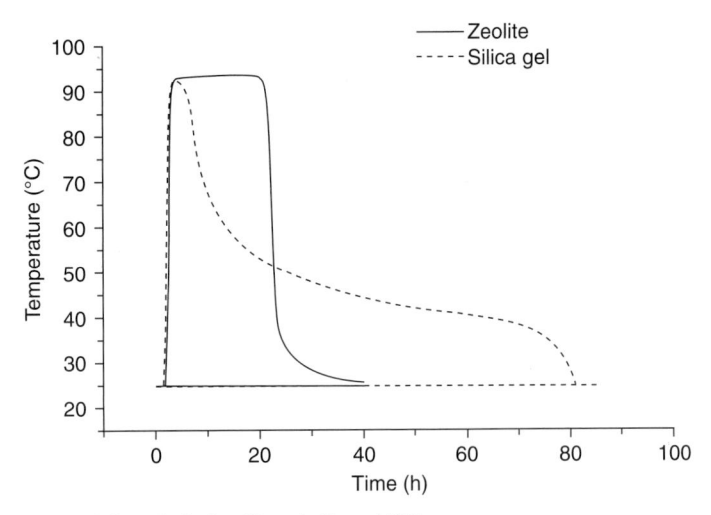

Figure 14 Thermal breakthrough curves (adsorption) of zeolite and silica gel [32].

Q_{bind} is the binding energy, caused by the adsorption forces:

$$Q_{bind} = \int_{C_{des}}^{C_{ads}} (\Delta F + T \times \Delta S)\, dC \qquad [41]$$

where $L(T)$ is the heat of evaporation for water vapour and $(\Delta F + T\Delta S)$ is the heat of binding taken from Dubinis theory of volume filling the water adsorption, which can be determined from the adsorption equilibrium.

Q_{ads} depends on the actual application.
For a heat pump, $Q_{ads} = Q_{des}$.
For long-term TES, Q_{sens} cannot be used due to thermal losses.
For a desiccant cooling system, only Q_{cond} can be used during adsorption.
The 'energy density' is defined as

$$\rho_Q = \frac{(Q_{cond} + Q_{bind})m_{sorb}}{V_{sorb}} = (Q_{cond} + Q_{bind})\rho_{sorb} \qquad [42]$$

where m_{sorb} is the mass of the adsorbent, V_{sorb} the volume of the adsorbent, and ρ_{sorb} the density of the adsorbent.

3.07.2.4 Comparison of Thermal Storage System Types

Comparison of different thermal storage techniques for solar space heating and hot water production applications is summarized in **Table 6** [14].

The main problem with water storage systems is the corrosion in long operation periods. Another disadvantage of water storage systems is that the volume of the storage may be very large for large heat storage requirements and therefore the whole system becomes very heavy. With large storage units, there is also the stratification problem. Scale formation is another problem with such systems.

With packed-bed storage systems, there is no corrosion or scale-forming problem, but the volume of the systems might be large with an increase in cost. On the other hand, by the use of phase change storage systems, large volumes required by the other type are eliminated. Because of the chemical interaction between the storage material and the container, storage material loses its energy storage characteristics after a period of time.

On weight basis, and even on volume basis, chemical storage has a greater capacity than other systems. High-pressure $CO-H_2$ mixtures, for example, have a storage capacity of an order of magnitude higher than liquid water (though less than salt hydrates and much less than metal hydrides). Although adequate thermodynamic data exist for most of the chemical reactions of interest, the chemical kinetics data are very scarce even for simple systems like methane–water.

3.07.3 Economics of TES

3.07.3.1 TES and Energy Savings

TES can be used to reduce energy consumption or to transfer an energy load from one period/place to another [15]. The reduced energy consumption can be achieved by storing excess thermal energy that would normally be released as water, such as heat produced by equipment and appliances, by lighting, and even by occupants.

Table 6 Comparison of different storage techniques for solar space heating and hot water production applications

	Sensible heat storage		Latent heat thermal storage material (PCM)
	Water	Rock	
Comparison between different heat storage media			
Operating temperature range	Limited (0–100 °C)	Large	Large, depending on the choice of the material
Specific heat	High	Low	Medium
Thermal conductivity	Low, convection effects improve the heat transfer rate	Low	Very low, insulating properties
Thermal storage capacity per unit mass and volume for small temperature differences	Low	Low	High
Stability to thermal cycling	Good	Good	Insufficient data
Availability	Overall	Almost overall	Dependent on the choice of material
Cost	Inexpensive	Inexpensive	Expensive
Comparison of heat transfer properties and life of different types of thermal storages			
Required heat exchanger geometry	Simple	Simple	Complex
Temperature gradients during charging and discharging	Large	Large	Small
Thermal stratification effect	Existent works positively	Existent works positively	Generally nonexistent with proper choice of material
Simultaneous charging and discharging	Possible	Not possible	Possible with appropriate selection of heat exchanger
Integration with solar heating/cooling systems	Direct integration with water systems	Direct integration with air systems	Indirect integration
Costs for pumps, fans, etc.	Low	High	Low
Corrosion with conventional materials of construction	Corrosion eliminated through corrosion inhibitors	Noncorrosive	Dependent on the choice of material
Life	Long	Long	Short

Adapted from Kakac S, Paykoc E, and Yener Y (1989) Storage of solar thermal energy. In: Kilkis B and Kakac S (eds.) *NATO ASI Series, Series E: Applied Sciences, Vol. 167: Energy Storage Systems*, pp. 129–161. Dordrecht: Kluwer Academic Publishers.

The main objective of most TES systems, which is to alter energy use patterns so that financial saving occurs, can be achieved in several ways as follows [15]:

- The consumption of purchased energy can be reduced by storing waste or surplus thermal energy available at certain times for use at other times. For example, solar energy can be stored during the day for heating at night.
- The demand of purchased electrical energy can be reduced by storing electrically produced thermal energy during off-peak periods to meet the thermal loads that occur during high-demand periods.
- The use of TES can defer the need to purchase additional equipment for heating, cooling, or air-conditioning applications and reduce equipment sizing in new facilities. The relevant equipment is operated when thermal loads are low to charge the TES and energy is withdrawn from storage to help meet the thermal loads that exceed equipment capacity.

3.07.3.2 Thermoeconomics of TES

The motivation and challenges for storing energy are focused mainly on three important facts [16]:

1. Energy security/reliability using new energy technology
2. Environmentally friendly techniques for climate protection, hence, contribution to environmental conservation – commitment for reduction of CO_2 – obligations of Convention on Climate Change, Kyoto Protocol
3. Economic feasibility using market principles.

Developing and deploying more efficient and environmentally friendly energy technology is critical to achieving the objectives of Energy security, Environmental protection, Economic growth and social development known as three Es. The mission is to implement an environmentally friendly energy system. If we are to achieve sustainable development, we will need to display greater responsibility for energy, economy, and environment.

Thermodynamic analysis (TA) identifies the sources of exergy losses due to irreversibilities in each process in a system. This will not guarantee that economical process modifications would be generated [12]. For that, relations between the energy efficiency and capital cost must be evaluated. Sometimes, improved energy efficiency will require more investment. TA is of considerable value where an efficient energy conversion is important. Optimization seeks the best solution under specific constraints, which usually determines the complexity of the problem. In every nonequilibrium system, an entropy effect leading to energy dissipation either within or through the boundary of the system exists.

Currently, TA has realized three main stages [12]:

1. First, the second-law analysis is mainly used in thermal engineering by combining the principles of thermodynamics with heat transfer and fluid mechanics to reduce entropy production.
2. Second, the exergy analysis combined the principles of thermodynamic with heat and mass transfer, fluid mechanics, and chemical kinetics that are widely used in the design and optimization of physical, chemical, and biological systems.
3. Finally, exergy analysis is combined with economic analysis, which is called thermoeconomics or exergoeconomics.

Thermoeconomics combines exergy analysis with economic analysis and calculates the efficiencies based on exergy; it assigns costs to exergy-related variables by using the 'exergy cost theory' and 'exergy cost balances'. Thermoeconomics can unify all balances – mass, energy, exergy, and cost by a single formalism. 'Extended exergy accounting' considers nonenergetic costs, such as financial, labor, and environmental remediation costs as functions of the technical and thermodynamic parameters of systems. There are two main groups of thermoeconomic methods: (1) cost accounting methods, such as exergy cost theory for a rational price assessment, and (2) optimization by minimizing the overall cost, under a proper set of financial, environmental, and technical constraints to identify the optimum design and operating conditions.

Structural theory facilitates the evaluation of exergy cost and incorporation of thermoeconomics functional analysis. It is a common formulation for the various thermoeconomic methods providing the costing equations from a set of modeling equations for the components of a system. The structural theory needs a productive structure displaying how the resource consumptions are distributed among the components of a system. The flows entering a component in the productive structure are considered as fuels F and flows leaving a component are products P. The components are subsystems with control volumes as well as mixers and splitters. Therefore, the productive structure is a graphical representation of the fuel and product distribution. All the flows are extensive properties, such as exergy. For any component j, or a subsystem, the unit exergy consumption x_c is expressed on a fuel–product basis by

$$x_{cj} = \frac{F_j}{P_j} = \frac{F_j}{X_j} \quad [43]$$

For linear modeling, the average costs of fuels and products are defined by

$$C_{jf}^* = \frac{\partial F_o}{\partial F_j} \quad C_{jP}^* = \frac{\partial F_o}{\partial P_j} \quad [44]$$

where F_o is the fuel to the overall system expressed as a function of the flow F_j or product P_j, respectively, and the other related parameters. Total annual production cost C_T in US$ is

$$C_T = \sum_{j=1}^{N} c_j X_j = \sum_{j=1}^{N} C_{ij} \quad [45]$$

where c_j is the specific cost of product in US$ kW^{-1}, C_{fj} is the cost of fuel, and X_j is the rate of exergy as product of component j in kilowatt and is expressed in terms of NTU using eqn [21].

$$X_j = \dot{m}_j C_p \left[NTU_j \Delta T_{lmj} - T_o \ln\left(\frac{T_{jl}}{T_o}\right) \right] \quad [46]$$

Some optimization techniques minimize the cost of product of a system or a component. The optimum total production cost rate with respect to NTU is obtained from

$$\frac{dC_T}{dNTU} = 0 \quad [47]$$

Thermoeconomics of latent heat storage systems involves the use of principles of thermodynamics, fluid mechanics, and heat transfer. Therefore, thermoeconomics may be applied to both the use of those principles and materials, construction, mechanical design, and a part of conventional economic analysis. The distinguished side of it comes from the ability to account the quality of energy and environmental impact of energy usage in economic considerations.

As an example, the seasonal solar energy storage with paraffin as PCM is studied. **Figure 15** shows the following three basic components: (1) solar air heaters, (2) latent heat storage, and (3) greenhouse.

1. System of packed bed solar air heaters: The system has a total solar heat collector area of 27 m^2 consisting of 18 packed bed solar air heaters. Each unit has 1.5 m^2 absorber area with a length of 1.9 m and width of 0.9 m. The Raschig ring type (traditionally used in distillation columns) of packing made of polyvinyl chloride with the characteristic diameter of 0.05 m is used within the airflow passage. The packing enhances the wall-to-fluid heat transfer by increasing the radial and axial mixing, as well as reducing the wall resistance. The volumetric flow rate of airflow is 600 m^3 h^{-1}.

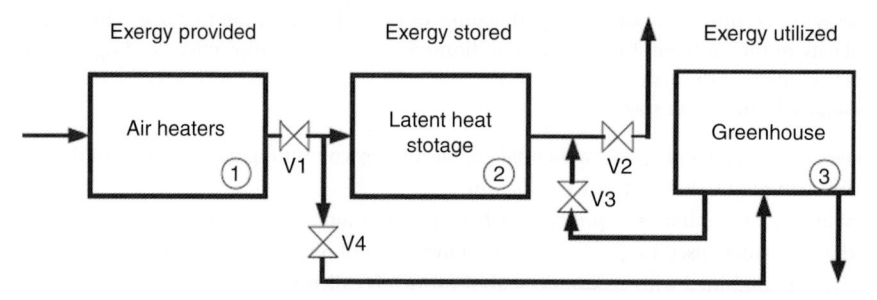

Figure 15 Productive structure with three components of the latent heat storage system representing exergy transformation [12].

2. Latent heat storage unit: A horizontal steel tank, 1.7 m long and 5.2 m wide, contains 6000 kg of technical grade of paraffin as PCM. Paraffin primarily consists of straight-chain hydrocarbons and very little amount of branching. The n-alkane content exceeds 75%. Commercial waxes may have a range of about 8–15 carbon number. Volume contraction is <12% during freezing. The tank is insulated with 0.05 m of glass wool. Inside the tank, there are two spiral coils made of perforated polyethylene pipes with a total length of 97 m and diameter of 0.1 m embedded into the PCM. The coils carry the warm airflow pumped from solar air heaters. Differential scanning calorimeter measurements show that the paraffin has a melting temperature range of 48–60 °C and ~190 kJ kg^{-1} of latent heat of melting. Paraffin wax freeze without subcooling and melt without segregation of components.
3. Greenhouse: The greenhouse with an area of 180 m^2 is covered by 0.35 mm thick polyethylene, and is aligned north to south. The floor area is 12 × 15 m and the height is 3 m. The latent heat storage tank carries 33.3 kg of paraffin wax per square meter of the greenhouse ground surface area. Heat storage unit connects the solar air heater system to the greenhouse with appropriate fans, valves, and piping. Whenever the temperature in the greenhouse drops below a set point, a fan circulates the air from greenhouse through the latent heat storage unit until the temperature reaches the required level.

Costs are the amount of resources consumed to produce a flow or a product. When exergy is added into a flow, the cost of flow leaving a component is equal to the cost of flow entering plus the fuel value of added exergy. When, on the other hand, exergy is removed, the fuel value of exergy is subtracted. The products and their average costs in the productive structure shown in **Figure 15** are summarized below:

- Component 1: Solar air heater system
  Added exergy provided by the solar air heater system can be expressed in terms of NTU and ΔT_{lm}:

$$\Delta X_1 = (X_{1p} - X_{1i}) = \dot{m}_1 C_p \left[NTU_1 \Delta T_{lm1} - T_o \ln\left(\frac{T_{1o}}{T_{1i}}\right) \right] \quad [48]$$

The airflow leaving the solar air heaters adds exergy, therefore its cost is

$$C_{1p} = C_{1i} + C_{1f} \quad [49]$$

where C_{1i} is the cost of the flow entering component 1 and C_{1f} is the fuel value of added exergy. Specific costs of warm air c_a and exergy c_{x1} are

$$c_a = \frac{C_{1p}}{X_{1p}} = \frac{C_{1pf}}{X_{1p}} \quad c_{x1} = \frac{C_{1f}}{\Delta X_1} \quad [50]$$

where C_{1pf} is the fuel value of the product leaving the solar air heating system.
- Component 2: Latent heat storage system
  Removed exergy by the latent heat storage system during charging is

$$\Delta X_c = (X_{cp} - X_{ci}) = \dot{m}_2 C_p \left[NTU_c \Delta T_{lmc} - T_o \ln\left(\frac{T_{co}}{T_{ci}}\right) \right] \quad [51]$$

Cost of the product after charging is

$$C_{cp} = C_{ci} + C_{cf} \quad [52]$$

Specific costs of the product leaving the latent heat storage unit c_c and the removed exergy c_{xc} are

$$c_c = \frac{C_{cp}}{X_{cp}} = \frac{C_{cpf}}{X_{cp}} \quad c_{xc} = \frac{C_{cf}}{\Delta X_c} \quad [53]$$

Discharging flow adds exergy from the latent heat storage system and is given by

$$\Delta X_d = (X_{dp} - X_{di}) = \dot{m}_3 C_p \left[NTU_d \Delta T_{lmd} - T_o \ln\left(\frac{T_{do}}{T_{di}}\right) \right] \quad [54]$$

Cost of discharging flow is

$$C_{dp} = C_{di} + C_{df} \quad [55]$$

Specific costs of discharging flow leaving the latent heat storage unit c_d and the added exergy c_{xd} are

$$c_d = \frac{C_{dp}}{X_{dp}} = \frac{C_{dpf}}{X_{dp}} \quad c_{xd} = \frac{C_{df}}{\Delta X_d} \quad [56]$$

- Component 3: Greenhouse
  Exergy change within the greenhouse is

$$\Delta X_3 = (X_{3p} - X_{3i}) = \dot{m}_3 C_p \left[NTU_3 \Delta T_{lm3} - T_o \ln\left(\frac{T_{3o}}{T_{3i}}\right) \right] \quad [57]$$

Exergy from the discharge flow is removed in the greenhouse, and the cost of flow leaving the greenhouse becomes

$$C_{3p} = C_{3i} - C_{3f} \quad [58]$$

Specific costs of flow leaving the greenhouse c_g and the exergy removed c_{xg} are

$$c_g = \frac{C_{3p}}{X_{3p}} = \frac{C_{3pf}}{X_{3p}} \quad c_{xg} = \frac{C_{3f}}{\Delta X_3} \quad [59]$$

The total cost of products of the three components would be

$$C_{pT} = C_{1p} + C_{cp} + C_{dp} + C_{3p} = c_a X_{1p} + c_c X_{cp} + c_d X_{dp} + c_g X_{3p} \quad [60]$$

Cost of a product for component j is based on a fuel–product basis $C_{jp} = C_{jpf}$, so that the total cost of products is

$$C_{pT} = C_{1p} + C_{cp} + C_{dp} + C_{3p} = C_{1pf} + C_{cpf} + C_{dpf} + C_{3pf} \quad [61]$$

Equation [61] may be used in eqn [47] to find an optimum value of NTU to minimize the total cost of production. Cost optimization basically depends on the tradeoffs between the cost of energy (fuel) and capital investment as seen in **Figure 16**. Working with compatible design and operating conditions, and new technologies, it is possible to recover more and more exergy in energy conversion systems. Implementing pollution charges and incentives for environmentally friendly technologies may reduce the cost of exergy loss.

Thermoeconomics of the latent heat storage system involves fixed capital investment, operational and maintenance cost, and exergy costs. Total fixed capital investment consists of the following:

- Direct expenses, such as equipment cost, materials, and labor
- Indirect project expenses, such as freight, insurance, taxes, construction, and overhead
- Contingency and contractor fee
- Auxiliary facilities, such as site development and auxiliary buildings.

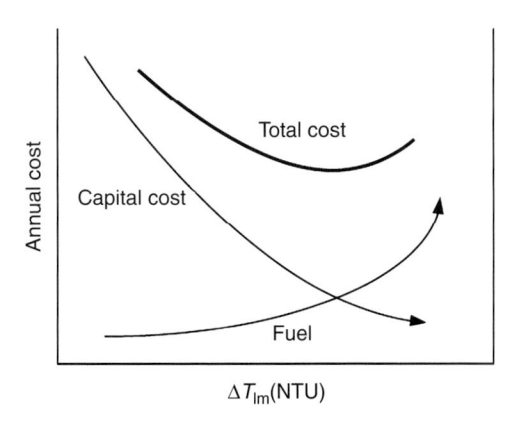

Figure 16 Annual cost optimization in thermoeconomics [12].

Table 7 Typical data used for thermoeconomic analysis of seasonal heat storage system [12]

Fixed capital investment for the components	$FCI_1 + FCI_2 + FCI_3 = \$200\,000 + \$200\,000 + \$100\,000 = \$500\,000$
Cost of land	$L = \$50\,000$
Working capital	$WC = 0.2(\$500\,000) = \$100\,000$
Yearly revenues or savings	$R = \$160\,000$
Total cost of production (COP)	$COP = C_{PT} = C_{1p} + C_{cp} + C_{dp} + C_{3p} = C_{1pf} + C_{cpf} + C_{dpf} + C_{3pf} = \$55\,000$
	$C_{1pf} = \$20\,000$, $C_{pf} = \$15\,000$
	$C_{dpf} = \$10\,000$, $C_{3pf} = \$10\,000$
Taxation rate	$t = 35\%$
Salvage value of the whole seasonal storage	$S = \$50\,000$
Useful life of the system	$n = 15$ years
Depreciation	10 years
Discount rate	$i = 8\%$

The analysis of a typical seasonal solar heat storage system considers the three basic components of a seasonal latent heat storage system (**Figure 15**) constructed after 1 year. **Table 7** shows the data used in thermoeconomic analysis.

Economic analysis can determine the discounted profitability criteria in terms of payback period (PBP), net present value (NPV), and rate of return (ROR) from discounted cash flow diagram, in which each of the annual cash flow is discounted to time zero for the latent heat storage system. PBP is the time required, after the construction, to recover the fixed capital investment. NPV shows the cumulative discounted cash value at the end of useful life. Positive values of NPV and shorter PBP are preferred. ROR is the interest rate at which all the cash flows must be discounted to obtain zero NPV. If ROR is greater than the internal discount rate, then the latent heat storage system is considered feasible.

Figure 17 shows the discounted cash flow diagram obtained from **Table 8** using the data in **Table 7**. An NPV of US$102 462.21 is obtained at the end of 15 years of useful life operation, which shows a profitable investment. Approximate discounted PBP is about 8 years. Discounted ROR is around 10.485%, which is greater than the internal interest rate of 8%. By changing the values of exergy costs in eqn [60], the cash flow diagram can be modified easily. Similar cash flow diagrams can be produced for individual components.

3.07.4 Case Studies

In this chapter, different case studies using TES in solar systems will be presented.

3.07.4.1 Combisystems

This is an example of a sensible storage system (liquid media).

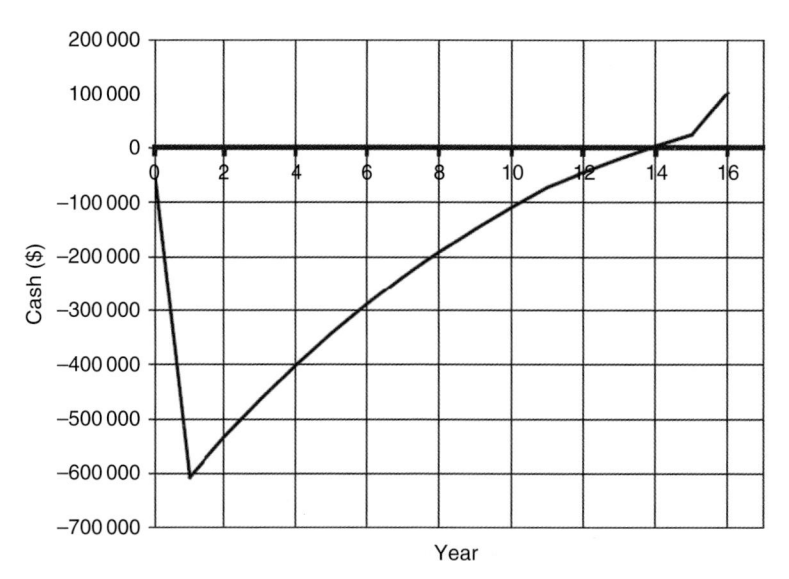

Figure 17 Discounted cash flow diagram for the productive structure of latent heat storage system with three components [12].

Table 8 Discounted cash flow estimations for a seasonal latent heat storage system [12]

n	FCI	D^a	A^b	R	COP	B^c	DCF	CCF
0	−50 000	0	500 000	0		−500 000	−50 000	−50 000
1	−500 000	0	500 000	0		−600 000	−555 555.6	−605 555.56
2	0	50 000	450 000	160 000	55 000	85 750	73 516.8	−532 038.75
3	0	50 000	400 000	160 000	55 000	85 750	6 807 111	−463 967.64
4	0	50 000	350 000	160 000	55 000	85 750	63 028.81	−400 938.83
5	0	50 000	300 000	160 000	55 000	85 750	58 360.01	−342 578.82
6	0	50 000	250 000	160 000	55 000	85 750	54 037.05	−288 541.77
7	0	50 000	200 000	160 000	55 000	85 750	50 034.3	−238 507.47
8	0	50 000	150 000	160 000	55 000	85 750	46 328.06	−192 179.41
9	0	50 000	100 000	160 000	55 000	85 750	42 896.35	−149 283.07
10	0	50 000	50 000	160 000	55 000	85 750	39 718.84	−10 956 422
11	0	50 000	50 000	160 000	55 000	85 750	36 776.71	−72 787.51
12	0	0	50 000	160 000	55 000	68 250	27 103.01	−45 684.50
13	0	0	50 000	160 000	55 000	68 250	25 095.38	−20 589.12
14	0	0	50 000	160 000	55 000	68 250	23 236.47	2 647.34
15	0	0	50 000	160 000	55 000	68 250	21 515.25	24 162.59
16	200 000	0	50 000	160 000	55 000	268 250	78 299.62	102 462.21

^{a}Depreciation: straight line method: $D = \frac{FCI - S}{n}$.
^{b}Book value: $A = FCI - \Sigma(D_k)$.
^{c}After tax cash flow: net profit + depreciation: $B = (R - COP - D_k)(1 - t) + D_k$.

One of the key elements of a solar heating system is the hot water store. The store has to fulfill several tasks as follows [17]:

- Deliver sufficient energy to the heat sink (with appropriate mass flow and temperature).
- Decoupling of mass flows of heat sources and heat sinks.
- Store heat from unsteady heat sources (solar) from times when excess heat is available to times when too little or no heat is available (either short-term storage from day to night or over one to a few days, or seasonal storage).
- Extend the running times for auxiliary heating devices in order to increase their efficiency and lower its startup–shutdown emissions.
- Allow a reduction in heating capacity of auxiliary heating devices.
- Store the heat at the appropriate temperature levels without mixing (stratification) in order to avoid exergy losses.

Solar combisystems (solar domestic hot water and heating systems) are the most complex short-term water storage tanks due to the fact that there are two different loads to supply using two separate heat sources, solar collectors and an auxiliary heat supplier. In these systems, the thermal store is normally the central part of the system, and heat is usually stored from both the solar collectors and the auxiliary heater. The two loads are often supplied from the store. In order to accomplish this, the store generally requires heat exchangers for the solar collector loop and for preparation of hot water, although immersed tanks or separate tanks can also be used for the latter. Due to the many options available, many different solutions have been developed and even marketed.

The design of the stores in solar combisystems greatly affects the overall system performance, making it necessary to have a good design [17]. This is also true for stores in solar hot water systems. Thus, specific testing methods have been developed to judge the properties of water stores in solar heating systems.

Figure 18 shows the principle of a water store with two energy inputs (solar and auxiliary) with water as the storage medium. In the following, some layout aspects of the tube connections to the different heat sources and heat sinks are described in order to show the complexity of such a system.

The hotter the water, the lower the density of the water becomes. Hot water thus naturally and stably finds its way above the layers of cold water. This phenomenon makes it possible to have stratification, with zones of different temperatures in one physical store. The zones indicated in **Figure 18** can therefore be at different temperatures, and more specifically at the temperatures required of the loads for domestic hot water and space heating. To keep stratification means that no temperature losses due to mixing of different temperatures in the store occur. Stratification allows an optimal use of the store with limited heat losses and in addition can be used to ensure that the collector inlet temperature is as low as possible. However, it is not obvious or easy to maintain good stratification in the store. In fact, the terms stratified and stratifying are used for slightly different phenomenon and approaches. The following diagrams and descriptions show important differences in how the store can be charged. The same distinctions can be applied to discharging the store. To maintain stratification, all charging and discharging must be done in a way to improve or maintain the stratification. If only one heat source or sink causes significant mixing, it can destroy the benefit of the stratification created by other sources/sinks.

The two criteria that need to be met if stratification is to be relevant are

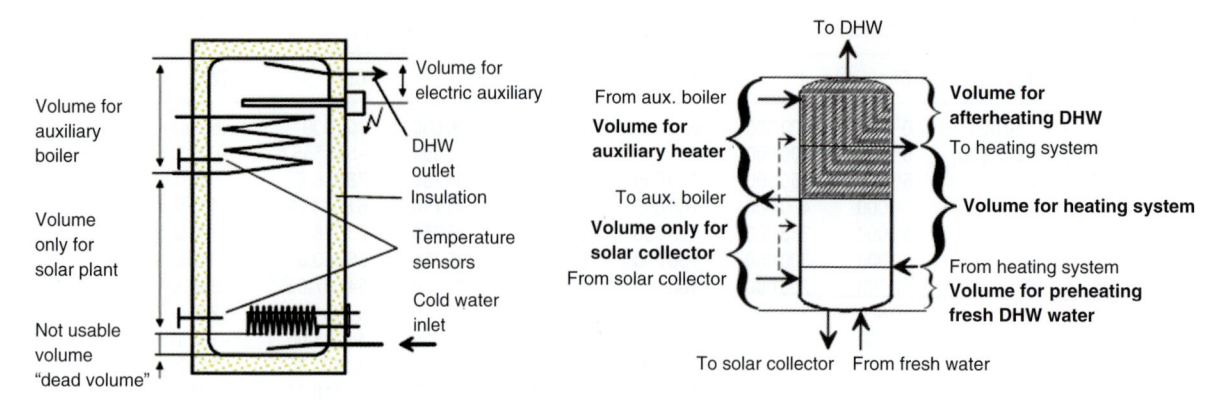

Figure 18 Zones for a hot water store of a domestic hot water (DHW) system (left) and a solar combisystem (right) [17].

1. the daily volume 'turnover' in the store should not be significantly more than the volume of the store itself, and
2. the heat source(s) should be able to generate a significant temperature difference, and in essence be capable of generating stratification in the store.

However, stratification is less important for certain systems and for certain store designs. For example, if the whole store is used for a small (<20 °C) temperature interval, then stratification leads to no significant benefits.

Figure 19 shows schematically what happens within the store when charging with an internal heat exchanger and with direct connections. The water heated by the internal heat exchanger starts to rise and mixes with the surrounding water. In this way, the heat is transferred to a large volume of water, which is heated slowly. The net result is usually a zone of uniform temperature above the heat exchanger. This zone extends as far as another zone with higher temperature, if one exists. Once the temperature of this higher zone is reached, both zones will be heated uniformly at the same temperature. Below the heat exchanger, the store is unaffected. The temperature sensor for the internal heat exchanger has to be placed in the region of the heat exchanger. If placed below, it would not measure the temperature increase during charging, and if placed above, it would give the signal for the heat source to start charging too late.

There is a small temperature gradient in the store at the same height as the heat exchanger. An electric element in the store acts in a similar way, but due to the relatively high power and small heat transfer area, the heated water does not mix fully with the surrounding store water, resulting in a small temperature gradient above the heater.

With a direct connection, there is some mixing in the store at the inlet. The degree of mixing is dependent on the inlet velocity and the difference in temperature of the incoming water and that of the store at the inlet. The zone above the inlet will be unaffected by the incoming water if the latter is colder (**Figure 20**, right). Beneath the inlet, the store water is pushed down and out through the outlet. However, if the incoming water is hotter than the upper zone, then heat will be transferred into that zone, causing mixing there, as well as into the volume below the inlet (**Figure 20**, left). A large volume is thus affected, and the temperature below the inlet will be significantly lower than that entering the store. The temperature of the inlet water from both the collector and the space heating circuits vary in time, and there will be times when the incoming water is hotter than the water in the store at the inlet, and other times it will be colder.

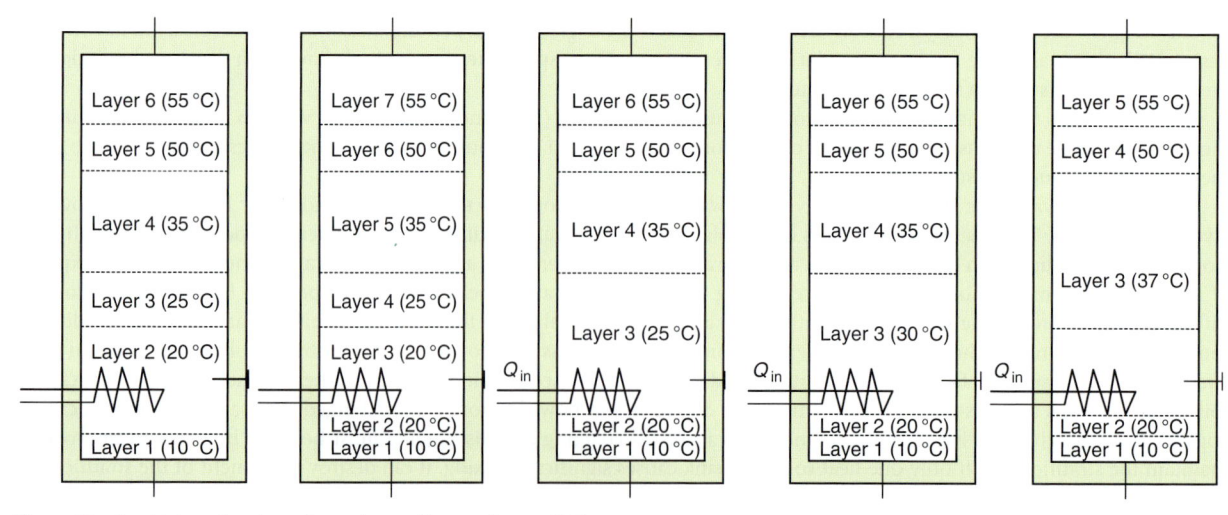

Figure 19 Combistore charging using an internal heat exchanger [17].

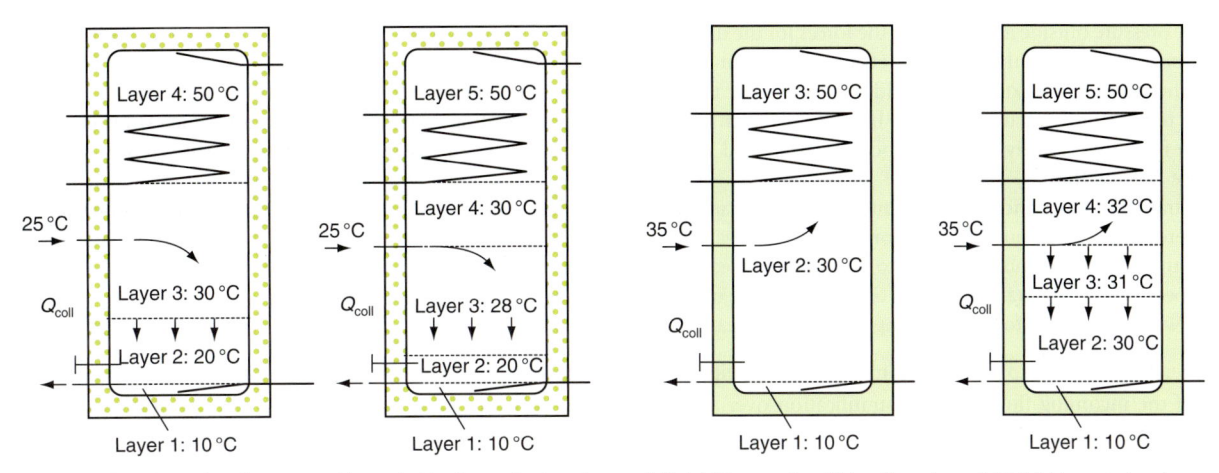

Figure 20 Charging using direct connections, that is, from a heat exchanger (left: inlet temperature higher than store, right: inlet temperature lower than store). The zone at the top of the tank with direct connections will be affected if the inlet temperature is higher than the temperature at the top of the tank [17].

Charging with direct connections thus tends to enhance stratification, with the volume of the zone increasing during charging. In contrast, charging with an internal heat exchanger tends to destroy stratification. In the store of a solar combisystem, there are several heat sources as well as sinks, and so the flows and stratification are complex.

Both the internal heat exchanger and the direct inlet are not perfect for creating stratification, so different methods have been applied to improve stratification. The first, and simplest, is to increase the number of internal heat exchangers, as illustrated in the store on the left side of **Figure 21**. This arrangement creates more zones between the heat exchangers and thus a greater degree of stratification. However, the whole of each zone gets heated or cooled by the heat exchangers, and the temperature in the zones does not change rapidly. In order to create a variable volume zone that can be heated or cooled quickly, several manufacturers have added a stratifying tube to the internal heat exchanger, as illustrated in the middle-left store shown in **Figure 21**. It uses an internal heat exchanger located in the stratifying tube. This tube then acts in a similar way to a direct inlet. However, the flow in the tube and thus the temperature at the outlet of the tube are dependent on the temperatures in the store as well as of the heat source, as the flow is the result of natural convection. This flow can vary considerably depending on the conditions within the store. Thus with this method, the water entering the store from the tube can be either hotter or colder than the surrounding water.

Another method is to use a stratifying unit with several outlets, as illustrated in the right-hand stores shown in **Figure 21**. This arrangement allows water to exit the unit at the height with approximately the same temperature in the store, thus maximizing stratification. This can be of benefit when the temperature inlet to the store varies with time, as it does with the solar input and the return from the heating circuit. Stratifier units are better than the other two, but require careful attention. The flow in the tube should be within a limited range, otherwise the water comes out at an incorrect height because the momentum in flow direction is higher than the force from density difference, making the flow bend towards an outlet. In addition, it is important to minimize drawing in of water through outlets into the passing flow in the tube, otherwise there is mixing on the way up, resulting in lower outlet temperatures. This is being performed by one-way flaps for the middle-right store and with a relatively large diameter of the stratifying tube for the store on the very right, which reduces the difference of the dynamic pressure in the tube compared to the

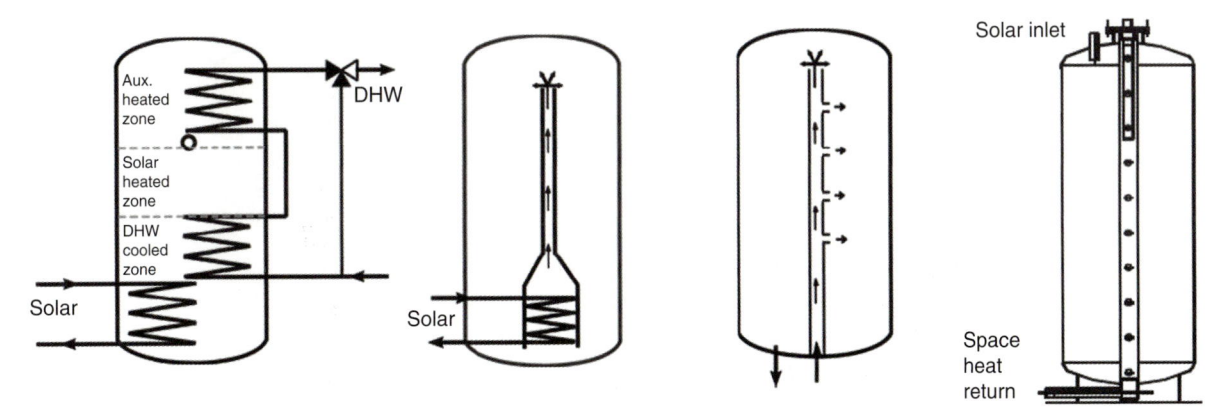

Figure 21 Four different methods of causing stratification several internal heat exchangers (left), stratifying tube with single outlet (middle-left), and stratifying units with multiple outlets (middle-right and right). The stratifying unit can be used with an internal heat exchanger or for other inlets that vary in temperature [17].

static pressure outside and therefore the forces for the drawing in of water. Of course, also the stratifying tube on the middle left side can be constructed with several outlets like the one in the middle right side.

The store on the extreme right side uses the same tube for the inlet of the secondary side of the collector (from the top inner tube to the stratifying tube) and the inlet of the return pipe from the space heating system from the bottom. Such stratifying units have been successfully used with both internal and external heat exchangers in the solar circuit and for the return from the space-heating loop.

Stratifying tubes and units with internal heat exchangers work with natural convection as mentioned above. It is important that the pressure drop through the tube or the unit, the heat exchanger effectiveness, and the expected heat transfer rate are matched so that the flow in the tube is similar to that in the collector circuit, thus ensuring low temperatures to the collector and high outlet temperatures. Both stratifying tubes and units can be used advantageously in low-flow systems.

Two general rules to avoid mixing or increased heat loss by pipes connected to the store are shown in **Figures 22** and **23**.

1. Vertical flow, inlet pipes to the tank should be equipped with a plate acting as a horizontal diffuser. Otherwise, the momentum of the incoming fluid destroys stratification over a significant height of the store. On the right side, a computational fluid dynamics simulation of an inlet pipe with and without a plate is shown. Another solution for this problem is shown in **Figure 22** on the right side. The inlet tube is directed horizontally into the store. So, no or only little vertical momentum occurs.
2. Horizontal pipes and vertical pipes to the top of the tank should be equipped with a thermosyphon break in order to prevent natural convection within the tube as shown in **Figure 23**. Such natural convection heats up the tubes without volume flow and therefore results in unnecessary heat losses.

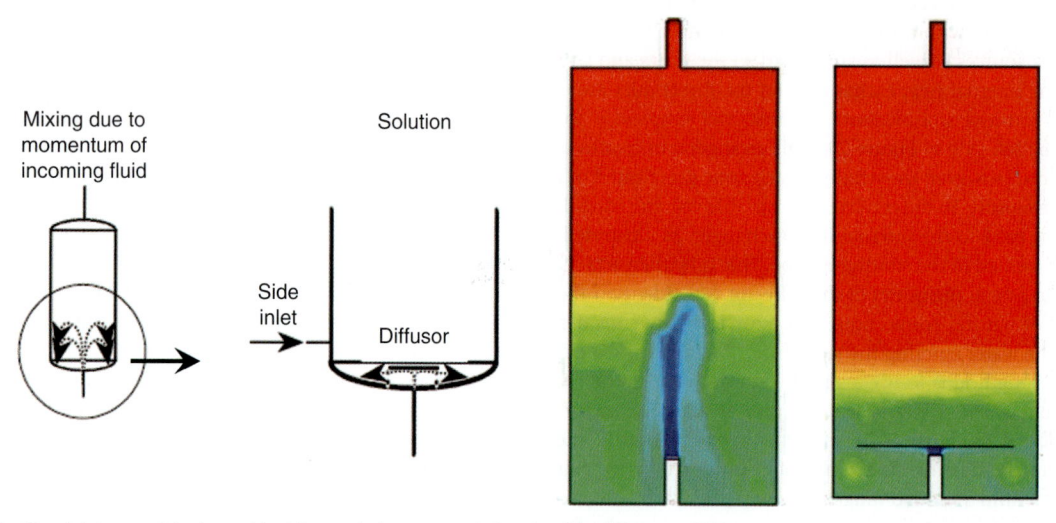

Figure 22 Flow inlet geometries to avoid mixing, and pipes connected to the side of the store [17].

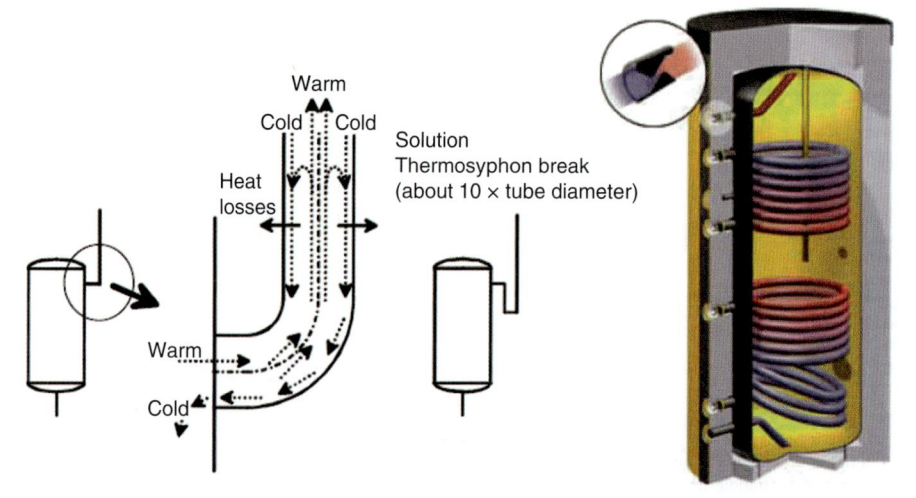

Figure 23 Thermosyphon break to avoid storage heat loss in connecting tubes [17].

3.07.4.2 BTES in a UK Office Building

This is an example of a sensible storage system (UTES).

In the autumn of 2000, the British Engineering Council awarded an Environmental Engineering award to the ground source heat pump project at Commerce Way, Croydon, Surrey [18]. This, one of the largest UK ground source projects, is a speculative-built industrial building of about 3000 m^2 with both offices and warehouse facilities (**Figure 24**). The building, which is leased by Ascom Hassler Ltd. (a Swiss-based IT company), is expected to have an annual cooling load of 100–125 MWh and a heating load of 90–100 MWh. Peak loads under hot summer conditions are anticipated to reach up to 130 kW.

The warehouse is heated or cooled using a low-temperature underfloor heating, with a water-to-water heat pump (26 kW). Total installed heating capacity is 225 kW, and maximum cooling capacity installed is 285 kW. As all geothermic heat pumps are connected in parallel to the pipe work supplying the source and return water, simultaneous cooling and heating loads are balanced in the building. During periods with a net cooling or net heating demand, the ground heat exchanger supplies the additional heat or cold. The ground loop heat exchanger consists of 30 U-loops (40 mm, PE PN16) installed in 100 m deep boreholes, with a distance of about 5 m between the boreholes. The boreholes were fully grouted with a bentonite–cement mixture.

Geology of the site has been described on the basis of three bore logs of the Geological Survey [19] in the vicinity and on the basis of the bore logs made during the drilling of a test borehole. Main geological sequence is as follows: a surface layer (1.5 m), Thanet Sands (1.5–13 m), and upper chalk (13–80 m) and middle chalk formation (80 m). Groundwater levels are at about 2 m below surface level. Groundwater flow is in a north–northwestern direction with an estimated Darcy flow of 20–25 m yr^{-1} in chalk formations and of between 75 and 100 m yr^{-1} in Thanet Sands.

The critical design parameters are the ground thermal conductivity, far-field temperature, and energy loads. The thermal ground parameters were measured on-site with an in situ thermal response test. Results of this test showed a thermal conductivity of 2.2 W m^{-1} K^{-1}, an average far-field temperature of 11.6 °C, and a geothermal gradient below 40 m of ~0.009 °C m^{-1}.

The average monthly fluid temperatures (**Figure 25**) in the ground loop heat exchanger were modeled using Earth Energy Designer (EED) [20] and GhlePro [21]. Clearly, the average temperatures in the ground tend to increase, from about 13.5 °C in the first year to about 17 °C in the 25th year. The installed geothermic heat pumps can operate efficiently within a temperature bandwidth of 0–30 °C, and design temperatures were selected accordingly. The limiting design temperature is the temperature during cooling peak loads, with a 30 °C limit.

A number of variables have been monitored with a relatively high frequency from September 2000 till July 2003 (20 min interval). Ambient temperatures (**Figure 26**) measured at Croydon are comparable to the design temperatures at High Holborn. It can be noted that the winters of 2000 and 2001 have been somewhat colder than normal, while summers (especially when maximum temperatures reached) have been quite a bit warmer in 2002 and 2003. The difference between minimum and maximum temperatures is much larger, as in the monitored data the temperatures are not averaged over a period of years.

Daily ambient and borehole temperatures monitored at the Croydon facility (**Figure 27**) also show a clear trend. Design limits of the borehole heat exchanger of 30 °C during heating and 0 °C during cooling have not been exceeded, but average winter temperatures have increased during the 2002–03 season with respect to previously recorded values. Minimum heat pump source temperature (ground loop heat exchanger return temperature) recorded throughout the period is 4.2 °C, maximum heat pump source temperature was 26.8 °C. The loads that have been recorded are shown in **Figure 28**. Clearly, the net cooling loads to the ground greatly exceed the heating loads. During the monitoring period, total heat extraction was 140 MWh (200 MWh design), and total heat injection was 441 MWh (368 MWh design). Heating loads are 30% lower than anticipated, while cooling loads are 20% higher. The original imbalance factor (cooling–heating) was 1.84, and in reality the imbalance is 3.15.

Figure 24 The Croydon Building, Commerce Way, Croydon, Surrey, UK [18].

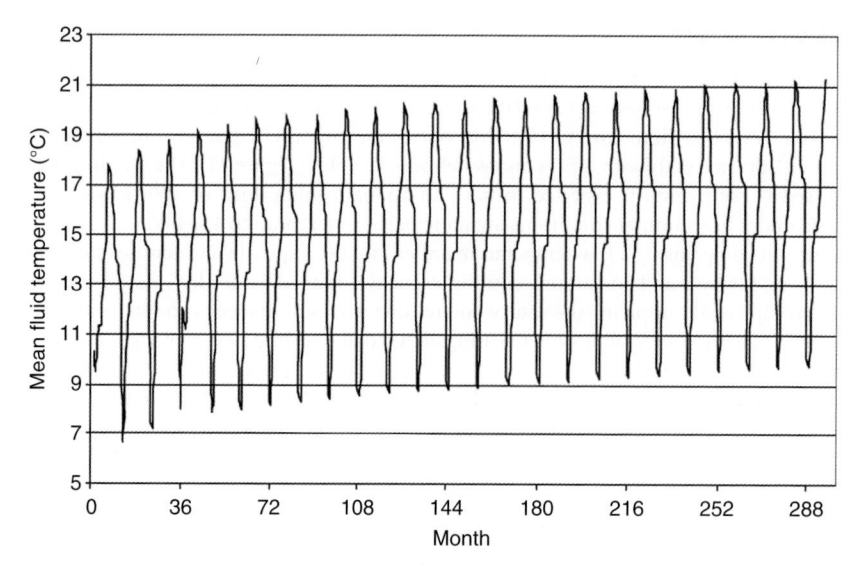

Figure 25 Average modeled monthly fluid temperatures in the ground loop heat exchanger, for 25 years [18].

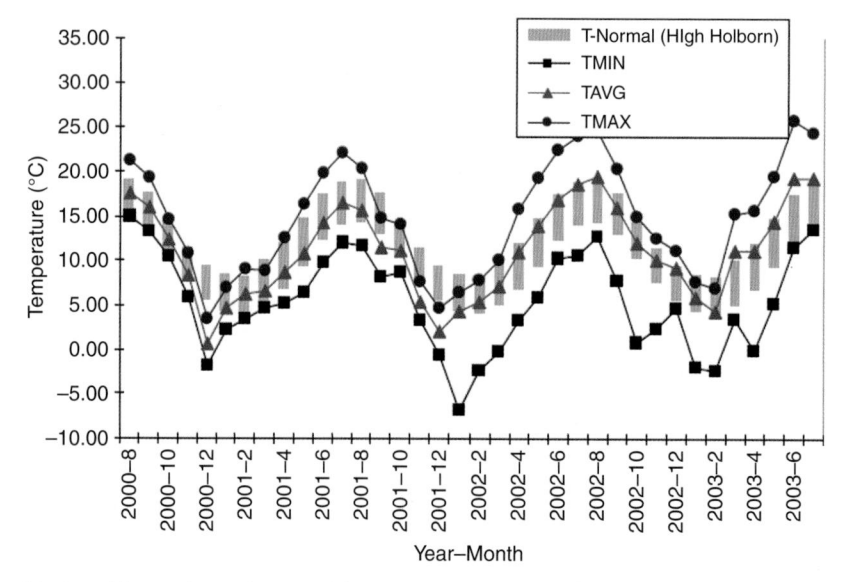

Figure 26 Average monthly day-minimum, day-maximum, and day-average temperatures at Croydon and average typical temperature range of the climate station High Holborn London Weather Centre (design temperatures) [18].

A direct comparison of the measured and design monthly loads is depicted in **Figure 29**. Here also, the trend of heating loads being smaller than anticipated while cooling loads being higher than anticipated is very clear. One of the main reasons for the difference in loads is the fact that occupancy level (number of people per square meter) was higher than anticipated.

The question of how well the borehole heat exchanger system holds up under these conditions is an interesting one. We compared the measured temperatures in the borehole heat exchanger system with the predicted temperatures using the design and measured loads. The EED program was used to calculate temperatures for the first year, and the analysis of the complete monitoring period was done using TRNSYS with the DST model [22]. **Figure 30** shows the simulated temperatures using the design and measured building heating and cooling loads.

Some interesting observations can be made from these figures. First of all, the measured temperatures and the calculated temperatures for the first year are all in fair agreement. The EED tends to overestimate temperatures during cooling when using the measured loads. The TRNSYS model, which has been used to predict temperatures for the complete monitoring series, predicts the increasing average store temperature relatively well. The measured fluid temperatures, however, show a higher temperature amplitude than the model calculations. Also, fluid temperatures in the 2001–02 winter seasons are much lower than expected, considering the measured loads.

During the normal life span of a building (25 years), the surplus of heat rejection would lead to increasing ground temperatures. This results in a less efficient heat pump operation and may even result in insufficient capacity during cooling peak demands. As a

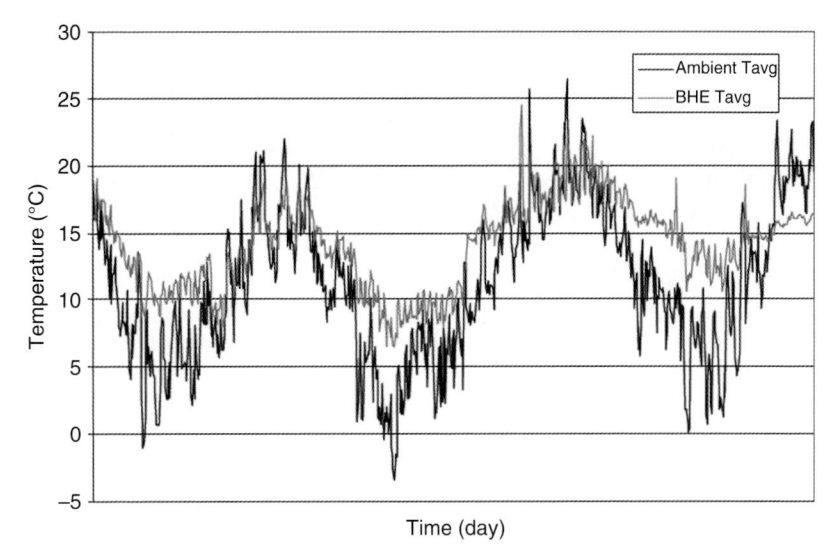

Figure 27 Average daily ambient and borehole heat exchanger temperatures at Croydon (period 2001–03) [18].

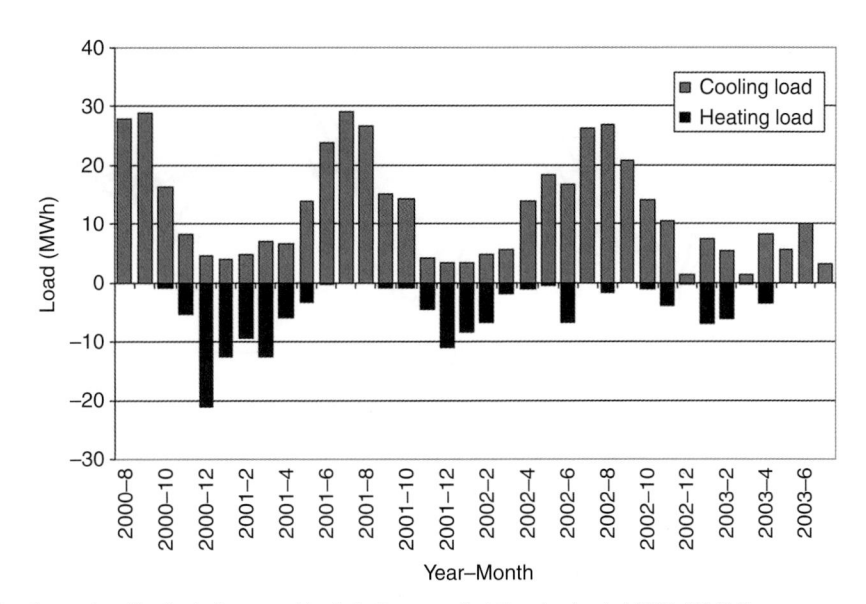

Figure 28 Monthly heating and cooling loads (measured loads to the ground) at Croydon (period 2001–03) [18].

solution a hybrid system, incorporating a dry cooler, was developed. The principal idea is to use the dry cooler to store cold in the wellfield during early spring when the required summer peak load of coolness can be generated very efficiently and cheaply. The operation and efficiency of the wellfield, the installed heat pump system, and the dry cooler is controlled and monitored under a Building Management System.

3.07.4.3 Molten Salts in High-Temperature Solar Power Plants

This is an example of a sensible storage system (liquid media).

Heat can be stored in the change of temperatures of substances that experience a change in internal energy. Besides the density and the specific heat of the storage material, other properties are also important for sensible heat storage: operational temperatures, thermal conductivity and diffusivity, vapor pressure, compatibility among materials stability, heat loss coefficient as a function of the surface areas to volume ratio, and cost [3].

Sensible TES consists of a storage medium, a container (commonly tank), and inlet–outlet devices. Tanks must both retain the storage material and prevent losses of thermal energy. The existence of a thermal gradient across storage is desirable. Different materials such as liquid media silicon and synthetic oils (very expensive materials) and nitrites in salts (with potential corrosion problems) can be used [3]. Nowadays, molten salts are the chosen liquid media in most commercial thermosolar plants.

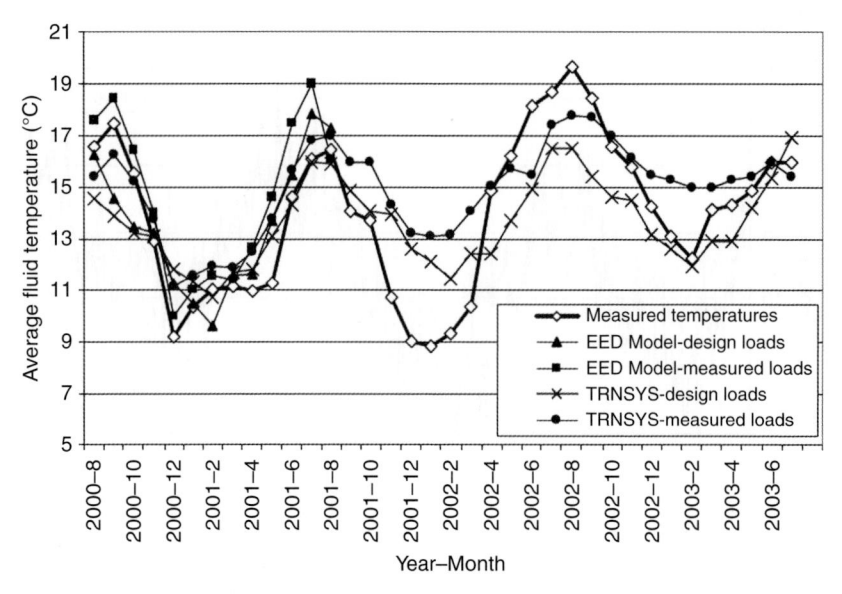

Figure 29 Comparison between design and measured monthly loads (period 2001–03) [18].

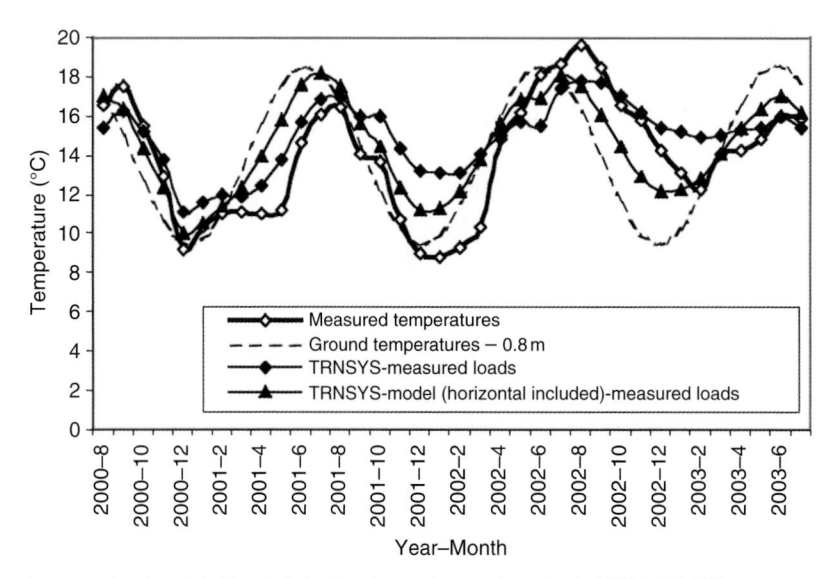

Figure 30 Comparison of measured and modeled borehole heat exchanger temperatures (period 2001–03) [18].

The use of molten salts or steam as an HTF and storage material at the same time eliminates the need for expensive heat exchangers. It allows the solar field to be operated at higher temperatures than what the current HTFs allow. This combination also allows for a substantial reduction in the costs of the TES system, improving the performance of the plant and reducing the levelized electricity cost. But in the case of molten salts, they freeze at relatively high temperatures (120–220 °C), and this means that special care must be taken to ensure that the salts do not freeze in the solar field piping during the night. Hence, routine freeze protection operation must be done by the thermal storage, increasing maintenance and operation (M&O) costs.

One of the active direct systems is the two-tank direct system, which consists of a storage system where the HTF is directly stored in a hot tank, in order to use it during cloudy periods or nights. The cooled HTF is pumped to the other tank, which is a cold tank, where it remains to be heated one more time. **Figure 31** shows the scheme of the plant Solar Tres that uses molten salts (NaNO$_3$ and KNO$_3$) as HTF [23].

The advantages of the two-tank solar systems are as follows: cold and heat storage materials are stored separately; low-risk approach; possibility to raise the solar field output temperature to 450–500 °C, thereby increasing the Rankine cycle efficiency of the power block steam turbine to the 40% range (conventional plants have a lower efficiency); and the HTF temperature rise in the collector field can increase up to a factor of 2.5 compared to the Solar Two project experience (located in Daggett, CA, built in 1995 and decommissioned in 1999), reducing the physical size of the thermal storage system.

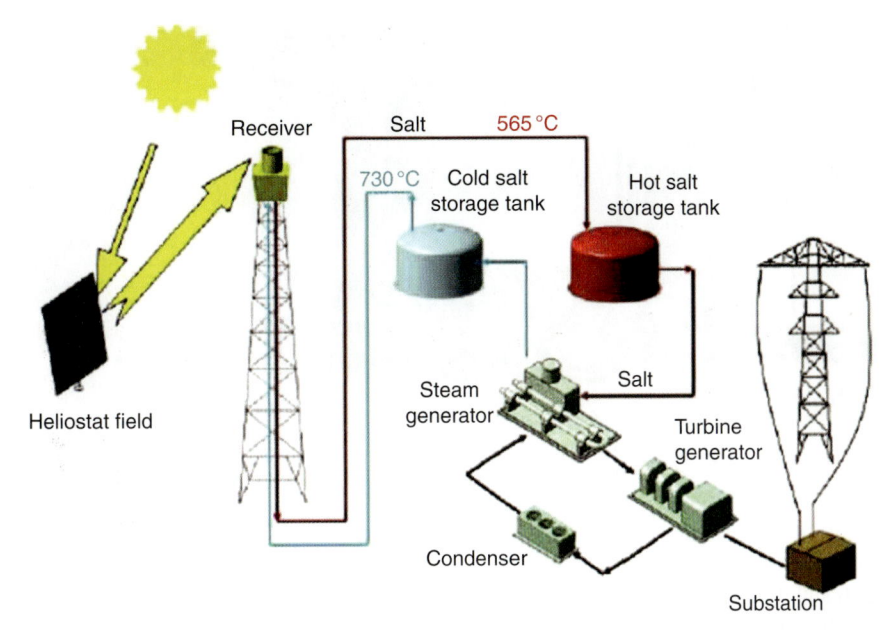

Figure 31 Scheme of installation of a central tower power plant (Planta Solar Tres), with direct two-tank and mineral oil-like storage systems [3, 23].

The disadvantages are very high cost of the material used as an HTF and storage material; high cost of the heat exchangers, the need for using two tanks instead of one; relatively small temperature difference between the hot and the cold fluid in the storage system; very high risk of solidification of storage fluid, due to its relatively high freezing point (which increases the M&O costs); the high temperature of both tanks leads to an increase of losses in the solar field; and the lowest cost TES design and operation does not correspond to the lowest cost of electricity (usually at night).

The development of this system started with the Solar One power plant. It was the first test of a large-scale thermal solar power tower plant. Solar One was designed by the Department of Energy (DOE), Southern California Edison, Los Angeles Department of Water and Power, and California Energy Commission. It was located in Daggett, CA, about 10 miles (16 km) east of Barstow. It operated from 1982 to 1988 [23].

This solar plant was provided with a central receiver system. It incorporated a thermal storage system that could be used to buffer the effects of clouds, and avoid interruptions of electricity supply to the grid. This TES was based on a one-tank thermocline storage concept, and consisted of a single tank filled with rocks and sand, using oil as the HTF. Several banks of exchangers allowed the heat to pass between the oil–rock storage tank and the steam cycles used in the receiver and turbine. The TES system extended the electrical production capability into the night.

According to the researchers, the project met most of its technical objectives by demonstrating the feasibility of generating power at 10 MW$_e$ for 8 h a day near summer solstice and 4 h a day near winter solstice. The average solar energy to electricity efficiency of the plant was about 16%.

In 1995, Solar One was converted into Solar Two by adding a second ring of 108 larger 95 m^2 heliostats around the existing Solar One, totaling 1926 heliostats with a total area of 82 750 m^2.

At Solar Two, the use of molten salts was found to be a solution to the problems of the storage system of Solar One. A consortium of enterprises led by Southern California Edison joined with US DOE retrofitted the Solar One. Solar Two was decommissioned in 1999 and was converted by the University of California, Davis, into an Air Cherenkov Telescope in 2001.

The storage system of Solar Two plant consisted of two flat-bottom, domed-roof, cylindrical, atmospheric tanks. The cold tank was fabricated from carbon steel and the hot tank from stainless steel (**Figure 32**). In order to monitor the level into the tank, each tank was equipped with bubbler level detectors [23].

The cold tank contained two active 25 kW$_e$ immersion heaters and one spare that maintained the tank at 290 °C when solar radiation was not enough, in order to avoid the molten salt temperature to decrease below the melting point. The sides and roof of the tank were insulated with 23 and 15 cm, respectively, of mineral wool blankets overlaid with 5 cm of fiberglass boards. The exterior of the tank was covered with aluminum jackets for weather protection, and the bottom of the cold tank was insulated with 41 cm of foam glass insulation under 10.2 m of the 11.4 m of diameter of the tank.

The hot tank contained three active 25 kW$_e$ immersion heaters and one spare that maintained the tank at 565 °C, in order to be able to keep generating power when solar radiation was not enough. The sides and roof of the tank were insulated with 46 and 30 cm, respectively, of mineral wool blankets overlaid with 5 cm of fiberglass boards. The exterior was covered with an aluminum jacket for weather protection. The bottom of the tank was insulated with 15 cm of insulating firebrick on top of 30 cm of foam glass insulation under 10.2 m of the 11.4 m of diameter of the tank. This plant has round-trip energy storage efficiencies of 97%.

Figure 32 View of two-tank storage system of Solar Two thermosolar plant: cold tank (left) and hot tank (right) [23].

An optimization of the thermal storage system involves the assessment of numerous parameters, including the inverse relationship between the surface area and cost of oil heat exchanger, the quantity and cost of the storage inventory, the surface area of the oil–salt heat exchanger, and the part of load performance penalty of the Rankine cycle when operating from thermal storage.

In an effort to reduce heat losses as the tanks were charged or discharged, piping was connected to the vents of the two tanks. This air will be conduced from the filled tank to the empty tank. Heat losses were measured once the vessel was at the steady state, and results showed that the thermal losses are basically a fixed value to the environment. **Table 9** shows the values of the losses in Solar Two plant.

The two-tank system implemented in this test is a relatively low-risk approach. No barriers to future implementation were evident. This experimental plant reached to demonstrate dispatching energy several times and the production of a constant output of electricity at night and through cloudy weather.

Placed on Fuentes de Andalucia, near to Seville (Spain), Solar Tres power plant is the first commercial solar plant with central receiver, which uses Solar One and Solar Two technology for commercial electrical production of 15 MW. A large molten nitrate salt storage tank is used giving the plant the ability to store 600 MWh, a storage system with 15 h of storage (**Figure 31**), which means that this plant can operate around 6500 h every year. This plant was built in 2008.

The thermal storage system, using molten salts as storage media (a mixture of $NaNO_3$ and KNO_3), is based on the two-tank system's direct technology, which means that the plant uses the same fluid as a working fluid that allows for collection, transport, and storage of the thermal energy with also very high efficiencies through the high top and differential temperatures.

The hot tank stores the molten salts at about 565 °C and was made from ASTM A240 Grade 347 stainless steel. The cold tank, made from ASTM A516 Grade 70 carbon steel, stores the molten salts at about 288 °C. The capacity of storage was 588 MWh_{th}. The large thermal storage capacity for very high utilization factors of the plant is above 70%.

3.07.4.4 Concrete and Other Solid Materials in High-Temperature Solar Power Plants

This is an example of a sensible storage system (solid media).

Solid media sensible storage systems are tested by DLR in Plataforma Solar de Almería (PSA). Solid media sensible heat storage units have been developed in the WESPE project [23], funded by the German government from December 2001 till December 2003, and storage temperatures of 325 °C have been reached. This project focusses on the development of an efficient and cheap sensible storage material, on the optimization of the tube register heat exchanger, and on the demonstration of this technology with a 350 kWh test unit.

In a solid media storage, the heat exchanger for the HTF is embedded in a solid matrix. The thermophysical properties of the solid storage materials, such as density, specific heat capacity, thermal conductivity, coefficient of thermal expansion (CTE), and cycling stability as well as availability, costs, and production methods are of great relevance.

Table 9 Values of thermal losses in tanks and sumps, of Solar Two plant, in every component, calculated and measured [23]

Major equipment	Calculated thermal loss (kW)	Measured thermal loss (kW)
Hot tank	98	102
Cold tank	45	44
Steam generator sump	14	29
Receiver sump	13	9.5

A high heat capacity reduces the storage volume and a high thermal conductivity increases the dynamics in the system. The CTE of the storage material should fit to the CTE of the material of the embedded metallic heat exchanger. A high cycling stability is important for a long lifetime of the storage. With respect to these techno-economic aspects, high-temperature-resistant concrete developed for parabolic trough power plants is proposed as suitable solid storage material [23].

Two different storage materials have been developed in parallel – as an innovative storage material, a castable ceramic and alternatively, a high-temperature concrete. Both the developed materials are principally composed of a binder system, aggregates, and a small amount of auxiliary materials.

The castable ceramic is based on a binder containing Al_2O_3. The binder is set chemically under ambient conditions and forms a solid, stable matrix, which encloses the aggregates. As main aggregate, iron oxides, accumulated as waste material in strip steel production, are used. Auxiliary materials are needed to improve the handling of the ready mixed material, for example, as accelerator or for reduction of viscosity.

For the high-temperature concrete, blast furnace cement is used as binder; again, iron oxides are used as main aggregate, as well as flue ash and again a small amount of auxiliary materials.

The material properties have been analyzed at DLR. Shear stress analysis has proven that the contact between the tubes and the solid is very good at ambient temperature as well as at elevated temperatures until 350 °C, even after 160 thermal cycles.

In an overall view, high-temperature concrete seems to be the most favorable material. Reasons are the lower costs, higher strength of the material, and easier handling of the ready-mixed material. However, further development of cracks in the test modules needs to be investigated, when cycling at operation temperature has been demonstrated. On the other side, castable ceramics has a 20% higher storage capacity and 35% higher thermal conductivity and still some potential for cost reduction.

Between 1991 and 1994, two concrete storage modules were tested at the storage test facility at the Centre for Solar Energy and Hydrogen Research (ZSW), a research center belonging to DLR, in Stuttgart. ZSW in collaboration with the companies ZUEBLIN and FLAGSOL examined during the period 2001–06 the performance, durability, and cost of using solid TES media in parabolic trough power plants. The system uses the standard HTF in the solar field, which transfers its heat through an array of pipe systems, imbedded in the solid storage media (**Figure 33**).

The main advantage of this approach is the low cost of the material, including a good contact between the concrete and piping, and the heat transfer rates into and out of the solid medium.

These tests took place at the PSA in southern Spain during 2001–06. DLR performed initial testing and found that both castable ceramic and high-temperature concrete were suitable for solid media, sensible heat storage systems. However, the high-temperature concrete is favored because of its lower costs, higher material strength, and easier handling. Moreover, there was no sign of degradation between the heat exchanger pipes and storage material.

A new test experiment was done in 2004 at the PSA. The thermal energy was provided by a parabolic trough loop with a maximum thermal power of 480 kW. Temperatures of storage reached were about 390 °C, with a range of 340–390 °C. The storage capacity for the ceramic storage unit is around 350 kWh, and the HTF was mineral oil.

The tube register design was found to be the best because heat transfer enhancement is important, the material to be used is concrete with quartz aggregates, and fins and other structures are not cost effective.

3.07.4.5 PCM in Buildings as Passive Energy System

This is an example of a latent storage system.

PCMs have been studied for thermal storage in buildings since 1980 [24]. These systems provide a higher thermal inertia to the building that, when combined with thermal insulation, can reduce the energy consumption of the building by absorbing the heat

Figure 33 View of high-temperature concrete storage system [23].

Figure 34 Demonstration cubicles in Puigverd de Lleida [24].

gains and reducing the heat flow. During daytime, the PCM can absorb part of the heat through the melting process, and during the night, the heat is released by solidification of the PCM, resulting in a lower heat flow from outdoors to indoors.

A long-term experiment is being developed at the University of Lleida (Spain), where different forms of PCMs are being tested in a pilot plant (**Figure 34**). Up to now, microencapsulated PCM was mixed in concrete without losing any of the concrete initial characteristics, achieving high energy savings in cooling power. Also, macroencapsulated PCMs were tested with typical Mediterranean constructive solutions. Macroencapsulated PCM was added in one conventional brick and in one alveolar brick cubicle (CSM panels, containing RT-27 and SP-25 A8, respectively) and the thermal behavior of the cubicles was studied. CSM panels are commercial products from Rubitherm (Germany); in fact, they are macroencapsulated PCMs. RT-27 is a commercial paraffin and SP-25 A8 is a commercial salt hydrate, both from Rubitherm (Germany).

The experimental setup consisted of seven identically shaped cubicles. The cubicles were designed with the help of TRNSYS, using the type developed by the authors for such application, and validated in the laboratory. To be able to compare the results, all cubicles had internal dimensions of 2.4 × 2.4 × 2.4 m. The cubicles are located in Puigverd de Lleida (Spain), which has a typical Spanish continental climate, with cold winters and warm and relatively dry summers. The important temperature oscillations during day and night make it very suitable for the PCM operation since the material can be melted during the day and solidified during the night. The PCMs tested were designed for cooling applications.

Two cubicles were built with concrete; one with conventional concrete and the other one with the modified concrete, which included microencapsulated PCM. Five other different cubicles were built using different Mediterranean typical constructive solutions [25].

In the concrete cubicles, the PCMs used were commercial microencapsulated material called Micronal PCM (from BASF) with a melting point of 26 °C, and a phase change enthalpy of 110 kJ kg^{-1}. Its mixture and inclusion in the concrete was developed within the MOPCON project, and the mechanical strength and thermal behavior were tested. It was found out that the new concrete reaches a compressive strength over 25 MPa and a tensile splitting strength over 6 MPa (after 28 days). These values open the opportunity for structural purposes.

The cubicles are apparently identical, built with the union of six concrete panels, but one of them contains about 5% in weight of PCM mixed with the concrete in three panels (south, west, and roof walls). The panels have a thickness of 0.12 cm. The distribution of the windows are as follows: one window of 1.7 × 0.6 m at the east and west walls, four windows of 0.75 × 0.4 m at the south wall, and the door in the north wall. It should be highlighted that the cubicles are not insulated, since the effect of the PCM alone was to be tested.

In the brick cubicles, the walls consist of perforated bricks (29 × 14 × 7.5 cm) with an insulating material (depending on the cubicle) on the external side, an air chamber of 5 cm, and hollow bricks. The roof was done using concrete precast beams and 5 cm of concrete slab [24]. The insulating material is placed over the concrete, protected with a cement mortar roof with an inclination of 3° and a double asphalt membrane. Three cubicles using different insulating solutions have been compared:

1. Reference cubicle (reference): This cubicle has no insulation.
2. Polyurethane (PU) cubicle: The insulation material used is 5 cm of spray foam PU.
3. PCM cubicle (RT-27 + PU): The insulation used is again 5 cm of spray foam PU and an additional layer of PCM. CSM panels containing RT-27 paraffin (**Table 10**) are located between the perforated bricks and the PU (in the southern and western walls and the roof).

Two different cubicles were built with alveolar brick:

1. Reference cubicle (alveolar): The alveolar brick has a special design that provides both thermal and acoustic insulation. No additional insulation was used in this cubicle.
2. PCM cubicle (SP-25 + alveolar): Several CSM panels containing SP-25 A8 hydrate salt (**Table 10**) are placed inside the cubicle, between the alveolar brick and plaster in order to increase the thermal inertia of the wall (in the southern and western walls and the roof).

The cubicles were instrumented with temperature sensors in every wall, temperature sensors in the middle of the room at a height of 1.2 and 2.0 m, and one heat flux sensor in the inside wall of the south panel. A meteorological station was installed nearby; this meteorological station measured outdoor temperature and wind speed. Also one irradiation sensor was set on top of each cubicle,

Table 10 Properties of the PCM used in the experimental setup in Puigverd de Lleida [24, 25]

Property	Micronal	RT-27	SP-25 A8
Melting point (°C)	26	28	26
Congealing point (°C)		26	25
Heat storage capacity (kJ kg^{-1})	110	179	180
Density (kg l^{-1})			
Solid		0.87	1.38
Liquid		0.75	
Specific heat capacity (kJ kg^{-1} K^{-1})			
Solid		1.8	2.5
Liquid		2.4	
Heat conductivity (W m^{-1} K^{-1})		0.2	0.6

giving the irradiation measures, and the possibility of shadows in each one. All the instrumentation is connected to a data logger connected to a computer to record the data obtained. Brick cubicles had a heat pump and its energy consumption was monitored.

Two different experiments were preformed in the experimental setup:

1. Free-floating temperature, where no cooling system is used. The temperature conditions inside the cubicles are compared. The ones with PCM are expected to have a better behavior.
2. Controlled temperature, where a heat pump is used to set a constant ambient temperature inside the cubicle. The energy consumption of the cubicles is compared. The cubicles using PCM are expected to have lower energy consumptions.

To see the details of the experiments, the measurements for 2 days for the south wall of the concrete cubicles are presented in **Figure 35** [25]. The following three points can be highlighted from the figure:

1. First, the cubicle without PCM had a maximum temperature that was 1 °C higher than the one with PCM, and the minimum temperature was 2 °C lower.
2. Second, the maximum temperature in the wall with PCM was reached about 2 h later without PCM, that is, the thermal inertia of the wall was higher.
3. Third, this thermal inertia appeared again in the afternoon due to the freezing of the PCM, but also earlier in the morning due to the melting of the PCM.

The effect of the thermal inertia is very interesting in commercial buildings, such as office buildings. A retard of 2 h in the heat wave would mean a decrease in the electrical consumption due to air conditioning.

The brick cubicles were equipped with a heat pump as a cooling system to simulate the real conditions of a house [24]. The energy consumption of the heat pump was measured to determine the real energy savings achieved when the cubicles remain within the comfort range.

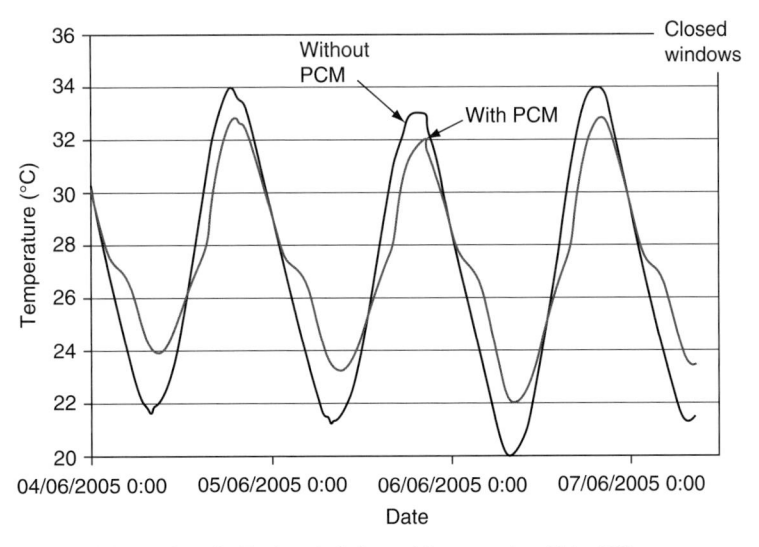

Figure 35 Detail of the temperature of the south wall with closed windows of the concrete cubicles [25].

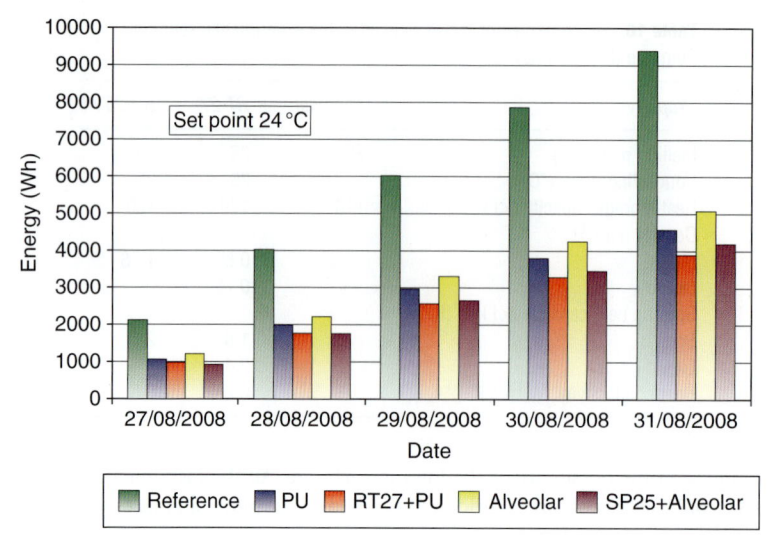

Figure 36 Accumulated energy consumption of the brick cubicles in Puigverd de Lleida [24].

Figure 36 presents the results of the controlled temperature experiments of the brick cubicles using a set point of 24 °C. The accumulated energy consumption of the reference cubicle is higher than that of all the other cubicles. The RT-27 + PU cubicle is the one with the lowest energy consumption, while the SP-25 + alveolar cubicle is the second one, consuming even less energy than the PU cubicle. Finally, the alveolar cubicle is the one that consumes more energy after the reference cubicle.

A moderate set point (like 24 °C) favors the PCM working conditions, since the temperature inside is close to the phase change range. Both PCM cubicles reduced the energy consumption compared with the same cubicle without PCM. The RT-27 + PU cubicle achieved a reduction of 15% compared to the PU cubicle, while the SP-25 + alveolar cubicle reached a 17% of energy savings compared to the alveolar one (**Table 11**). Moreover, the SP-25 + alveolar cubicle presents lower energy consumptions than the PU cubicle.

From the energy consumption of each cubicle, the CO_2 emissions to the atmosphere can be estimated. Considering the Spanish electricity production share, a CO_2 emission rate of 572.9 g kWh^{-1} is determined. **Table 12** presents the CO_2 emissions and savings for each cubicle.

Table 11 Accumulated energy consumption and savings for the different cubicles [24]

	Energy consumption[a] (Wh)	Energy savings[b] (Wh)	Energy savings[b] (%)	Improvement[c] (%)
Reference	9376	0	0	
PU	4583	4793	51.12	0
RT-27 + PU	3907	5469	58.33	14.75
Alveolar	5053	4323	46.11	0
SP-25 + alveolar	4188	5188	55.33	17.12

[a]Set point of 24 °C during 5 days.
[b]Referred to the reference cubicle.
[c]Referred to the cubicle with analog constructive solution and without PCM.

Table 12 CO_2 emissions to the atmosphere due to the energy consumption of the cubicle [24]

	Energy consumption[a] (kWh yr^{-1} m^{-2})	CO_2 emissions (kg yr^{-1} m^{-2})	CO_2 savings[b] (kg yr^{-1} m^{-2})	CO_2 improvement[c] (kg yr^{-1} m^{-2})
Reference	29.3	16.8	0.0	
PU	14.3	8.2	8.6	0.0
RT-27 + PU	12.2	7.0	9.8	1.2
Alveolar	15.8	9.1	7.7	0.0
SP-25 + alveolar	13.1	7.5	9.3	1.6

[a]Set point of 24 °C during 90 days per year (cooling demand).
[b]Referred to the reference cubicle.
[c]Referred to the cubicle with analog constructive solution and without PCM.

The results of the concrete cubicles show the energy storage in the walls by encapsulating PCM and the comparison with conventional concrete without PCMs, leading to an improved thermal inertia as well as lower inner temperatures. These results demonstrate a real opportunity in energy savings for buildings [25].

The thermal inertia seen in all experiments shows that all PCMs included in the cubicle walls freeze and melt in every cycle. The results also showed that night cooling is important to achieve this full cycle every day.

The results with brick cubicles present similar tendencies than those observed in the concrete cubicles [24]. However, some problems with the solidification of the PCM during the night were observed. Therefore, a cooling strategy (either natural or mechanical) must be defined to improve the performance of the PCM under free-floating conditions.

Additional experiments using a heat pump to set and control the inside temperature of the cubicles were performed. The experiments demonstrated that the energy consumption of the cubicles containing PCM was reduced by about 15% compared to the cubicles without PCM. This demonstrates the significant contribution and the potential of PCM use in building envelopes for energy saving and thermal comfort in a real house-shaped cubicle.

The new results demonstrate the good behavior, energy savings, and technical viability of using macroencapsulated PCM in typical Mediterranean constructive solutions. Moreover, about 1–1.5 kg yr^{-1} m^{-2} of CO_2 emissions were saved in the PCM cubicles due to the reduction of the energy consumption. This reduction can help to mitigate the climate change and the global warming by means of a more efficient and sustainable use of energy.

3.07.4.6 PCM in Buildings as Active Energy System

This is an example of a latent storage system.

The idea of improving the thermal comfort of lightweight buildings by integrating PCMs into the building structure has been investigated in various research projects over several decades. The option to microencapsulate PCM, a key technology that overcomes many of these problems, may make PCM products accessible for the building industry [26].

Building materials with integrated PCMs are used to cool buildings passively. During the day, the PCM stores surplus heat energy, which is released in the night (by night aeration). The PCM thereby is not a replacement of usual cooling applications but it is part of the whole cooling concept.

The development of these materials started at the Fraunhofer ISE (Germany) in 1998 with a project about latent heat storage in building materials raised by the BMWi. By now, different products are available in stores, for example, a PCM plaster with 20% PCM that has a heat capacity of 20 J g^{-1} in its melting range (**Figures 37** and **38**).

Figure 39 shows the result of a measurement where two identical rooms were compared with each other – one with PCM plaster on the walls and the ceiling and the other one is the reference room with conventional materials. Over a longer period of time, the wall temperature in the PCM room was constantly lower (up to 4 K) than in the reference room.

The test rooms were built as a typical lightweight construction consisting of gypsum plasterboard mounted on wooden slats with insulation [26]. This construction is mounted on the 14 cm thick PU foam insulation of the cabin. Both test rooms were equipped with conventional venetian blinds as external shading devices, and the ventilation profile could be controlled. During the measurements, both test rooms were run with the same conditions.

By using PCM plaster and adequate night aeration, it is possible to achieve a much more comfortable ambient temperature without any active cooling system. Similar results are possible with other PCM materials.

Passive systems and therefore passive cooling with PCM are highly dependent on low temperatures during the night. Without these low temperatures, the storage cannot be discharged completely. This leads to less usable storage for the next day and therefore the building tends to overheat faster.

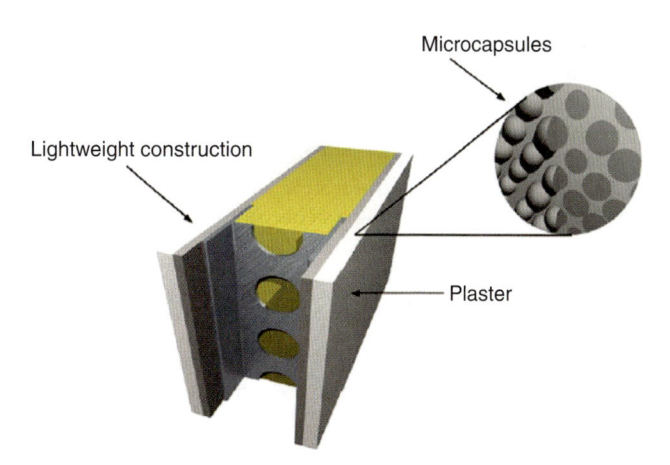

Figure 37 Schematic view of a lightweight wall. The PCM microcapsules are integrated into the interior Blaster [26].

Figure 38 PCM plaster developed at Fraunhofer ISE (Germany) to increase the heat capacity of the building [27].

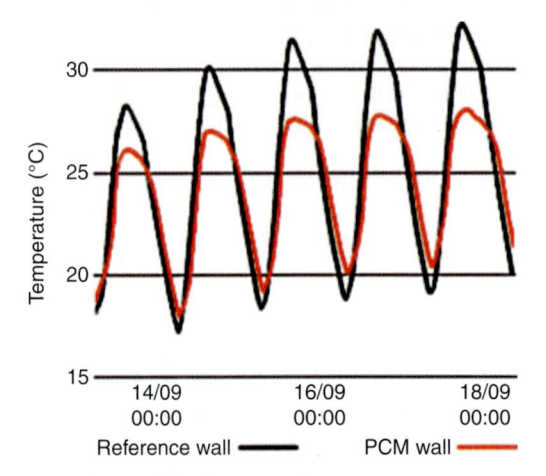

Figure 39 Results of two identical rooms finished with plaster, one with PCM and the other without PCM [27].

Passive cooling of buildings is mainly restricted by two factors: first, the heat transmission between the air and the wall limits the heat quantity, which can be charged and discharged in a 24 h cycle. Increasing the thickness of the PCM layer, therefore, does not automatically lead to larger usable heat capacity. Second, the system is highly dependent on colder air temperatures during the night. In hot summer nights, the storage may not be completely discharged. This leads to less available storage during the day.

Active cooling systems in combination with PCM building materials are one way to solve this problem [27]. For this purpose, chilled ceilings were examined (**Figure 40**). Water is actively pumped through capillary tubes that are surrounded by PCM grout and PCM plaster developed in previous projects. The PCM passively buffers large parts of the heat that would have to be actively chilled in conventional systems. Only the heat overrun has to be chilled by an active chiller.

Chilled ceilings with PCM allow a smaller chiller to be installed. Because of the PCM buffering ability, the chiller does not need to cool down the whole peak load. So we can use alternative heat sinks like well water or heat pumps that would not have enough power to cool conventional systems. Up to now, active cooling systems with PCM are only used and examined in testing facilities.

3.07.4.7 Seasonal Storage of Solar Energy

This is an example of a closed adsorption system.

Long-term heat storage is one of the main challenges for an effective year-round use of thermal solar energy [28]. Therefore, high energy density heat stores are the focus of an increasing amount of research efforts.

In the framework of the HYDES project [29], AEE INTEC in Austria has built a first prototype in order to observe the performance of a sorption system combined to solar collectors of 20.4 m^2 for heating and domestic hot water production. This was a closed adsorption system using silica gel–H$_2$O.

Figure 40 Actively chilled PCM system with capillary tubes [27].

The major objectives of the HYDES project were the development of a high energy density heat storage system based on closed cycle adsorption processes suitable for the long-term storage of low-temperature heat and the testing of this system in the application of seasonal storage of solar thermal energy for space heating purposes under different climatic and system conditions [28].

To charge the system, the silica gel is heated through a heat exchanger with energy from solar collectors at about 88 °C; water vapor is released (desorption) and condensed in a condenser by an external cooler. The condensed vapor and the dry adsorbent are then stored separately with only sensible heat loss. In discharging period, the stored water is evaporated in an evaporator connected to a silica gel store that adsorbs the vapor and releases the useful heat. The experimental results achieved are 20% less than theoretical predictions from simulations (storage density: 150 kWh m^{-3} of silica gel) [29].

The complete system is shown in **Figure 41**. In summer, during the charging of the storage, heat from the solar collectors is delivered to the three adsorbers. The heat input has to be realized by heat exchangers, which are located within a packed bed of silica gel. The desorbed water vapor is condensed at the evaporators/condensers and the heat of condensation is transferred as waste heat to a cooling fan. During the discharging in winter, low-temperature heat from the solar collectors is used for the evaporation of the water in the evaporators/condensers. The heat of adsorption is collected by the inner heat exchangers within the adsorbers and is delivered to the heating system of the building. In this configuration, the heat needed for evaporation during the discharging is not coming from the ambience, because the temperature level would be too low. It is provided by the solar collectors at a higher temperature.

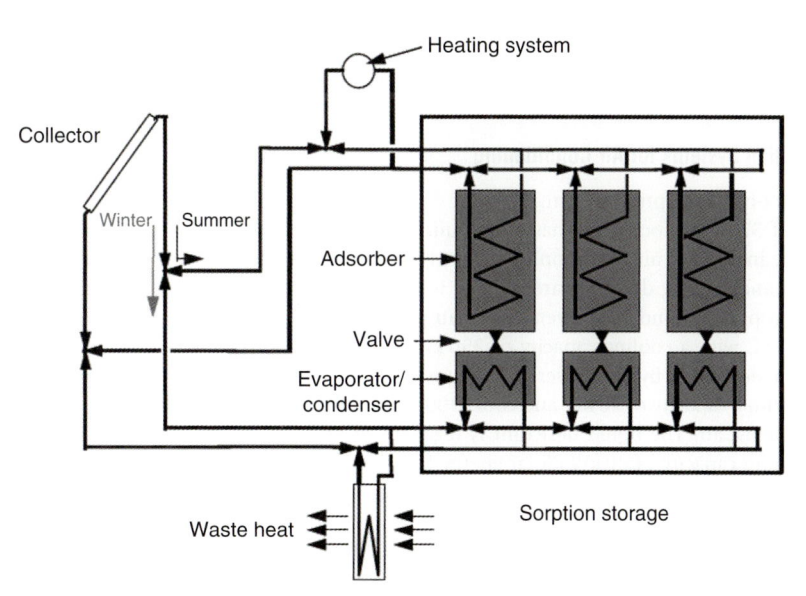

Figure 41 Closed sorption storage system for seasonal storage [28].

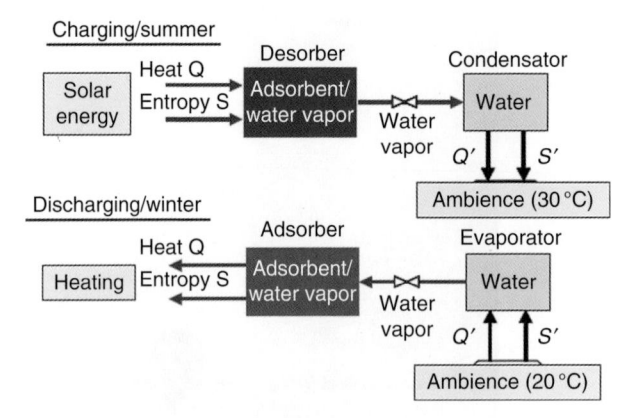

Figure 42 Seasonal storage of solar energy as an indirect heat storage [28].

Seasonal storage with sorption storage systems is strongly influenced by the changes in ambient temperature between winter and summer. A reduction of the thermal COP_{th} (besides the reduction due to the irreversibilities of the converter at charging and discharging) will be demonstrated in the following example. The charging process takes place in the summer time at ambient temperature $T_{AC} = 30\ °C$, while the discharging happens in winter at $T_{DC} = -20\ °C$. This leads to a reduction of the ideal ratio between the discharged amount of heat Q_D and the heat charged to the storage Q_C:

$$\frac{Q_D}{Q_C} = \frac{\left(1 - \frac{T_{AC}}{T_C}\right)}{\left(1 - \frac{T_{AD}}{T_D}\right)} = 0.6$$

In this example [28], the charging temperature T_C and the discharging temperature T_D are both chosen to be $100\ °C$. In most applications, T_C is less than T_D, which leads to a further decrease in COP_{th}. The system is schematically shown in **Figure 42**.

The MODESTORE project was the occasion of development of a 'second generation' prototype and the integration of essential components (reactor and heat exchangers) into a block unit [29]. But the performance achieved with this unit failed to meet the expectations; the material storage density dropped to only $50\ kWh\ m^{-3}$, that is, 30% less efficient than water storage. Indeed, experiments showed that the temperature lift is not sufficient over water content of the silica gel of about 13%. In addition, the temperature levels of flat-plate solar collectors and available heat sinks cannot allow desorption under water content of 3%; the material has to operate in a water content range of 3–13%. The study has concluded about the unsuitability of the silica gel–H_2O combination for seasonal storage and has suggested for further projects on other materials combination such as some zeolites. However, a storage plant is actually in experimentation for a field test with silica gel–H_2O. The main industrial partner of the project is currently commercializing this technology as heat pumps without storage.

A prototype storage module has been developed (**Figure 43**) [30]. The upper part contained the adsorber and a spiral heat exchanger. In the center, there was a vertical channel for vapor diffusion. The spiral heat exchanger consisted of perforated sheet copper with copper pipes soldered to it. The lower part contained the heat exchanger that served as evaporator and condenser. At the bottom, the container was connected to a second container that held the water that was not adsorbed. For desorption, the water was pumped from the storage module as it accumulated at the bottom. For adsorption, water was led into the bottom of the storage container and heated.

3.07.4.8 Open Absorption Systems for Air Conditioning

This is an example of an open absorption system.

An office building of $5700\ m^2$ floor space has been built in Amberg (Germany) by the architects Hart & Flierl for Prochek Immobilien GmbH. The innovative air-conditioning concept using solar energy was worked out by M. Gammel, an engineering consultant. The heating and cooling demands are 35 and $30\ kW\ m^2\ yr^{-1}$, respectively. These are covered by thermally activated ceilings, assisted by appropriately conditioned ventilation air [31].

Well water of $12-14\ °C$ with a cooling capacity of $250\ kW$ is used for cooling the ceilings in summer. A solar-driven liquid desiccant cooling system, developed by ZAE Bayern (Germany), dehumidifies outside air by a liquid desiccant, a concentrated salt solution of LiCl–H_2O, with a capacity of $70\ kW$ and cools $300\ m^3\ h^{-1}$ of air supply with a capacity of $80\ kW$ by cold recovery from evaporatively cooled exhaust air. The liquid desiccant is regenerated by solar thermal from a $70\ m^2$ flat-plate collector array at $70-80\ °C$ with a maximum capacity of $40\ kW$. Solar energy for air conditioning is stored efficiently in about $10\ m^3$ of desiccant solution. Summer air conditioning uses only solar energy, except for pumps and fans [31].

A sketch of the system for heating, cooling, and hot water production for a restaurant within the building is shown in **Figure 44**. The thermally activated ceilings are divided into 16 zones, the air handling system into 20 zones, which allows separate cost calculation for different departments even if the division of the floor space should be changed in the future. The maximum cooling capacity delivered by the well water is $250\ kW$.

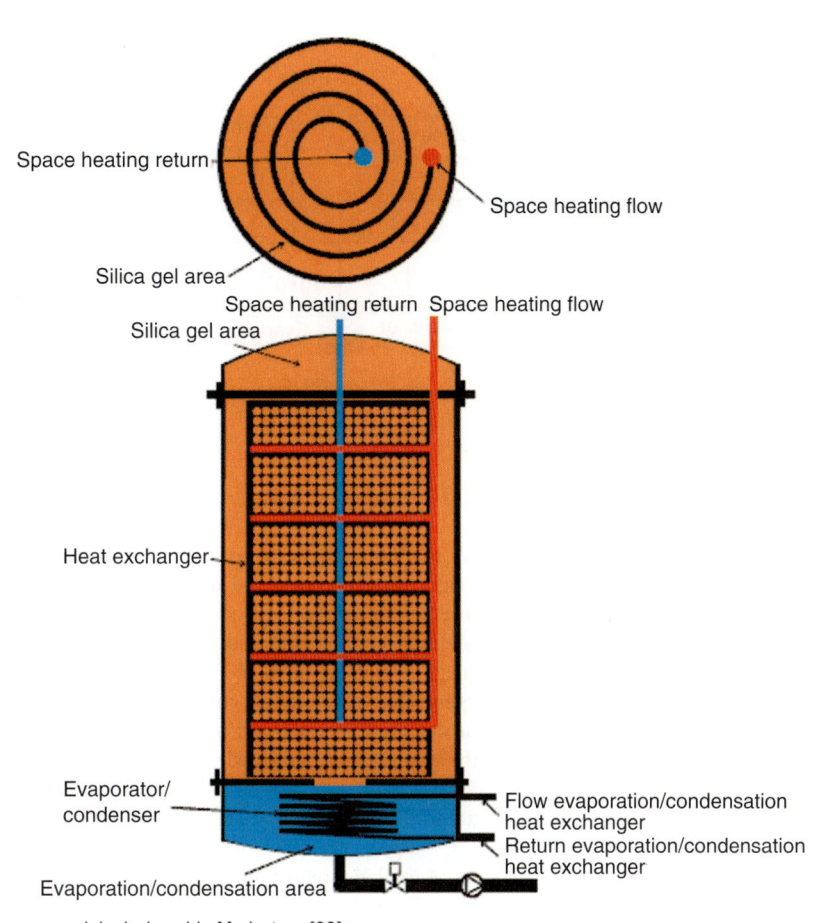

Figure 43 Prototype storage module designed in Modestore [30].

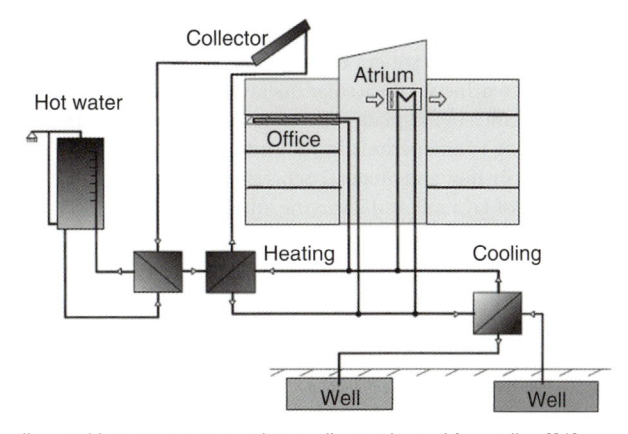

Figure 44 Sketch of the heating, cooling, and hot water system, where well water is used for cooling [31].

In summer, the ventilation air has to be dehumidified to keep the required comfort and to prevent condensation on cold ceilings. The air dehumidification is done by a liquid desiccant dehumidification and cooling system (**Figure 45**). Warm and humid air outside is cooled and dried in a special dehumidifier by a concentrated LiCl salt solution before it is blown into the atrium of the building. From there, several air handling units draw the air into the offices and provide additional cooling on demand.

The exhaust air of the building is collected in three exhaust air handling units. Indirect evaporative coolers exploit the remaining cooling capacity of the exhaust air and cool the air supply in the dehumidifier via a water loop. The cold recovery makes the system more efficient. Depending on the ambient conditions, the predicted thermal COP of the system is 1.2–2. In hot and humid climates, the COP will be close to 1.

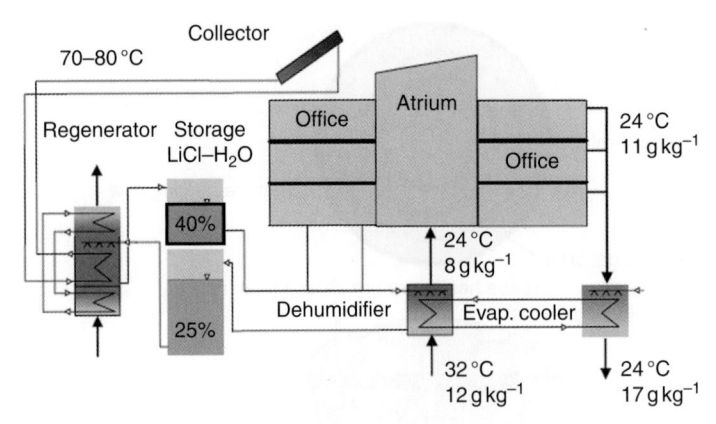

Figure 45 Air dehumidification by a liquid desiccant storage system [31].

A special low-flow technique enables the dehumidifier to dilute the desiccant significantly when drying the air. The salt concentration changes from 40% to about 28% of its weight. Concentrated and diluted solutions are stored separately. The dehumidification process can be operated as long as the concentrated solution is available. The system of concentrated and diluted solutions stores energy very efficiently. The energy storage density reaches up to about 300 kWh m^{-3} related to the volume of the diluted solution. Since a chemical potential is stored, the storage is nondegrading, and no insulation of the storage tanks is required.

When solar energy is available, the diluted solution is regenerated to its original concentration in a regenerator, at temperatures of 70–80 °C. At this temperature, water evaporates from the desiccant solution and is taken to the ambient by an airflow through the regenerator. The LiCl does not evaporate. It remains in the solution and in the cycle. Heat recovery for the airflow is used to keep up the thermal coefficient of performance.

The desiccant cooling system is designed for a maximum airflow of 30 000 m^3 h^{-1}. The design point for cooling is defined as 32 °C and 12 g kg^{-1} outside air state and 24.5 °C and 8.5 g kg^{-1} supply air state. Under these conditions, the air cooling demand is about 80 kW and the air dehumidification demand is 70 kW. A total air-conditioning capacity of 150 kW is required.

The system concept is to use solely solar energy, and no additional fossil fuel should be used. Therefore, the required storage volume and the investment costs for collector array and storage have been calculated as a function of collector array size and solar fraction. A computer simulation of the system has been made evaluating the seasonal performance of the system under the meteorological conditions of Amberg. **Figure 46** shows the results.

On the right-hand side of **Figure 46**, lines of constant collector array size indicate the storage volume needed to achieve a certain solar fraction. The larger the collector array size, the smaller is the required volume of the stored desiccant for a given solar fraction. The left-hand side of **Figure 46** shows the related investment costs. A collector array size of 60 m^2 and a storage volume of 8.5 m^3 turn out to be the most economic solution to achieve 100% solar operation.

A solar collector array of 70 m^2 of highly efficient flat-plate collectors has been installed, providing a maximum thermal power of about 40 kW. Solar energy is collected during sunny periods in the early season and stored for several weeks until the energy is needed in short dehumidification periods in July and August. Separate tanks of 12 m^3 volume are used to store diluted and concentrated solutions, containing 3000 kg of LiCl salt and a varying amount of water.

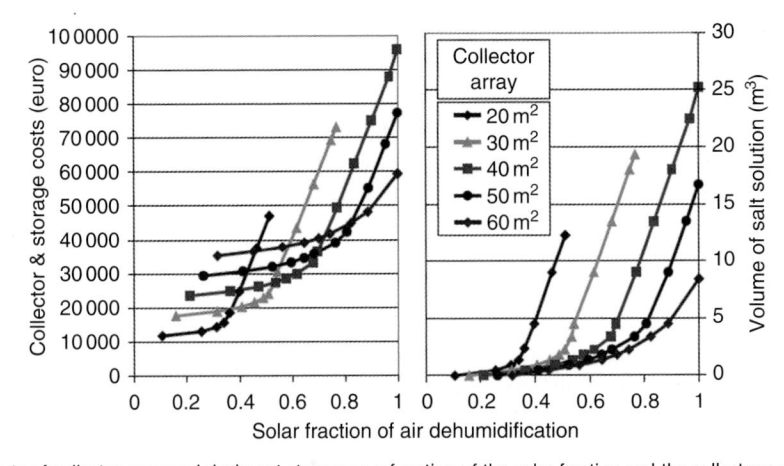

Figure 46 Investment costs of collector array and desiccant storage as a function of the solar fraction and the collector array size [31].

The desiccant cooling system can provide up to 20 MWh yr^{-1} of cooling and dehumidification energy. This includes the energy delivered by the cold recovery system. In addition to the regeneration of the desiccant solution, the collector array has the potential to deliver about 11 MWh yr^{-1} of hot water for the restaurant or the heating of the building. A connection to the heating system of the building, however, is not yet installed.

The necessary electrical energy for operating the desiccant system has been calculated to be about 1.5 MWh yr^{-1}. Compared to a conventional system using vapor compression cooling and gas heating, about 6 MWh of electrical energy and 11 MWh of thermal energy per year can be saved.

The well water cooling system provides a cooling energy of 150 MWh yr^{-1} and needs about 10 MWh of electrical energy. A conventional vapor compression system would need about 50 MWh of electrical energy per year.

The total investment costs of the desiccant cooling system including collector array, cold recovery, storage, and controls have been planned to be about €300 000; this is €2000 per kilowatt, respectively, or €10 per cubic meter per hour. The final costs have not yet been evaluated.

References

[1] Mehling H and Cabeza LF (2008) *Heat and Cold Storage with PCM: An Up to Date Introduction into Basics and Applications.* Heidelberg, Berlin: Springer.
[2] Dincer I and Rosen MA (2002) Thermal energy storage (TES) methods. In: Dincer I and Rosen MA (eds.) *Thermal Energy Storage: Systems and Applications*, pp. 93–212. New York, NY: John Wiley & Sons.
[3] Gil A, Medrano M, Martorell I, et al. (2010) State of the art on high temperature thermal energy storage for power generation. Part 1 – concepts, materials and modellization. *Renewable and Sustainable Energy Reviews* 14: 31–55.
[4] Buchlin JM (1989) Experimental and numerical modeling of solar energy storage in rockbeds and encapsulated phase change packings. In: Kilkis B and Kakac S (eds.) *NATO ASI Series, Series E: Applied Sciences, Vol. 167: Energy Storage Systems*, pp. 249–301. Dordrecht: Kluwer Academic Publishers.
[5] Kalogirou S (2009) *Solar Energy Engineering: Processes and Systems.* California: Elsevier.
[6] Nielson C, Akbarzedeh A, Andrews J, et al. (2005) The history of solar pond science and technology. *Proceedings of the International Solar Energy Society*, Orlando, FL, USA
[7] Andersson O (2007) Aquifer thermal energy storage (ATES). In: Paksoy HO (ed.) *NATO Sciences Series, II. Mathematics, Physics and Chemistry, Vol. 234: Thermal Energy Storage for Sustainable Energy Consumption: Fundamentals, Case Studies and Design*, pp. 155–176. Dordrecht: Springer.
[8] Witte HJL (2007) Advances in geothermal response testing. In: Paksoy HO (ed.) *NATO Sciences Series, II. Mathematics, Physics and Chemistry, Vol. 234, Thermal Energy Storage for Sustainable Energy Consumption: Fundamentals, Case Studies and Design*, pp. 177–192. Dordrecht: Springer.
[9] Nagano K (2007) Energy pile system in new building of Sapporo City University. In: Paksoy HO (ed.) *NATO Sciences Series, II. Mathematics, Physics and Chemistry, Vol. 234: Thermal Energy Storage for Sustainable Energy Consumption: Fundamentals, Case Studies and Design*, pp. 245–253. Dordrecht: Springer.
[10] Zalba B, Marín JM, Cabeza LF, and Mehling H (2003) Review on thermal energy storage with phase change: Materials, heat transfer analysis and applications. *Applied Thermal Engineering* 23: 251–283.
[11] Cabeza LF (2005) Storage techniques with phase change materials. In: Hadorn JC (ed.) *Thermal Energy Storage for Solar and Low Energy Buildings*, pp. 77–105. Spain: Universitat de Lleida.
[12] Demirel Y (2007) Heat storage by phase changing materials and thermoeconomics. In: Paksoy HO (ed.) *NATO Sciences Series, II. Mathematics, Physics and Chemistry*, Vol. 234: *Thermal Energy Storage for Sustainable Energy Consumption: Fundamentals, Case Studies and Design*, pp. 133–151. Dordrecht: Springer.
[13] Kato Y (2007) Chemical energy conversion technologies for efficient energy use. In: Paksoy HO (ed.) *NATO Sciences Series, II. Mathematics, Physics and Chemistry, Vol. 234: Thermal Energy Storage for Sustainable Energy Consumption: Fundamentals, Case Studies and Design*, pp. 377–391. Dordrecht: Springer.
[14] KaKac S, Paykoc E, and Yener Y (1989) Storage of solar thermal energy. In: Kilkis B and Kakac S (eds.) *NATO ASI Series, Series E: Applied Sciences, Vol. 167: Energy Storage Systems*, pp. 129–161. Dordrecht: Kluwer Academic Publishers.
[15] Dincer I and Rosen MA (2002) Thermal energy storage and energy savings. In: Dincer I and Rosen MA (eds.) *Thermal Energy Storage: Systems and Applications*, pp. 235–258. Chichester: John Wiley & Sons.
[16] Evliya H (2007) Energy storage for sustainable future: A solution to global warming. In: Paksoy HO (ed.) *NATO Sciences Series, II. Mathematics, Physics and Chemistry, Vol. 234: Thermal Energy Storage for Sustainable Energy Consumption: Fundamentals, Case Studies and Design*, pp. 87–99. Dordrecht: Springer.
[17] Streicher W and Bales C (2005) Combistores. In: Hadorn JC (ed.) *Thermal Energy Storage for Solar and Low Energy Buildings*, pp. 29–40. Spain: Universitat de Lleida.
[18] Witte HJL and Van Gelder AJ (2007) Three years monitoring of a borehole thermal energy store of a UK office building. In: Paksoy HO (ed.) *NATO Sciences Series, II. Mathematics, Physics and Chemistry, Vol. 234: Thermal Energy Storage for Sustainable Energy Consumption: Fundamentals, Case Studies and Design*, pp. 205–219. Dordrecht: Springer.
[19] British Geological Survey (1997).
[20] Eskilson P, Hellström G, Claesson J, (2000) Earth Energy Designer.
[21] Spitler JD (2000) GLHEPRO – A design tool for commercial building ground loop heat exchangers.
[22] Hellström G (1989) *Duct Ground Heat Storage Model, Manual for Computer Code.* Sweden: Department of Mathematical Physics, University of Lund.
[23] Medrano M, Gil A, Martorell I, et al. (2010) State of the art on high-temperature thermal energy storage for power generation. Part 2 – Case studies. *Renewable and Sustainable Energy Reviews* 14: 56–72.
[24] Castell A, Medrano M, Martorell I, et al. (2010) Experimental study of using PCM in brick constructive solutions for passive cooling. *Energy and Buildings*, 42: 534–540.
[25] Cabeza LF, Castellón C, Nogués M, et al. (2007) Use of microencapsulated PCM in concrete walls for energy savings. *Energy and Buildings* 39: 113–119.
[26] Schossig P, Henning H-M, Gschwander S, and Haussmann T (2005) Micro-encapsulated phase-change materials integrated into construction materials. *Solar Energy Materials and Solar Cells* 89: 297–306.
[27] www.ise.fraunhofer.de (accessed June 2010)
[28] Hauer A (2007) Adsorption systems for TES – Design and demonstration projects. In: Paksoy HO (ed.) *NATO Sciences Series, II. Mathematics, Physics and Chemistry, Vol. 234: Thermal Energy Storage for Sustainable Energy Consumption: Fundamentals, Case Studies and Design*, pp. 409–427. Dordrecht: Springer.
[29] Edem N'Tsoukpoe K, Liu H, Pierrès NL, and Luo L (2009) A review on long-term sorption solar energy storage. *Renewable and Sustainable Energy Reviews* 13: 2385–2396.
[30] Jaehning D, Hausner R, Wagner W, and Isaksson C (2006) *Thermo-Chemical Storage for Solar Space Heating in a Single-Family House.* USA: Ecostock.
[31] Hauer A and Lävemann E (2007) Open adsorption systems for air conditioning and thermal energy storage. In: Paksoy HO (ed.) *NATO Sciences Series, II. Mathematics, Physics and Chemistry, Vol. 234: Thermal Energy Storage for Sustainable Energy Consumption: Fundamentals, Case Studies and Design*, pp. 429–444. Dordrecht: Springer.
[32] Hauer A (2007) Sorption theory for thermal energy storage. In: Paksoy HO (ed.) *NATO Sciences Series, II. Mathematics, Physics and Chemistry, Vol. 234: Thermal Energy Storage for Sustainable Energy Consumption: Fundamentals, Case Studies and Design*, pp. 393–408. Dordrecht: Springer.

3.08 Photovoltaic/Thermal Solar Collectors

Y Tripanagnostopoulos, University of Patras, Patras, Greece

© 2012 Elsevier Ltd. All rights reserved.

3.08.1	**Introduction**	256
3.08.1.1	The Origins of PV/T Solar Energy Collectors	256
3.08.1.2	Categorization of PV/T Collectors	256
3.08.1.3	History of PV/T Collectors	258
3.08.1.3.1	Early work on PV/T collectors	258
3.08.1.3.2	The development of PV/T collectors	258
3.08.2	**Aspects of PV/T Collectors**	259
3.08.2.1	Electrical and Thermal Conversion of the Absorbed Solar Radiation	259
3.08.2.2	The Effect of Illumination and Temperature to the Electrical Performance of Cells	261
3.08.2.3	Design Principles of Flat-Plate PV/T Collectors	263
3.08.2.4	Concentrating PV/T Collectors	265
3.08.2.5	Aspects for CPVs	267
3.08.2.6	Application Aspects of PV/T Collectors	268
3.08.2.7	Economical and Environmental Aspects of PV/T Collectors	269
3.08.3	**PV/T Collector Performance**	269
3.08.3.1	PV/T Collector Analysis Principles	269
3.08.3.2	Flat-Plate PV/T Collectors with Liquid Heat Recovery	270
3.08.3.2.1	PV/T-water collector energy balance equations	270
3.08.3.2.2	PV/T collector thermal losses	271
3.08.3.2.3	The electrical part of the PV/T collector	271
3.08.3.2.4	Thermal energy of PV/T collector	271
3.08.3.2.5	Thermal energy of PV/T collector	271
3.08.3.3	Flat-Plate PV/T Collectors with Air Heat Recovery	271
3.08.3.3.1	PV/T-air collector energy balance equations	272
3.08.3.3.2	Pressure drop	272
3.08.3.3.3	Influence of geometrical and operational parameters	273
3.08.3.4	PV/T-Air Collector in Natural Airflow	274
3.08.3.4.1	Analysis of airflow rate	274
3.08.3.4.2	Estimation of heat transfer coefficient, h_c, and friction factor, f	275
3.08.3.5	Design of Modified PV/T Systems	276
3.08.3.6	Hybrid PV/T System Design Considerations	277
3.08.3.6.1	PV/T collector efficiency test results	278
3.08.3.7	Thermosiphonic PV/T Solar Water Heaters	279
3.08.4	**Application of PV/T Collectors**	280
3.08.4.1	Building Application Aspects	280
3.08.4.1.1	PV/T collectors in the built environment	280
3.08.4.1.2	The booster diffuse reflector concept	281
3.08.4.2	PV/T Collectors Applied to Buildings	282
3.08.4.2.1	PV/T-water collectors	282
3.08.4.2.2	PV/T-air collectors	285
3.08.4.3	The PVT/DUAL System Concept	286
3.08.4.3.1	Modified PVT/DUAL systems	286
3.08.4.4	PV/T–STC Combined Systems	287
3.08.4.5	FRESNEL/PVT System for Solar Control of Buildings	289
3.08.4.6	CPC/PVT Collector New Designs	291
3.08.4.7	PV/T Collectors in Industry and Agriculture	292
3.08.4.7.1	PV/T collectors in industry	292
3.08.4.7.2	PV/T in agriculture	294
3.08.4.7.3	PV/T collectors combined with other renewable energy sources	295
3.08.4.7.4	Commercial PV/T collectors	295
3.08.5	**Epilog**	296
References		296

3.08.1 Introduction

3.08.1.1 The Origins of PV/T Solar Energy Collectors

Solar energy conversion systems as thermal collectors and PVs are devices that absorb solar radiation and convert it to useful energy as thermal and electrical, respectively. Flat-plate solar thermal collectors, vacuum tube solar thermal collectors, compound parabolic concentrating (CPC) solar collectors, Fresnel lenses, and parabolic trough concentrating (PTC) collectors with linear absorbers are typical devices that are mainly used to convert solar radiation into heat, while parabolic dish-type, circular Fresnel lenses, and tower-type concentrating solar energy systems are the systems that convert the absorbed solar radiation into heat, a following process converts the heat to power and further to electricity. On the other hand, PVs are the main type of solar devices that convert solar radiation directly into electricity. Typically, PVs are made from silicon-type modules, semiconductors based on polycrystalline silicon (pc-Si), monocrystalline silicon (c-Si), and amorphous silicon (a-Si) modules. In terrestrial applications, the pc-Si type PV modules are the most widely applied, and new types of PVs, such as cadmium telluride (CdTe), copper indium gallium selenide (CIGS), dye-sensitized solar cells (DSSCs), and so on, have been introduced to the market. Silicon-type PVs are still the main cell types in applications because they have longer durability and higher efficiency. The PVs that are based on other materials than on silicon would follow in applications in the next years, mainly in the built sector. The conversion rate of solar radiation into electricity by PVs depends on cell type and is between 5% and 20%. Thus, the greater part of the absorbed solar radiation by PVs is converted into heat (at about 60–70%), increasing the temperature of cells. This effect results in the reduction of their electrical efficiency and there is an essential difference between solar thermal collectors and PVs regarding the required conditions for their effective operation. The solar thermal collectors aim to achieve higher absorber temperature in order to provide heat removal fluid (HRF) efficiently and at higher temperature, while the PV cells operate at lower temperatures in order to achieve higher efficiency in their electrical output.

In the case of PV modules that are installed in parallel rows on horizontal plane of ground or building roof, the exposure of both PV module surfaces to the ambient permits their natural cooling, but in facade or inclined roof installation on buildings, the thermal losses are reduced due to the thermal protection of PV rear surface and PV modules operate at higher temperatures. This undesirable effect can be partially avoided by applying a suitable heat extraction with a fluid circulation, keeping the electrical efficiency at a satisfactory level. In the case of using air as HRF, the contact with PV panels is direct (PV/T-air collectors), while in the case of using liquids, mainly water (PV/T-water collectors), the contact is through a heat exchanger. PV modules that are combined with thermal units, where circulating air or water of lower temperature than that of the PV module is heated and forwarded for use, constitute hybrid PV/T systems and provide electrical and thermal energy, therefore increasing the total energy output from PV modules. PV/T systems have been introduced since the mid-1970s, but they were not developed in the same way as the well-known solar thermal collectors and PVs. PV/T systems were first suggested, experimented, and analyzed by Martin Wolf in 1976 [1], and in the following years, many studies were carried out by other researchers. Commercial PV/T systems have been on market for about 20 years, although they have not yet been accepted as solar energy systems of high performance. These solar devices are still at their beginning, and in most cases, they are applied for demonstration purposes, except PV/T-air systems have been on the facades of buildings, where PV cooling is critical to avoid electrical output reduction and this method is standard practice in building-integrated photovoltaics (BIPVs) applications. In addition to flat-type PV/T collectors based on typical PV modules, concentrating photovoltaic/thermal (CPVT) collectors have been developed combining reflectors or lenses with concentrating-type cells, aiming at cost-effective conversion of solar energy.

3.08.1.2 Categorization of PV/T Collectors

PV/T solar energy systems can be divided into three systems according to their operating temperature: low- (up to about 50 °C), medium- (up to about 80 °C), and high-temperature (>80 °C) systems. The hybrid PV/T systems that are referred to applications of very low temperatures (30–40 °C) are associated with air or water preheating and are considered the most promising PV/T category. The PV/T systems that use typical PV modules and provide heat above 80 °C have lamination problems due to the high operating temperatures and need further development. In PV/T systems, although electrical and thermal output is high if operated at low temperatures, the main aim is to provide heat at a considerable fluid temperature to be useful for practical applications, also keeping the electrical output at a satisfactory level. The electrical and thermal output, although is of different value, could be added in order to give a figure of the hybrid system total (electrical and thermal) energy output, and new devices are in development toward cost-effective and of low environmental impact solar energy conversion systems.

The flat-type PV/T solar systems can be effectively used in the domestic and in the industrial sectors, mainly for preheating water or air. Hybrid PV/T systems can be applied mainly in buildings for the production of electricity and heat and are suitable for PV applications under high values of solar radiation and ambient temperature. In **Figure 1**, the two basic forms of PV/T collectors, with and without additional glazing, are shown. In these devices, water or air is circulated in thermal contact with the PV, exchanging heat. When air is used, the contact with PV panels is direct, while in the case of using liquids, the contact is made through a heat exchanger. The water-cooled PV modules (PV/T-water systems) are suitable for water heating, space heating, and other applications (**Figures 1(a)** and **1(b)**). Air-cooled PV modules (PV/T-air systems) can be integrated on building roofs and facades, and apart from the electrical load, they can cover building heating and air ventilation needs (**Figures 1(c)** and **1(d)**). PV/T solar collectors integrated on building roofs and facades can replace separate installation of thermal collectors and PVs, resulting in cost-effective application

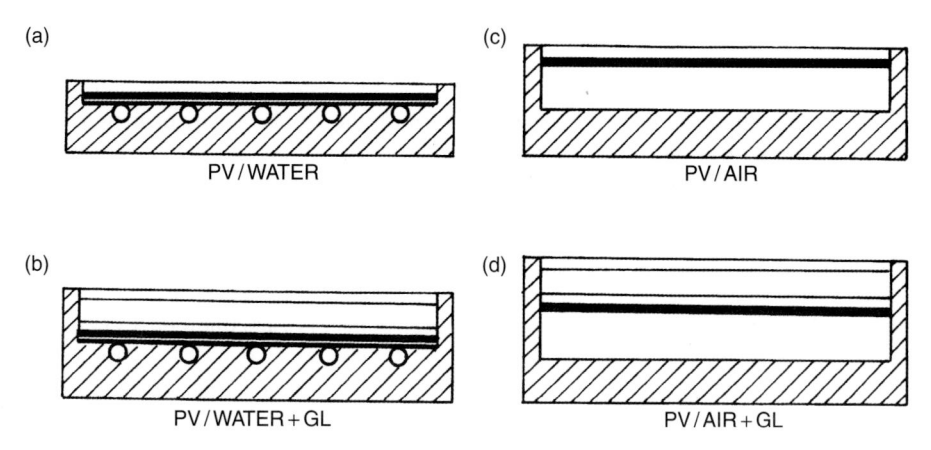

Figure 1 Cross-section of PV/T experimental models for water and air heating [2].

of solar energy systems. To increase system operating temperature, an additional glazing is used (**Figures 1(b)** and **1(d)**), but this results in a decrease of the PV module electrical output because an amount of the incoming solar radiation is absorbed and another part is reflected away, depending on the angle of incidence. These new solar devices can be mainly used for residential buildings, hotels, hospitals, and other buildings; to cover agricultural and industrial energy demand; and also to simultaneously provide electricity and heat in several other sectors.

In PV/T system applications, the production of electricity is of priority; therefore, it is necessary to operate the PV modules at low temperatures in order to keep PV cell electrical efficiency at a sufficient level. This requirement limits the effective operation range of the PV/T unit to low temperatures; thus, the extracted heat can be used mainly for low-temperature applications such as space heating, water or air preheating, and natural ventilation in buildings. Water-cooled PV/T systems are practical systems for water heating in domestic buildings but their application is limited up to now. Air-cooled PV modules have been applied to buildings, integrated usually on their southern inclined roofs or facades. In PV/T systems, the electrical output from PV modules can be increased contributing to building space heating during winter and ventilation during summer, thus avoiding building overheating. PV/T-water systems are promising solar energy systems and they are under development to become cost-effective for commercial applications. Some new systems have been introduced in the market, but with limited use so far.

Natural or forced air circulation is a simple and low-cost way to remove heat from PV modules, but it is less effective at low latitudes where ambient air temperature is over 20 °C for many months during the year. In BIPV applications, unless special precautions are taken, the increase of PV module temperature can result in the reduction of PV efficiency and the increase of undesirable heat transfer to the building, mainly during summer. In air-cooled hybrid PV/T systems, the air channel is usually mounted at the rear of the PV module. Air of lower temperature than that of the PV modules, usually ambient air, is circulating in the channel, and PV cooling as well as thermal energy collection can be achieved. In this way, the PV electrical efficiency is kept at a sufficient level and the collected thermal energy can be used for the building's thermal needs. Regarding water heat extraction, the water can circulate through pipes in contact with a flat sheet placed in thermal contact with the PV module's rear surface. In PV/T systems, the thermal unit for air or water heat extraction, the necessary fan or pump, and the external ducts or pipes for fluid circulation constitute the complete system.

Hybrid PV/T systems can be applied, apart from the building sector, to the industrial and agricultural sectors, as high quantities of electricity and heat are needed to cover the energy demand of production procedures. In most industrial processes, electricity for the operation of motors and other machines and heat for water, air, or other fluid heating and for physical or chemical processes is necessary; this makes hybrid PV/T systems promising devices for an extended use in this field adapting several industrial applications (such as washing, cleaning, pasteurizing, sterilizing, drying, boiling, distillation, polymerization, etc.). In the agricultural sector, typical forms or new designs of PV/T collectors can be used as transparent cover of greenhouses and applied for drying and desalination processes, providing the required heat and electricity. The combination of solar radiation concentration devices with PV modules is a viable method to reduce system cost, replacing the expensive cells with a cheaper solar radiation concentrating system. Besides, concentrating photovoltaics (CPVs) present higher efficiency than the typical ones, but this can be achieved in an effective way by keeping PV module temperature as low as possible. The concentrating solar systems use reflective (mirrors) and refractive (lenses) optical devices and are characterized by their concentration ratio C or CR. The CPVT solar system consists of a simple reflector, properly combined with the PV/T collectors; tracking flat reflectors; parabolic trough reflectors; Fresnel lenses; and dish-type reflectors. In CPVT systems with medium or high CR values, the system operation at higher temperatures makes the application field wider, but requires PV modules that suffer temperatures up to about 150 °C, as it is possible to produce steam or achieve higher temperatures by the heat extraction fluid.

Apart from the individual use of hybrid PV/T systems, they can also be applied to buildings combined with other renewable energy sources, such as geothermal, biomass, or wind energy. When geothermal energy is used for space heating and cooling of residential, office, and industrial buildings, shallow ground installations of heat exchangers are applied combined with heat pumps (HPs). In these installations, the PVs can provide the necessary electricity for the operation of the HPs, while the thermal units of the PV/T system can boost the extracted heat from the ground. In the case of using biomass, PV/T collectors can be used to preheat the water and store it in a hot water storage tank, while the main heating is performed by the biomass boiler. In combination with PVs, small wind turbines can provide electricity. PV/T systems can effectively replace typical PV modules and new concepts are rising, with the supplementary operation, in some applications, of solar energy and wind energy subsystems.

Life-cycle assessment (LCA) methodology and cost analysis for typical PV and PV/T systems can give an idea for the environmental impact and the practical use of these systems. These analyses should consider the materials used and the application aspects, and as PV/T collectors substitute both electricity and heat, calculations confirm their environmental advantage compared with standard PV modules. Regarding PV/T system applications, modeling tools (such as TRNSYS methodology and others) can be used to get a clear idea about practical aspects, including their cost-effectiveness. In the literature, a reader can find some review papers on PV/T collectors and among them are the works of Charalambous et al. [3], Zondag [4], and Chow [5]. PVT Roadmap [6], a European guide for the development and market introduction of PV-Thermal technology, is one of the basic brochures that provide information on solar energy technology. In addition, under Task 35 of the International Energy Agency (IEA-SHC/Task35), studies on the technology and application of PV/T systems have been performed, and through international meetings, aspects on these new solar energy systems have been recorded. A brief history of PV/T systems is following, recording the main original published works in *Solar Energy* journals and conference proceedings.

3.08.1.3 History of PV/T Collectors

3.08.1.3.1 *Early work on PV/T collectors*

Theoretical and experimental studies referred to hybrid PV/T systems with air and/or water heat extraction from PV modules. In 1978, Wolf [1] and Kern and Russel [7] were the first who presented the design and performance of water- and air-cooled PV/T systems, while Hendrie in 1979 [8] and also Florschuetz [9] included PV/T modeling in their works. Two years later, numerical methods predicting PV/T system performance were developed by Raghuraman [10], and after few years, computer simulations were studied by Cox and Raghuraman [11]. A low-cost PV/T system with transparent-type a-Si cells was proposed by Lalovic [12], and results from an applied air-type PV/T system are given by Loferski et al. [13]. After the 1980s, Bhargava et al. [14], Prakash [15], and Garg and Agarwal [16] presented the same aspects of a water-type PV/T system. Following these works, Sopian et al. [17] and Garg and Adhikari [18] presented a variety of results regarding the effect of design and operation parameters on the performance of air-type PV/T systems. Because of their easier construction and operation, hybrid PV/T systems with air heat extraction were more extensively studied, mainly as an alternative and cost-effective solution to the installation of PV modules on building roofs and facades. Apart from the works on practical aspects, a general analysis of ideal PV and solar thermal converters was presented by Luque and Marti [19] to show the potential of these systems.

3.08.1.3.2 *The development of PV/T collectors*

Following the above-referred studies, test results from PV/T systems with improved air heat extraction are given by Ricaud and Roubeau [20] and from roof-integrated air-cooled PV modules by Yang et al. [21]. Regarding BIPVT systems, Posnansky et al. [22], Ossenbrink et al. [23], and Moshfegh et al. [24] include in their works considerations and results on these systems. Later, Brinkworth et al. [25], Moshfegh and Sandberg [26], Sandberg and Moshfegh [27], Brinkworth [28, 29], and Brinkworth et al. [30] present design and performance studies regarding air-type building-integrated hybrid PV/T systems. In addition, the works of Eicker et al. [31], which give monitoring results from a BIPV PV/T system that operates during winter for space heating and during summer for active cooling, and of Bazilian et al. [32], which evaluate the practical use of several PV/T systems with air heat extraction in the built environment, can be referred. These works were the first steps of the studies on the BIPV concept, applying effectively also PV cooling.

Large surfaces on the facade and roof of buildings are available and suitable for incorporating PV modules. Such incorporation has been referred to as BIPV technology and accounts for a significant portion in urban applications of PV systems in buildings. BIPV technology has provided practical applications of PV/T-air systems and built examples exist across the world [32–34]. In BIPV, a cavity is created behind the PV module for air circulation to cool the PV module and the preheated air can be used for the thermal needs of the building. Further, with installed BIPV panels, the solar energy absorbed and transmitted through the building fabric is reduced, hence decreasing the cooling load in summer. Several experimental and simulation studies on BIPV systems have appeared recently and most of them are focused on the ventilated PV facade [35–40]. BIPV is a sector of a wider PV module application, and the works of Hegazy [41], Chow et al. [42], and Ito and Miura [43] give interesting modeling results on air-cooled PV modules. Recently, the works on building-integrated, air-cooled PVs include studies on the multioperational ventilated PVs with solar air collectors [44], ventilated building PV facades [40, 45, 46], and the design procedure for cooling air ducts to minimize efficiency loss [47]. A study on several PV/T collectors, glazed and unglazed, using diffuse reflectors has been presented by Tripanagnostopoulos et al. [2] and also a theoretical and experimental work on improved PV/T-air collectors was performed by Tonui and Tripanagnostopoulos [48–50], while a detailed study using CFD methodology for air-cooled PVs was presented by Gan [51] and the performance of a building-integrated PV/T collector by Anderson et al. [52]. The energy performance for three PV/T configurations for a house [53] gives interesting information. Toward the effective use of PV/T-air collectors for buildings and a life-cycle cost analysis [54] shows that c-Si PVs are preferable for buildings with limited mounting surface area, while a-Si PVs are more suitable for urban and remote places.

Water heat extraction is more expensive than air, but as water from mains does not often exceed 20 °C and ambient air temperature is usually higher during summer in low latitude countries, the water heating can be used during all seasons at these locations. The liquid-type hybrid PV/T systems are less studied than air-type systems, and the works that follow the first period of PV/T system development are of Bergene and Lovvik [55] for a detailed analysis on liquid-type PV/T systems; of Elazari [56] for the design, performance, and economic aspects of a commercial-type PV/T water heater; of Hausler and Rogash [57] for a latent heat storage PVT system; and of Kalogirou [58] with TRNSYS results for water-type PV/T systems. Later, Huang et al. [59] presented a PV/T system with hot water storage, and Sandness and Rekstad [60] gave results for PV/T collectors with polymer absorber. Dynamic 3D and steady-state 3D, 2D, and 1D models for PV/T prototypes with water heat extraction have been studied by Zondag et al. [61]. PV/T systems with water circulation in channels attached to PV modules have also been suggested by Zondag et al. [62], and a work on the energy yield of PV/T collectors [63], a PV/T collector modeling using finite differences [64], and some PV/T-water prototypes were extensively studied by Busato et al. [65]. Following the above works, modeling results [42, 66], the study on domestic PV/T systems [67], the performance and cost results of a roof-sized PV/T system [68], the theoretical approach for domestic heating and cooling with PV/T collectors [69], the performance evaluation results [70], floor heating [71], and HP PV/T system [72] can be referred. Aiming at domestic hot water, hybrid PV/T-water collectors can replace the typical flat-plate collectors in the thermosiphonic systems. Works on this kind of solar devices have been performed by Kalogirou [58, 73–75]. In addition, PV/T solar water heaters of integrated collector storage (ICS) type [76] have been suggested.

In order to achieve cost-effective solar energy systems by reducing cell material and to provide HRF at higher temperatures, PV/T collectors can be effectively combined with solar radiation concentrating devices, thus forming the CPVT systems. CPVs are more sensitive than thermal collectors to the density of solar radiation on the absorber surface, and to avoid reduction of the electrical output from the cells, a homogenous radiation distribution is necessary. Flat and curved reflectors, Fresnel lenses, and dielectric lens-type concentrators combined with PVs are the most widely studied CPVT collectors. Reflectors of low concentration have been studied by Sharan et al. [77], Al-Baali [78], and Garg et al. [79] in the first years, while later, flat- or CPC-type reflectors combined with PV/T collectors have been proposed by Garg and Adhikari [80], Brogren et al. [81, 82], Karlsson et al. [83], Brogren et al. [84], Tripanagnostopoulos et al. [2], Othman et al. [85], Mallick et al. [86], Nilsson et al. [87], Robles-Ocampo et al. [88], and Kostic et al. [89]. For medium concentration ratios, PV/T systems of linear parabolic reflectors [90], linear Fresnel reflectors [91], compound reflector system [92], linear Fresnel lenses [93], and also Fresnel lenses combined with CPC secondary concentrators for building integration [94] have been investigated.

Economic aspects on PV/T systems are given by Leenders et al. [95], while the environmental impact of PV modules by using the LCA methodology has been extensively used at University of Rome 'La Sapienza', where Frankl et al. [96] presented LCA results on the comparison of PV/T systems with standard PV and thermal systems, confirming the environmental advantage of PV/T systems. LCA results for water and air-type PV/T collectors [97, 98] are compared with standard PV modules and give an idea about the positive environmental impact for low-temperature heating of water or air through the PV/T collectors. The application of PV/T systems in industry is suggested as a viable solution for a wider use of solar energy systems [99], and TRNSYS results for PV/T-water collectors, calculated for three different latitudes [100], show the benefits of these systems. The combination of PV/T absorbers with linear Fresnel lenses is suggested for integration on building atria or greenhouses to achieve solar control in illumination and temperature of the interior space, providing also electricity and heat [101]. Apart from single-type PV/T collectors, some new PV/T devices were suggested, combining heating of water and air [101, 102]. PV/T collectors have been suggested to be coupled with HPs [103] or to achieve cost-effective desiccant cooling [104], while some agricultural applications of PV/T collectors [79, 105–109] show the wide range of their usage.

Commercial flat-type PV/T collectors are few and the market is still at the beginning of its growth. Regarding CPVT collectors, there are some steps toward producing PV/T systems operating at higher temperature and some commercial CPVT collectors have been introduced to the market. The take-off procedure of all these solar energy conversion devices has been delayed, but the future looks brighter as the demand for renewable energy in buildings will be higher due to environmental concerns and fuel cost increase, and PV/T collectors can adapt energy load with limitations in the availability of external building surface. In addition, the agricultural and industrial sectors would be possibly a viable field for the wider application of PV/T collectors, if conventional energy sources become more expensive and environmental requirements more severe.

3.08.2 Aspects of PV/T Collectors

3.08.2.1 Electrical and Thermal Conversion of the Absorbed Solar Radiation

Solar thermal collectors are solar radiation conversion systems that collect and transform solar energy into heat, with efficiencies depending on the operating temperature and ranging usually between 30% and 80%. PVs are the solar devices that convert solar energy into electricity through the PV effect and their efficiency, for one sun isolation, is between 5% and 20%, depending on the cell technology. Apart from these two solar energy devices with the definite conversion mode, the PV/T solar energy collector is a third type of solar devices, which is a hybrid solar energy system providing simultaneously electricity and heat. This system has different design and operation characteristics from the other two types and aims mainly to improve the overall conversion efficiency of the absorbed solar energy by the PVs. A brief description on the main properties of PVs is presented, to combine the physics of PV cells with thermal collectors, including also the materials used for heat extraction from the cells and the basic application and economical and environmental aspects.

PV cells are generally classified as either crystalline or thin film. c-Si and pc-Si PV modules have the largest share in the market. a-Si modules have a smaller share of total PV production, while thin-film technologies and organic PVs are still a minority in the market. A c-Si module consists of individual PV cells connected together by soldering and encapsulated between a transparent front cover, usually glass and weatherproof backing material, usually plastic. Thin-film modules are constructed from single sheets of thin-film material and can be encapsulated in the form of a flexible or fixed module with transparent plastic or glass as front material. The modules are typically framed in anodized aluminum frames suitable for mounting and are guaranteed up to 20 years or more by the manufacturers. CPV systems use reflectors and lenses to focus sunlight onto the solar cells or modules, hence increasing their efficiencies, reducing also the size of PV modules. CPVs present conversion efficiencies of 30% under concentration, and multijunction solar cells have recently exceeded 40% under 1000 suns.

Parabolic dishes and Fresnel-type, parabolic trough reflectors, and CPC reflectors, made from glass mirrors or aluminum, are the systems used for solar concentrating systems. The Fresnel lenses are widely applied in CPVs and most of them are made from acrylic, while new solar lenses are based on silicon-on-glass (SOG). GaAs cells have higher conversion efficiencies, can operate at higher temperatures, and are often used in CPV modules and space applications, but are substantially more expensive. PV modules are also classified according to their output power under standard test conditions, defined as irradiance of $1000\,\mathrm{W\,m^{-2}}$ at AM1.5 solar spectrum and module temperature $25\,°C$. The c-Si cells produce electrical power between 1 and 1.5 W under standard test conditions and is supplied at voltage output of 0.5–0.6 V. PV modules, which consist of a number of cells in series and in parallel, are available with typical ratings between 50 and 300 W.

PV modules are usually applied to solar farms, for the generation of grid-connected electricity, to residential and office buildings, to industry, and so on. PV cells use sunlight with photon energy equal to or larger than the energy gap E_g. This energy gap differs for each cell type: for c-Si cells 1.12 eV, for a-Si cells 1.75 eV, for CdTe cells 1.45 eV, for CIS cells 1.05 eV, and for GaAs cells 1.42 eV. Each photon creates an electron–hole pair and the energy in excess of E_g is dissipated as heat, while photons with lower energy than E_g cannot generate electron–hole pair resulting to keep electricity conversion efficiencies low and up to a level of 30%. To generate an electric current, these light-created electron–hole pairs must be separated before being recombined and this is achieved through the built-in electric field associated with the p–n junction; however, not all of the light can be converted into electricity.

The energy that is not converted into electricity increases cell temperature, resulting in considerable reduction of the open-circuit voltage. In such a case, although the short-circuit current is slightly increased, the reduction of open-circuit voltage is much more and results in the reduction of the electrical output. The main reason for the higher reduction of open-circuit voltage is that the temperature rise increases the diffusion current, which results in a decrease of the charges at the edges of cell, thus reducing the voltage. The effect of voltage reduction is smaller for cells with higher band gap compared with cells with lower values of Si and Ge. In the case of c-Si cells, electrical output is reduced with a rise in operating temperature of about 0.4–0.5% K^{-1}; for a-Si cells 0.2% K^{-1}, while for CIS is 0.36% K^{-1}, CdTe is 0.25% K^{-1}, and GaAs is 0.24% K^{-1}. This performance is affected by the low or high heat transmission from cells to ambient. **Figure 2** shows the decrease of PV module electrical efficiency according to the cell temperature, for typical pc-Si unglazed and glazed PV modules. In case of direct mounting of PV modules on a building facade or roof, their rear surface is thermally protected due to contact with the construction material of the building and cells become warmer than when mounted on horizontal building roofs or ground surface and having both sides exposed to ambient air.

To avoid PV electricity efficiency reduction due to temperature rise of cells, it is logical to remove the excessive heat. In addition, the current status of the commercial flat-plate PV modules is that 5–20% of the incident solar radiation is transformed into electricity and the rest appears as heat. Thus, PV modules need cooling to keep their electrical efficiency at an acceptable level and there is also a higher potential of heat production from a given PV module to be used in a sensible way. In the case of combining PV cells with solar radiation concentration devices used to achieve a reduction of cell material and to increase electrical efficiency, cell cooling is necessary because of heating due to the higher density of solar radiation on cell surface and thus a passive or an active heat extraction should be applied. In the case of active PV cooling, water, air, or any other fluid can be circulated to remove the heat,

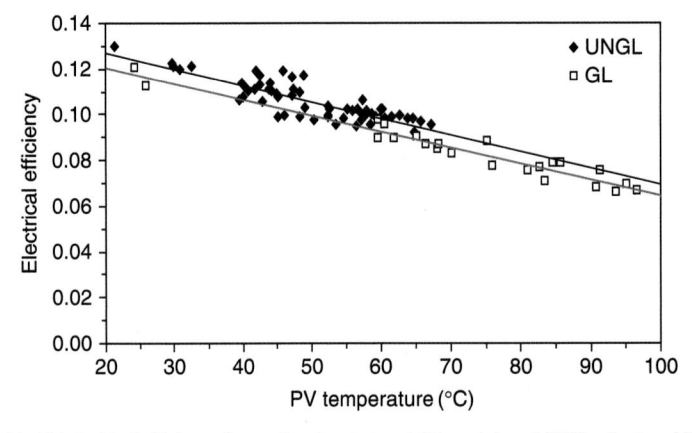

Figure 2 The temperature effect to PV electrical efficiency for unglazed and glazed PV modules of PV/T collectors [49].

which is transferred to a thermal load or storage and the solar device is therefore the PV/T collector. PV/T collectors aim to increase the conversion rate of the incoming solar radiation on the PVs and to improve the total (electrical and thermal) energy output from them.

To improve thermal performance of PV/T collectors, an additional glazing can be applied above the PV module. In this case, the electrical efficiency of the PV cells is reduced because of the optical losses from the additional glazing, while the temperature of cells is increased, which obviously results in electrical efficiency decrease. The calculation of the absorbed solar radiation by the PV module is done in a similar way as in flat-plate solar thermal collectors, considering the optical properties of glazing and the PV module. The prediction of the operating temperature of the PV module is complicated and several formulas have been suggested [110–113]. In PV/T collectors, the thermal part affects the electrical part and PV cell temperature is the result from the incoming solar radiation, ambient temperature, wind speed, and circulating HRF temperature. An estimation of cell temperature for PV/T collectors affected by convection on both their surfaces or having thermally insulated rear surface and operating also under the effect of an additional reflector can be used for various applications [97, 98]. The results from these studies show that the PV/T collectors present lower electrical output and higher thermal output in the case of collector rear surface attached on building roofs or facades, as they have an additional insulation on their back side. PV/T collectors that can transmit heat to the ambient from the front and the rear present higher electrical output and moderate thermal output, as cells keep their temperature relatively low. These results show that in the inclined roof or facade, integration of PV/T modules decreases electrical performance and increases their thermal performance.

PV/T systems operate in a similar way to the typical solar thermal collectors and can have liquid, usually water, or air as the HRF, defining therefore the two main types: the PV/T-water and PV/T-air collectors. Water-type PV/T collectors are suitable for domestic, agricultural, or industrial applications to heat water, while air-type PV/T systems can be applied in buildings as ventilated BIPV systems either on the facade or on the roof or on both and to preheat air that can be used for heating or cooling of the building, depending on the season. PV/T-air systems are cheaper than PV/T-water type solar collectors, since air can be heated directly by the PV modules (thus less material for a heat exchanger is used); hence, it is cost-effective for large-scale applications; in addition, they have no boiling corrosion or freezing problems associated usually with water-type PV/T system and leakage is not very critical. However, the performance of PV/T-air type collectors is lower than PV/T-water type systems due to poor thermophysical properties of air compared with water, and hence require heat transfer augmentation. Another option of PV/T collector application is the combination with HPs to adapt building space heating load from the increase of the coefficient of performance (COP) of the HP by the heated fluid of PV/T thermal energy and to drive the HP by the electricity from the PVs. PV/T collectors can also be applied for space cooling, desalination, drying procedures, and other applications.

3.08.2.2 The Effect of Illumination and Temperature to the Electrical Performance of Cells

Convectional PV/T solar collectors usually consist of two parts, solar radiation absorbers and the heat extraction units. The fraction of the absorber plate area covered by the PV cells is given in terms of cells packing factor (PF). The PF of a PV/T collector is defined as the fraction of the area occupied by the cells to the total module surface area (**Figure 3**). In the partially filled design, the spaces between adjacent rows of the cells allow some of the incident solar radiation to pass through and get absorbed directly by the secondary absorber plate [114]. The PF in PV/T systems is selected depending on the output load, either electrical load (electrical priority operation (EPO)) or thermal load (thermal priority operation (TPO)) [115]. The EPO has higher PF (usually ≥ 0.7), hence is optimized for electrical power, while the TPO has lower packing factor, hence optimized for thermal production. The PV cells are of higher cost when compared with other components in a PV/T collector, and under normal circumstances, the electrical power is given a priority. On the other hand, the TPO relies very much on the direct absorption by the secondary absorber of solar radiation that passes through the intercell spacing to increase the heat extraction from the back of the cells. Thus, PF determines the ratio of electricity to heat and characterizes the practical use of PV/T modules, with PV cells to be the main system part.

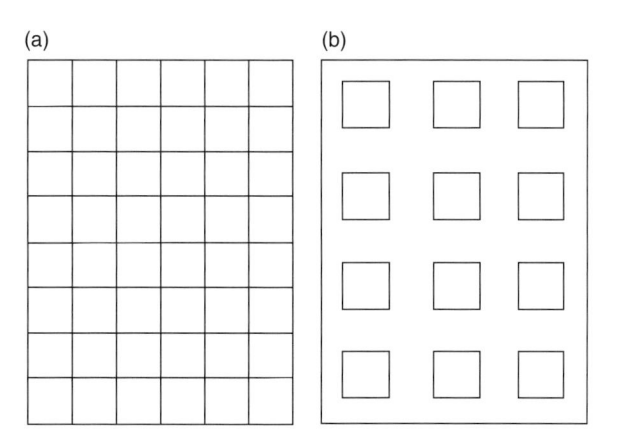

Figure 3 PV/T collectors with different packing factor (PF) of pasted cells: (a) 100% and (b) 25%.

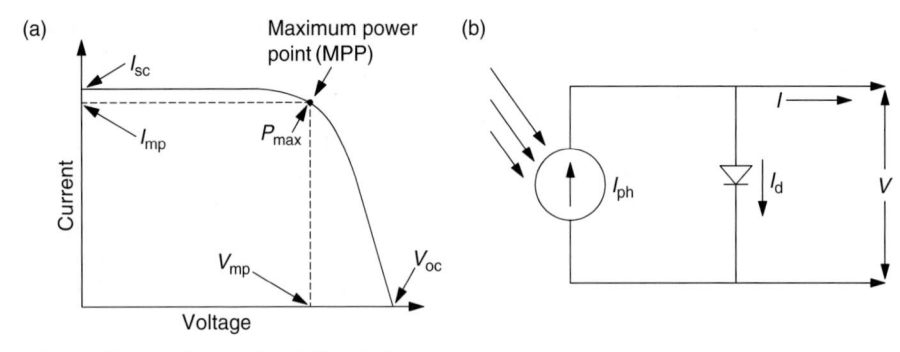

Figure 4 I–V curve of an (a) illuminated solar cell and (b) equivalent circuit.

The current–voltage (I–V) curves are used to characterize illuminated PV systems and a typical I–V curve is shown in **Figure 4(a)**, where open-circuit voltage V_{oc}, short-circuit current I_{sc}, maximum voltage V_{mp}, and maximum current I_{mp} are shown. The point where the product of I_{mp} and V_{mp} is maximum is called the maximum power point (MPP), which gives the maximum power, P_{max}, from a solar cell for the prevailing weather conditions and the load impedance. The fill factor (FF) of a solar cell is defined as

$$\text{FF} = \frac{V_{max} \times I_{max}}{V_{oc} \times I_{sc}} \quad [1]$$

The I–V characteristics can be described numerically by considering the equivalent circuit of a solar cell, as shown in **Figure 4(b)**, where the solar cell is modeled by a current source in parallel with a diode, representing the p–n junction. From **Figure 4(b)**, the output current, I, is equal to the difference between the photon-generated current I_{ph} and the diode current I_d as

$$I = I_{ph} - I_d \quad [2]$$

The diode current, I_d, is given by the diode equation

$$I_d = I_o \left(\exp\left(\frac{qV}{kT}\right) - 1 \right) \quad [3]$$

Substituting eqn [2] into eqn [3] yields

$$I = I_{ph} - I_o \left(\exp\left(\frac{qV}{kT}\right) - 1 \right) \quad [4]$$

where I_o is the diode reverse saturation current, q is the electronic charge, k is the Boltzmann constant, and T is the absolute cell temperature (K). Equation [3] describes the I–V characteristic of any PV system quantitatively. When the cell is short-circuited and $V = 0$, as in eqn [4], the short-circuit current flows in the reverse direction to that in a biased PV cell and is given by

$$I_{sc} = I_{ph} \quad [5]$$

When there is no bias, that is, no load or open circuit, then $I = 0$ and the open-circuit voltage is obtained from eqn [4] as

$$V_{oc} = \frac{kT}{q} \ln\left(\frac{I_{ph}}{I_o} + 1\right) \quad [6]$$

Thus, eqns [5] and [6] show, respectively, that I_{sc} is directly proportional to I_{ph} and V_{oc} varies logarithmically with I_{ph}, hence the effective solar irradiance intensity. I–V graphs of any PV device depend mainly on the solar irradiance and cell's operating temperature (**Figure 5**). The electrical efficiency of a solar cell falls as the temperature increases, mainly due to a reduction in V_{oc}, typically −2.3 mV/°C for c-Si solar cells [116]. The temperature rise of a PV cell tends to increase the I_{sc}, but marginally

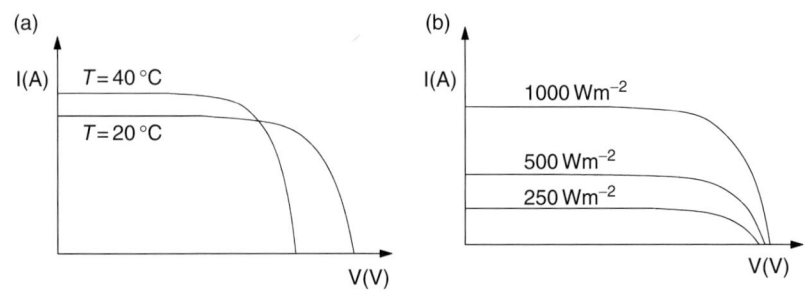

Figure 5 Typical I–V characteristics at different (a) temperatures and (b) intensities.

(≈6 μA/°C per cm^2 of cell area), hence is less pronounced and usually neglected in the PV designs. As the cell operating temperature increases, the band gap of an intrinsic semiconductor shrinks, making V_{oc} to decrease but allows more incident light to be absorbed, increasing the number of mobile charge carriers created, hence the increase in I_{sc}. The photogenerated carriers increase linearly with solar intensity due to the expected increase in the probability of photons with sufficient energy to create electron–hole pairs, which increases the light-generated current.

PV/T solar systems can simultaneously give electrical and thermal output, achieving also PV cooling and a higher energy conversion rate of the absorbed solar radiation. In PV/T modules, PV cells are placed on the absorber plate or the PV module acts as the absorber plate of a standard solar thermal collector. In this way, the waste heat from the PV module is directly transferred into air, water, or to phase-change materials (PCMs) that can store the heat to be used when needed. PV/T collectors can be analyzed regarding the conversion of the incoming solar radiation on their aperture area into electricity, with the electrical efficiency η_{el} and the conversion into heat, with the thermal efficiency η_{th}, and adding these two efficiencies the total conversion efficiency η_t is obtained:

$$\eta_t = \eta_{el} + \eta_{th} \qquad [7]$$

The total efficiency does not correspond to a well-defined energy conversion efficiency rate, as it includes two forms of energy of different values. Considering thermodynamics, the transformation of heat to power corresponds to the temperature difference between the 'hot' and the 'cold' level, while the electricity can be converted to power almost totally. Thus, to normalize the heat with the electricity of a PV/T collector, it is necessary to consider the HRF temperature. The efficient operation of PV/T collector regarding the electrical output is obtained for low operating temperatures of PV module, in order to avoid its reduction due to temperature rise. On the other hand, the efficient operation of a PV/T collector regarding the thermal output is obtained when the system can operate at higher temperatures with satisfactory efficiency. Actually, for low PV/T collector operating temperatures, both electrical and thermal efficiencies are high but the produced heat is of low thermodynamic value, as it corresponds to HRF of low temperature. Thus, in PV/T collectors, there is a conflict between electrical and thermal operation and this is the 'Achilles heel' of these new solar energy systems, and in the case of system operation at higher temperatures to obtain HRF at a useful application temperature, the electricity output of system is lower. A formula that can be used to calculate PV module temperature is a function of the ambient temperature T_a and the incoming solar radiation G and is given by Lasnier and Ang [110]:

$$T_{PV} = 30 + 0.0175(G - 300) + 1.14(T_a - 25) \qquad [8]$$

This relation is used for standard pc-Si PV modules. For the a-Si PV modules, their lower electrical efficiency results in slightly higher PV module temperature compared with pc-Si PV modules. For this reason, the following formula can be applied:

$$T_{PV} = 30 + 0.0175(G - 150) + 1.14(T_a - 25) \qquad [9]$$

In PV/T systems, PV temperature depends also on the system operating conditions and mainly on heat extraction fluid mean temperature. In PV/T systems, the PV electrical efficiency η_{el} can be considered as a function of the parameter $(T_{PV})_{eff}$, which corresponds to the PV temperature for the operating conditions of the PV/T systems. This effective value $(T_{PV})_{eff}$ can be obtained by

$$(T_{PV})_{eff} = T_{PV} + (T_{PV/T} - T_a) \qquad [10]$$

The operating temperature $T_{PV/T}$ of the PV/T system corresponds to the PV module and to the thermal unit temperatures and can be determined approximately by the mean fluid temperature. This modified formula corresponds to the increase of PV operating temperature due to the reduced heat losses to the ambient from the PV/T system.

3.08.2.3 Design Principles of Flat-Plate PV/T Collectors

The PV/T collectors are similar devices to solar thermal collectors, as both consist of a solar radiation absorber, thermal insulation at the nonilluminated surfaces of the device, and a glazing to keep thermal losses low from a system surface that faces the sun. The absorber includes a heat extraction unit for water or air circulation and heat extraction should have a good thermal contact with the absorber, the PV module. The glazing contributes to a higher thermal performance and reduces thermal losses as in typical thermal collectors, but due to optical losses (reflection, absorption), the electrical output of the PV module is lower than without using glazing. The most usual case to construct a PV/T collector is to attach a heat exchanger at the rear surface of a PV module. The common type of PV/T-water systems is the flat-plate solar thermal collector with PV cells pasted on the absorber plate, which was the usual way of construction of PV/T collectors during the first decade of their development. The adhesive used to bond the cell to the thermal absorber plate is made from a special material with good thermal conductivity but poor electrical conductivity to have good heat transfer from the cells to the absorber plate (hence to HRF) and simultaneously preventing short circuiting of the cells. PV/T-air systems, on the other hand, can have a ventilating air passage either in front or behind or on both sides of the PV module. Later, and in most of the studied PV/T collectors, a heat extraction element, for water or air circulation, is directly mounted on typical form PV modules, with most of them attached at the rear side of it. The PV/T-water system can be without or with an additional glazing (PV/T-water + GL), which results in higher thermal output (as it contributes to the reduction of thermal losses) but increases optical losses (reflection and absorption of solar radiation), thus reducing the electrical efficiency. In the case of using air as HRF, the system is the PV/T-air, also in the form without or with additional glazing (PV/T-air + GL). In **Figure 6**, the cross-section of both types is shown.

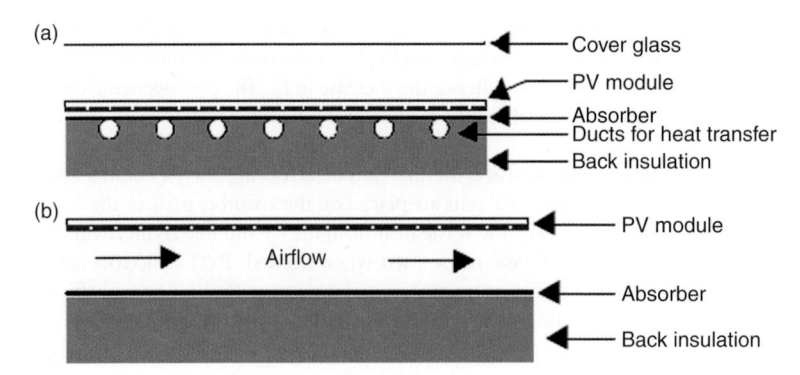

Figure 6 Typical (a) PV/T-water collector and (b) PV/T-air collector.

The dual behavior of PV/T collector design creates a dilemma to the PV/T collector designer concerning whether the emphasis should be given to the electrical or thermal energy output. The solution of partially covered absorber surface with cells (PF value, **Figure 3**) is good for the thermal part but not effective for the electrical output. In some commercial PV/T collectors, the cells are pasted on the additional glazing and not on the thermal absorber, in order to minimize the electrical energy reduction by the optical losses and the higher operating temperatures. The PF affects in all cases the electrical and thermal output, but PV/T manufacturers have not yet achieved optimal collectors considering both properties and most PV/T collectors use a typical PV module as absorber.

The Si-type PV modules are the most stable modules up to now, aiming to be used for the conversion of solar radiation into heat, in addition to electricity. Thus, c-Si, pc-Si, and a-Si PV modules of several sizes can be used, with c-Si type giving higher electrical and lower thermal output and the a-Si type giving higher thermal and a lower electrical output. The pc-Si module type gives satisfactory results for both electricity and heat, and due to the high efficiency and moderate cost, it can be considered an effective PV module for most of the applications of PV/T collectors. PV/T-water systems use mainly metallic absorber plates with pipes for water circulation, although polymer absorber plates have also been reported [60]. The water circulates usually inside the pipes that are attached to the absorber plate rear surface and collects the heat from the absorber. The collector back and sides are insulated to reduce heat loss from these surfaces. The PV/T-water systems can operate with forced circulation by a pump (pumped system) or by natural (thermosiphonic flow) circulation of the heat transfer fluid. Another approach for the water flow and heat recovery is to circulate it through flat channels over and under the PV module [4]. In PV/T-air collectors, a suitably constructed air gap is attached behind the absorber plate with the PV cells pasted below, though other designs exist. The air can be circulated by either natural or forced ventilation, which defines the kind of PV/T-air collector. The thermal energy in the PV/T-air collectors can also be transferred to other media such as water through an air/water heat exchanger.

In PV/T-air systems, the PV modules are used as absorbers and the air duct can be attached above, behind, or mounted at both of their sides. The PV module is heated by the incident solar radiation and a part of this heat is transferred to the air channel by convection and radiation. The radiation heat transfer carries heat energy from the PV rear surface to the back wall of the air channel which raises its temperature. The net radiant heat gained by the back wall is in turn transferred to the airflow by convection and a small fraction is lost to the ambient through the back insulation. Thus, the air in the duct receives heat from both the rear surface of the PV module and the back wall of the air channel during the day, and gets heated resulting in higher outlet temperature, hence heat production in terms of hot air. The thermal efficiency depends on the airflow mode, channel depth, and airflow rate. Natural air circulation constitutes a simple and low-cost method of heat removal from PV modules but it is less efficient. Forced air circulation is more efficient but additional energy supply to the pump or fan reduces the net electrical gain of the system. Small channel depth and high flow rate results in increased heat extraction but then results in high pressure drop in the forced flow operation. The increased pressure drop leads to increased fan power, which reduces the system net electrical output power. Therefore, the evaluation of the total energy yield of a PV/T-air collector in forced flow systems should account for the electrical energy required by the fan.

Comparing air with water heat extraction, the lower density of air results in the air heat extraction being less efficient than water heat extraction. To increase the thermal efficiency of air heat extraction, the PV/T-air collector design with air ducts over and under PV module, the two-pass PV/T-air system [17], has been suggested. This PV/T-air collector design is efficient if low-temperature air (e.g., ambient air) is inserted into the front air channel and then circulated through the second air channel at the back side of the PV absorber, but it is less efficient if air of higher temperature is inserted into the front air channel, because system thermal losses are increased. Another mode for heat extraction improvement is to place fins attached to the PV rear surface or on the opposite air channel wall (as in FIN modification), or the interposition of a thin metallic sheet (as in TMS modification) inside the air channel [48–50]. These modifications (**Figure 7**) are of low cost and a low additional pressure drop is present in the air channel. The TMS modification also plays the role of a heat shield, reducing the heat transmission to the building envelope when the PV/T-air collectors are attached on facade or inclined roof. This reduction has a positive result to the energy demand of the building, avoiding an amount of electricity consumption for driving the air-conditioning system of the building, if there are high values of solar radiation input and high ambient temperatures. Another design is the PV/T-air system, where cells are pasted on a thermal absorber with fins attached on the back of the thermal absorber [85]. In addition to PV/T-water and PV/T-air collectors, two alternative

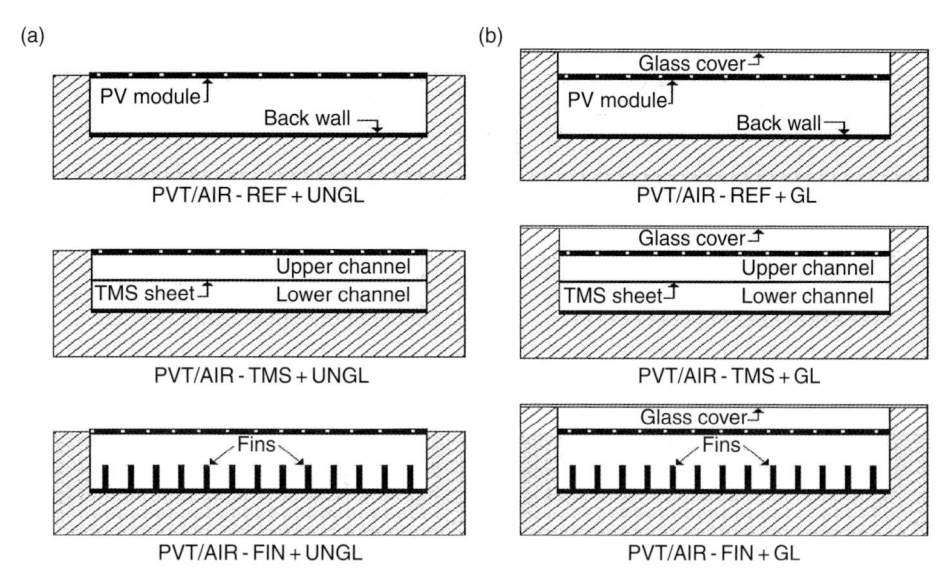

Figure 7 Modified air channels in (a) unglazed and (b) glazed PV/T-air collectors [49].

designs have been proposed, with water and air heat extraction. The first type consists of an air channel behind a PV module, where a conductive plate with pipes for water circulation is attached at the rear of the PV module and can operate with water or air heat extraction [101]. The air heat extraction has also some improvements to increase thermal efficiency. Regarding the second type, there is an arrangement of successive rows of PV cells that are cooled by air ducts at the PV module rear sides and thermal absorbers consisting of fins with pipes for water heat extraction [102].

Another option for PV/T collector application is the hybrid thermosiphonic system, consisting of PV/T collectors, which have usually an additional glazing to suppress system thermal losses and a hot water storage tank, in a similar form as the typical flat-plate thermosiphonic systems. Apart from a commercial model [56], there are some publications on this issue [58, 73, 75], analyzing system operation and application aspects. Thermosiphonic-type PV/T systems are considered as alternatives to typical domestic solar hot water units, aiming to replace them as providing electricity in addition to hot water. Although PV/T-thermosiphonic systems are promising devices for domestic applications, there are some additional problems with their performance. The additional glazing and the higher cell operating temperature, in order to achieve a considerable level of water temperature, result in the reduction of system electrical output. On the other hand, PV cells are not usually constructed with low ε coating, and the inevitable thermal resistance between PV cells and the water heat extraction unit are two obstacles that lower thermal performance compared with the typical thermosiphonic systems. The above reasons compel PV/T-thermosiphonic systems to require a larger aperture surface area than thermosiphonic systems for the same stored hot water quantity. An improvement to system total energy output is the placement of an adjusted flat reflector in front of the PV/T collector. Considering the use of c-Si, pc-Si, and a-Si cells for the PV module of the PV/T collector in the thermosiphonic system, a-Si cells result in higher thermal output because of their lower conversion rate to electricity. In this case, PV/T collectors should be of larger aperture surface to produce the same electrical output as of c-Si or pc-Si cells. The PF is also important and affects the electrical and thermal performance of PV/T-thermosiphonic collector, as considering its thermal behavior, in low PF values, the system is closer to the typical thermosiphonic mode. For high PF value, the thermal output is reduced and the system is less effective in water heating.

3.08.2.4 Concentrating PV/T Collectors

Several investigations resulted to lower the cost of PVs increasing also their electrical efficiency, but their payback time has not been reduced enough to be considered as cost-effective. The combination of solar radiation concentration devices with PV modules is up to now the most viable method to reduce system cost, replacing the expensive cells with a cheaper solar radiation concentrating systems, which converge the solar rays to a PV module of smaller surface area than aperture. Although CPV solar energy systems present higher efficiency than the typical flat PV modules, concentration is more important in cases where there is a high ratio of beam solar radiation; however, homogenous distribution on PV cells is required for effective cooling to keep their temperature low. For PV cooling, the water or air heat extraction can avoid the efficiency reduction due to the PV module temperature increase. Concentrating solar energy systems should use a system to track the sun and only the very low concentration ($C < 2$) devices can be stationary. The distribution of the solar radiation on the cell surface and its temperature rise are two problems that affect its electrical output. The uniform distribution of the concentrated solar radiation on cell surface and the application of a suitable cooling mode contribute in all cases to an effective system operation, considering the achievement of the maximum electrical output. Nonuniformity is due to mirror geometry or shape error, which even if small, has a significant effect on the flux profile. The passive (heat sink) and active (heat extraction by water or air circulation) cooling of cells are the usual modes to keep their temperature at an acceptable level. In general, PV/T collectors can be divided into three systems according to their operating temperature: low- (up to about 50 °C), medium- (up to about 80 °C), and high-temperature (>80 °C) systems. The PV/T systems based on typical PV modules that aim to provide heat above 80 °C have lamination problems due to the high operating temperatures and need further development. As extension of the simple cooling mode of CPV, the CPVT solar systems are a follow-up stage of CPV and of typical PV/T systems.

The concentrating solar energy systems use reflective (flat or curved mirrors) and refractive (mainly Fresnel lenses) optical devices. CPV module efficiencies are up to 40%, with respect to the incident direct solar radiation. Plane and curved reflectors are often used to increase the density of solar radiation on the focal point or on the focal line, while Fresnel lenses that are inexpensive and lightweight plastic material have also been developed to adapt solar radiation concentrating requirements for PV and PV/T systems The concentrator material should be inexpensive compared with the cells, as it corresponds to 5, 20, 100, or more times larger aperture than them and also durable for a long period, aiming to adapt the life of cells (more than 20 years).The solar energy systems are characterized by their concentration ratio C (or CR), expressed in X suns and are combined with 'linear focus' (2D) or 'point-focus' (3D) absorbers for low ($C<10X$), medium ($C<100X$), or high ($C>100X$) values. The low concentrating ratio systems are of particular interest to be combined with PVs as they are of linear geometry and thus one tracking axis is enough for their efficient operation. In low CPVs, c-Si PV modules are the most usual type for low CPV systems but their electrical output is reduced by the temperature increase and the nonuniform distribution of solar radiation on their surface, but in contrast to c-Si cells of typical PV modules (flat type), the temperature coefficient of efficiency reduction is lower for concentrating-type c-Si cells ($0.25\% \, K^{-1}$). Cells of GaAs have higher conversion efficiency than c-Si cells and can operate more effectively in higher temperatures but are of substantially higher cost. Thin-film PVs like Cu-In-Ga-Se$_2$ (CIGS) are less sensitive to the nonuniform distribution of solar radiation but they are still of lower efficiency than crystalline silicon cells. Recently, CPV efficiencies exceed 40% for systems of 1000 suns on multijunction cells. On the other hand, low CPVs are mostly with static concentrators (no movements to track the sun), but the nonuniform distribution of solar radiation on the surface of cells decrease their electrical efficiency. In some systems, bifacial cells are used in order to adapt concentrating system geometry, reducing in this way the cell material [117–120].

The high-concentration solar energy systems use only direct solar radiation. The diffuse solar radiation is partially absorbed by the very low-concentration systems and mainly by the static concentrators. The concentrated solar radiation on the absorber is limited by thermodynamics, solar disk diameter, and the concentrator geometry [121], while the ratio of the radiation on the absorber to the incoming one determines the optical concentration of the system. Solar thermal concentrating systems aim to energy applications of high-temperature requirements. In concentrating systems, the absorber surface area is smaller than the system aperture surface area and this contributes to lower system thermal losses with respect to the solar radiation exposed surface. To avoid radiation thermal losses, the absorber should be covered by a low emission infrared coating (low ε selective absorber). The suppression of convection thermal losses is achieved by using transparent covers, or with fluid circulation pipes inside evacuated tubes. CPVs differ from the solar thermal concentrating collectors because high temperatures reduce their efficiency and it is energetically preferable to operate at lower possible temperatures. In addition, the distribution of concentrated solar radiation on PV cells is critical for their electrical efficiency, while in concentrating solar thermal collectors, the short width of the solar radiation absorber results in an effective heat transmission by conductivity and the requirement for a high homogeneity of the concentrated solar radiation on the thermal absorber surface is not particularly significant.

Concentrators definitely have the potential to be comparative on cost but they must be effectively designed to benefit from this. The solar radiation concentration devices are the reflectors (such as flat, V-trough, CPC, cylindrical parabolic, dishes, etc.) and the lenses (such as linear Fresnel lenses, point-focus Fresnel lenses, dielectric type lenses, etc.). Recently, advanced technology Fresnel lens concentrators have been developed and commercial models are on the market, and most of them are of the 3D type with a large number of grooves. Regarding reflectors, for high CPV systems the parabolic dish type has been mostly used until now, with tower-type concentrators to be promising for the future. For medium CPV systems, Fresnel lenses, Fresnel reflectors, and parabolic trough reflectors have been studied. Comparison results [122–124] give an idea about the benefits of CPV systems. In low CPV flat and curved reflectors, Fresnel lenses and dielectric lens-type concentrators have been studied. Among them are the V-trough systems, CPC-type reflectors [80, 81, 125–132], refractive concentrators [117, 133, 134], linear Fresnel lenses [135–137], and linear Fresnel reflectors [92, 191]. Regarding dielectric lens-type concentrators, optical results show that for 3D static acrylic lens concentrators, a reduction of 62% in cell surface is achieved [133, 134, 138]. In medium CPVs, 2D concentrators have been applied, with the best-known being the Euclides system [139], which consisted of a parabolic trough reflector and flat-type absorber of PV cell strips on the focal line. In the point focus (3D) CPV systems, the Fresnel lens is the most-used concentrating optical medium with fewer applications of reflector-type concentrators [140–145].

In CPV systems, the cell temperature increase is controlled by applying a passive cooling mode, using heat sinks of several geometries. If PV cell temperature rise is high and the system needs active cooling, water or air circulation through a heat exchanger in thermal contact with PV cells removes the heat and rejects it. If this heat is not rejected to ambient but is transferred to storage or is suitably used to cover a thermal load, then the solar device can be considered as a hybrid CPVT system. Few CPVT systems have been studied till now and most of them are of low to medium concentrating ratio. CPVT systems consist of a solar radiation concentration system and their thermal unit operates with water, air, or other fluid circulation to extract the heat and keep PV temperature as low as possible. They can simultaneously provide electricity and heat, like the flat-type PV/T collectors, but due to the higher level of achieved fluid temperature, these devices aim to become more practical and cost-effective. CPVT collectors can be combined with low-, medium- or high-concentration devices, but so far, only systems of low and medium concentration ratios have been mainly developed. In CPVT collectors, the PV part is sensitive to the distribution of solar radiation and its homogeneity is of importance, while the thermal part is almost unaffected due to the high conductivity of the absorber.

3.08.2.5 Aspects for CPVs

In linear CPV and CPVT systems, the longitudinal radiation flux profile along the string of cells is affected by the shape of mirror, shading due to receiver supports, and gaps in the illumination. The flux profile is not the same for all cells in series and this limits the current and thus their performance. Maximum deviation from the ideal shape of the system is less than 1 mm and even small deviations from the perfect shape can cause significant nonuniformities in the flux at the focal line. In these cases, a reduction in short-circuit current and open-circuit voltage is observed, reducing finally the electrical output of the cells used. Another effect is that the temperature in locations of high solar radiation input can be 10–15 °C higher than elsewhere in the cell, reducing the open-circuit voltage. In the absence of a flux modifier, the electrical losses are in the order of 5–15%. In addition, other optical losses due to tracking process, wind, and high ratio of diffuse solar radiation cause a further reduction of the final system electrical output. High concentration ratio CPV systems, mainly of 3D Fresnel lens type constituting large arrays of panels that track the sun, are considered suitable for solar farms. Other technologies, such as panels of small parabolic reflectors, dish-type concentrators, and recently tower-type CPV, have also been developed. In Fresnel lens and small parabolic reflector CPV systems, passive heat sink is the main mode of cell cooling. In dish- and tower-type concentrators, PV cells cannot be passively cooled and an active mode is necessary; thus, new CPVT systems are considered to be an optimal solution. Regarding 2D CPV systems, linear Fresnel lenses, Fresnel reflectors, and cylinder-parabolic reflectors have been developed, using a water circulation mode to cool PV strips as an effective mode to provide heat in addition to electricity generation, while some CPVT systems have been introduced in the market recently.

Concentrating systems with CR > 2.5X use a system to track the sun, and for systems with CR < 2.5X, stationary concentrating devices can be used [121]. The low concentration ratio systems (C < 10X) are of particular interest for the PVs as they are of linear geometry and thus one tracking axis is enough for their efficient operation. The distribution of solar radiation on a PV module and its temperature rise affect the electrical output. The uniform distribution of the concentrated solar radiation on the PV surface and the application of a suitable cooling mode contribute to an effective system operation, considering the achievement of the maximum electrical output. The typical one sun cells convert the absorbed solar radiation into electricity at a relatively low efficiency, between 5% and 20%. These cells can be modified to operate also under low-concentration solar radiation (up to about 5X), but they present a reduction of their electrical efficiency due to the increase of temperature, thus they need cooling to keep a satisfactory electrical performance. For solar energy systems of higher concentration ratios, the suitable cells are mainly multijunction cells. Among the types of Si cells, the c-Si PV cells are the most usual type for low CPV systems, but their electrical output is strongly negatively affected by temperature increase, while the nonuniform distribution of solar radiation on their surface is another important reason for their efficiency decrease and the homogenous distribution of solar radiation on their surface is necessary.

In high CPVs, the sun tracking point-focus (3D) Fresnel lenses and reflective dishes are the most usual optical systems for solar energy concentration. In low CPVs, flat and curved reflectors, Fresnel lenses, and dielectric lens-type concentrators are the most widely studied. The solar energy devices in this field include V-trough reflectors, CPCs-type reflectors, several refractive concentrators, linear Fresnel lenses and Fresnel reflectors, or other types of concentrating systems and also systems with bifacial PV modules. Regarding the V-trough reflectors, the planar reflectors are used to increase solar radiation on the PV module surface, with sun tracking to result in a uniform distribution of solar radiation. These are simple devices, achieving concentration ratios up to about 2 with east–west- or north–south-orientated reflectors. CPC type is another category of devices that are coupled with PV modules. Most of them are static concentrators (no movements to track the sun), but the nonuniform distribution of solar radiation on the surface of cells decrease their electrical efficiency. In some systems, bifacial cells are used in order to adapt to the concentrating system geometry, reducing in this way the cell material, and for this purpose, dielectric lens-type concentrators have been investigated.

In CPVT systems, reflectors of low concentration, either of flat type as presented by Sharan *et al.* [77], Al-Baali [78], and Garg *et al.* [79] or of CPC type as proposed by Garg and Adhikari [80], Brogren *et al.* [81], Karlsson *et al.* [83], Brogren *et al.* [84], and Othman *et al.* [85], have been suggested in order to increase the thermal and electrical output of PV/T systems. A combination of Fresnel lenses with linear PV/T absorbers has been suggested by Jirka *et al.* [137], and Tripanagnostopoulos [93] studied for application to building atria and greenhouses to achieve, in addition to the electricity and heat production, an effective solar control of the interior spaces. For medium concentration ratios, CPVT systems of linear parabolic reflectors [90] or linear Fresnel reflectors [91] and linear-type Fresnel lenses [93, 94, 137] have been investigated. In very low concentration ratio, CPVT systems [86, 87, 116, 125, 128] and the stationary system consisting of flat booster diffuse reflectors [2, 89, 101] constitute the first works on this field.

The design of a PV cooling device depends on the material and the geometry of the concentrator, the system operating temperature, and the tracking requirements. In the case of concentrating systems that use single cells under high concentration, the usual cooling mode is passive cooling by heat sinks. For 3D Fresnel lenses, in the absence of PV cooling the cell temperatures may exceed 300–400 °C, but a thermal conductive plate or an air convective heat extraction by fins can achieve effective PV cooling, keeping cell temperature under 80 °C. In these concentrators, the cells are under the lens and they do not cause energy reduction from the optical losses due to shading. On the contrary, in 3D reflector-type concentrators, only fin-type heat sinks are suitable for passive cooling, as the cells are in front of the reflector and any wide in surface additional element may cause significant shading. Recently, the concept of a solar tower with a field of tracking reflectors is in development, in order to be applied also to PVs. In this case, the PVs are cooled by a liquid heat extraction system with forced circulation through pipes and transferring the heat from the tower down to the ground for use.

In linear (2D) concentrating systems, the cooling mode is usually a duct or tube, which is in thermal contact with the linear row of cells through which there is a circulation of water or another suitable liquid, to extract the heat and transfer it out of the CPVT system for use. This cooling mode can be easily applied to the linear concentrating systems using either a reflective (e.g., parabolic trough, Fresnel reflectors, CPC reflectors) or refractive (e.g., Fresnel lens, dielectric) optical system. In low CPVs constituting flat-type PV modules (e.g., V-trough, planar reflectors), the cooling mode is usually a conductive plate with pipes placed in thermal contact at the rear of the PV module and thermally insulated from its outer ambient surface, to keep system thermal losses low. An interesting low-concentrating system combined effectively with PV/T collectors is static diffuse reflectors, placed in front of flat-plate PV/T collectors, installed in parallel rows on a horizontal building roof or ground surface. The diffuse reflector contributes to a low, but considerably useful, additional solar radiation on the PV surface, which can give 20% or more energy output annually, with a very low additional cost [2]. Recently, some commercial types of CPVT collectors were introduced in the market and among them are systems based on CPC reflectors, linear Fresnel reflectors, slightly curved Fresnel-type reflectors, and parabolic dish reflectors.

3.08.2.6 Application Aspects of PV/T Collectors

The operating temperature of a PV/T collector affects the electrical power output of the PV module, and for maximum electrical production, the PV/T collector should operate at low temperature as much as possible under the prevailing weather conditions of solar radiation, ambient temperature, and wind speed. This can be achieved by circulating a fluid much colder than the PV module with proper flow rate, but this would result in a low temperature rise of the fluid, hence low thermal output. Thus, a PV/T system desired for electrical power production results in lower outlet temperatures of the fluid that are useful for low-temperature applications such as space heating (air) or water preheating for domestic or industrial use and swimming pool heating. The operation at higher temperatures is more useful for thermal applications requiring medium temperatures around 55 °C such as the solar domestic hot water (SDHW) systems. The use of PV/T systems with additional glazing is interesting mainly for the increase of system thermal output, because the PV electrical efficiency is reduced.

The intensity of solar radiation on PV module surface affects the rise of PV temperature. Considering the integration of PV/T systems on building facades, the modules are usually in a vertical position and the incoming solar radiation is reduced, mainly in low latitude countries, as the angle of incidence is large in most days of the year. During summer the sun's altitude is high, resulting in lower intensity on the module plane, also mainly in low latitude countries. In tilted installed PV/T collectors on buildings or in parallel rows on the horizontal building roof, the solar input is higher and this results in higher PV module temperature. The performance of PV/T-air systems depends on air channel depth, system tilt, airflow mode, and flow rate. The air channel depth affects the air heat extraction and the thermal efficiency is increased for smaller depth, but the pressure drop must also be taken into consideration for the determination of the additional electrical power input from the fan.

The reduction of temperature has a positive effect on the electricity output but it affects the practical value of cells to be used as thermal absorbers because the low temperature is of lower value for the thermal applications. PV/T collectors are efficient and therefore useful, mainly for lower-temperature applications, such as for water or air preheating in low temperatures (30–40 °C). In other applications, the building integration of PV/T collectors is practical when the available external surface area of building facade and roof is not enough for the installation of a considerable number of solar thermal collectors and PV modules (in number or in square meter). This requirement is obvious often in multiflat residential buildings, in hotels, athletic centers, and so on, where the thermal and electrical demand is high and the available installation surface area is small. In these cases, the PV/T collectors are more useful than separate thermal collectors and PV modules and it is the main application that could be considered as cost-effective. Another useful application of PV/T collectors, considering mainly PV/T-air collectors, is their use for space heating during winter and space cooling (by enhancing the air ventilation) during summer. In these applications, when these solar devices (the PV/T collectors) are directly mounted on a building facade or inclined roof, the building overheating from the transmitted heat by PV modules can also be avoided.

Industry is the sector responsible for the consumption of about one-third of total energy demand in most developed countries. PV/T collectors can significantly contribute to this load, as both electricity and heat are necessary in most industrial processes. Industrial buildings usually have large available surfaces suitable for the installation of solar thermal collectors of PVs and hybrid PV/T collectors. The application of solar energy systems in industry is still at low installation level, because the cost of conventional energy sources (e.g., oil, gas, electricity) is still kept low. The technological improvements and the rise of conventional energy cost would result in a wider application of solar energy systems, assisted also by other renewable energies such as geothermal and biomass and this penetration will contribute to the saving of conventional energy sources and environmental protection. PV/T collectors could play an important role to this as industry has a high ratio of low-temperature heat demand, and even if the collectors provide preheated fluid, it is very useful for the final energy contribution of solar energy systems. Flat-type PV/T collectors can contribute to warm water and air, while in the case of CPVT collectors, the demand in higher temperatures (such as cooling, steam for heating, or other processes) can also be covered. A similar situation is also in the use of PV/T collectors in agricultural applications. Solar drying and desalination processes can be adapted well with PV/T collectors and is a promising technology for the future. The first work on industrial applications of PV/T collectors refers to the application for water and air heating [99]. Later, a study using TRNSYS calculations [100] shows the interesting results from the use of PV/T collectors in the industrial processes.

3.08.2.7 Economical and Environmental Aspects of PV/T Collectors

Cost issues are important for all energy systems and hybrid PV/T collectors should overcome cost problems of both thermal collectors and PVs so as to achieve an optimized combination. The complete PV/T systems, apart from the separate electrical and thermal part of the modules, include the additional components called the balance-of-system (BOS) for electricity and heat. Because of the BOS, the final energy output is reduced by about 15% due to the electrical and thermal losses from one part to the other. The cost payback time (CPBT) of standard PVs for applications and without subsidies is about 15–20 years (considering market prices of 2010). PV/T systems present lower values of CPBT (about 10 years) if they are operated at low temperatures, whereas CPBT is higher for higher system operating temperatures because electrical and thermal efficiencies are reduced [97, 98].

Aspects and cost analysis results for standard PV modules [146, 147] and PV/T systems [58, 95] give an idea for the practical use of PVs. The consideration of the environmental impact of PV modules by using LCA methodology has been presented for typical PV systems [148–153], for comparison of CPV and non-CPV systems [122], as well as for domestic PV/T systems [67]. The LCA method has been extensively used at the University of Rome 'La Sapienza', starting with a PhD thesis [154] on LCA for PV systems and following the study on the simplified life-cycle analysis in buildings [155] and the overview and future outlook of LCA for PVs [156]. In addition, the comparison of PV/T systems with standard PV and thermal systems [96] confirmed the environmental advantage of PV/T systems. An extended work on LCA results for PV/T collectors has been performed [97, 98] with the LCA results from a specific software (SimaPro 5.1). These results refer to PV and glazed and unglazed PV/T solar systems on horizontal and tilted building roofs and for operation at three temperature levels. In addition, the use of a booster diffuse reflector between the parallel rows for the horizontal installations is suggested and the corresponding results are presented, aiming to achieve more effective PV and PV/T applications. The calculated energy performance, the LCA results, and the estimated CPBT of all systems can be considered useful as guidelines for the application of the studied standard PV and the newly suggested PV/T systems. In addition, the work of Beccali et al. [104] gives a figure of cost and environmental impact of PV/T collectors.

LCA methodology aims at assessing the potential environmental impacts of a product or a service during its whole life cycle. In studying PV/T systems, an installation should be considered according to all subparts such as PV modules, electrical BOS (inverter and cables), mechanical BOS, PV module and PV/T system support structures for both horizontal and tilted roof installation, the hydraulic circuit, aluminum reflectors, and heat recovery unit (HRU), with or without additional glazed covering. For all system components, the environmental indicators should be calculated from raw material extraction to end of life disposal. The main contribution (more than 99%) to the total impacts comes from the PV system itself, that is, from the production of all its components, including mechanical and electrical BOS. Despite that the disposal phase contribution is almost negligible, a sensitivity analysis is necessary to be performed in order to estimate the potential benefits of a 'controlled' system disposal for the considered PV/T collectors including BOS (both mechanical and electrical), hydraulic circuit, HRU, and other components, while LCA data should be also considered for PV modules recycling [157].

As for the system production, by means of an *ad hoc* contribution analysis performed only for the PV system production phase, nearly the whole of the impacts (96–97%) are due to PV module production, while barely significant are the shares of other system components, such as support structures or electric and electronic devices. In the case of complicated PV/T systems (such as with glazed covering, aluminum reflectors, etc.), PV modules' share of the total impacts is considerably lower, between 60% and 65%, and relevant contributions come from the additional components needed for heat recovery, reflection, and so on. The glazed HRU impacts come from copper (pipes and heat exchanger), aluminum (collector frame and collector back cover), glass (glazed covering), and polyurethane foam (insulation). The impacts of the reflectors are due to their high aluminum content, while for the mechanical BOS, most of the impact is due to the hydraulic circuit that is constituted by copper (heat exchanger in the storage tank) and galvanized iron (connecting pipes and water storage tank). As to aluminum products, recycled aluminum content of 30% can be assumed.

3.08.3 PV/T Collector Performance

3.08.3.1 PV/T Collector Analysis Principles

PV/T collectors are still under development and some technical improvements are necessary for them to become practical devices for cost-effective commercial applications. There are several modes of water circulation and heat extraction, but more practical is considered to circulate water through pipes in contact with a flat sheet, placed in thermal contact with the PV module rear surface. Regarding air-type PV/T systems, an air channel is usually mounted at the back of the PV modules. Air of lower temperature than that of PV modules, usually ambient air, is circulating in the channel and thus both PV cooling and thermal energy collection can be achieved. Natural or forced air circulation is a simple and low-cost method to remove heat from PV modules, but it is less effective at low latitudes, where ambient air temperature is over 20 °C for many months of the year. In PV/T systems, the thermal unit for water or air heat extraction, the necessary fan or pump, and the external ducts or pipes for fluid circulation constitute the complete system.

To increase the system operating temperature, an additional glazing is used, but this results in a decrease of the PV module electrical output because an amount of solar radiation is absorbed and another is reflected away, depending on the angle of incidence. In PV/T systems, the cost of the thermal unit is the same, irrespective of the PV module construction, whether with c-Si, pc-Si, or a-Si type of cells.

The PV/T concept has been in existence for nearly three decades now and has been discussed in numerous publications. Among the first works on the theoretical study of flat-plate PV/T systems are that on the extension of the Hottel–Whillier–Bliss equation to model PV/T systems [9], where a linear relationship between the cell efficiency and its operating temperature was proposed, and on the elaborate numerical models for both water-type and air-type PVT systems [10]. The theoretical model is based on the definition of equations describing the energy flows, both thermal and electrical. Considering a simplified model, the main assumptions made are the 1D steady-state heat transfer, the negligible thermal capacities of the collector components, and the heat transfer from the absorber, which is the PV module, to the conductive plate and the pipes for the PV/T-water, or to the air duct for the PV/T-air collector. The top optical losses are accounted by the product $(\tau\alpha)$, where τ is the transmittance of the front protective glass (for the unglazed PV/T-type collector) plus the transmittance of the additional glass cover (for the glazed PV/T type) and α is the absorptance of solar radiation by the cells.

The optical losses are subtracted from the incident solar radiation to get the net energy available for conversion into heat and electricity. The node temperatures of the PV/T collector are assumed to be uniform throughout the respective surfaces, and the collector aperture area is equal to the front area of the PV module designated by A_{pv}, while the active convective surface of the back wall and sides is denoted by A_{int}. For both PV/T-type collectors, the equations of energy balance are the same and the main difference lies in the heat transfer to the HRF and the pressure drop in the fluid circulation duct. There are several studies for the energy analysis of PV/T collectors and among them the works of Hendrie [8], Florschuetz [9], Raghuraman [10], Cox and Raghuraman [11], Moshfegh and Sandberg [26], Brinkworth et al. [30], Hegazy [41], Chow et al. [42], Ito with Miura [43], Busato et al. [65] and Ji et al. [158] can be referred. In the following text, the basic energy equations for PV/T collectors are presented, followed by experimental results from tested prototypes.

3.08.3.2 Flat-Plate PV/T Collectors with Liquid Heat Recovery

3.08.3.2.1 PV/T-water collector energy balance equations

The PV/T collector can be considered as a kind of solar thermal collector, which has PV cells to absorb solar radiation and a fluid heat extraction unit, constituting the collector thermal part for the circulation of the HRF. In PV/T-water collectors, the heat extraction unit is usually a heat conductive plate with pipes for the circulation of the water in thermal contact with the PV rear, while in PV/T-air collectors, it is usually an air duct placed at the rear of the PV. In addition, a glazing can be used to reduce PV/T collector thermal losses or the collector can be unglazed to avoid reduction in the electrical output due to the reflection and absorption optical losses by the glazing. The PV/T collector also has thermal insulation at the nonilluminated collector parts, similar to the way this is applied to the typical solar thermal collectors. The flat-plate PV/T collector with water heat extraction can be analyzed in a similar way as a flat-plate thermal liquid collector using the Hottel–Whillier–Bliss model [159] modified by Florschuetz [9]. As shown in **Figure 8**, the collector consists of the PV module, as absorber, a sheet with the pipes (ducts for heat transfer), thermal insulation, and additional glazing (cover transparent plate). The PV/T-water steady-state energy balance equation is as follows:

$$Q_s = Q_u + Q_L + Q_{OL} + Q_{el} \qquad [11]$$

Q_s is the incoming solar power on PV module aperture area $A_{pv}(m^2)$, Q_{OL} the optical losses, Q_u the useful power to the HRF, Q_L the thermal losses, and Q_{el} the electrical power extracted.

These parameters are calculated from the following equations:

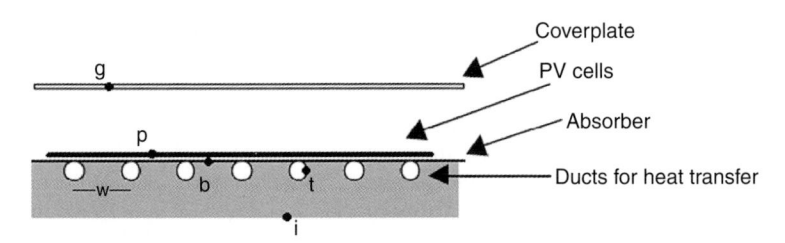

$$Q_s = A_{pv}G \qquad [12]$$

$$Q_u = \eta_{th} A_{pv} G \qquad [13]$$

$$Q_{OL} = (1 - (\tau\alpha))A_{pv}G \qquad [14]$$

Figure 8 Cross-section of PV/T-water collector with cover plate (PVT/GL).

$$Q_{el} = \eta_{el} A_{pv} G \quad [15]$$

G is the incident solar radiation (Wm^{-2}s^{-1}), η_{th} and η_{el} the thermal and the electrical efficiency, respectively, and τa the transmittance–absorptance product of the device.

3.08.3.2.2 PV/T collector thermal losses
Total thermal losses of PV/T collector U_L include top losses U_t, back losses U_b, and edge losses U_e:

$$U_L = U_t + U_b + U_e \quad [16]$$

The thermal losses are calculated using wind convection heat transfer coefficient and radiation heat transfer from glazing or from PV module to sky [159]. Considering a modified heat losses coefficient $\overline{U_L}$ to give the reduced thermal losses due to the energy rejection by the electricity, it can be calculated by

$$\overline{U}_L = U_L - \tau a \eta_{ref} \beta_{ref} G \quad [17]$$

3.08.3.2.3 The electrical part of the PV/T collector
The electrical efficiency of the PV module η_{el} depends on the temperature T_{pv} and is given by the formula [9]

$$\eta_{el} = \eta_{ref}\left(1 - \beta_{ref}(T_{pv} - T_{ref})\right) \quad [18]$$

where β_{ref} is the temperature factor of PV efficiency and η_{ref} the electrical efficiency for the reference temperature T_{ref}.

3.08.3.2.4 Thermal energy of PV/T collector
The thermal efficiency of the collector η_{th} is the useful energy Q_u to the incoming solar energy G and collector aperture surface area A_c:

$$\eta_{th} = \frac{Q_u}{A_c} G \quad [19]$$

$$Q_u = A_c \left[S - U_L\left(T_{p,m} - T_a\right)\right] \quad [20]$$

where $T_{p,m}$ is the mean temperature of absorber plate, T_a the ambient temperature, and S the absorbed solar energy per unit aperture surface.

3.08.3.2.5 Thermal energy of PV/T collector
Using the heat removal efficiency factor F_R and inlet HRF temperature T_i, the useful thermal energy Q_u is obtained from

$$Q_u = A_c F_R [S - U_L (T_i - T_a)] \quad [21]$$

The steady-state efficiency η_{th} modified by Florschuetz [9] for PV/T collectors is

$$\eta_{th} = \overline{F_R}\left[\tau a\left(1 - \eta_{pv}\right) - \overline{U_L}\left(\frac{T_{wi} - T_a}{G}\right)\right] = \frac{\dot{m}C_p(T_{wo} - T_{wi})}{A_c G} \quad [22]$$

where η_{pv} is the electrical efficiency of PV module for ambient conditions, U_L the thermal coefficient of total thermal losses, F_R the heat removal factor of the collector, $\dot{m}$ the mass flow rate of the HRF, and C_p the specific heat of water.

3.08.3.3 Flat-Plate PV/T Collectors with Air Heat Recovery

In most air solar collectors, the air circulates through a channel formed between the solar radiation absorber and system thermal insulation, and in some other systems through channels on both absorber sides, in series or in parallel flow. The usual heat extraction mode is the direct air heating from absorber rear surface by natural or forced convection and the thermal efficiency depends on channel depth, airflow mode, and airflow rate. Small channel depth and high flow rate not only increase heat extraction but also pressure drop, which reduces the system net energy output in the case of forced airflow, because of the increased power for the fan. In applications with natural air circulation, the small channel depth reduces airflow and therefore the heat extraction. In these systems, a large depth of air channel (minimum 0.1 m) is necessary [14]. Several publications are referred to investigations on air heating solar collectors. The simpler modification is the roughened opposite air channel wall surface [160, 161], by which up to about 30% heat extraction increase can be achieved. Better results give the addition of several types of ribs in the air channel [162, 163]. More efficient is considered the mounting of vortices [164–169], which contribute to about 4 times better performance in heat transfer. Other modifications that have been suggested for the improvement of heat extraction in the air channel are the use of pins, matrices, porous materials, and perforated plates. Fins on the absorber back surface, on the opposite air channel wall, or on both surfaces [170], as well as joining these two surfaces [171], are interesting and practical modifications to enhance the heat transfer in the air channel. Some other finned absorber geometries [172, 173] give satisfactory results, making promising this type of air channel modification. Air collectors based on perforated plates have also been used in combination with PV modules, extracting heat from them and thus cooling them and keeping their electrical efficiency at an acceptable level (PV/T system of SolarWall). Considering PV/T collectors, almost all works are referred to water- or air-cooled PV/T systems. The only PV/T collector with dual operation, such as heating water and air, is the Multi Solar System (from Millenium Ltd.), which was briefly presented by Elazari [56]. This collector is mainly applied for water heating, but its design is also considered effective for air heating. An extensive research on PV/T collectors has been performed with improved modifications [48–50, 174–176].

3.08.3.3.1 PV/T-air collector energy balance equations

In the analysis of PV/T-air collector performance, the energy balance and thermal losses equations used in PV/T-water collectors can also be applied. In a detailed analysis, the air duct dimensions and other air circulation channel geometrical and airflow characteristics should be considered. The modified overall heat loss coefficient $\overline{U}_L$ and heat removal factor $\overline{F}_R$ for the PV/T-air collectors can also be obtained from the formulas of Florschuetz [9]. The $\overline{F}_R$ is described by the modified collector efficiency factor $\overline{F}'$ and the two parameters differ from those of the flat-plate thermal collectors because of the modified value of U_L, but retain their general expressions as given by Duffie and Beckman [159].

For the PV/T-air collector, the parameter $\overline{F}'$ is calculated from the following modified equation from Duffie and Beckman [159]:

$$\overline{F}' = \left[1 + \frac{\overline{U}_L(h_c + h_r)}{h_c^2 + 2h_c h_r}\right]^{-1} \quad [23]$$

where h_c and h_r are the convective and radiative heat transfer coefficients in the air duct.

The relationship between $\overline{F}'$ and $\overline{F}_R$ is given by Florschuetz [9] as

$$\overline{F}_R = \frac{\dot{m} C_p}{A_{pv} \overline{U}_L}\left[1 - \exp\left(-\frac{A_{pv} \overline{U}_L \overline{F}'}{\dot{m} C_p}\right)\right] \quad [24]$$

where $\dot{m}$ and C_p are airflow rate and specific heat capacity of air. The steady-state thermal efficiency of the PV/T-air collector is calculated from the measured data from

$$\eta_{th} = \frac{\dot{m} C_p (T_{out} - T_{in})}{A_a G} \quad [25]$$

The forced convection heat transfer coefficient in the air channel is assumed to be constant for all channel walls to ease the calculations. In the case of short-length PV/T modules (≈1 m), the correlation of Tan and Charters [177] can be used (which includes the effect of thermal entrance length of the air duct) to compute Nusselt number, hence forced convection heat transfer coefficient. Reynolds number Re and hydraulic diameter are determined from their usual expressions, and Prandtl number Pr is usually 0.7 for air.

3.08.3.3.2 Pressure drop

Any heat transfer augmentation is accompanied by an increase in pressure drop, and since it determines the fan power, it is important to evaluate pressure drop in order to determine and compare the required pumping power. In principle, it is expected that there is an increase in electrical output power. In PV/T systems, the thermal and electrical output in relation with the temperature range of operation, as well as the cost of the additional thermal unit, determine the effectiveness of these devices regarding their practical application. In these systems, the electricity is of priority due to the higher cost of the PV module compared with that of the thermal unit, but, on the other hand, the total energy output (electrical + thermal) is usually considered for the estimation of the effectiveness of system modification improvements. The analysis of pressure drop is derived by applying Bernoulli's law and energy equation to a given system and making assumptions to the system under consideration [178]. For forced flow, the driving force is provided by the fan, which does some work by pushing air through the fan head H_p. The opposing forces are represented by the total head loss H_L, which includes major losses due to friction between channel walls and airstream represented by friction head H_f and the minor losses caused by any obstruction that hinders smooth flow of air from inlet to outlet, evaluated as the product of loss coefficient k_i and available velocity head, $v^2/2g$. The head loss is then given as the sum of major and minor losses:

$$H_p = H_L = H_f + \sum_i k_i \frac{v^2}{2g} \quad [26]$$

The loss coefficients k_i for the PV/T-air collector in **Figure 9** include the effect of entrance, exit, and the two 90° turns inside the channels, and loss coefficients at these four places are summed to give the total loss coefficient k, using the values given by Young et al. [179], while the major head loss H_f can be determined from the Darcy–Weisbach equation [178]:

$$H_f = \frac{v^2}{2g} f\left(\frac{L}{D_H}\right) \quad [27]$$

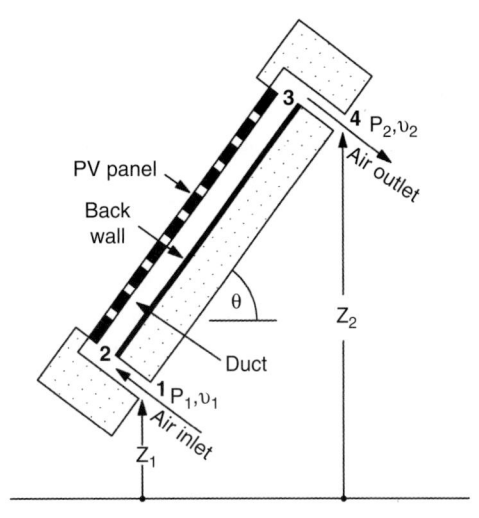

Figure 9 Cross-section of the PV/T-air collector with indication of vents [50].

The pressure drop ΔP is then calculated from the following equation:

$$\Delta P = g\rho H_P \qquad [28]$$

where g is the gravitational acceleration and ρ is the mean air density inside the channel.

The parameter f in eqn [27] is the friction factor and can be calculated from the equations given by Incropera and DeWitt [180]:

$$f = 64 Re^{-1} \quad \text{(Laminar flow, Re} \leq 2300) \qquad [29]$$

$$f = 0.316\, Re^{-0.25} \quad \text{(Turbulent flow up to } \sim 2 \times 10^4) \qquad [30]$$

The electrical power required also depends on the fan efficiency η_{fan} and the motor efficiency η_{motor}, and the power required P is given by

$$P = \frac{\dot{m}\Delta P}{\rho} = \frac{\dot{m}\Delta P}{\rho \eta_{\text{fan}}\eta_{\text{motor}}} \qquad [31]$$

3.08.3.3.3 Influence of geometrical and operational parameters

From the work of Tonui and Tripanagnostopoulos [49], it shows that T_{PV} and T_{w} increase with increasing channel depth. This is attributed to the decreased air velocity; hence, heat transfer coefficient as the channel depth widens resulting in lower heat extraction from the module leading to higher PV and back wall temperatures, and thus, air outlet temperature reduces with increasing channel depth. The thermal and electrical efficiency are reduced with increasing channel depth. The reduced thermal efficiency is due to reduced flow rate, while the decrease of electrical efficiency is due to the increase in PV temperature as the depth widens. The pumping power is high (high pressure drop) at small channel depth due to the increased airflow rate, hence more frictional losses, and the pump must use more power to overcome them. Air mass flow rate decreases T_{pv}, T_{w}, and T_{out} as more and more air volume is available to take away more heat from the channel walls, hence decreasing PV and back wall temperatures, while electrical and thermal performance increases with flow rate and tends to reach constant value at high airflow rate.

For glazed systems, similar trends as those displayed by unglazed systems are observed for the characteristic temperatures considering that glazing increases the operating temperature of the systems, as observed also by Garg and Adhikari [18]. The pressure drops in the glazed systems are equal to those of unglazed systems since the duct geometries remain basically the same, except for the small changes in the thermophysical properties of air, which may affect the Reynolds number but are small enough and can be neglected. However, the glazed system has higher thermal efficiency than the unglazed system due to the reduced thermal losses, but lower electrical efficiency as a result of more absorption and reflection losses in the glass cover and higher PV module temperature. Similar results are observed for varying air mass flow rate. It has been observed [49] that the thermal efficiency increases with increasing channel length and approaches a constant value as the collector length increases. The electrical efficiency, on the other hand, reduces with increasing channel length as the PV temperature increases with the collector length; hence; there is a decrease in electrical efficiency. The additional glazing increases the thermal efficiency of the PV/T-air collector but lowers the electrical efficiency. The PV panel is of higher cost in any PV/T system and electricity production is of priority; hence, glazed PV/T systems may not be recommended on the basis of reduced electrical power unless the system is optimized for heat production.

Both small channel depth and high flow rate yield higher thermal output and higher electrical efficiency and may be recommended for efficient PV/T-air collectors but result in more pressure drop, hence pumping power and running cost of the systems. System optimization in channel depth and air mass flow rate can result in a higher performance and low running cost. Regarding collector length, thermal efficiency increases with collector length and approaches saturation value at collector length of about 8–10 m. It is also seen that the electrical efficiency decreases with collector length and is attributed to the increase in PV module temperature with collector length.

3.08.3.4 PV/T-Air Collector in Natural Airflow

The air velocity in natural or free flow in air ducts has been shown to vary across the duct as well as in the flow direction with small numerical values [25, 47, 181]. The induced airflow rate needs to be determined for the analysis of any natural flow systems, which normally entails measurement of the air velocity in the flow duct. The uncontrollable behavior of airflow requires high-accuracy simultaneous multiple velocity measurements to predict the airflow rate [182]. Another study on thermosiphon air mass flow rate is that of Trombe, as reported by Kalogirou et al. [183], and a CFD work is referred to BIPV [51]. The air velocity is about 0.1 ms^{-1} according to the measured (using tracer gas technique) results by Sandberg and Moshfegh [184]. Brinkworth et al. [25] have also noted that air velocity of about 0.1 ms^{-1} is expected and suggested laser Doppler anemometry to be used for reliable and accurate measurements. The buoyancy force (heat) is the driving force in natural flow systems and controls the induced flow rate through the air channel. The pressure difference between the inlet and outlet due to local wind effect at these points may also assist or oppose the induced flow, but it can be ignored for simplicity.

The buoyant force is a complex function of design and operating parameters such as incident solar radiation, geometry, orientation, ambient temperature, and so on. High air temperature rise in the channel creates higher buoyancy forces, which causes a larger airflow rate through the collector. The opposing forces are the frictional losses between duct walls and airflow as well as pressure gradients created at the entrance, exit, and any control device included in the flow channel. At steady state, the buoyancy force and the opposing forces balance and control the induced airflow rate in the channel under the operating conditions and is the basis used to derive the flow rate. Wind affects collector performance in an unpredicted way, due to the Bernoulli effect at inlet and outlet vents of air channel, increasing or decreasing the natural airflow rate and resulting in unstable system operation. Also, higher values of wind speed result in lower PV module temperature, depending also on the ambient temperature. For these reasons, the calculation is complex and it is difficult to predict the wind effect on the system. The following analysis on natural airflow PV/T-air collectors is included in the work of Tonui and Tripanagnostopoulos [50].

3.08.3.4.1 Analysis of airflow rate

The expression for the induced airflow rate by natural convection in steady-state analysis is based on Bernoulli's equation from inlet (location 1) to outlet (location 4) of the airflow channel (**Figure 9**):

$$P_1 + \frac{\rho_1 v_1^2}{2} + \rho_1 g z_1 - \frac{fL}{D_H}\frac{v^2}{2} - k_1\frac{\rho_1 v_1^2}{2} - (k_2 + k_3)\frac{\rho v^2}{2} = P_2 + \frac{\rho_2 v_2^2}{2} + \rho_2 g z_2 + k_4\frac{\rho_2 v_2^2}{2} \qquad [32]$$

Considering simplifying assumptions both vents at inlet (1) and outlet (2) are open to the atmosphere, hence $P_1 = P_2$, and inlet ambient air is considered as an infinite reservoir with negligible velocity, hence $v_1 \approx 0$ [178]. Considering these assumptions, eqn [32] reduces to

$$\rho_1 g z_1 - \rho_2 g z_2 = \frac{\rho_2 v_2^2}{2} + \frac{fL}{D_H}\frac{\rho v^2}{2} + (k_2 + k_3)\frac{\rho v^2}{2} + k_4\frac{\rho_2 v_2^2}{2} \qquad [33]$$

The left-hand side represents the buoyancy force that drives the air up the channel and the first term on the right-hand side represents the kinetic energy gained by the accelerated air at the exit. The second term on the right-hand side is the friction loss between duct walls and airflow, while the other terms are minor losses due to the change in direction of airflow (90° turns at location 2 and 3) and exit vent (4). The buoyancy term is derived for 1D 'fictitious loop analysis' for naturally ventilated buildings [30, 185], and using the expression for buoyancy term from these references on the left-hand side of eqn [33] yields

$$(\rho_1 - \rho_2)gL \sin \theta = \frac{\rho_2 v_2^2}{2} + \frac{fL}{D_H}\frac{\rho v^2}{2} + (k_2 + k_3)\frac{\rho v^2}{2} + k_4\frac{\rho_2 v_2^2}{2} \qquad [34]$$

where ρ_1 and ρ_2 are the air densities at inlet and outlet vents, respectively, and v_2 and v are the air velocities at the outlet vent (4) and main air channel, respectively. The parameters k_1, k_2, k_3, and k_4 in above equations are constants called loss coefficients at the respective locations in **Figure 9** given by the subscripts and are due to contraction and expansion associated to inlet (1) and outlet (4) vents, respectively, or change in direction of airflow (2 and 3). Their products with available velocity head ($v^2 g^{-1}$) at these locations describe the minor losses. The entrance and exit vents have reentrant angles and the accepted values are $k_1 = 0.5$ and $k_4 = 1$, while $k_2 = k_3 = 1.1$ [179]. The parameter D_H is the hydraulic diameter of the air duct and equals 4 times the cross-sectional area of the duct divided by the wetted perimeter. The continuity equation and the simplified relationship between temperature and density (Boussinesq approximation) are given, respectively, by

$$\dot{m} = \rho A_{ch} v = \rho_2 A_2 v_2 \qquad [35]$$

and

$$\rho_T = \rho \beta T \qquad [36]$$

where A_{ch} and A_2 are channel and exit vent areas, respectively, ρ_T is the density of air at any temperature T, and $\beta = 1/T_f$, with $T_f = (T_{in} + T_{out})/2$.

Using eqns [35] and [36] to eliminate v_2, ρ_1 and ρ_2 in eqn [34] gives

$$\beta L g \sin\theta (T_{out} - T_{in}) = \frac{v^2}{2}\left[\frac{fL}{D_H} + \beta T_{out}(1+k_4)\left(\frac{A_{ch}}{A_2}\right)^2 + (k_2 + k_3)\right] \qquad [37]$$

The expression for the induced air velocity v is obtained by rearranging eqn [37], and using the k_i values for our system yields

$$v^2 = 2g\beta L \sin\theta (T_{out} - T_{in})\left[2.2 + \frac{fL}{D_H} + 2\beta T_{out}\left(\frac{A_{ch}}{A_2}\right)^2\right]^{-1} \qquad [38]$$

Equation [38] gives the magnitude of the velocity induced in the air channel, and together with eqn [35], the induced air mass flow rate is given by

$$\dot{m}^2 = 2g\beta L \sin\theta (A_{ch}\rho)^2 (T_{out} - T_{in})\left[2.2 + \frac{fL}{D_H} + 2\beta T_{out}\left(\frac{A_{ch}}{A_2}\right)^2\right]^{-1} \qquad [39]$$

The useful heat gain by the induced airflow is given by the following equation:

$$Q_u = \dot{m}C_p(T_{out} - T_{in}) = \eta_{th}A_{pv}G \qquad [40]$$

Substituting $(T_{out} - T_{in})$ from eqn [40] in eqn [39] and with some little manipulations we get

$$\dot{m} = \left(\frac{2g\beta (A_{ch}\rho)^2 A_{pv}\eta_{th}GL\sin\theta}{C_p\left[2.2 + fL/D_H + 2\beta T_{out}(A_{ch}/A_2)^2\right]}\right)^{\frac{1}{3}} \qquad [41]$$

3.08.3.4.2 Estimation of heat transfer coefficient, h_c, and friction factor, f

The airstream in the duct receives heat from channel surfaces in contact with by convection heat transfer process and is characterized by the convection heat transfer coefficient h_c. To ease the analysis, the value of h_c between the PV rear, back, and side walls and airstream is assumed to be equal. The induced air velocity in the channel is influenced by h_c and the friction factor, f, and among many mathematical models for calculating these quantities, the correlation of Smolec and Thomas [186] can be applied. The convection heat transfer coefficient, h_c, is a complex quantity since it depends on many parameters, for example, thermophysical properties of fluid, flow type, and so on, and normally calculated from Nusselt number, Nu, which depends on Raleigh number, Ra, for the natural convection case:

$$h_c = \frac{k}{D_H}\text{Nu} \qquad [42]$$

Smolec and Thomas [186, 187] suggested the use of Tsuji and Nagano [188] correlation to calculate the Nusselt number for their Trombe wall arguing that the Tsuji and Nagano analyzed heat transfer of natural convection and wall shear stress along a vertical flat plate and that the system dimensions and temperature range were similar to their work. The Tsuji and Nagano [188] derived the following equations for laminar and turbulent flow, respectively:

$$\text{Nu}_L = 0.378\,\text{Ra}^{1/4} \qquad [43]$$

and

$$\text{Nu}_L = 1.2\,\text{Ra}^{1/3} \qquad [44]$$

Equation [43] applies for $\text{Ra} > 8 \times 10^8$ and eqn [44] applies for $\text{Ra} > 3.5 \times 10^9$. Chow et al. [42] observed that the knowledge of average Nusselt number permits the determination of the overall heat transfer rate for natural convection and suggested to use the expression introduced by Randall et al. [189] for vertical enclosures:

$$\text{Nu} = 0.0965\,\text{Ra}^{0.29} \qquad [45]$$

The Raleigh number, Ra, is given as the product of Grashof number, Gr, and Prandtl number, Pr (i.e., Ra = GrPr). Pr is usually 0.7 for air and the Grashof number is defined from

$$\text{Gr} = \frac{L^3\rho^2 g\beta\Delta T}{\mu} \qquad [46]$$

where ΔT is the temperature difference between the PV rear surface and the channel back wall. The Grashof number used here is modified by replacing g by $g\sin\theta$ to account for the inclination of the studied PV/T systems. The results of Smolec and Thomas [187] showed that the Tsuji and Nagano equations give lower values of h_c than Randall expression. The friction factor f in the above equations is calculated from the equation given by Tsuji and Nagano [188] for laminar (eqn [47]) and turbulent (eqn [48]) flow, as suggested by Smolec and Thomas [186] for their Trombe wall:

$$f = 1.906\left(\frac{\text{Gr}}{\text{Pr}}\right)^{1/12} \quad [47]$$

and

$$f = 1.368\left(\frac{\text{Gr}}{\text{Pr}}\right)^{1/11.9} \quad [48]$$

The parametric analysis shows that the induced mass flow rate, hence thermal efficiency, decreases with increasing ambient (inlet) temperature and increases with increasing tilt angle for a given insolation level. The results also show that there is an optimum channel depth at which mass flow rate, hence thermal efficiency, is a maximum, and for the studied systems, the optimum channel depth occurs between 0.05 and 0.1 m. The thermal performance also increases with increasing exit area of the channel, and for higher performance, the exit vent area should not be restricted but made as large as possible, probably equal to the duct cross-sectional area.

3.08.3.5 Design of Modified PV/T Systems

Elements with a variation of geometries can be placed between the PV module and the opposite channel wall, or on the wall, by which a more efficient air heat extraction is achieved. Roughening the opposite channel wall with ribs or/and using a wall surface of high emissivity, a considerable and low-cost air heating improvement can be adapted (**Figure 10(a)**). In addition, corrugated sheet inside the air channel along the airflow can be attached on the PV rear surface and opposite channel wall surface (**Figure 10(b)**). An alternative modification is to put lightweight pipes along the airflow in the air channel, with slight elasticity to achieve satisfactory thermal contact with the PV rear surface and channel wall (**Figure 10(c)**). These pipes are heated by conduction, convection, and radiation from the PV rear surface and can contribute to air heat extraction, avoiding also the undesirable increase of the opposite channel wall surface temperature [174].

Although the above heat transfer improvements result in efficient air heating, two other low-cost modifications can be applied. By these improvements, satisfactory air heating, reduced PV module temperature, and low increase of the opposite channel wall

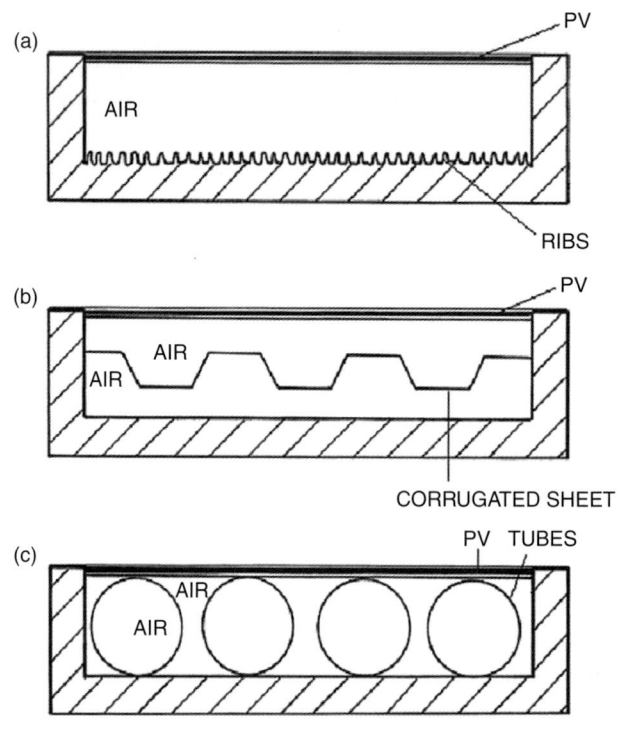

Figure 10 Air heat extraction improvements to the PV/T-air system, (a) roughened with ribs the opposite air channel wall modification, (b) interposition of a corrugated sheet, and (c) placement of tubes inside air channel [101].

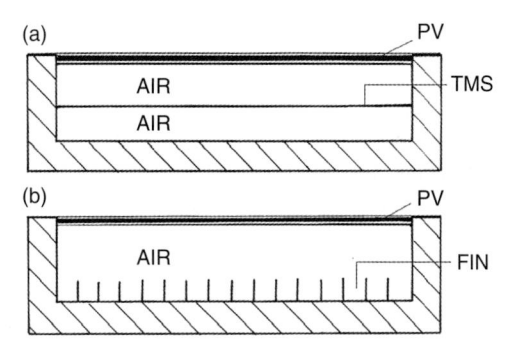

Figure 11 Air heat extraction improvement by using (a) a thin metallic sheet inside air channel (TMS modification) and (b) fins on the opposite air channel wall (FIN modification) [101].

temperature are achieved [174]. The first is the thin, flat metallic sheet (TMS-type modification) inside the air channel and along the airflow (**Figure 11(a)**). This TMS element doubles the heat exchanging surface area in the air channel and reduces the heat transmittance to the back air channel wall of the PV/T system. The second modification is the fins on the opposite air channel wall and along airflow (**Figure 11(b)**, FIN-type modification) and facing the PV rear surface (**Figure 11(b)**), by which, the heat exchange surface is increased 2 times or more depending on the fin density and dimensions [170]. Fins can also be attached at the PV rear surface, but although they can contribute to the achievement of higher heat extraction, they increase the system cost because they should be laminated to PV modules and the higher module weight increases the transportation cost. The cross-section of the typical PV/T-air collector and the two modified systems are shown in **Figure 12**. The mounting of fins at the opposite of the PV module channel wall can be applied separately on the building tilted roof or the facade and has practical interest regarding flexibility and cost. The typical as well as the modified PV/T-air collectors can be used for space heating of buildings during winter and for space cooling during summer with a natural ventilation mode and by the creation of a strong upward airstream (solar chimney effect).

3.08.3.6 Hybrid PV/T System Design Considerations

Natural air circulation constitutes a simple and low-cost method to remove heat from PV modules and to keep the electrical efficiency at an acceptable level. Forced air circulation is more efficient but the additional energy supply to the pump reduces the net gain of the system in electricity. The direct heat extraction from the PV rear surface by using a liquid circulation could be an efficient mode of PV cooling. To avoid problems due to the electrical conductivity of water, a heat exchanger in thermal contact with the PV rear surface should be used. The operating temperature of the thermal unit in hybrid PV/T systems affects the electrical efficiency of the PV module. To maximize the electrical output, the PV module should be at a lower operating temperature under certain conditions of incoming solar radiation intensity, ambient air temperature, and wind speed. This can be achieved by using the HRF at the lower possible temperature at the system input, with a proper flow rate for a low fluid temperature rise in the system. This requirement gives output temperatures useful for water preheating, water heating in swimming pools, building space heating, and air and water preheating in industry. The operation of the thermal unit at higher temperatures results in a decrease in PV efficiency. In PV building installations at locations with high solar input and high ambient temperatures, liquid PV cooling can be considered as the most efficient mode for water preheating all year, with air heat extraction for smaller periods in the case of space heating (winter) and natural ventilation (summer).

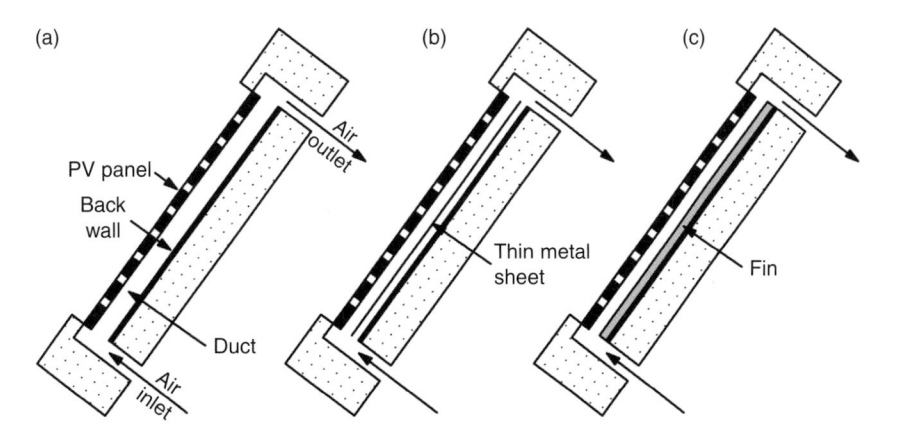

Figure 12 Cross-section of the typical (a) PV/T-air collector and the collectors with (b) TMS and (c) FIN modifications [50].

In all hybrid PV/T system applications, the additional cost of the complete thermal part (such as heat extraction from PV modules, working fluid and flow mode, circulation pipes, pumps, system thermal energy storage, etc.) is compared with the cost of the plain PV installation, calculating the electrical output gain by the PV cooling procedure, in order to optimize the system and make it cost-effective. The added thermal unit must be durable, as PV cooling may give to solar cells a longer time of acceptable operation than that corresponding to plain PV applications. The cost of the added thermal system can be the same for all PV types used in hybrid systems, for the same heat extraction mode and equal aperture area of PV installation, but the thermal efficiency differs with the PV type, with higher values for a-Si PV modules because of their lower electrical efficiency and lower optical losses. Air heat extraction from PV modules is used in hybrid PV/T systems and several projects aim at cost-effective devices with increased total energy output.

These improvements together with projected lower costs of the PV component of hybrids will aid the market penetration of these systems. Water is more suitable for the weather conditions and the building needs in lower latitude countries as freezing is not usual, and air is better for applications in higher latitudes as it is unaffected by low ambient temperatures and freezing. For PV/T-water collectors at locations with low ambient temperatures, an antifreezing solution is necessary.

3.08.3.6.1 PV/T collector efficiency test results

PV/T collector testing can give efficiency results similar to typical solar thermal collectors. From the work of Tripanagnostopoulos *et al.* [2, 190], one can have comparative steady-state outdoor test results for PV/T-water and PV/T-air collectors using two types of commercial Si modules, pc-Si and a-Si modules, as solar radiation absorbers, having a thin copper sheet with copper pipes in thermal contact with it, used for the heat extraction unit. The tested collectors are of unglazed (without additional glass cover) and of glazed type (GL), having also thermal insulation on their back and edges to reduce thermal losses from the nonilluminated parts of the collector. In hybrid systems with circulating air, the thermal unit is simpler, with the formation of an air duct between the PV rear surface and the collector thermal insulation. The width of the air channel affects the heat extraction, with higher values for smaller width and lower for larger width, and as smaller width increases, the pressure drops; considering Bhargava *et al.* [14], an air channel with minimum width $w = 0.1$ m can balance the thermal output of air heating system with the needed electrical energy input for the fan.

Test results for thermal and electrical steady-state efficiency for PV/T-air UNGL and PV/T-air GL collectors, with pc-Si and a-Si PV modules, are shown in **Figure 13**. The corresponding cost increase of hybrid systems with a-Si PV modules is relatively higher (about double) compared with that of pc-Si PV modules, with equal aperture area for both PV module types. This is because the thermal unit is of the same cost, but the a-Si PV modules are of lower cost (almost half) compared with pc-Si PV modules.

Considering the incoming solar radiation G on aperture area A_a of the tested systems, the fluid mass flow rate $\dot{m}$, the fluid temperature rise $(T_o - T_i)$, and the fluid specific heat c_p, the steady-state thermal efficiency η_{th} of the tested PV/T systems is calculated by the relation $\eta_{th} = \dot{m} c_p (T_o - T_i)/A_a G$ and it is determined relative to $\Delta T / G$ (with $\Delta T = T_i - T_a$, fluid input temperature T_i and ambient temperature T_a). During the tests, the PV electrical output is connected to a load and the values of current I_m (in A) and voltage V_m (in V) at MPP of PV module operation are used to determine the PV module electrical efficiency η_{el} for system aperture area A_a by the relation: $\eta_{el} = I_m V_m / A_a G$. In hybrid PV/T systems, the total efficiency η_{tot} corresponds to the sum of the electrical efficiency η_{el} and the thermal efficiency η_{th} of the system, for certain operating conditions.

Comparative tests of PV/T systems with water and air for heat extraction (PV/WATER and PV/AIR) and of a plain PV module with both surfaces free to ambient (PV/FREE) and another with back thermal insulation (PV/INSUL) show the effect of the heat extraction mode used on the electrical efficiency, compared with that of PV/INSUL, that simulates PV installed on a building facade or inclined roof, and with that of PV/FREE, the simpler type of the used PV systems. **Figure 14** shows the comparative results from which water cooling is proven as the most effective for the production of electricity and the insulated PV cells the worst case.

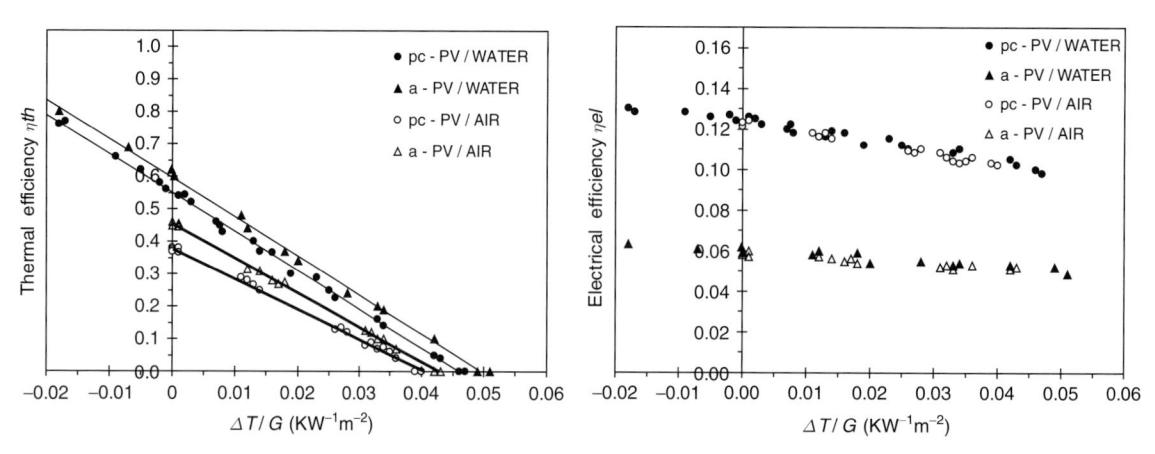

Figure 13 Thermal η_{th} and electrical η_{el} efficiency curves of tested systems: pc-PV/WATER, a-PV/WATER, pc-PV/AIR, and a-PV/AIR collectors, as function of $\Delta T/ G$[2].

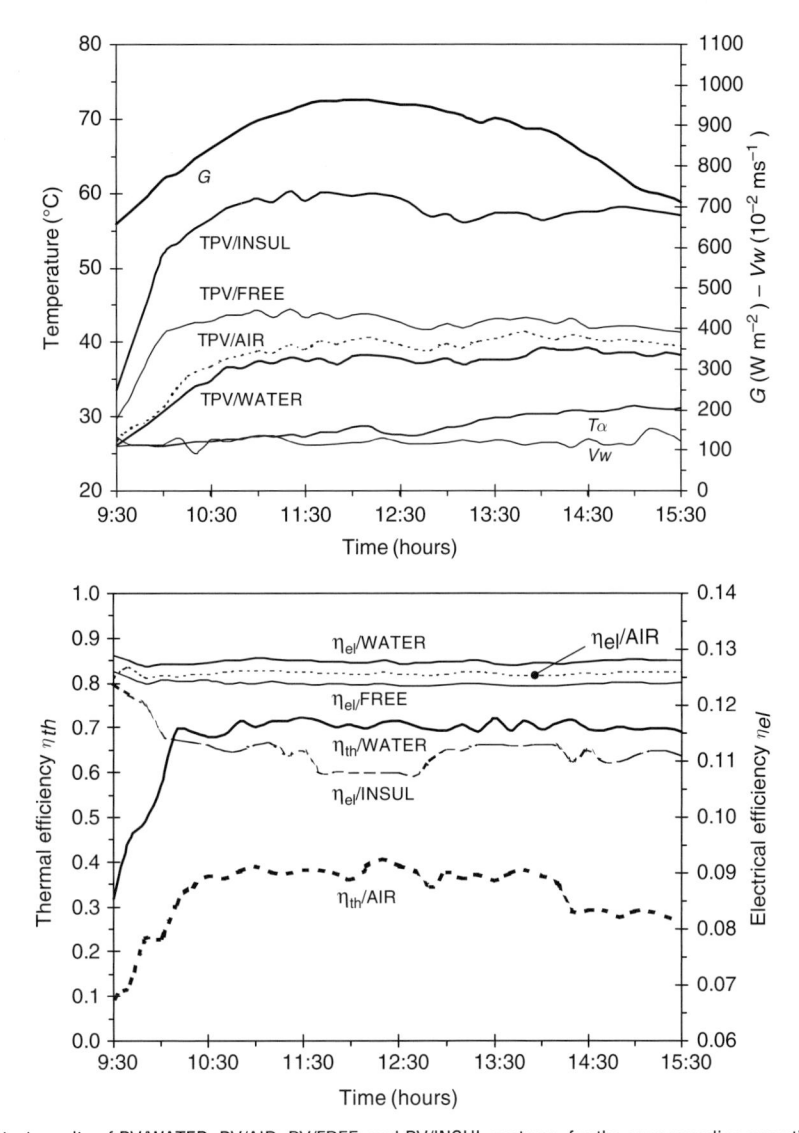

Figure 14 Comparative test results of PV/WATER, PV/AIR, PV/FREE, and PV/INSUL systems, for the corresponding operating conditions [2].

3.08.3.7 Thermosiphonic PV/T Solar Water Heaters

Thermosiphonic systems heat water (or a heat transfer fluid) and they do not use pumps and controls to transfer the water heated by solar energy to a hot water storage tank, instead they use natural convection to transport it from the collector to storage. The water in the collector expands, becoming less dense as the sun heats it and rises through the collector into the top of the storage tank. There it is replaced by the cooler water that has sunk to the bottom of the tank, from which it flows down the collector and circulation continually as long as there is sunshine [191]. In thermosiphonic systems, the collector is connected to a water storage tank, which is at a higher position to avoid reverse operation during the night. To avoid water freezing in the tubes of the collector, a heat exchanger is used in the storage tank and the HRF is water with antifreeze liquid.

The typical collector employed in thermosiphonic units is the flat-plate, while evacuated tube-type collectors have been also introduced to the market lately, with increasing application rate. In the case of using PV/T collectors instead of flat-plate or evacuated tube collectors, the new solar devices are the hybrid PV/T-thermosiphonic solar water heaters whose absorbing surface is a PV module or PV cells pasted on a thermal absorber. Such systems provide both electricity and hot water and can be used alternatively to typical thermosiphonic solar water heaters. There are some studies on PV/T-thermosiphonic systems, which include material on their design and performance [58, 74, 192, 193], while a commercial PV/T-thermosiphonic collector (MSS, Elazari, 1998) has been introduced to the market. PV/T systems have usually a PV aperture surface area of about 2–5 m^2 and water storage tank of 100–300 l and are mainly suitable to be installed in single-family houses.

In the work of Kalogirou and Tripanagnostopoulos [192], a PV/T-thermosiphonic system is modeled with the well-known TRNSYS program. The systems were simulated on an annual basis at three different latitudes, Nicosia, Cyprus (35°); Athens, Greece (38°); and Madison, Wisconsin (43°). The first two locations represent locations with hot summer weather and mild winters,

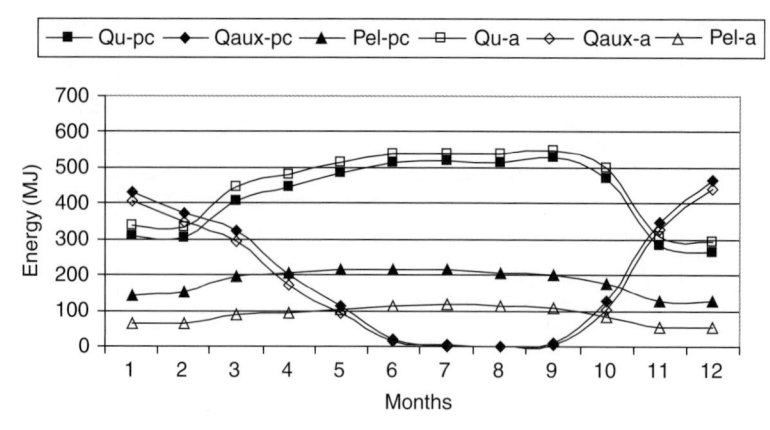

Figure 15 TRNSYS results for a PV/T-thermosiphonic collector with operation at Athens [192].

whereas the latter represents a location with mild summer and severe winter and was used to find out the difference in system performance, for comparison purposes. For each of these three locations, a typical meteorological year (TMY) file is required in simulations. With respect to the water consumption and although the hot water demand is subject to a high degree of variation from day to day and from consumer to consumer, it is impractical to use anything but a repetitive load profile. Consequently, the total thermal energy requirement is reasonably constant throughout the year and the simulation assumes a daily hot water consumption of 120 l at 50 °C for a family of four (30 l per person).

The pc-Si PV modules give higher total energy output compared with a-Si PV modules; however, the a-Si gives more useful thermal energy and thus higher solar contribution to water heating. In cold climates and although the overall performance of the hybrid system is reduced due to excessive cloudiness, the comparative performance of the PV is better because of operation at a lower environmental temperature. The annual results for the PV/T-thermosiphonic system show that pc-Si cells produce more electrical energy (P_{el}) than the corresponding a-Si cells. This is due to the higher efficiency of pc-Si cells.

The a-Si cells produce more useful thermal energy (Q_u) in all three locations considered. For Nicosia and Athens, both types of cells cover all thermal energy required for hot water production in the summer months as represented by the zero or near zero auxiliary energy required (Q_{aux}). For Madison, where the temperatures and available solar radiation are lower, a substantial amount of thermal energy is covered in summertime, but some thermal auxiliary is still required. All systems represent a substantial thermal energy collection and a good electrical performance throughout the year (**Figure 15**).

A general comment on the monthly performance of the systems, as indicated in **Figure 15**, is that the useful thermal energy (Q_u) of the a-Si cells is slightly higher than the corresponding value of the pc-Si cells by an equal amount in each month, which is also reflected on the auxiliary thermal energy required to cover the hot water load. However, the electrical energy produced by the pc-Si cells is much higher than the a-Si ones due to their higher electrical efficiency. Diesel and electricity are used as backup auxiliaries of the thermal energy. This is to account for houses that produce hot water with diesel through the central heating system and those that use electric immersion heaters. As the unit cost of electricity is higher than that of fuel, in the case where an electric immersion heater is used, the solar energy replaces a more expensive fuel. Regarding the benefits of commercial PV/T solar water heaters, it is estimated that in the case of cost reduction by mass production and considering that the produced heat replaces electricity, the PV/T-thermosiphonic system can become cost-effective for practical applications.

The results show that the electrical production of the system employing pc-Si cells is more than the a-Si cells, but the solar thermal contribution is slightly lower. A nonhybrid PV system produces about 40% more electrical energy, but the PV/T-thermosiphonic system covers also, depending on the location, a large percentage of the hot water needs of the buildings considered. The derived TRNSYS results give an account of the energy and cost benefits of the studied PV/T systems with thermosiphon water flow. The overall energy production of the hybrid units is lower than the typical flat-plate thermosiphonic systems and some improvements are necessary. Additionally, the economics of the systems considered show that for locations with higher available solar radiation, like Nicosia and Athens, the economics give better figures. Additionally, although a-Si PV panels are much less efficient than the pc-Si ones, they give better figures due to their lower initial cost, that is, they have better cost/benefit ratio. In the case where there are considered subsidies, the PV/T-thermosiphonic system has a better future for application.

3.08.4 Application of PV/T Collectors

3.08.4.1 Building Application Aspects

3.08.4.1.1 PV/T collectors in the built environment

In new buildings or retrofitting, the emphasis is addressed to the effective use of passive and active solar energy systems to partial or entire adaptation of the demand for natural lighting, space heating and cooling, air ventilating, domestic hot water, and electricity. The facades and the horizontal or inclined roofs of buildings constitute appropriate surfaces for an expanded use of solar thermal collectors (STC) and PVs, and their effective integration should be adapted in a harmonic way to the building architecture. The several types and forms of STC and PV constitute new and interesting systems, which can be easily integrated to the buildings, giving new shapes and a symbol of the ecological concept. It is also a new material in the architect's hands, ready to be shaped and create alternative buildings. The emerging concerns for environmental protection and global energy saving have introduced new architectural design rules, aiming at buildings of reduced energy consumption with effective integration of solar energy systems in combination with satisfactory esthetics. Solar energy systems are installed on the roof or the facade of buildings to cover hot water and space heating/cooling needs and provide electricity for lighting, operation of electric devices, and so on. The application of STC and PV is actually useful and efficient, considering the total energy consumption of buildings. Apart from the typical form of solar energy conversion systems, the new devices, the hybrid PV/T collectors, can play a significant role.

In PV/T collectors, the reduction of temperature has a positive effect to the electricity output but it affects the practical value of cells to be used as thermal absorbers because the low temperature is of less value for thermal applications. PV/T collectors are efficient mainly for lower-temperature applications such as water or air preheating (30–40 °C). Building integration of PV/T collectors is considered practical when the available external surface area of building facade and roof is not enough for the installation of a considerable number of solar thermal collectors and PV modules. In multiflat residential buildings, hotels, athletic centers, and other buildings, the thermal and electrical demand is high and the available installation surface area is small; thus, PV/T collectors are more practical than separate thermal collectors and PV modules. Another useful application of PV/T collectors, mainly of the PV/T-air collectors, is for space heating during winter and space cooling (by enhancing the air ventilation), during summer. In these applications, when these solar devices are directly mounted on a building facade or inclined roof, the building overheating from the heat that is provided by PV modules can also be avoided.

In BIPV applications on facade and inclined roof, the rear surface of PV modules is thermally protected from back thermal losses and cell temperature rise resulting in electrical efficiency reduction. In addition, heat from PV modules is transmitted to the building, mainly during summer. In this case, the building temperature rises above the acceptable comfort level and more electrical energy is needed to cover the increased load of the air-conditioning system to reject this undesirable heat out to the ambient and to cool the building. In higher latitude applications, this effect is less significant, as building needs for space heating is almost all year and ambient air temperature is not high enough during summer to demand building cooling. To avoid overheating, apart from increased wall thermal insulation, another mode is to use hybrid PV/T solar systems, which can extract the surplus heat and contribute to building energy needs. PV/T systems are appropriate for installation in buildings with both thermal and electricity needs. They can be placed on their facade and roof, and one type of solar module (in form and color) can be used instead of separate PV panels and solar thermal collectors, in side-by-side installation, aiming to a practical utilization of the available surface of the building. Horizontal and tilted roof installations are more practical at low latitudes, while building facade and high tilted roof installations are more effective for medium and high latitude applications because of the lower sun altitude angles. In facade and tilted roof-integrated PV/T systems, the additional back thermal protection increases the thermal efficiency of the system, but the lower thermal losses keep PV temperature at a higher level, therefore they are operating with reduced electrical efficiency.

Considering the BIPV and PV/T systems, there are some operational and architectural aspects. In PV/T systems, the cost of the thermal unit is the same, irrespective of the PV module construction, whether with c-Si, pc-Si, or a-Si type of cells. Thus, the ratio of the additional cost of the mounted thermal unit per PV module area cost is different and is almost double in case of using a-Si compared with c-Si or pc-Si PV modules. The complete PV/T systems include the necessary additional components (BOS for the electricity and the BOS hydraulic system for the heat) and therefore the final energy output is reduced due to the electrical and thermal losses from one part to the other. Considering the installation of solar energy systems on building roofs or facades, the combination of PV/T collectors with solar thermal systems have some esthetic problems due to the different size and appearance. The problem can be overcome if there is a harmony in size and if the color of solar thermal collector absorber adapts esthetically with the color of PV cells.

A combined system suitable for application on building atria is the Fresnel lenses with linear PV/T absorbers, which apart from electricity and heat production, the system can operate as transparent material that controls the lighting and temperature of building interior spaces [101, 137]. In addition, stationary symmetric or asymmetric CPC reflectors can be effectively combined with linear strip-type PV modules and flat thermal absorbers, resulting in novel PV/T systems [101, 194]. Low-concentration solar energy configurations have been investigated and studied regarding the effect of the concentrator geometry to the PV electrical output. Flat diffuse reflectors provide an almost uniform distribution of the solar radiation on PV surface, linear Fresnel lenses additionally achieve solar control of interior spaces, and CPC reflectors effectively combine PV strips with flat solar thermal absorbers. These new concentrating collectors can be integrated on buildings being adapted with their architecture and contributing to their energy and esthetic requirements. Based on the investigated CPV and CPVT systems, some new architectural designs have been suggested [194], giving a better idea about their esthetic integration in the building structure.

3.08.4.1.2 The booster diffuse reflector concept

Considering PV/T solar systems installed on horizontal building roofs, the parallel rows keep a distance from one to the other in order to avoid PV module shading. A cost-effective modification is to place stationary flat diffuse reflectors (**Figure 16**) between the PV modules from the top side of one row to the bottom side of the next row. This installation increases solar input on PVs almost all year, resulting in PV/T system electrical and thermal output increase. An extended work on PV/T collectors combined with booster diffuse reflectors shows the positive effect of this modification [2, 97, 101, 195]. The diffuse reflectors differ from the specular reflectors, as they avoid the illumination differences on the PV module surface and the reduction of electrical efficiency, because they

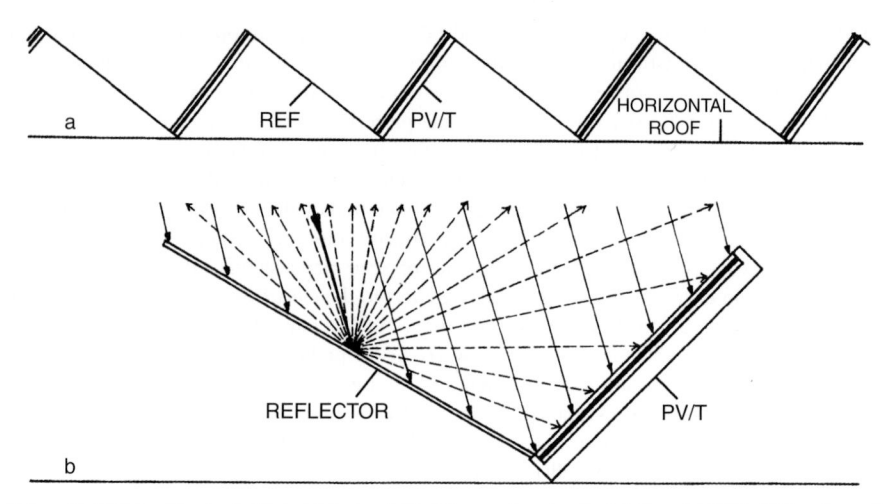

Figure 16 PV/T systems with booster diffuse reflectors: (a) horizontal building roof system installation; (b) PV/T+REF system with indication of diffuse and reflected solar rays [2].

provide an almost uniform distribution of reflected solar radiation on PV module surface. In addition, diffuse reflectors are cheaper and can be combined easily with typical size PV modules. Although diffuse reflectors result in lower radiation on system absorbers than for the specular reflectors, they do not cause PV electrical efficiency drop as they provide an almost uniform distribution of the reflected solar radiation on the PV module surface. Diffuse reflectors can be effectively applied in the residential and the industrial sectors, overcoming some limitations of PV/T systems. In the case of domestic use systems, the booster reflectors can be of diffuse or specular type, depending on the installation flexibility for orientation adjustments to the sun and also application requirements. The diffuse reflectors can operate without (or few) adjustments, but with lower additional solar input to the PV modules, while the specular reflectors need more adjustments but their contribution to solar input increase is higher.

In concentrating solar devices, the concentration ratio C is determined by the ratio of the system aperture area to the absorber surface area. The calculation of thermal (η_{th}) and electrical (η_{el}) efficiencies can be based on net incoming solar radiation G and not on $C \cdot G$, in order to get the 'effective' values of the efficiencies, considering that the additional solar input from the reflector rises η_{th} and η_{el} which increase both the electrical and thermal output. This provides a clearer figure of the achieved performance from the systems with and without diffuse reflectors.

The work on PV/T collectors with diffuse reflectors includes test results for a variable percentage of the additional solar radiation from the diffuse reflector, with respect to its electrical efficiency as a function of PV module temperature. The concentration factor C that corresponds to a homogeneous increase of the incoming solar radiation on PV module surface has value $C = 1$ for net solar input (without additional solar radiation from the diffuse reflector) and there is $C = 1.1$ for an effective 10% additional solar input, and so on, up to $C = 1.5$ for 50% additional solar input on the PV module. Higher values of factor C are not usually achieved in practice, because of the limits from geometry by the use of diffuse reflectors. Thermal performance of hybrid PV/T systems with booster diffuse reflectors depends on the fluid input temperature, ambient temperature, incident net solar radiation, and the concentration factor. In practice, the additional solar radiation is not uniformly distributed on the PV module surface, and an effective concentration factor C_t can be considered that corresponds to the solar radiation profile from bottom to top of the PV module surface. The η_{el} values versus the concentration factor for pc-Si PV modules are presented in **Figure 17**, based on the net solar radiation on the PV module ('effective' n_{el}) to get the electrical output in comparison to that without a diffuse reflector (results for $C = 1$).

From the results of **Figure 17**, a mean electrical efficiency drop of 0.08% per K of PV temperature increase is observed. In the same work, test results for PV/T-water and PV/T-air collectors without and with additional glazing (GL) are presented. In **Figure 18** the thermal efficiency results and in **Figure 19** the electrical efficiency results give an idea about the performance of the studied hybrid pc-Si PV/T systems with water or air heat extraction, especially regarding their combination with additional glazing and/or diffuse reflector. The use of PV/T systems with additional glazing is interesting mainly for the increase of system thermal output, because the PV electrical efficiency is reduced or remains the same in the case of using both glazing and booster diffuse reflectors. From the results obtained, it is observed that there is an important increase of thermal and electric energy attribution due to use of diffuse booster reflectors. More results are included in some other works [93, 97, 98], while the works from some other authors on PV/T collectors with booster reflectors give similar results [88, 89].

3.08.4.2 PV/T Collectors Applied to Buildings

3.08.4.2.1 PV/T-water collectors

Practical considerations in PV/T system design and applications include the evaluation of the thermal and electrical efficiency with respect to system cost. The ratio of the additional cost of the mounted thermal unit per PV module area cost is different and is almost double in the case of using a-Si compared with c-Si or pc-Si PV modules. The hybrid PV/T systems consisting of PV modules freely exposed to ambient temperature without any thermal protection have high top thermal losses and therefore the achieved operating

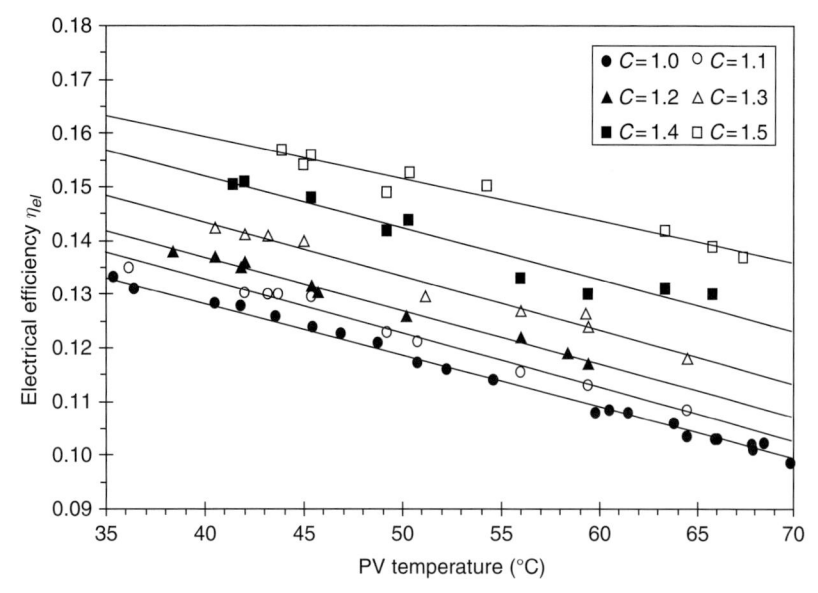

Figure 17 Results of PV/T system electrical efficiency η_{el} for the diffuse reflector with $C = 1$ to $C = 1.5$ (step 0.1) and for variable pc-PV module operating temperature [2].

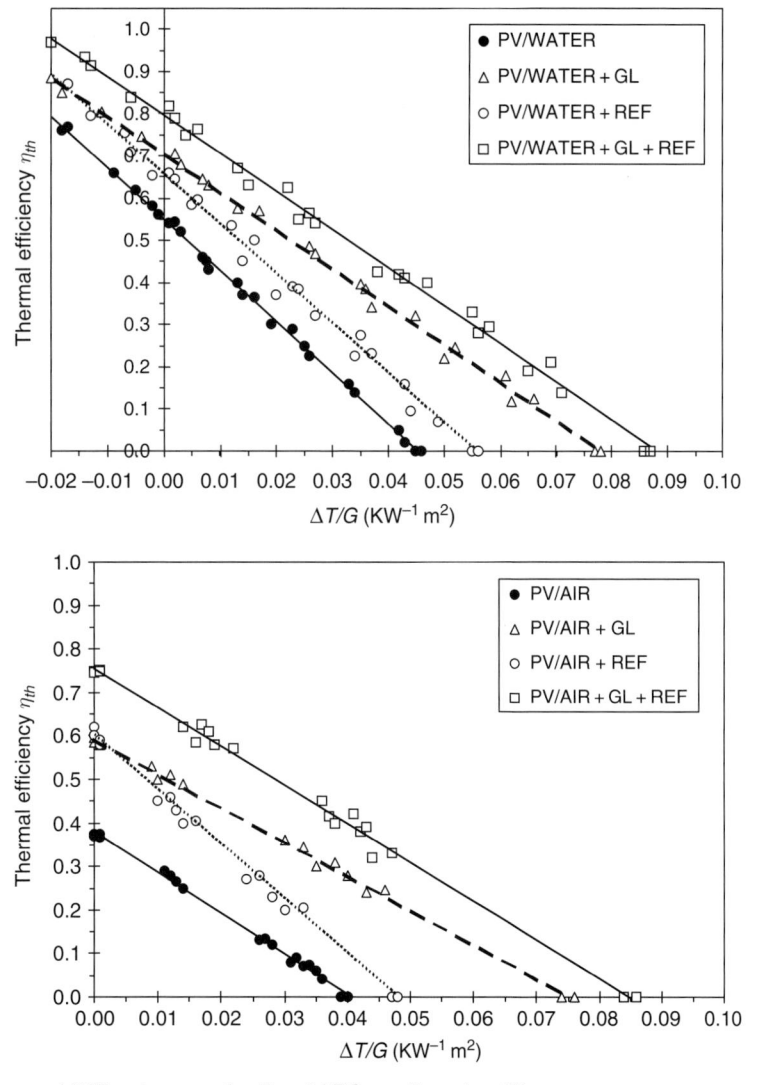

Figure 18 Thermal efficiency η_{th} of PV/T systems as a function of $\Delta T/G$ operating values [2].

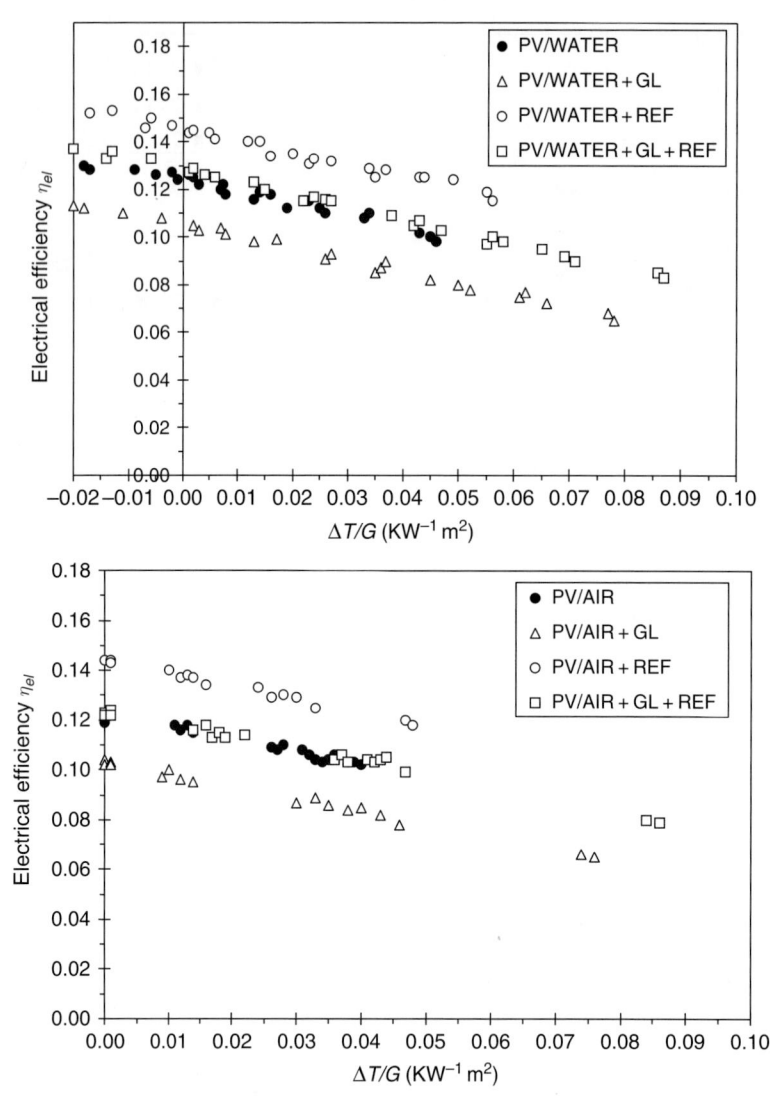

Figure 19 Electrical efficiency η_{el} of PV/T systems for the corresponding $\Delta T/G$ values [2].

temperature is not high. To increase the system operating temperature, an additional transparent cover is necessary, although this lowers the PV module electrical output because of the increasing reflection and absorption of the solar radiation. Horizontal and tilted roof installations are more viable at low latitudes, while building facade (and high tilted roof) installations are more effective for medium and high latitude applications because of the lower sun altitude angles. A study on energy performance, on LCA, and life cost analysis on PV/T-water collectors [97] shows the limitations and perspectives of these systems. These collectors are shown in **Figure 20** for the unglazed and the glazed type, indicating also their mounting on tilted building roofs. Considering PV/T systems installed on horizontal roofs, a minimum distance between the parallel rows is needed in order to avoid mutual shading of PV modules. An installation of stationary flat diffuse reflectors placed properly between the PV modules (**Figure 21**) increases solar input on PV modules almost all year, resulting in an increase of electrical and thermal output. The tilted roof-integrated systems show an additional thermal insulation on their rear surface, compared with the ones installed on horizontal roofs with convection thermal losses from both sides.

The complete systems include the necessary additional components (BOS for the electricity and the BOS hydraulic system for the heat) and therefore the final energy output is reduced due to the electrical and thermal losses. Considering operation of PV/T-water collectors in 25, 35, and 45 °C, both electrical and thermal energies decrease with temperature rise, although higher temperature values are more effective in practical thermal applications. The additional glazing results in lower electrical output, but achieves higher thermal output. The use of a diffuse reflector between parallel rows of PV/T collectors increases both electrical and thermal output and can be considered as an effective system modification. The installation on tilted building roofs reduces electrical output but increases thermal output. Regarding CPBT of PV/T collectors, the glazed systems give better results, mainly in replacing electricity. The application of the diffuse reflector is positive up to about 10% in the reduction of CPBT. In tilted roof installed systems, the conversion of solar radiation into heat is more efficient (lower thermal losses) than to electricity (higher cell

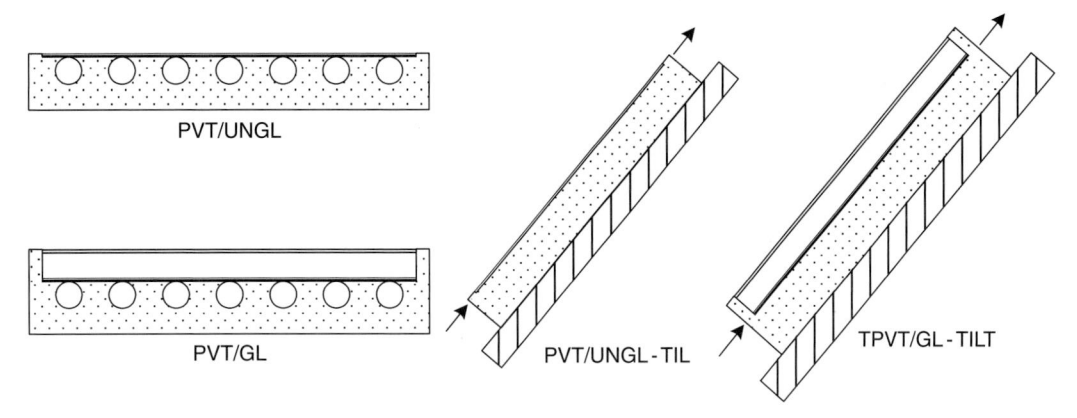

Figure 20 Cross-section of the studied PV/T-water systems [97].

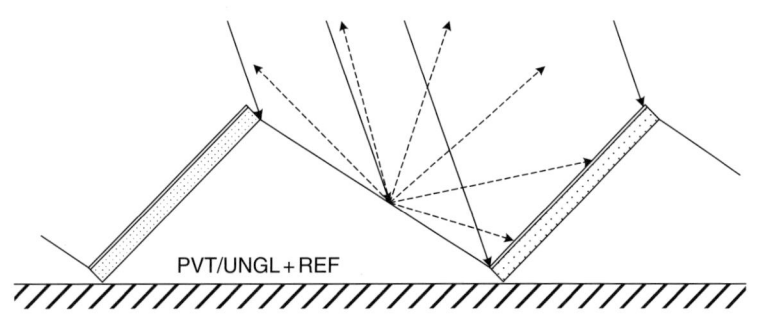

Figure 21 The booster diffuse reflectors for horizontal roof installation of PV and PV/T systems [97].

temperature) compared with horizontal roofs, but regarding cost, they have almost the same CPBT. Considering energy payback time (EPBT) and CO_2 payback time (CO_2 PBT), the best results are for system operation at 25 °C.

Regarding the contribution of the stationary diffuse reflector, the solar input increase effect is positive in all cases. The system that combines the higher total energy output with the lower values of CPBT, EPBT, and CO_2 PBT is the glazed-type PV/T system. This system can be used on horizontal or tilted building roofs, with better performance for the horizontal roofs and is much more effective when combined with diffuse reflectors. Thus, the heat extraction from PV modules results in cost-effective solar devices, with positively impacted environmental performance, compared with standard PV modules. This advantage of the hybrid PV/T solar systems makes them attractive for a wider application of PVs, providing heat apart from electricity and therefore increasing the total efficiency of the converted solar radiation into useful energy.

3.08.4.2.2 PV/T-air collectors

A similar study [98] gives results for the application of hybrid PV/T-air collectors to buildings. In this study, three scenarios (**Figure 22**) regarding the use of the extracted heat from the PV/T-air systems were considered, based on the following hypothesis:

1. The heated air is used for 12 months. This consideration is for reference purposes and corresponds to the application of annual needs in heated air, as, for example, in some industries.

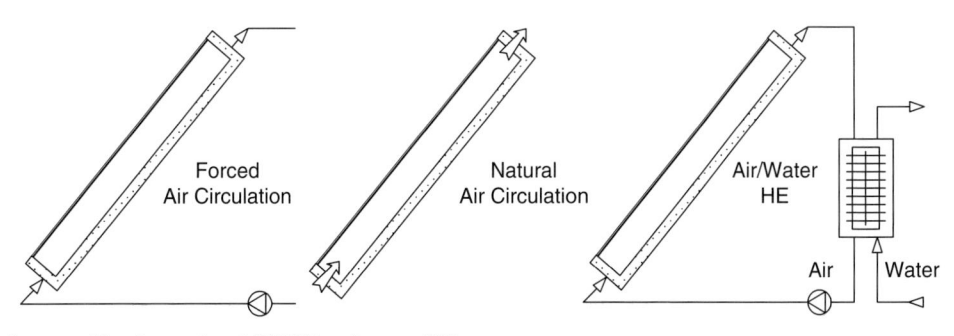

Figure 22 The three considered scenarios of PVT/AIR system use [98].

2. The heated air is used for 6 months (November–April, in the northern hemisphere), while for the remaining 6 months (May–October), the heated air is ejected to the ambient, cooling the PV modules only. This consideration corresponds to typical PV/T-air applications with space heating of buildings during winter.
3. The heated air is used 12 months, 6 months (November–April) for the effective use of air (e.g., for space heating of buildings) and 6 months (May–October) for water preheating through a heat exchanger. The thermal output in water preheating is lower than that of the air heating only, as there are additional thermal losses in the air–water heat exchanger.

The experimental results show that total energy output (electrical plus thermal) of PV/T-air collectors is higher than that of standard PV modules. Considering only electrical output, the glazed-type PV/T-air collectors present lower values due to the optical losses and higher PV temperature. The suggested low-cost modification in the air channel results in higher energy output. The calculated thermal output for the heated air for 6 months is almost 40% of the reference mode for the 12 months. In the case of water preheating for the remaining 6 months, the total thermal energy output can be considered satisfactory as it is about 75% of the reference mode of the 12 months. System operation for 12 months for air heating gives the maximum economic and energy gain, but it can be considered mainly for industrial use, as in building applications the heated air is not directly useful during the summer season. For the second and third scenarios, the third one is better, while the diffuse reflector results in better values in all considered cases. Regarding EPBT and CO_2 PBT, all PV/T collectors present lower values than the typical PV module, which gives a value of more than 3 years.

3.08.4.3 The PVT/DUAL System Concept

The different design and operation of PV/T-water and PV/T-air type collectors has, as a result, some limitations in their application. The PV/T-water collectors can effectively operate in all seasons, mainly for application at locations in low latitudes where favorable weather conditions regarding the efficient operation of the thermal collectors usually exist, or marginally in medium latitudes to avoid freezing. On the other hand, the PV/T-air collectors can effectively operate mainly at locations of medium and high latitudes without freezing problems, but for low latitude applications the summer period with the high ambient temperatures, PV cooling by the circulating air is less effective. In addition, the hot air is not useful to the buildings during summer, except if the system is used to enhance natural ventilation by the solar chimney effect, but in this case the heated air is usually rejected to the ambient. A combination of both heat extraction modes in one device is interesting and could possibly overcome the limitations of the two PV/T-type collectors. One of the first commercial PV/T collectors (MSS, Millenium Electric) is based on this concept [56], while the works of Tripanagnostopoulos [93] and Assoa et al. [102] suggest such a type of PV/T collectors and give design details and results from tested experimental models.

In the work of Assoa et al. [102], the PV/T collector absorber consisted of separate parts for the water and air heat extraction, under the same aperture surface, where a part of it is used for the PV cells. In the work of Tripanagnostopoulos [93], the collector aperture consisted of a commercial pc-Si PV module and the heat from it is removed by water or air depending on the weather conditions and building needs. This PV/T collector with the dual heat extraction operation (PVT/DUAL [93, 190]) is of flat form and can be easily applied to building roofs and facades or other applications (in industry and agriculture). The water heat extraction could be performed during periods of high ambient temperatures, as water from mains is not usually over 20 °C, while the air heat extraction part of the collector operates when the ambient temperature is low. Care should be taken to drain the water from the pipes when ambient air drops below zero and operates the system only with the air circulation (except if antifreezing liquid is used), while under mild weather conditions, both heat extraction modes can operate if it is useful for the application. In the dual PV/T collector, both water and air heat exchangers (WHE and AHE) are employed together in the same device, and among the three arrangement modes (**Figure 23**), the WHE placed in thermal contact with the back surface of PV module and the AHE forming the thermal insulation envelope (MODE A) is the most effective for water and air heating. This mode has an advantage in water heat extraction as the WHE is in thermal contact with the PV rear surface, but air heat extraction is through the WHE back side. In this mode, the air heat extraction is improved because the pipes of the WHE increase the heat exchanging surface inside the air channel.

3.08.4.3.1 Modified PVT/DUAL systems

The PVT/DUAL collector can be further modified, applying some elements in the air channel for heat exchanging improvement [93]. The first modification is the TMS modification, with the interposition of a thin metallic sheet element in the air channel (PVT/DUAL-TMS model), the second is the FIN modification, mounting fins inside the air channel and on the opposite air channel wall (PVT/DUAL-FIN model), and the third is the TMS/RIB modification, where the TMS element is combined with the roughened opposite channel wall by small ribs (PVT/DUAL-TMS/RIB model). These three modified PVT/DUAL collectors are shown in **Figure 24**. The modifications improve air heat extraction by the additional heat exchange surface inside the channel. The use of the TMS element (**Figure 24(a)**) operates also as a shield, protecting the opposite air channel wall from the heat flow from the PV rear surface to it; thus, it is suitable to avoid undesirable building overheating. In the second modified model, the PVT/DUAL-FIN, fins of Π profile form the fin plate element with their flat vertical surfaces being parallel to the airstream and increasing the heat exchanger surface of the FIN element (**Figure 24(b)**). The third modified model, the PVT/DUAL-TMS/RIB, is similar to the first model, but ribs (of about 5 mm) can be formed on the opposite air channel wall (**Figure 24(c)**). By this model, the advantages of TMS and FIN modifications are combined. The modified PVT/DUAL collectors can be effectively combined with flat diffuse reflectors, which are mainly applied in horizontal building roof installations, with the collectors placed in parallel rows and reflectors to fill the available space between them. In

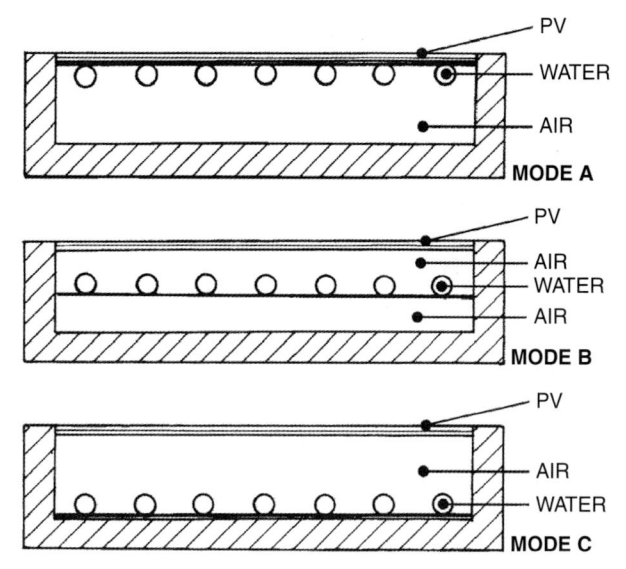

Figure 23 Alternative PVT/DUAL design modes [101].

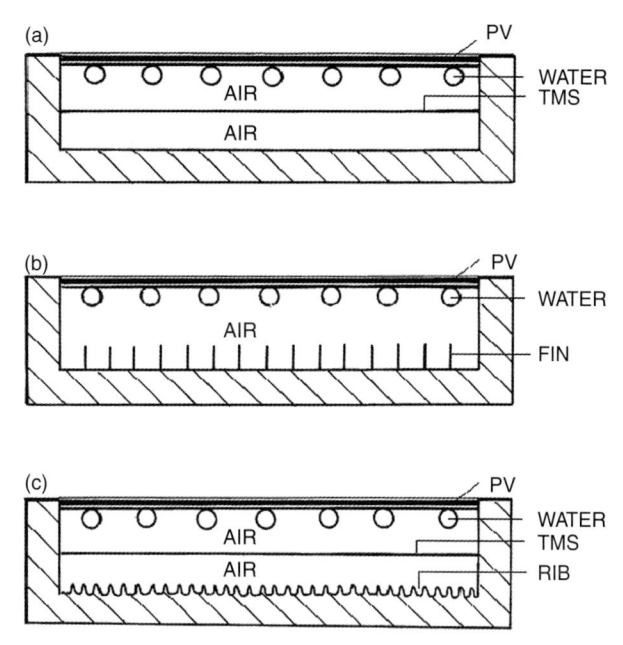

Figure 24 Modified PVT/DUAL solar systems (a) TMS, (b) FIN, and (c) TMS/RIB [93].

Figure 25, the experimental results of PVT/DUAL collector with FIN (left) and TMS/RIB (right) are presented, showing the positive effect by the contribution of a 35% additional radiation on a PV/T aperture from a diffuse reflector [93].

3.08.4.4 PV/T–STC Combined Systems

The requirement for the low operating temperature of cells limits the efficient temperature range of PV/T systems and the extracted heat can be used mainly for space heating, water or air preheating, and also for natural ventilation in buildings. In order to use PV/T collectors more efficiently in both electricity and heat production, they should operate at low temperatures. The disadvantage of low output water temperature from PV/T-water collectors can be overcome if this system is used to preheat the water of a typical solar thermal collector (STC) system [196]. The extracted warm water from a PV/T collector is circulated through a heat exchanger placed at the lower – and cooler – part of the hot water storage tank of an STC system. The heated water in the collectors of the STC system can circulate through a heat exchanger placed higher inside the water storage and providing heat at a higher temperature. In this way, the PV/T collectors preheat the stored water, while the collectors of the STC system are used for the main water heating.

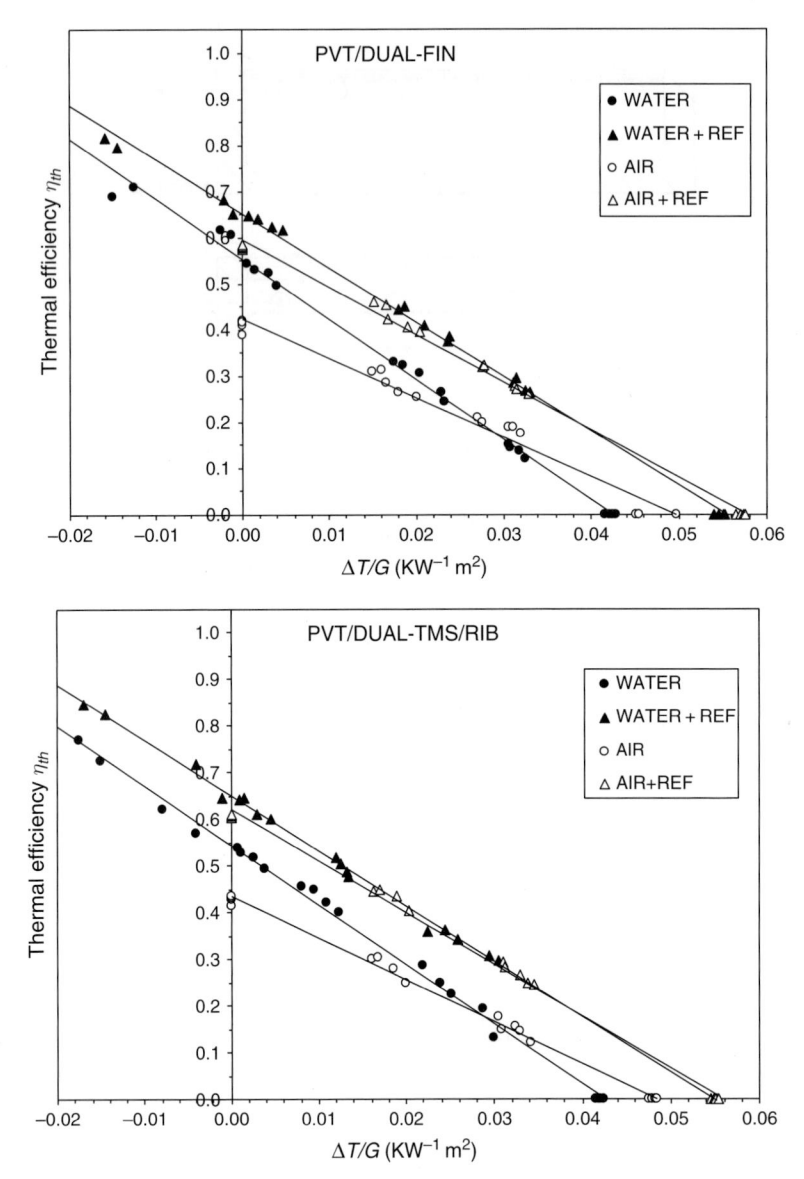

Figure 25 Thermal efficiency results of PVT/DUAL-FIN and PVT/DUAL-TMS/RIB type collector regarding water and air heat extraction, in typical form and with diffuse reflector [93].

The typical solar thermal collectors do not have the limitations of PV/T systems, as they can be constructed with black selective absorbers and double-glazing to reduce thermal losses and they do not include PV cells to be sensitive in their efficiency for higher temperatures. Therefore, PV/T collectors are not efficient in higher operating temperatures. In the combined PV/T–STC system, the HRF from a PV/T collector transfers its heat to the water inside the storage tank, for example, of a flat-plate thermosiphonic unit (FPTU) system, through a heat exchanger (HE) placed at the lowest part of the tank (**Figure 26**(a)). On the other hand, the HRF of the FPTU system transfers the heat from the collectors to the middle and higher part of the stored water inside the tank through a suitably mounted HE. A similar system can be achieved in the case of using evacuated tubes instead of flat-plate collectors.

A second PV/T–STC system is the PV/T–ICS system (**Figure 26**(b)). ICS systems are considered alternative solar devices to FPTU systems and consist of one or more water storage tanks, where all or a part of their tank surface is exposed for the absorption of solar radiation. ICS systems have simpler construction and lower cost than FPTU systems, as they consist of a solar collector and a water storage tank mounted together in the same device. Thermal protection of the storage tank is less effective in ICS systems compared with the fully protected tank of the thermosiphonic systems. The combination of PV/T collectors with ICS systems can be achieved by two operating modes, the natural or the forced circulation of the HRF through pipes in the bottom of the water storage tank of the ICS system. In the case of natural flow, low-height PV/T modules are adapted with the low height of ICS collectors and particularly for the horizontal water storage tank.

The PV/T collectors can also be combined with an array of solar thermal collectors (PV/T–ATC). The typical thermal collector array is usually connected to one large water storage tank and the array of PV/T collectors are connected to the same water storage

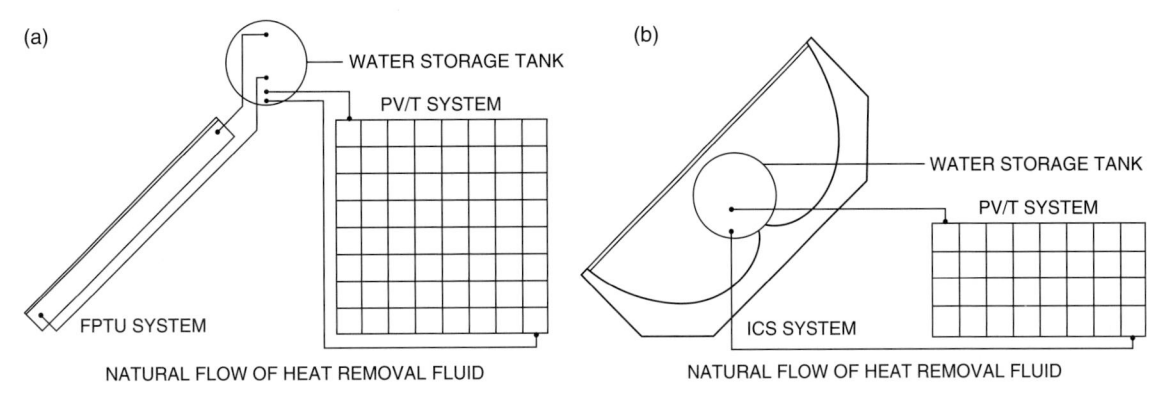

Figure 26 The (a) PV/T–FPTU and (b) PV/T–ICS systems with natural flow operation mode [196].

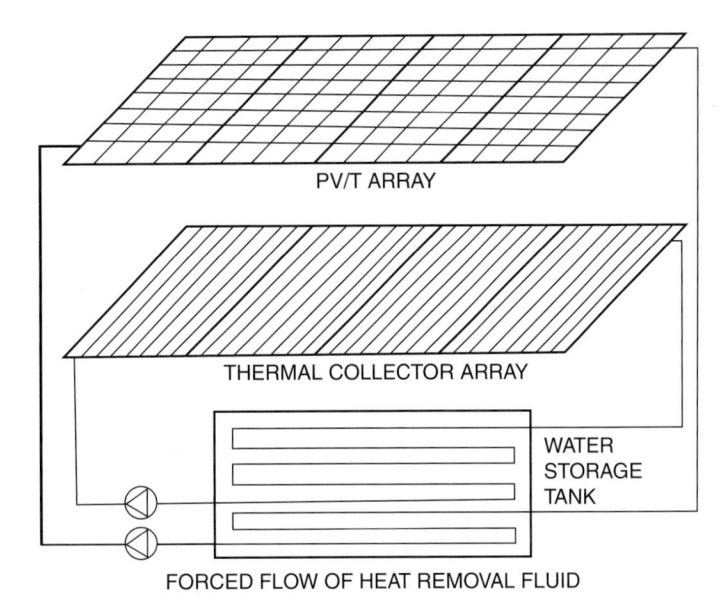

Figure 27 The PV/T–ATC system forced flow mode [196].

tank. In this combination the HRF with forced flow transmits the heat from the PV/T collectors to the water storage tank through the HE (usually of pipe type). The HE is placed – as in the above cases – inside the lower part of the storage tank to have thermal contact with the cooler water in the tank (**Figure 27**). The thermal collectors provide the storage tank with heat of higher temperature than the PV/T system, as they can operate efficiently at higher temperatures without the above limitations of the PV/T collectors mentioned previously.

3.08.4.5 FRESNEL/PVT System for Solar Control of Buildings

The daylight that penetrates the transparent apertures of a building affects illumination and temperature of the interior spaces. In addition to typical windows, the sunspace, the atrium, the gallery, or other light-guide designs are used in architecture to provide more solar radiation into the building. These constructions are used to replace artificial illumination and thus to save electricity, but daylight plays a more important role considering visual comfort, communication effectiveness, and other aspects. In addition, the distribution of daylight on external and internal building services results in most cases to nonuniform energy flow and therefore solar control is often necessary. The visible spectrum of solar radiation affects illumination, while the infrared part causes mainly the heating effect when absorbed by the building elements.

In medium and high latitude countries, the amount of solar energy is not usually enough and artificial light and heat supply is needed for most months of the year. On the contrary, in low latitude countries, the incoming solar radiation is more than necessary for visual and thermal comfort and its reduction is a common practice. A part of the incoming solar radiation is absorbed by the building structure and another part is transmitted in the interior spaces through the windows, thus increasing the temperature of the building. Despite the reduction of the undesirable excess solar radiation, the high level of ambient temperature is also a significant factor for building overheating. Passive and active cooling methods are necessary to be applied, and considering sustainability, solar energy technologies can contribute to cover the cooling load.

The application of new transparent materials, like the linear Fresnel lenses, can achieve illumination and temperature control of buildings and extract the surplus solar radiation from the interior space in the form of electricity and heat to satisfy building energy demand. The use of Fresnel lenses as a transparent covering material for lighting and energy control of internal spaces has been introduced by Jirka et al. [137], but is marginally applied so far. Considering this concept, a further study was performed [101] giving experimental results using the same type of Fresnel lenses. The Fresnel lenses are combined with small width absorbers of thermal, PV, or hybrid PV/T collectors to extract the concentrated solar radiation in the form of heat, electricity, or both for simultaneous or later use in greenhouses [197] and buildings [101]. The extracted energy can be stored as heat (e.g., hot water storage) to be used during the night or as electricity (batteries or electricity grid) to cover the electrical needs. The Fresnel lens concept is suggested for solar control of building interior spaces in order to keep the illumination and the temperature at the comfort level. The lighting level of an atrium (or of other space with a transparent cover) can be controlled by absorbing the greater part of the incident solar radiation and leaving the rest of the radiation – mainly the diffuse – to keep a minimum illumination level of the internal space. In this way, the Fresnel lens system is a kind of active shading device by which an amount of the transmitted solar radiation is not reflected or rejected to ambient (as is done by most shading techniques), but it can also be used to cover the thermal and electrical needs of the building. Recently, some work on dome-type linear Fresnel lenses has been performed [94], which aims also to building-integrated concentrating PV/T collectors.

Glass-type Fresnel lenses are of smaller concentration ratio due to fabrication limitations and thus it is difficult to construct lenses with smaller glass groove size and to achieve sharper focal images. This can be done more easily with plastic Fresnel lenses, but they are less durable in UV, heat, and so on. The glass-type Fresnel lenses are durable to long-term operation (UV and temperature resistant), suitable for installation as transparent covers of atria, sunspaces, greenhouses, and so on. The lenses can be mounted as stationary on inclined roofs (or facades) and movable linear absorbers can track the converged solar rays either automatically or manually. In linear Fresnel lenses, applications with North–South (polar) axis mounting, the focal line is moving from morning to evening, while for a East–West axis, mounting (horizontal) needs less orientation adjustments.

The hybrid PV/T collectors can be combined with linear Fresnel lenses (**Figure 28**) and aim to maximize the energy conversion from Fresnel lens-type solar energy systems. The advantage of Fresnel lenses to separate the direct part from the diffuse solar radiation makes them suitable for illumination control in the building interior spaces such as atria, galleries, and sunspaces (**Figure 29**), providing light of suitable intensity level and without sharp contrasts. The direct part of the incident solar radiation can be concentrated on an absorber strip (**Figure 30**(b)) located at the focal position of the applied optical system and can be taken away to achieve lower illumination levels and also to avoid the overheating of the space (**Figure 30**(a)). The Fresnel lens is a nonimaging concentrator and therefore the refracted rays form a diffused image of sun at the focal line. In **Figure 28** (right), six types of possible solar radiation absorbers are included, where in the first line are the fins with pipe type for water heating, the air duct for air heating, and the PV-type absorber. In the second line, there are the hybrid PV/T-type absorbers for water heating, for air heating, and also for water heating with additional glazing and thermal insulation.

These systems can be used for illumination control during the day, and by storing the surplus energy for space heating during the night can contribute in the ventilation needs during the day and apply illumination by artificial light during the night or they can cover other building electrical loads. In low-intensity solar radiation, due to the position of the sun relative to the building roof

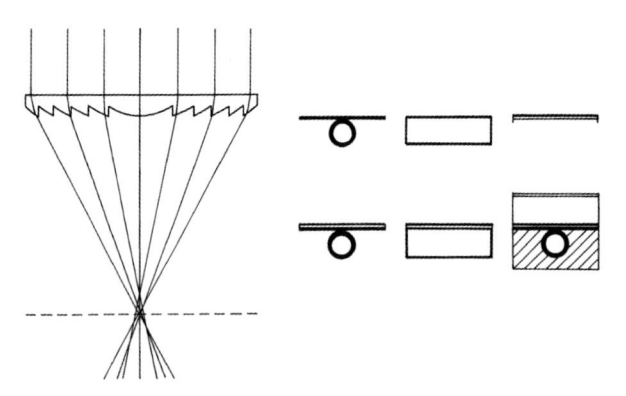

Figure 28 The Fresnel lens and the linear absorbers [101].

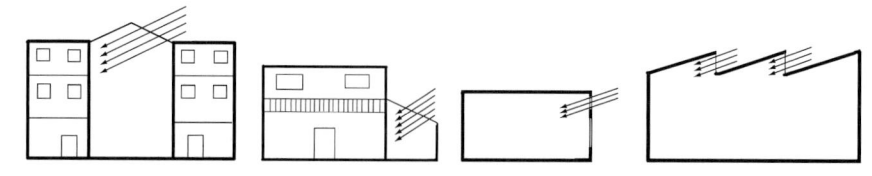

Figure 29 Examples of Fresnel lens application on transparent covers of buildings [101].

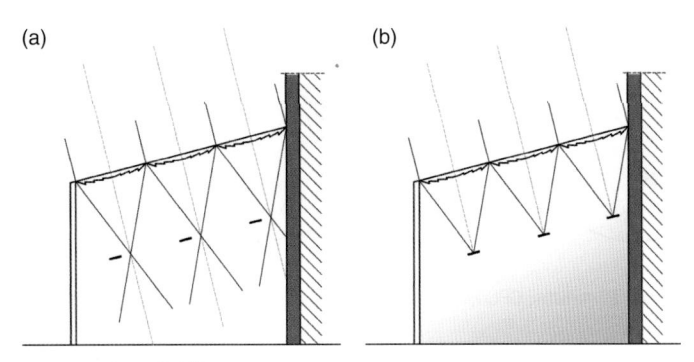

Figure 30 The absorbers (a) out and (b) in focus [101].

(low sun altitude) or because of the clouds, the absorbers can be out of focus leaving the light to come into the interior space and to keep the illumination at an acceptable level. This investigation differs from the other optical devices for building shading and cooling and is a low-cost method for illumination and temperature control of building interior spaces supplying additionally electricity and heat.

The linear Fresnel lens can be combined with linear multifunction absorbers that can convert the concentrated solar radiation into heat, electricity, or both (**Figure 28**, right). These compound systems can adapt illumination control during the day, as of a sunspace (**Figure 30(a)**), storing the surplus energy for space heating during the night, to contribute to the ventilation needs during the day and to cover other building electrical loads. In low-intensity solar radiation, due to the position of the sun relative to the building roof (low sun altitude) or because of the clouds, the absorbers can be out of focus (**Figure 30(a)**) leaving the light to come into the interior space and to keep the illumination at an acceptable level.

The effect of the Fresnel lens system on the temperature of a building interior space with transparent cover is shown in **Figure 31**, indicating the effect without natural ventilation of the interior space (**Figure 31(a)**) and with natural ventilation of this space (**Figure 31(b)**). Test results [101] showed that a considerable lighting and temperature reduction in the interior space is achieved. The cooling effect by the suggested system can adapt about 50% of the needs, only from the heat extraction by the absorber operation, which can be higher if we consider that the fan or AC operation is provided with electricity from the PVs.

3.08.4.6 CPC/PVT Collector New Designs

Low-concentration solar energy configurations using CPC reflectors have been investigated, but few are concerned with PV/T absorbers. CPVT collectors based on CPC reflectors show that they are a promising technology (MaReCo type [87, 132]), mainly for high latitudes. Luminescent concentrators with cells on side edges of an absorbing plate have been suggested [198], where a thermal collector can receive and convert to heat the nonabsorbed solar radiation from the above plate. A different approach for low-concentration CPV solar systems has been suggested last year [194], where stationary symmetric or asymmetric CPC reflectors are combined with PV absorber strips, which are tracking the converged reflected solar radiation and thermal absorbers receive the diffuse radiation as well as the nonabsorbed solar radiation by the PV absorber strips. These new concentrating collectors can be integrated on buildings being adapted with their architecture and contributing to the energy and its esthetic requirements. A first system is the stationary symmetric CPC reflector (**Figure 32(a)**) with flat bifacial absorber, where two PV strips can track the converged solar radiation on each absorber side and absorb the concentrated solar radiation to convert it into electricity. The nonabsorbed beam solar radiation and the diffuse solar radiation are absorbed by the flat bifacial thermal absorber and can

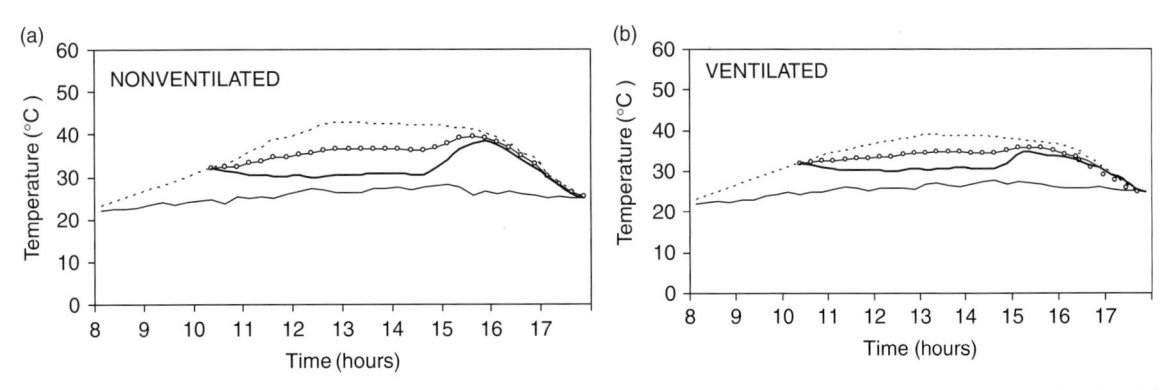

Figure 31 Results for system operation at 20 and 50 °C from 10:30 to 14:30 h without openings (nonventilated) and with openings (ventilated) for natural cooling [101].

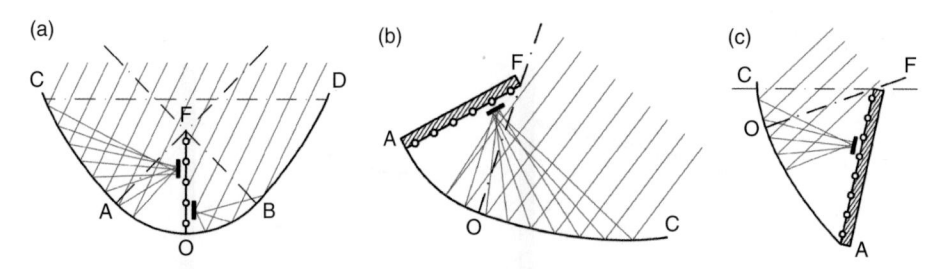

Figure 32 The symmetric CPC/PVT and asymmetric CPC/PVT concept using stationary CPC reflectors and tracking PV strip absorbers [194].

be taken away to a thermal storage (or directly to the use) by the circulation of a HRF. The PV strips operate in a similar way as in the Fresnel lens device. A second CPC-type concentrating design is the asymmetric CPC reflector (**Figures 32(b)** and **32(c)**) where the thermal component is a thermal collector and the PV strip is moving in front of the thermal absorber tracking the converged radiation. In this system, the parabola axis can be directed to the higher altitude of sun (summer solstice, **Figure 32(b)** and alternatively can be directed to the lower sun altitude (winter solstice, **Figure 32(c)**). In these devices, the nonabsorbed converged solar radiation and diffuse solar radiation are also absorbed by the well thermally insulated flat absorber to heat a circulating liquid.

3.08.4.7 PV/T Collectors in Industry and Agriculture

Hybrid PV/T systems can be applied, apart from the built sector, to the industrial and agricultural sectors, as high quantities of electricity and heat are also needed to cover the energy demand of production processes. In most industrial processes, electricity for the operation of motors and other machines and heat for water, air, or other fluid temperature rise and for physical or chemical processes is necessary; this makes hybrid PV/T systems promising devices for extended use in this field adapting several industrial applications (such as washing, cleaning, pasteurizing, sterilizing, drying, boiling, distillation, polymerization, etc.). The most suitable use of PV/T systems is the application that needs heat in medium (60–80 °C) and mainly in low (< 50 °C) temperatures, as both the electrical and the thermal efficiency of the PV/T system can be kept at an acceptable level. The fraction of heat demand at low temperatures is high, especially in food, wine, beer, beverage, paper, and textile industries. In these industrial processes, the heat demand could be up to 80% of the overall thermal energy needs in these sectors. Although solar energy can adapt to the energy requirements of the industrial processes, the penetration of solar thermal systems in industry is very low considering the total industrial heat demand. In many industries, the thermal load is so high that there is no need for storage of solar energy; thus, the PV/T systems are of lower cost. Most solar applications for industrial processes that use thermal collectors have been on a relatively small scale, are mostly experimental in nature, and only a few large systems are in use worldwide. The PV/T plants could be installed on the ground or on either flat or sawtooth roofs or on facades. PV/T-water systems could heat up water for washing or cleaning processes and PV/T-air systems could provide hot air for drying processes in food, beverage, or textile industries. Regarding electricity, PV modules are also applied to few industrial buildings, although large surfaces are available for their installation. Among the few publications for the industrial applications of PV/T collectors, a study on the possible use of PV/T collectors is given by Battisti and Tripanagnostopoulos [99] and a TRNSYS analysis for the application to three different locations by Kalogirou and Tripanagnostopoulos [100]. Referring to the agricultural sector, PV/T collectors can be applied to greenhouses, for drying, and also for desalination processes, providing the required heat and electricity. Some works on this field that can be referred are of Garg et al. [79], Sopian et al. [105], Othman et al. [106], Rocamora and Tripanagnostopoulos [107], Souliotis and Tripanagnostopoulos [197], Nayak and Tiwari [108], and Kumar and Tiwari [109].

3.08.4.7.1 PV/T collectors in industry

In most industrial processes, both electricity and heat are necessary and these make hybrid PV/T systems promising devices for an extended use in this field. Electricity is more expensive than heat and the use of PV modules could be considered useful, although a large surface is needed to adapt the energy load to the industrial processes. As the heat and the electrical load is usually too much to be covered completely by the solar energy systems, only a small part can be satisfied in most cases. The electrical needs can be easily covered with the PVs, as they correspond to a certain voltage and power. The heat differs from the electricity, as the operating temperature is the critical parameter.

PV/T systems can be used in several industrial applications for medium (60–80 °C) or mainly low (< 50 °C) temperatures. Several types of PV/T systems could be used, depending on the temperature required for the heated fluid and its final use. For example, water-cooled PV/T systems could heat up water for washing or cleaning processes. In addition, low-cost reflectors, such as white painted surfaces or other cheap diffuse reflectors [190] could increase the thermal energy output, thus making this suggestion of practical interest.

Large-scale solar applications for processing heat benefit from the effect of scale. Therefore, the investment costs should be comparatively low, even if the costs for the collectors are higher. The principle of operation of components and systems for hot water production applies directly to industrial process heat applications. The central system for heat supply in most factories uses hot water at a temperature needed in the different processes. Hot water can be used either for preheating used for processes (washing, dyeing, etc.) or for direct coupling of the solar system to an individual process. In the case of water preheating, higher efficiencies are obtained due to the low input temperature to the solar system; thus, low-technology collectors can work effectively and the required load supply temperature has no or little effect on the performance of the solar system.

In a solar process heat system, interfacing of the collectors with conventional energy supplies must be done in a way compatible with the process. The easiest way to accomplish this is by using heat storage, which can also allow the system to work in periods of low irradiation and/or nighttime. Industries show high demand of both heat and electricity and the hybrid PV/T systems could be used as solar cogeneration plants in order to meet these requirements. The use of solar plants in industry is currently marginal (< 1%) compared with their use in residential buildings, hotels, and other sectors. PV/T-water and PV/T-air type systems can be used considering the suitable fluid for the processes. Both types can be operated all year round and this is the main advantage of applying PV/T systems in industry compared with the residential buildings where the systems are not useful in all seasons (mainly the PV/T-air). A commercial system suitable for industrial applications is the mounting of typical PV modules on perforated metallic external walls, forming a kind of PV/T system (SolarDuct from SolarWall).

The industrial heat demand represents about one-third of the total energy demand in most European countries and low- and medium-temperature heat requirements (up to 250 °C) cover about 7% of the total energy needs in all sectors. The fraction of heat demand at temperatures up to 250 °C is high, especially in the food industry, the wine, beer and beverage industry, the textile industry, and the automobile industry where shares could be between 60% and 100% of the overall thermal energy needs of these sectors. PV/T systems could be used to produce heat for low- and medium-temperature processes, such as washing, cleaning, pasteurizing, sterilizing, drying, boiling, distillation, polymerization, and so on. Several studies carried out in the past years showed that the potential for the penetration of the solar thermal systems in industry is about 4% of the total industrial heat demand. The coupling of the PV/T systems with the conventional heat supply system can take place in several ways: direct coupling to a specific process, preheating of air and water, or steam generation in the central system. In many industries, the heat demand is so high that there is no need for storage of solar energy, thus allowing PV/T systems to be of lower cost.

When process heat is required at temperatures higher than 80–100 °C, concentrating PV/T systems should be used, able to effectively provide heat transfer fluid in this temperature range. By means of such systems, a significant solar fraction could be obtained, taking into account also that the industrial heat demand is often very high. This could be a problem, since generally the available surface for the installation of solar systems on the factory roof or on the ground is a limiting factor. The concentrating PV/T systems could belong to three main categories: flat plate with stationary booster reflectors, CPC systems, parabolic trough with sun tracking devices and dish-type systems. Although PV/T collectors are promising solar energy devices to cover energy demand in industry, it is very important to take into account the investment cost, since the price of the conventional fuel for industrial users is often very low and an expensive PV/T system could mean not having economic payback time.

Most solar applications for industrial processes that use thermal collectors have been on a relatively small scale, are mostly experimental in nature, and only a few large systems are in use worldwide. The use of solar energy systems in the commercial and industrial sector is currently insignificant compared with their use in the household sector. PV/T systems can be applied to several industries, but the most suitable should be the applications that need heat in medium (< 100 °C) and mainly in low (< 60 °C) temperatures, as in these cases electrical and thermal efficiencies can be kept at an acceptable level. For the industrial applications where water or air is useful to be preheated in very low temperatures (< 40 °C), PV/T unglazed systems can be used, which show good electrical and thermal efficiency, relative low cost, and could operate with suppressed thermal losses by applying cheap back insulation layers.

In order to improve the system thermal and electrical output, stationary booster diffuse reflectors could be mounted between the parallel rows of solar flat-plate PV/T modules. Such a solution is viable for industrial sawtooth roofs, flat roofs, or even for ground installation (**Figure 33**). The booster diffuse reflectors could lead to a remarkable increase of the PV/T system thermal output, up to 100% for higher operating temperatures and to overcome the reduction of the electrical output due to the additional glazing used for the increase of the provided heat. In addition, it should be highlighted that low-cost reflectors, such as white painted surfaces or other cheap diffuse reflectors, could allow the increase of the thermal output, thus making this suggestion economically viable.

Another work referring to industrial application of PV/T collectors is the work of Kalogirou and Tripanagnostopoulos [100], where PV/T systems consisting of pc-Si and a-Si PV modules are modeled and simulated with TRNSYS program for industrial process heat with load supply temperature 60 and 80 °C. The results show that the electrical production of the system employing

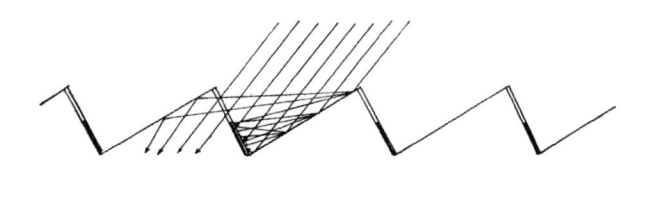

Figure 33 Booster diffuse reflectors combined with the sawtooth roof of industrial buildings [99].

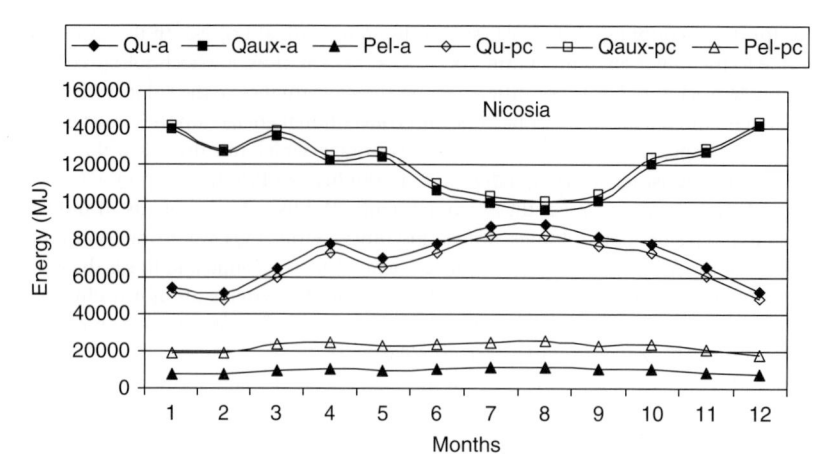

Figure 34 Monthly useful, auxiliary, and electrical energy of the 80 °C load temperature industrial process heat system for Nicosia [100].

pc-Si PV modules is more than the a-Si PV modules but the solar thermal contribution is slightly lower. A nonhybrid PV system produces about 25% more electrical energy, but the present system covers also, depending on the location, a large percentage of the thermal energy of the industry considered.

The overall energy production of the system is increased with economic viability in applications where higher load temperature process heat is required. Additionally, the economics of the systems considered show that for locations with higher available solar radiation, like Nicosia and Athens, the economics give better figures. Also, although a-Si PV modules are much less efficient than the pc-Si PV modules, they give better economic figures due to their lower initial cost, that is, they have better cost/benefit ratio. In **Figure 34**, the obtained results for Nicosia are presented.

3.08.4.7.2 PV/T in agriculture

The dual operation of PV/T collectors to absorb solar radiation and to convert it to electricity and heat makes them suitable to adapt effectively with agricultural applications. Greenhouses need heating in winter and cooling/ventilation during summer and PV/T collectors can cover these loads, while lighting control of the interior space is important almost all year round and Fresnel lenses combined with linear PV/T absorbers could contribute effectively. Drying is also an agricultural procedure where PV/T collectors can play an important role. In addition, desalination and water treatment for irrigation are other possible application of PV/T collectors.

For greenhouses, the main actions that are concerned with PV/T collectors are the temperature and illumination control of their interior spaces. At some periods, mainly during summer, the high quantity of radiation has a negative result in the greenhouse cultivation both in lighting and temperature and its reduction is necessary. In low latitude countries, such as Spain, Greece, and other Mediterranean countries, the radiation fulfills sufficiently the needs of the plants that are cultivated in the greenhouses in summer and other periods. Several methods are addressed to control the irradiation and the temperature of greenhouses and among them are shading, passive and dynamic ventilation, and water evaporation. Besides, daylight is an essential plant growth factor and greenhouses have to be built with light translucent covers in the most effective way depending on daily and seasonal needs. Among the materials used for covering the greenhouses, glass is the most stable material with satisfactory optical and thermal properties. Plastics are cheaper than glass, but most of them are of lower performance regarding illumination and thermal properties. An alternative transparent cover to the usual glass panes for greenhouses is the glass-type Fresnel lens. The use of Fresnel lenses combined with solar energy absorbers instead of typical glazing on the roof of greenhouses, which aim to improve lighting and adapt the energy needs of greenhouses, has been introduced by Jirka et al. [137, 199] and followed by Souliotis et al. [197] with extended PV/T collector results in the work of Tripanagnostopoulos [93].

Another case for solar control of greenhouses is to mount properly PV/T collectors on the roof, covering a small part of them to minimize the reduction of the solar radiation that enters the greenhouse interior space. The greenhouses should have east–west orientation, with the solar systems facing south. The application of PV/T systems with dual (water and air) heat extraction mode is proposed for greenhouse ventilation and energy load covering. The PV modules provide electrical energy to the loads (such as fans, window-opening motors, artificial lighting, irrigation equipment, etc.) all year. In the summer, the heat extraction from PV modules is made by air, which is conducted outside through the roof openings for the ventilation of the greenhouse. During the winter, the heat extraction is achieved by water, which can be stored and circulated later (during the night) through the heat exchangers inside the greenhouse in order to cover the space heating needs. The design and performance of the dual-type PV/T system for greenhouses are included in the work of Rocamora and Tripanagnostopoulos [107] and **Figure 35** gives a schematic of the PV/T integration. The PV/T collectors can be effectively used as part of the greenhouse roof, and to minimize the shading of the interior space, they should cover a small percentage of the roof surface, which should not exceed 10%. The new dual-type PV/T system is without back insulation, because the thermal losses are reduced due to the higher temperature greenhouse inner space and therefore the heat exchanger sheet (that is attached on the PV rear surface) is exposed directly to the greenhouse inner air. The PV module absorbs solar radiation and operates like a solar chimney, and thus a higher natural flow rate of the air circulation toward the greenhouse roof

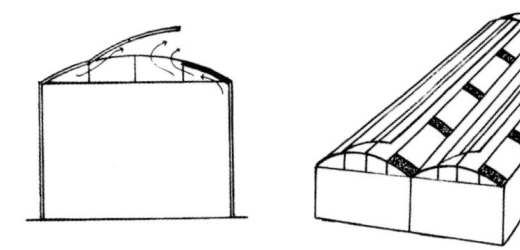

Figure 35 Integration of dual-type PV/T collectors on greenhouse roof [107].

openings can be achieved. In the case of extremely higher ambient temperatures, the dynamic ventilation of the greenhouse is necessary, where a part of the produced electricity from the PV modules can be used to operate the ventilation fans.

Apart from solar energy to greenhouses, solar drying is also an effective application field for PV/T collectors, mainly of the PV/T-air collectors. Some work on this subject has been performed, aiming to combine the drying effect with new PV/T-air design investigations. The work of Garg et al. [79] is one of the first for solar drying with PV/T collectors. Other works that can be referred are the investigations of Sopian et al. [105] and of Othman et al. [85, 106]. These PV/T collectors are considered cost-effective as their efficient operation is adapted to the favorable weather conditions and drying procedure requirements. Another issue for effective agricultural application of PV/T collectors is water treatment and desalination. The work of Kumar and Tiwari [109] is a recent example for an active solar still system. Apart from flat-type PV/T collectors, the concentrating PV/T systems seem to be promising solar devices as they can provide HRFs at higher temperatures. CPVT collectors are more useful for applications that require temperatures above 60 °C, a temperature that can be considered a limit for the efficient operation of flat-type PV/T collectors.

Desalination is also a very promising field as the electricity from PV can drive the reverse osmosis unit and the extracted heat to achieve preheating toward an effective procedure. Although PV/T collectors are suitable for agricultural procedures, examples for their application are quite few, but they are promising for a wider application in future years.

3.08.4.7.3 PV/T collectors combined with other renewable energy sources

Energy saving in all sectors and energy production by renewable energy sources (RESs) is the possible energy resource in the near future. In many cases, one energy source is not enough or it is not cost-effective to cover the load and should be combined with other sources. Solar thermal collectors are usually combined with geothermal energy or biomass boilers to adapt building energy needs in heating and cooling demand. The PV/T collector is a new opportunity for an effective combination of solar energy in heating systems with shallow depth geothermal energy. In that case, the low-temperature water from the ground can be boosted by the PV/T collectors and increase the HP COP, while the produced electricity from the PVs to cover the electricity load demand of HPs. Another interesting combination is to adapt PV/T collectors with biomass boilers. In this system, the PV/T collectors can provide water preheating, as the most effective for both PV and thermal unit operation because low temperature has the effect of maximizing the electrical and thermal output. In this combination, the biomass boiler can cover the main heating of the system.

PV/T collectors can be combined also with wind energy systems and mainly with small wind turbines (WTs). Wind energy is a very promising renewable energy source, estimated to cover 20% of the global electrical energy demand in 2020. The facades and the horizontal or inclined roofs of buildings are appropriate surfaces for the application of PV/T collectors, while small wind turbines can be mounted on building roofs, mainly at locations with satisfactory wind velocity potential. In this system, the surplus of electricity from wind turbines – if not used or stored in batteries – can increase the temperature of the thermal storage tank of the solar thermal unit. In the PV/T/WT systems, the output from the solar component depends on the sunshine time and the output of the wind turbine part depends on the wind speed and duration and it is obtained at any time of day or night. Thus, PV/T and WT subsystems can supplement each other to cover building electrical load. In this concept, the hot water storage tank of a PV/T system is proposed to be the energy storage for the surplus of energy from PV and WT subsystems [200].

3.08.4.7.4 Commercial PV/T collectors

Commercial PV/T collectors have not been developed and applied as solar thermal collectors and PVs. The commercial model that has been first introduced in the market is the Multi Solar System (MSS) from Millenium Electric, which is a flat-type PV/T collector for water and air heating. Other commercial flat-type PV/T collectors are Twinsolar (Grammer) Solar, SolarVenti (Aidt Miljo), TIS (Secco Sistemi), SolarDuct (SolarWall), PVTWIN, SES, Solimpeks, Solarhybrid, and so on. Regarding hybrid CPVT collectors, in the market there are products from Heliodynamics, Arontis (Absolicon), Power-Spar, ZenithSolar, and so on. The practical application of commercial PV/T collectors is mainly limited to the PV/T-air collectors as air cooling is a usual practice for BIPVs and the use of the heated air for building heating during winter and ventilating during summer is a simple and rather cost-effective technique. The conflict between PV cells' efficient operation in lower temperatures and thermal unit useful heat output in higher temperatures affects both subsystems. The CPVT systems could, perhaps, bridge this gap and become really useful for practical applications.

3.08.5 Epilog

The PV modules that are combined with thermal units, where circulating air or water of lower temperature than that to which the PV module is heated, constitute the hybrid PV/T collectors and simultaneously provide electricity and heat, increasing the total energy output from the PVs. PV/T collectors are classified as PV/T-water and PV/T-air collectors, depending on the heating medium used. In PV/T-air collectors, the contact of air with PV panels is direct, while in PV/T-water collectors, the water heating is usually through a heat exchanger. In addition to PV/T collectors that heat only water or only air, a collector type with dual operation may be designed, which can heat water or air or both. Apart from the use of the flat-type PV/T collectors, which are based on the use of typical PV modules, there have been developed CPV/T collectors using reflectors or lenses and concentrating-type cells, aiming at cost-effective conversion of solar energy.

In this chapter, the main principles and studies performed on hybrid PV/T collectors were presented, giving details of PV/T solar collector designs, operation, performance, and application aspects. The basic PV/T collector designs were described and the operation and performance of these new collector devices were analyzed. A great part of the material included in this chapter was based on the work and the experience from the research activities of the Solar Energy Laboratory of the Department of Physics at the University of Patras (UP-SEL), Greece. The work on PV/T collectors started over 20 years ago, after a first stage of research on solar thermal collectors and mainly on work on low-concentration collectors. During this period, several PV/T collector designs were constructed in the laboratory and were tested outdoors in the experimental site of the Department of Physics building roof. A great part of the research that constitutes the material for this chapter was funded by the Greek State and from European projects (Building Impact and PV-Catapult), while many key points for the work, the understanding, and the PV/T system improvements has come from participation of the author in the EU Project meetings, from the International Conferences, and the discussions with other researchers at all of these events.

PV/T collectors are promising solar devices but suffer from the 'temperature conflict', where the best for the PV part is not as good for the thermal part. The operation of PV/T collectors in low temperatures results in the increase of total energy output, but the heated fluid is less useful for practical applications regarding the temperature achieved. A possible field for the application of PV/T collectors is the building sector where the available surface for the installation of solar thermal collectors and PVs is limited and the use of PV/T collectors looks like a 'one-way' solution. Besides residential buildings, hotels, hospitals, and athletic centers are possible future sectors for the application of PV/T collectors, while industrial and agricultural processes are open fields for these collectors, especially if they satisfy some other additional energy loads. A possible case for the wider application of PV/T collectors is the CPVs, where PV cell cooling is necessary in order to keep electrical efficiency at a sufficient level and this requirement can be combined with a higher-temperature HRF. Another critical parameter is cost. The additional thermal component increases the system cost, so the final energy gain should overcome this extra cost in order to get a cost-effective collector.

Concluding, it is environmentally, energetically, and economically necessary to avoid the free heat transmission from the PVs to the ambient but this should be done in the most sustainable and cost-effective way and PV/T collectors are a promising way of achieving this target.

References

[1] Wolf M (1976) Performance analyses of combined heating and photovoltaic power systems for residences. *Energy Conversion and Management* 16: 79–90.
[2] Tripanagnostopoulos Y, Nousia Th, Souliotis M, and Yianoulis P (2002) Hybrid photovoltaic/thermal solar systems. *Solar Energy* 72: 217–234.
[3] Charalambous PG, Maidment GG, Kalogirou SA, and Yiakoumetti K (2007) Photovoltaic thermal (PV/T) collectors: A review. *Applied Thermal Engineering* 27: 275–286.
[4] Zondag HA (2008) Flat-plate PV-thermal collectors and systems: A review. *Renewable and Sustainable Energy Reviews* 12: 891–959.
[5] Chow TT (2010) A review on photovoltaic/thermal hybrid solar technology. *Applied Energy* 87: 365–379.
[6] PVT ROADMAP (2006) *A European Guide for the Development and Market Introduction of PV-Thermal Technology*. www.pvtforum.org
[7] Kern EC and Russel MC (1978) Combined photovoltaic and thermal hybrid collector systems. In: *Proceedings of the 13th IEEE Photovoltaic Specialists*, pp. 1153–1157. Washington, DC, USA.
[8] Hendrie SD (1979) Evaluation of combined photovoltaic/thermal collectors. In: *Proceedings of the International Conference ISES*, vol. 3, pp. 1865–1869. Atlanta, GA, USA, 28 May–1 June.
[9] Florschuetz LW (1979) Extention of the Hottel–Whillier model to the analysis of combined photovoltaic/thermal flat plate collectors. *Solar Energy* 22: 361–366.
[10] Raghuraman P (1981) Analytical predictions of liquid and air photovoltaic/thermal, flat-plate collector performance. *Journal of Solar Energy Engineering* 103: 291–298.
[11] Cox CH and Raghuraman P (1985) Design considerations for flat-plate photovoltaic/thermal collectors. *Solar Energy* 35: 227–241.
[12] Lalovic B (1986–87) A hybrid amorphous silicon photovoltaic and thermal solar collector. *Solar Cells* 19: 131–138.
[13] Loferski JJ, Ahmad JM, and Pandey A (1988) Performance of photovoltaic cells incorporated into unique hybrid photovoltaic/thermal panels of a 2.8 KW residential solar energy conversion system. In: *Proceedings of the 1988 Annual Meeting*, pp. 427–432. American Solar Energy Society, Cambridge, MA, USA.
[14] Bhargava AK, Garg HP, and Agarwal RK (1991) Study of a hybrid solar system: Solar air heater combined with solar cells. *Energy Conversion and Management* 31: 471–479.
[15] Prakash J (1994) Transient analysis of a photovoltaic-thermal solar collector for co-generation of electricity and hot air/water. *Energy Conversion and Management* 35: 976–972.
[16] Garg HP and Agarwal PK (1995) Some aspects of a PV/T collector/forced circulation flat plate solar water heater with solar cells. *Energy Conversion and Management* 36: 87–99.
[17] Sopian K, Liu HT, Yigit KS, *et al.* (1996) Perfromance analysis of photovoltaic thermal air heaters. *Energy Conversion and Management* 37: 1657–1670.
[18] Garg HP and Adhikari RS (1997) Conventional hybrid photovoltaic/thermal (PV/T) air heating collectors: Steady-state simulation. *Renewable Energy* 11: 363–385.
[19] Luque A and Marti A (1999) Limiting efficiency of coupled thermal and photovoltaic converters. *Solar Energy Materials and Solar Cells* 58: 147–165.
[20] Ricaud A and Roubeau P (1994) Capthel, a 66% efficient hybrid solar module and the Ecothel co-generation solar system. In: *Proceedings of IEEE First World Conference on Photovoltaic Energy Conversion*, pp. 1012–1015. Waikoloa, Hawaii.

[21] Yang HX, Marshall GH, and Brinkworth BJ (1994) An experimental study of the thermal regulation of a PV-clad building roof. In: *Procedings of the 12th European Photovoltaic Solar Energy Conference*, pp. 1115–1118. Amsterdam, The Netherlands, 11–15 April.
[22] Posnansky M, Gnos S, and Coonen S (1994) The importance of hybrid PV-building integration. In: *Proceedings of the First World Conference on Photovoltaic Energy Conversion*, pp. 998–1003. Waikoloa, HI, USA, 5–9 December.
[23] Ossenbrink HA, Rigolini CO, and van der Vebbe O (1994) Building integration of an amorphous silicon photovoltaic façade. In: *Proceedings of the IEEE 1st World Conference on PV Energy Conversion*, pp. 770–773. Hawaii, USA, 5–9 December.
[24] Moshfegh B, Sandberg M, Bloem JJ, and Ossenbrink H (1995) Analysis of fluid flow and heat transfer within the photovoltaic façade on the ELSA building. In: *JRC ISPRA Proceedings of the 13th European PV Solar Energy Conference*, p. 2215. Nice, France, 23–27 October.
[25] Brinkworth BJ, Cross BM, Marshall RH, and Hongxing Y (1997) Thermal regulation of photovoltaic cladding. *Solar Energy* 61: 169–179.
[26] Moshfegh B and Sandberg M (1995) Investigation of fluid flow and heat transfer in a vertical channel heated from one side by PV elements, Part I – Numerical study. *Renewable Energy* 8: 248–253.
[27] Sandberg M and Moshfegh B (2002) Buoyancy-induced air flow in photovoltaic facades: Effect of geometry of the air gap and location of solar cell modules. *Building and Environment* 37: 211–218.
[28] Brinkworth BJ (2000) A procedure for routine calculation of laminar free and mixed convection in inclined ducts. *International Journal of Heat Fluid Flow* 21: 456–462.
[29] Brinkworth BJ (2000) Estimation of flow and heat transfer for the design of PV cooling ducts. *Solar Energy* 69: 413–420.
[30] Brinkworth BJ, Marshall RH, and Ibarahim Z (2000) A validated model of naturally ventilated PV cladding. *Solar Energy* 69: 67–81.
[31] Eicker U, Fux V, Infield D, and Mei Li (2000) Heating and cooling of combined PV-solar air collectors facades. In: *Proceedings of the 16th European PV Solar Energy International Conference*, pp. 1836–1839. Glasgow, UK, 1–5 May.
[32] Bazilian M, Leeders F, van der Ree BGC, and Prasad D (2001) Photovoltaic cogeneration in the built environment. *Solar Energy* 71: 57–69.
[33] Benemann J, Chehab O, and Schaar-Gabriel E (2001) Building-integrated PV modules. *Solar Energy Materials and Solar Cells* 67: 345–354.
[34] Chow TT (2003) Performance analysis of photovoltaic-thermal collector by explicit dynamic model. *Solar Energy* 75: 143–152.
[35] Krauter S, Arauja RG, Schroer S, et al. (1999) Combined photovoltaic and solar thermal systems for facade integration and building insulation. *Solar Energy* 67: 239–248.
[36] Davies MW, Fanney AH, and Dougherty BP (2001) Prediction of building integrated photovoltaic cell temperatures. *Journal of Solar Energy Engineering* 123: 200–210.
[37] Lee WM, Infield DG, and Gottschalg R (2001) Thermal modeling of building integrated PV systems. In: *Proceedings of the 17th PV Solar Energy Conference*, pp. 2754–2757. Munich, Germany, 22–26 October.
[38] Mei L, Infield D, Eicker U, et al. (2003) Thermal modelling of a building with an integrated ventilated PV façade. *Energy and Building* 35: 605–617.
[39] Mondol JD, Yohanis YG, Smyth M, and Norton B (2005) Long-term validated simulation of a building integrated photovoltaic system. *Solar Energy* 78: 163–176.
[40] Infield D, Mei L, and Eicker U (2004) Thermal performance estimation for ventilated PV facades. *Solar Energy* 76: 93–98.
[41] Hegazy AA (2000) Comparative study of the performances of four photovoltaic/thermal solar air collectors. *Energy Conversion and Management* 41: 861–881.
[42] Chow TT, Hand JW, and Strachan PA (2003) Building-integrated photovoltaic and thermal applications in a subtropical hotel building. *Applied Thermal Engineering* 23: 2035–2049.
[43] Ito S and Miura N (2003) Usage of a DC fan together with photovoltaic modules in a solar air heating system. In: *Proceedings (CD-ROM) ISES World Congress*. Göteborg, Sweden, 14–19 June.
[44] Cartmell BP, Shankland NJ, Fiala D, and Hanby V (2004) A multi-operational ventilated photovoltaic and solar air collector: Application, simulation and initial monitoring feedback. *Solar Energy* 76: 45–53.
[45] Guiavarch A and Peuportier B (2006) Photovoltaic collectors efficiency according to their integration in buildings. *Solar Energy* 80: 65–77.
[46] Charron R and Athienitis AK (2006) Optimization of the performance of double-facades with integrated photovoltaic panels and motorized blinds. *Solar Energy* 80: 482–491.
[47] Brinkworth BJ and Sandberg M (2006) Design procedure for cooling ducts to minimise efficiency loss due to temperature rise in PV arrays. *Solar Energy* 80: 89–103.
[48] Tonui JK and Tripanagnostopoulos Y (2007) Improved PV/T solar collectors with heat extraction by natural or forced air circulation. *Renewable Energy* 32: 623–637.
[49] Tonui JK and Tripanagnostopoulos Y (2007) Air-cooled PV/T solar collectors with low cost performance improvement. *Solar Energy* 81: 498–511.
[50] Tonui JK and Tripanagnostopoulos Y (2008) Performance improvement of PV/T solar collectors with natural air flow operation. *Solar Energy* 82: 1–12.
[51] Gan G (2009) Numerical determination of adequate air gaps for building: Integrated photovoltaics. *Solar Energy* 83: 1253–1273.
[52] Anderson TN, Duke M, Morrison GL, and Carson JK (2009) Performance of a building integrated photovoltaic/thermal (BIPVT) solar collector. *Solar Energy* 83: 445–455.
[53] Pantic S, Candanedo L, and Athienitis AK (2010) Modeling of energy performance of a house with three configurations of building – Integrated photovoltaic – Thermal systems. *Energy and Buildings* 42: 1779–1789.
[54] Agrawal B and Tiwari GN (2010) Life cycle cost assessment of building integrated photovoltaic thermal (BIPVT) systems. *Energy and Buildings* 42: 1472–1481.
[55] Bergene T and Lovvik OM (1995) Model calculations on a flat-plate solar heat collector with integrated solar cells. *Solar Energy* 55: 453–462.
[56] Elazari A (1998) Multi Solar System – Solar multimodule for electrical and hot water supply for residentially building. In: *Proceedings of 2nd World Conference on Photovoltaic Solar Energy Conversion*, pp. 2430–2433. Vienna, Austria, 6–10 July.
[57] Hausler T and Rogash H (2000) Latent heat storage of photovoltaics. In: *Proceedings of 16th European PV Solar Energy Conference*, vol. 3, pp. 265–2267, 1–5 May, Glasgow, UK.
[58] Kalogirou SA (2001) Use of TRNSYS for modelling and simulation of a hybrid PV-thermal solar system for Cyprus. *Renewable Energy* 23: 247–260.
[59] Huang BJ, Lin TH, Hung WC, and Sun FS (2001) Performance evaluation of solar photovoltaic/thermal systems. *Solar Energy* 70: 443–448.
[60] Sandness B and Rekstad J (2002) A photovoltaic/thermal (PV/T) collector with a polymer absorber plate-experimental study and analytical model. *Solar Energy* 72: 63–73.
[61] Zondag HA, De Vries DW, Van Helden WGJ, et al. (2002) The thermal and electrical yield of a PV-thermal collector. *Solar Energy* 72: 113–128.
[62] Zondag HA, De Vries DW, Van Helden WGJ, et al. (2003) The yield of different combined PV-thermal collector designs. *Solar Energy* 74: 253–269.
[63] Santbergen R, Rindt CCM, Zondag HA, and van Zolingen RJC (2010) Detailed analysis of the energy yield of systems with covered sheet-and-tube PVT collectors. *Solar Energy* 84: 867–878.
[64] Notton G, Cristofari C, Mattei M, and Poggi P (2005) Modelling of a double-glass photovoltaic module using finite differences. *Applied Thermal Engineering* 25: 2854–2877.
[65] Busato F, Lazzarin R, and Noro M (2008) Experimental analysis of photovoltaic cogeneration modules. *International Journal of Low Carbon Technologies* 3–4: 221–244.
[66] Jie J, Chow TT, and He W (2003) Dynamic performance of hybrid photovoltaic/thermal collector wall in Hong Kong. *Building and Environment* 38: 1327–1334.
[67] Coventry JS and Lovegrove K (2003) Development of an approach to compare the 'value' of electric and thermal output from a domestic PV/thermal system. *Solar Energy* 75: 63–72.
[68] Bakker M, Zondag HA, Elswijk MJ, et al. (2005) Performance and costs of a roof-sized PV/thermal array combined with a ground coupled heat pump. *Solar Energy* 78: 331–339.
[69] Vokas G, Christandonis N, and Skittides F (2006) Hybrid photovoltaic-thermal systems for domestic heating and cooling: A theoretical approach. *Solar Energy* 80: 607–615.
[70] Tiwari A and Sodha MS (2006) Performance evaluation of solar PV/T system: An experimental validation. *Solar Energy* 89: 751–759.
[71] Fraisse G, Menezo C, and Johannes K (2007) Energy performance of water hybrid PV/T collectors applied to combisystems of direct solar floor type. *Solar Energy* 81: 1426–1438.
[72] Fang G, Hu H, and Liu X (2010) Experimental investigation on the photovoltaic-thermal solar heat pump air-conditioning system on water-heating mode. *Experimental Thermal and Fluid Science* 34: 736–743.
[73] Chow TT, He W, and Ji J (2006) Hybrid photovoltaic-thermosyphon water heating system for residential application. *Solar Energy* 80: 298–306.
[74] He W, Chow TT, Ji J, et al. (2006) Hybrid photovoltaic and thermal solar-collector designed for natural circulation of water. *Applied Energy* 83: 199–210.

[75] Kalogirou SA and Tripanagnostopoulos Y (2006) Hybrid PV/T solar systems for domestic hot water and electricity production. 2006. *Energy Conversion and Management* 47: 3368–3382.
[76] Tripanagnostopoulos Y, Nousia Th, and Souliotis M (1998) Hybrid PV-ICS systems. In: *Proceedings of the International Conference WREC V*, pp. 1788–1791. Florence, Italy, 20–25 September.
[77] Sharan SN, Mathur SS, and Kandpal TC (1985) Economic evaluation of concentrator-photovoltaic systems. *Solar & Wind Technology* 2: 195–200.
[78] Al-Baali AA (1986) Improving the power of a solar panel by cooling and light concentrating. *Solar & Wind Technology* 3: 241–245.
[79] Garg HP, Agarwal PK, and Bhargava AK (1991) The effect of plane booster reflectors on the performance of a solar air heater with solar cells suitable for a solar dryer. *Energy Conversion and Management* 32: 543–554.
[80] Garg HP and Adhikari RS (1999) Performance analysis of a hybrid photovoltaic/thermal (PV/T) collector with integrated CPC troughs. *International Journal of Energy Research* 23: 1295–1304.
[81] Brogren M, Ronnelid M, and Karlsson B (2000) *Proceedings of the 16th European PV Solar Energy Conference*, vol. 3, pp. 2121–2124. Glasgow, UK, 1–5 May.
[82] Brogren M, Nostell P, and Karlsson B (2000) Optical efficiency of a PV-thermal hybrid CPC module for high latitudes. *Solar Energy* 69: 173–185.
[83] Karlsson B, Brogren M, Larsson S, et al. (2001) A large bifacial photovoltaic-thermal low-concentrating module. In: *Proceedings of the 17th PV Solar Energy Conference*, pp. 808–811. Munich, Germany, 22–26 October.
[84] Brogren M, Karlsson B, Werner A, and Roos A (2002) Design and evaluation of low-concentrating, stationary, parabolic reflectors for wall-integration of water-cooled photovoltaic-thermal hybrid modules. In: *Proceedings of the International Conference PV in Europe*, pp. 551–555. Rome, Italy, 7–11 October.
[85] Othman MYH, Yatim B, Sopian K, and Bakar MNA (2005) Performance analysis of a double-pass photovoltaic/thermal (PV/T) solar collector with CPC and fins. *Renewable Energy* 30: 2005–2017.
[86] Mallick TK, Eames PC, and Norton B (2007) Using air flow to alleviate temperature elevation in solar cells within asymmetric compound parabolic concentrators. *Solar Energy* 81: 173–184.
[87] Nilsson J, Hakansson H, and Karlsson B (2007) Electrical and thermal characterization of a PV-CPC hybrid. *Solar Energy* 81: 917–928.
[88] Robles-Ocampo B, Ruiz-Vasquez E, Canseco_Sanchez H, et al. (2007) Photovoltaic/thermal solar hybrid system with bifacial PV module and transparent plane collector. *Solar Energy Materials and Solar Cells* 91: 1966–1971.
[89] Kostic Lj, Pavlovic TM, and Pavlovic ZT (2010) Optimal design of orientation of PV/T collector with reflectors. *Applied Energy* 87: 3023–3029.
[90] Coventy J (2005) Performance of a concentrating photovoltaic/thermal solar collector. *Solar Energy* 78: 211–222.
[91] Rosell JI, Vallverdu X, Lechon MA, and Ibanez M (2005) Design and simulation of a low concentrating photovoltaic/thermal system. *Energy Conversion and Management* 46: 3034–3046.
[92] Tyukhov I, Simakin V, Smirnov A, and Poulek V (2009) Combined PV/T system based on concentrator with vertical p-n junctions solar cells. In: *Website Proceedings of the International Workshop on Concentrating Photovoltaic Optics and Power*. Darmstadt, Germany, 9–10 March 2009.
[93] Tripanagnostopoulos Y (2007) Aspects and improvements of hybrid photovoltaic/thermal solar energy systems. *Solar Energy* 81(9): 1117–1131.
[94] Chemisana D and Ibanez M (2010) Linear Fresnel concentrators for building integrated applications. *Energy Conversion and Management* 51: 1476–1480.
[95] Leenders F, Shaap AB, and van der Helden BGC (2000) Technology review on PV/thermal concepts. In: *Proceedings of the 16th European PV Solar Energy Conference*, pp. 1976–1980. Glasgow, UK, 1–5 May.
[96] Frankl P, Gamberale M, and Battisti R (2000) Life cycle assessment of a PV cogenerative system: Comparison with a solar thermal and a PV system. In: *Proceedings of the 16th European PV Solar Energy Conference*, pp. 1910–1913. Glasgow, UK, 1–5 May.
[97] Tripanagnostopoulos Y, Souliotis M, Battisti R, and Corrado A (2005) Energy, cost and LCA results of PV and hybrid PV/T solar systems. *Progress in Photovoltaics: Research and Applications* 13: 235–250.
[98] Tripanagnostopoulos Y, Souliotis M, Battisti R, and Corrado A (2006) Performance, cost and life-cycle assessment study of hybrid PVT/AIR solar systems. *Progress in Photovoltaics: Research and Applications* 14: 65–76.
[99] Battisti R and Tripanagnostopoulos Y (2005) PV/thermal systems for application in industry. In: *Proceedings (CD-ROM) of the 20th European Photovoltaic Solar Energy Conference*, paper 6CV.2.3. Barcelona, Spain, 6–10 June.
[100] Kalogirou SA and Tripanagnostopoulos Y (2007) Industrial application of PV/T solar energy systems. *Applied Thermal Engineering* 27(8–9): 1259–1270.
[101] Tripanagnostopoulos Y, Siabekou C, and Tonui JK (2006) The Fresnel lens concept for solar control of buildings. *Solar Energy* 81(5): 661–675.
[102] Assoa YB, Menezo C, Fraisse G, et al. (2007) Study of a new concept of photovoltaic-thermal hybrid collector. *Solar Energy* 81: 1132–1143.
[103] Jie J, Keliang L, Chow TT, et al. (2008) Performance analysis of a photovoltaic heat pump. *Applied Energy* 85: 680–693.
[104] Beccali M, Finocchiaro P, and Nocke B (2009) Energy and economic assessment of desiccant cooling systems coupled with single glazed air and hybrid PV/thermal solar collectors for applications in hot and humid climate. *Solar Energy* 83: 1828–1846.
[105] Sopian K, Liu HT, Kakac S, and Veziroglu TN (2000) Perfromance of a double pass photovoltaic thermal solar collector suitable for solar drying systems. *Energy Conversion and Management* 41: 353–365.
[106] Othman MYH, Sopian K, Yatim B, and Daud WRW (2006) Development of advanced solar assisted drying systems. *Renewable Energy* 31: 703–709.
[107] Rocamora MC and Tripanagnostopoulos Y (2006) Aspects of PV/T solar system application for ventilation needs in greenhouses. *Acta Horticulturae* 719: 239–245.
[108] Nayak S and Tiwari GN (2008) Energy and exergy analysis of photovoltaic/thermal integrated with a solar greenhouse. *Energy and Buildings* 40: 2015–2021.
[109] Kumar S and Tiwari A (2010) Design, fabrication and performance of a hybrid photovoltaic/thermal (PV/T) active solar still. *Energy Conversion and Management* 51: 1219–1229.
[110] Lasnier F and Ang TG (1990) *Photovoltaic Engineering Handbook*, p. 258. Princeton, NJ: Adam Higler.
[111] Skoplaki E, Boudouris AG, and Palyvos JA (2008) A simple correlation for the operating temperature of photovoltaic modules of arbitrary mounting. *Solar Energy Materials and Solar Cells* 92: 1393–1402.
[112] Skoplaki E and Palyvos JA (2009) Operating temperature of photovoltaic modules: A survey of pertinent correlations. *Renewable Energy* 34: 23–29.
[113] Skoplaki E and Palyvos JA (2009) On the temperature dependence of photovoltaic module electrical performance: A review of efficiency/power correlations. *Solar Energy* 83: 614–624.
[114] Aste N, Beccali M, and Solaini G (2003) Experimental validation of a simulation model for a PV/T collector. *ISES Solar World Congress*, CD-ROM., Göteborg, Sweden, 14–19 June.
[115] Fujisawa T and Tani T (1997) Annual exergy evaluation on photovoltaic-thermal hybrid collector. *Solar Energy Materials and Solar Cells* 47: 135–148.
[116] Markvart T (ed.) (2000) *Solar Electricity*, 2nd edn. Chichester, UK: John Wiley & Sons.
[117] Edmonds IR, Cowling IR, and Chan HM (1987) The design and performance of liquid filled stationary concentrators for use with photovoltaic cells. *Solar Energy* 39: 113–122.
[118] Hernandez M, Mohedano R, Munoz F, et al. (2000) New static concentrator for bifacial photovoltaic solar cells. In: *Proceedings of the 16th European Photovoltaic Solar Energy Conference*, pp. 2394–2397. Glasgow, UK, 1–5 May.
[119] Ortabasi U (1997) Performance of a 2X cusp concentrator PV module using bifacial solar cells. In: *Proceedings of the 26th IEEE Photovoltaic Specialist Conference*, Anaheim, CA, USA, 30 Sept.–3 Oct., pp. 1177–1181.
[120] Moehlecke A, Zanesco I, Pan AC, et al. (2001) Photovoltaic module with colored diffuse reflectors. In: *Proceedings of the 17th European Photovoltaic Solar Energy Conference*, pp. 785–787. Munich, Germany, 22–25 October.
[121] Winston R (1974) Principles of solar concentrators of a novel design. *Solar Energy* 16: 89–95.

[122] Wheldon A, Bentley R, Whitfield G, *et al.* (2005) Payback times for energy and carbon dioxide: Comparison of concentrating and non-concentrating PV systems. In: *Proceedings of the* 16th European PV Solar Energy Conference, pp. 2622–2625. Glasgow, UK, 1–5 May.
[123] Whitfield GR and Bentley RW (1998) Development and testing of optical concentrators for small PV systems. In: *Proceedings of the 2nd World Conference on PV Solar Energy Conversion*, pp. 2181–2184. Vienna, Austria.
[124] Verlinden PJ, Terao A, Daroczi S, *et al.* (2000) One-year comparison of a concentrator module with silicon point-contact solar cell to a fixed flat plate module in northern California. In: *Proceedings of the 16th European PV Solar Energy Conference*, pp. 2367–2370. Glasgow, UK, 1–5 May.
[125] Gordon JM, Kreider JF, and Reeves P (1991) Tracking and stationary flat plate solar collectors: Yearly collectible energy correlations for photovoltaic applications. *Solar Energy* 47: 245–252.
[126] Klotz FH, Noviello G, and Sarno A (1995) PV V-trough systems with passive tracking: Technical potential for mediterranean climate. In: *Proceedings of the 13th European Photovoltaic Solar Energy Conference*, pp. 372–375. Nice, Paris, 23–27 October.
[127] Fraidenraich N (1998) Design procedure of V-trough cavities for photovoltaic systems. *Progress in Photovoltaics: Research and Applications* 6: 43–54.
[128] Poulek V and Libra M (2000) TRAXLE™ the new line of trackers and tracking concentrators for terrestrial and space applications. In: *Proceedings of the 16th European Photovoltaic Solar Energy Conference*, pp. 2453–2546. Glasgow, UK, 1–5 May.
[129] Goetzberger A (1998) Static concentration systems with enhanced light concentration. In: *Proceedings of the 20th IEEE Photovoltaic Specialists Conference*, pp. 1333–1337, Las Vegas, NV, USA.
[130] Zanesco I and Lorenzo E (2002) Optimisation of an asymmetric static concentrator: The PEC-44D. *Progress in Photovoltaics: Research and Applications* 10: 361–376.
[131] Mohedano R, Benitez P, and Minano JC (1998) Cost reduction of building integrated PV's via static concentration systems. In: *Proceedings of the 2nd World Conference and Exhibition on Photovoltaic Solar Energy Conversion*, pp. 2241–2244. Vienna, Austria, 6–10 July.
[132] Nilsson J, Leutz R, and Karlsson B (2004) Improving asymmetrical CPCs for photovoltaics by using microstructured reflectors. In: *Proceedings of the 19th European Photovoltaic Solar Energy Conference*, pp. 2094–2097. Paris, France, 7–11 June.
[133] Yoshioka K, Goma S, Hayakawa S, and Saitoh T (1997) Preparation and properties of an experimental static concentrator with a new three-dimensional lens. *Progress in Photovoltaics: Research and Applications* 5: 139–145.
[134] Zacharopoulos A, Eames PC, McLarnon D, and Norton B (2000) Linear dielectric non-imaging concentrating covers for PV integrated building facades. *Solar Energy* 68: 439–452.
[135] Nabelek B, Maly M, and Jirka VI (1991) Linear Fresnel lenses, their design and use. *Renewable Energy* 1: 403–408.
[136] Kaminar N, McEntee J, Stark P, and Curchod D (1991) SEA 10*X* concentrator development progress. In: *Proceedings of the 22nd IEEE Photovoltaic Specialists Conference*, pp. 529–532. Las Vegas, NV, USA.
[137] Jirka V, Kuceravy V, Maly M, *et al.* (1998) The architectural use of glass raster lenses. In: *Proceedings of the World Renewable Energy Congress V*, Florence, Italy, 20–25 September 1998, part III, pp. 1595–1598.
[138] Shaw NC and Wenham SR (2000) Design of a novel static concentrator lens utilising total internal reflection surfaces. In: *Proceedings of the 16th European Photovoltaic Solar Energy Conference*, pp. 2342–2345. Glasgow, UK, 1–5 May.
[139] Luque A, Sala G, Arboiro JC, *et al.* (1998) Some results of the Euclides photovoltaic concentrator prototype. *Progress in Photovoltaics: Research and Applications* 5: 195–212.
[140] Rumyantsev VD, Heim M, Andreev VM, *et al.* (2000) Concentrator array based on GaAs cells and Fresnel lens concentrators. In: *Proceedings of the 16th European PV Solar Energy Conference*, pp. 2312–2315. Glasgow, UK, 1–5 May.
[141] James LW and Williams JK (1978) Fresnel optics for solar concentration on photovoltaic cells. In: *Proceedings of the 13th Photovoltaic Specialist Conference 1978*, New York, USA, pp. 673–679.
[142] Lorenzo E and Sala G (1979) Hybrid silicon-glass Fresnel lens as concentrator for photovoltaic applications. In: *ISES Conference, Silver Jubilee Congress*, pp. 536–539. Atlanta, GA, USA.
[143] O'Neil MJ, Walters RR, Perry JL, *et al.* (1990) Fabrication, installation and initial operation of the 2000 sq. m. linear fresnel lens photovoltaic concentrator system at 3M/Austin (Texas). In: *Proceedings of the 21th IEEE PV Specialists Conference*, pp. 1147–1152. Kissimmee, FL, USA.
[144] Bottenberg WR, Kaminar N, Alexander T, *et al.* (2000) Manufacturing technology improvements for the PVI SUNFOCUS™ concentrator. In: *Proceedings of the 16th European PV Solar Energy Conference*, pp. 2233–2236. Glasgow, UK, 1–5 May.
[145] Kritchman EM, Friesem AA, and Yekutieli G (1979) Efficient Fresnel lens for solar concentration. *Solar Energy* 22: 119–123.
[146] Evtuhov V (1979) Parametric cost analysis of photovoltaic systems. *Solar Energy* 22: 427–433.
[147] Hynes KM, Pearsall NM, Shaw M, and Crick FJ (1995) An assessment of the energy requirements of PV cladding systems. In: *Proceedings of the 13th European Photovoltaic Solar Energy Conference*, pp. 2202–2205. Nice, France, 23–27 October.
[148] Hynes KM, Baumann AE, and Hill R (1994) An assessment of the environmental impacts of thin film cadmium telluride modules based on life cycle analysis. In: *Proceedings of the 1st World Conference on PV Energy Conversion*, pp. 958–961. Waikoloa, HI, USA, 5–9 December.
[149] Keoleian GA and Lewis GMc-D (1997) Application of life-cycle energy analysis to photovoltaic module design. *Progress in Photovoltaics: Research and Applications* 5: 287–300.
[150] Alsema EA, Frankl P, and Kato K (1998) Energy pay-back time of photovoltaic energy systems: Present status and prospects. In: *Proceedings of the 2nd World Conference and Exhibition on Photovoltaic Solar Energy Conversion*, pp. 2125–2130. Vienna, Austria, 6–10 July.
[151] Kato K, Murata A, and Sakuta K (1998) Energy pay-back time and life-cycle CO_2 emission of residential PV power system with silicon PV module. *Progress in Photovoltaics: Research and Applications* 6: 105–115.
[152] Dones R and Frischknecht R (1998) Life-cycle assessment of photovoltaic systems: Results of Swiss studies on energy chains. *Progress in Photovoltaics: Research and Applications* 6: 117–125.
[153] Alsema EA (2000) Energy pay-back time and CO_2 emissions of PV systems. *Progress in Photovoltaics: Research and Applications* 8: 17–25.
[154] Frankl P (1996) 'Analisi del ciclo di vita di sistemi fotovoltaici' (LCA of Photovoltaic Systems). PhD Dissertation Thesis, Università di Roma 'La Sapienza', Roma, May 1996. Available at the Dipartimento di Meccanica e Aeronautica, Università di Roma 'La Sapienza', Roma, or at the Biblioteca Nazionale, Roma.
[155] Frankl P, Masini A, Gamberale M, and Toccaceli D (1998) Simplified life-cycle analysis of PV systems in buildings: Present situation and future trends. *Progress in Photovoltaics: Research and Applications* 6(2): 137–146.
[156] Frankl P (2002) Life cycle assessment (LCA) of PV systems: Overview and future outlook. In: *Proceedings of the International Conference PV in Europe*, pp. 588–592. Rome, Italy, 7–11 October.
[157] Frisson L, Lieten K, Bruton T, *et al.* (2000) Recent improvements in industrial PV module recycling. In: *Proceedings of the 16th European PV Solar Energy Conference and Exhibition*, pp. 2160–2163. Glasgow, UK, 1–5 May.
[158] Ji J, He H, Chow TT, *et al.* (2009) Distributed dynamic modelling and experimental study of PV evaporator in a PV/T solar: Assisted heat pump. *International Journal of Heat and Mass Transfer* 52(5–6): 1365–1373.
[159] Duffie JA and Beckman WA (1991) *Solar Engineering of Thermal Processes*. New York: John Wiley & Sons.
[160] Prasad BN and Saini JS (1991) Optimal thermohydraulic performance of artificially roughened solar air heaters. *Solar Energy* 47: 91–96.
[161] Bhavnani SH and Bergles AE (1990) Effect of surface geometry and orientation on laminar natural convection heat transfer from a vertical flat plate with transverse roughness elements. *International Journal of Heat and Mass Transfer* 33: 965–981.
[162] Han JC and Park JS (1988) Developing heat transfer in rectangular channels with rib turbulators. *International Journal of Heat and Mass Transfer* 31: 183–195.
[163] Gupta D, Solanki SC, and Saini JS (1993) Heat and fluid flow in rectangular solar air heater ducts having transverse rib roughness on absorber plates. *Solar Energy* 51: 31–37.

[164] Turk AY and Junkhan GH (1986) Heat transfer enhancement downstream of vortex generators on a flat plate. In: *Proceedings of 8th International Heat Transfer Conference*, Hemisphere, New York, USA, vol. 6, pp. 2903–2908.
[165] Biswas G and Chattopadhyay H (1992) Heat transfer in a channel with built-in wing-type vortex generators. *International Journal of Heat and Mass Transfer* 35: 803–814.
[166] Zhu JX, Fiebig M, and Mitra NK (1995) Numerical investigation of turbulent flows and heat transfer in a rib-roughened channel with longitudinal vortex generators. *International Journal of Heat and Mass Transfer* 38: 495–501.
[167] Tiggelbeck St, Mitra NK, and Fiebig M (1993) Experimental investigations of heat transfer enhancement and flow losses in a channel with double rows of longitudinal vortex generators. *International Journal of Heat and Mass Transfer* 36: 2327–2337.
[168] Brockmeier U, Guentermann Th, and Fiebig M (1993) Performance evaluation of a vortex generator heat transfer surface and comparison with different high performance surfaces. *International Journal of Heat and Mass Transfer* 36: 2575–2587.
[169] Fiebig M (1998) Vortices, generators and heat transfer. *Chemical Engineering Research and Design* 76: 108–123.
[170] Garg HP and Datta G (1989) Performance studies on a finned-air heater. *Energy* 14: 87–92.
[171] Garg HP, Jha R, Choudhury C, and Datta G (1991) Theoretical analysis on a finned type solar air heater. *Energy* 16: 1231–1238.
[172] Pottler K, Sippel CM, Beck A, and Fricke J (1999) Optimized finned absorber geometries for solar air heating collectors. *Solar Energy* 67: 35–52.
[173] Naphon P (2005) On the performance and entropy generation of the double-pass solar air heater with longitudinal fins. *Renewable Energy* 30: 1345–1357.
[174] Tripanagnostopoulos Y, Nousia Th, and Souliotis M (2000) Low cost improvements to building integrated air cooled hybrid PV-thermal systems. In: *Proceedings of the 16th European PV Solar Energy Conference*, vol. 2, pp. 1874–1899. Glasgow, UK, 1–5 May.
[175] Tripanagnostopoulos Y, Nousia Th, and Souliotis M (2001) Test results of air cooled modified PV modules. In: *Proceedings of the 17th PV Solar Energy Conference*, pp. 2519–2522. Munich, Germany, 22–26 October.
[176] Tripanagnostopoulos Y, Tzavellas D, Zoulia I, and Chortatou M (2001) Hybrid PV/T systems with dual heat extraction operation. In: *Proceedings of the 17th PV Solar Energy Conference*, pp. 2515–2518. Munich, Germany, 22–26 Oct.
[177] Tan HM and Charters WWS (1969) Effect of thermal entrance region on turbulent forced-convective heat transfer for an asymmetrically rectangular duct with uniform heat flux. *Solar Energy* 12: 513–516.
[178] Esposito A (1998) *Fluid Mechanics with Applications*. Upper Saddle River, NJ: Prentice-Hall.
[179] Young FD, Munson BR, and Okiishi TH (1997) *A Brief Introduction to Fluid Mechanics*. New York: John Wiley & Sons.
[180] Incropera FB and DeWitt DP (1996) *Fundamentals of Heat and Mass Transfer*. New York: John Wiley & Sons.
[181] Moshfegh B and Sandberg M (1998) Flow and heat transfer in the air gap behind photovoltaic panels. *Renewable and Sustainable Energy Reviews* 2: 287–301.
[182] Dascalaki E, Santamouris M, Argiriou A, *et al.* (1996) On the combination of air velocity and flow measurements in single side natural ventilation configurations. *Energy and Building* 24: 155–165.
[183] Kalogirou SA, Florides G, and Tassou S (2002) Energy analysis of buildings employing thermal mass in Cyprus. *Renewable Energy* 27: 353–368.
[184] Sandberg M and Moshfegh B (1996) Investigation of fluid flow and heat transfer in a vertical channel heated from one side by PV elements, Part II: Experimental study. *Renewable Energy* 8(1–4): 254–258.
[185] Ibarahim Z, Marshall RH, and Brinkworth BJ (1999) Simplified loop analysis for naturally ventilated channel heated from one side by PV elements. In: *Proceedings of UK-ISES Silver Jubilee Conference*, pp. 69–74. Brighton, UK, May.
[186] Smolec W and Thomas A (1994) Problems encountered in heat transfer studies of Trombe wall. *Energy Conversion and Management* 35: 483–491.
[187] Smolec W and Thomas A (1993) Theoretical and experimental investigations of heat transfer in a Trombe wall. *Energy Conversion and Management* 34: 385–400.
[188] Tsuji T and Nagano Y (1988) Characteristics of a turbulent natural convection boundary layer along a vertical flat plate. *International Journal of Heat and Mass Transfer* 31: 1723–1734.
[189] Randall KR, Mitchell JW, and El-Wakil MM (1979) Natural convection heat transfer characteristics of flat plate enclosures. *American Society of Mechanical Engineers Journal of Heat Transfer* 101: 120–125.
[190] Tripanagnostopoulos Y, Bazilian M, Zoulia I, and Battisti R (2002) Hybrid PV/T system with improved air heat extraction modification. In: *Proceedings of the International Conference on PV in Europe*, pp. 718–721. Rome, Italy, 7–11 October.
[191] Kalogirou SA (2009) *Solar Energy Engineering: Processes and Systems*. Burlington, MA: Academic Press.
[192] Kalogirou SA, Florides G, Tsipas D, *et al.* (2008) A TRNSYS model of a hybrid PV/T solar collector system. In: *Proceedings (in CD) of International Conference WREC X*. Glasgow, Scotland, 19–25 July.
[193] Tripanagnostopoulos Y, Souliotis M, Makris Th, *et al.* (2009) Design and performance of a hybrid PV/T solar water heater. In: *Proceedings (in CD) of the 7th General Conference of the BPU (BPU7) Organized by the Hellenic Physical Society*. Alexandroupolis, Greece, 9–13 September.
[194] Tripanagnostopoulos Y (2008) Building integrated concentrating PV and PV/T systems. In: *Proceedings of the International Conference Eurosun*. Lisbon, Portugal, 7–10 October.
[195] Tripanagnostopoulos Y and Iliopoulou A (2007) Improved designs for low concentration photovoltaics. In: *Proceedings of the 22nd PVSEC International Conference*. Milan, Italy, 3–7 September.
[196] Tripanagnostopoulos Y (2006) Cost effective designs for building integrated PV/T solar systems. In: *Presented in 21st European PV Solar Energy Conference*. Dresden, Germany, 4–6 September.
[197] Souliotis M, Tripanagnostopoulos Y, and Kavga A (2006) The use of Fresnel lenses to reduce the ventilation needs of greenhouses. *Acta Horticulturae* 719: 107–113.
[198] Petrova-Koch V, Hezel R, and Goetzberger A (2008) High-efficient low-cost photovoltaics: Recent developments. *Springer Series in Optical Sciences* 140: 177–181.
[199] Jirka V, Kuceravy V, Maly M, *et al.* (1999) Energy flow in a greenhouse equipped with glass raster lenses. *Renewable Energy* 16: 660–664.
[200] Tripanagnostopoulos Y, Souliotis M, Makris Th, and Chemisana D (2010) Effective combination of solar and wind energy systems. In: *Proceedings of International Conference on Hybrid-PV and Mini Grid*. Tarragona, Spain, April.

3.09 Solar Selective Coatings

P Yianoulis and M Giannouli, University of Patras, Patras, Greece
SA Kalogirou, Cyprus University of Technology, Limassol, Cyprus

© 2012 Elsevier Ltd. All rights reserved.

3.09.1	Introduction	301
3.09.1.1	Introductory Remarks and Definitions	302
3.09.1.2	Definitions of Some Key Optical Properties	303
3.09.2	**Classes of Selective Absorbers**	**304**
3.09.2.1	Intrinsic Materials or Mass Absorbers – A Single Material Is Used Exhibiting the Desired Selectivity	304
3.09.2.2	Tandem Stacks or Inverse Tandem Stacks of a Reflecting Surface and a Semiconductor on Top of It	305
3.09.2.2.1	Some simple methods for the preparation of 'tandem stacks'	305
3.09.2.2.2	Silicon and/or germanium on proper base surfaces	306
3.09.2.2.3	Inverse tandem stacks	306
3.09.2.3	Multilayer Stacks (Interference Stacks)	306
3.09.2.4	Metal Particles in a Dielectric or Metal Matrix (Cermets)	307
3.09.2.5	Surface Roughness	308
3.09.2.6	Quantum Size Effects	309
3.09.3	**Characterization of Selective Surfaces**	**309**
References		**310**
Further Reading		**312**

Glossary

Absorptance The ratio of the radiant flux absorbed by a body to that incident upon it. Spectral absorptance refers to absorptance measured at a specified wavelength. Care must be taken not to confuse it with 'absorbance'.
Band gap The minimum energy separation between the highest occupied state and the lowest empty state that determines the temperature dependence of the electrical conductivity of a pure semiconductor.
Cermet Metal–dielectric composites, a composite structural material of a heat-resistant compound (such as titanium carbide, chromium oxide, etc.) and a metal (such as nickel, chromium, etc.).
Emittance (or emissivity) The ratio of heat emitted by a body to that emitted by a blackbody at the same temperature. It takes values from 0 to 1. A blackbody by definition has emissivity 1. A perfect reflector would have emittance 0.
Evaporation The deposition by sublimation of a material to form a film or any other deposited form.
Morphology The external form and structure of a material or topographic features.
Reflectance The fraction of incident electromagnetic power that is reflected at an interface.
Reflectance spectrum or spectral reflectance curve The plot of the reflectance as a function of wavelength.
Reflectivity The reflectance of the surface of a material of very large thickness. The reflectivity is an intrinsic property of the material and it is measured with the material, theoretically, filling half of all space. Therefore, the term reflectivity applies to thick reflecting objects.
Sputtering The process of removing atoms from the surface of a material (target) by impact with high-energy ions, and by this process a metallic film is deposited.

3.09.1 Introduction

Spectrally selective coatings, or solar selective coatings in particular that are of interest here, are used in solar thermal collectors or solar collector systems, in general, to enhance the efficiency of photothermal conversion and the useful heat collected, especially at elevated temperatures. Their use is especially important for high-temperature applications. The spectral selectivity of a solar absorber is characterized (or determined) by its high 'absorptance' α in the short-wavelength region of the solar radiation of about 0.3–3 μm and low 'emittance' ε at the far-infrared (IR) region of the spectrum corresponding to the blackbody thermal emittance at the operating temperature of the absorber (i.e., about 2–25 μm). Typical values for these properties of selective surfaces are 0.90 for absorptance and 0.10 for the emittance. However, respective values in the range from 0.8 to 0.99 and from 0.01 to 0.3 have been obtained experimentally.

It is of interest to define a more representative figure of merit of a selective surface, based on its overall energetic performance. Usually, 'selectivity' is defined as the ratio of the absorptance to emittance (α/ε) in the spectral regions mentioned earlier. This ratio can vary with temperature and depends on the exact function of wavelength of the two quantities α and ε. The ideal characteristics of a photothermal converter are approximated by an absorber reflector tandem, the reflector coated with a highly absorbing layer over the short-wavelength region which is transparent in the far-IR region.

3.09.1.1 Introductory Remarks and Definitions

'Solar absorbers' are used as a first step for the photothermal conversion of solar energy. They should absorb as much as possible in the spectral region of the solar radiation, which is contained in the region of about 0.3–3 μm. They are heated by this process at a temperature of operation that can be low, as in the case of domestic hot water collectors, or at higher temperatures required for some industrial applications and for the conversion of heat to electricity using an appropriate thermodynamic cycle. It is obvious that it is required to reduce the thermal losses and thus the energy radiated by the absorber to the environment. It should be pointed out that ordinary black paint has high absorption, satisfying the first requirement, but it has also high emissivity in the thermal infrared (TIR), and thus its selectivity is low. Therefore, in general, ordinary black surfaces are not selective surfaces. Selective surfaces are designed to take advantage of the different wavelength regions of incident solar radiation and the emitted thermal radiation from the absorbing surface. Selective surface coatings play an important role when the working temperatures are above 100 °C. Radiative losses become large at medium and especially at high temperatures (>400 °C). At these higher temperatures, evacuated tubes and selective absorbers are used to reduce convective and radiative losses; the systems utilizing these collectors are of the concentrating type.

In the following, the subscript or superscript 's' is used to show that a physical quantity is measured over the short-wavelength spectrum, that is, in the region of about 0.3–3 μm. In a more rigorous definition, the value of the corresponding physical quantity will be taken as a weighted average, taking into account the average distribution of the solar intensity as a function of wavelength. Then the quantity will be characterized by s, to show that its value is valid for the 'short-wavelength' or solar wavelength region.

Similarly, the subscript or superscript ℓ is used to show that a physical quantity is measured over the long-wavelength spectrum or the TIR, that is, in the region of about 2–25 μm. Strictly, the value of the quantity will be taken as a weighted average taking into account the average distribution of the blackbody intensity with the wavelength at the operating temperature of the absorber according to Planck's law. The quantity then will be characterized as 'long-wavelength' or TIR wavelength region.

In this chapter, when it is obvious that we are referring to the absorptance in the s region and the emittance in the ℓ region, we may drop the use of the subscripts (or superscripts) s or ℓ.

The spectral distribution of solar radiation and the TIR radiation emitted by bodies heated at the usual operating temperatures of solar absorbers do not overlap significantly. The blackbody emission (i.e., energy emitted within a given wavelength interval) at absolute temperature T is given by Planck's law eqn [2]. From this law, it follows that the spectral regions s and ℓ are in well-separated parts of the spectrum. This is the physical basis that permits us to use surfaces that have different absorption, reflection, and emitting properties in the short- and long-wavelength regions as stated before. Such surfaces can be designed for maximum absorption of solar radiation and minimum emittance in the TIR. These surfaces are called 'selective'. Therefore, the spectral selectivity stands on the fact that the solar spectrum and the thermally emitted radiation (as given by Planck's law) are in different areas and do not overlap.

The desired spectral selectivity can be achieved by several techniques and engineering of the absorbing surfaces, using to our advantage the physics of thin solid films and dispersions of metal particles in a dielectric matrix. An 'ideal selective surface' should have an absorptance α as presented in general in **Figure 1**. The absorptance α must approach as close to 1 as possible in the 'short-wavelength' region and as close to 0 as possible in the long-wavelength or TIR wavelength region. This follows from Kirchhoff's law (see Section 3.09.1.2) as we must have ε as nearly equal to 0 as possible in the TIR wavelength region. In between is the transition spectral region, which must be as abrupt as possible and at a 'critical wavelength', λ_c. For most applications, λ_c has a value in the

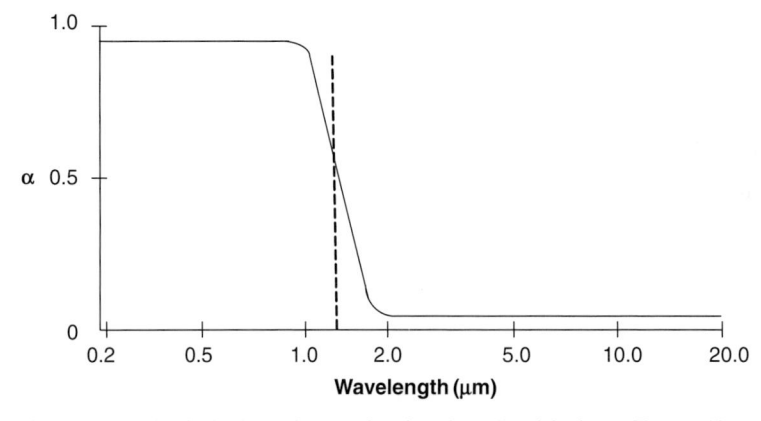

Figure 1 The absorptance α of a hypothetical ideal selective surface as a function of wavelength is shown. The transition spectral region, which must be as abrupt as possible, is shown here in the region of 1–1.8 μm. The critical wavelength λ_c is indicated by the vertical dashed line at around 1.3 μm.

spectral region of 1–3 μm. The exact value of λ_c depends on the operating temperature of the photothermal converter and on the concentration factor of the solar radiation, if an optical system is used for this purpose.

3.09.1.2 Definitions of Some Key Optical Properties

For electromagnetic radiation in general, a flow of photons with energy is given by

$$E = hf = \frac{hC}{\lambda} \qquad [1]$$

where h is Planck's constant (6.626×10^{-34} Js), f is the frequency of light, λ is the wavelength, and C the velocity of light. The velocity of light C in a material is connected with its index of refraction n by the equation $C = \frac{C_o}{n}$ where C_o is the velocity of light in vacuum.

The blackbody emission (i.e., energy emitted within a given wavelength interval) at absolute temperature T is given by Planck's law:

$$E_\lambda = \frac{C_1}{\lambda^5}\left(\frac{1}{e^{C_2/\lambda T}-1}\right) \qquad [2]$$

In eqn [2], the constants are $C_1 = 3.742 \times 10^{-16}$ Wm^2 and $C_2 = 0.014388$ mK.

Wien's law gives the wavelength λ_{max} for which the thermal emission from eqn [2] has a maximum. This is related to temperature (T) by

$$\lambda_{max} T = 2897.8 \; (\mu m\, K) \qquad [3]$$

Using this equation, it can be found that the spectral distribution of thermal radiation emitted by bodies at operating temperatures of solar absorbers, as stated earlier, has a maximum around 10 μm (long-wavelength radiation: symbol ℓ), while the solar spectrum has a maximum at about 0.55 μm (short-wavelength radiation: symbol s). The equivalent temperature of the sun may be taken as 5900 K for the application in eqns [2] and [3] for the solar spectrum. The exact solar spectrum is available from measurements with the attenuation caused by atmospheric absorption at sea level and various zenith angles of the sun (i.e., air mass values) or extra-terrestrially from satellites without the atmospheric absorption. These results provide fine details that are not covered by this general picture. However, for most practical cases, these equations can be used.

Also from Planck's law the total power emitted by a blackbody, per unit area for all wavelengths can be found. This is the well-known Stefan–Boltzmann law:

$$E = \int_0^\infty E_\lambda d\lambda = \sigma T^4 \qquad [4]$$

The constant $\sigma = 5.6697 \times 10^{-8}$ W m^{-2}K^4 is called Stefan–Boltzmann constant.

The absorptance a is defined as the absorbed fraction of light of a specified wavelength when it falls on the surface. This quantity is a function of wavelength and can differ in various parts of the spectrum. It is obvious that we are interested mainly in a^s in this chapter.

The emittance ε of a surface is defined as the emitted fraction of light, at a specified wavelength, from the surface over that emitted from a blackbody at the same temperature T. This quantity is also a function of wavelength and can differ in various parts of the spectrum. We are interested mainly in ε^ℓ in this chapter. At this point, we should also point out that ε in general, as also ε^ℓ in particular, depend on the temperature of the sample.

All materials absorb, reflect, and transmit radiant energy. The incident (monochromatic) radiation I_o on a surface is partly absorbed, reflected, and transmitted through it. The equation of energy conservation then may be written as

$$I_o = I_a + I_r + I_t \qquad [5]$$

Dividing both sides of this equation by I_o, the following very useful relation can be obtained:

$$\alpha(\lambda) + \rho(\lambda) + \tau(\lambda) = 1 \qquad [6]$$

where α is the absorptance, ρ is the reflectance, and τ is the transmittance of the surface. Equation [6] can be stated in words as the sum of absorptance, reflectance, and transmittance of a surface is 1.

Strictly speaking, this equation is valid for monochromatic radiation. In some cases, this is indicated by showing the explicit dependence on λ, or the subscript λ at the symbols of the quantities involved. These quantities may vary considerably over a wavelength range of interest for some materials. If the optical characteristics of a body do not change with λ, this is called 'gray body'. For an ideal blackbody, $\varepsilon(\lambda) = 1$ and $\alpha(\lambda) = 1$ for all λ. It is obvious that we can extend eqn [6] by the principle of superposition for any region of the spectrum with well-defined spectral distribution of the radiation. Therefore, in general, eqn [6] can be written as $\alpha + \rho + \tau = 1$.

For opaque surfaces, we have $\tau = 0$ and we obtain

$$\alpha(\lambda) + \rho(\lambda) = 1 \qquad [7]$$

At this point, it is useful to apply the known Kirchhoff's law:

$$\varepsilon(\lambda) = \alpha(\lambda) \qquad [8]$$

From eqns [7] and [8], we obtain the very useful relation for selective surfaces:

$$\varepsilon(\lambda) + \rho(\lambda) = 1 \qquad [9]$$

Equation [9] implies that a reflective surface (ρ almost equal to 1) is a poor emitter for a specified wavelength or wavelength region. This is a very important fact concerning the study of selective surfaces. Also, from eqns [7] and [9], it can be deduced that the graph for the reflectance for an ideal selective surface is close to 0 for the s wavelength region, while it rises sharply at a wavelength λ_c which is called critical wavelength, and remains close to 1 for wavelengths longer than λ_c (see **Figure 1**). It is stressed once more that the critical wavelength depends on the temperature of the absorber and the concentration of solar radiation if an optical system is used for this purpose.

3.09.2 Classes of Selective Absorbers

Many methods and materials or material combinations have been used for obtaining the desired property of spectral selectivity. The various selective absorbers can be divided into the following categories [1]:

1. Intrinsic materials or mass absorbers.
2. Tandem stacks and inverse tandem stacks.
3. Multilayer stacks (interference stacks).
4. Metal particles in a dielectric or metal matrix (cermets).
5. Surface roughness.
6. Quantum size effects (QSEs).

These are examined in the following sections.

3.09.2.1 Intrinsic Materials or Mass Absorbers – A Single Material Is Used Exhibiting the Desired Selectivity

The range of single materials having the desired selective properties as they are defined before is extremely restricted. Here we are interested mainly with the type of 'selective absorbing materials' (SAMs) used as absorbers. However, we should note that there exists also another very important class of 'selective transmitting materials' (STMs) that are transparent in the short-wavelength (solar wavelength) region and reflective in the long-wavelength region (TIR). These are mainly used as layers on windows. Details are given in Chapter **3.01** of this volume. Their function is to let solar radiation in, but restrict the thermal radiative losses to the ambient. It is obvious that this second category is interesting for use also on the transparent covers of solar collecting systems besides the well-known use for windows in buildings. For completeness, we refer briefly to them.

Tin oxide (SnO_2) and indium oxide (In_2O_3) are naturally selective materials that can be used as STMs. For SnO_2, the solar transmittance is $\tau^s = 0.75$ and the reflectance in the TIR is $\rho^\ell = 0.7$. In_2O_3 has similar properties. These values are very modest and the use of them for this purpose is rather limited. The main use of these materials is as thin films for windows (as STMs) and for transparent conductive coatings. For the latter use, doping is used to improve conductivity. The main doping material for SnO_2 is fluoride (F). Also for many cases, the mixed oxide is used, under the name ITO, standing for the mixed substance indium tin oxide. Through the years, many interesting results have been obtained. The appealing property of this mixed oxide is that it can have an abrupt transition from transmission in the short-wavelength range to the reflecting state in the IR. This abrupt change occurs at the desired spectral region around 2 μm. An interesting application is for transparent covers for solar collectors. For this use, the internal absorptance of the films should be minimized. The experimental results were very encouraging but the current price of indium as a metal prevents the widespread use of these films. Very early in the development of this field, it was found that a small amount of SnO_2 in In_2O_3 can give very good results, with the transmission in the short wavelength τ^s of about 0.9 and reflection in the TIR at ρ^ℓ of about 0.85 [2]. The interesting point in this case is that the transition region is very abrupt, as we want it to be, and at about 1.8 μm.

Hafnium carbide (HfC) is a semiconductor known for a very long time to exhibit natural selectivity as a SAM [1]. The TIR reflectance ρ^ℓ is about 0.9 and ε^ℓ is about 0.1, which is very good, but it has relatively low absorptance α^s of about 0.7. HfC is an attractive material for applications at very high temperatures of absorbers because of its high melting point. Actually, it has the highest melting point of any compound. Other carbides have similar physical properties. In order to use these materials profitably for solar energy applications as an absorber, the absorptance must be increased in the short wavelengths by the methods described for the next categories. For example, it can be combined with an antireflective layer, or to arrange the absorber in order to have two reflections for the incident radiation [1, 3].

Rare earth hexaborides, in general, have optical properties that are also of interest. From them in particular, lanthanum hexaboride (LaB_6) has reflectance in the TIR ρ^ℓ of about 0.9 and solar transmittance τ^s of about 0.85, if it is used with an antireflective coating to reduce reflectance at the short wavelengths. Rare earth hexaborides belong in the class of STMs. In most cases of semiconductors in the class of STMs, they have high indices of refraction in the short wavelengths, and for this reason, it is required to have an antireflection coating deposited on top of them for best performance [1].

As has already been mentioned, the intrinsic absorbers are materials in which the selectivity is an intrinsic property of the material, consequently, they are structurally more stable but optically less effective than multilayer stacks. No natural materials exhibit intrinsically the required selective properties, but some of them approach these properties. Research in intrinsic absorbers has not given impressive results up to now. Intrinsic materials are finding use as a component in high-temperature absorber composite coatings and multilayer absorbers. We should point out that intrinsic solar selective properties are found in transition metals and semiconductors, but both need to be modified considerably in order to be finally used as intrinsic absorbers [4].

3.09.2.2 Tandem Stacks or Inverse Tandem Stacks of a Reflecting Surface and a Semiconductor on Top of It

Sometimes, this category is also characterized by the name 'semiconductor–metal tandems'. The semiconductor is deposited in the form of a film few micrometers thick and absorbs the short-wavelength radiation. It is placed on top of a reflective metal film, which provides low thermal emittance and is reflective for short-wavelength radiation. Tandem stacks were first deposited for the construction of a 'black searchlight mirror' in 1964 by Hass [1, 5]. This black mirror is reflective for the TIR and absorbing in the short wavelength. Germanium (Ge) was used as a semiconductor on top of an aluminum reflector. The semiconductor Ge has a band gap of 0.7 eV and is transparent for TIR. Seraphin has done much work for the development of such stacks [6]. Among other materials that were used long ago is another well-known semiconductor, lead sulfide (PbS, Eg = 0.4 eV). Another semiconductor that has been used extensively is Si (Eg = 1.1 eV) [7].

The basic optical component of a semiconductor–metal tandem is obviously the semiconductor. The transition region of the tandem stack is connected with the semiconductor band gap as can be seen from the following reasoning. The semiconductors absorb short-wavelength radiation according to their band gaps. For an ideal two-energy level system, we have from eqn [1] by putting in the physical constants involved:

$$\lambda_{max} = \frac{1.24}{Eg} \quad [10]$$

In eqn [10], Eg is the energy difference in eV and λ_{max} is the maximum wavelength in μm to which the absorption extends (absorption edge). For a semiconductor, the band gap Eg can be used in eqn [10]. Therefore, if the semiconductor has a band gap of 1.24 eV, it cannot absorb at longer wavelengths than 1 μm, and for a band gap of about 0.5 eV, at no longer wavelengths than 2.5 μm. From the same formula, we find that the value 2.0 μm for the 'cutoff wavelength' corresponds to a band gap of 0.62 eV. It is evident that the wavelength for transition from transparent to reflective depends on the band gap of the semiconductor and it is important to be as abrupt as possible. Again, it should be noted here that the semiconductor absorbs the short-wavelength radiation and the underlying metal provides low emittance for the desired spectrally selective properties of the stack.

The required thickness of the semiconductor depends on the absorption coefficient of the semiconductor at short wavelengths. For silicon, it can be found from the absorption data that the required thickness is around 3–5 μm. Of course, it is required to reduce the thickness in order to save expensive material. Interference effects in the stack design may be used profitably in order to reduce the thickness. It has been reported that layers of Si of about 1.5 μm in thickness can be used in this way [3].

The tandem can be extended by the incorporation of more layers that act as antireflection coatings, if they are needed. This may be useful in most cases as the semiconductors have high refractive indices, resulting in large reflectance losses. The concept of two basic layers is maintained, but by including additional layers, more efficient and durable tandem stacks can be produced.

Ideally, it is preferable to have simple methods of preparation of tandem stacks. Methods that have been used include vacuum evaporation of the layers, chemical vapor deposition (CVD), and simple heating in the air. The silicon-based designs that have been produced by CVD are known to be suitable for mid- to high-temperature applications [6]. Electrochemical selective coatings can be prepared in principle. The main difficulty is to have uniform behavior of the electrochemically produced coatings. The parameter of interest is the plating current that must be varied during deposition for best results. A well-known electrochemical selective coating is the black nickel that can be deposited in the form of a tandem stack. Black nickel selective coatings were developed first by Tabor, as early as in 1955. The method of production was electrochemical deposition.

3.09.2.2.1 Some simple methods for the preparation of 'tandem stacks'

Unfortunately, there are no simple methods for the preparation of tandem stacks in the form of paints, as one would desire. It has been reported that lightly 'smoking' the surface of a mirror gives a simple tandem stack, as the 'carbon layer' is opaque to the short wavelengths, but transparent to TIR. These surfaces are not very stable as the carbon particles are removed easily and it is impossible to find a suitable binder in order to solve this problem. The physical properties of the binder do not match the requirements.

'Oxidized metal surfaces' offer a relatively simple method for preparing tandem stacks. Oxidation of Type 410 stainless steel by heating it in the air at 750 °C shows a specular reflectance in the short wavelengths that is reduced considerably, but in the transition region (i.e., in the region of 1–3 μm), the change in reflectance is very gradual [1]. The 'selectivity', defined as the ratio $\alpha^s/\varepsilon^\ell$, is only about 3 limiting the possible applications to concentrating collectors requiring modest selectivity. The oxidation of stainless steel is a simple method and can be used accordingly. Titanium (Ti) is a metal that can be used in the same way to prepare an oxide layer on its surface. The oxidation is achieved by heating it in the air at 425 °C for a time period from 100 to 300 h. Heating time increase has as a result the increase of the transition region from about 1 to 3 μm. The transition in this case is also very gradual. The selectivity is again moderate [1].

3.09.2.2.2 Silicon and/or germanium on proper base surfaces

Si was placed over aluminum (Al) substrates [1]. The Si thickness was 0.5 mm. The reflectance in the visible is that of bulk Si (>30%) and is not low enough. It can be reduced by using a thin layer of SiO_2 as an antireflecting layer for Si. Nickel (Ni) was also used as a substrate in some stacks with relatively good results. In more advanced multilayer designs, both Si and Ge have been used to produce a multilayer stack that is close to an ideal selective surface [1, 3]. It has a double minimum for the specular reflectance at about 0.5 and 1 μm, a very sharp increase in reflectance at about 1.5 μm, and the reflectance in the TIR is about 0.97. The substrate in this stack was silver and the Si/Ge layer is antireflected with a double layer composed of silicon nitride and silicon dioxide (Si_3N_4/SiO_2) [1, 3].

Important developments were in the direction of using optically thin layers. Interference fringes appear in the specular reflectance versus wavelength graphs from such thin films. Simulation tools are very useful in the design of advanced stacks of multiple coatings [3, 6, 8]. In principle, such stacks can be developed as to take advantage of interference effects that cancel out reflected light in the short wavelengths with almost zero reflectance at 550 nm where the maximum of the solar spectrum occurs. The use of Ag substrate with Si and Ge is an example of such a stack. In most cases, the final product includes also very thin diffusion barriers in the form of additional thin films in the stack. These are necessary for ensuring long-term stability of the product and ensure that there is no mixing of the various layers by ion diffusion between layers occurs. A good example of such diffusion layer is Cr_2O_3. Modern vacuum deposition techniques such as magnetron sputtering fabrication in the industry and electron beam (e-beam gun) evaporation in the scientific laboratories have made the thin sold film deposition straightforward and very precise. Thickness measurements of the films are performed *in situ* during deposition using special quartz crystal sensors. The work in this direction is developed in parallel with that required for developing STMs for energy saving applications [9–11].

3.09.2.2.3 Inverse tandem stacks

It is possible to put the TIR emission suppression layer on the top and the absorbing material, for the short wavelengths, at the bottom. In this case, the top material can be an STM that is transparent in the short-wavelength (solar wavelength) region and reflective in the long-wavelength region (TIR). Tin oxide (SnO_2) and indium oxide (In_2O_3) are suitable materials as seen earlier. Fluoride (F) is often used as a doping material for SnO_2. The mixed oxide can also be used, under the name indium tin oxide (ITO). The absorbing material can be Si as described before, or any other suitable absorber as Ge, or lead sulfide (PbS). The top layer should be designed to be as transparent as possible for the solar wavelength region of the spectrum.

3.09.2.3 Multilayer Stacks (Interference Stacks)

In this class, as many layers of metal and dielectric may be used as needed to achieve the desired results. One simple construction can include a metal substrate on which to deposit the next layers, a reflective metal film, a first dielectric material, a semitransparent thin metal film, a second dielectric material, and finally an antireflection coating. As substrates, stainless steel, molybdenum, copper, aluminum, and other metals can be used. On the substrate, a highly reflective film is deposited. It can be omitted if the substrate surface is highly reflective by a proper process like polishing. However, the quality of the reflecting surface is ensured at best by vacuum deposition. Then a semiconductor as the first dielectric layer is deposited. The reflectance versus wavelength curve then shows a lowering of the reflectance in the short-wavelength region, as desired, but this is not as low and broad as we would like it to be. To achieve this, one may add a second very thin, semitransparent metal reflecting layer over the first dielectric. This is similar to the Fabry–Perot interferometer [12]. This has as a result the strengthening of the reflected wave and maximizing the interference in the first dielectric layer. The thickness of this metal film is generally < 10 nm.

Then a second dielectric layer is deposited in order to complete the basic four-layer stack; this minimizes the reflection and thus maximizes the absorption in the short-wavelength region. Typically, now in this region we have two reflection minima as shown in **Figure 2**. It also broadens the absorption region in the short-wavelength region, which is the low-reflectance region in the figure. It should be noted that the effect of the two reflecting layers is to strengthen the reflected wave and thus maximize the internal interference in the first dielectric. The second dielectric is necessary to get the overall general result as it appears in this figure.

It is also possible to deposit an antireflection coating on top of the second dielectric layer to have a five-layer optimized stack. This minimizes the reflection losses from the top of the stack as solar light enters the selective surface. The series of layers as described can be repeated for an even better result [1]. However, one must be careful as to the cost-effectiveness of such a solution. Studies show that it will pay only in very special applications.

The multilayer interference stack absorbers can be designed so that they are optimized for very efficient selectivity. The physics of the multilayer absorber is well understood, and modeling can easily be carried out [8, 12–16]. The optical properties of a given multilayer can be computed. The overall design and selection of materials can be facilitated by this process [17]. Depending on the materials used, multilayer interference stacks have high solar absorption, low thermal emittance, and can be stable, depending on the materials chosen, at elevated temperatures (≥ 400 °C). For high-temperature applications, several multilayer absorbers using

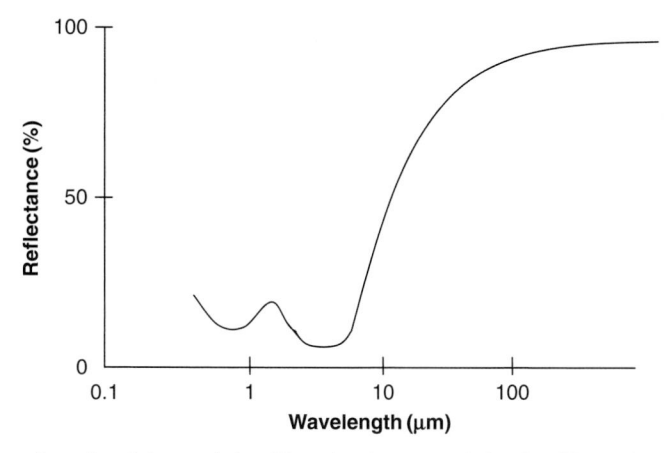

Figure 2 Reflectance as a function of wavelength for a typical multilayer interference stack absorber. The two interference minima and the transition spectral region can be noted.

different metals (e.g., Al, Mo, Ag, Cu, Ni, W, and Cr) and dielectric layers (e.g., Al_2O_3, SiO_2, CeO, ZnS, Cu_2O, and Cu_2S) have been used [18, 19]. In the older literature, there is an ambiguity as to the exact chemical species involved [1]. It should be pointed out that there are two oxides of copper: CuO and Cu_2O. CuO decomposes to Cu_2O at 1026 °C. Cu_2O, which is the more stable form, is a material with good intrinsic selectivity [1]. In the same way from the sulfides, Cu_2S is the more stable form and CuS decomposes to the former at temperatures over 100 °C. Selectivity can be achieved by placing either Cu_2O or Cu_2S over a reflecting Cu surface. Care must be taken in this case so that the underlying reflecting Cu surface does not react with oxygen or sulfur; otherwise, the selectivity disappears.

Tabor [20] has done early development work for selective black Ni coatings by electroplating. The plating bath he used contained both Ni and Zn ions. The coatings consist of bright Ni on a Cu substrate and the dielectric in the stack is ZnS. The results show good selectivity with the characteristic double minimum in the short-wavelength region and a transition wavelength in the 1–5 μm region, depending on the thickness of the ZnS layer over the base layer of reflective Ni. Later, Honeywell produced black Ni also by electrodeposition and post-deposition annealing at 500 °C for 15 h. The results showed that we could have a considerable shift of the transition region to longer wavelengths. This had as a result the increase of the absorptance to 0.98.

Overall, these developments at Honeywell showed that the heat treatment of the absorber after preparation and the variation of the thickness of the ZnS layer permitted very good values of overall selectivity to be achieved [1]. They are produced very early, and became commercially available, selective absorbers of black Ni in large sizes that were used in solar installations in the United States. The same researchers have also produced molybdenum (Mo)-based multilayer interference stack absorbers for space applications. They used Al_2O_3, CeO, or both as dielectric materials in the stack. The transition is steep and appears at 2.0 μm, but the TIR reflectance is relatively low, below 0.9. To improve this, they used a thin layer of Ag or Au on top of Mo. The problem with Au was that it disappears by diffusion in the Mo base. Ag is more durable and it is possible to use a thin buffer layer of a dielectric to avoid the diffusion problem [1, 21].

Both Al and W have been used as metal bases in the multilayer interference stack absorbers for their good reflection properties in the TIR. They both withstand high temperatures and can be deposited by sputtering, evaporation, and by CVD. The best results for W are achieved by the CVD method. Al can be effectively applied by all these methods. Cu is also giving very good results as a base film. It has high TIR reflectance and it has the advantage of being a relatively low-cost material. On the negative side is its reactivity with O and S at high temperatures, which destroys the selectivity of the film by forming CuO and CuS or the more stable versions Cu_2O and Cu_2S, as mentioned before, at elevated temperatures.

It has been found that copper and its oxides create an arrangement with reflective, transparent, and highly absorbing states. Cu_2O can be transformed reversibly to opaque metallic copper films when reduced in an alkaline electrolyte. Also the Cu_2O films transform reversibly to black copper (II) oxide when cycled at more anodic potentials. Copper oxide to copper switching covers a large dynamic range in luminous transmittance.

An excellent choice of a stack has been found to be a silver base with Cu_2S, as a dielectric, on top of it and a second Ag metal film on the top of Cu_2S. The transition wavelength is in the 1.4–1.8 μm spectral region. It is very abrupt and the selectivity is very good [1, 21]. From the other metals that have been mentioned, nickel and chromium produce excellent selective absorbing surfaces. Black chrome can be produced electrochemically by sputtering and by CVD. These procedures can give results that differ significantly as to their optical and thermo-mechanical properties. The absorptance α is about 0.95 and the emittance ε can be from 0.03 to 0.25 [1, 22].

3.09.2.4 Metal Particles in a Dielectric or Metal Matrix (Cermets)

Fine metal particles in a dielectric or ceramic matrix, or a porous oxide impregnated with metal, are generally called 'cermets' [4]. These highly absorbing metal–dielectric composites are transparent in the TIR region of the spectrum (3–25 μm), while they are highly absorbing in the solar wavelength region because of interband transitions in the metal and the small particle resonance [23].

When deposited on a highly reflective mirror, it forms a selective surface with high solar absorptance and low thermal emittance. The high absorptance may be intrinsic, geometrically enhanced (by surface texturing), or both. An important parameter is the metal volume fraction of the cermets, which may vary on purpose with depth to achieve an optimized performance.

Many materials have been used for the preparation and study of solar absorbers based on cermet coatings: Mo–Al_2O_3 [24], Ni–Al_2O_3 [25], Pt–Al_2O_3 [26], W–AlN [27], gold–magnesia (Au–MgO) [28], and black chrome (Cr–Cr_2O_3) [22] have been reported. The last one being one of the first combinations of material studied. The list is not exhaustive and we suggest the interested reader to consult also the references in these papers for a more complete appraisal of the literature.

Nanomaterials have also being used as cermets during the last years. These efforts focus the attention on metal nanoparticles in order to produce 'nanocermets'. They are comprised of Ag or Au metal nanoparticles embedded in a dielectric matrix and have attracted attention for their potential use in different applications like photochromic, photoelectrochemical applications solar energy conversion, optical waveguides, and gas sensors [29–33]. The deposition techniques mentioned already can be applied in this class of materials. One can produce the composite coatings with the well-known methods as co-deposition of metal and insulator materials by physical vapor deposition (PVD), CVD, electroplating, anodization, and inorganic pigmentation of anodized aluminum.

There are basically two types of metal–dielectric composite coatings, the metal-pigmented alumina and the graded cermet selective coatings [23]. Metal-pigmented alumina selective coatings use oxide coatings obtained from the phosphoric anodization of aluminum. The oxide coating consists of a compact barrier layer and a porous alumina layer whose pores are perpendicular to the aluminum. The pores can be impregnated with Ni, V, Cr, Co, Cu, Mo, Ag, and W as rod-like particles 30–50 nm in diameter and 300 nm long [34]. In a graded cermet, the reflectance from the cermet is reduced by gradually increasing the metal volume fraction, and as a consequence, the refractive index, as a function of depth from the surface to the base of the film. PVD or CVD techniques can be used for most graded cermets. By controlling the PVD parameters, the microstructure of the oxides can be affected with a porous to columnar structure, and by co-deposition, the pores can be filled with metal by evaporation or sputtering [4].

The solar absorptance in cermets is mainly determined by the response of the absorbing particles. There is a shift of the absorption and scattering cutoffs to higher wavelengths when the particle radius, r, increases. This effect is accompanied by a reduction in the maximum of the scattering and absorption efficiencies. This follows the law $1/r$ [35]. It should be noted that thicker cermets are needed to reach the same low reflectance in the visible region as seen for larger particles. Additionally, thermal emittance strongly increases as the thickness of cermet increases due to IR absorption. Reducing the thickness and increasing the metallic concentration in the same proportion can reduce emittance. The absorbing cermet layer consists of inherently high-temperature materials that can have either a uniform or graded metal content. The metal–dielectric concept offers a high degree of flexibility and the solar selectivity can be optimized by the proper choice of constituents, particle concentration, size, shape, coating thickness, and orientation. The solar absorptance can be increased with a suitable choice of substrates and antireflection layers, which can also provide protection from environmental moisture, thermal oxidative degradation, and other degrading factors. The powdered semiconductor–reflector combination can be included in this category, where the solar selective properties of the semiconductor, inorganic metal oxides, organic black pigments, and metal-dust-pigmented selective paints can be considered.

Based on computer modeling, a double-cermet film structure can also be developed that has higher photothermal conversion efficiency than surfaces using a homogeneous cermet layer or a graded film structure. It was found that it is easier to deposit the double-cermet selective coating than graded-cermet layer selective surfaces. In double-cermet solar coatings, solar radiation is effectively absorbed internally and additionally by phase interference. The typical double-cermet layer film structure from surface to substrate consists of an AR layer that enhances solar absorption, an absorbing layer composed of two homogenous cermet layers, a low-metal-volume fraction cermet layer on a high-metal-volume fraction cermet layer, and a metallic IR reflector layer to reduce substrate emittance [36–39].

3.09.2.5 Surface Roughness

When a surface has characteristic 'roughness dimension' that is smaller than the wavelength of light impinging on the surface, it behaves like a mirror. On the contrary, it may strongly absorb light of smaller wavelength. In this case, high solar absorptance is enhanced by 'multiple reflections' among pyramidal, dendrite, or porous microstructure. Sometimes, the materials with this property are called 'wavefront discriminating materials'. The surface roughness can be used to produce different effects in the visible and TIR. Some surfaces can be made to appear rough to obtain spectral selectivity by 'optical trapping' of solar energy. In other cases, one can use naturally occurring rough surfaces for the same purpose. There are procedures, such as etching by a proper acid, that produce such a structure. It is called 'surface texturing'. Properly textured surfaces appear rough and absorb solar energy while appearing highly reflective and mirror-like to thermal energy. The selective properties depend on the ratios of mean height deviations and distance to the wavelength [40]. The emittance is also affected and can be adjusted by modifying the microstructure of the coatings with ion beam treatments [41]. The orientation of a textured material (surface) affects these optical properties and can improve the absorption and emissivity of a spectrally selective material.

Fine grinding and sandblasting can also be used to produce surface roughness and then the deposition of a selective coating on this surface gives low emittance and high solar absorptance. CuO deposition on metal substrates produces surface roughness and enhances selectivity [42]. Additionally, PbS on Al gave good results [43]. In general, deposition of some materials on metal gives enhanced selectivity. Chemically, etching of a tin-doped In_2O_3 film to form a transparent microgrid has been reported. Using photolithography, one can make holes of about 2.5 μm [7]. Reactive sputtering or ion etching with fluorocarbon gases such as CF_4

has been used with photolithography to produce square-wave gratings with micron and submicron periodicities [44]. Additionally, a vapor-phase transport process using catalyzed epitaxial crystal growth was used recently to synthesize high-density arrays of ZnO–Ag nanowires that are hexagonal in cross section and have 70–100 nm diameters [45].

It has been known for a long time that needle-like, dendrite, or porous microstructures of the same magnitude as the wavelength of solar radiation have both wavelength and directional selectivity, which is not very sensitive to the severe environmental effects such as oxidation or thermal shocks, which lower significantly the lifetime of conventional multilayer selective coatings [3]. For all the above cases, it is important that the surface of the microstructure is protected from damage by abrasion or contact to other objects. The initial selection of a material with high inherent absorption coefficient can optimize the absorptance [4, 23].

3.09.2.6 Quantum Size Effects

These effects can be utilized to achieve high absorption in the short-wavelength region as defined earlier while maintaining a low TIR emittance. As it is expected, a substantial confinement must be reached in space in order to see the QSEs. They have indeed been observed to occur in ultrathin films and dots. The critical thickness for the QSE in a metal film is 2–3 nm, and for a degenerate semiconductor, 10–50 nm. This is a direct consequence of the basic physical laws as there are about $10^{22}\,\mathrm{cm}^{-3}$ free electrons in a metal and only $10^{16}\,\mathrm{cm}^{-3}$ free charge carriers in a degenerate semiconductor.

QSEs in indium antimonide (InSb) films have been detected by many experimental procedures. The work function dependence on thickness is obtained in a most straightforward way from photoelectric emission threshold measurements and can be compared with results obtained with the retarding potential method. The measured work functions as derived from both methods are comparable. They are less than the corresponding bulk values, according to current theoretical predictions. The interband energy gap can be determined from photoelectric absorption band edge data; its value differs with respect to the bulk one, by the location of the first allowed energy subband, in the conduction band, due to the presence of QSE.

A QSE material and a metallic substrate can be combined to construct a selective absorber. This effect has been observed in vacuum-deposited InSb on silver and aluminum substrates. The InSb (degenerate semiconductor) film was deposited in vacuum on a heated substrate (at about 1000 °C). At that temperature, the material could evaporate. Fortunately, the dissociation temperature is substantially higher and this was possible without dissociation of InSb. Tandem systems were realized using as absorber a film of InSb and a layer of Ag or Al acting as reflector. Heating measurements were performed and compared with analogous measurements performed with conventional systems. Different thicknesses, both of the InSb film and metallic layer, were tested. To improve the collection efficiency, tandem systems, where the absorber is made up by several layers of InSb of various thicknesses separated by plastic layers, were also tested. The absorption coefficient was measured for this film for various film thicknesses by Mancini and co-workers [46]. Similar results are observed in semiconductors exhibiting sharp conduction band minima. This would require a low value of the ratio of electron effective mass to that of its free mass in the thin film [1, 3, 6, 47, 48]. Also AlN films were deposited by reactive DC magnetron sputtering. The films are usually analyzed with X-ray diffraction and Auger electron spectroscopy (AES). There is a correlation between deposition parameters and crystal growth. Depending on the deposition parameters, films can present a hexagonal wurtzite (*P6mm*) or cubic zinc-blende (*Fm3m*) microstructure. Oxygen appears to induce amorphous growth on films and some distortion of the lattice parameters. For the film with cubic microstructure, AES transitions detected near the surface level at 56 and 66 eV are usually attributed to aluminum oxide (Al_xO_y), AlN, and metallic Al.

The QSE can play an important role in multilayer selective absorbers. Frequently, thin metallic layers are used between dielectric layers. These layers are responsible for high solar energy absorption; QSE may help explain the phenomena. The major drawback in utilizing this effect in a realistic solar absorber is the stability and continuity of composition of the coating upon cyclic heating and atmospheric exposure. To understand and apply the QSE, further work must be performed on various semiconductors and metals [47–50]. One of the problems is agglomeration that appears when the thin solid metal films, such as silver, are deposited. This is particularly serious when the film is heated at very high temperatures. Then the film may shrink into islands [1, 11, 12, 51]. Fully oxidized chromium (Cr_2O_3) was used in the form of a very thin film to act as a protective layer against agglomeration and also as a diffusion barrier preventing ion mixing.

3.09.3 Characterization of Selective Surfaces

It is very important to be able to characterize the surfaces of selective coatings microscopically. Modern instruments offer a plethora of methods and allow us to improve the deposition of the films that are required. Good optical measurements are also needed. Reflectance measurements are sometimes used to derive both the absorptance and the emittance of various materials. In practice, both absorptance and emittance are integrated values; however, emission meters are employed to measure emittance. Some authors in their reports use direct beam spectral reflectance measurements to characterize their samples, while others use hemispherical spectral reflectance and calorimetric methods. On the other hand, many do not even report the techniques used to obtain their values. As a result, in some cases, discrepancies due to equipment and techniques exist and absolute values for any one particular surface are not well defined [47].

It is important to have methods that provide reliable characterization of selective coatings, regarding the layer-by-layer and also their final optical properties. Using standard spectrophotometers, solar reflectance is usually measured in the 0.3–2.5 μm wavelength range at near-normal incidence angle, that is, nearly zero. This leads to unrealistically high predictions for efficiencies at high temperatures, as the emittance in the TIR is systematically underestimated [23, 52].

For some materials, the measured emittance data depend rather significantly with temperature. For this reason, the emittance measurements should be carried out at the expected operating temperatures. It must also be realized that the actual performance of a solar absorber operating at high temperatures may not correspond to the calculated emittance because small errors in measured reflectance (ρ) can lead to large errors in the expected small values of emittance (ε) [53]. It is important to remember that the emittance is a property of the material and depends strongly on the surface condition of the material, such as the surface roughness and the presence of surface films or oxide layers [54]. The morphology of the deposited coatings is affected considerably by the substrate roughness. It is a good laboratory practice to measure the emittance of the product after the deposition of each coating on the previously deposited combination of films on the substrate. The uncoated substrate should also be measured.

Absorbers with low emittance need to be chosen especially for high-temperature applications. It should be pointed again that the thermal radiative losses of the absorber increase in proportion to the fourth power of temperature. For this reason, it is extremely important to measure the emittance at the operating high temperature and other associated physical and chemical conditions [53]. Estimating the emittance from spectral data taken at room temperature, it is assumed that the spectral characteristics do not change with increasing temperature, which is only valid if the material is invariant and does not undergo a phase change (e.g., titanium containing materials), breakdown, or undergo oxidation (e.g., paints and some oxide coatings) at higher temperatures. Therefore, it is important before using high-temperature emittance, estimated from room temperature data, that the estimated data are verified with high-temperature emittance measurements for each selective coating.

Selective coatings can degrade at high temperature because of thermal load (i.e., oxidation), high humidity or water condensation on the absorber surface, corrosion from chemicals in polluted atmosphere, diffusion processes (i.e., interlayer substitution), chemical reactions, and poor interlayer adhesion [55]. The requirement is long-term stability for absorber coatings. At high temperatures, thermal emittance is the dominant source of losses, and the requirement of low emittance often leads to complex designs that are frequently susceptible to degradation at the working temperature [4].

Thermal stability is sometimes based on the thermal properties of the individual materials or the processing temperature parameters; the actual durability data, however, are rarely known for high-temperature absorber coatings. Durability or thermal stability is typically tested by heating the selective coating in a vacuum oven or in air for a relatively short duration (100 s). Degradation of high-temperature absorbers usually causes increase in emittance; therefore, emittance is a sensitive indicator to monitor degradation in the normal case where emittance changes with exposure.

The International Energy Agency (IEA) Task X has proposed a 'performance criterion' (PC) for flat-plate collector selective absorber testing (nonconcentrating, or at most 1–2 × sunlight intensity). The PC describes the influence in the change of solar absorption ($\Delta \alpha_s$) and emittance ($\Delta \varepsilon$) on the solar fraction:

$$\text{PC} = -\Delta \alpha_s + 0.25 \times \Delta \varepsilon \leq C \quad [11]$$

The minus sign in eqn [11] before $\Delta \alpha_s$ gives a positive result for the first term, as the deterioration of the selective paint reduces its solar absorption, and for this reason, $\Delta \alpha_s$ has a negative value. For the second term $\Delta \varepsilon$ on the contrary, the deterioration increases its value and this gives again a positive result for the second term. The constant C is usually taken to be equal to 0.05. This choice of C is equivalent to a decrease in the annual solar fraction of 5%. A lifetime of 25 years for the collector is also taken as a reasonable expectation. Service lifetime testing for this criterion is performed by exposing the absorber coatings for 200 h at 250 °C. If the material survives, it is exposed for 75 h at 300 °C, followed by 600 h at 40 °C and 95% relative humidity, and then for 85 h at 60 °C and 95% relative humidity [4, 55–57]. After exposure testing, the emittance is typically measured at 100 °C.

No criterion has been developed for testing the service of selective coatings for very high-temperature applications. Degradation of very high-temperature absorbers usually causes increased emittance. The emittance is a sensitive indicator to monitor degradation in the normal case where emittance changes with exposure. It is of interest to note here that while the emittance of many materials after exposure to high temperatures does not return to the original value, for some materials the emittance changes at high temperatures and returns to the original value after cooling to room temperature. Therefore, it is important to verify for each selective coating that the emittance does not change during the heat cycle. Capability must be built to allow spectrally selective coatings to be exposed and measured at their operating temperatures and conditions for longer periods of time to determine the durability and thermal stability of materials. A practical universal criterion for high-temperature selective surfaces (concentrating applications) is needed [4].

References

[1] Meinel AB and Meinel MP (1977) *Applied Solar Energy*, ch. 9. Reading, MA: London; Amsterdam: Addison-Wesley Publishing Co.
[2] Blandenet G and Lagarde SJ (1975) In: Blocher *et al.* (eds.) *Proceedings of the Chemical Vapor Deposition Conference*. Princeton, NJ: Electrochemical Society, Inc.
[3] Seraphin BO and Meinel AB (1976) Photothermal energy conversion. In: Seraphin BO (ed.) *Optical Properties of Solids: New Developments*, ch. 17, pp. 926–1018. Amsterdam, The Netherlands: North Holland Publishing Co.
[4] Kennedy CE (2002) Review of mid- to high-temperature solar selective absorber materials. *Technical Report NREL/TP-520-31267*, pp. 1–53. Golden, CO: National Renewable Energy Laboratory.
[5] Drummeter LF and Hass G (1964) In: Hass G (ed.) *Physics of Thin Films*, vol. 2, p. 305. New York: Academic Press.

[6] Seraphin BO (1979) Chemical vapor deposition of thin semiconductor films for solar energy conversion. *Thin Solid Films* 57(2): 293–297.
[7] Agnihotri OP and Gupta BK (1981) *Solar Selective Surfaces*. New York: Wiley-Interscience.
[8] Macleod HA (1988) *Thin-Film Optical Filters*, 2nd version. Bristol, UK: Adam Hilger Ltd.
[9] Leftheriotis G, Yianoulis P, and Patrikios D (1997) Deposition and optical properties of optimized ZnS/Ag/ZnS thin films for energy saving applications. *Thin Solid Films* 306: 92–99.
[10] Leftheriotis G and Yianoulis P (1999) Characterization and stability of low emittance multiple coatings for glazing applications. *Solar Energy Materials and Solar Cells* 58: 185–197.
[11] Griffiths PW, Di Leo M, Cartwright P, et al. (1998) Fabrication of evacuated glazing at low temperatures. *Solar Energy* 63: 243–249.
[12] Hecht E (1987) *Optics*, 2nd edn. Reading, MA: Addison–Wesley. ISBN 0-201-11609-X.
[13] Rancourt JD (1996) *Optical Thin Films: User Handbook, Vol. 37*. Bellingham, WA: SPIE Press.
[14] Pulker HK (1999) *Coatings on Glass*, 2nd edn. Amsterdam, The Netherlands: Elsevier.
[15] Kaiser N and Pulker HK (eds.) (2003) *Optical Interference Coatings*. Berlin, Germany: Springer.
[16] Gläser HJ (2008) History of the development and industrial production of low thermal emissivity coatings for high heat insulating glass units. *Applied Optics* 47(13): C193–C199.
[17] Andersson Å, Hunderi O, and Granqvist CG (1980) Nickel pigmented anodic aluminum oxide for selective absorption of solar energy. *Journal of Applied Physics* 51: 754–764.
[18] Schmidt RN, Park KC, Torberg RH, and Jensen JE (1963) *High Temperature Solar Coatings, Part I: AST-TDR-63-579*. Hopkins, MN: Honeywell Corporation.
[19] Schmidt RN, Park KC, and Jensen JE (1964) *High Temperature Solar Coatings, Part II: ML-TDR-64-250*. Hopkins, MN: Honeywell Corporation.
[20] Tabor H (1962) Selective surfaces. *Solar Energy* 6(3): 112–113.
[21] Meinel AB, Mc Kenney DB, and Beauchamp WT (1974) *Solar Selective Coatings, NSF/RANN/SE/GI-41895/PR/74/4, NTIS*. Washington, DC: US Department of Commerce.
[22] Smith GB, Mcphedran RC, and Derrick GH (1985) Surface structure and the optical properties of black chrome. *Applied Physics A* 36: 193–204.
[23] Kalogirou SA and Kelires PC (2009) Absorber coatings for parabolic trough collectors: A review. In: *Proceedings of HPC'2009 Conference on Heat Power Cycles on CD-ROM*. Berlin, Germany.
[24] Zhang Q-C, Yin Y, and Mills RD (1996) High efficiency Mo–Al$_2$O$_3$ cermet selective surfaces for high-temperature application. *Solar Energy Materials and Solar Cells* 40: 43–53.
[25] Stephen T, Sathiaraj R, Thangaraj H, et al. (1991) Optical properties of selectively absorbing R.F. sputtered Ni–Al$_2$O$_3$ composite films. *Thin Solid Films* 195: 33–42.
[26] Vien TK, Sella C, Lafait J, and Berthier S (1985) Pt–Al$_2$O$_3$ selective cermet coatings on super alloy substrates for photo thermal conversion. *Thin Solid Films* 126: 17–22.
[27] Zhanga Q-C and Shenb YG (2004) High performance W–AlN cermet solar coatings designed by modeling calculations and deposited by DC magnetron sputtering. *Solar Energy Materials and Solar Cells* 81: 25–37.
[28] Maziere-Bezes D and Valignat J (1982) Optical properties of gold-magnesia selective cermets. *Solar Energy Materials* 7: 203–211.
[29] Radeka M, Gorzkowska-Sobas A, Zakrzewska K, and Sobas P (2004) Nanocermet TiO$_2$:Au thin film electrodes for wet electrochemical solar cells. *Opto-Electronics Review* 12(1): 53–56.
[30] Cho S, Lee S, Lee TS, et al. (2007) Microstructural effect on optical properties of Au:SiO$_2$ nanocomposite waveguide films. *Journal of Applied Physics* 102: 123501–123505.
[31] Okumu J, Dahmen C, Sprafke AN, et al. (2005) Photochromic silver nanoparticles fabricated by sputtering deposition. *Journal of Applied Physics* 97: 094305 (6pp.).
[32] Zakrzewska K, Radecka M, Kruk A, and Osuch W (2003) Noble metal/titanium dioxide nanocermets for photoelectrochemical applications. *Solid State Ionics* 157: 349–356.
[33] Barshilia HC, Kumar P, Rajam KS, and Biswas A (2011) Structure and optical properties of Ag/Al$_2$O$_3$ nanocermet solar selective coatings prepared using unbalanced magnetron sputtering. *Solar Energy Materials and Solar Cells* 95: 1707–1715.
[34] Niklasson GA and Granqvist CG (1991) In: Granqvist CG (ed.) *Materials Science for Solar Energy Conversion Systems*, ch. 4. Oxford, UK: Pergamon.
[35] Arancibia-Bulnes CA, Estrada CA, and Ruiz-Suárez JC (2000) Solar absorptance and thermal emittance of cermets with large particles. *Journal of Physics D: Applied Physics* 33: 2489–2496.
[36] Zhang Q-C and Mills DR (1992) Very low emittance solar selective surfaces using new film structures. *Journal of Applied Physics* 72: 3013–3021.
[37] Zhang Q-C and Mills DR (1992) High solar performance selective surface using bi-sub layer cermet film structures. *Solar Energy Materials and Solar Cells* 27: 273–290.
[38] Zhang Q-C, Mills DR, and Monger A (1994) *Thin Film Low Loss Selective Surface*. Australia Patent 646,172, University of Sydney.
[39] Zhang Q-C, Mills DR, and Monger A (1996) Thin Film Solar Selective Surface Coating. US Patent 5,523,132, University of Sydney.
[40] Cuomo JJ, Ziegler JF, and Woodall JM (1975) A new concept for solar energy thermal conversion. *Applied Physics Letters* 26(10): 557–559.
[41] Kussmaul M, Mirtich MJ, and Curren A (1992) Ion beam treatment of potential space materials at the NASA Lewis Research Center. *Surface and Coatings Technology* 51: 299–306.
[42] Kokoropoulos P, Salam E, and Daniels F (1959) Selective radiation coatings: Preparation and high temperature stability. *Solar Energy* 3(4): 19–23.
[43] Williams DA, Lappin TA, and Duffie JA (1963) Selective radiation properties of particulate coatings. *Transactions of the ASME Journal of Engineering Power* 85(3): 213–219.
[44] Lehmann HW and Widmer R (1978) Profile control by reactive sputter etching. *Journal of Vacuum Science and Technology* 15(2): 319–326.
[45] Huang MH, Mao S, Feick H, et al. (2001) Room-temperature ultraviolet nanowire nanolasers. *Science* 292(5523): 1897–1899.
[46] Burrafato G, Pennisi A, Giaquinta G, et al. (1976) Thin film solar acceptors. In: Ketani MA and Soussou JE (eds.) *Heliotechnique and Development, Proceedings of the International Conference*, vol. 1, pp. 180–187. Dhahran, Saudi Arabia, 2–6 November 1975. Cambridge, MA: Development Analysis Associates, Inc. (A77-19043 06-44).
[47] Lampert CM (1979) Coatings for photothermal energy collection. I. Selective absorbers. *Solar Energy Materials* 1(5–6): 319–341.
[48] Hahn RE and Seraphin BO (1978) Spectrally selective surfaces for photothermal solar energy conversion. In: Hass G (ed.) *Physics of Thin Films: Advances in Research and Development*, vol. 10, pp. 1–69. New York: Academic Press.
[49] Lampert CM (1979) Microstructure of a black chrome solar selective absorber. *Solar Energy Materials* 1: 81–92.
[50] Ehrenreich H and Seraphin BO (1975) *Report on the Symposium on The Fundamental Optical Properties of Solids Relevant to Solar Energy Conversion*, pp. 20–23. Tucson, AZ, November.
[51] Leftheriotis G, Papaefthimiou S, and Yianoulis P (2000) Development of multilayer transparent conductive coatings. *Solid State Ionics* 136–137: 655–661.
[52] Seiffert C, Eisenhammer T, Lazarov M, et al. (1993) *Test Facility for Solar Selective Materials*, vol. 2, pp. 321–325. Budapest, Hungary: ISES Solar World Congress.
[53] Brunotte A, Lazarov M, and Sizmann R (1992) Calorimetric measurements of the total hemispherical emittance of selective surfaces at high temperatures. In: Hugot-Le Goff A, Granqvist CG, and Lampert CM (eds.) *Proceedings of the SPIE*, vol. 1727, pp.149–160. Washington: Bellingham.
[54] Pettit RB (1975) *Total Hemispherical Emittance Measurement Apparatus for Solar Selective Coatings, SAND-75-0079*. Albuquerque, NM: Sandia National Laboratory.
[55] Brunold S, Frei U, Carlsson B, et al. (2000) Accelerated life testing of solar absorber coatings: Testing procedure and results. *Solar Energy* 68(4): 313–323.
[56] Carlsson B, Möller K, Köhl M, et al. (2000) Qualification test procedure for solar absorber surface durability. *Solar Energy Materials and Solar Cells* 61(3): 255–275.
[57] Yianoulis P and Giannouli M (2008) Thin solid films and nanomaterials for solar energy conversion and energy saving applications. *Journal of Nano Research* 2: 49–60.

Further Reading

Duffie JA and Beckman WA (1991) *Solar Energy of Thermal Processes*, 2nd edn. New York: Wiley.
Gordon J (2001) *Solar Energy: The State of the Art*. International Solar Energy Society. London: James and James (Science Publishers).
Heavens OS (1991) *Optical Properties of Thin Solid Films*. New York: Dover. ISBN 0-486-66924-6.
Kalogirou S (2009) *Solar Energy Engineering: Processes and Systems*. Burlington, MA: Academic Press; Elsevier Science, ISBN: 978-0-12-374501-9.
Macleod HA (1988) *Thin-Film Optical Filters*, 2nd version. Bristol, England: Adam Hilger Ltd.

3.10 Glazings and Coatings

G Leftheriotis and P Yianoulis, University of Patras, Patras, Greece

© 2012 Elsevier Ltd. All rights reserved.

3.10.1	**Introduction**	315
3.10.1.1	Summary	315
3.10.1.2	Historical Development of Glass Manufacture	315
3.10.1.3	Modern Windows	316
3.10.1.4	Emerging Technologies	316
3.10.2	**Thermal and Optical Properties of Glazing and Coatings**	316
3.10.2.1	General Considerations	316
3.10.2.1.1	Solar irradiation	316
3.10.2.1.2	Optical properties of a glazing	317
3.10.2.1.3	Definitions of useful terms	317
3.10.2.1.4	Basic laws for solar and thermal radiation	318
3.10.2.2	Optical Analysis of Glazing and Coatings	319
3.10.2.2.1	Basic laws for the refraction and transmission of radiation	319
3.10.2.2.2	Combined absorption and reflection for total transmittance	320
3.10.2.3	Thermal Properties	321
3.10.2.3.1	Theoretical background	321
3.10.2.3.2	Practical considerations	322
3.10.2.3.3	Other useful terms	322
3.10.3	**Low-Emittance Coatings**	323
3.10.3.1	General Considerations	323
3.10.3.2	Solar Control Versus Thermal Insulation	323
3.10.3.3	Deposition Methods	324
3.10.3.3.1	Thermal evaporation	324
3.10.3.3.2	Electron beam gun evaporation	324
3.10.3.3.3	Sputtering	324
3.10.3.3.4	Chemical methods	324
3.10.3.4	Types of Coatings	325
3.10.3.4.1	Doped metal oxides	325
3.10.3.4.2	Coatings with metal layers	325
3.10.3.4.3	Use of interface layers	327
3.10.3.4.4	Application of a chemically and mechanically resistant top layer	327
3.10.3.4.5	Development of asymmetrical coatings	327
3.10.3.4.6	Development of Ag-based coatings resistant to high temperatures	327
3.10.3.4.7	Development of coatings with double Ag layers	327
3.10.3.5	Conclusions – Resumé	327
3.10.4	**Glass and Windows**	327
3.10.4.1	Float Glass	327
3.10.4.1.1	Manufacture	328
3.10.4.2	Toughened Glass	328
3.10.4.2.1	Manufacture and properties	329
3.10.4.3	Use of Glass in Solar Collectors	329
3.10.4.3.1	Light admittance	329
3.10.4.3.2	Weather protection and heat loss suppression	330
3.10.4.4	Windows in the Built Environment	330
3.10.4.5	Single-Glazed Windows	331
3.10.4.5.1	Clear single glazing	331
3.10.4.5.2	Tinted single glazing	331
3.10.4.5.3	Reflective single glazing	331
3.10.4.5.4	Low-emittance single glazing	331
3.10.4.5.5	Self-cleaning single glazing	331
3.10.4.6	Multiple-Glazed Windows	332
3.10.4.6.1	Double glazing	332
3.10.4.6.2	Triple and quadruple glazing for ultrahigh thermal insulation	333
3.10.4.7	Window Frames	333

3.10.4.7.1	Aluminum	333
3.10.4.7.2	Wood and wood composites	333
3.10.4.7.3	Plastics (vinyl, fiberglass, thermoplastics)	334
3.10.4.7.4	Hybrid	334
3.10.4.7.5	Effect of frames on the window thermal properties	334
3.10.4.8	Spacers and Sealants	335
3.10.4.9	Emerging Technologies	336
3.10.4.10	Conclusions – Epilogue	336
3.10.5	**Evacuated Glazing**	336
3.10.5.1	Operating Principles	336
3.10.5.2	Technology and Related Problems	336
3.10.5.3	The State of the Art	337
3.10.5.4	Comparison with Conventional Glazing	338
3.10.5.5	Electrochromic Evacuated Glazing	338
3.10.5.6	Conclusions	339
3.10.6	**Transparent Insulation**	339
3.10.6.1	Historical Background	339
3.10.6.2	Optical and Thermal Properties	339
3.10.6.3	Types of Available Materials	340
3.10.6.3.1	Granular aerogels	340
3.10.6.3.2	Monolithic silica aerogel	341
3.10.6.3.3	Glass capillary structures	341
3.10.6.4	Conclusions	342
3.10.7	**Chromogenic Materials and Devices**	342
3.10.7.1	Introduction	342
3.10.7.2	Electrochromics	342
3.10.7.3	Electrochromic Devices: Principles of Operation and Coloration Mechanisms	343
3.10.7.4	Materials for Electrochromic Devices	344
3.10.7.4.1	Transparent electrical conductors	344
3.10.7.4.2	Active electrochromic film	344
3.10.7.4.3	Ion storage and protective layers	345
3.10.7.4.4	Protective layers – magnesium fluoride	346
3.10.7.5	Performance of a Typical EC Device	346
3.10.7.6	Photoelectrochromics	346
3.10.7.7	Gasochromics	350
3.10.7.8	Thermochromics	350
3.10.7.9	Metal Hydride Switchable Mirrors	350
3.10.7.10	Other Switching Devices	350
3.10.7.10.1	Suspended particle devices	351
3.10.7.10.2	Polymer-dispersed liquid crystal devices	351
3.10.7.10.3	Micro-blinds	351
3.10.7.11	Conclusions – Epilogue	351
References		351
Further Reading		354
Relevant Websites		354

Glossary

Double, triple, or multiple glazing Glazing with two, three, or more parallel glass sheets, placed at a short distance, with the air gap between them hermetically sealed.

Electrochromic windows Windows that can change their color and appearance with the application of an electrical potential.

Evacuated glazing Double glazing with vacuum established in the air gap between the two glass sheets, for minimizing heat losses.

Float glass Glass produced by the 'float' method, in which the molten glass literally floats on a tin bath.

Low-e coatings Transparent thin films with low emittance, usually deposited on the surface of glass to reduce the emitted thermal losses.

Transparent insulation Materials that combine high thermal resistance and visible transparency.

3.10.1 Introduction

3.10.1.1 Summary

Windows are key elements of a building as they play an important role in many of its functions: They allow the continuity of indoor/outdoor space by visible light admittance (which is very important esthetically and psychologically). They play a significant part in the energy balance of the building through 'solar gains' (desirable in winter and undesirable in summer) and thermal losses. They contribute to the daylighting of rooms and present a shield from weather elements (rain, wind, dust, noise). By proper design, the windows can perform all of the above functions. Glazing also plays a significant role in solar thermal collectors by admitting solar radiation and by reducing thermal losses to the environment.

The most important breakthrough in the flat glass industry is undoubtedly the development of the float process. It has revolutionized glass manufacturing and led to the production of high-quality windows. Nowadays, multiple glazing with high visible transmittance and increased thermal insulation is the state of the art in the fenestration market. The incorporation of various thin film coatings (such as low emissivity (low-e), reflective, self-cleaning) has added value to the glazing products. Emerging technologies such as evacuated glazing (EG), aerogels, and chromogenics promise that in the years to come, new improved products with even better properties will appear.

Nowadays, the technology of windows has advanced to such an extent that optimum performance windows are produced commercially, each type tailored for a specific need. Different optimization criteria apply for windows depending on climate, use of the building (residential/commercial), dimensions, and other characteristics. Thus, there is a multitude of solutions available in the market, ranging from low-performance, inexpensive single glazing to highly insulated triple glazing; and furthermore, to self-cleaning windows that remove dirt from their exterior surfaces, 'smart' electrochromic (EC) windows that alter their color on demand, and so on. Emerging technologies such as EG, chromogenics, and aerogels promise that in the years to come, new improved products with even better properties will appear.

3.10.1.2 Historical Development of Glass Manufacture

It is of interest to know that primitive windows were just holes in the walls. In the next step of the development, they were covered with cloth, wood, or paper and then came the possibility to be closed or opened by the use of appropriate shutters. Later, windows were built so that they could accomplish a double task: to transmit light and protect the inhabitants from the extreme environmental conditions. Glass was used for this function. The Romans used glass as a material for windows in Alexandria in the second century AD. They used cast glass windows (with poor optical properties.) for this purpose [1]

The word *window* appears for the first time in the early thirteenth century, and it was referring to an unglazed hole in a roof. In English the word *fenester* was used in parallel until the eighteenth century. Today, to describe the array of windows within a facade, we use the word fenestration.

Until the seventeenth century, window glass was cut from large disks of crown glass. Larger sheets of glass were made by blowing large cylinders that were cut open and flattened, and then cut into panes. Most window glass in the early nineteenth century was made using the cylinder method. The 'cylinders' were 2.0–2.5 m long and 250–350 mm in diameter, limiting the width that panes of glass could be cut, and resulting in windows divided by transoms into rectangular panels. The first advances in automated glass manufacturing were patented in 1848 by Henry Bessemer, an English engineer. His system produced a continuous ribbon of flat glass by forming the ribbon between rollers. This was an expensive process, as the surfaces of the glass needed polishing. If the glass could be set on a perfectly smooth body this would cut costs considerably. Attempts were made to form flat glass on a molten tin bath, notably in the United States. Patents were awarded in 1902 and 1905 to H. Hill and H. Hitchcock [2], but this process was unworkable. Before the development of float glass, larger sheets of plate glass were made by casting a large puddle of glass on an iron surface, and then polishing both sides – a costly process. From the early 1920s, a continuous ribbon of plate glass was passed through a lengthy series of in-line grinders and polishers, reducing glass losses and cost. Glass of lower quality, sheet glass, was made by drawing upward a thin sheet from a pool of molten glass, held at the edges by rollers. As it cooled the rising sheet stiffened and could then be cut. The two surfaces were not as smooth or uniform, and of lower quality than those of float glass. This process was in use for many years after the development of float glass [3]. Between 1953 and 1957, Sir Alastair Pilkington and Kenneth Bickerstaff of the UK's Pilkington Brothers developed the first successful commercial application for forming a continuous ribbon of glass using a molten tin bath on which the molten glass flows unhindered under the influence of gravity [4]. The success of this process lay in the careful balance of the volume of glass fed onto the bath, where it was flattened by its own weight [4]. In January 1959, Pilkington made public its new technology, which led to rapid growth in the production of high-quality glass. Full-scale profitable sales of float glass were first achieved by Pilkington in 1960. In the Soviet Union, a two-stage molding method was developed in 1969 (USSR Inventor's Certificate nos. 230393 and 556593, US patent no. 4081260), and a float glass production line was put into service manufacturing commercial products. In 1974, PPG Industries (the United States) patented its own method for float glass production (US patent no. 3843346) [2].

The float method is the standard method for glass production nowadays: Over 90% of flat glass produced worldwide is float glass. As of 2009, the world float glass market, not including China and Russia, is dominated by four companies: Asahi Glass, NSG/Pilkington, Saint-Gobain, and Guardian Industries. Other companies include PPG, Central Glass, Hankuk, Visteon, and Cardinal Glass Industries. The flat glass market is expected to reach 39 million tons by 2010 [3].

3.10.1.3 Modern Windows

Modern windows became possible with the perfection of the industrial process for glassmaking and the deposition of appropriate thin films on transparent surfaces leading to the use of low-e coatings. Low-e coatings are spectrally selective thin films that add value to plain glass enabling it to perform multiple functions as part of fenestration systems: daylighting of buildings and at the same time suppression of radiative heat losses. There are two broad categories of coatings: doped metal oxides and metal-based stacks. The former are less expensive, they can be deposited on glass by spray pyrolysis immediately after it leaves the float line, and they are better suited for thermal insulation, in cold climates. The latter comprises three to five thin film stacks, which require advanced equipment for their production (such as sputtering in high vacuum) and accurate thickness control. They are more expensive, but more versatile: they can be tailored on demand either for solar control or for thermal insulation. Recent advances in the glazing industry (especially in the metal-based coatings field) have led to widespread production of low-e coatings for fenestration, automotive, and architectural applications. Furthermore, these coatings exhibit electronic conductivity and are being used as transparent conductors (TCs) in a multitude of devices, such as light-emitting diodes, displays, dye-sensitized and organic solar cells, smart switchable windows, and gas sensors. This wide range of applications brings these films in the forefront of high technology.

3.10.1.4 Emerging Technologies

In recent years, materials science and technology have gained a great impetus. New materials and devices with amazing properties and functions are being developed. Research teams worldwide continuously come forward with new concepts. These advances could have a significant impact in the architectural sector as they could bring about a new concept, the 'dynamic building', for example, a building with the capacity to adapt itself to the prevailing weather conditions to save energy and to improve the occupants' comfort. Windows play a key role in the dynamic building concept, as they should be dynamic and reversibly altering their optical properties on demand. To that end, a multitude of materials are being developed, under the collective name of 'chromogenic materials'. Coming from the Greek 'χρώμα' (chroma) and 'γεννώ' (genno), their name implies that they 'create color'. Indeed, these materials, switch from a transparent state to a colored-absorptive one, or to a reflective-mirror-like one, under the influence of electrical potential (electrochromics), heat (thermochromics), gases (gasochromics), or light (photochromics and phototelectrochromics). Furthermore, there is a large variety of chromogenic material at different degrees of maturity. Some others have found their way to the markets, while yet others are unlikely to ever leave the laboratory bench. Chromogenic devices are believed to become the smart windows of tomorrow and to eventually dominate the fenestration market, much as float low-e glass is a standard today. Their widespread use in buildings could improve living conditions of inhabitants, reduce the building energy consumption – both for cooling and for artificial lighting – and have a positive environmental impact.

3.10.2 Thermal and Optical Properties of Glazing and Coatings

3.10.2.1 General Considerations

We give in this section the basic equations and definitions related to the thermal and optical properties of the solar radiation and the general environment. Windows are used to permit the entrance of natural light into the buildings (daylighting) and at the same time to allow visual contact with the outside environment. For these reasons, large windows create a pleasant feeling to the inhabitants. On the other hand, we can have huge thermal losses through them in cold climates (winter case) and undesired heat gains in hot climates, especially if they receive direct solar radiation (summer case). However, the solar heat gains are very welcome during winter and for this reason the appropriate arrangement of windows is a basic element for the bioclimatic design of buildings. In principle, walls can be insulated thermally very well, but the same is very difficult for windows as they must be transparent. Simple, single-pane windows may exhibit, in some cases, about 10 times larger heat loses compared to a standard wall of the same surface area. Advanced double-pane windows have only about 3 times the corresponding losses of a wall or even less. Special products have been developed for this purpose as we describe them in detail in this chapter. We note here that usually transparent materials are used, but for special uses both translucent and transparent materials can be used.

3.10.2.1.1 Solar irradiation

We start with some important considerations about the solar irradiation data, as they are needed for the study of optical and thermal properties of glazing and coatings. For this purpose, we rely mainly on field-measured meteorological data or predictions from well-known models that are capable for providing such data for the regions that have been modeled. Meteorological hourly data exist for several locations of most countries. These files usually include solar irradiation, ambient temperature, relative humidity, wind direction, and speed, and they are very useful for long-term energetic predictions.

The solar irradiation consists of two components: (1) direct and (2) diffuse irradiation. The direct irradiation component (symbol I_b, from beam radiation) is the solar radiation coming directly from the sun to the point of observation without scattering or absorption from the molecules and particles of the atmosphere. The diffuse irradiation is the irradiation received after it has been scattered by these molecules and particles. For example, during a cloudy day the light consists mainly of diffuse irradiation. The instruments used for the measurement of direct irradiation are called actinometers or pyrheliometers. They consist of a tube directed toward the sun with collimators inside, which do not permit the diffuse rays into the instrument, and a black absorbing surface at the bottom of the tube. The solar direct irradiation is absorbed at the base of the tube heating the instrument. Appropriate thermocouples placed there give a signal in millivolts that is calibrated to give the accurate reading of the direct irradiation (in W m^{-2}). The apparatus includes a manual tracking mechanism for aiming at the sun. In addition, at the entrance of the tube, there is a filter wheel so that spectral measurements can also be taken in various spectral regions.

The total irradiation (I or I_{tot}) is measured using an instrument called a pyranometer. It usually consists of black (absorbing) and white regions and multiple thermoelectric elements connected to them, all under a double glass dome, which is transparent to the solar radiation. The output is calibrated to give the total solar irradiation. With the same instrument, we measure the diffuse irradiation (I_d) by placing a small disk (or a band) to shadow it at a distance before the pyranometer glass dome. However, if the direct component I_b (the beam irradiation) is known from the measurement that we have described before using the pyrheliometer, we can find the diffuse component I_d indirectly from the following formula:

$$I_d = I - I_b \quad [1]$$

It is obvious that these three quantities are related and it is usually preferable to measure I and I_b directly and get I_d from eqn [1]. If these quantities are measured on a horizontal plane, we use the corresponding symbols: I_{dh}, I_h, and I_{bh}, where the index h stands for horizontal.

When we consider a windowpane, or any other surface having any orientation in space, for many applications, we need to measure or calculate the total solar irradiation (I_p) on that surface. I_p can be measured placing a pyranometer parallel to the surface. It can be also calculated from eqn [2], assuming for the diffuse irradiation, in a first approximation, an isotropic distribution over the sky and then calculating its contribution from the solid angle exposed to the sky dome (second term). In this equation, the first term on the right-hand side gives the direct component on the plane we are examining. We add the reflected total radiation from the ground as well (third term) to get the final result as given by [5]

$$I_p = I_{bh}\left(\frac{\cos\theta}{\cos\theta_z}\right) + I_{dh}\left(\frac{1+\cos\beta}{2}\right) + I_h\left(\frac{1-\cos\beta}{2}\right)\rho_g \quad [2]$$

In addition to the symbols introduced before, we use θ for the angle of incidence (angle between the beam irradiation and the normal to the surface), θ_z for the zenith angle (angle between the vertical and the beam radiation), and ρ_g the albedo (reflectance of the ground). The angle between the plane of the pane and the horizontal plane is β (tilt angle).

Equation [2] may be used to find the total radiation received by a surface (as a windowpane) when we have measured the radiation components on the horizontal plane. Assume that the diffuse radiation has an isotropic distribution as an approximation. Corrections have been provided for an even better approximation (e.g., see References 5 and 6]). They are based on the fact that the diffuse solar radiation in an area around the direction of the sun is more intense (circumsolar). In general, we should take three components for the diffuse radiation from the sky: isotropic, circumsolar, and horizon (coming from a belt near the horizon).

3.10.2.1.2 Optical properties of a glazing

The optical properties of a glazing depend on material properties and on the incidence angle of the irradiation on them. The incidence angle of the direct irradiation is measured experimentally, but it can also be calculated for a certain place and time by finding the position of the sun and, consequently, the direction of beam radiation in relation to the surface normal [5]. For the diffuse radiation, we can proceed by an approximation as we have described before [5]. Modern technology allows the deposition of thin film coatings on large areas of glass. Low-e coatings can be applied reducing heat loss problems as well as problems with overheating because they also reflect in the far infrared (IR) radiation [7, 8]. For this reason large-area windows can be used now in buildings.

The optical properties and the energy performance of a glazing are interrelated. Double-glazed units (DGUs) are common, while triple-glazed units (TGUs) are rather uncommon, their use being restricted to very harsh environments. The surfaces and panes are numbered starting with 1 for the outside surface of the outer pane (the surface facing the environment outside that belongs to the first pane). Then 2 is the inner surface of the outer pane and so on. Also, it is common now to seal the glazed unit using spacers and to create what is called an insulated glass unit (IGU). The handling of the window is more efficient in this way. In some cases the air gap is filled with inert, low thermal conductivity, gases such as Ar or Kr. Advanced glazing, creating and maintaining vacuum in the gap, has been proposed and prototypes have been studied, for extremely low heat transfer [9]. The unit is completed with a frame. We focus mainly on the glazed part of windows in this chapter.

3.10.2.1.3 Definitions of useful terms

At this point it is useful to introduce some definitions that are commonly used for the optical and thermal properties of glazing and coatings. We then give the equations for the dependence of various physical quantities on the angle of incidence.

Total solar transmittance (T_{sol}, expressed as a percent or a number between 0 and 1) is the ratio of the total solar energy in the solar spectrum (wavelength 300–3000 nm of the solar spectrum) that is allowed to pass through a glazing, to the amount of total solar energy falling on it. In other words, solar transmittance is the portion of total solar energy that is transmitted through the glazing.

Total solar reflectance (R_{sol}, expressed usually as a percent or a number between 0 and 1) is the ratio of the total solar energy that is reflected outward by the glazing system to the amount of total solar energy falling on it. We should note that for windows with different films on the two sides the reflectance will depend on the side of the window surface exposed to the sun. In a similar manner for DGU and TGU, it depends on the sequence of any existing films.

Total solar absorption or absorptance (A_{sol}, expressed usually as a percent or a number between 0 and 1) is the ratio of the total solar energy absorbed by a glazing system to the amount of total solar energy falling on it. The Greek letter α (lower case) is also used as a symbol for the absorption and the same is valid for τ and ρ.

We should point out here that the solar transmittance and solar reflectance can be measured directly. It is usually then easier to calculate solar absorption from the following basic equation, which is an expression of the energy conservation:

$$T_{sol} + R_{sol} + A_{sol} = 1 \quad\quad [3a]$$

Solar transmittance is one of the most important physical parameters as it gives the entry of solar energy through the glazing, or any protective envelope in general. It affects the total heat transfer, but other factors are needed also to determine the total heat transfer. Test methods exist that can give the value of transmittance *in situ* or *ex situ*. A measurement method of solar transmittance for various materials can be devised by using the sun (or artificial sun) as the energy source, an enclosure, and a pyranometer. Sometimes, in addition to transparent, we have to design methods that are appropriate for special cases such as for translucent, patterned, or corrugated materials. Some methods can be applied at a small sample area, or others may give an average over a large area, as the need arises. Methods also exist that are used to measure transmittance of glazing materials for various angles of incidence up to nearly 80° relative to the normal incidence. However, some methods allow measurements of the solar transmittance only at near-normal incidence.

Visible light transmittance (T_{vis}) is the ratio of the total visible solar energy (in the range 400–750 nm of the solar spectrum) that can pass through a glazing system to the amount of total visible solar energy falling on the glazing system.

Visible light reflectance (R_{vis}) is the percent of total visible light reflected by a glazing system.

Visible light absorption reflectance (A_{vis}) is the percent of total visible light absorbed by a glazing system. Again the sum of the previous three quantities is 1.

Ultraviolet transmittance (T_{UV}) It is the ratio of the total ultraviolet (UV) solar energy (range 300–400 nm of the solar spectrum) that is allowed to pass through a glazing system to the amount of total UV solar energy falling on the glazing system.

There are practical reasons for the interest in the absorption of light in the UV region of the solar spectrum because it contributes to the deterioration and fading of materials (as, e.g., fabrics and furnishing). Obviously we can define the other two quantities for the UV part of the solar spectrum.

Luminous transmittance (T_{lum}) is defined as

$$T_{lum} = \frac{\int f(\lambda)\, T(\lambda)\, d\lambda}{\int f(\lambda)\, d\lambda} \quad\quad [3b]$$

with $f(\lambda)$ being the relative sensitivity of the human eye in the photopic state (see **Figure 1**) and $T(\lambda)$ the transmittance spectrum of a glazing system. The luminous transmittance is in effect the visible transmittance weighed by the human eye sensitivity. It provides a quantitative representation of the impression of a glazing system to our vision.

Similarly, we can also define the *luminous reflectance* (R_{lum}) and *luminous absorption* (A_{lum}). Again, the sum of the previous three quantities is 1.

3.10.2.1.4 Basic laws for solar and thermal radiation

The electromagnetic radiation (solar and thermal that is of interest here) is a flow of photons with energy

$$E = h \times f = \frac{h \times c}{\lambda} \quad\quad [4a]$$

where h is the Planck's constant (6.626×10^{-34} Js), f the light frequency, λ the wavelength, and c the velocity of light.

The thermal emission of a black body at absolute temperature T is given by Planck's law:

$$E_\lambda = \frac{C_1}{\lambda^5} \cdot \left(\frac{1}{e^{C_2/\lambda T} - 1} \right) \quad\quad [4b]$$

the numerical values of the constants C_1 and C_2 being 3.742×10^{-16} W m^2 and 0.014 388 m °K, respectively [10].

Wien's law gives the wavelength λ_{max} for which the thermal emission has a maximum related to T by

$$\lambda_{max} T = 0.2897 \quad (\text{cm K}) \quad\quad [4c]$$

Using this equation we find that the spectral distribution of thermal radiation emitted by bodies at or around ambient temperatures has a maximum around 10 μm (long-wavelength radiation: symbol ℓ), while the solar spectrum at 0.55 μm (short-wavelength radiation: symbol s). The solar spectrum is available from measurements with the attenuation caused by atmospheric absorption at sea level or extraterrestrial from satellites without it. The equivalent temperature of the sun (more specifically of the photosphere that emits most of the solar spectrum) is at 5900 K. In **Figure 1**, we show the spectral distribution of solar radiation after passing through the atmosphere (measured in W m^{-2} per unit wavelength, left curve). On the right in the same figure, we show the curve for

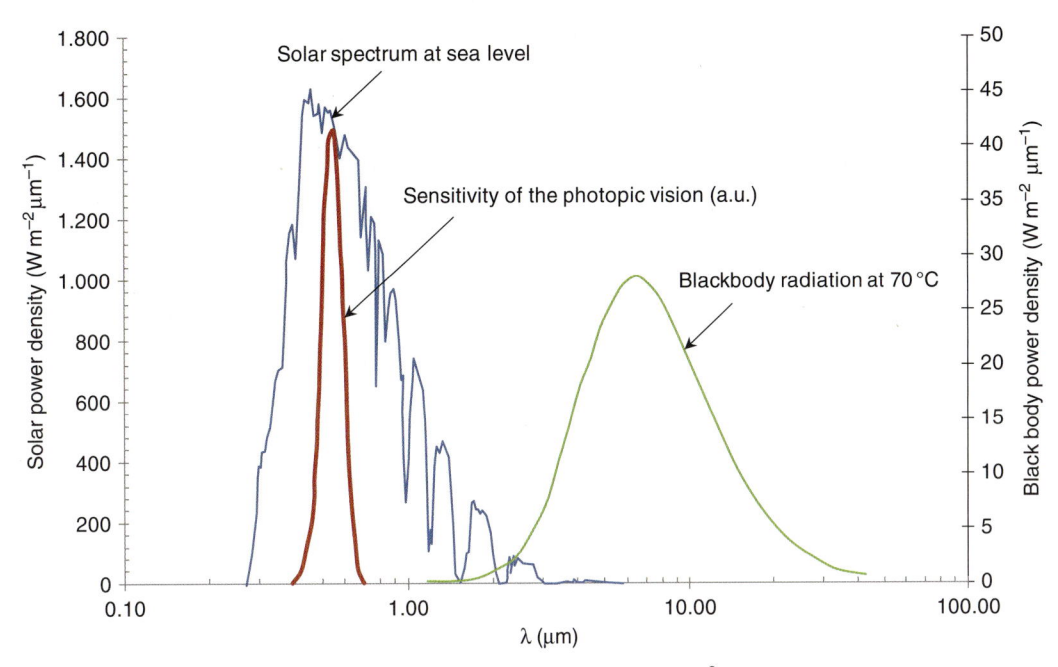

Figure 1 Spectral distribution of solar radiation after passing through the atmosphere (in W m^{-2} per unit wavelength, left curve). On the right, we show thermal radiation at a typical temperature of a body with $\varepsilon = 1$ (black body). Note the different scales on the two sides. The relative efficiency of the human eye is also shown (in arbitrary units, red line) at the region near the maximum of the solar spectral distribution.

thermal radiation at a typical near ambient temperature of a body with $\varepsilon = 1$ (black body). We note the very different scales on the two sides. The relative efficiency of the human eye is also shown (in arbitrary units, red line) at the region near the maximum of the solar spectral distribution.

From Planck's law we can also find the total power emitted per unit area by integration of the spectral distribution for all wavelengths (Stefan–Boltzmann law):

$$E = \int_0^\infty E_\lambda \, d\lambda = \sigma T^4 \qquad [4d]$$

The constant $\sigma = 5.6697 \times 10^{-8}$ W m^{-2} K^{-4} is called Stefan–Boltzmann constant.

The blackbody, for example, the perfect absorber and emitter, is an ideal concept. All real materials have a no zero reflectance and as a result, they emit less radiation than a blackbody. To express this fact, eqn [4d] can be modified for the case of a gray body with radiation properties independent of wavelength:

$$E = \varepsilon \sigma T^4 \qquad [4e]$$

with ε the body 'emittance' or 'emissivity', which represents the ratio of the electromagnetic radiation emitted by a surface to the intensity that would be emitted by a black body at the same temperature (T). Emittance can be monochromatic (for a given wavelength) or directional (at a given angle). In most practical situations, the 'total hemispherical' emittance is used by integration over all wavelengths (total) and over all directions of the hemisphere enclosing the emitting surface (hemispherical).

The radiation exchange between two bodies (1 and 2) depends on their emittance (ε_1 and ε_2, respectively), their temperature (T_1 and T_2, respectively), and their geometry. To express the latter, the *configuration factor* $F_{1 \to 2}$ is used. It is a geometrical factor giving the fraction of radiation emitted by surface 1 that is intercepted by surface 2.

It can be derived easily that for two large parallel surfaces with $S_1 = S_2 = S$, we have that the configuration factor $F_{1 \to 2} = 1$ and the exchange of thermal radiation is [5]

$$\frac{Q}{S} = \frac{\sigma(T_2^4 - T_1^4)}{(1/\varepsilon_1 + 1/\varepsilon_2) - 1} \qquad [4f]$$

3.10.2.2 Optical Analysis of Glazing and Coatings

3.10.2.2.1 *Basic laws for the refraction and transmission of radiation*

To calculate the optical properties under a given angle of incidence θ_1 of a ray of light on glass, we remind the basic equations for the refraction of light [10]. Snell's law gives the *refraction angle* θ_2, going from air (medium 1) into medium 2 (glass). C_1 and C_2 are the values of the velocity of light in media 1 and 2, respectively. The index of refraction of glass relative to air (or vacuum) is $n = 1.526$ for the most common type of glass. Symbols $n_{2,1}$ and n_{20}, n_{10} are also used for the relative and absolute indices of refraction as shown in the following equations:

$$n = \frac{\sin \theta_1}{\sin \theta_2} \quad \text{Snell's law} \quad \left(n = \frac{n_{20}}{n_{10}} = \frac{C_1}{C_2} \equiv n_{2,1} \right) \quad [5]$$

We note also that the velocity of light C in a material is connected with its index of refraction by the equation (C_o is the velocity of light in vacuum): $C = C_o/n = \lambda f$.

The *reflectivity* r (or reflectance) of a surface is the ratio of the intensity of reflected light to that of incident nonpolarized light is given by the well-known Fresnel equation [5, 6]:

$$r(\theta_1) = \frac{I_r}{I_i} = \frac{1}{2}\left[\frac{\sin^2(\theta_2 - \theta_1)}{\sin^2(\theta_2 + \theta_1)} + \frac{\tan^2(\theta_2 - \theta_1)}{\tan^2(\theta_2 + \theta_1)} \right] = \frac{1}{2}[r_\mathrm{I} + r_\mathrm{II}] \quad [6]$$

For a given material (n known) and θ_1 known, from eqn [5] we can find θ_2, and from eqn [6] the reflectance r. In this equation, the two terms in the bracket represent the reflectance for the perpendicular and parallel polarization, respectively. For example, for glass ($n = 1.526$) and $\theta_1 = 60°$, we have from eqn [5] $\theta_2 = 34.58°$ and from eqn [6] $r(60°) = 0.093$, that is, 9.3% of the light beam is reflected. When $\theta_1 = 0°$ (perpendicular incidence), $\theta_2 = 0°$ and from eqn [6] we derive:

$$r(0) = \frac{(n-1)^2}{(n+1)^2} \quad [7]$$

The result then is $r(0) = 0.043$ (4.3% of the light beam is reflected). Naturally when light goes through a flat glass plate, it is reflected on both surfaces as it is found from eqns [5] and [6].

If we add the intensity of all rays passing after multiple reflections (method of ray tracing) we find for the transmittance of the plate for one component of polarization, normal to the plane of incidence:

$$\tau_1 = (1 - r_1)^2 \sum_{n=0}^{\infty} r_1^{2n} = \frac{(1-r_1)^2}{(1-r_1^2)} = \frac{1-r_1}{1+r_1} \quad [8]$$

The same is derived for the other polarization component (parallel) $\tau_{11} (1-r_{11})/(1+r_{11})$.

Then the *total transmittance* τ_r is

$$\tau_r = \frac{1}{2}\left(\frac{1-r_1}{1+r_1} + \frac{1-r_{11}}{1+r_{11}} \right) \quad [9]$$

For a system of N parallel plates, it can be proved in the same way (method of ray tracing) that the transparency for the combined system is

$$\tau_{rN} = \frac{1}{2}\left(\frac{1-r_1}{1+(2N-1)r_1} + \frac{1-r_{11}}{1+(2N-1)r_{11}} \right) \quad [10]$$

We have assumed zero absorption up to now and we must consider it next. The system of N parallel plates is very useful in modeling of the transparency of double and triple glazing.

The results from the last two equations for $0 < \theta_1 < 50°$ give transmittance that is almost constant, but for $\theta_1 > 60°$ the transmittance is decreasing at a fast rate with the angle of incidence [5].

3.10.2.2.2 Combined absorption and reflection for total transmittance

Now we turn to the combined problem. The absorption for the light traveling the path $L/\cos \theta_2$, where L is the thickness of the plate and θ_2 the angle of diffraction, the intensity of radiation is found from the differential equation:

$$dI_\lambda(x) = -K_\lambda I_\lambda(x)\, dx \quad [11]$$

After integration, we get for the ratio of the transmitted radiation over the total incident radiation:

$$\tau_\alpha = \exp\left(\frac{-KL}{\cos \theta_2} \right) \quad [12]$$

K is the coefficient of extinction of the material of the plate. We note that in eqn [11] we indicated the dependence on the wavelength. In eqn [12], we consider a properly weighted value of K in the solar spectrum region, for example, if we consider solar energy.

We can follow again the ray-tracing method and get a general equation. The exact result is not very useful here. Instead, we can use the approximate final result [5]:

$$\tau \approx \tau_r \tau_\alpha \quad [13]$$

For the practical applications, as solar energy, the total transmittance is approximately equal to the product of the two transmittances due to reflection and absorption separately.

At this point it is useful to recall Kirchhoff's law:

$$\varepsilon(\lambda) = a(\lambda) \qquad [14]$$

Also the consequence of energy conservation:

$$\tau(\lambda) + a(\lambda) + \rho(\lambda) = 1 \qquad [15]$$

Similar equations follow for a weighted integration over some definite spectral distribution, as the solar irradiance, usually denoted by the index sol, or simply s from the initial of short-wavelength radiation, to distinguish from long-wavelength (or thermal) radiation.

For the absorptance (the ratio of radiant energy absorbed by the pane to that incident upon it) we have

$$a \approx 1 - \tau_a \qquad [16]$$

And for the reflectance

$$\rho = 1 - a - \tau \approx \tau_a - \tau_r \tau_a \qquad [17]$$

Equations [13], [16], and [17] can be used for more than one plate. In this case, we should use the total thickness of the system for L and also use eqn [10] instead of eqn [9] for τ_r.

3.10.2.3 Thermal Properties

3.10.2.3.1 Theoretical background

Our purpose is to establish the energy evaluation of windows and show how we can find the energy gains and losses. In our analysis, we are using the well-known thermal resistance concept that simplifies calculations. It is based on the solution of the differential equation for heat conduction:

$$\rho c \frac{\partial T}{\partial t} = A + k \nabla^2 T \qquad [18]$$

where A is the rate of heat production per unit volume in the material, at the point we consider, c the specific heat of the material, and ρ its density. T is the absolute temperature and t the time. The coefficient of thermal conductivity k depends on the material, being small for insulating materials and large for good heat conductors. It depends also on temperature, but for relatively small variations of temperature and the kind of materials we consider it is constant to a very good approximation. The heat flow per unit time and unit area (vector **f**) is given by Fourier's law

$$\mathbf{f} = -k(\text{grad}T) = -k(\nabla T) \qquad [19]$$

Now, if we solve eqn [18] for a problem and find T, then from eqn [19] we can find the heat flow. For the case of a flat wall, or window, with $A = 0$ and heat flowing at the direction perpendicular to the wall plane, eqn [18], simplifies to the Laplace equation $\nabla^2 T = 0$ and we find for the steady state the result:

$$q = \frac{T_1 - T_2}{((x_2 - x_1)/kS)} \qquad [20]$$

The numerator is the temperature difference between the two faces of the wall or window and is analogous to the voltage difference. Also q is the current i in the completely analogous electrical problem. The quantity in the denominator is the thermal resistance $R = D/kS$, where $D = x_1 - x_2$ is the wall (or window) thickness. If we consider the heat flow per unit time and unit area: $f = |\mathbf{f}| = q/S$, then the thermal resistance per unit area will be $r = D/k$.

For the thermal flow through a glazing we should, in addition to conduction, consider also radiation and, for the air or gas spaces between multiple glass panes, convection. For a single glass, we have to consider the internal and external space heat transfer coefficients h_i and h_o. Then according to the law of addition of heat resistances if D is the thickness of the glass and k its coefficient of thermal conductivity, reminding also that the conductance h is the inverse of the corresponding resistance, we have for the total heat transfer coefficient U, the equation:

$$U^{-1} = \frac{1}{h_i} + \frac{D}{k} + \frac{1}{h_o} \qquad [21]$$

For DGU we have:

$$U^{-1} = \frac{1}{h_i} + \frac{D_1}{k_1} + \frac{D_2}{k_2} + \frac{1}{h_g} + \frac{1}{h_o} \qquad [22]$$

where h_g is the gas conductance for the space between the two glass panes. For triple glass or more, the extension is obvious if we apply the thermal resistance method.

The values for h_g, h_i, and h_o in these equations can be determined by using basic experimental or theoretical procedures that are outside of the scope of this chapter. The interested reader can find details in ASHRAE [11]. It will be sufficient to state that all depend on the emissivity of the corresponding surfaces involved for each of them and a number of other factors. For h_i, which also depends on the inside radiation and convection and is easier to find, we usually give a typical value: $h_i = 8$ W m^{-2} K^{-1}. The outside coefficient may vary considerably because it depends on wind velocity and direction as well on the rest environmental conditions. We may take the standardized value $h_o = 23$ W m^{-2} K^{-1}. The gap (gas or air) conductance h_g depends on the temperature, the thermal conductivity of the gas, density, specific heat, viscosity, and the width of the gas space. The inclination to the vertical also affects its value [12].

3.10.2.3.2 Practical considerations

The U-value (or factor) is the overall heat transfer coefficient for a glazing system. It is defined as the rate at which heat is transmitted through it, per unit surface area per unit temperature difference between its two sides. It is measured in watts per square meter per degree Kelvin (W m^{-2} K^{-1}). The U-value is a function of the materials and the detailed construction of the glazing system. U-value ratings for windows generally have values between 1 and 10 W m^{-2} K^{-1}. The U-value of a window assembly is affected by the physical properties of the frame, glass, thin film coatings, and spacers. The lower the U-value, the greater a window's resistance to heat flow, and the better is its insulating value. The symbol U (or U_w) is used for the value referring to the whole window, U_C the value at the center of glass, and U_F (or U_{fr}) the value for the frame.

In some cases we may encounter the term R-value, which is the inverse of the U-value. The R-value is usually cited when discussing wall and ceiling insulation values and rarely for windows and other fenestration products. The higher the R-value, the better insulated is the wall or window, and it is more effective in keeping out the heat (and cold).

In practice, to facilitate thermal calculations for a window, we consider three zones: glazed, frame, and edge zone (**Figure 2**). The edge zone is approximately taken to be about 6 cm wide [11, 13, 14].

Then an average value, $\langle U \rangle$, can be found from the following equation:

$$\langle U \rangle = U_{fr} A_{r,fr} + U_{ed} A_{r,ed} + U_{gl} A_{r,gl} \qquad [23]$$

where fr stands for frame, ed for edge, gl for the center glazed area, and $A_{r,x}$ the relative area of x to the total. For example $A_{r,fr} = A_{fr}/A_{total}$. It is also common (in Europe) to use a linear heat flow coefficient $\Psi_{fr,gl}$ for the edge zone so that the term in the middle (edge) in the above equation is replaced by $\Psi_{fr,gl} (L_{fr,gl}/A_{total})$, where $L_{fr,gl}$ is the length of the borderline between the frame and the edge. Obviously, the units for $\Psi_{fr,gl}$ are W m^{-1} K^{-1} while those for U are W m^{-2} K^{-1}.

3.10.2.3.3 Other useful terms

At this point it is useful to mention some other terms that are related to the energy performance of glazing.

Solar gain (or solar heat gain) (SHG) in general refers to the heat increase of a structure (or object) in a space that results from absorbed solar radiation. Objects intercepting sunlight absorb the radiation and as a result their temperature is increased. Then, of course, part of the heat is reradiated at far-IR wavelengths. If a glass pane (or other material) is placed between the solar irradiation and the objects intercepting it, that is, transparent to the shorter wavelengths and not to the longer, then the solar irradiation has as net result an increase in temperature (solar gain).

This is the general principle on which the greenhouse effect is based and has become well known in the context of global warming. The amount of solar gain increases with increasing incoming irradiation from the sun and with the ability of the intervening materials to transmit *short-wavelength (solar) radiation* and in part to absorb small fraction of it. It is useful to include a low-emittance coating in order to reflect the *long-wavelength (thermal) radiation* back into the space protected by glazing. In passive solar building design, for example, the aim is to maximize solar gain from the building in order to reduce space heating demand (winter) and to control it in order to minimize cooling requirements (summer). The composition and coatings on glass for the building glazing can be manipulated to optimize the greenhouse effect, while the pane size, position, and shading can be used to optimize solar gain. Solar gain can also be transferred to the building by indirect or isolated solar gain systems. Objects having large thermal capacity are used to smooth out the fluctuations during the day, and to some extent between days.

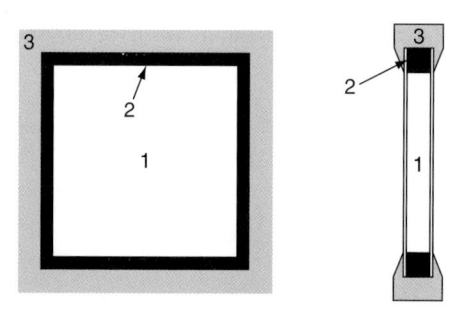

Figure 2 The areas used for the thermal analysis of a typical window: 1, glazing; 2, spacer; and 3, frame.

Solar heat gain coefficient (SHGC) is the fraction of incident solar irradiation admitted through a window, both directly transmitted and absorbed, and subsequently released inward. SHGC is given as a number between 0 and 1. The lower a window's SHGC, the less solar heat it transmits in the protected space. SHGC is used in the United States.

g-Value is the coefficient commonly used in Europe while shading coefficient (SC) is an older term that is still sometimes used in the United States. The relationship between SHGC and SC is as follows: SHGC = SC × 0.87.

SC values are calculated using the sum of the primary solar transmittance and the secondary transmittance. Primary transmittance is the fraction of solar radiation that directly enters a building through a window compared to the total solar insolation, the amount of radiation that the window receives. The secondary transmittance is the fraction of heat flowing inside the space from the window, compared to the total solar insolation.

Total solar energy rejected (%) is the percent of incident solar energy rejected by a glazing system. It is to the sum of the solar reflectance and the part of solar absorption that is reradiated as thermal energy outward.

Shading coefficient (SC) is the ratio of the SHG through a given glazing system to the SHG under the same conditions for clear, double-glass window. The SC defines the solar control capability of the glazing system and it is useful when discussing the properties of fenestration and shading devices. In other words, the SC gives the solar energy transmittance through windows.

3.10.3 Low-Emittance Coatings

3.10.3.1 General Considerations

Low-e coatings are thin films that exhibit spectral selectivity: they are highly transparent in the visible (VIS) part of the electromagnetic spectrum (from 0.4 to 0.7 µm), highly reflective in the IR (for wavelengths higher than 0.7 µm), and absorbing in the UV (e.g., below 0.4 µm).

Transparent materials with low-e properties can exist because of the following laws of physics: (1) the Stefan–Boltzmann law and the Wien displacement law, which state that the heat exchange by radiation between surfaces is characterized by their thermal emittance and that the maximum of emitted radiation from a body occurs at a specific wavelength, related to its temperature. For materials at room temperature, this wavelength is about 10 µm away from the visible part of the spectrum. (2) Drude theory and the Hagen–Rubens law, which state that the free carrier plasma in electrically conductive materials has a cutout frequency below which all incoming electromagnetic radiation is rejected (e.g., reflected) and that the IR reflectivity is directly related to the electrical conductivity of the material. Thus, it is possible to decouple the visible light spectrum from that of thermal radiation and to have surfaces with properties being entirely different with regard to thermal and visible radiation. Furthermore, it becomes clear that for a film to exhibit low-e properties it is necessary to possess electronic conductivity.

Low-e coatings were first envisaged for use in transparent heat-insulating glazing. Although they were already known from the 1960s, the main thrust in their development took place after the petroleum crisis in 1974, as is the case for most of the renewable energy materials. In the 1980s and 1990s, low-e glass products dominated the markets. Nowadays, use of low-e glass in architecture is very common, and in many countries it is mandatory by law to increase the energy efficiency of buildings, to promote rational use of energy, and to reduce CO_2 emissions. The most prominent companies in this field are Pilkington, PPG, Saint-Gobain, AGC (former Glaverbel), Nippon Sheet Glass Co. (NSG), and Guardian. Links to their Internet sites appear in the webpage list.

Apart from their use in buildings, these coatings have a number of diverse applications, emerging from their electrical conductivity, which enables them to serve as TCs in a multitude of devices such as dye-sensitized and organic solar cells, smart switchable windows, gas sensors, light-emitting diodes, and displays. This wide range of applications brings these thin films in the forefront of high technology.

3.10.3.2 Solar Control Versus Thermal Insulation

In **Figure 3** appear the transmittance and reflectance spectra of plain glass and of a typical low-e coating. The intensity of the solar radiation on the Earth's surface is also presented for comparison. As can be seen in that figure, the transmittance of plain glass is high throughout the visible part of the spectrum, up to 2 µm, well into the IR region, apart from a dip at about 1 µm, related to the amount of Fe_2O_3 that is present in the glass [15]. It is also evident that in the thermal radiation region (around 10 µm) both reflectance and transmittance of plain glass remain low, and by Kirchhoff's law (i.e., $\alpha + \rho + \tau = 1$, $\varepsilon = \alpha$ in thermal equilibrium) the absorptance (and consequently the emittance) of glass is considerable. On the other hand, the transmittance of a typical low-e coating follows closely the solar spectrum in the visible and diminishes in the IR. The coating reflectance has the opposite behavior: it remains low in the visible and increases in the IR. By Kirchhoff's law, at 10 µm, the absorptance (and emittance) of the coating is low, as it exhibits high reflectance. Thus, the low-e coating acts as a spectrally selective filter, which allows passage of the visible (and possibly some of the near IR) and rejects the far IR. Depending on the wavelength (λ_T) at which transition from high transmittance to high reflectance occurs (e.g., when $\tau \approx 50\%$ and $\rho \approx 50\%$), we can distinguish two broad categories of low-e coatings: (1) those intended for solar control, with $\lambda_T \approx 0.7$ µm, which reject the solar IR spectrum and (2) those intended for thermal insulation, with $\lambda_T \approx 2$ µm, which transmit the solar IR. The former are suitable for warm climates, the latter being suitable for cold climates in which solar gains are desirable.

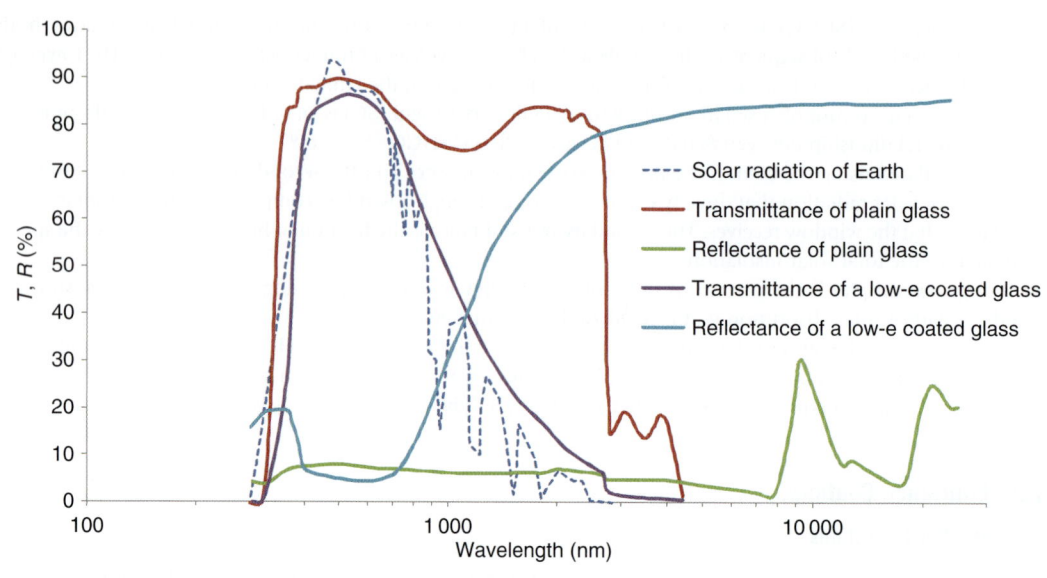

Figure 3 Optical properties of plain glass and a typical low-emissivity (low-e) coating. Adapted from Schaefer C, Brauer G, and Szczyrbowski J (1997) Low emissivity coatings on architectural glass. *Surface and Coatings Technology* 93: 37–45, with permission.

3.10.3.3 Deposition Methods

Thin film deposition and optical design of coatings constitute a vast technological field [16–18], and here only the most common methods are presented.

3.10.3.3.1 Thermal evaporation

The raw material of the film is placed in a crucible and heated in vacuum so that a vapor transfers material to an adjacent surface (the substrate) at a sufficient rate [19].

3.10.3.3.2 Electron beam gun evaporation

Instead of thermally heating the raw material, which can be ineffective in cases of compounds with low thermal conductivity (as are dielectrics), an electron beam springing from a metal at high temperature can be deflected into the crucible by a magnetic field [20]. Momentum transfer from the incident electrons heats the material. This method is versatile as the electron beam can be manipulated (in a way similar to that of a cathode ray tube) to heat uniformly all the material in the crucible. The beam intensity can also be altered in order to maintain constant deposition rates. Electron guns with multiple crucibles are available for the sequential deposition of different materials within the same vacuum chamber, without interrupting the vacuum. To improve the stoichiometry of compounds, reactive evaporation can be used, with the presence of a gas (usually O_2) in the vacuum chamber that is incorporated in the film structure. To enhance the film packing density, ion-assisted evaporation can be used: The substrate is bombarded by energetic ions of an inert gas (usually Ar) during deposition and the resulting film becomes more compact. The e-gun method is widely used in the optics industry for the production of antireflection coatings, optical filters, etc.

3.10.3.3.3 Sputtering

In this method, a plasma of inert and/or reactive gases (such as Ar, O_2) is created in a low pressure, and energetic ions in the plasma dislodge chunks of the raw material from a solid plate (known as the target). These chunks are deposited on the substrate [21, 22]. Depending on the gas discharge method used to create the plasma, one can distinguish between radio frequency (RF), medium frequency (MF), or direct current (DC) sputtering. Furthermore, magnetrons are used to increase the efficiency of the electrons in ionizing the Ar atoms by trapping the electrons near the target, and thus we have Twin-mag, pulsed magnetron sputtering, etc. The sputtering method is applied for the deposition of industrial metal-based low-e coatings on large areas.

Evaporation and sputtering are also known as physical vapor deposition (PVD) methods.

3.10.3.3.4 Chemical methods

In order to avoid vacuum that entails expensive (and sensitive) equipment, chemical deposition methods have been developed. A widespread and relatively simple method is the sol–gel deposition that involves immersion of a substrate in a chemical solution, withdrawal at a controlled rate, and subsequent heat treatment [23]. Alternatively, the chemical solution can be applied by spray or by spin coating. In the latter, the substrate is rotating and as a result, the chemical solution is spread evenly on its surface. Chemical vapor deposition (CVD) uses heat to decompose a vapor of a precursor chemical to make a thin film of a desired composition [24, 25]. A variation of the CVD technique is called spray pyrolysis; a fluid containing the precursor is then sprayed onto a hot substrate. This method is used on a large scale for deposition of tin oxide-based films on hot glass as it comes out from the float glass production and is transferred to the cooling stage. Electrochemical techniques include cathodic electrodeposition from a chemical solution and anodic conversion of a metallic surface – especially of Al – to form a porous oxide. A disadvantage of the chemical methods is the inevitable presence of traces in the resulting films of the precursors used, due to limitations in the heat treatment phase. These traces may impede the film performance or reduce their service life by unwanted side reactions. Furthermore, environmental and health hazards from the compounds involved can be a concern.

3.10.3.4 Types of Coatings

Two groups of materials are of particular interest for use as low-e coatings: (1) doped metal oxides and (2) film combinations that incorporate metal layers. The typical thickness of the first group of films is on the order of 10^{-1} μm. They are hard, compact, strongly adherent to glass, chemically inert, their luminous and near-IR absorbance can be low, and their thickness does not affect electrical resistance. The thickness of the second group of films is on the order of 10^{-2} μm and they are soft, porous, poorly adherent to glass substrates, and chemically reactive. In this group of films, the electrical resistance is strongly thickness-dependent.

3.10.3.4.1 Doped metal oxides

Low-e coatings based on doped metal oxides comprise a host lattice (usually In_2O_3, SnO_2, or ZnO) that is doped by metal or halide atoms. The most common representatives of this group of films are tin-doped indium oxide (In_2O_3:Sn, usually called ITO), fluorine-doped tin oxide (SnO_2:F, usually called TFO), and gallium-doped zinc oxide (ZnO:Ga, usually called GZO). Doping is accomplished either by adding a higher-valence metal, by replacing some oxygen with fluorine, or by oxygen vacancies. The compounds mentioned above have wide enough band gaps to allow considerable transmission in the visible and doping is feasible to a level high enough to render the materials IR reflecting and electrically conducting. In doped metal oxides, the degree of doping determines the position of the transition wavelength (λ_T): the higher the doping, the more metal-like the films are and λ_T appears at lower wavelengths. However, in these films, doping cannot be brought to a sufficiently high level required for solar control, their λ_T usually lies in the near IR and, thus, doped metal oxide coatings are used mostly for thermal insulation. The main advantage of the doped metal oxides, compared to metal-based films, is the chemical and mechanical stability, which allows their use on glass surfaces exposed to ambient conditions. This is why these films are referred to as 'hard coatings'.

The development of these materials has reached maturity, and numerous commercial products are available in the market for windows and other architectural applications. Most of these films are prepared by spray pyrolysis and their typical thickness is on the order of 10^{-1} μm. Typical properties of such coatings are as follows: $T_{lum} \approx 90\%$, $T_{sol} \approx 75\%$, $\varepsilon \approx 0.20$.

Although doped metal oxide coatings are well established, intense research activity continues in the field. The research effort is directed toward the development of alternative host materials and dopants, as well as multiphase mixtures of known materials, in order to improve various properties of the coatings, such as electrical conductivity, optical transmission, hardness, and adherence. [15]. Some of the combinations reported in the literature are the following [15]: ITO:ZnO, ITO:Ti, In_2O_3–ZnO (IZO), In_2O_3:Ti, In_2O_3:Mo, In_2O_3:Ga, In_2O_3:W, In_2O_3:Zr, In_2O_3:Nb, $In_{2-2x}M_xSn_xO_3$ with M being Zn or Cu, ZnO:(Al,F), ZnO:B, ZnO(Ga,B), $Zn_{0.9}Mg_{0.1}O$:Ga, and many others.

3.10.3.4.2 Coatings with metal layers

In this type of coatings, the highly reflective metal film (that would otherwise be opaque in the visible) is sandwiched between two dielectric layers that have an antireflective effect: with an appropriate index of refraction and thickness, the light beams reflected on the front and back surfaces of each of the dielectric layers are of opposite phase and of nearly equal amplitude. Thus, they interfere destructively and as a result, the film reflectivity is diminished. One is then led to dielectric/metal/dielectric (D/M/D hereafter) multilayers. Dielectrics with high refractive indices, usually metal oxides, such as TiO_2, ZnO, ZnS, SnO_2, Bi_2O_3, and In_2O_3, are suitable. Appropriate metals are the so-called 'noble' ones, such as Ag, Au, Cu, and Al (given in order of decreasing performance). Of all these metals, Ag is the most suitable, due to its low absorption in the visible. Coatings based on Au or Cu have inferior optical properties and a characteristic golden brown color.

To achieve high transmittance, the metal layer needs to be as thin as possible. The growth mechanism of metal layers on glass [26–28] imposes the limit: in the initial stages of their development on glass and other dielectric materials, metal films form tiny nuclei. With material continuously added on the substrate, these nuclei grow via surface diffusion and direct impingement, into islands that are discontinuous and possess a fractal nature. Further thickening of the metal film leads to large-scale coalescence and to continuous films. The coalescence thickness is about 15 nm for thermally evaporated Ag films [26, 27] and can be reduced to about 9 nm using other methods such as sputtering and ion-assisted deposition [27].

In these stacks, the metal layer thickness governs the coating properties. With the metal thickness increasing, the coating electronic conductivity increases, and its thermal emittance and luminous transmittance decrease. In **Figure 4** appears the measured emittance of evaporated ZnS/Ag/ZnS coatings versus Ag layer thickness [8]. An abrupt decrease of emittance with increasing Ag thickness can be observed below coalescence, in the range 10–15 nm. For continuous Ag films, thicker than 15 nm, the values of emissivity continue to decrease with increasing thickness, but at a lower rate. The figure of merit $\eta = T_{lum}/\varepsilon$ also shown in **Figure 4**, indicates that for this type of films, an optimum can be found at around 22 nm of Ag.

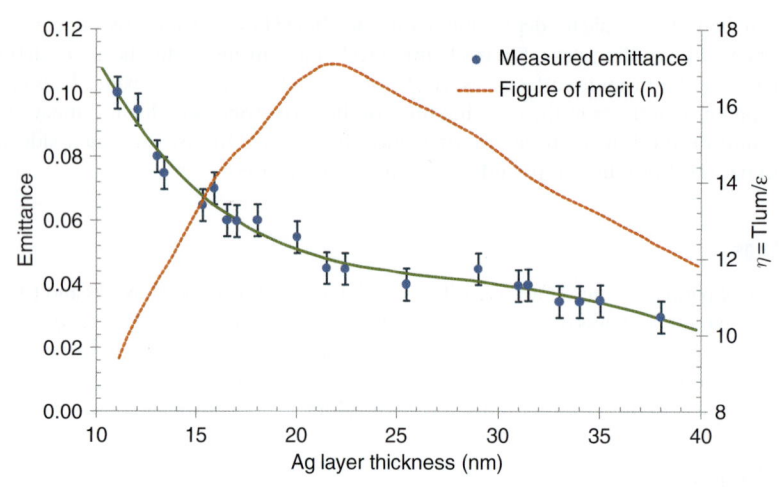

Figure 4 Emissivity and figure of merit of ZnS/Ag/ZnS coatings vs. Ag thickness. Adapted from Leftheriotis G and Yianoulis. P (1999) Characterization and stability of low emittance multiple coatings for glazing applications. *Solar Energy Materials and Solar Cells* 58: 185–197, with permission.

The D/M/D coatings are more versatile than doped metal oxides. It is possible to optimize them either for thermal or for solar control through proper selection of the thickness of each individual layer with use of standard thin film optics software and the 'characteristic matrix' formulation [8]. Typical thicknesses and properties of D/Ag/D films are as follows: 40/20/40 nm for solar control ($T_{lum} \approx 85\%$, $T_{sol} \approx 50\%$, $\varepsilon \approx 0.05$) and 30/10/30 nm for thermal insulation ($T_{lum} \approx 87\%$, $T_{sol} \approx 72\%$, $\varepsilon \approx 0.15$). Deposition of such extremely thin stacks requires exact growth control of each individual layer. Furthermore, optical interference between different layers causes the whole coating to fail, should only one layer deviate from the desirable thickness. The major disadvantage of D/M/D coatings is their lack of durability. They are sensitive to environmental exposure and degrade with time as atmospheric gases and Ag diffuse into the dielectric layer and react with each other [29]. They cannot withstand heat treatment above 200–250 °C [8]. For these reasons they are referred to as 'soft coatings'. To resolve these problems and to improve the low-e coatings' properties intense research work is being carried out worldwide [15]. Indeed, work has been reported recently on ZnS/Ag/ZnS, ZnO/Ag/ZnO, ZnO/Cu/ZnO, IZO/Al/GZO, ZnO:Al/Ag/ZnO:Al, TiO$_2$/Ag/TiO$_2$, and many others [15].

Typical optical transmission properties of Ag-based low-e coatings are shown in **Figure 5**. Therein appear ZnS/Ag/ZnS stacks optimized for maximum transmittance at 550 nm, ZnS/Cu/Ag/ZnS and ZnS/Al/Ag/ZnS coatings with ultrathin (less than 5 nm) Cu or Al films added on Ag to improve emittance and provide thermal stability. Finally, five-layer stacks of the form ZnS/Ag/ZnS/Ag/ZnS have been developed to provide nearly zero emittance (less than 0.02). These coatings and their properties are indicative of the recent technological developments in the field, which have already been adopted by the glazing industry. Indeed, Ag-based thin films for energy-efficient fenestration are now highly optimized, and a very large number of products with specified thermal, solar, and luminous properties are available on the market. Commercial metal-based coatings are prepared by sputtering, as this technique permits accurate thickness control and in-line coating of large areas. It is remarkable that with the sputtering method, thickness control approaching atomic precision is feasible in a high-performance production environment and handling of glass sheets up to 30 m^2 in size is made possible. The optimization of commercial Ag-based low-e coatings has been brought about by several breakthroughs presented in the following paragraphs [8, 30].

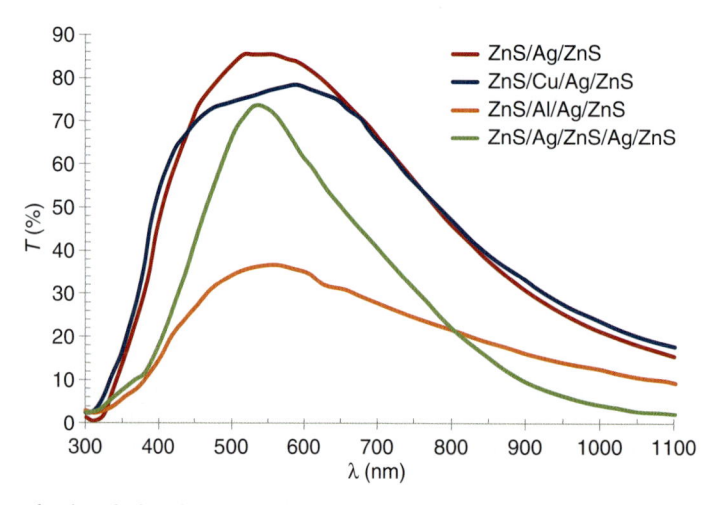

Figure 5 Transmittance spectra of various Ag-based low-emissivity (low-e) coatings. Adapted from Leftheriotis G, Yianoulis P, and Patrikios D (1997) Deposition and optical properties of optimized ZnS/Ag/ZnS thin films for energy saving applications. *Thin Solid Films* 306: 92, with permission.

3.10.3.4.3 Use of interface layers
Interfaces are ultrathin, optically neutral layers, used to improve the coating properties: A 5 nm-thick ZnO interface (also called the 'seed layer') intervenes between the dielectric film and the Ag layer. It is used as substrate for the Ag layer to enhance the Ag film uniformity, pushing the coalescence threshold down to 10 nm. Thus, coatings with the lowest thermal emissivity and the highest luminous transmittance result. Furthermore, a 2–4 nm-thick TiO_x interface, also called 'sacrificial layer', grown on top of the Ag film prevents oxidation of the Ag layer during the reactive deposition of the covering oxide layer. It also protects the Ag film from oxygen permeation that decreases the age resistance of the coating. This development was implemented industrially in the mid-1990s.

3.10.3.4.4 Application of a chemically and mechanically resistant top layer
An oxynitride (such as SiN_xO_y) improves the mechanical and age resistance of Ag-based low-e coatings. This development was industrially applied after the implementation of the dual magnetrons as a sputtering tool since the end of the 1990s.

3.10.3.4.5 Development of asymmetrical coatings
Asymmetrical coatings incorporate dielectric layers with different refractive indices. Compared to symmetrical layer structures, such layer systems result in higher transmittance (due to better antireflection of Ag) and possess neutral color, granting a higher market acceptance. They also exhibit lower color sensitivity for individual layer thickness variations, resulting in a coating process with less waste. In this field, fundamentally theoretical and practical developments were performed by Grosse et al. [31]. Since the end of the 1990s, the changeover from symmetrical to asymmetrical Ag layer systems has been accomplished by degrees by all low-e manufacturers.

The structure of a typical coating incorporating the advances mentioned above is glass/TiO_2 ($n = 2.5$)/ZnO/Ag/TiO_x/SnO_2 ($n = 2.0$)/SiN_xO_y, achieving $T_{lum} = 80\%$, $T_{sol} = 60\%$, and $\varepsilon = 0.10$. A double glazing with such a coating and Ar gas filling the air gap exhibits a U-value equal to $1.1\ W\ m^{-2}\ K^{-1}$.

3.10.3.4.6 Development of Ag-based coatings resistant to high temperatures
Since the 1980s, Ag layer systems resistant to high temperatures have been developed for the production of bent coated car windshields at temperatures up to 650 °C. This was achieved with use of suboxide dielectric layers (usually TiO_x, $x < 2$) and/or ultrathin Ti interface layers that protected the Ag layer against oxidation during annealing. Later, this knowledge was transferred to the production of heat-strengthened glass. Since the end of the 1990s, heat-resistant Ag-based layer systems have been marketed for heat-strengthened architectural glass. A specific characteristic of these coatings is that they are opaque and absorbing in the as prepared state (due to the presence of Ti and suboxide films). They become optically transparent and heat reflective after annealing at high temperatures, as the opaque films are oxidized and become clear (Ti and TiO_x absorb oxygen and are transformed into TiO_2).

3.10.3.4.7 Development of coatings with double Ag layers
Coatings in the form of D/Ag/D/Ag/D were proposed by Berning [26], in the early 1990s. It is essentially two D/Ag/D stacks put together, with the middle dielectric layer being twice as thick as the other two. The layer structure also contains interface (seed and sacrificial) layers above and below the Ag films. Insulating glass units with such a coating exhibit reduced heat transmittance ($\approx 0.1\ W\ m^{-2}\ K^{-1}$) compared to units with single Ag layer systems, but its selectivity effect on solar radiation is much higher (see **Figure** 5). It must be stated that double Ag layer coatings are costly to produce. At the moment, solar control glasses with such coatings are a trendsetter for car and architectural glazing all over the world.

3.10.3.5 Conclusions – Resumé
Low-e coatings are spectrally selective thin films that add value to plain glass enabling it to perform multiple functions as part of fenestration systems: daylighting of buildings and at the same time suppression of radiative heat losses. There are two broad categories of coatings: doped metal oxides and metal-based stacks. The former are less expensive, they can be deposited on glass by spray pyrolysis immediately after it leaves the float line, and they are better suited for thermal insulation, in cold climates. The latter comprises three to five thin film stacks that require advanced equipment for their production (such as sputtering in high vacuum) and accurate thickness control. They are more expensive, but more versatile: they can be tailored on demand either for solar control or for thermal insulation. Recent advances in the glazing industry (especially in the metal-based coatings field) have led to widespread production of low-e coatings for fenestration, automotive, and architectural applications. Furthermore, these coatings exhibit electronic conductivity and are being used as TCs in a multitude of devices, such as light-emitting diodes, displays, dye-sensitized and organic solar cells, smart switchable windows, and gas sensors. This wide range of applications brings these films in the forefront of high technology.

3.10.4 Glass and Windows

3.10.4.1 Float Glass
Float glass is the basic glass from which almost all the flat glass products are derived. It is produced by the 'float' process that involves the flotation of molten glass on a bath of liquid tin, producing a perfectly flat surface on both sides. The glass has no wave or distortion and is nowadays the standard method for glass production: over 90% of flat glass produced worldwide is float glass.

3.10.4.1.1 Manufacture

The raw materials used for the production of float glass typically consist of 72.6% sand (silicon dioxide), 13.0% soda (sodium carbonate), 8.4% limestone (calcium carbonate), 4.0% dolomite, and 1.0% alumina. Another 1.0% of various additives is also present. These are compounds for the adjustment of the physical and chemical properties of the glass, such as colorants and refining agents. The raw materials are mixed in a batch mixing process, then fed together with suitable cullet (waste glass), in a controlled ratio, into a furnace operating at approximately 1500 °C. Common flat glass furnaces are 9 m wide, 45 m long, and contain more than 1200 tons of glass. Once molten, the temperature of the glass is stabilized to approximately 1200 °C to ensure a homogeneous specific gravity. The molten glass is fed into a 'tin bath', a bath of molten tin (about 3–4 m wide, 50 m long, and 6 cm deep), through a delivery canal [32]. The amount of glass allowed to pour onto the molten tin is controlled by a gate. Once poured onto the tin bath, the glass spreads out in the same way that oil spreads out if poured onto a bath of water. In this situation, gravity and surface tension result in the top and bottom surfaces of the glass becoming approximately flat and parallel. The molten glass does not spread out indefinitely over the surface of the molten tin. Despite the influence of gravity, it is restrained by surface tension effects between the glass and the tin. The resulting equilibrium between the gravity and the surface tension defines the equilibrium thickness of the molten glass (T), given by the relation [33]:

$$T^2 = (S_g + S_{gt} + S_t)\frac{2\rho_t}{g\rho_g(\rho_t - \rho_g)} \quad [24]$$

with ρ_g the glass density; ρ_t the tin density; S_g, S_{gt}, and S_t the values of surface tension at the glass–air, glass–tin, and tin–air interfaces, respectively. For standard soda-lime-silica glass under a protective atmosphere and on clean tin, the equilibrium thickness is approximately 7 mm.

Tin is suitable for the float glass process because it has a high specific gravity, is cohesive, and is immiscible into the molten glass. Tin, however, is highly reactive with oxygen and oxidizes in a natural atmosphere to form tin dioxide (SnO_2). Known in the production process as dross, the SnO_2 adheres to the glass. To prevent oxidation, the tin bath is provided with a positive pressure-protective atmosphere consisting of a mixture of nitrogen and hydrogen. The glass flows onto the tin surface forming a floating ribbon with perfectly smooth surfaces on both sides and an even thickness. As the glass flows along the tin bath, the temperature is gradually reduced from 1100 °C until the sheet can be lifted from the tin onto rollers at approximately 600 °C. The glass ribbon is pulled off the bath by rollers at a controlled speed. Variation in the flow speed and roller speed enables glass sheets of varying thickness to be formed. Top rollers positioned above the molten tin may be used to control both the thickness and the width of the glass ribbon. Once off the bath, the glass sheet passes through a lehr kiln for approximately 100 m, where it is further cooled gradually so that it anneals without strain and does not crack from the change in temperature. On exiting the 'cold end' of the kiln, the glass is cut by machines. A block diagram of the float process is shown in **Figure 6**.

3.10.4.2 Toughened Glass

Toughened glass is physically and thermally stronger than regular glass. The principle of toughened glass relies on the fact that the faster contraction of the glass surface layer during cooling induces compressive stress in the surface of the glass balanced by tensile stress in the body of the glass as shown in **Figure 7**. The greater the surface stress, the smaller the glass particles that will result in case the glass is broken. Surface compressive stresses increase the glass strength. This is because any surface flaws tend to be pressed closed by the retained compressive forces, while the core layer remains relatively free of the defects, which could cause crack initiation. For glass to be considered toughened, the surface compressive stress should be a minimum of 69 MPa. For it to be considered safety glass, the surface compressive stress should exceed 100 MPa. There are two main types of commercial heat-treated glass: heat strengthened and fully tempered. Heat-strengthened glass is twice as strong as common glass while fully tempered glass is typically 4–6 times stronger and can withstand heating in microwave ovens.

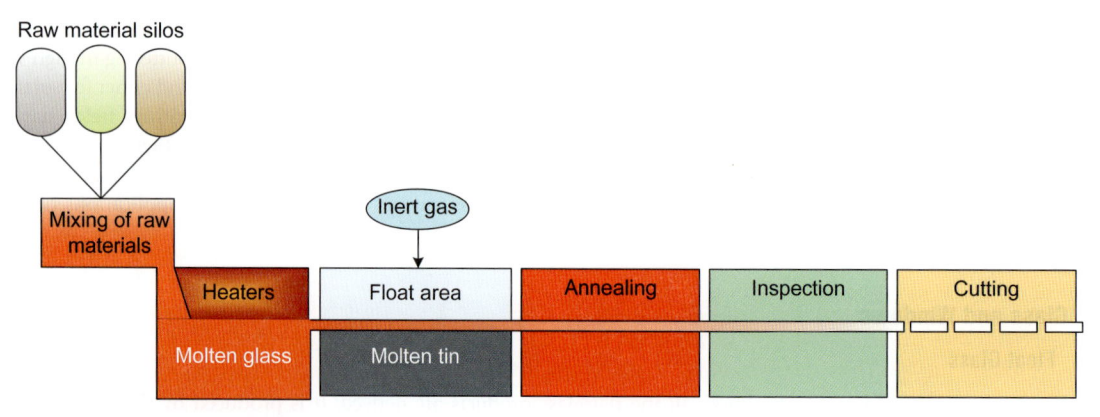

Figure 6 Block diagram of a typical float line.

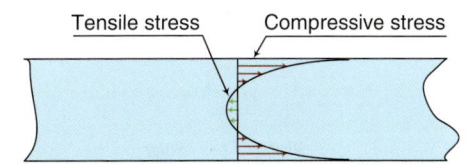

Figure 7 Stress distribution of glass due to tempering.

3.10.4.2.1 Manufacture and properties

Toughened glass is made from annealed glass via a thermal tempering process. The glass is placed onto a roller table, taking it through a furnace that heats it above its annealing point of about 720 °C. The glass is then rapidly cooled by forced convection with use of air drafts. As a result, the external layers of the glass plate solidify earlier than the internal part. Stresses are generated during this process as shown in **Figure 7**. An alternative chemical process involves forcing a surface layer of glass at least 0.1 mm thick into compression by ion exchange of the sodium ions in the glass surface with the 30% larger potassium ions, by immersion of the glass into a bath of molten potassium nitrate. Chemical toughening results in increased toughness compared with thermal toughening, and can be applied to glass objects of complex shape [34].

Toughened glass has several disadvantages, all due to its pronounced stress pattern:

- It must be cut to size or pressed to shape before toughening and cannot be reworked once toughened. The same applies to polishing the edges or drilling holes.
- It is most susceptible to breakage due to edge damage as the tensile stress is a maximum there. Shattering can also occur in the event of a hard impact in the middle of the glass pane or if the impact is concentrated (e.g., striking the glass with a point).
- Using toughened glass can pose a security risk in some situations because of the tendency of the glass to shatter completely upon hard impact rather than leaving shards in the window frame. In Reference 35, it is stated that "The security value of tempered glass is questionable. Although it will resist a brick or rock, it is susceptible to sharp instruments such as ice picks or screwdrivers. When attacked in this manner, tempered glass tends to crumple easily and quietly, leaving no sharp edges."
- The surface of toughened glass is not as hard as that of plain glass and is more susceptible to scratching. To prevent this, toughened glass manufacturers apply various coatings or laminates to the surface of the glass.
- Tempered glass has wavy surfaces, caused by contact with the rollers. This waviness is a significant problem in the manufacturing of thin film solar cells [36].

3.10.4.3 Use of Glass in Solar Collectors

Glass plays an important role in thermal solar collectors, serving several purposes: It enables light admittance onto the collector absorber, protects the absorber from weather elements (rain, dust, etc.), and provides some insulation against heat loss from the collector front surface. An optimum solar collector glazing must perform well all three functions.

3.10.4.3.1 Light admittance

As can be seen in **Figure 3**, plain float glass exhibits high transmission in the visible and near IR, apart from a reduction in the wavelength range from 700 to 1500 nm. This dip in transmittance is associated with iron compounds present in the glass, especially iron trioxide, Fe_2O_3. The larger the iron content of the glass, the less transparent it becomes. Glass with high iron content (0.5% and above) has a greenish appearance and poor transmittance. As can be seen in **Figure 3**, the plain glass reflectance in that range is low, thus the loss of transmittance is due to absorption. This is very inconvenient from the solar collector point of view, as at this range, there is a significant amount of solar radiation that cannot reach the absorber. In order to rectify this situation, glass with low iron content (about 0.02% Fe_2O_3) has been developed. This improves the glass T_{vis} value from 88% (a value typical of a 6 mm-thick clear float glass, see **Table 1**) to 91%.

Further improvement in the glass transmittance can be effected by reduction of reflectance (which is about 8% in the visible, as can be seen in **Figure 3** and **Table 1**). There are two types of reflectance: diffuse and specular (mirror-like). The former is caused by the roughness of the reflecting surface and can be suppressed by a treatment of the glass surfaces called 'etching' [5]: The glass is dipped into a silica-saturated fluorosilicic acid solution, which smooths its surface, reducing R_{vis} to 2%. The latter (specular) reflectance is caused by refractive index mismatch between glass and air (1.5 and 1.0 respectively). The use of thin films with refractive indices in between 1.5 and 1.0 and of appropriate thickness can cause the reflected light beams originating from the air/film and film/glass surfaces to have equal magnitude and opposite phase. The two beams then cancel out suppressing reflectance and increasing transmittance. These films are the well-known 'antireflection' coatings, used in optical lenses. A glass with anti-reflection coatings on both sides can achieve R_{vis} values as low as 1% [5]. However, as the production cost of such coatings is rather high, they are not very common in solar collector covers.

Table 1 Mid-pane values of optical and thermal performance indicators for various types of coatings

No	Type of glazing	T_{vis}	R_{vis}	T_{sol}	R_{sol}	A_{sol}	g-value (SHGC)	SC	U-value Air filled (WK^{-1}m^{-2})	U-value Gas filled (WK^{-1}m^{-2})
	Single Glazing									
1	Clear, 6 mm thick	88	8	79	7	14	0.82	0.95	5.7	
2	Tinted, 6 mm thick	50	5	47	5	48	0.60	0.68	5.7	
3	Reflective	31	42	24	47	29	0.38	0.44	5.6	
4	TI Low-e 6 mm thick, indoors	67	25	58	19	23	0.62	0.71	3.8	
5	TI Low-e, 10 mm thick, indoors	65	24	53	17	30	0.58	0.66	3.7	
6	Self-cleaning, 6 mm thick	83	14	79	13	8	0.81	0.93	5.9	
	Double glazing (all panes 6-mm thick) OUTDOORS | INDOORS									
7	Clear | Clear	79	14	64	12	24	0.72	0.82	2.9	2.8
8	Tinted | Clear	44	7	38	7	55	0.48	0.55	2.7	2.6
9	Reflective | Clear	49	39	28	43	29	0.31	0.36	2.7	2.6
10	TI Low-e | Clear	73	17	55	15	30	0.69	0.79	1.7	1.5
11	SC Low-e | Clear	70	10	38	28	34	0.43	0.49	1.4	1.1
12	Self-cleaning/SC Low-e | Clear	67	16	36	32	32	0.40	0.46	1.4	1.1
13	Tinted SC Low-e | Clear	49	39	28	42	30	0.31	0.36	1.4	1.3
14	SC Low-e | TI Low-e	53	22	29	34	37	0.34	0.40	1.3	1.1
15	TI Low-e | TI Low-e	56	31	42	23	35	0.53	0.60	1.5	1.3
	Triple glazing (all panes 6 mm thick)									
16	Clear | Clear | Clear	70	19	52	15	33	0.63	0.73	1.8	1.7
17	TI Low-e | Clear | Clear	55	32	39	24	37	0.50	0.57	1.3	1.2
18	SC Low-e | Clear | Clear	62	14	33	29	38	0.39	0.45	1.0	0.9
19	Self-cleaning/SC Low-e | Clear | TI Low-e	54	20	28	35	37	0.35	0.40	0.8	0.7
	Quadruple glazing (all panes 6 mm thick)									
20	Clear | Clear | Clear | Clear	63	23	43	17	40	0.57	0.65	1.3	1.2
21	TI Low-e | Clear | Clear | Clear	50	35	33	25	42	0.45	0.52	1.0	0.9
22	SC Low-e | Clear | Clear | Clear	56	17	28	31	41	0.36	0.45	0.9	0.7
23	SC Low-e | Clear | Clear | TI Low-e	52	18	26	31	43	0.34	0.39	0.7	0.6

SC, solar control; TI, thermal Insulation.
(|) Symbolizes the gap between glass panes.

3.10.4.3.2 Weather protection and heat loss suppression

The use of tempered (toughened) glass is common in solar collectors to withstand blizzard attacks. Furthermore, appropriate edge sealing is required to prevent moisture ingress and air infiltration.

As regards heat losses, glass effectively suppresses convective losses to the environment (compared to an unglazed collector) but as it exhibits significant emittance (~0.84), it suffers from radiation losses, especially during nighttime. To improve the performance of glass in this respect, one could use the low-e coatings presented in the previous section. However, these coatings would also reduce light admittance, as can be seen in **Figure 3**. A more appropriate solution is to stop the heat from being emitted from the absorber surface, using 'selective' absorbers that exhibit high absorptance and low emittance. The analysis of selective absorbers is beyond the scope of this chapter.

3.10.4.4 Windows in the Built Environment

A window can be split into two parts: the glass, which occupies 80–90% of its area, and the frame, which is used to support the glass pane on the building walls and to act as a peripheral seal.

In **Table 1** appear the mid-pane values of optical and thermal performance indicators for various types of glazing. They have been calculated with use of the Pilkington 'Spectrum' online tool according to the following standards:

- EN 410 for optical properties in the visible and solar part of the spectrum (T_{vis}, R_{vis}, T_{sol}, R_{sol}, A_{sol}) and for g-value.
- EN 673 for *U*-value.

The results derived by this piece of software have been cross-checked and validated with equivalent results from the literature [37–42].

The values of **Table 1** are typical for state-of-the-art commercial products that abound in the market. They are used to compare different glazing types that are presented in the following sections.

3.10.4.5 Single-Glazed Windows

3.10.4.5.1 Clear single glazing
The simplest type of window consists of a single clear uncoated glass. It provides the highest visible transmittance but exhibits large thermal losses. Furthermore, such a glazing does not provide sufficient sound insulation and suffers from mist condensation. Nowadays, the use of such glazing is limited to low-cost solutions or to retrofitting of windows in historical buildings that do not possess thick enough frames to accommodate double glazing.

3.10.4.5.2 Tinted single glazing
Tinted glass is a normal float glass containing colorants. Colored glass is an important architectural element for the exterior appearance of facades. It is also used in interior decoration (doors, partitions, staircase panels, mirrors). Its production is the same as that of clear float glass apart from the addition of appropriate colorants to the standard raw materials. Colorants are mostly metals, each producing a different color, depending on its nature and its concentration in the glass. Some of the most common colorants and the colors they produce are the following: iron/green, brown, blue; manganese/purple; chromium/green, yellow, pink; vanadium/green, blue, gray; copper/blue, green, red; cobalt/blue, green, pink; nickel/yellow, purple; cadmium sulfide/yellow; titanium/purple, brown; cerium/yellow; carbon and sulfur/amber, brown; selenium/pink, red; gold/red.

Due to its high extinction coefficient, low transmittance, and high absorptance, tinted glass is often called 'absorptive'. The low visible transmittance reduces the quantity of daylight admitted indoors. Its primary use in windows is therefore to reduce glare and excessive solar transmission. As the reduction in light transmission is effected through absorption, such glazing exhibit high SHGCs: the absorbed radiant energy is initially transformed into heat within the glass, thus raising the glass temperature. A significant amount of it is then reemitted indoors. Tinted glazing allows a greater reduction in visible transmittance (T_{vis}) than in SHGC due to reemission, as can be seen in **Table 1**. In a practical situation, transmittance in the visible and SHGC are required to increase (winter, cold climates) or to decrease (summer, hot climates) simultaneously by a similar degree. Thus, single-tinted glazings are far from achieving optimum performance. To rectify this situation, other, more appropriate solutions have been developed such as spectrally selective coatings with light blue/green tint having higher visible performance and lower SHG (glazing no. 13 in **Table 1** is one such example).

3.10.4.5.3 Reflective single glazing
A reflective coating can be added to glass to increase the reflectivity of its surface, in order to achieve a considerable reduction in solar gains. The reflective coating usually consists of thin metallic or metal oxide layers, and comes in various metallic colors such as bronze, silver, or gold. The SHGC varies with the thickness and reflectivity of the coating, and its location in the glazing system. While some reflective coatings must be protected by sealing in cavity (e.g., those based on noble metals), others are durable and can be added on exposed surfaces. It can be seen in **Table 1** that a reflective coating changes very little the U-value of single glazing that is dominated by convection (between glass and the surrounding air) and conduction (through the glass). Similar to that of tinted glass, the visible transmittance of reflective glass declines more than its SHGC. Architects are generally fond of reflective glazing because of its glare control and appealing outside appearance. However, the usage is limited by its sun mirror effect that may cause disturbances on traffic roads and nearby buildings. Also in well-illuminated rooms, the loss of visual privacy and outside views at night can be a concern to the occupants.

3.10.4.5.4 Low-emittance single glazing
Low-e coatings can be added to float glass to achieve either solar control or thermal insulation. The materials and properties of low-e coatings have already been covered extensively. The performance of single low-e-coated glazing depends on the position of the coating (indoors or outdoors). The correct placement of the coating is indoors in order to suppress long-wave radiative heat losses to the environment. In that configuration, the heat emitted from indoors is reflected back into the room. Otherwise (e.g., with the low-e coating facing outdoors), the heat would have been absorbed by the glass, raising its temperature, which would have caused an increase of convective heat losses. The glass thickness also plays a role in the performance of such a glazing, especially in SHGC (or g-value), as can be seen in **Table 1**. Low-e-coated glass is very popular in modern architecture over the world, mostly in conjunction with double glazing. The market share is over 30% of the fenestration products installed in the United States [13].

3.10.4.5.5 Self-cleaning single glazing
Self-cleaning glazing [43, 44] have an additional coating on their external surface that is exposed to weather elements and gets dirty with time. This coating is a nanostructured TiO_2 film (less than 1 μm thick). TiO_2 is a semiconductor with a band gap of 3.2 eV. Under UV light irradiation, electrons and holes are produced in the conduction and valence band of the film, respectively, in accordance to the following reaction: $TiO_2 + h\nu\,(>3.2\,\text{eV}) \rightarrow e^- + h^+$. The holes and electrons can react with molecules adsorbed on the film surface as follows: The holes oxidize water molecules to hydroxyl radicals and the electrons react with oxygen to form peroxide radicals, which in turn can react with electrons and protons to produce hydrogen peroxide. These highly reactive radicals

332 Components

and hydrogen peroxide decompose dirt particles deposited on the glass surface. This phenomenon is called 'photocatalysis' and it was first reported by Fujishima and Honda [45]. Furthermore, TiO_2 thin films possess another interesting property: they are water repellent. Rainwater that lands on the glass surface does not adhere on it. Instead, droplets are formed that drip down the window washing away the decomposed dirt particles. Hence, the self-cleaning action works in two stages: breakdown of dirt under UV irradiation and removal of dirt by the rainwater. Self-cleaning glass is particularly suited for highly glazed, tall buildings in which glass cleaning is time consuming and costly. The reduction of glass cleaning costs brought about by the use of self-cleaning glass can counterbalance (or even overcome) the increased cost of glass. Nowadays, there are several glass manufacturers that produce self-cleaning products. However, research is still active in this field, aiming to improve the photocatalytic efficiency by use of visible light instead of UV, by increase of the TiO_2 porosity and by use of alternative materials (such as ZnO, SnO_2, and CeO_2) and their combinations [43, 44]. TiO_2 is a high index of refraction material and its application on the external glass surface is expected to increase reflectance. Indeed, in **Table 1**, it can be seen that windows with self-cleaning glass exhibit slightly lower visible transmittance, higher reflectance, and slightly lower g-value. No significant effect can be observed in U-values.

3.10.4.6 Multiple-Glazed Windows

Multiple panes with air-sealed cavities can be used to improve the glazing thermal insulation properties without undue reduction in transmittance and in heat gains. The fabrication of multiple glazing (double, triple, quadruple) poses new challenges to the manufacturers: the cavity must be air and moisture proof, thus appropriate sealants (called 'spacers') must be developed. Furthermore, the spacers must be able to accommodate the thermal stress and the differential expansion of the two (or more) glass sheets. They are also required to be thermally insulating, otherwise edge losses may exceed the extra insulation multiple glazing offer. To minimize heat losses through multiple glazing, one needs to reduce not only the peripheral heat losses (e.g., conduction through the spacers) but also the heat transferred through the air gap. The latter can be caused either by thermal conductance of the air (or gas) through an unduly short gap or by convection in case the gap is too large. An optimum of the gap width can be found at about 14–16 mm [46], as can be seen in **Figure 8**. At that distance both heat transfer mechanisms are counterbalanced and the heat loss is minimized. Inert gases have a similar behavior: Ar has an optimum similar to air (14 mm). The optimum for Kr and Xe is 10 and 6 mm, respectively [46]. The optimum distance depends on the thermophysical properties of the various gases (e.g., thermal conductivity, thermal diffusivity, and viscosity). Different types of multiple glazing are presented next.

3.10.4.6.1 Double glazing

As can be seen in **Table 1**, the U-value of a double glazing with two clear panes is 49% lower than that of a similar single pane window. The improvement of the window thermal properties comes at a price of a 12% reduction in SHGC, which is more than acceptable. In situations where further reduction of solar gains is desirable, tinted and reflective glass can offer a decrease in g-value between 30% and

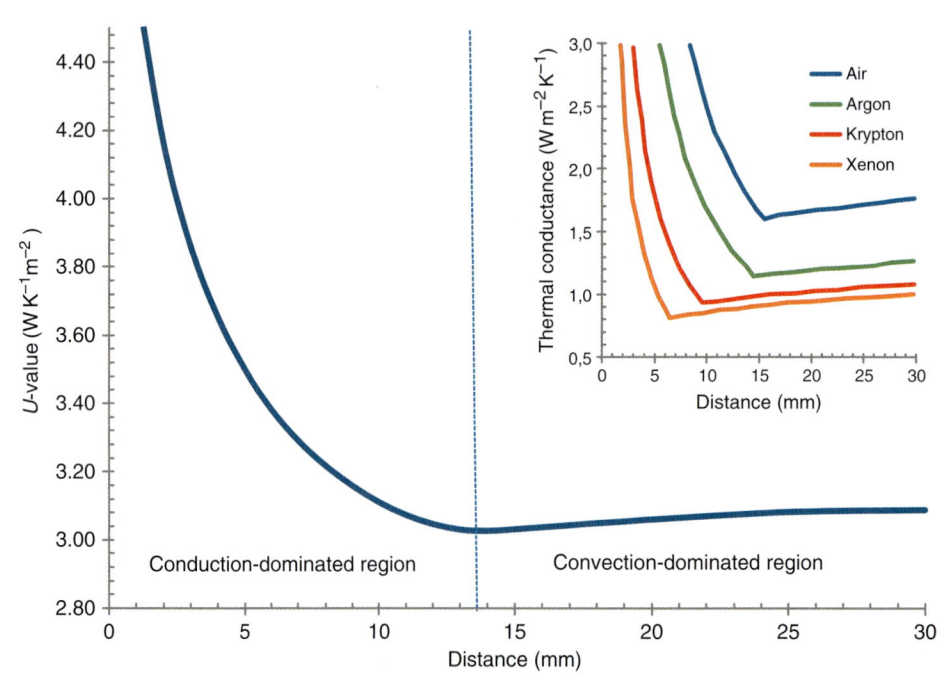

Figure 8 U-value vs. distance of glass panes for a double glazing with two clear panes. Calculated using LBNL 'Window 5.2'. (Inset) Conductive and convective heat transport in a glazing cavity as a function of distance between panes for air and inert gases. Adapted from Manz H (2008) On minimizing heat transport in architectural glazing. *Renewable Energy* 33: 119–128, with permission.

60%. As with single glazing, the *U*-value of double-glazed windows with tinted or reflective glass are not affected considerably. Low-e coatings, on the other hand, further improve thermal insulation, halving the clear double glazing *U*-value. Depending on the type of low-e coating, different properties can be obtained (e.g., solar control, with suppressed solar gains, or thermal insulation with high solar gains), each appropriate for a different climate type and application. The placement of low-e coating on the window assembly plays a marginal role on the overall window properties. Usually these coatings are placed within the air gap for protection reasons. The outdoors pane is preferred by glass manufacturers to be the coated one, with the indoors pane being clear glass, as this configuration is more efficient in blocking thermal radiation from the inside (in a similar way as in the case of single glazing but less pronounced). Using two coatings on both panes is not favored by glass manufacturers. Indeed, as follows by comparison of windows 10 and 15 of **Table 1**, the use of two low-e coatings instead of one causes a 23% reduction in SHGC and an 11% reduction in *U*-value, which are small compared to the increase of the window cost, which could be 1.5 times higher or more. Of the double glazing appearing in **Table 1**, the most effective ones in terms of thermal insulation seem to be those with the solar control coatings.

Further reductions in *U*-values are possible with use of a less conductive and more viscous inert gas. Manufacturers use Ar, Kr, Xe, and mixtures of these as filling gases. They are nontoxic, nonreactive, clear, and odorless. As can be seen in **Table 1**, the effect of filling the gap with an inert gas is a reduction in *U*-values in the range of $0.1-0.3 \, W \, m^{-2} \, K^{-1}$ depending on the glazing configuration. Thus, highly insulating windows benefit more from the use of inert gases, as the relative change in *U*-value is larger. The biggest problem with inert gases is that their retention in the glazing is questionable. As with all gases, they tend to diffuse through the seals and to escape through microcracks in the sealing materials. Keeping the gas within the window unit depends largely on the quality of the design and construction, materials in use, and assembly, particularly the sealing techniques. As a result of all these improvements, state-of-the-art double glazings with *g*-values up to 0.49 and *U*-values down to $1.1 \, W \, m^{-2} \, K^{-1}$ have been achieved.

3.10.4.6.2 Triple and quadruple glazing for ultrahigh thermal insulation

In heating-dominated climates with extremely low temperatures, the *U*-values of double glazing are not low enough to ensure acceptable thermal losses of buildings. In these environments, triple and quadruple glazing are used, having *U*-values down to $0.6 \, W \, m^{-2} \, K^{-1}$. The price to be paid is the reduction in solar gains, and increase of the window dimensions, weight, and cost. In high-tech triple and quadruple glazing, Kr or Xe are used as the filling gases to reduce the overall width of the window. These gases allow placement of the glass panes at shorter distances (see the inset of **Figure 8**).

3.10.4.7 Window Frames

Frames are very important in glazing systems. Not only do they hold windows in place but they also act as a peripheral seal. The thermal properties of the frame play a significant role in the overall *U*-value of the window. Nowadays, a variety of window frames is available, ranging from wood (the material used traditionally) to aluminum, plastics, and various other composite materials. Next, the different frame types are presented in order of decreasing thermal conductivity [47–49].

3.10.4.7.1 Aluminum

Aluminum is a light, strong, and durable material that can be easily extruded into complex shapes. Aluminum frames are available in anodized and factory-baked enamel finishes that are extremely durable and require virtually no maintenance. However, aluminum as a window frame material is not very efficient in terms of thermal insulation. As a metal, it exhibits high thermal conductance, greatly raising the overall *U*-value of a window unit. For this reason (and also for economizing on materials), the aluminum frame profiles are hollow with complex shapes, in an effort to create air enclaves.

In hot climates, where solar gain suppression is often more important than heat losses, improving the insulating value of the frame can be much less important than using a higher-performance glazing system. In cold climates, on the other hand, a simple aluminum frame can easily become cold enough to condense moisture or frost on the surfaces of window frames. Even more than the problem of heat loss, the condensation problem has led to the development of better insulating aluminum frames. The most common solution to the heat conduction problem of aluminum frames is to provide a 'thermal break' by splitting the frame components into interior and exterior pieces and use a less conductive material to join them. Current technology with standard thermal breaks has decreased aluminum frame *U*-values from roughly 10 to about $6 \, W \, m^{-2} \, K^{-1}$.

3.10.4.7.2 Wood and wood composites

The traditional window frame material is wood, because of its availability and ease of milling into the complex shapes required to make windows. Wood is favored in many residential applications because of its appearance and traditional place in house design. From a thermal point of view, wood-framed windows perform well with frame *U*-values in the range of $2-3 \, W \, m^{-2} \, K^{-1}$. The disadvantages of wooden frames are that they are not as durable as other materials and require maintenance (with paint or lacquer) to last longer.

A variation of the wood-framed window is to clad the exterior face of the frame with either vinyl or aluminum, creating a permanent weather-resistant surface. Clad frames thus have lower maintenance requirements, while retaining the attractive wood finish on the interior.

Alternatively, composite wood products, such as particle board and laminated strand lumber, in which wood particles and resins are compressed to form a strong composite material have also been used to produce window frames that have similar thermal properties of wood. New materials have emerged recently, such as wood/polymer composites that are extruded into a series of lineal shapes for window frame and sash members. These composites are very stable and have the same or better structural and thermal properties as conventional wood, with better moisture resistance and more decay resistance.

3.10.4.7.3 Plastics (vinyl, fiberglass, thermoplastics)

Vinyl, also known as polyvinyl chloride (PVC), is a very versatile plastic with good insulating properties. Vinyl window frames do not require painting and have good moisture resistance. Because the color goes all the way through, there is no finish coat that can be damaged or deteriorate over time – the surface is therefore maintenance-free. Some vinyl window manufacturers are now offering surface treatments such as laminates (wood veneer, paintable/stainable, maintenance-free) and coatings. The main disadvantage of vinyl is that, like all polymers, its long chains tend to break up under UV irradiation. Thus, the material ages and loses its properties. Recent advances have improved resistance to degradation from sunlight and temperature extremes. In terms of thermal performance, vinyl frames are comparable with wood, while there are minor differences, depending on the frame construction. Small, hollow chambers within the frame reduce convection exchange, as does adding an insulating material.

Window frames can also be made of glass-fiber-reinforced polyester, or fiberglass, which is pultruded or extruded into lineal forms and then assembled into windows. These frames are dimensionally stable and have air cavities (similar to vinyl). When the cavities are filled with insulation, fiberglass frames have thermal performance superior to wood or vinyl (similar to insulated vinyl frames). Because the material is stronger than vinyl, it can have smaller cross-sectional shapes and thus less area. Another polymer-based approach is to use extruded engineered thermoplastics, another family of plastics used extensively in automobiles and appliances. Like fiberglass, they have some structural and other advantages over vinyl. Usually these high-performance frames are used with high-performance glazing.

3.10.4.7.4 Hybrid

Manufacturers are increasingly turning to hybrid frame designs that use two or more frame materials to produce a complete window system. The wood industry has long built vinyl- and aluminum-clad windows to reduce exterior maintenance needs. Vinyl manufacturers and others offer interior wood veneers to produce the finish and appearance that many homeowners desire. Split-sash designs may have an interior wood element bonded to an exterior fiberglass element. We are likely to see an ever-increasing selection of such hybrid designs as manufacturers continue to try to provide better-performing products at lower cost.

3.10.4.7.5 Effect of frames on the window thermal properties

It is evident that the frame chosen for a given type of glazing must possess similar thermal properties. A highly insulating frame with a single glazing is a waste and, similarly, a simple, aluminum frame is not suitable for a superinsulating triple glazing. The ideal frame for a given glazing is one that does not increase the whole window U-value above the mid-pane value. To match the different types of windows to appropriate frames in terms of thermal properties, simulations of the whole window assembly and its thermal performance must be carried out. Such results are presented in **Table 2** in which appear the U-values of various combinations of frames and glazing for typical residential windows (0.8 × 1.2 m). They are simulations obtained with the 'Window 5.2' and 'Therm 5.2' software developed by Lawrence Berkeley National Laboratory [50, 51]. The mid-pane U-values of **Table 1** have also been added for comparison. It follows from **Table 2** that most frame and glazing combinations have U-values higher than the mid-pane ones of equivalent glazing. At best, insulating frames keep the window U-value equal to the mid-pane one. It is also clear that plain aluminum frames are not suitable even for a single clear glass. Their use is only justified in hot climates where the reduction of thermal losses is not a priority. Aluminum frames with thermal break are suitable for single glazing. Wood, composites, and vinyl are suitable for double glazing with clear glass panes. For the more advanced glazing with low-e coatings either double or triple, insulated vinyl or fiberglass frames are necessary. It should also be noted that the frame effects are more pronounced in smaller windows, which have a larger edge-to-area ratio. The frame rebate (e.g., the amount of glazing covered by the frame) also influences

Table 2 *U*-values of windows with different types of glazing and frames

Type of glazing	Type of frame				
	Mid-pane	Aluminum	Aluminum with thermal break	Wood, wood clad, vinyl, composite	Vinyl insulated, fiberglass
Clear, 6 mm thick	5.7	6.6	5.7	–	–
OUTDOORS | INDOORS					
Clear | Clear	2.9	4.3	3.6	2.9	–
TI Low-e | Clear (gas filled)	1.5	3.5	2.8	2.1	1.6
SC Low-e | Clear (gas filled)	1.1	3.4	2.7	1.9	1.5
TI Low-e | Clear | Clear (gas filled)	1.2	–	–	1.6	1.3
SC Low-e | Clear | Clear (gas filled)	0.9	–	–	1.6	1.0

SC, solar control; TI, thermal insulation.
(\|) Symbolizes the gap between glass panes.

the thermal properties of the window: the larger the rebate, the lower the heat loss, as the glass edges that are potential thermal bridges are 'buried' within insulated material and the thermal conduction path through which heat must pass increases [9].

3.10.4.8 Spacers and Sealants

Modern multiple glazing include spacer bars that hold the glass panes at a fixed distance apart and a sealant (called primary seal) placed around the outer perimeter to hold the window together. The primary seal is usually a thermosetting polyisobutylene or butyl rubber. The application of an additional layer of sealant to the shoulder of the spacer bar (termed secondary seal) creates an extra barrier that reduces the overall vapor permeability of the glazing. The secondary seal is polysulfide, polyurethane, silicone, hot melt butyl, or an epoxy glue. In glazing incorporating inert gases, an additional gas-retention seal (in the form of adhesive tape) is added [47, 48, 50]. In **Figure 9**, the sketch of a double glazing is shown. The typical cross section of such a glazing and the various components discussed above are also highlighted.

The spacer bar has a profile depth of 6–8 mm. Its width can be varied to give a cavity of 6–20 mm. The spacer bar is hollow and a desiccant is incorporated into it to absorb the moisture trapped between the panes during manufacture of the glazing, as well as moisture that permeates during its service life.

As in the case of frames, the spacer material is of great importance for the thermal properties of the window.

Aluminum has excellent structural properties, but as a conductor of heat it represents a significant thermal 'short circuit' at the edge of the window, which reduces the benefits of improved glazing. In addition to the increased heat loss, the colder edge is more prone to condensation.

To address this problem, window manufacturers have developed a series of edge systems, including solutions that depend on material substitutions as well as new designs. One approach to reducing heat loss has been to replace the aluminum spacer with a metal that is less conductive, for example, stainless steel, and change the cross-sectional shape of the spacer. These designs are widely used in windows today.

Another approach is to replace the metal with insulating materials. The most commonly used design incorporates spacer, sealer, and desiccant in a thermoplastic compound that contains a blend of desiccant materials and a thin, fluted metal shim of aluminum or stainless steel. Another approach uses an insulating silicone foam spacer that incorporates a desiccant and has a high-strength adhesive at its edges to bond to glass. The foam is backed with a secondary sealant. Both extruded vinyl and fiberglass spacers have also been used instead of metals.

There are several hybrid designs that incorporate thermal breaks in metal spacers or use one or more of the elements described above. Some of these are specifically designed to accommodate three- and four-layer glazings incorporating stretched plastic films. All are designed to interrupt the heat transfer pathway at the glazing edge between two or more glazing layers.

The effort to develop 'warm' edge materials with improved thermal insulation is justified by the fact that the thermal effect of a spacer extends beyond its physical size, to a peripheral band 60–70 mm wide. The contribution of this 'glass edge' to the total window U-value depends on the size of the window: glass edge effects are more pronounced in smaller windows, which have a larger edge-to-area ratio. For a typical residential-size window (0.8×1.2 m), changing from a standard aluminum edge to a good-quality warm edge can reduce the overall window U-factor by approximately $0.1 \text{ W m}^{-2} \text{ K}^{-1}$. Apart from the reduction of thermal losses, another benefit is the rise in interior surface temperature at the bottom edge of the window, which is the most prone to condensation part of the glazing.

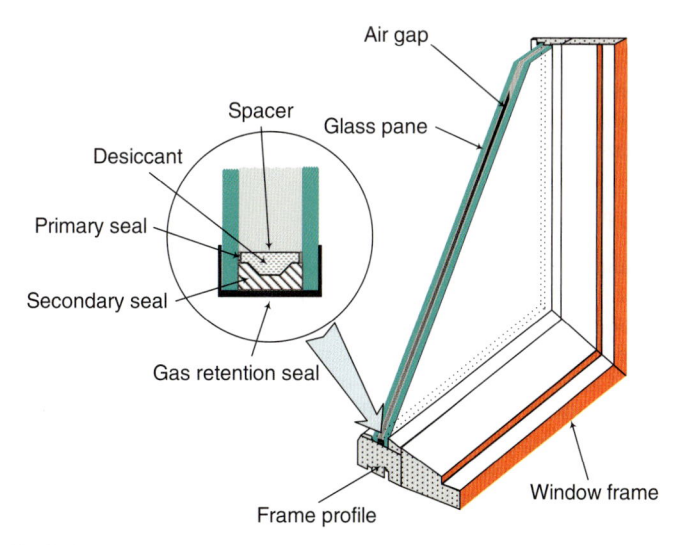

Figure 9 Sketch of a typical double glazing.

3.10.4.9 Emerging Technologies

In a continuous effort to improve the performance of windows, various innovative technologies are emerging. These are as follows [37]:

- *Evacuated glazing.* By replacing the air gap with a vacuum, better thermal insulation is expected, as convection and conduction losses are eliminated. However, new challenges emerge, such as the retention of vacuum, heat transfer through the pillars used to hold the glass panes apart, accommodation of differential expansion of the two glass panes, sound insulation issues, and more.
- *Aerogel glazing.* Use of aerogels (microporous insulating material such as granular silica) can lead to highly insulated glazing either translucent or transparent.
- *Switchable glazing.* They are intended for dynamic solar control in 'smart' buildings that adapt their envelope to changing climatic conditions. There are many different designs, such as ECs that change their color reversibly from transparent to dark blue upon application of a DC voltage, gasochromics that perform the same task with use of H_2 gas, thermochromics in which the color change is triggered by heat, liquid crystal, suspended particles, and metal hydride devices with reflectance modulation (they switch between a mirror and a transparent state), and others.

All these emerging technologies will be presented in the following sections.

3.10.4.10 Conclusions – Epilogue

The most important breakthrough in the flat glass industry is undoubtedly the development of the float process. It has revolutionized glass manufacturing and led to the production of high-quality windows. Nowadays, multiple glazing with high visible transmittance and increased thermal insulation are the state of the art in the fenestration market. The incorporation of various thin film coatings (such as low-e, reflective, self-cleaning) have added value to the glazing products. Emerging technologies such as EG, ECs, and aerogels promise that in the years to come, new improved products with even better properties will appear.

3.10.5 Evacuated Glazing

3.10.5.1 Operating Principles

There are two basic problems with the DGUs that need to be solved, for at least some applications demanding very good insulation. The first is that the *U*-value cannot become lower than a limit, which appears to be approximately $1 \, W \, m^{-2} \, K^{-1}$. TGUs and quadruple-glazed units can be used for this purpose in demanding or very harsh environments. However, this choice introduces the second difficulty, which is lack of space and the lowering of *U*-value is still less than desired in the case of DGU. In addition, the TGU is necessarily more expensive and heavy than is desired for most applications. The problem of space and weight is serious and the tables in the preceding section show this. The EG was proposed to reply to these challenges.

It was proposed that a solution would be to evacuate the space between the two panes. This could improve the heat-insulating characteristics to a very low *U*-value, as there is no convective heat transfer, leaving only the radiative heat transfer. The last can be reduced to a minimum by using special low-e coatings on the inner two glass surfaces, or at least on one of them. The glass must be supported internally using the tiny pillars, or else the atmospheric pressure will cause implosion.

We must also stop the glass panes from collapsing and touching each other internally, because of the forces on the outer two planes (surfaces 1 and 4). The small (typical diameter 0.2–0.4 mm) supporting glass or metal pillars are placed at regular distances about 20–40 mm from each other in a square arrangement to avoid the problem of reduction of optical clarity (transparency), as shown in **Figure 10**. This distance is a critical parameter for the thermal and optical characteristics of the EG.

After this short description of the operating principles, we may state that with the EG, we try to eliminate completely the convective heat losses in double-glazed windows by evacuating the space between the two glass units.

3.10.5.2 Technology and Related Problems

For the heat transfer, if there is vacuum in the space between the two glass panes, the conductance h_g in eqn [22] becomes very small. The typical EG unit consists of two glass panes sealed hermetically (gastight seal) around their edge so that vacuum can be maintained in the space between the two glass panes (**Figure 10**). Low-e coatings are used on the internal glass surfaces (2 and 3 or only on one of them) to reduce the only remaining mode of heat transfer, the radiative heat transfer.

The EG concept is very advanced and some basic problems must find better solutions. Further research is needed for a smart design and a breakthrough in the details of its production that will make it attractive for the companies to produce and the consumers to use it. Transparent low e-coatings (both hard and soft) are used on one or both of the inner surfaces and this is crucial as otherwise the heat exchange by radiation would wipe out the advantage of the vacuum for extremely low heat transfer.

Benson *et al.* [52] tried a production method forming the edge seal of the glazing by laser heating in vacuum. During the process, the entire glass structure was maintained at high temperature to reduce stresses in the glass. Practical difficulties in the sealing method prevented this technique from being widely implemented. In addition, it was recognized that it would be necessary to

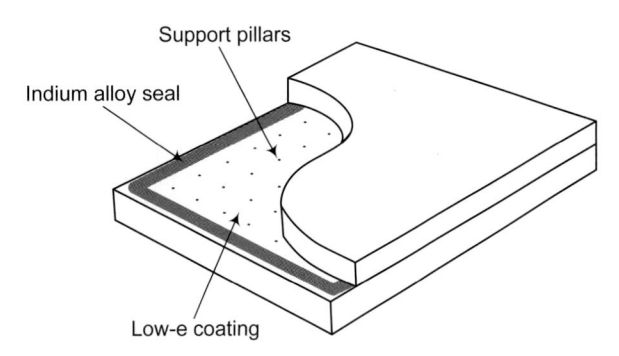

Figure 10 Construction and operating principle of a typical evacuated glazing with the support pillar array and the indium alloy vacuum seal.

include getters within the device in order to remove gas that was emitted by the glass while it was still hot, after the edge seal had been completed.

Several factors influence the optimal separation of the glass sheets. On the one hand, we are constrained to have a small separation, on the order of 1 mm, as otherwise the mechanical energy stored in the EG device could be hazardous in the case of breakage. On the other hand, there is a low separation limit that is determined by the following factors [53]:

1. Due to the large distributed impedance to gas flow between the closely spaced glass sheets, long evacuation times may occur.
2. Evanescent field radiative coupling between the internal surfaces of the cavity may result in enhanced heat exchange and flow through the evacuated space [54].
3. Interference fringes due to reflections from the internal surfaces may have visual unpleasant effects.

Clugston and Collins [53] applied a method of using glass, of the same kind as the panes, to seal the two glass panes at the outside edge. A small tube about 4 mm long, with 1 mm internal diameter, was sealed on an appropriate hole in one glass plate with solder glass. Evacuation was performed through this tube and the outer end of it is fused to seal the vacuum. They described the determination of the time required to evacuate such a device through the small pump-out tube. The same researchers have developed also an approximate analytic method for this study. The numerical results have been validated by experimental measurements. It was shown that samples of about 1 m^2 and internal gap of 0.2 mm could be evacuated in a few minutes through the small pump-out tube. Therefore, the evacuation time in the production process of EG is determined mainly by the heating cycles required for the outgassing of the internal glass surfaces. The pressure in the evacuated space should be kept below 1.5×10^{-3} mbar, so that the heat flow through the glazing by gas conduction is negligible.

The optimum distance between successive pillars is determined by the following opposite requirements. When the distance is relatively large, a problem arises because of the tendency of the glass to bend over the glass beads causing disturbing reflections. Closer bead spacing minimizes the optical anomalies, but denser spacing increases the thermal losses and optical intrusion.

3.10.5.3 The State of the Art

As we have already mentioned, it is necessary to use support pillars to maintain the separation of the glass sheets under the force from atmospheric pressure. The design of the pillar array also involves careful optimization as we have two competing factors: heat flow through the pillars and mechanical stresses in glass sheets and pillars. Pillars are about 0.2–0.5 mm in diameter; they are placed at distances, on a square matrix, that may vary from 25 to 50 mm [7, 9, 53, 55–57]. Experimental and theoretical results enable an assessment of the design choice of the internal gap in EG. The need to avoid optical interference fringes, and to ensure that significant evanescent field radiative heat flow does not occur, gives a lower limit of 0.1 mm for the dimension of the gap. The constraint to keep mechanical energy associated with the evacuated volume small, for safety, imposes an upper limit of 1 mm for the gap. It is fortunate that the dimensions of practical pump-out tubes can be chosen to give evacuation time of less than 1 min in this range of gap sizes, for samples of realistic dimensions. This time required to establish vacuum in EG is dominated by the time required for the outgassing process.

Stable EG units were initially produced around 1990 [52, 55]. All early attempts, as well as the later fabrication of evacuated experimental glazing units [58], necessitate temperatures above 450 °C for edge sealing. This is an energy-intensive process and permits the use of only hard low-e coatings. These are essentially metal oxides, as SnO_2 with fluorine as a doping material. The hard coatings have an emissivity in the IR that cannot be lower than 0.15 and this has resulted in their inability to reduce radiative heat transfer across the unit below a certain limit. In addition, we should emphasize that the emittance of the hard coatings becomes even higher at the high temperatures used for edge seal fabrication. The emittance is increased irreversibly at very high temperatures. For example, the emittance after fabrication at temperatures above 450 °C was measured to be 0.25 [56, 57]. There is, on the other hand, a possibility to use special coatings that have been described earlier in this chapter. The idea to use soft coatings (of the type D/M/D), which can have very low-e, forces one to be able to seal the double glass using lower temperatures of fabrication (typically 190 °C or lower), as this is near the upper temperature limit that these films can endure [7, 9]. Soft coatings can have much lower emittance to thermal (long-wave) radiation in the range 3–30 μm and, for this reason, are desirable. The value for the emittance can be as low as 0.02 (e.g., ZnS/Ag/ZnS) [7, 8, 59, 60]. In addition to the very low e, it is claimed that one can save thermal processing energy at this lower temperature.

Another problem to be solved with the EG technology is the maintenance of adequate vacuum for a long time. This depends on the outgassing from the glass surfaces after sealing. It is preferable that the film deposition and the evacuation and sealing are done in one process. With this method, the glass surfaces are still hot and have no chance to be covered by adsorbed molecules from the atmosphere. Even in this case, getters are required to absorb gases that are released or infiltrate through glass surfaces and seals.

Deterioration of the EG can appear from the action of the UV part of the solar spectrum, from moisture, and from thermal gradients as well as from rapid thermal transients. The last come from partial exposure to the sun (partial shading effect), from weather changes, or in general from any factor that creates temperature differences across the glazing. In addition, the EG system is subject to stresses [55] due to the glass contact with pillars (compressive stresses on the inner surfaces) and radial tensile stresses on the outer surfaces. The glass panes are subject to forces from atmospheric pressure leading to bending stress.

As we have already mentioned, to use soft low-e coatings, we must search for solutions other than solder glasses because they have too high a melting temperature to be used for sealing around the edge. Other adhesives (epoxy-based, silicone tapes or compounds containing silicone) have also been found inappropriate for this purpose. It is known that for stable vacuum seals in cryogenic systems, copper or indium under compression is used [9, 61–69]. These metals have high ductility and can follow surface contours. Indium is also used in electron tube manufacture as a soft-metal pressure sealant for glass-to-glass and glass-to-ceramic interfaces [70]. Indium was finally selected for the following additional reasons: (1) Indium has a low vapor pressure at ambient temperatures. (2) With indium we avoid glass breakage during thermal cycling when we join materials with incompatible coefficients of thermal expansion. (3) Compressing an indium wire between two glass panes forms a vacuum seal that may be not very strong, but can be improved by adding an adhesive around the periphery of the glass to provide the required strength characteristics. In **Figure 10** the indium-based seal is illustrated schematically. One can easily imagine an epoxy-based material at the periphery of the glass panel to complete the seal, strengthening the overall mechanical stability of the system.

For the formation of the indium seal, an indium or indium alloy wire is used. An oxide layer covers the wire and must be removed by the use of dilute hydrochloric acid [71]. During sealing experiments [9], it was found that after cleaning we should have an inert atmosphere or vacuum for the successful completion of the fabrication. Experiments have shown that using indium alloy (which is half the cost of pure indium) we have a smaller problem of surface oxidation [9]. Another problem has to do with the connection of the two ends of the wire. A hermetic seal can be achieved by either increasing the indium wire compression ratio or forming the indium seal at elevated temperatures, under vacuum conditions [9]. It was also found that increasing the diameter of the wire increases the movement of indium during the formation of the seal and effectively removes the surface layer, isolating and minimizing regions where nonbonding occurred. When indium alloy is used to form the edge seal, it melted and bonded well with the glass when heated. The alloy needed to be kept molten using a soldering iron [9].

NSG has developed the world's first commercialized vacuum glazing product known as SPACIA. The glazing consists of two 3, 4, or 5 mm sheets of glass, separated by pillars 0.5 mm in diameter and 0.2 mm high (e.g., a 0.2 mm vacuum spacing gap is formed), spaced on a regular Cartesian grid at 20 mm centers. NSG now produce three different systems: SPACIA, SPACIA 21, and Laminated SPACIA with U-values ranging from 1.5 to 0.7 W m^{-2} K^{-1}. Its thin structure (6–10 mm thick) is particularly well suited for the replacement of single panes in old houses without changing the existing traditional frames.

3.10.5.4 Comparison with Conventional Glazing

For the prediction of heat transfer through the indium and adhesive layers of the edge seal and through the pillars, detailed computational modeling is required [9, 72]. A transient finite volume approach [73] was adopted for these calculations. The calculated [9] center-pane overall heat loss coefficient, for a system in which 6 mm glass panes were used and the pillar separation was 40 mm, was 0.36 W m^{-2} K^{-1}. The visible transmittance under these parameters is $\tau_{vis} = 0.72$. We state for comparison that noble gas-filled glazing systems have center-pane U-value of 0.9 W m^{-2} K^{-1}.

The low-temperature sealing method with indium alloy wire under vacuum has several benefits over the laser based or other high-temperature manufacturing techniques. The most important is that we can use 'soft' coatings [7–9, 60] of lower emittance. Another advantage is the lower energy that is required for the manufacture of the integrated sealing and that the use of a pump-out tube is eliminated [9].

3.10.5.5 Electrochromic Evacuated Glazing

A combination of evacuated and EC glazing has been developed, combining optimum dynamic control of the solar radiation that is allowed to enter into buildings with a high degree of thermal insulation [74]. These advanced glazing systems can be manufactured today using EG in combination with EC glazing. The optimization of the EC device materials (EC, ion storage (IS), protective layers, TCs, and polymer electrolytes) and the refinement of sealing methods for EG made this possible [74, 75].

Prototypes of EC EG with dimensions up to 40 cm × 40 cm have been fabricated using vacuum techniques and chemical methods. The prototypes exhibited excellent optical and thermal performance, with a contrast ratio up to 1 : 32, coloration efficiency (CE) up to 92 cm^2 C^{-1}, and mid-pane U-values as low as 0.86 W m^{-2} K^{-1} [74, 75]. Such a glazing can be used in building applications to improve occupant thermal comfort, to contribute to a reduction in space heating and cooling loads, and to allow for increased areas of fenestration reducing artificial lighting loads [74, 75]. Their durability in relation to real working environmental conditions has been assessed through indoor and outdoor testing. These factors reduce the energy demand for the building and, therefore, contribute to the reduction of CO_2 emissions

3.10.5.6 Conclusions

In practical EG, the vacuum must be maintained over 20 years for the window to work in a satisfactory way. This is a crucial factor for this product. A laser has been used experimentally to seal the borosilicate glass edges; other methods of glass welding at high temperatures are used now. However, most of the soft-coat low-e coatings cannot withstand the high heat of laser welding. The hard coatings can withstand these temperatures but their emissivity is considered too high for effective vacuum windows. A hermetic seal can be achieved by indium wire forming an indium seal at lower temperatures under vacuum conditions and permitting the use of soft-coat low-e coatings of emissivity as low as 0.02.

In conclusion we may state that with this technology we can achieve a U-value lower than 0.5 W m^{-2} K^{-1} in evacuated DGUs with a soft-coat low-e coating deposited on the internal glass surface (or surfaces) to further reduce the radiation exchange heat losses in the space between the two glasses. The lowest limits to the U-value cannot be pushed further down because of the heat loss via thermal bridging through the pillars and the edge seal.

A combination of evacuated and EC glazing has been developed experimentally and is of interest. Its durability in relation to real working environmental conditions has been assessed through indoor and outdoor testing. This glazing can be used in building applications to improve occupant thermal comfort, to contribute to a reduction in space heating and cooling loads, and to allow for increased areas of fenestration for the reduction of artificial lighting. These factors reduce the energy demand of buildings and contribute to the overall reduction of CO_2 emissions [74, 75].

3.10.6 Transparent Insulation

3.10.6.1 Historical Background

From the early days of solar energy applications, it became apparent that transparent insulation (TI) materials could be used profitably in reducing the heat transport, in many systems requiring transparency, starting from active solar systems (thermal collectors, concentrating systems, solar cookers) to passive solar buildings and other applications [76–78]. Research and development on TI systems has been ongoing for 30 years now. TI materials (TIMs) are used to replace standard opaque insulation materials. Efforts were made to apply suitable honeycomb materials between the two flat covers of a solar thermal collector or between the absorber and the single cover to reduce heat transport by convection and radiation. In window technology, TIMs can be used to fill the space of a DGU for achieving even lower U-values. Using TIMs we may not have clear view since they exhibit high levels of light scattering. They are geometric structures made from plastic or glass and generally distort the image of the objects (nonimaging display). They usually have the form of honeycombs, slats, or tubes and show very high light scattering. There is an interesting material, called 'aerogel', with insulating properties that we describe in detail later. It is a very promising candidate for modern applications.

Experiments with TIMs were performed on buildings during 1982 and 1983 and showed promising results [76]. The results appeared particularly attractive for retrofitting purposes of existing buildings. For south facades during a sunny period in January, a mean flux of 9 W m^{-2} into the house (through the walls) was observed. For the entire heating season, the extrapolated value was 16 W m^{-2}. The beneficial effect is combined with heat storage and damping of temperature fluctuation in masonry walls, as was also demonstrated. In general, the use of solar energy in passive buildings can be realized with a plethora of ideas that include the use of TI. TIMs have the interesting property of being transparent or translucent to solar radiation while at the same time they act as heat insulation. Elements made of TIM can be attached to the walls of buildings and thus permit the utilization of solar energy for heating. Theoretical and validated experimental relations were given for the dependence of heat flux and conversion efficiency of radiation into useful heat. This depends on the thermal resistance of the components. Calculations using meteorological data show that with material parameters achievable with the present technology, the use of TI may lead to significant contributions to heating and energy savings.

Very early attempts to use TIMs were made by Prof. Francia who was primarily interested in obtaining very high temperatures with solar tower systems. He also proposed the use of honeycomb structures in solar collectors. Prof. Francia showed how the honeycomb could effectively reduce the radiation losses within a solar collector and reduce the overall heat transport to the environment. Also hotbox solar cookers have been realized with TIMs.

3.10.6.2 Optical and Thermal Properties

The optical and heat transport properties of TIMs are important for all applications that we mention here. In buildings, the use of TIMs can reduce heat losses, controlling indoor temperatures, at the same time allowing considerable solar radiation transmittance of more than 50% in the visible part of the spectrum. Solar transmittance and reflectance are very important properties for TIMs in solar energy applications. The spectral transmittance is derived as a weighted average over the solar spectrum (300–3000 nm). When we examine clear glazing units, we should compare them by the normal transmittance. If we consider a good honeycomb material and measure the transmittance for normal incidence, we find that it is slightly less than 1, as the parallel light passes unobstructed. This result is independent of the length of the cells. In comparison, other TIMs may have very different optical properties. For granular aerogel, there is a scattering resulting in small angular variation of the transmittance. Therefore, this quantity does not reveal the honeycomb quality.

We have the problem of standardization and characterization of TIM, as the quality of samples varies and this may not give reproducible results. Solar transmittance and heat conductance are available for the most important material classes [79, 80].

The optical and heat transport in TIMs, as well as the light scattering and corrugation of cell walls, has been treated theoretically [81]. Spectral transmittance measurements of TIMs as the hemispherical–hemispherical transmittance are given as a function of thickness and are available for several commercial products. A proper quantity for material comparisons is the transmittance for diffuse irradiation. This does not differ much from the annual average transmittance and is almost independent of orientation and tilt of the material plane. The light transmittance and reflectance are important for visual evaluation and for daylighting systems. For energy considerations the directional-hemispherical quantities are needed, while for daylighting the complete bidirectional characteristics are also important.

The heat transport in TIMs is usually dominated by the radiative heat transfer. Other modes of the heat transfer, conduction through the structure and convection of the filling gas, may be usually neglected. The reason is the semitransparency of most materials to radiation in the thermal wavelength range. This is rather pronounced in cellular structures such as honeycombs and capillaries, but even in aerogel, which is optically thick at most thermal wavelengths, a radiative window exists where the extinction is relatively small. The dominance of the radiative mode results in a heat conductance varying approximately with T^3, where T is the absolute temperature. Another consequence of this semitransparent quality is that the equivalent heat conductivity including all heat transport modes (i.e., heat conductance × sample thickness) is not constant with thickness.

3.10.6.3 Types of Available Materials

TIMs are usually structures with small cells that are designed to suppress convection and to reduce radiative heat exchange. This is achieved by absorption and reemission of IR photons through the structure. The material content of these products is high, on the order of 20–50 kg m^{-3}. The types of structures used are capillaries, small-diameter tubes, and honeycombs. The easiest to make are the rectangular or rhombic structures that can collapse to a two-dimensional shape, but hexagonal cells are also used. The tiny cells have the form of square and hexagonal honeycombs or capillaries of width 2–5 mm (**Figure 11**). These may be extruded polycarbonate (PC) honeycombs or capillary materials with tubular cells. The material can be PMMA (polymethylmethacrylate), PC, or other plastics satisfying the obvious requirement of stability to UV. For higher temperatures, as for example in a solar fluid collector for process heat, the proper material is the APEC (polyester carbonate) capillary. A polyacrylate variation (KAMAX®) has been produced with sufficient temperature stability and good optical properties.

However, product uniformity and cell quality is frequently a problem for materials with small cell structure. In the following paragraphs, the most promising TIMs are presented. TIMs are usually specific to certain applications. These range from windows to transparent covers for flat-plate solar collectors. The deterioration of the system performance is usually not dramatic under regular use. It is impracticable to optimize TI products for such divergent requirements.

Aerogel materials have good insulating properties and are transparent. The structure of aerogel is porous with pore sizes on the order of few tens of nanometers (**Figure 12**). It is sometimes referred to as 'silicate foam' as the chemical organization is SiO$_2$ with extended –O–Si–O– bonds. They are as transparent as glass and have a very good U-value, on the order of 0.5 W m^{-2} K^{-1}. The optical properties are a result of light scattering in the material. We have aerogels in two different forms: (1) monolithic silica aerogel (MSA) or monolithic tiles and (2) granular filling material.

These materials can be used in windows (filling the inner space in a double window) and cover systems because of their transparency and insulating properties.

3.10.6.3.1 Granular aerogels

The granular silica aerogels (GSAs) may be produced under supercritical drying. The granulate sizes range from 1 to 10 mm in diameter. The product has been developed for application as a filling material for double-glazed translucent glazing units (**Figure 13**). The GSA is produced industrially. Granule distribution, mechanical stability, and hydrophobicity have been improved.

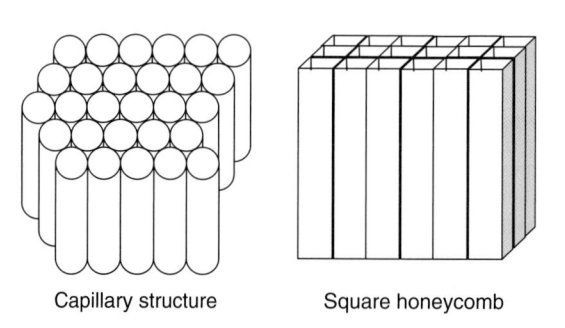

Figure 11 Basic types of structures used for transparent insulation (TI) materials (capillaries and honeycombs).

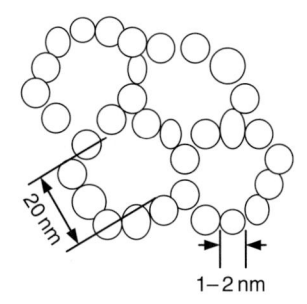

Figure 12 The nanostructured form of aerogels.

Figure 13 The principle of operation of granular aerogel in double glazing.

It is obvious from basic physics that the granule size influences the heat transport and optical properties. We note that the transmitted light in GSAs is diffused and as a consequence they are appropriate for translucent walls and glazing units that are produced for daylighting applications. The heat conductivity is in most cases slightly higher for granules than for monolithic tiles. This may be attributed to the special porous structure of this form.

3.10.6.3.2 Monolithic silica aerogel

The MSA is a material that has much potential of improvement, and for this reason we may state that it is still in experimental form. It is a nanoporous medium with many interesting physical and chemical properties [81]. We can produce MSA by supercritical drying from a starting material called alcogel. The final product (MSA) has densities in the range of 100–150 kg m^{-3}. We can also obtain densities between 3 and 500 kg m^{-3} by a variation of production methods. There are problems to produce large flat tiles (larger than 60 cm × 60 cm × 2 cm) without cracks. Water resistance should be improved. It is used for solar collectors and other thermal applications.

The material presents a reddish color under transmission and blue under reflection. This is due to bulk scattering of light from the small pores. Optically, the material is clear and the solar transmittance is especially high [81].

The characteristic equivalent conductivity of MSA at room temperature is about 2×10^{-2} W m^{-1} K^{-1}. This corresponds to nonevacuated material. Xerogels are dried differently and are much clearer than aerogels. Xerogels have higher densities, and the corresponding conductivity is usually above 3×10^{-2} W m^{-1} K^{-1}. The heat transport is well understood. Gaseous conduction is principally reduced by the Knudsen effect within the small pores. Evacuating down to 1 mbar is adequate to eliminate gas conduction almost completely. The radiative heat transport is the main part, influenced also by water adsorption [82–84].

3.10.6.3.3 Glass capillary structures

For solar thermal applications, for example, solar thermal collectors, the material that is used must endure any temperatures that are developed either under regular use or under stagnation conditions. The stagnation temperature of a solar thermal collector depends on the U-value of the collector and consequently on the honeycomb thickness as well as on the environmental conditions. A plastic structure used as TI has this severe limitation. The usual or extreme temperatures in flat-plate collectors are such that the plastic TI does not hold up to the collector stagnation temperature. Additional design measures may be taken by putting more air gaps and special films can prevent melting. Another more drastic solution in such applications is to use glass as an alternate material instead of plastic as it does not become softer below 450 °C. This temperature covers very well the needs. Nevertheless, there are some drawbacks: (1) glass has higher density and (2) has also higher heat conductivity. For this reason, we have to optimize the glass TI with respect to material content. Also we need to reach competitive prices in comparison to plastic materials. The glazing company Interpane produced glazing filled with glass silica aerogel (GSA) commercially.

Experiments using glass tubes may give relatively large U-values if one is not careful enough as in early experimental work [85]. Recent efforts to develop glass capillary structures for TI with satisfactory U-values proved to be successful [86, 87]. Uniform, large-diameter tubes, 7–8 mm, can be produced successfully. Regular appearance, uniformity of production, heat resistance, and very good optical properties make glass tubes an attractive TIM for transparent walls or special windows for daylighting. The regular pattern that may be obtained with filled glazing is rather attractive for architectural purposes.

3.10.6.4 Conclusions

The experience gained up to this date shows that the potential of these materials for high temperature or storage systems is high. Although there exist alternative structures, the materials described seem to be the most promising ones. Further improvements might be possible in the future, mainly in transmittance as a result of better production technologies but also in the U-value due to optimization of the geometry. All the materials we have described may not be used in ordinary windows. There is, however, an increasing market for special (nonview) glazing, as skylights, light-transmitting covers over entrances, or windows. Their advantages include (1) uniform light distribution, (2) no direct shades, and (3) reduced direct glare.

The constant light distribution is combined with low heat losses and supplementary light gains. All these advantages are very important for many applications. The achievements with new TIMs depend critically on the concurrence of high-quality optical and thermal properties. The cost is also critical and we should strive to develop further economical production techniques [88]. The big disadvantage of honeycomb structures is that they need unusually wide gaps to obtain U-value on the order of $1.0\,\mathrm{W\,m^{-2}\,K^{-1}}$. Special spacer and edge seal technology is needed for the accommodation of very thick products. Because of the different nature of the material types treated, it is difficult to compare materials in a fair way. Similar optical and thermal properties may be achieved with different thickness. Normal incidence transmittance is a good indicator of aerogel quality but not for honeycombs.

Granular aerogel has been publicized to reach good energy efficiency with conventional glazing thickness. The constraint for this type of product is the cautious filling and sealing after lowering the pressure to about 0.1 atm.

3.10.7 Chromogenic Materials and Devices

3.10.7.1 Introduction

In recent years, materials science and technology has gained a great impetus. New materials and devices with amazing properties and functions are being developed. Research teams worldwide continuously come forward with new concepts. These advances could have a significant impact in the architectural sector as they could bring about a new concept, the 'dynamic building', for example, a building with the capacity to adapt itself to the prevailing weather conditions to save energy and to improve the occupants' comfort. Windows play a key role to the dynamic building concept, as they too should be dynamic, reversibly altering their optical properties on demand. To that end, a multitude of materials are being developed, under the collective name of 'chromogenic materials'. Coming from the Greek 'χρώμα' (color) and 'γεννώ' (give birth – create), their title describes them as materials that 'create color'. Indeed, these materials, switch from a transparent state to a colored-absorptive one, or to a reflective-mirror-like one, under the influence of electrical potential (electrochromics), heat (thermochromics), gases (gasochromics), or light (photochromics and photoelectrochromics). In this section, the advances in the field of chromogenic materials and devices are presented.

3.10.7.2 Electrochromics

ECs represent the most mature of the chromogenic technologies that are applicable to windows. Since the discovery of electrochromism in WO_3 and MoO_3 in the late 1960s by Deb and co-workers [89], a considerable research effort has been directed toward EC devices and materials, as it has been realized that an EC window has several advantages compared to conventional shading and solar control devices: It does not impede visibility through the window as blinds and curtains do, while it provides glare control and thermal comfort management. It has no moving parts and as a result, minimum maintenance costs. It requires low-voltage power supply (it can even be powered by photovoltaics (PVs) [89]), and it can be integrated into the central power management of the building. It has practically infinite coloration stages. It can block both direct and diffuse solar radiation, unlike passive shading devices. Unlike tinted glass, it can become transparent during the early morning and afternoon hours to improve natural lighting conditions. Furthermore, it has low energy consumption (typically $8\,\mathrm{W\,m^{-2}}$), which is nearly zero when the glazing is kept at constant conditions. This is due to the very high open-circuit memory of the device [90]. An EC window can outperform the best currently available window systems (in most applications) [91] and has lower annual energy demand than an opaque insulating wall [92]. The primary energy benefits are the following: reduced cooling, heating, and ventilation loads, and the ability to replace, at a considerable part, artificial electric lighting use by managing daylight admittance. In a recent study [93], EC windows have been found to outperform PV facades in terms of energy savings. The findings indicate that the energy benefit that results from replacing standard glazing with EC glazing may exceed that of PV facade for the majority of cases studied.

In addition, the architectural and aesthetic appeal of a dynamic control that the EC coating technology offers is difficult to quantify but it will be a major contributing factor for its selection for many building applications. Many design decisions are made not only on the basis of 'payback' but also on the basis of style and appearance.

The aforementioned research effort has come to fruition, as several companies worldwide have announced development of commercial EC glazing for architectural applications during the past years [94–97]. The performance of commercial devices is limited by several factors. They have rather limited transmittance modulation (50–15% for E-Control by Pilkington, 70–20% for Eclipse Energy Systems Inc., 72–17% for Asahi, and 62–3.5% for SAGE Glass®) [94–97]. A wider range (e.g., 75–1%) would allow better control of solar gain. They suffer from defects that are developed during extended operation: these can be dark spots or pinholes (up to 3 mm in diameter and as many as 3 spots per m^2) that are no longer electrochromically active, dust, and metallic particles (due to the preparation technique problems), which cause electric leakage and hence low production yields. Large-area devices also suffer from uneven coloration and degrade after prolonged operation (typically 5% degradation in maximum transmittance). Furthermore, they have a rather limited lifetime: 6000 coloration/bleaching cycles per 5 years for Pilkington E-Control, while the devices developed by SAGE and Asahi are designed for a lifetime of 10 years. As these devices were only produced during the past several years, there are not yet available comprehensive long-term operational performance data.

Another limiting factor to commercialization of EC glazing is the high cost of the devices, which is approximately €1000 m^{-2}, that is, one order of magnitude higher than that of a typical thermally insulating glazing (~€100 m^{-2}).

Consequently, the research effort in this field is still ongoing, trying to address the following issues:

- Cost reduction, by use of alternative, less expensive deposition techniques
- Improvement of the durability of the devices
- Enhancement of their transmittance modulation for better solar control
- Use of alternative materials (especially nano- or microstructured ones) that could solve existing limitations in switching speed
- Improvement of the theoretical understanding of the coloration mechanisms, and the electrochemical processes involved

3.10.7.3 Electrochromic Devices: Principles of Operation and Coloration Mechanisms

A typical EC device has a five-layer structure (as shown in **Figure 14**), consisting of

- a transparent electronically conductive film (TC) deposited on glass, usually TFO (SnO_2:F) or ITO (In_2O_3:Sn);
- an EC film (usually WO_3);
- an ion conducting electrolyte (EL) in liquid, gel, or solid state;
- an IS layer; and
- a second transparent conductive film (TC).

The five-layer structure is therefore: glass/TC/EC/EL/IS/TC/glass. The operation of such an EC cell is as follows: a voltage applied across the two electrodes forces the Li^+ ions (or protons depending on the electrolyte type) from the electrolyte into the active EC layer. Electrons are also injected from the external circuit into the layer for charge equilibration, changing its electronic density and

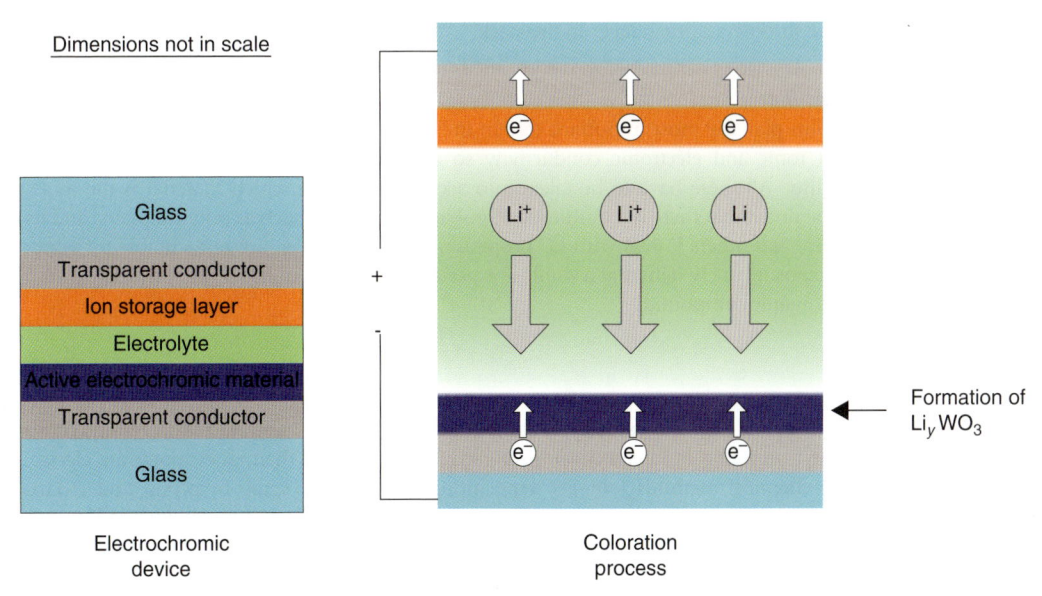

Figure 14 Structure and operation of a typical electrochromic device.

causing coloration of the material. Reversal of the voltage polarity causes movement of ions and electrons in the opposite directions than before and as a result, the material is bleached. This phenomenon can be described as a redox reaction, and in the case of Li ion intercalation into tungsten oxide (WO_3), the following equation applies:

$$x\text{Li}^+ + xe^- + \text{WO}_3 \leftrightarrow \text{Li}_x\text{WO}_3 \quad [25]$$

The above equation describes the intercalation of Li$^+$ into the oxide matrix. However, it does not provide information on the coloration mechanism. During the above process, coloration occurs when the number of W^{5+} oxidation states in the lattice increase. Today it is widely believed that the observed optical absorption during coloration of amorphous WO_3 films is caused by small polaron transitions between two nonequivalent sites. The localized electrons in WO_3 polarize the surrounding lattice forming small polarons, which absorb the incident photons and hop from one site to another. The controversy centers on whether the two transition sites between which the polarons hop are W^{5+} and W^{6+} [98], or W^{5+} and W^{4+} [99]. These intervalence transitions can be described by the following expressions:

$$h\nu + \text{W}^{5+}(A) + \text{W}^{6+}(B) \rightarrow \text{W}^{5+}(B) + \text{W}^{6+}(A) \quad [26]$$

$$h\nu + \text{W}^{5+}(A) + \text{W}^{4+}(B) \rightarrow \text{W}^{5+}(B) + \text{W}^{4+}(A) \quad [27]$$

Models based on eqn [26] do not offer a satisfactory interpretation of some important experimental observations (such as the role of the oxygen deficiency in the CE and the differences between the ratio of Li$^+$ or H$^+$ in the colored WO_3 films). The exclusive use of eqn [27] certainly leads to a better explanation of the experimental results [99], but does not take into account the existing role of the mechanism described by the expression [26]. The combination of both mechanisms is evidently a more acceptable way to describe these phenomena and steps in this direction have already been reported [89, 100]. However, a comprehensive explanation of the chromic mechanisms of WO_3 is still elusive.

3.10.7.4 Materials for Electrochromic Devices

3.10.7.4.1 *Transparent electrical conductors*

Transparent electrically conductive coatings are crucial for the operation of EC devices, as they convey electrical signals from the external circuit leading to coloration/bleaching. An optimum TC for an EC device should exhibit high electronic conductivity – low sheet resistance and minimum obstruction of the visible light. The most suitable materials are the well-known low-e coatings. These have been covered extensively in a previous section. Doped metal oxides are the most obvious choice given their low cost and durability.

However, the metal-based soft films possess several advantages: EC windows could benefit from the use of such multilayered coatings as transparent electrodes since commercially produced EC windows would consist of two transparent sheets, one with the EC device and another with the low-e film. An all-solid-state integrated low-e-EC window can be produced on a single substrate with use of solid ion conductors. Apart from solar control, suppression of emissive heat losses and prevention of overheating by the solar IR radiation, the integration of low-e coatings within the EC device could simplify the preparation of the window and possibly reduce costs. Furthermore, the high electron conductance of the metal film would improve the electrical performance of the device. To date, only ZnS/Ag/ZnS stacks have been used as TCs in EC devices [60, 101, 102]. They exhibited improved electrical and thermal properties, but lacked in their optical behavior due to optical interference between different layers. These issues could be further improved by careful control of the thickness of each layer in the stack.

3.10.7.4.2 *Active electrochromic film*

The properties of the active EC film play the most important role in the overall performance of an EC device. An ideal EC film should have large CE, sufficient ionic and electronic conductivity so as its coloration/bleaching time is acceptable, cycling reversibility, stability, and durability. All these have to be taken into account to decide which material is the most suitable for viable EC devices. It should also be noted that there is a multitude of polymer materials (such as polythiophene and its derivatives, viologens, metallophthalocyanines, and others [103]) with EC properties. These, however, are not suitable for windows, as they cannot withstand the prolonged exposure to UV light that a window experiences throughout its service life [104]. Thus, the quest for suitable materials is limited to inorganic compounds.

3.10.7.4.2(i) Tungsten oxide

WO_3 is the most common EC material. Its broad range of color variation, hardness, and cycling durability renders it the best candidate among inorganic EC materials. It is also extensively studied and the literature abounds with reports on its properties. Similarly, a broad range of preparation routes has been developed: vacuum techniques (thermal evaporation, electron beam gun deposition, and sputtering) and chemical methods (sol–gel deposition, spin coating, spray pyrolysis, and electrodeposition) [105–108]. The film morphology and structure strongly depend on the preparation method: it is well known [105] that sputtered WO_3 films tend to be polycrystalline while thermally evaporated and e-gun deposited ones are amorphous [102]. Sol–gel derived films are known to be amorphous or polycrystalline with grains of various sizes, according to solution chemistry and post-deposition treatment [109, 110]. The morphology of spray pyrolysis WO_3 films strongly depends on the substrate temperature during their fabrication [106, 108]. As for electrodeposited films, a variety of morphologies and microstructures can be obtained by variation of the starting materials and of the solution chemistry [111–115], by alterations in the applied voltage and current [112], and by post-deposition thermal treatment [116].

The surface morphology and microstructure of WO_3 films determines their EC performance. Films that possess an 'open' structure, caused by high porosity or by extensive grain boundaries, are more suitable to function as ECs since their form facilitates the intercalation of metal ions responsible for coloration [111, 112].

The typical thickness of EC WO_3 films ranges from 300 to 600 nm. Evaporated and chemically derived films are nearly stoichiometric with an O:W ratio ranging from 2.83 to 2.97, as can be confirmed by X-ray photoelectron spectroscopy (XPS) measurements [110, 117, 118]. Critical performance parameters of the films are their Li^+ diffusion coefficient during the formation of Li_xWO_3 (typical given values are in the range of 1.5×10^{-9} to 3×10^{-12} cm^2 s^{-1}), the charge capacity of the films (which is about 20 mC cm^{-2}), and the CE of EC devices defined as

$$CE(\lambda) = \frac{\Delta OD(\lambda)}{Q} \quad [28]$$

with $\Delta OD(\lambda) = \log(T_{bleached}(\lambda)/T_{colored}(\lambda))$ the change in optical density, $T_{bleached}$ and $T_{colored}$ the EC cell transmittance in the bleached and colored state, respectively, and Q the intercalated charge density (=inserted charge/device area). Typical CE values for WO_3-based EC devices are 40 cm^2 C^{-1} at 550 nm (point of highest sensitivity for the human eye) and 60 cm^2 C^{-1} at 650 nm.

3.10.7.4.2(ii) Molybdenum oxide

EC coloration has been reported for molybdenum oxide (MoO_3) films prepared by evaporation, sputtering, and chemical methods [105]. The absorption spectra of Li_xMoO_3 films are fairly similar to those of Li_xWO_3, and their characteristic color is purplish blue. The coloration phenomena are comparable to those observed in WO_3 films and a-MoO_3 as well as crystalline films have been investigated [105]. The CEs (at 500 nm) vary between 10 and 50 cm^2 C^{-1} for amorphous and polycrystalline films. The use of MoO_3 in EC devices is hindered by its inferior cycling stability, as compared to WO_3. On top of that, MoO_3 cannot be prepared by certain techniques (e-gun deposition, for example), due to its magnetic properties.

3.10.7.4.2(iii) Prussian blue

Prussian blue (PB) is a dark blue pigment, synthesized for the first time in Berlin around the year 1706 [119, 120]. It was named 'Preußisch blau' and 'Berlinisch Blau' by its first trader [121]. PB is a common pigment, used in paints, and it is the traditional 'blue' in blueprints. Two formulae have been postulated for PB, one of them contains the ion K^+ in the crystal lattice and is called 'soluble PB', $KFe[Fe(CN)]$, and the other, without K^+, is called 'insoluble PB', $Fe[Fe(CN)]$ [122]. Neff deposited PB for the first time in the form of a film on solid electrodes [123]. The coloration and bleaching reaction for this material is as follows:

$$\underset{\text{(blue, PB)}}{Fe_4^{III}[Fe^{II}(CN)_6]_3} + 4M^+ + 4e^- \rightleftharpoons \underset{\text{(bleached, PW)}}{M_4Fe_4^{II}[Fe^{II}(CN)_6]_3} \quad [29]$$

with M^+ a metal species (such as H^+, Li^+, or Na^+). The material cycles between two different states: the colored one (Prussian blue, PB) and the bleached one (Prussian white, PW). It should also be noted that the coloration of PB is 'anodic', complementary to that of WO_3: It is colored in the as prepared state and becomes transparent upon intercalation of metal ions and electrons. Thus, apart from being used as an active EC material, it has also been used as complementary to WO_3 in devices of the form WO_3/electrolyte/PB. Its widespread use is hindered by stability problems: Although it can withstand some 20 000 coloration–bleaching cycles, it has poor at-rest stability (bleached-state degradation) that is associated with trapping of H_2O in PW [124]. Recently, nanocomposite PB films consisting of ITO nanoparticles and PB have been developed with promising properties [125]. In such films, ITO is serving as a medium layer for PB to gain larger operative reaction surface area.

3.10.7.4.3 Ion storage and protective layers

The purpose of an IS layer is to store temporarily the ions that color the active EC film. The IS film accepts and stores ions at the bleached state of the EC device improving its performance. There are two strategies for IS in ECs: (1) the first is use of a separate film dedicated to this purpose. The familiar five-layer structure thus results. The IS film can exhibit complementary coloration to the EC layer, serving a double purpose and contributing to the increase of the CE of the device. It may also be passive, with no significant change of its optical properties. (2) The other alternative is to avoid the use of a separate layer and to combine the IS function with either ionic or electronic conductivity. Thus, IS can be done within the electrolyte or the TC of the device and a four-layer structure results.

3.10.7.4.3(i) Vanadium pentoxide

V_2O_5 thin films exhibit anodic coloration, complementary to that of WO_3 and a large charge capacity. Their thickness ranges from 300 to 500 nm. V_2O_5 films possess a layered morphology, suitable for fast insertion/extraction of ions. To function optimally in EC devices, IS films need to be doped with Li ions before they are incorporated into the devices. V_2O_5 can be Li^+ doped using two techniques, either electrochemical doping or doping in vacuum [102]. The charge capacity of the films thus doped is about 27 mC cm^{-2} resulting in an intercalation parameter y (in Li$_y$V$_2$O$_5$) of 1.3. V$_2$O$_5$ films are thermally stable up to 500 °C. However, they degrade upon prolonged exposure to moisture, as water molecules are inserted in the oxide structure reducing the number of V=O terminal bonds. Although V$_2$O$_5$ seems to be an ideal IS material, it has several disadvantages: it is toxic and corrosive to metals at high temperatures making its handling problematic. Polycrystalline and sol–gel V$_2$O$_5$ films are known to degrade at high degrees of lithiation, due to phase transition effects. Finally, a sharp absorption edge that reaches up to the visible causes V$_2$O$_5$ films to have a yellowish tint that is not much appreciated in the fenestration business.

3.10.7.4.3(ii)   Other IS materials
To avoid the above-mentioned problems, other materials have been sought. Two such materials are NiO and CeO$_2$. They are stable and transparent in the visible (NiO films exhibit complementary coloration, taking a brownish color), but with limited charge capacity. CeVO$_4$ is another candidate material that occurs in nature. Its structure consists of VO$_4$ tetrahedra sharing corners and edges with CeO$_8$ dodecahedra. Thin films of CeVO$_4$ have been prepared by sol–gel techniques. They have promising properties: medium to high charge capacity and high transparency, although they present some stability problems.

Another route to better IS layers is the use of film mixtures. A successful example of this kind is the CeO$_2$–TiO$_2$ combination. As can be seen in **Table 3**, introduction of TiO$_2$ into the CeO$_2$ matrix greatly increases charge capacity, probably due to grain boundary-assisted diffusion. The two materials are arranged in separate nanometer size grains. XPS experiments suggest that the Ti oxidation state does not change during Li$^+$ intercalation. Thus, titanium oxide does not act as an intercalation host. Its role is to improve the access of ions to the CeO$_2$ sites. The optimum atomic composition was found to be 50% Ce and 50% Ti. Apart from TiO$_2$, other metal oxides (ZrO$_2$, Al$_2$O$_3$, SiO$_2$) and even WO$_3$ have been used in conjunction with CeO$_2$ with inferior properties. Apart from inorganic compounds, polyaniline (PANI) and carbon-based materials have also been used in the form of micron-scale lines or dots. The latter result in devices with limited transparency (T_{lum} = 50%).

3.10.7.4.4   Protective layers – magnesium fluoride
The need for an IS layer could be alleviated with use of an appropriate gel electrolyte (with thickness on the order of 0.2–0.5 mm) that can serve the double purpose of ion transfer and storage. In that case, a protective layer will be required to block the Li ions from penetrating the TC film during bleaching of the device. An appropriate material for this purpose is magnesium fluoride (MgF$_2$). It is a neutral, low refractive index material that adheres well to glass and other substrates and it can be prepared easily by e-beam gun evaporation to a thickness of about 150–200 nm.

3.10.7.5   Performance of a Typical EC Device

In **Figure 15** appear the transmittance spectra of a 40 cm × 40 cm EC glazing of the form glass/TC (SnO$_2$:F)/350 nm WO$_3$/0.25 mm electrolyte/150 nm MgF$_2$/TC/glass [74] together with pictures of the devices in the bleached and colored states. The device was colored galvanostatically, with the application of a constant current pulse, and the color intensity was regulated by the current application time. The inserted charge during each coloration cycle was 4.6 mC cm^{-2}. The luminous transmittance of the device decreased from 62.8 to 6.1 (see **Figure 15**) giving a contrast ratio value of 10 : 1. The device could be fully bleached by reversing the polarity of the applied current pulses. The CE of the prototype at 550 and 650 nm was as follows: CE$_{550}$ = 42.7 cm^2 C^{-1} and CE$_{650}$ = 54.1 cm^2 C^{-1}.

The environmental impact of such a device has been assessed with use of energy life cycle analysis [75, 126]. The total production energy was found to be 2261 MJ, of which 91% is allocated to the frame, about 7% to fabrication processes, and the remaining 2% to the embodied energy of the raw materials. Various scenarios for EC operation were compared with respect to the induced heating – cooling loads and energy savings. When the EC window prototype was used instead of a single glass in heating-dominated areas and large facades for a maximum expected lifetime of 25 years, the reduction in energy consumption can reach up to 54%, corresponding to 6388 MJ. Based on the conducted analysis, 0.9 years of operation of the prototype window are required to compensate the production energy of the plain EC device. This time period is extended to 8.9 years when the aluminum frame is taken into account, proving its extensive energy contribution. The total cost savings range from €228 to €569 m^{-2} glass for 10 and 25 years of EC window operation, respectively. It was also found that an EC window, implemented in cooling-dominated areas and operated with an optimum control strategy for the maximum expected lifetime (25 years), can reduce the building energy requirements by 52%. Furthermore, the total energy savings provided will be 33 times more than the energy required for its production while the emission of 615 kg CO$_2$ equivalent per EC glazing unit can be avoided. The reduction of the purchase cost (to €200 m^{-2}) and the increase of the lifetime (above 15 years) were found to be the two main targets for achieving both cost and environmental efficiency.

3.10.7.6   Photoelectrochromics

A less developed and very promising category of devices is that of photoelectrochromics (PECs thereafter). They were first presented by Bechinger *et al.* [127] and Gregg [128] as electrochemical cells consisting of two electrodes separated by a redox electrolyte, an EC, and a dye-sensitized PV one, the latter powering the coloration of the former, in response to the incoming solar radiation. Later, it has been realized that in the above configuration, coloration and bleaching are competing processes, and as a result, such devices

Table 3 Properties of materials for electrochromic devices

	Material	Method of preparation	Thickness (nm)	Type of coloration	Charge capacity ($mC\,cm^{-2}$)	Luminous transmittance (%) (Bleached/colored)	Stability durability
Electrochromic layer	WO_3	e-gun, sputtering, chemical methods (sol–gel, electrodeposition)	350–500	Cathodic	20–40	80/10	Stable, more than 5 000 voltammetric cycles
	MoO_3	Thermal evaporation, sputtering, chemical methods	300–400	Cathodic	~20	85/20	Unstable above 5 000 cycles
	Prussian Blue	Chemical methods, mostly electrodeposition	300–600	Anodic, also used as IS layer	~20	70/10	Stable up to 20 000 cycles, degrades at rest
Transparent conductor	SnO_2:F (TFO)	Spray pyrolysis	>1000	NA	NA	~90	Hard coating, stable up to 350 °C
	In_2O_3:Sn (ITO)	Spray pyrolysis	>1000	NA	NA	~90	Hard coating, stable up to 350 °C
	ZnS/Ag/ZnS	e-gun, sputtering	40/10/40	NA	NA	~85	Soft coating, stable up to 259 °C, optical interference problems
Ion storage-protective layer	V_2O_5	e-gun, sputtering, chemical methods	300–500	Anodic	30 (maximum)	70/60	Stable up to 500 °C, degrade with moisture, unstable due to phase transitions
	CeO_2	e-gun, sputtering, chemical methods	150–500	Passive	10	90	Stable
	CeO_2-TiO_2	Sputtering, chemical methods	150–450	Passive	20–50	80	10% reduction of charge capacity after 300 cycles
	NiO	Sputtering (low yield), chemical methods	200–400	Anodic	1	70/50	Stable up to 1 200 cycles
	MgF_2	e-gun, sputtering, chemical methods	150–200	Passive	5	95	Stable, optically neutral

NA, Not applicable

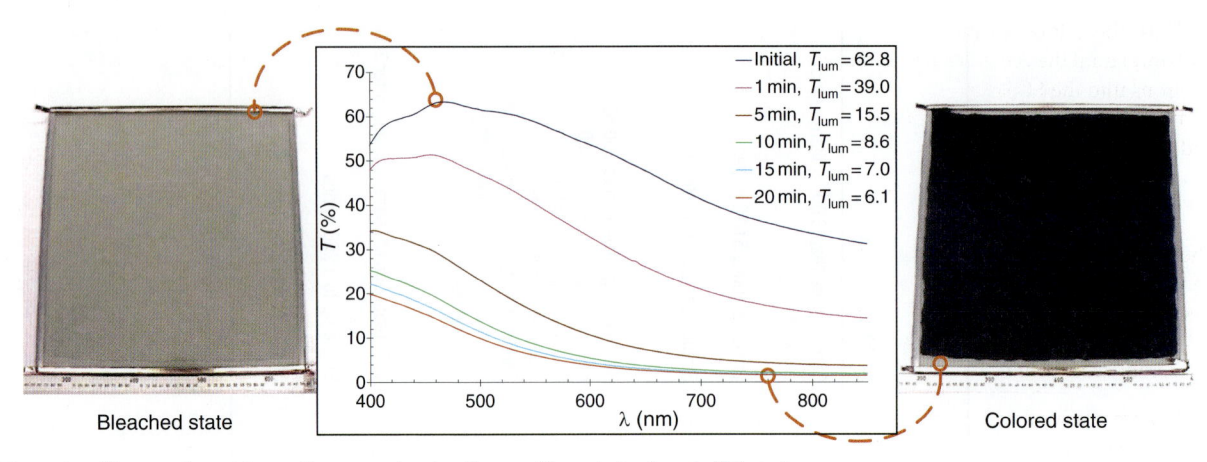

Figure 15 Photographs and transmittance spectra of a 40 cm × 40 cm electrochromic (EC) device.

exhibit limited coloration and slow bleaching [129]. A different configuration with both EC and PV layers on one electrode (as shown in **Figure 16**) has been proposed to enhance the device performance [129, 130].

A typical layout of such a device is shown in **Figure 16** and consists of the following:

1. A glass coated with a transparent conductive oxide (TCO; such as SnO_2:F or ITO)
2. An EC layer (usually WO_3) of optical quality
3. A nanostructured wide band gap semiconductor film (usually TiO_2) sensitized by an appropriate dye
4. An electrolyte with high ionic and low electronic conductivity that contains a redox couple (such as I^-/I_3^-) and Li ions
5. A counterelectrode consisting of a TCO with a thin Pt layer.

Parts 1, 3, 4, and 5 of the above device comprise a dye-sensitized solar cell that is used to provide the electrical potential and electronic charge required to cause coloration of the EC layer. The coloration and bleaching sequences of a PEC device involve six different processes as shown (in parentheses) in **Figure 16**. Indeed, upon radiation, incident light on the sensitized TiO_2 surface absorbed by the dye excites the dye molecules from the ground state to an excited state (1). Electrons of sufficient energy are injected into the TiO_2 conduction band (2) and are then transferred in the conduction band of WO_3. Lithium ions intercalate into the WO_3 layer (3) in order to keep the charge balance. Intercalation of Li ions and electrons results in the coloration of the WO_3 film (eqn [25]). Coloration is possible only under open circuit.

Ionized dye molecules are reduced by iodide ions according to the reaction [131]:

$$2S^+ + 3I^- \Rightarrow 2S^0 + I_3^- \qquad [30]$$

with S^0, S^+ the ground and ionized state of the dye molecule, respectively.

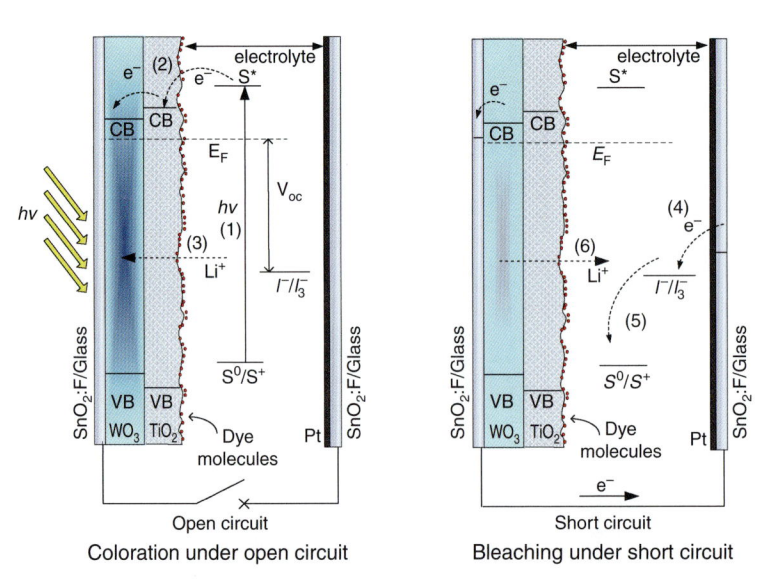

Figure 16 Layout and operation of a typical photoelectrochromic (PEC) device.

Thus, the coloration process can go on until either all iodide ions in the electrolyte are transformed to triiodide or (most probably) until the generated photovoltage equals the electromotive force (EMF) of the Li$_x$WO$_3$ film preventing further diffusion of electrons into the EC layer.

Under short circuit in the dark, electrons flow through the external circuit and reduce the triiodide ions at the counterelectrode, with the reaction being catalyzed by the Pt layer (4):

$$I_3^- + 2e^- \overset{(Pt)}{\Rightarrow} 3I^- \qquad [31]$$

Then, the iodide ions move from the counterelectrode to the TiO$_2$ surface and reduce the ionized dye molecules (5), according to eqn [30]. In this way, triiodide ions are produced at the dye/electrolyte interface and are consumed at the electrolyte/counterelectrode interface. Lithium ions are transferred back to the electrolyte and the WO$_3$ film is bleached.

Compared to ECs, the PEC devices are considerably more complicated. They possess, however, several advantages that make their study worthwhile:

- They are passive devices that do not require external power for their operation.
- Unlike EC windows, the speed of coloration and bleaching does not depend on the device area, but only on the internal electrical field generated by the PV unit. Thus, coloration times realized by small laboratory samples are also applicable to large-area windows.
- As these devices incorporate solar cells, they can also produce electricity acting as semitransparent PVs.
- By proper combination of the EC and semiconductor layer thickness, various colors (apart from the well-known WO$_3$ blue) can be obtained during coloration, as can be seen in **Figure 17**, in which appear the chromaticity diagrams for EC and PEC devices.

Unlike ECs, PEC devices are still at an early stage in their development. Until now, there are no commercial PEC products. Only experimental laboratory samples and demonstration prototypes have been reported in the literature with dimensions up to $10 \times 10\,cm^2$ [131–137]. There are still quite a few obstacles to be overcome before PECs can find their way to commercial applications:

- PECs exhibit a limited transmittance in the visible $T_{lum} = 51$–62% mostly due to the intense absorption of the dye in that part of the spectrum.
- They do not exhibit sufficient endurance to continuous cycling (less than 1000 coloration bleaching cycles). This can be caused by degradation of the PV cells or by side reactions taking place into the electrolyte.
- They exhibit poor at-rest stability and gradually degrade after about 50 days of storage.

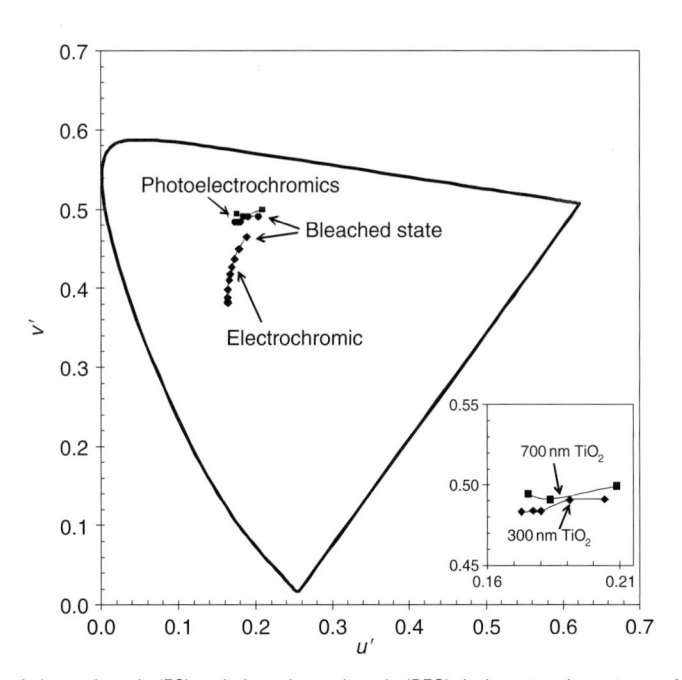

Figure 17 Chromaticity diagram of electrochromic (EC) and photoelectrochromic (PEC) devices at various stages of coloration. (Inset) Different color coordinates for PEC devices with different TiO$_2$ layers, make color tailoring possible.

3.10.7.7 Gasochromics

Gasochromic devices consist of an EC film (such as WO_3) deposited directly on glass (no TC is required here) [131]. On top of the EC film, an ultrathin layer of an appropriate catalyst, such as Pt, is added. For the coloration of gasochromic devices a flow of H_2 gas is needed. The hydrogen molecules are adsorbed onto the film surface, they are dissolved into H atoms by the catalyst, they are further ionized to form protons and electrons at the Pt/WO_3 interface, and they finally diffuse into the oxide matrix. Electrons lead to a reduction of tungsten and to coloration, while protons are believed to react with oxygen to form water and create oxygen vacancies in WO_3. The films are bleached by fluxing them with oxygen, Ar, or Ar–O_2 mixtures so as to remove hydrogen and to restore the oxygen vacancies.

A similar behavior has also been observed for lanthanides (Y, La, Ce, Pr, Nd, Sm, Eu, Gd, Tb, Dy, Ho, Er, Tm, Yb, and Lu) as well as for palladium-coated magnesium lanthanide alloys. These materials exhibit the 'switchable mirror effect' discovered accidentally by Griessen and co-workers, during their quest for high critical temperature (T_c) superconductors [138]. They reversibly go through an optical transition by variation of the hydrogen concentration and exhibit three different optical states: a color-neutral transparent state at high hydrogen concentration, a nontransparent dark absorbing state at intermediate hydrogen pressures, and a highly reflective metallic state at low hydrogen pressures. The ratio in transmission between the transparent state and the reflecting state is more than 1000 [139]. Such materials could also serve as gasochromic films.

The attractive element in gasochromics is their simplicity. They do away with TCs, electrolytes, IS layers, and counterelectrodes that are necessary in ECs and PECs. Favorable performance characteristics have been reported for such devices [140]: Switching times below 10 s, a range in the solar transmittance of 72–5%, and endurance of 10 000 cycles. The major disadvantage of gasochromics is the very method used for their coloration. Indeed, windows with gas inlets and outlets are rather awkward, and can be used in special applications only. The authors believe that it is very difficult for them to gain acceptance in the domestic sector. Furthermore, the use of hydrogen (a combustible gas) gives rise to safety concerns.

3.10.7.8 Thermochromics

Thermochromic materials undergo a structural transformation at a certain T_c that affects their optical properties. The most common material is vanadium dioxide, VO_2. This oxide exists under six crystallographic structures. One of these allotropic varieties is characterized by a thermochromic transition, associated with a first-order monoclinic to tetragonal reversible structural change at $T_c = 68\,°C$ [141]. Below T_c, the structure is monoclinic, which is semiconducting with a small gap of 0.7 eV and relatively nonabsorbing in the IR. Above T_c, the structure transforms to a metallic tetragonal one, which is reflective in the IR. This property of VO_2 could be applied for the production of switchable glazing that become reflective above a T_c, thus rejecting the incident solar energy during hot summer days. However, as the switching control is effectively 'built-in' the material, there is little room for control by the user. Taking into account that the temperature of 68 °C is too high for practical applications, the research effort in this field has been directed toward lowering the T_c. This can be achieved by replacement of some vanadium in VO_2 by other metals (W, Mo, Rh, etc.) or by replacement of some oxygen by fluorine. Mixing of VO_2 with other compounds (CeO_2–VO_2) is also an option. Thermochromics are still in the materials development stage, although Pleotint LLC (www.pleotint.com) has come up with a thermochromic glazing named 'SRT'.

3.10.7.9 Metal Hydride Switchable Mirrors

These materials function in much the same way as the lanthanides described in the section Gasochromics, with the difference that ions are inserted or extracted through an electrolyte with the application of an electric potential and that Li^+ is used instead of H^+. Metal hydride switchable mirrors are based on rare earths and their alloys, or on mixtures of magnesium and transition metals [142]. Typical representatives of this family are antimony and bismuth, which exhibit very high reflectance modulation due to lithiation in the visible and substantial in the near-IR range, as well as high transmittance modulation at all wavelengths above the absorption edge. The most transparent state corresponds to Li_3Sb. Similar performance was achieved with Bi films. Li_3Sb is yellow-green and Li_3Bi is yellow in transmitted light. Addition of other metals in the structure can improve performance. The metals (Cu or Ag) take the place of lithium, resulting in Li_2MSb, for example, where M = Cu or Ag, reducing the amount of lithium required for switching and decreasing the resulting volume expansion of the material [143].

In a similar way, copper and its oxides produce a system with reflective, transparent, and highly absorbing states. Cu_2O can be transformed reversibly to opaque metallic copper films when reduced in an alkaline electrolyte. In addition, the same Cu_2O films transform reversibly to black copper(II) oxide when cycled at more anodic potentials. Copper oxide-to-copper switching covers a large dynamic range, from 85% to 10% luminous transmittance, with a CE of about 32 $cm^2\,C^{-1}$ [144].

All of the above systems suffer from gradual degradation with cycling, mainly due to the large volume expansion they undergo during lithiation and the corresponding stress imposed on the films. For example, during conversion of Cu to Cu_2O, a 65% volume change takes place [143]. These devices are still under development with no commercial products available.

3.10.7.10 Other Switching Devices

There are many more families of switching devices, intended for uses other than solar control (displays or privacy glass). They are presented next, for completeness and because some of them could eventually spill over into the dynamic solar control market.

3.10.7.10.1 Suspended particle devices

In suspended particle devices (SPDs), a thin film laminate of rodlike particles suspended in a fluid is placed between two glass or plastic layers. When no voltage is applied, the suspended particles are arranged in random orientations and tend to absorb light, so that the glass panel looks dark (or opaque), blue, or, in more recent developments, gray or black. When voltage is applied, the suspended particles align and let light pass. SPDs can be dimmed, and allow instant control of the amount of light passing through. A small but constant electrical current is required for keeping the SPD device in its transparent stage. SPD devices have typical transmission ranges of 0.79–0.49 and 0.50–0.04, a switching time of 100–200 ms, and require 65–220 VAC (volt alternating current) to operate [104].

3.10.7.10.2 Polymer-dispersed liquid crystal devices

In these devices, liquid crystals are dissolved or dispersed into a liquid polymer. Solidification or curing of the polymer follows, during which the liquid crystals become incompatible with the solid polymer and form droplets throughout the solid polymer. The polymer is sandwiched between two glass sheets coated with transparent electrodes. With no applied voltage, the liquid crystals are randomly arranged in the droplets, resulting in scattering of light as it passes through the smart window assembly. This results in the translucent, 'milky white' appearance. When a voltage is applied to the electrodes, the electric field formed between the two transparent electrodes on the glass causes the liquid crystals to align, allowing light to pass through the droplets with very little scattering and resulting in a transparent state. The degree of transparency can be controlled by the applied voltage. This is possible because at lower voltages, only a few of the liquid crystals align completely in the electric field, so only a small portion of the light passes through while most of the light is scattered. As the voltage is increased, fewer liquid crystals remain out of alignment, resulting in less light being scattered. Most of the devices offered today commercially operate in on or off states only, even though the technology to provide for variable levels of transparency is easily applied. Large-area windows are available in sizes up to $1.0 \times 2.8\,m^2$, and operate between 24 and 120 V [104]. This technology has been used in interior and exterior settings for privacy control (e.g., conference rooms, intensive-care areas, bathroom/shower doors) and as a temporary projection screen. It has been marketed under the name of '3G Switchable Film/Glass' and 'Polyvision Privacy Glass'. New generation nanotechnology switchable films with improved transparency are offered by Polytronix Inc. and Scienstry, with working voltages lowered to the 12–48 VAC range; the lower driving voltage could extend life expectancy to some extent. However, the devices require continuous power resulting in a power consumption of 5 up to $20\,W\,m^{-2}$, while their long-term UV stability and their high cost are still issues to be resolved.

3.10.7.10.3 Micro-blinds

Micro-blinds control the amount of light passing through in response to applied voltage. They are composed of rolled thin metal blinds on glass. They are very small and thus practically invisible to the eye. The metal layer is deposited by magnetron sputtering and patterned by laser or lithography process. The glass substrate includes a thin layer of a TCO layer. A thin insulator is deposited between the rolled metal layer and the TCO layer for electrical disconnection. With no applied voltage, the micro-blinds are rolled and let light pass through. When there is a potential difference between the rolled metal layer and the transparent conductive layer, the electric field formed between the two electrodes causes the rolled micro-blinds to stretch out and thus block light. The micro-blinds have several advantages including switching speed (milliseconds), UV durability, customized appearance, and transmission. The micro-blinds are currently under development. Commercial products are expected to emerge soon.

3.10.7.11 Conclusions – Epilogue

It has been demonstrated in this part that there is a large variety of chromogenic materials at different degrees of maturity. Others have found their way to the markets, while others are unlikely to ever leave the laboratory bench. Chromogenic devices are believed to become the smart windows of tomorrow and to eventually dominate the fenestration market, much as float low-e glass is a standard today. Their widespread use in buildings could improve living conditions of inhabitants, reduce the building energy consumption – both for cooling and for artificial lighting – and have a positive environmental impact.

References

[1] http://en.wikipedia.org/wiki/Window and related links in this site.
[2] Kondrashov VI, Fainberg EV, and Bezlyudnaya VS (2000) Development of float process in sheet glass production. *Glass and Ceramics* 57: 195–198.
[3] http://en.wikipedia.org/wiki/Float glass and related links in this site.
[4] Pilkington LAB (1969) Review lecture. The float glass process. *Proceedings of the Royal Society of London. Series A, Mathematical and Physical Sciences* 314(1516): 1–25.
[5] Duffie JA and Beckman WA (1991) *Solar Engineering of Thermal Processes*, 2nd edn. USA: Wiley.
[6] Kalogirou S (2009) *Solar Energy Engineering: Processes and Systems*, . USA: Academic Press, Elsevier ScienceISBN: 978-0-12-374501-9.
[7] Leftheriotis G, Yianoulis P, and Patrikios D (1997) Deposition and optical properties of optimized ZnS/Ag/ZnS thin films for energy saving applications. *Thin Solid Films* 306: 92.
[8] Leftheriotis G and Yianoulis P (1999) Characterization and stability of low emittance multiple coatings for glazing applications. *Solar Energy Materials and Solar Cells* 58: 185–197.
[9] Griffiths PW, Di Leo M, Cartwright P, *et al.* (1998) Fabrication of evacuated glazing at low temperatures. *Solar Energy* 63: 243–249.
[10] Hecht E (1987) *Optics*, 2nd edn.. Reading, MA: Addison–Wesley, ISBN 0-201-11609-X.

[11] Arasteh DK, Reilly MS, and Rubin MD (1989) A versatile procedure for calculating heat transfer through windows. *ASHRAE Transactions* 95(2): 755–765.
[12] Raithby GD and Hollands KGT (1998) Natural convection. In: Rohsenhow WM, Hartnett JP, and Cho YI (eds.) *Handbook of Heat Transfer*, 3rd edn., pp. 4.40–4.62. New York, NY: McGraw-Hill.
[13] ASHRAE (2001) *Fundamentals Handbook*, . US: ASHRAEISBN 1-883413-88-5.
[14] Gordon J (ed.) (2001) *Solar Energy: The State of the Art*, ch. 2: *Glazing and Coatings*, pp. 29–107. Germany: International Solar Energy Society.
[15] Granqvist CG (2007) Transparent conductors as solar energy materials: A panoramic review. *Solar Energy Materials and Solar Cells* 91: 1529–1598.
[16] Rancourt JD (1996) *Optical Thin Films: User Handbook*, vol. PM37. Bellingham, USA: SPIE Press.
[17] Pulker HK (1999) *Coatings on Glass*, 2nd edn. Amsterdam, The Netherlands: Elsevier.
[18] Kaiser N and Pulker HK (eds.) (2003) *Optical Interference Coatings*. Berlin, Germany: Springer.
[19] Bunshah RF, Blocher JM Jr., Bonifield TD, *et al.* (1982) *Deposition Technologies for Films and Coatings*. Park Ridge, USA: Noyes.
[20] Smith DL (1995) *Thin-Film Deposition*. New York, NY: McGraw-Hill.
[21] Mahan JE (2000) *Physical Vapor Deposition of Thin Films*. New York, NY: Wiley.
[22] Wasa K and Hayakawa S (1992) *Handbook of Sputter Deposition Technology*. Park Ridge, USA: Noyes.
[23] Klein LC (ed.) (1994) *Sol–Gel Optics: Processing and Applications*. Dordrecht, The Netherlands: Kluwer.
[24] Morosanu CE (1990) *Thin Films by Chemical Vapour Deposition*. Amsterdam, The Netherlands: Elsevier Science.
[25] Pierson HO (1999) *Handbook of Chemical Vapor Deposition: Principles, Technology, and Applications*, 2nd edn. Park Ridge, USA: Noyes.
[26] Berning PH (1983) Principles of design of architectural coatings. *Applied Optics* 22: 4127–4141.
[27] Granqvist CG (1985) Spectrally selective coatings for energy efficiency and solar applications. *Physica Scripta* 32: 401.
[28] Lee CC, Chen S, and Jaing C (1996) Optical monitoring of silver-based transparent heat mirrors. *Applied Optics* 35: 5698.
[29] Ando E and Miyazaki M (1999) Moisture degradation mechanism of silver-based low-emissivity coatings. *Thin Solid Films* 351: 308–312.
[30] Gläser HJ (2008) History of the development and industrial production of low thermal emissivity coatings for high heat insulating glass units. *Applied Optics* 47(13): C193, C199.
[31] Grosse P, Hertling R, and Müggenburg T (1997) Design of low-E systems based on three layer coating. *Journal of Non-Crystalline Solids* 218: 38–43.
[32] de Jong BHWS (2010) Glass. *Ullmann's Encyclopedia of Industrial Chemistry*, 7th edn., ISBN 9783527306782, vol. A12, pp. 365–432. Weinheim, Germany: VCH Publishers.
[33] Rawson H (1974) Physics of glass manufacturing processes. *Physics in Technology* 5: 91–114.
[34] Pfaender HG (1996) *Schott Guide to Glass*. New York, NY: Chapman and Hall.
[35] O'Block RL, Donnermeyer JF, and Doeren SE (1991) *Security and Crime Prevention*. Stoneham, MA: Butterworth-Heinemann.
[36] Walecki W and Szondy F (2008) Integrated quantum efficiency, topography, and stress metrology for solar cell manufacturing: real space approach. *Proceedings of SPIE* 7048: 704804.
[37] Bahaj ABS, Patrick PAB, and James MF (2008) Potential of emerging glazing technologies for highly glazed buildings in hot arid climates. *Energy and Buildings* 40: 720–731.
[38] Chow T.-tai, Li C, and Lin Z (2010) Innovative solar windows for cooling-demand climate. *Solar Energy Materials and Solar Cells* 94: 212–220.
[39] Werner A and Roos A (2003) Simulations of coatings to avoid external condensation on low U-value windows. *Optical Materials* 30: 968–978.
[40] Singh MC, Garg SN, and Jha R (2008) Different glazing systems and their impact on human thermal comfort – Indian scenario. *Building and Environment* 43: 1596–1602.
[41] Nilsson AM and Roos A (2009) Evaluation of optical and thermal properties of coatings for energy efficient windows. *Thin Solid Films* 517: 3173–3177.
[42] Roos A and Karlsson B (1994) Optical and thermal characterization of multiple glazed windows with low U-values. *Solar Energy* 52(4): 315–325.
[43] Zhao X, Zhao Q, Yu J, and Liu B (2008) Development of multifunctional photoactive self-cleaning glasses. *Journal of Non-Crystalline Solids* 354: 1424–1430.
[44] Brook LA, Evans P, Foster HA, *et al.* (2007) Novel multifunctional films. *Surface and Coatings Technology* 201: 9373–9377.
[45] Fujishima A and Honda K (1972) Electrochemical photolysis of water at a semiconductor electrode. *Nature* 238: 37–38.
[46] Manz H (2008) On minimizing heat transport in architectural glazing. *Renewable Energy* 33: 119–128.
[47] http://www.efficientwindows.org.
[48] Garvin SL and Wilson J (1998) Environmental conditions in window frames with double-glazing units. *Construction and Building Materials* 12: 289–302.
[49] Gustavsen A, Petter Jelle B, Arasteh D, and Kohler C (2007) *State-of-the-Art Highly Insulating Window Frames – Research and Market Review*, Project report no 6. Oslo, Norway: SINTEF Building and Infrastructure.
[50] Mitchell R, Kohler C, Arasteh D, *et al.* (2006) THERM 5.2/WINDOW 5.2 NFRC Simulation Manual, (LBNL-48255), Berkeley, USA. Available from http://windows.lbl.gov/software/NFRC/NFRCSim5.2-2006-Cover-Chptr01.pdf.
[51] http://windows.lbl.gov/software/software.html.
[52] Benson DK, Smith LK, Tracy CE, *et al.* (1990) Vacuum window glazing for energy-efficient buildings. *Internal Report SERI/TP-212-3684*, Solar Energy Research Institute. Golden, Colorado, USA: National Renewable Energy Laboratory.
[53] Clugston DA and Collins: RE (1994) Pump down of evacuated glazing. *Journal of Vacuum Science and Technology A* 12(1 Jan/Feb): 241–247.
[54] Polder D and Van Hove M (1971) Theory of radiative heat transfer between closely space bodies. *Physical Review B* 4: 3303.
[55] Collins RE and Robinson SJ (1991) Evacuated glazing. *Solar Energy* 47: 27–38.
[56] Collins RE, Davis CA, Dey CJ, *et al.* (1993) Measurement of local heat-flow in flat evacuated glazing. *International Journal of Heat and Mass Transfer* 36: 2553–2563.
[57] Collins RE, Simko T, Wilson C, *et al.* (1997) Final Report of Project B5: Evacuated Glazing. International Energy Agency, Solar Heating and Cooling Programme, Task 18 Advanced Glazings, T18/B5/FPR/97.
[58] Granqvist CG (1989) Materials for energy efficient windows. *Proceedings of the Workshop on Materials Science and the Physics of Non-Conventional Energy Sources*. September, Trieste, Italy: ICTP.
[59] Johnson TE (1991) *Low-e Glazing Design Guide*. Stoneham, MA: Butterworth-Heinemann.
[60] Leftheriotis G, Papaefthimiou S, and Yianoulis P (2000) Development of multilayer transparent conductive coatings. *Solid State Ionics* 136–137: 655–661.
[61] Jones EA and van der Sluijs JCA (1972) On indium seals in low temperature devices. *Cryogenics* 12: 135–136.
[62] Kh KV (1973) A low temperature indium seal. *Cryogenics* 13: 732–733.
[63] Agarwal KL and Betterton JO Jr. (1974) On low temperature indium seals. *Cryogenics* 14: 520–521.
[64] Lipsett FR (1966) Cold welded indium low temperature window seal. *Review of Scientific Instruments* 37: 229.
[65] Lim CC (1986) Indium seals for low-temperature and moderate-pressure applications. *Review of Scientific Instruments* 57: 108–114.
[66] Saeki H, Ikeda J, and Ishimaru H (1989) Optical window sealed with indium for ultrahigh vacuum. *Vacuum* 39: 563–564.
[67] Shuvalov AS and Filatovskii LA (1979) Fabrication of indium seals by prepressing. *Instrumentation and Experimental Techniques* 22: 1177–1178.
[68] Vos J and Kingma R (1967) Helium-II-tight high pressure seal for optical windows. *Cryogenics* 7: 50–51.
[69] Turkington RR and Harris-Lowe RF (1984) Note on the design of simple indium O-ring seals. *Review of Scientific Instruments* 55: 803–805.
[70] Neuhausen RG (1979) Pressure-made soft-metal vacuum seals for glass and ceramics. *Vacuum* 29: 231–235.
[71] Lewis BG (1995) *Sealing Vacuum and Cryogenic Components with Indium*. pp. 21–23. Lexington, MA: CryoGas International.
[72] Eames PC and Norton B (1993) A validated unified model for optics and heat transfer in line-axis concentrating solar energy collectors. *Solar Energy* 50: 339–355.
[73] Patanker SV (1980) *Numerical Heat Transfer and Fluid Flow*. New York, NY: Hemisphere.
[74] Papaefthimiou S, Leftheriotis G, Yianoulis P, *et al.* (2006) Development of electrochromic evacuated advanced glazing. *Energy and Buildings* 38: 1455–1467.
[75] Syrrakou E, Papaefthimiou S, and Yianoulis P (2006) Eco-efficiency evaluation of a smart window prototype. *Science of the Total Environment* 359: 267–282.

[76] Goetzberger A, Schmid J, and Wittwer V (1984) Transparent insulation system for passive solar energy utilization in buildings. *International Journal of Solar Energy* 2: 289–308.
[77] Goetzberger A, Dengler J, Rommel M, *et al.* (1992) A new transparently insulated bifacially irradiated solar flat-plate collector. *Solar Energy* 49: 403–411.
[78] Nahar NM (2001) Design, development and testing of a double reflector hot box solar cooker with a transparent insulation material. *Renewable Energy* 23: 167–179.
[79] Platzer WJ (1992) Directional-hemispherical solar transmittance data for plastic honeycomb-type structures. *Solar Energy* 49/5: 359–370.
[80] Platzer WJ (1992) Total heat transport data for plastic honeycomb-type structures. *Solar Energy* 49/5: 359–370.
[81] Rubin M and Lampert CM (1983) Transparent silica aerogels for window insulation. *Solar Energy Materials* 7: 393–400.
[82] Stangl R, Platzer WJ, and Wittwer V (1994) New methods of characterizing the thermal properties of silica aerogel/xerogel. *Proceeding of SPIE International Symposium on Optical Material Technology for Energy Efficiency and Solar Energy Conversion XIII*, Freiburg, Germany, 18–22 April.
[83] Caps R, Döll G, Fricke J, *et al.* (1989) Thermal transport in monolithic silica aerogel. *Proceedings of the 3rd International Symposium on Aerogels, Physics Applied* C4/4: 113–120.
[84] Einarsrud M-A, Hæreid S, and Wittwer V (1993) Some thermal and optical properties of a new transparent silica xerogel material with low density. *Solar Energy Materials and Solar Cells* 31/3: 341–348.
[85] Buchberg H and Edwards DK (1976) Design considerations for solar collectors with cylindrical glass honeycombs. *Solar Energy* 18: 193–203.
[86] Diehm W and Jaeger L (1993) First results on the development and production of glass capillaries for TI applications. In: Jesch L (ed.) *Proceedings of TI6*, Birmingham, pp. 118–121, 3–5 June.
[87] Perincioli L and Mühlethaler F (1993) Using glass capillaries as TIM. In: Jesch L (ed.) *Proceeding of TI6*, Birmingham, pp. 122–125, 3–5 June.
[88] Florides G, Tassou S, Kalogirou S, and Wrobel L (2002) Measures used to lower building energy consumption and their cost effectiveness. *Applied Energy* 73(3–4): 299–328.
[89] Deb SK (2008) *Solar Energy Materials and Solar Cells* 92: 245.
[90] http://www.econtrol-glas.de/en/econtrol-minusglass/product-description/
[91] Lee ES, Yazdanian M, and Selkowitz SE (2004) The energy-savings potential of electrochromic windows in the US commercial buildings sector. *LBNL-54966 Report*, April 30, Available from http://gaia.lbl.gov/btech/papers/54966.pdf.
[92] Selkowitz SE, Rubin M, Lee ES, and Sullivan R (1994) A review of electrochromic window performance factors. Presented at the *SPIE International Symposium on Optical Materials Technology for Solar Energy Conversion XIII*, Freiburg, Germany.
[93] Mardaljevic J and Nabil A (2008) *Lighting Research and Technology* 40: 55–72.
[94] Nagai J, McMeeking GD, and Saitoh Y (1999) Durability of electrochromic glazing. *Solar Energy Materials and Solar Cells* 56: 309.
[95] SAGE Electrochromics Inc., wwww.sage-ec.com.
[96] ECLIPSE Energy Systems Inc., http://eclipsethinfilms.com
[97] EControl_technical specifications, available from http://www.econtrol-glas.de/fileadmin/user_upload/PDF/EControl_technical_specifications_20100901.pdf
[98] Schirmer OF, Wittwer V, Bauer G, and Brandt G (1977) Dependence of WO_3 electrochromic absorption on crystallinity. *Journal of the Electrochemical Society* 124: 749.
[99] Zhang J, Benson DK, Tracy CE, *et al.* (1997) Chromic mechanism in amorphous WO_3 films. *Journal of The Electrochemical Society* 144: 2022.
[100] Lee S, Cheong HM, Zhang J, *et al.* (1999) Electrochromic mechanism in $a\text{-}WO_{3-y}$ thin films. *Applied Physics Letters* 74: 242.
[101] Leftheriotis G, Papaefthimiou S, and Yianoulis P (2000) Integrated low emittance-electrochromic devices incorporating ZnS/Ag/ZnS coatings as transparent conductors. *Solar Energy Materials and Solar Cells* 61: 107.
[102] Papaefthimiou S, Leftheriotis G, and Yianoulis P (2001) Advanced electrochromic devices based on WO_3 thin films. *Electrochimica Acta* 46: 2145.
[103] Carpi F and De Rossi D (2006) Colours from electroactive polymers: Electrochromic, electroluminescent and laser devices based on organic materials. *Optics and Laser Technology* 38: 292–305.
[104] Baetens R, Jelle BP, and Gustavsen A (2010) Properties, requirements and possibilities of smart windows for dynamic daylight and solar energy control in buildings: A state-of-the-art review. *Solar Energy Materials and Solar Cells* 94: 87–105.
[105] Granqvist CG (1995) *Handbook of Inorganic Electrochromic Materials*. Amsterdam, The Netherlands: Elsevier Science.
[106] Bathe SR and Patil PS (2007) *Solar Energy Materials and Solar Cells* 91: 1097–1101.
[107] Ortega JM, Martınez AI, Acosta DR, and Magana CR (2006) Structural and electrochemical studies of WO_3 films deposited by pulsed spray pyrolysis. *Solar Energy Materials and Solar Cells* 90: 2471–2479.
[108] Patil PS, Nikam SB, and Kadam LD (2001) Influence of substrate temperature on the properties of sprayed WO_3 thin films. *Materials Chemistry and Physics* 69: 77–83.
[109] Livage J and Ganguli D (2001) Sol-gel electrochromic coatings and devices. A review. *Solar Energy Materials and Solar Cells* 98: 365–381.
[110] Leftheriotis G, Papaefthimiou S, Yianoulis P, *et al.* (2003) Structural and electrochemical properties of opaque sol-gel deposited WO_3 layers. *Applied Surface Science* 218: 275–280.
[111] Yang B, Li H, Blackford M, and Luca V (2006) Novel low density mesoporous WO_3 films prepared by electrodeposition. *Current Applied Physics* 6: 436–439.
[112] Zhong Q and Colbow K (1991) Electrochromic properties of cesium tungstate with pyrochlore structure. *Thin Solid Films* 205: 85–88.
[113] Leftheriotis G and Yianoulis P (2008) Development of electrodeposited WO3 films with modified surface morphology and improved electrochromic properties. *Solid State Ionics* 179: 2192.
[114] Deepa M, Srivastava AK, Sharma SN, *et al.* (2008) Microstructural and electrochromic properties of tungsten oxide thin films produced by surfactant mediated electrodeposition. *Applied Surface Science* 254: 2342–2352.
[115] Yu Z, Jia X, Du J, and Zhang J (2000) Electrochromic WO_3 films prepared by a new electrodeposition method. *Solar Energy Materials and Solar Cells* 64: 55–63.
[116] Srivastava AK, Deepa M, Singh S, *et al.* (2005) Microstructural and electrochromic characteristics of electrodeposited and annealed WO_3 films. *Solid State Ionics* 176: 1161–1168.
[117] Siokou A, Ntais S, Papaefthimiou S, *et al.* (2004) Influence of the substrate on the electrochromic characteristics of lithiated α-WO3 layers. *Surface Science* 566–568: 1168.
[118] Leftheriotis G, Papaefthimiou S, Yianoulis P, and Siokou A (2001) Effect of the tungsten oxidation states in the thermal coloration and bleaching of amorphous WO3 films. *Thin Solid Films* 384: 298.
[119] Bartoll J, Jackisch B, Most M, *et al.* (2007) Vogtherr: Early Prussian blue. Blue and green pigments in the paintings by Watteau, Lancret and Pater in the collection of Frederick II of Prussia *TECHNE* 25: S39–S46.
[120] Bartoll J (2008) The early use of Prussian blue in paintings. *9th International Conference on NDT of Art*, Jerusalem, Israel, 25–30 May. Retrieved from 22 January 2010 at http://www.ndt.net/article/art2008/papers/029bartoll.pdf
[121] Frisch JL (1976) Briefwechsel mit Gottfried Wilhelm Leibniz. In: Fischer LH (ed.) *Berlin, Stankiewicz Buchdruck, 1896*. Hildesheim/New York, NY: Georg Olms Verlag.
[122] Schaefer C, Brauer G, and Szczyrbowski J (1997) Low emissivity coatings on architectural glass. *Surface and Coatings Technology* 93: 37–45.
[123] Neff VD (1978) Electrochemical oxidation and reduction of thin films of prussian blue. *Journal of The Electrochemical Society* 125: 886.
[124] Kuo-Chuan Ho (1999) Cycling and at-rest stabilities of a complementary electrochromic device based on tungsten oxide and Prussian blue thin films. *Electrochimica Acta* 44: 3227–3235.
[125] Cheng K-C, Chen Fu-R, and Kai Ji-J (2007) Electrochromic property of nano-composite Prussian blue based thin film. *Electrochimica Acta* 52: 3330–3335.
[126] Syrrakou E, Papaefthimiou S, and Yianoulis P (2005) Environmental assessment of electrochromic glazing production. *Solar Energy Materials and Solar Cells* 85: 205–240.
[127] Bechinger C, Ferrere S, Zaban A, *et al.* (1996) Photoelectrochromic windows and displays. *Nature* 383: 608–610.
[128] Gregg B (1997) Photoelectrochromic cells and their applications. *Endeavour* 21(2): 52–55.
[129] Hauch A, Georg A, Krašovec UO, and Orel B (2002) Comparison of photoelectrochromic devices with different layer configurations. *Journal of The Electrochemical Society* 149(9): H159–H163.

[130] Hauch A, Georg A, Baumgartner A, et al. (2001) New photoelectrochromic device. *Electrochimica Acta* 46: 2131–2136.
[131] Georg A, Georg A, Graf W, and Wittwer V (2008) Switchable windows with tungsten oxide. *Vacuum* 82: 730–735.
[132] Hsu CY, Lee KM, Huang JH, et al. (2008) A novel photoelectrochromic device with dual application based on poly(3,4-alkylenedioxythiophene) thin film and an organic dye. *Journal of Power Sources* 185: 1505–1508.
[133] Krašovec UO, Topic M, Georg A, et al. (2005) Preparation and characterisation of nano-structured WO3-TiO2 layers for photoelectrochromic devices. *Journal of Sol-Gel Science and Technology* 36: 45–52.
[134] Georg A and Krašovec UO (2004) New photoelectrochromic window. *Proceedings of the 5th ICCG*, Saarbruecken.
[135] Krašovec UO, Georg A, Georg A, et al. (2004) Performance of a solid-state photoelectrochromic device. *Solar Energy Materials and Solar Cells* 84: 369–380.
[136] Teowee G, Gudgel T, McCarthy K, et al. (1999) User controllable photochromic (UCPC) devices. *Electrochimica Acta* 44: 3017–3026.
[137] Georg A and Krašovec UO (2006) Photoelectrochromic window with Pt catalyst. *Thin Solid Films* 502: 246–251.
[138] Aruna I, Malhotra LK, and Mehta BR (2006) Switchable metal hydride films. In: Gschneidner KA Jr., Bünzli J-CG, and Pecharsky VK (eds.) *Handbook on the Physics and Chemistry of Rare Earths*, ch. 228, vol. 36. Amsterdam, The Netherlands: Elsevier B.V.
[139] van der Sluis P, Ouwerkerk M, and Duine PA (1997) Optical switches based on magnesium lanthanide alloy hydrides. *Applied Physics Letters* 70: 3356–3358.
[140] Georg A, Graf W, Neumann R, and Wittwer V (2000) Mechanism of the gasochromic coloration of porous WO3 films. *Solid State Ionics* 127: 319–328.
[141] Hollands KGT, Wright JL, and Granqvist CG (2001) Glazings and coatings. In: Gordon JM (ed.) *Solar Energy. The State of the Art. ISES Position Papers*, May 2001.
[142] Richardson TJ, Slack JL, Armitage RD, et al. (2001) Switchable mirrors based on nickel-magnesium films. *Applied Physics Letters* 78: 3047. [80: 1349, 2002].
[143] Richardson TJ (2002) New electrochromic mirror systems. *5th International Meeting on Electrochromism*, Golden, CO, August 2002.
[144] Richardson TJ, Slack JL, and Rubin MD (2001) Electrochromism in copper oxide thin films. *Electrochimica Acta*. 46: 2281.

Further Reading

[1] Advances in Window Technology: 1973–1993, Aresteh D, Lawrence Berkeley Laboratory, LBL-36891, 1995. Available from http://gaia.lbl.gov/btech/papers/36891.pdf.
[2] Aruna I, Malhotra LK, and Mehta BR (2006) Switchable metal hydride films. In: Gschneidner KA Jr., Bünzli J-CG, and Pecharsky VK (eds.) *Handbook on the Physics and Chemistry of Rare Earths*, ch. 228, vol. 36. Amsterdam, The Netherlands: Elsevier B.V.
[3] ASHRAE (2001) *Handbook of Fundamentals*. Atlanta, GA: ASHRAE.
[4] Baetens R, Jelle BP, and Gustavsen A (2010) Properties, requirements and possibilities of smart windows for dynamic daylight and solar energy control in buildings: A state-of-the-art review. *Solar Energy Materials and Solar Cells* 94: 87–105.
[5] Bange K (1999) Colouration of tungsten oxide lms: A model for optically active coatings. *Solar Energy Materials and Solar Cells* 58: 1–131.
[6] Çengel YA (2003) *Heat Transfer: A Practical Approach*, 2nd edn., pp. 489–499. New York, NY: McGraw-Hill.
[7] Deb SK (2008) Opportunities and challenges in science and technology of WO_3 for electrochromic and related applications. *Solar Energy Materials and Solar Cells* 92: 245–258.
[8] Duffie JA and Beckman WA (1991) *Solar Engineering of Thermal Processes*, 2nd edn. USA: Wiley.
[9] Gläser HJ (2008) History of the development and industrial production of low thermal emissivity coatings for high heat insulating glass units. *Applied Optics* 47(13): C193, C199.
[10] Gordon J (ed.) (2001) *Solar Energy: The State of the Art*. Germany: International Solar Energy Society.
[11] Granqvist CG (1995) *Handbook of Inorganic Electrochromic Materials*. Amsterdam, Netherlands: Elsevier Science.
[12] Granqvist CG (2004) Solar energy materials. In: Cleveland CJ, (eds.) *Encyclopedia of Energy*, vol. 3, pp. 845–858. Oxford, UK: Elsevier.
[13] Granqvist CG (2007) Transparent conductors as solar energy materials: A panoramic view. *Solar Energy Materials and Solar Cells* 91: 1529–1598.
[14] Granqvist CG (2006) Solar energy materials. *Kirk-Othmer Encyclopedia of Chemical Technology*, 5th edn., vol. 23, pp. 1–32. Hoboken, USA: Wiley.
[15] Gustavsen A, Jelle BP, Arasteh D, and Kohler C (2007) S*tate-of-the-Art Highly Insulating Window Frames – Research and Market Review, Project report no 6*, Oslo, Norway: SINTEF Building and Infrastructure.
[16] Kalogirou S (2009) *Solar Energy Engineering: Processes and Systems*, ch. 2. USA: Academic Press, Elsevier Science. ISBN: 978-0-12-374501-9.
[17] Klein LC (ed.) (1994) *Sol–Gel Optics: Processing and Applications*. Dordrecht, The Netherlands: Kluwer.
[18] Muneer T 2000 *Windows in Buildings: Thermal, Acoustic, Visual, and Solar Performance*, 1st edn. Oxford, UK: Architectural Press.
[19] Shelby JE 2005 *Introduction to Glass Science and Technology*, 1st edn. Cambridge, UK: The Royal Society of Chemistry.
[20] Standard NFRC (National Fenestration Rating Council) 100: Procedure for determining fenestration product thermal properties. Available from: http://www.nfrc.org/documents/1997_NFRC100.pdf.
[21] Mitchell R, Kohler C, Arasteh D, et al. (2006) THERM 5.2/WINDOWS 5.2 NFRC Simulation Manual (Report LBNL-48255, Berkeley, USA. Available from http://windows.lbl.gov/software/NFRC/NFRCSim5.2-2006-Cover-Chptr01.pdf.

Relevant Websites

Manufacturers of Float and Low-e Glass

http://www.agc-flatglass.eu (former Glaverbel) – AGC Glass Europe
http://www.guardian.com – Gaurdian.
http://www.nsggroup.net – NSG Group.
http://www.pilkington.com – Pilkington.
http://corporateportal.ppg.com – PPG Industries.
http://www.saint-gobain.com – Saint-Gobain.

Manufacturers of Commercial Electrochromic Products

http://www.chromogenics.se – ChromoGenics.
http://eclipsethinfilms.com – Eclipse Energy Systems Inc.
http://www.econtrol-glas.de – Econtrol-Glas.
http://www.gentex.com – Gentex Corporation.
http://www.gesimat.de – GESIMAT.
http://www.sage-ec.com – SAGE Electrochromics Inc.

Manufacturers of Suspended Particle, Liquid Crystal, and Thermochromic Devices

http://www.dreamglass.es – DreamGlass.
http://www.innovativeglasscorp.com – Innovative Glass Corporation.
http://www.pleotint.com – Pleotint LLC.
http://www.refr-spd.com – Research Frontiers Inc.
http://www.SmartGlassinternational.com – SmartGlass International.

Others

http://www.advancedglazings.com – Advanced Glazings.
http://www.efficientwindows.org (Window-frame specifications) – Efficient Windows Collaborative.
http://www.cenerg.ensmp.fr (Education of Architects in Solar Energy and Environment, section 3.1) – Mines ParisTech.
http://windows.lbl.gov (WINDOWS software) – Windows & daylighting.

3.11 Modeling and Simulation of Passive and Active Solar Thermal Systems

A Athienitis, Concordia University, Montreal, QC, Canada
SA Kalogirou, Cyprus University of Technology, Limassol, Cyprus
L Candanedo, Dublin Institute of Technology, Dublin, Ireland

© 2012 Elsevier Ltd. All rights reserved.

3.11.1	Introduction	359
3.11.2	Passive Solar Design Techniques and Systems	359
3.11.2.1	Direct-Gain Modeling	361
3.11.2.1.1	Transient heat conduction and steady-periodic (frequency domain) solution	362
3.11.2.1.2	Building transient response analysis	367
3.11.2.1.3	Simplified analytical direct-gain room model and solution (passive)	369
3.11.3	PV/T Systems and Building-Integrated Photovoltaic/Thermal (BIPV/T) Systems	379
3.11.3.1	Integration of Solar Technologies into the Building Envelope and BIPV/T	379
3.11.3.2	A Simplified Open-Loop PV/T Model	381
3.11.3.3	Transient and Steady-State Models for Open-Loop Air-Based BIPV/T Systems	381
3.11.3.3.1	Air temperature variation within the control volume	383
3.11.3.3.2	Radiative heat transfer	383
3.11.3.3.3	Inlet air temperature effects	383
3.11.3.4	Heat Removal Factor and Thermal Efficiency for Open-Loop BIPV/T Systems	388
3.11.4	Near-Optimal Design of Low-Energy Solar Homes	389
3.11.4.1	Envelope and Passive Solar Design	390
3.11.4.1.1	HVAC and renewable energy systems	391
3.11.4.2	Overview of the Design of Two Net-Zero Energy Solar Homes	394
3.11.5	Active Solar Systems	396
3.11.6	The f-Chart Method	396
3.11.6.1	Performance and Design of Liquid-Based Solar Heating Systems	400
3.11.6.1.1	Storage capacity correction	401
3.11.6.1.2	Collector flow rate correction	401
3.11.6.1.3	Load heat exchanger size correction	401
3.11.6.2	Performance and Design of Air-Based Solar Heating Systems	402
3.11.6.2.1	Pebble-bed storage size correction	402
3.11.6.2.2	Airflow rate correction	402
3.11.6.3	Performance and Design of Solar Service Water Systems	403
3.11.6.4	General Remarks	403
3.11.7	Utilizability Method	404
3.11.7.1	Hourly Utilizability	404
3.11.7.2	Daily Utilizability	406
3.11.7.3	Design of Active Systems with Utilizability Methods	407
3.11.7.3.1	Hourly utilizability	407
3.11.7.3.2	Daily utilizability	408
3.11.8	The $\bar{\Phi}$, f-Chart Method	408
3.11.8.1	Storage Tank Losses Correction	410
3.11.8.2	Heat Exchanger Correction	410
3.11.9	Modeling and Simulation of Solar Energy Systems	410
3.11.9.1	The F-Chart Program	411
3.11.9.2	The TRNSYS Simulation Program	411
3.11.9.3	WATSUN Simulation Program	413
3.11.10	Limitations of Simulations	415
References		415

Nomenclature

A collector exposed area, m^2; collector area, m^2
A_c cross-sectional area, m^2
A_{cv} area of the control volume, m^2
b conditions at bulk temperature
C_{min} minimum capacitance of the two fluid streams in the heat exchanger, W °C^{-1}
c_p specific heat capacity of the air, J kg^{-1} K^{-1}

d tube diameter, m
D_h hydraulic diameter of the cavity, m
E_p electric power, W
f friction factor
F_e emissivity factor, $1/(1/\varepsilon_2 + 1/\varepsilon_3 - 1)$
$F_{plate,insu}$ view factor between plate and insulation
F_R collector heat removal factor
G total incident solar radiation, W m^{-2}
g gravitational acceleration, m s^{-2}
Gr Grashof number, $g\beta(T_w - T_{bulk})D_h^3/v^2$
$\overline{Gr}_b$ Grashof number, $(\varrho_b - \bar{\rho})d^3g/\varrho_b^2$
Gr_q Grashof number based on heat flux q_w, $(g\beta q_w D_h^4)/(v^2 k)$
Gr_x Grashof number based on inlet distance, $x^3 g\beta(T_w - T_{bulk})/v^2$
h hour angle in degrees at the midpoint of each hour, degrees
h_o, h_w exterior/wind convective heat transfer coefficient, W m^{-2} K^{-1}
h_r cavity radiative heat transfer coefficient, W m^{-2} K^{-1}
h_{ro} exterior radiative heat transfer coefficient, W m^{-2} K^{-1}
h_{ss} sunset hour angle, degrees
h'_{ss} sunset hour angle on the tilted surface, degrees
$\overline{H}_t$ monthly average daily total radiation on the tilted collector surface, MJ m^{-2}
h_{cb}, h_{ct} convective heat transfer coefficient in cavity, W m^{-2} K^{-1}
h_{ci} convective heat transfer coefficient in attic, W m^{-2} K^{-1}
I_t total radiation incident on the collector surface per unit area, kJ m^{-2}
k thermal conductivity, W m^{-1} K^{-1}
L length of the channel, m; total heating load during the integration period; monthly heating load or demand, MJ; local latitude, degrees
L_s solar energy supplied to the load, GJ
L_u useful load, GJ
m average mass flow rate, kg s^{-1}
M actual mass of storage capacity, kg
$\dot{m}_a$ actual collector flow rate per square meter of collector area, l s^{-1} m^{-2}
$M_{b,a}$ actual pebble storage capacity per square meter of collector area, m^3 m^{-2}
$M_{b,s}$ standard storage capacity per square meter of collector area, 0.25 m^3 m^{-2}
$\dot{m}_s$ standard collector flow rate per square meter of collector area, l s^{-1} m^{-2}
$M_{w,a}$ actual storage capacity per square meter of collector area, l m^{-2}
$M_{w,s}$ standard storage capacity per square meter of collector area, 75 l m^{-2}
N number of days in a month
N_{DR} diffusivity ratio
N_u Nusselt number, $hD_h k^{-1}$
P_{elect} electrical power per unit area, W m^{-2}
Pe Peclet number, RePr
Pr Prandlt number (v/α)
q_{rad} radiative heat exchange between cavity surfaces per unit area, W m^{-2}

q_{rec} heat recovered in the control volume per unit area, W m^{-2}
q_w heat flux on the wall, W m^{-2}
Qin_{cv} convective heat transfer rate in control volume, W
$Qrad_{cv}$ radiative heat transfer rate in control volume, W
Ra Rayleigh number, $GrPr = g\varrho^2 c_p \beta(T_w - T_{bulk})D_h^3/(\mu k) = g\beta(T_w - T_{bulk})D_h^3/v\alpha$
$\overline{R}_B$ monthly mean beam radiation tilt factor
Re Reynolds number, $\varrho V D_h/\mu$
Re_x Reynolds number based on inlet distance, $\varrho V x/\mu$
R_{insu} insulation R-value, m^2 K W^{-1}
R_{mix} combined thermal resistance, m^2 K W^{-1}
$R_{plywood}$ plywood layer R-value, m^2 K W^{-1}
R_s ratio of standard storage heat capacity per unit of collector area of 350 kJ m^{-2} °C^{-1} to actual storage capacity
R_{Tefzel} Tefzel R-value, m^2 K W^{-1}
t time from midnight, h
T_a ambient temperature, °C
$\overline{T}_a$ monthly average ambient temperature, °C
T_b air bulk temperature in the control volume, °C
T_{dp} dew point temperature, °C
T_i inlet collector fluid temperature, °C
T_{inlet} inlet air temperature, °C
T_{insu} interior side temperature of the insulation, °C, or in K for radiative heat transfer computation
T_m mains water temperature, °C
T_o, T_a exterior air temperature, °C
T_{outlet} outlet air temperature, °C
T_{plate} interior side temperature of the metal sheet, °C, or in K for radiative heat transfer computation
T_{PVMID} temperature of the photovoltaic (PV) module at midpoint, °C
T_{PVTOP} temperature of the PV module at its external surface, °C
$\overline{T}_s$ monthly average storage tank temperature, °C
T_{sky} sky temperature, K
T_w minimum acceptable hot water temperature, °C
U wetted perimeter, m
U_L energy loss coefficient, kJ m^{-2}-K^{-1}
$(UA)_L$ building loss coefficient and area product used in degree-day space heating load model, W K^{-1}
V average air velocity in the channel, m s^{-1}
V_w average wind velocity, m s^{-1}
W air moisture content, kg$_v$ (kg$_a$)$^{-1}$
W_{PV} width of the control volume, m
x distance from inlet of flow channel, m

Greek Letters

α solar absorptivity; thermal diffusivity $(=k/\varrho c_p)$, m^2 s^{-1}
β thermal expansion coefficient, 1/T or PV module temperature coefficient, (%K^{-1})
β_{mp} maximum power point PV module temperature coefficient, %K^{-1}
δ declination
Δt_L number of seconds during a month the load is required, s
Δx length of the control volume, m
ε_L effectiveness of the load heat exchanger

$\varepsilon_1, \varepsilon_2, \varepsilon_3$ long-wave emissivities
η_e electrical efficiency
η_{PV} electrical efficiency of the PV module
η_{STC} electrical efficiency at standard test conditions
θ incidence angle, degrees
μ dynamic or absolute viscosity, $kg\,m^{-1}s^{-1}$
v kinematic viscosity, $m^2\,s^{-1}$
$\bar{\rho}$ average air density $1/(T_w - T_b) \iint_{T_b}^{T_w} \rho dT$, $kg\,m^{-3}$
ϱ air density, $kg\,m^{-3}$
σ Stefan–Boltzmann constant, $W\,m^{-2}\,K^{-4}$
$(\tau\alpha)$ effective transmittance–absorptance product
$\overline{(\tau\alpha)}$ monthly average value of $(\tau\alpha)$
φ tilt angle, degrees

3.11.1 Introduction

There are two principal categories of building solar heating and cooling systems: passive and active. Passive systems integrate into the structure of the building technologies that admit, absorb, store, and release solar energy, thereby reducing the need for electricity use to transport fluids. In contrast, active systems also include fans and pumps controlled to move air and heat transfer fluids, respectively, for space heating and/or cooling and domestic hot water (DHW) heating.

Current international trends, which are expected to continue, will increasingly rely on a combination of active and passive solar systems as enabling technologies for net-zero energy solar buildings (NZESBs) – solar buildings that produce as much energy as they consume over a year. Similarly, hybrid systems – active/passive and thermal/electric – will gain popularity, such as the photovoltaic/thermal (PV/T) systems that are described later in this chapter.

This section presents approaches that are used for modeling and simulating both passive and active solar systems. First, techniques are discussed for modeling direct gains, analyzing transient responses of buildings, and developing simplified analytical thermal models of direct-gain rooms. Next, methods are presented for the thermal analysis of hybrid PV/T collectors and building-integrated photovoltaic (BIPV) systems. Then, to conclude the section, an overview of the design of two net-zero energy houses is described.

In the second part of the chapter, various design methods are presented that include the simplified f-chart method, which is suitable for both solar heating and solar cooling of buildings, as well as for domestic water heating systems, utilizability Φ, and the $\overline{\Phi}$, f-chart methods. Subsequently, various packages for advanced modeling and simulation of active systems are presented.

Finally, it should be noted that the components and subsystems discussed in other chapters of this volume may be combined to create a wide variety of building solar heating and cooling systems.

3.11.2 Passive Solar Design Techniques and Systems

Passive solar technologies do not use fans or pumps in the collection and usage of solar heat. Instead, these technologies use the natural modes of heat transfer to distribute the thermal energy of solar gains among different spaces. When applied to buildings, this generally refers to passive energy flows among rooms and envelope, such as the redistribution of absorbed direct solar gains or night cooling [1]. Buildings that use primarily these technologies to reduce heating and/or cooling energy consumption are called 'passive solar buildings' (i.e., a building that uses solar gains to reduce heating and possibly cooling energy consumption based on natural energy flows – radiation, conduction, and natural convection). The major driving forces for thermal energy transfer in a passive solar building are long-wave thermal radiation exchanges and natural convection, that is, buoyancy [1].

Passive technologies are integrated within the building and may include:

1. 'Near-equatorial facing windows' with high solar transmittance and high thermal resistance. These properties maximize the amount of direct solar gains into the living space, while reducing envelope heat losses and gains in the heating and cooling seasons, respectively. Skylights are often employed for daylighting in office buildings and in sunspaces (solaria).
2. *Building-integrated thermal storage*. Thermal storage, which is commonly referred to as thermal mass, may consist of sensible heat storage materials, such as concrete or brick, or phase-change materials. Two design options are 'isolated thermal storage' passively coupled to a fenestration system or solarium/sunspace and 'collector-storage walls'. A collector-storage wall – known as a Trombe wall – consists of thermal mass that is placed directly in front of the glazing; however, this system has not gained much acceptance since it limits the views to the outdoor environment. Direct-gain systems are the most common implementation of thermal storage.
3. *Airtight insulated opaque envelope*. Such an envelope reduces heat transfer to and from the outdoor environment, but must be chosen to be appropriate for the local climate. In most climates, this energy efficiency aspect is an essential part of the passive design. A solar technology that may be employed in conjunction with opaque envelopes is transparent insulation combined with thermal mass to store solar gains in a wall so as to turn it into an energy-positive element.
4. *Daylighting technologies and advanced solar control systems*. These technologies provide passive daylight transmission. They include electrochromic and thermochromic coatings, motorized shading (internal, external) that may be automatically controlled, and fixed shading devices, particularly for daylighting applications in the workplace. Newer technologies, such as transparent photovoltaics (PV) panels, can also generate electricity.

Passive solar heating systems are generally divided into two categories: direct gain and indirect gain. Four common types of passive solar systems are shown in **Figure 1**.

Direct-gain systems have two essential components: near-equatorial facing windows that transmit incident solar radiation and thermal mass distributed in the interior surfaces of the room to store much of that radiation. Since the direct-gain zone of a building collects, stores, and releases thermal energy from the sun, it is not only technologically simple but also one of the most thermodynamically efficient solar systems – it is essentially a live-in solar collector, in which thermal comfort must be satisfied and very often visual comfort as well with glare reduction measures. Although technologically simple, these systems require proper integration with the active (heating, ventilation, and air-conditioning (HVAC)) systems to achieve

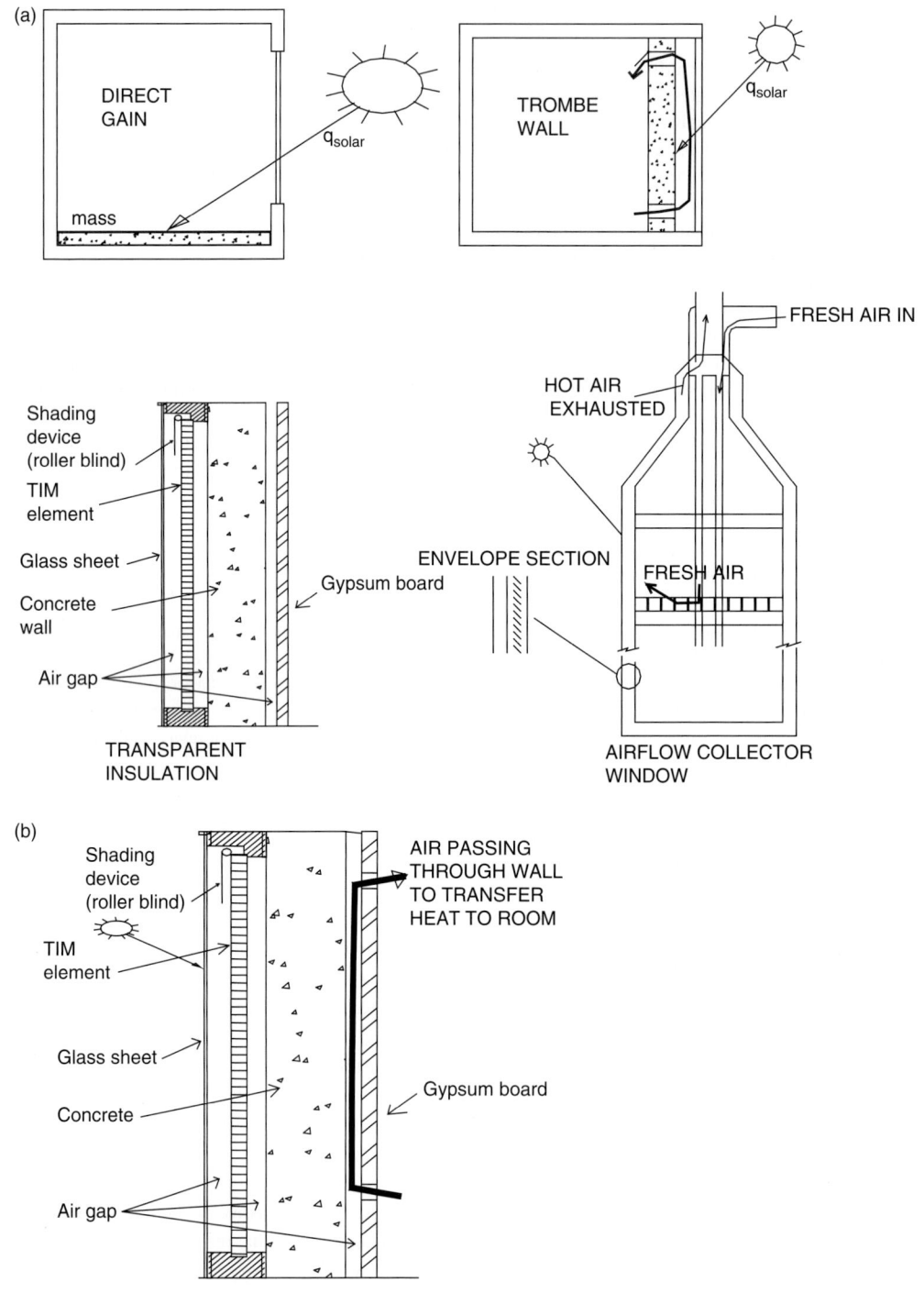

Figure 1 (a) Common types of passive systems. (b) Transparent insulation and an option for air circulation in a wall accelerate heat release.

high performance. In the case of the workspace such as offices integration with design and operation of the lighting system is also essential.

Thermal storage is essential in direct-gain systems since it performs two important roles: storing much of the absorbed direct gains for slow release and maintaining satisfactory thermal comfort conditions by limiting the rise in maximum operative (effective) room temperature [2].

The key design choices for such a system are type, quantity, and position of thermal mass, as well as the choice of window area and type. To satisfy thermal comfort requirements, the ratio of peak solar heat gains to thermal mass should not exceed the maximum room temperature swing; this can be determined using dynamic thermal analysis.

In indirect-gain systems, the thermal storage mass is separated from the main building envelope. Such systems include Trombe wall (i.e., collector-storage wall) systems, transparent insulation systems, and air heating systems (i.e., airflow windows and solar collectors) (**Figure 1**). Various controlled devices may be employed such as motorized reflective shades and controlled inlet/outlet dampers to control transmission of solar heat gains and the rate of their release from the thermal storage layers (**Figure 1(b)**).

3.11.2.1 Direct-Gain Modeling

The primary objective in the design of a direct-gain solar building or thermal zone is to achieve high savings in energy consumption through optimal utilization of passive solar gains, while preventing frequent room overheating above the acceptable comfort limit.

During the thermal analysis stage of a solar building, it is necessary to determine heating loads and room temperature fluctuations either for design days or with given typical annual weather data. For sizing equipment and components, it is desirable to evaluate the building response under extreme weather conditions for many design options, each time changing only a few of the building parameters, until an optimum or acceptable response is obtained. For a solar building that includes direct gain as its main solar energy utilization mechanism, it is also essential to study the free (passive) response of the building as it enables the designer to determine the relation between room temperature fluctuation and storage of passive solar gains.

There are two main steps in creating a mathematical model that describes the heat transfer processes in a solar building. First, the thermal exchanges must be modeled as accurately as is practical; while a high level of precision is desired, too much complexity can limit the model's usefulness in analysis and design. Second, an appropriate method of solution must be chosen to determine the room temperature and auxiliary energy loads. The type of solution may be numerical or analytical, as long as the variables of interest can be determined. As an optional third step, a method of analyzing the system without simulation can be developed.

The degree of detail and model resolution required during the analysis of a building depends on the stage of the design. For the early stages of design, a steady-state or an approximate dynamic model is often adequate. However, more detail is required for a preliminary design, taking into account all objectives of thermal design and the specific characteristics of the system considered.

Modeling the radiant heat exchanges of the zone interior is more important with direct-gain than with indirect-gain systems and generally requires more modeling detail. In designing direct-gain buildings (i.e., a building with at least one direct-gain room), a key objective is to store energy in the walls during the daytime for release at night without having uncomfortable temperature swings.

A basic characteristic of passive solar building is the strong convective and conductive coupling between adjacent thermal zones. This coupling is very important between equatorial-facing direct-gain rooms that receive a significant amount of solar radiation transmitted through large windows and adjacent rooms that receive very little solar radiation. For example, heat transfer by natural convection through a doorway connecting a warm direct-gain room or a solarium and a cool north-facing room can be an effective way of heating the cool room.

The design of direct-gain buildings can be separated into two phases. First involves the determination of room temperature swings on relatively clear days during the heating season (assuming no active or passive cooling) in order to decide how much storage mass to include so as to ensure that overheating does not occur frequently. Second, to determine the optimum amount of insulation and window area and type, the net increase in the mean (daily or monthly) room temperature above the ambient temperature due to the solar gains is calculated, or auxiliary heating loads are computed until the desired energy savings are achieved.

Periodic conditions are usually assumed (explicitly or implicitly) in dynamic building thermal analysis and load calculations. Heating or cooling load, that is, the auxiliary heat energy input/removal required to maintain comfort conditions, is usually calculated for a design day. The peak heating load is used to size heating equipment and the peak cooling load to size cooling equipment.

The following three types of approximations are commonly introduced in mathematical models to facilitate the representation of building thermal behavior:

1. *Linearization of heat transfer coefficients*. Convective and radiative heat transfers are nonlinear processes, and the respective heat transfer coefficients are usually linearized so that equations to derive system energy balance can be solved by direct linear algebraic techniques and possibly represented by a linear thermal network.
2. *Spatial and/or temporal discretization*. The equation describing transient heat conduction is a parabolic, diffusion-type partial differential equation. Thus, when finite-difference methods are used, a conducting medium with significant thermal capacity such as concrete or brick must be discretized into a number of regions, commonly known as control volumes, which may be modeled by lumped network elements (thermal resistances and capacitances). Also, time domain discretization is required in which an appropriate time step is employed. In response factor methods, only time discretization is necessary. For frequency domain analysis, none of these approximations are required; in periodic models however, the number of harmonics employed must be kept within reasonable limits.

3. *Approximations for reduction in model complexity – selecting model resolution.* These approximations are employed in order to reduce the required data input and the number of simultaneous equations to be solved or to enable the derivation of closed-form analytical solutions. They are by far the most important approximations. Examples include combining radiative and convective heat transfer coefficients (so-called film coefficients commonly employed in building energy analysis), assuming that many surfaces are at the same temperature, or considering certain heat exchanges as negligible.

A major aspect of the modeling process considers heat conduction in the building envelope. In most cases relating to heating or cooling load estimations, energy savings calculations, and thermal comfort analysis, it is generally accepted that one-dimensional heat conduction may be assumed. Thermal bridges such as those present around corners and at the structure are generally accounted for in calculating the effective thermal resistance of building envelope elements. However, the thermal storage process may usually be adequately modeled as a one-dimensional process for insulated buildings.

Direct-gain zone modeling entails certain important requirements in addition to those involved in traditional building modeling. In particular, there is an increased need to deal with thermal comfort requirements and a need to allow the room temperature to fluctuate in order to enable storage of direct solar gains in building-integrated exposed thermal mass.

Calculation of peak heating and cooling loads – a major aspect of heating and cooling equipment sizing – needs to take into account the building thermal storage capacity and dynamic variation of solar radiation and outdoor temperature in order to avoid oversizing of HVAC systems. For most mild temperate climates, a heat pump will provide an efficient auxiliary heating and cooling system. Well-insulated buildings with effective shading systems and natural ventilation will have a reduced need for auxiliary cooling. Similarly, appropriate sizing of the fenestration systems facing the equator will meet most heating requirements on sunny days.

Frequency domain analysis techniques with complex variables are usually employed for steady-periodic analysis of multilayered walls and zones. They provide a convenient mean for periodic analysis, in which parameters like magnitude and phase angle of room temperatures and heat flows are obtained.

Generally, materials with significant thermal storage capacity must be modeled, particularly room interior layers. The thermal properties of major thermal storage materials and a few other materials (for comparison) are given in **Table 1**. Generally, thermal mass has high thermal capacitance but low thermal resistance. For example, a 1 m² concrete block that is 10 cm thick can store (for 1 °C temperature rise)

$$Q = c_p \rho \, \text{Vol} \, \Delta T = 840 \, \text{J kg}^{-1} \, °\text{C} \times 2200 \, \text{kg m}^{-3} \times 0.10 \times 1 \, \text{m}^2 \times 1 \, °\text{C}$$
$$Q = 184\,800 \, \text{J}$$

By contrast, its thermal resistance is negligible ($0.1/1.73 = 0.058 \, \text{K W}^{-1}$). The properties of concrete can vary considerably with density and moisture content.

3.11.2.1.1 Transient heat conduction and steady-periodic (frequency domain) solution

The equation describing heat conduction is a parabolic, diffusion-type partial differential equation. Thus, the use of finite-difference methods requires the discretization of a conducting medium with significant thermal capacity into a number of regions which are modeled by lumped elements. Also, time domain discretization is required in which an appropriate time step is employed. In response factor methods, only time discretization is necessary.

Table 1 Properties of thermal mass and other building materials [3, 4]

Material	Mass density (kg m⁻³)	Thermal conductivity (W m⁻¹ K⁻¹)	Specific heat (J kg⁻¹ K⁻¹)
Heavyweight concrete	2243	1.73	840
Clay tile	1121	0.57	840
Gypsum	1602	0.73	840
Gas-entrained concrete	400	0.14	1000
Water	1000	0.58	4200
Plasterboard	840	0.16	950
Expanded polystyrene	25	0.035	1400
Timber			
Softwood	630	0.13	1360
Hardwood	630	0.15	1250
Plywood	530	0.14	1214
Chipboard	800	0.15	1286
Common brick (full)	1922	0.727	840
Stone			
Granite	2600	2.50	900
Limestone	2180	1.59	720
Sandstone	2000	1.30	712
Marble	2500	2.00	802
Screed finish (lightweight)	1200	0.41	840

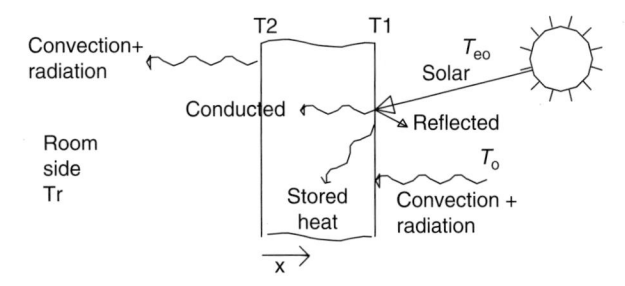

Figure 2 Heat exchanges in a wall layer with absorption of solar radiation (T_o, ambient temperature; T_{eo}, sol-air temperature [3]).

For frequency domain analysis, none of these approximations are required; in periodic models however, the number of harmonics employed must be kept within reasonable limits. Frequency domain analysis techniques with complex variables are usually employed for steady-periodic analysis of multilayered walls. They provide a convenient means for periodic analysis, in which the main parameters of interest are the magnitude and phase angle of room temperatures and heat flows.

First, the frequency domain solution of heat transfer in multilayered walls is determined (see **Figure 2**). Consider a slab and assume one-dimensional transient conduction with uniform properties k, ρ, c, then

$$\alpha \frac{\partial^2 T}{\partial x^2} = \frac{\partial T}{\partial t} \qquad [1a]$$

where thermal diffusivity $\alpha = k/(\rho c)$.

The application of a Laplace transform to eqn [1a] converts it to an ordinary differential equation as follows (s is the Laplace domain variable):

$$\alpha \frac{d^2 T}{dx^2} = sT \qquad [1b]$$

This is an ordinary differential equation which may be solved for $T(x)$ while keeping s as a constant:

$$T\{x,s\} = c_1 e^{\gamma x} + c_2 e^{-\gamma x}, \quad \text{where } \gamma = \sqrt{\frac{s}{\alpha}} \qquad [2a]$$

Note: the Laplace transform of eqn [1a] assumes the initial condition $T\{x, t=0\} = 0$. This is acceptable as the aim is to derive steady-periodic (or frequency domain) solutions.

Rewrite eqn [2a] as

$$T\{x,s\} = M \cosh(\gamma x) + N \sinh(\gamma x) \qquad [2b]$$

Heat flux q' is obtained by differentiating eqn [2b]:

$$q' = -k \frac{dT}{dx} \Rightarrow q'\{x,s\} = -M k \gamma \sinh(\gamma x) - N \sinh(\gamma x) \qquad [3]$$

At each surface, the following temperatures and heat fluxes are obtained:

$$\begin{aligned} T_1\{x=0,s\} &= M \\ q'_1\{x=0,s\} &= -Nk\gamma \\ T_2\{x=L,s\} &= M \cos h(\gamma L) + N \sin h(\gamma L) \\ q'_2\{x=L,s\} &= M k \gamma \sin h(\gamma L) + N k \gamma \cos h(\gamma L) \end{aligned} \qquad [4]$$

The above equations for the conditions at the two surfaces may be expressed in the so-called cascade equation matrix form [4] as follows (assuming that heat flux q' is positive into the wall on both sides):

$$\begin{bmatrix} T_1 \\ q_1 \end{bmatrix} = \underbrace{\begin{bmatrix} \cos h(\gamma L) & \sin h(\gamma L)/k\gamma \\ k\gamma \sin h(\gamma L) & \cos h(\gamma L) \end{bmatrix}}_{\text{two port cascade matrix}} \cdot \begin{bmatrix} T_2 \\ -q'_2 \end{bmatrix} \qquad [5]$$

The constant k is the thermal conductivity, x is the thickness, and γ is equal to $(s/\alpha)^{1/2}$, s being the Laplace transform variable and α being the thermal diffusivity. For admittance calculations, $s = j\omega$, where $j = \sqrt{-1}$ and $\omega = 2\pi/P$. For diurnal analysis, the period $P = 86\,400$ s. For a multilayered wall, the cascade matrices for each successive layer are multiplied to get an equivalent wall cascade matrix that relates conditions at one surface of the wall to those at the other surface, thus eliminating all intermediate nodes with no approximation required and no discretization:

$$\begin{bmatrix} T_1 \\ q'_2 \end{bmatrix} = \begin{bmatrix} A_1 & B_1 \\ C_1 & D_1 \end{bmatrix} \cdot \begin{bmatrix} A_2 & B_2 \\ C_2 & D_2 \end{bmatrix} \cdots \begin{bmatrix} A_N & B_N \\ C_N & D_N \end{bmatrix} \cdot \begin{bmatrix} T_N \\ -q'_N \end{bmatrix} \qquad [6]$$

The effective wall cascade matrix is expressed as follows:

$$\begin{bmatrix} T_1 \\ q'_1 \end{bmatrix} = \begin{bmatrix} \overline{A} & \overline{B} \\ \overline{C} & \overline{D} \end{bmatrix} \cdot \begin{bmatrix} T_N \\ -q'_N \end{bmatrix} \quad [7]$$

The cascade matrix for a simple conductance (per unit area), u, can be shown to be given by $\begin{bmatrix} 1 & 1/u \\ 0 & 1 \end{bmatrix}$.

Usually, the variables of primary interest are the surface temperatures of the room interior. Consider, for example, a wall made up of an inner (room side) storage mass layer and insulation on the exterior. This can be represented by

$$\begin{bmatrix} T_1 \\ q'_1 \end{bmatrix} = \underbrace{\begin{bmatrix} D & B \\ C & D \end{bmatrix}}_{\substack{\text{mass} \\ \text{cascade} \\ \text{matrix}}} \cdot \underbrace{\begin{bmatrix} 1 & 1/u_o \\ 0 & 1 \end{bmatrix}}_{\substack{\text{insulation} \\ \text{and air cascade} \\ \text{matrix}}} \cdot \begin{bmatrix} T_2 \\ -q'_2 \end{bmatrix} = \underbrace{\begin{bmatrix} D & D/u_o + B \\ C & C/u_o + D \end{bmatrix}}_{\text{wall cascade matrix}} \cdot \begin{bmatrix} T_2 \\ -q'_2 \end{bmatrix} \quad [8]$$

3.11.2.1.1(i) Admittance transfer functions for walls

The above cascade equations for walls may be utilized to obtain frequency domain (admittance) transfer functions for walls that can be used for steady-periodic analysis or controls and system dynamics studies.

Simple Fourier series models for outside temperature or sol-air temperature and solar radiation are used for steady-periodic thermal analysis of wall heat flow. Frequency domain transfer functions such as the wall admittance are studied in terms of magnitude and phase lag and are then used together with Fourier series models for weather variables to determine the steady-periodic thermal response of walls. The technique is applied to passive solar analysis and design.

Significant insight into the dynamic thermal behavior of walls may be obtained by studying their admittance transfer functions (magnitude and phase angle) as a function of frequency, thermal properties, and geometry.

Figure 3 shows conceptually how wall response to weather inputs (e.g., $T \sin(\omega t)$) may be obtained for one harmonic, and the time lag between the input and output waves. For inputs with more than one harmonic, the total response may be obtained by superposition of the response harmonics.

The thermal admittance of a wall is a transfer function parameter useful for analysis of the effects on room temperature of cyclic variations in weather variables such as solar radiation, outside temperature, and dynamic heat flows under steady-periodic conditions.

There are two transfer functions of primary interest, namely, the self-admittance Y_s relating the effect of a heat source at one surface to the temperature of that surface and the transfer admittance Y_t relating the effect of an outside temperature variation to the resulting heat flow at the inside surface.

These two transfer functions are determined as demonstrated in the following model [5]. The wall in **Figure 4** consists of insulation and thermally nonmassive layers (low thermal capacity) with conductance u per unit area, and a thermally massive layer of thickness L.

The Norton equivalent network for a wall with a specified temperature on one side (such as basement temperature or sol-air temperature) is obtained from the cascade form of the wall equations which relates temperature and heat flow at one surface to those at the other surface. The cascade form of the equations is derived by first taking the Laplace transform of the one-dimensional heat diffusion equation to obtain an ordinary differential equation (as previously described) which can then be readily solved to relate heat flux and temperature at one surface of a one-dimensional medium to those at the other surface as follows (based on eqn [5]):

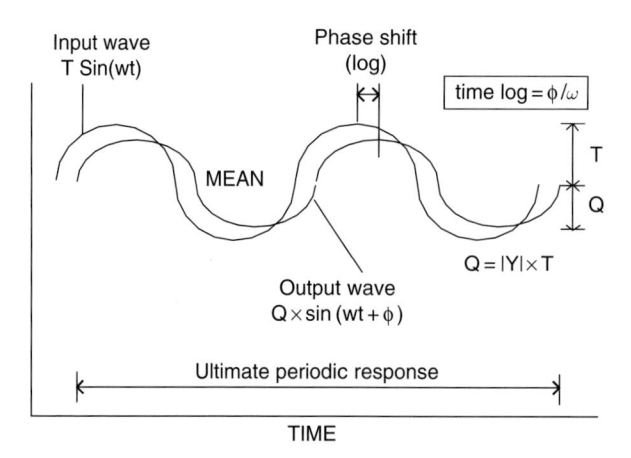

Figure 3 Schematic of temperature and heat flow waves (Y = admittance transfer function with magnitude $|Y|$ and phase angle φ).

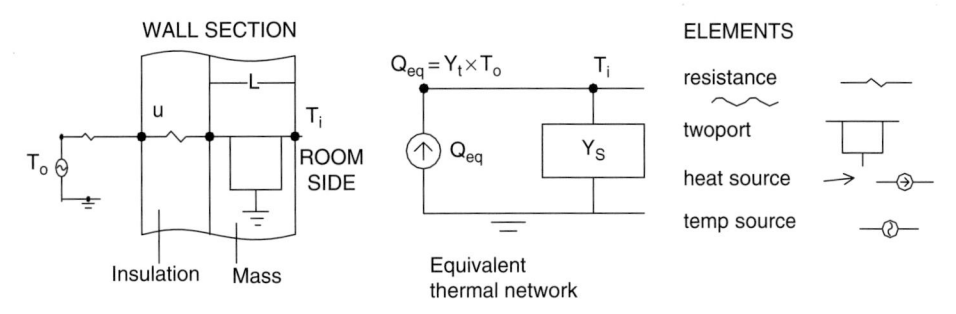

Figure 4 Exterior wall with massive interior layer and equivalent thermal network (for a wall with incident solar radiation, replace T_o with the sol-air temperature T_{eo}).

$$\begin{bmatrix} T_1 \\ q'_1 \end{bmatrix} = \begin{bmatrix} D & B \\ C & D \end{bmatrix} \begin{bmatrix} T_2 \\ -q'_2 \end{bmatrix}$$

where

$$D = \cos h(\gamma x)$$
$$B = \frac{\sin h(\gamma x)}{k\gamma}$$
$$C = k\gamma \sin h(\gamma x)$$
[9]

and q' is assumed to be positive into the slab (on both sides). As explained above, the cascade matrix for a multilayered wall is obtained by multiplying the cascade matrices for consecutive layers. Usually, the temperatures of interest are either the inside or the outside temperatures. In this way, wall intermediate layer nodes and their temperatures are eliminated. A linear subnetwork connected to a network at only two terminals (a port) can be represented by its Norton equivalent, consisting of a heat source and an admittance connected in parallel between the terminals [5].

The admittance is the subnetwork equivalent admittance as seen from the connection port (the two terminals), and the heat source is the short-circuited heat flow at the port. Consider, for example, the wall in **Figure 4**, assumed to be made up of an inner layer of storage mass of uniform thermal properties and an insulation layer with negligible thermal capacity, also of uniform thermal properties. The region behind the thermal mass may be represented by equivalent conductance U in series with the outside temperature T_o (for exterior walls the sol-air temperature T_{eo}). The conductance U combines the insulation resistance and a film coefficient. The determination of Y_s (called the wall self-admittance) and the equivalent source Q_{sc} produced by the transformation will now be explained. The first step is obtaining the total cascade matrix by multiplying the cascade matrix for the storage mass layer by that for u (note: $u = U/A$):

$$\begin{bmatrix} T_s \\ q_s \end{bmatrix} = \begin{bmatrix} D & B \\ C & D \end{bmatrix} \begin{bmatrix} 1 & 1/u \\ 0 & 1 \end{bmatrix} \begin{bmatrix} T_o \\ -q_o \end{bmatrix}$$
[10]

After the multiplication, T_s is temporarily set to 0 (short-circuit) to get the Norton equivalent source as

$$Q_{eq} = -Y_t T_o$$
[11]

where the transfer admittance Y_t is given by

$$Y_t = \frac{-A}{\dfrac{A \cos h(\gamma x)}{u_o} + \dfrac{\sin h(\gamma x)}{k\gamma}}$$
[12a]

The transfer admittance has been multiplied by the area A to obtain its total value. To obtain Y_s, T_o is temporarily set to 0, and the admittance as seen from the interior surface is obtained, yielding (after multiplying by A)

$$Y_s = \frac{A\left(\dfrac{u_o}{A} + k\gamma \tan h(\gamma x)\right)}{\dfrac{u_o}{k\gamma A}\tan h(\gamma x) + 1}$$
[12b]

If there is no thermal mass, the simple equality $Y_s = -Y_t = u_0$ is obtained. A similar result is derived for windows in eliminating all nodes exterior to the inner glazing. An important result is obtained for an infinitely thick wall or a wall with no heat loss at the back (adiabatic surface, or high amount of insulation $u_o \approx 0$); in this case, Y_s is given by

$$Y_s = A k \gamma \tan h(\gamma x)$$
[12c]

Thick walls have admittance that is close to that given by the above equation. When the penetration depth, given by

$$d = \sqrt{\frac{2k}{c_p \rho \omega}} = \sqrt{\frac{2\alpha}{\omega}}$$
[12d]

is significantly less than the wall thickness, then the wall behaves like a semi-infinite solid.

The magnitude and phase angle (and time lag/lead) of a transfer function such as Y_s and Y_t are computed by means of complex variables.

3.11.2.1.1(i)(a)   Analysis   Substantial insight into wall and building thermal behavior may be gained by studying the magnitude and phase angle of important transfer functions such as Y_s and Y_t [6]. The time lead d_s of Y_s is the time difference between the peak of a sinusoidal input function, such as solar radiation in the case of the room interior surface, and the resulting peak of the interior surface temperature T_i. Now, consider the variation of wall thermal admittance with thermal mass thickness L for the fundamental frequency (one cycle per day, $n=1$) for unit wall area. Note that the diurnal ($n=1$) frequency is important in the analysis of variables with a dominant diurnal harmonic such as solar radiation. High frequencies are important in analyzing the effect of varying heat inputs such as those due to on/off cycling of a furnace.

Compare two walls, one with a concrete interior and the other with a softwood interior. The exterior insulating layer of both walls has insignificant thermal capacity, and its thermal resistance is 2.5 RSI. The concrete is assumed to have a specific heat capacity of 800 J kg^{-1} °C^{-1}, a density of 2200 kg m^{-3}, and a thermal conductivity of 1.7 W m^{-1} K^{-1}. The softwood has a specific heat capacity of 1360 J kg^{-1} °C^{-1}, a density of 630 kg m^{-3}, and a thermal conductivity of 0.13 W m^{-1} K^{-1}.

The results presented below are specific to this concrete, but they generally indicate the expected trends for concrete, brick, and masonry-type materials. Note that the thermal conductivity of these materials increases with moisture content and density. **Figure 5** shows an extremely important result in steady-periodic analysis of building thermal response – the fact that there exists a certain wall thermal mass thickness that will reduce room temperature fluctuations most – in this case for $L=0.2$ m for concrete, corresponding to the maximum admittance. Therefore, this is the optimum thermal mass thickness for passive solar design because the dominant harmonic component of solar radiation is that corresponding to one cycle per day.

As indicated in **Figure 6**, the magnitude of wall admittance (for mass thickness of 20 cm) increases with frequency (decreases with period). The magnitude of wall admittance is also higher for concrete than for softwoods. Thus, the inside room temperature fluctuations are smaller for high-frequency fluctuations in internal heat gains in the case of the concrete wall. For harmonic numbers higher than about eight – that is, periods less than 3 h – the wall behaves like an infinitely thick solid; in this case, the phase angle is 45°.

The variation of transfer admittance Y_t with mass thickness is depicted in **Figure 7**. In this case, the magnitude of Y_t decreases with thickness, and therefore, fluctuations in the sol-air temperature are significantly modulated as they are transmitted to the room interior. This is a well-known phenomenon, efficiently employed in traditional architecture in adobe buildings. The time lag of the heat gains transmitted ($q = Y_t \times T_{eo}$) into the interior is the time lag of Y_t. This time lag increases to about 7.5 h for a mass thickness of 30 cm.

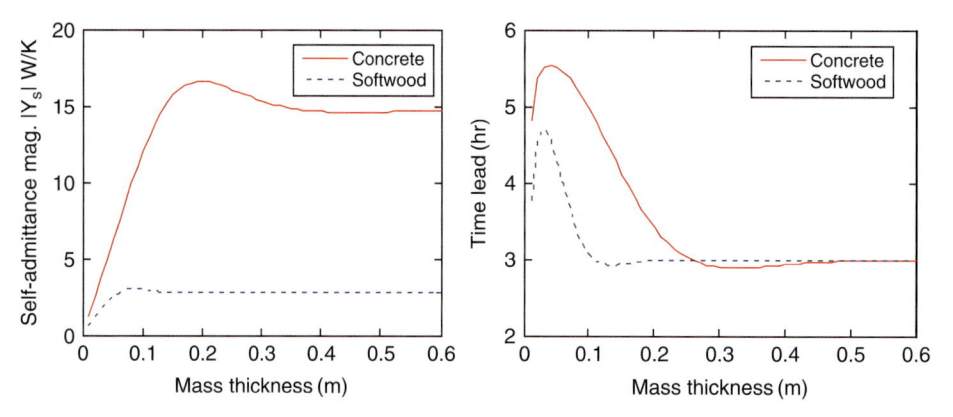

Figure 5 Variation in self-admittance and its time lead with mass thickness and material type for the one cycle per day harmonic.

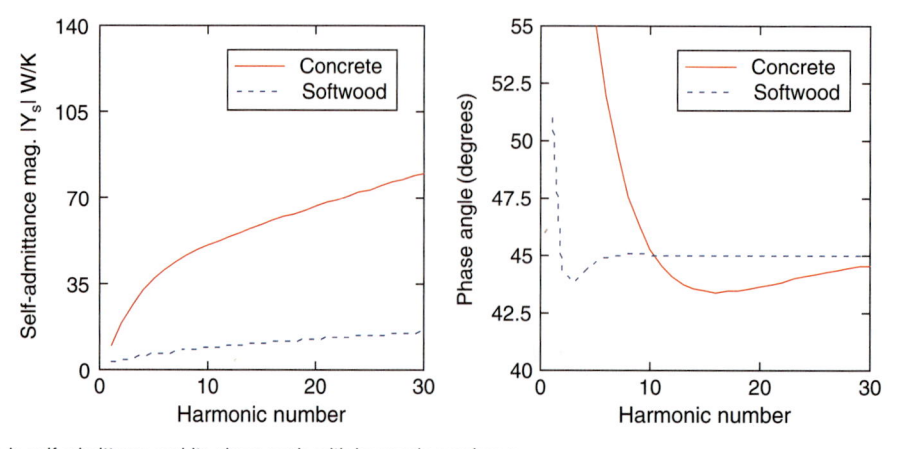

Figure 6 Variation in self-admittance and its phase angle with harmonic number n.

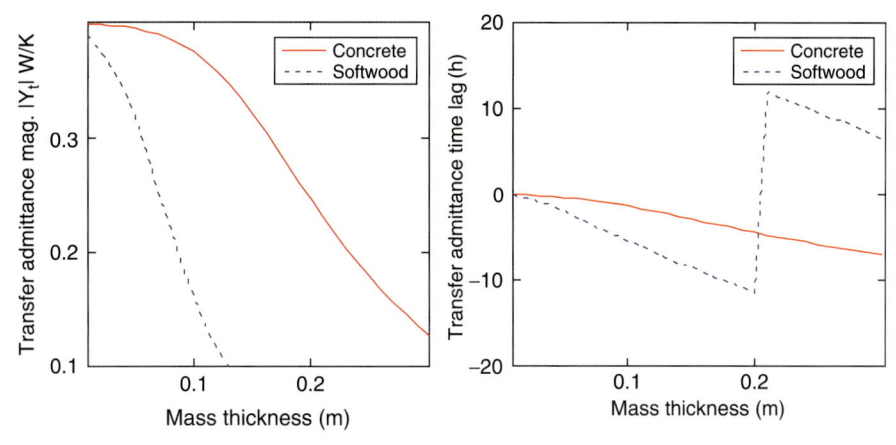

Figure 7 Variation in transfer admittance and its time lag with mass thickness.

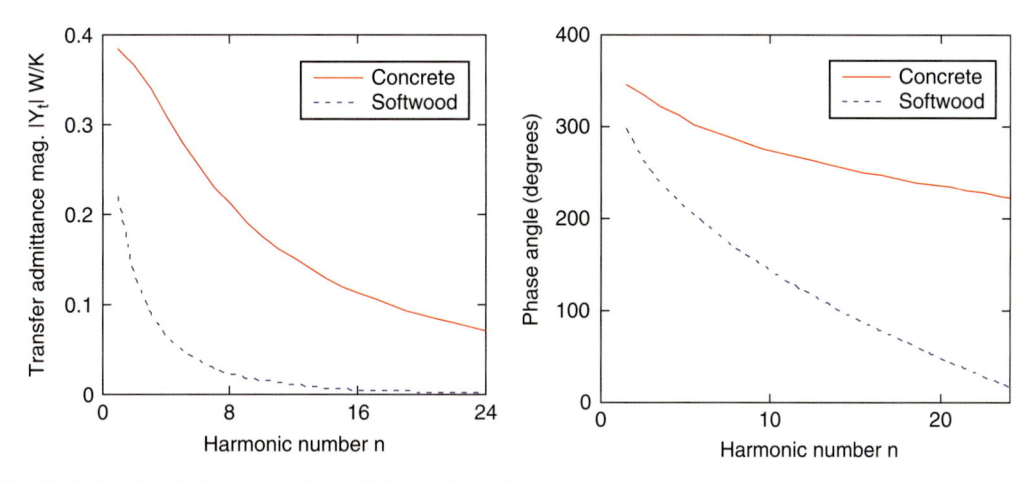

Figure 8 Variation in transfer admittance magnitude with harmonic number n.

The time delay in the transmission of a heat wave through a wall is another positive effect of thermal mass in addition to the attenuation of temperature swings. Thus, the peak heat gains through the structure coincide with cooler outside conditions when natural ventilation may be employed to reduce total instantaneous cooling loads.

Figure 8 shows that the magnitude of the transfer admittance decreases relatively fast with increasing harmonic number n and decreasing period. Thus, the heat gain fluctuations transmitted into the room as a result of sol-air temperature fluctuations are significantly reduced at high frequencies. For example, a temperature fluctuation (amplitude of wave) of 10 °C in sol-air temperature will result in a heat gain fluctuation of about: $0.1\,\text{W}\,°\text{C}^{-1} \times 10\,°\text{C} = 1\,\text{W}$ per square meter of wall.

3.11.2.1.2 Building transient response analysis

Transient thermal analysis of walls or zones may be performed with the following objectives:

1. Peak heating/cooling load calculations.
2. Calculation of dynamic temperature variation within walls, including solar effects, room temperature swings, and condensation on wall interior surfaces; two-dimensional steady-state temperature profiles in walls (e.g., for investigation of thermal bridge effects).

For a multilayered wall, an energy balance is applied at each node at regular time intervals to obtain the temperature of the nodes as a function of time. These equations may be solved with the implicit method as a set of simultaneous equations or with the explicit method which involves a forward progression in time from a set of initial conditions. Mixed differencing schemes are also often used in building simulation.

Here we consider the finite-difference thermal network approach. In this approach, each wall layer is discretized (divided) into a number of sublayers (regions). Each region is represented by a node and is assumed to be isothermal. Each node (i) has a thermal capacitance (C_i) associated with it and resistances connecting it to adjacent nodes.

Wall transient thermal response analysis with finite-difference techniques may generally provide a more accurate estimation of temperatures and heat flows owing to the capability to model nonlinear effects such as convection and radiation. One disadvantage is that the initial conditions are usually unknown. Thus, the simulation is repeated until a steady-periodic response is obtained.

In the transient one-dimensional finite-difference method, each wall layer is represented by one or more sublayers (regions) – also known as control volumes. Each region is represented by a central node with a thermal capacitance C connected to two thermal

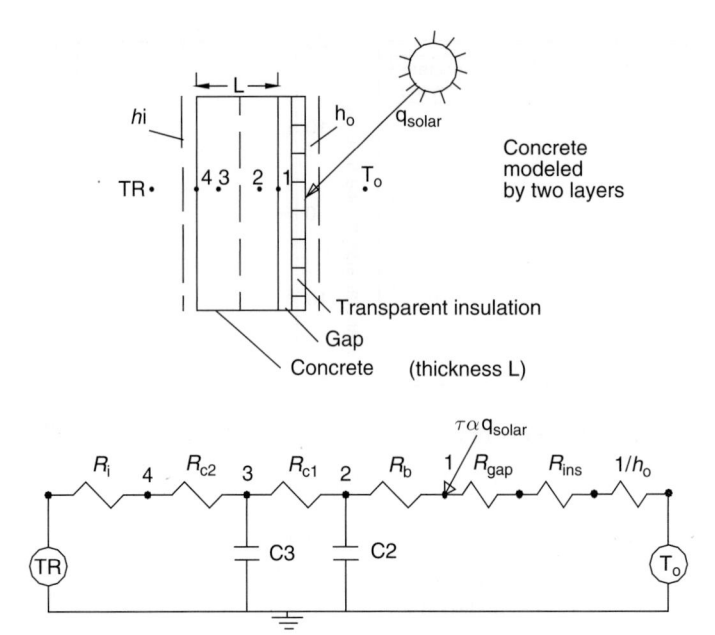

Figure 9 Wall with transparent insulation and its thermal network.

resistances, each equal to half the *R*-value of the layer (**Figure 9**). Thus, the finite-difference thermal network model for the wall consists of two capacitances for the concrete thermal capacity and interconnecting thermal resistances. The energy balance for the thermal network is as follows:

$$T_{i,p+1} = \frac{\Delta t}{C_i}\left(q_i + \sum \frac{T_{j,p}-T_{i,p}}{R_{t,j}}\right) + T_{i,p} \quad [13]$$

Subscript *i* indicates the node for which the energy balance is written, and *j* indicates all nodes connected to node *i*, while *p* is the time interval; q_i represents a heat source at node *i*, such as solar radiation.

The time step is selected on the basis of the following condition for numerical stability:

$$\Delta t \leq \min\left(\frac{C_i}{\sum_j \frac{1}{R_{i,j}}}\right) \quad [14]$$

for all nodes *i*.

The explicit finite-difference method is particularly suitable for the modeling of nonlinear heat diffusion problems such as heat transfer through the building envelope. It can easily accommodate nonlinear heat transfer coefficients and control actions.

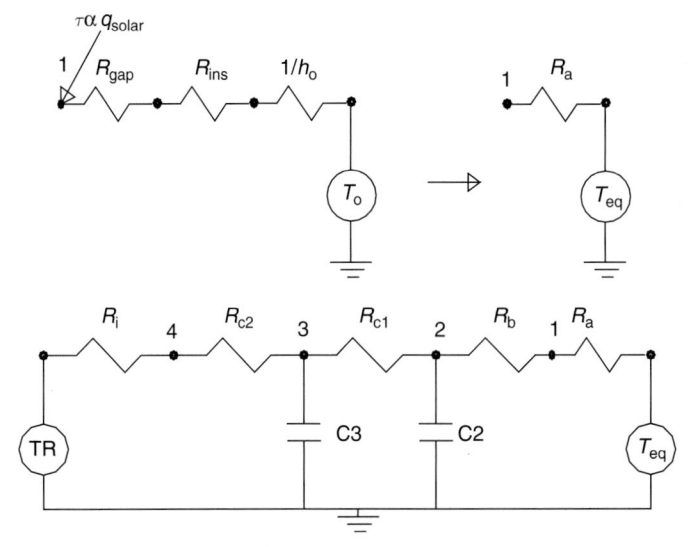

Figure 10 Simplified thermal network for **Figure 9**.

$L = 0.20\,\text{m}$ $A = 1 \cdot \text{m}^2$ concrete thickness and face area (perpendicular to heat flow)

Concrete properties: $c = 800 \cdot \dfrac{\text{joule}}{\text{kg} \cdot \text{degC}}$ $k = 1.7 \cdot \dfrac{\text{watt}}{\text{m} \cdot \text{degC}}$ $\rho = 2200 \cdot \dfrac{\text{kg}}{\text{m}^3}$

 specific heat   conductivity   density

Film coefficients: $h_i = 10\,\dfrac{\text{watt}}{\text{m}^2 \cdot \text{degC}}$ $h_o = 20\,\dfrac{\text{watt}}{\text{m}^2 \cdot \text{degC}}$

$\tau\alpha = 0.7$ effective transmittance–absorptance of transparent insulation system and concrete face)

$R_{ins} = 0.5 \cdot \text{m}^2 \dfrac{\text{degC}}{\text{watt}}$ $R_{gap} = 0.3\,\text{m}^2 \dfrac{\text{degC}}{\text{watt}}$ transparent insulation and gap resistances

$R_a = \dfrac{R_{gap} + R_{ins} + \dfrac{1}{h_o}}{A}$ $R_a = 0.85\,\dfrac{\text{degC}}{\text{watt}}$ resistance from outside to concrete face

$R_c = \dfrac{L}{k \cdot A}$ total concrete resistance $R_b = \dfrac{R_c}{4}$ $R_b = 0.029\,\dfrac{\text{degC}}{\text{watt}}$

$R_{c1} = \dfrac{R_c}{2}$ $R_{c1} = 0.059\,\dfrac{\text{degC}}{\text{watt}}$ $R_{c2} = \dfrac{R_c}{4}$ $R_i = \dfrac{1}{A \cdot h_i}$ $R_i = 0.1\,\dfrac{\text{degC}}{\text{watt}}$

$C2 = \rho \cdot c \cdot \dfrac{L}{2} \cdot A$ $C2 = 1.76 \times 10^5\,\dfrac{\text{joule}}{\text{degC}}$ $C3 = C2$ thermal capacitance for each layer

Stability test

$TS = \left(\dfrac{C2}{\dfrac{1}{R_a + R_b} + \dfrac{1}{R_{c1}}}\quad \dfrac{C3}{\dfrac{1}{R_{c1}} + \dfrac{1}{R_{c2} + R_i}} \right)$ The time step Dt should be lower than the minimum of the two values in the vector TS

$TS = (9.704 \times 10^3 \quad 7.118 \times 10^3)\,\text{s}$

$\Delta t_{critical} = \min(TS)$ $\Delta t_{critical} = 7.118 \times 10^3\,\text{s}$ $\Delta t = 1800\,\text{s}$

$i = 0., 1.. 96$ number of time steps $t = 0\,\text{s},\,1800\,\text{s}..\,172\,800\,\text{s}$

Figure 11 Computations of finite-difference model in MathCad [6].

Figure 9 shows the thermal network for a wall with transparent insulation. The wall consists of an exterior layer of transparent insulation, an air cavity, and a thermal storage layer of concrete. The thermal circuit represented in Figure 9 can be simplified by using the equivalent sol-air temperature and equivalent resistance. The simplification and the resulting thermal network are shown in Figure 10.

The specific calculations for the above model developed in MathCad [6] are shown in Figures 11 and 12, and the resulting temperature variation of a south-facing wall for two winter days with high solar gains is shown in Figure 13. For summer simulations, a shutter is assumed to be closed in the air cavity, reflecting outwards 90% of transmitted solar gains.

3.11.2.1.3 Simplified analytical direct-gain room model and solution (passive)

An analytical model can provide insight into passive solar design and quick comparison of design options. A simple analytical model based on the admittance method is presented below. The room is shown schematically in Figure 14. The walls (all of which are external) are assumed to be made up of an inner lining of storage mass material of uniform thermal transport properties and outer insulating layers with negligible thermal storage capacity. Walls with storage mass are assumed to be at the same surface temperature, and they are thus treated as one exterior wall, which is modeled as a two-port distributed element as previously

Assume $w = 2\dfrac{\pi}{86\,400} \cdot \dfrac{\text{rad}}{\text{s}}$ frequency based on period of one day

$T_o(t) = \left(5 \cdot \cos\left(w \cdot t + 3 \cdot \dfrac{\pi}{4}\right) - 10\right) \cdot \text{degC}$ outside temperature

$f(t) = 500 \cdot \cos[w \cdot (t - 43\,200\,\text{s})] \cdot \text{watt}$ $q_{\text{solar}}(t) = \text{if}(f(t) > 0 \cdot \text{watt}, f(t), 0 \cdot \text{watt})$ incident solar radiation modeled as half-sinusoid

$T_{\text{eq}}(t) = T_o(t) + q_{\text{solar}}(t) \cdot \tau\alpha \cdot R_a$ equivalent 'sol-air' temperature at node 1 (concrete surface)

$T_R = 22 \cdot \text{degC}$ room temperature

Initial estimates of temperatures $\begin{pmatrix} T_{20} \\ T_{30} \end{pmatrix} = \begin{pmatrix} 10 \\ 10 \end{pmatrix} \cdot \text{degC}$

Simulation for nodes with capacitances:

$$\begin{pmatrix} T2_{i+1} \\ T3_{i+1} \end{pmatrix} = \begin{bmatrix} \dfrac{\Delta t}{C2} \cdot \left(\dfrac{T_{\text{eq}}(i \cdot \Delta t) - T2_i}{R_a + R_b} + \dfrac{T3_i - T2_i}{R_{c1}} \right) + T2_i \\ \dfrac{\Delta t}{C3} \cdot \left(\dfrac{T2_i - T3_i}{R_{c1}} + \dfrac{T_R - T3_i}{R_i + R_{c2}} \right) + T3_i \end{bmatrix}$$

Finite-difference simulation (i is present time, and $i+1$ the next time step)

Calculaiton of intermediate temperatures

$T4_i = T_R + R_i \cdot \dfrac{T3_i - T_R}{R_{c2} + R_i}$ $T1_i = T2_i + R_b \cdot \dfrac{T_{\text{eq}}(i \cdot \Delta t) - T2_i}{R_a + R_b}$

Figure 12   Computations of finite-difference model in MathCad.

described in section 3.11.2.1.1, and its internal surface is assumed to be uniformly irradiated by solar radiation. The important temperatures are also shown in **Figure 14**: the storage mass internal surface temperature T_s, the (double-glazed) window internal glazing temperature T_{wi}, the room air temperature T_{ai}, and the outdoor air temperature T_o.

The thermal network, shown in **Figure 15**, contains several conductances; the equivalent conductance U_{inf} due to infiltration heat loss links T_{ai} and T_o. Convective conductances U_{sa} and U_{aw} link T_{ai} with T_s and T_{wi}, respectively, while the radiative conductance U_{sw} links T_s and T_{wi}. Combined radiative and convective conductances U_{wi} and U_{wo} thermally link T_{wi} with T_{wo} and T_o, respectively. The components outside the thermal mass have been replaced in **Figure 16** by an equivalent conductance U_o in series with the sol-air temperature T_{eo} associated with the external wall surface. The conductance U_o combines the insulation resistance R_{ins} and the external surface radiative–convective conductance (equal to $A_o h_o$). While the model as just described assumes a uniformly distributed storage mass, by a small extension it can model a situation where some of the walls (normally the ceiling) are nonmassive, by modeling them as conductances in parallel with U_{inf}. Therefore, U_{inf} is replaced by $U_{\text{inf}} + U_{\text{nonmassive}}$.

The network also contains several heat sources. The major source S_s is the solar radiation transmitted through the window and absorbed by the storage mass. Sources S_{wi} and S_{wo} are the rates at which solar radiation is absorbed (uniformly) by the inner and outer glazings, respectively.

A delta to star transformation permits the network in **Figure 15** to be reduced to that in **Figure 16**. This transformation has permitted a 'natural' representative room temperature T_{ei} to be obtained at an important node; T_{ei} is a weighted average of T_{ai}, T_{wi}, and T_s:

$$T_{ei} = \frac{U_{ew} T_{wi} + U_{ea} T_{ai} + U_{es} T_s}{U_{ew} + U_{ea} + U_{es}} \quad [15a]$$

where

$$U_{ew} = U_{sw}\left(1 + \frac{U_{aw}}{U_{sa}}\right) + U_{aw} \quad [15b]$$

$$U_{ea} = U_{aw}\left(1 + \frac{U_{sa}}{U_{sw}}\right) + U_{sa} \quad [15c]$$

$$U_{es} = U_{sw}\left(1 + \frac{U_{sa}}{U_{sw}}\right) + U_{sa} \quad [15d]$$

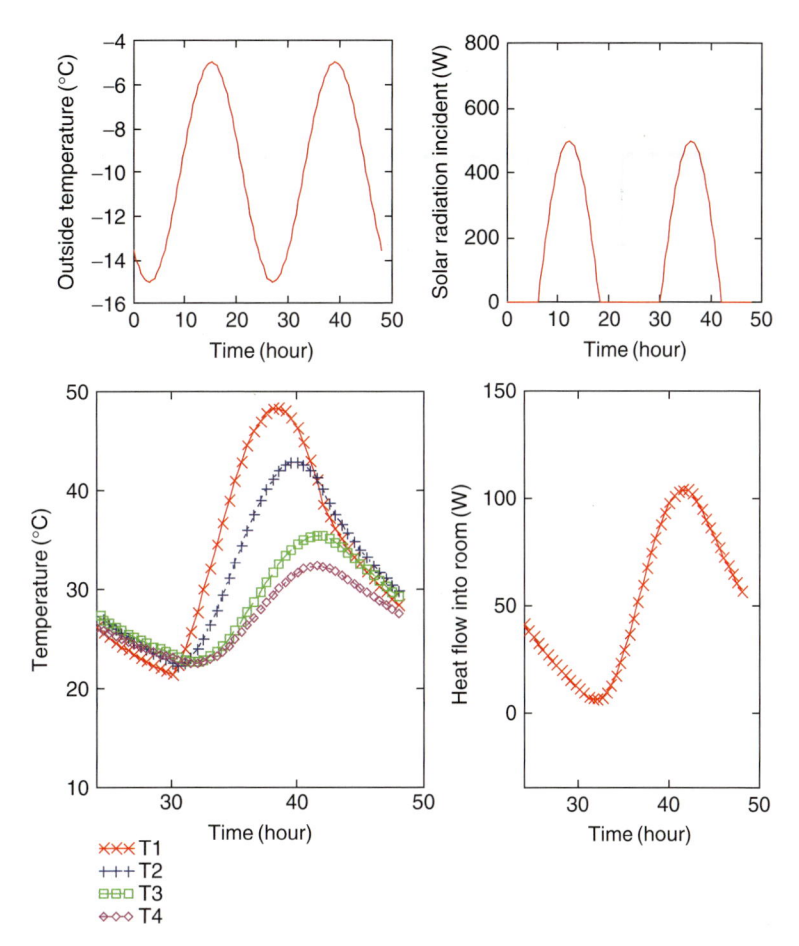

Figure 13 Weather conditions and temperature variation under clear winter conditions for a wall with transparent insulation.

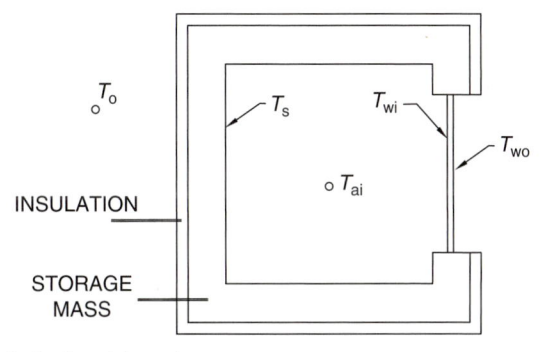

Figure 14 Direct-gain room with uniformly distributed thermal storage mass.

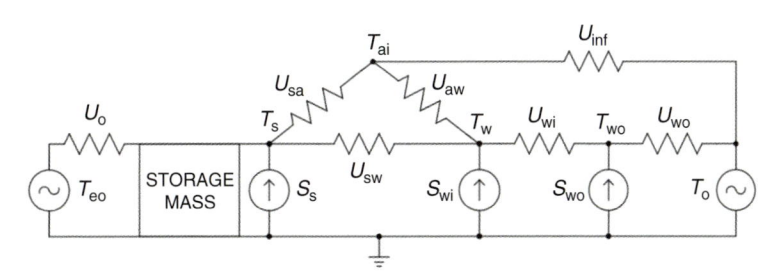

Figure 15 Thermal network for room with wall model by distributed RC element.

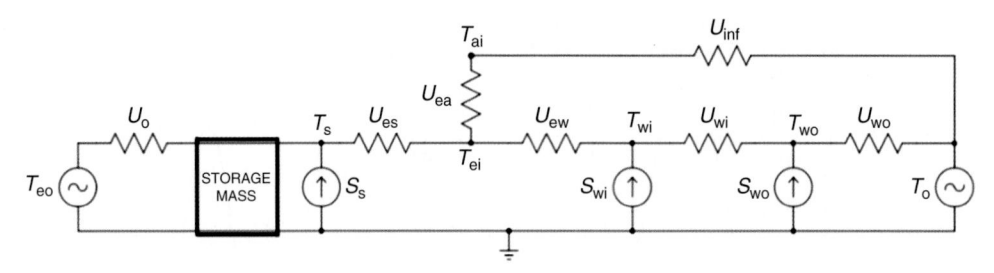

Figure 16 Thermal network after delta-to-star transformation.

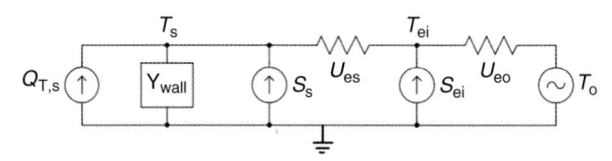

Figure 17 Simplified thermal network.

The temperature T_{ei} can serve as a representative 'sensed' temperature because it should closely follow the effective temperature that would be felt by an occupant who senses, through radiant exchange, the temperature of the room surfaces, and through convective exchange, the room air temperature.

More simplifications are applied to obtain the simplified network in **Figure 17**. The first transforms the minor sources S_{wi} and S_{wo} to the equivalent source S_{ei} given by

$$S_{ei} = \frac{U_{ew}[S_{wi}(h_i + h_o) + S_{wo}h_i]}{h_i h_o A_w + (h_i + h_o)U_{ew}} \quad [16a]$$

$$S_{ei} = \frac{U_{ew}[S_{wi}(h_i + h_o) + S_{wo}h_i]}{[h_i h_o A_w + (h_i + h_o)U_{ew}]} \quad [16b]$$

Source S_{ei} represents the portion of solar radiation, which is absorbed in the glazings and then transferred to the room interior by thermal radiation or convection. After S_{ei} has been obtained, the equivalent conductance U_{eo} coupling T_{ei} and T_o can be determined as

$$U_{eo} = \frac{1}{\left[\frac{1}{U_{ew}} + \frac{1}{U_{wi}} + \frac{1}{U_{wo}}\right]} + \frac{1}{\left[\frac{1}{U_{ea}} + \frac{1}{U_{inf}}\right]} \quad [17]$$

$$U_{eo} = \frac{1}{\left[\frac{1}{U_{ew}} + \frac{1}{U_{wi}} + \frac{1}{U_{wo}}\right]} + \frac{1}{\left[\frac{1}{U_{ea}} + \frac{1}{U_{inf}}\right]} \quad [18]$$

(If there is no mass on the ceiling, the ceiling is modeled as a pure conductance in parallel with U_{inf}, and its conductance is added to U_{inf} in eqn [18]). Both S_{ei} and S_s are proportional to the solar irradiance on the window, so that S_{ei} is expected to be proportional to S_s. It was found that S_{ei} is typically about 4% of the magnitude of S_s (for standard double glazing and midlatitudes in winter). S_{ei} can be transformed to node s and added to S_s. Thus, S_s is multiplied by the appropriate transformation factor so as to include the effect of S_{ei}; this factor is equal to $[1 + ((S_{ei}/S_s)U_{es}/(U_{es} + U_{eo}))]$.

The final simplification is replacement of the wall by its Norton equivalent, which is determined as explained above. The variable of interest here is the interior surface temperature T_s, unimportant nodes are eliminated by this transformation, and the resulting network consists of only two-terminal components. These two simplifications yield the network in **Figure 17**. The Norton equivalent consists of Y_{wall} (called the wall self-admittance in the previous section) and the equivalent source $Q_{T,s}$ given by:

$$Q_{T,s} = -Y_{seo}T_{eo} \quad [19]$$

where the transfer admittance Y_{seo} is given by

$$Y_{seo} = -\frac{A_s}{\left[\frac{A_s \cos h(\gamma x)}{U_o} + \frac{\sin h(\gamma x)}{k\gamma}\right]} \quad [20]$$

The wall self-admittance is given by

$$Y_{wall} = \frac{A_s\left[\left(\frac{U_o}{A_s}\right) + k\gamma E\right]}{\left[\left(\frac{U_o}{k\gamma A_s}\right)E + 1\right]} \quad [21]$$

where $E = \tan h(\gamma)$.

3.11.2.1.3(i) Important design approximation

For rooms with well-insulated walls and high mass (more than 10 cm of concrete or equivalent), the approximate wall self-admittance can be calculated with the following equation:

$$Y_{\text{wall}} \approx A\,k\gamma\,\tan\,h(\gamma x) \qquad [22\text{a}]$$

For very thick mass (more than 25 cm of concrete or equivalent), the wall may be approximated to a semi-infinite solid with admittance equal to

$$Y_{\text{wall, semi-inf}} \approx A\,k\gamma \qquad [22\text{b}]$$

In both of the above cases, the transfer admittance (for all frequencies apart from the mean) is negligible.

The solutions for T_s and T_{ei} are readily obtained from a heat balance at the two nodes (note that S_{ei}, a small source, is not explicitly included in the heat balance as it has been transformed to node s and added to S_s). The storage mass surface temperature is found to be given by

$$T_s(\omega) = \frac{S_s + Q_{T,s} + U_L T_o}{Y_s} \qquad [23\text{a}]$$

where Y_s is the total room admittance as seen from the port formed by the reference and the T_s node, given by

$$Y_s = Y_{\text{wall}} + U_L \qquad [23\text{b}]$$

where

$$U_L = \frac{1}{\dfrac{1}{U_{\text{es}}} + \dfrac{1}{U_{\text{eo}}}} \qquad [23\text{c}]$$

The conductance U_L represents the total loss conductance between the storage mass interior surface and the ambient temperature T_o.

The representative room temperature (expected to be close to the operative room temperature [3]) can be shown to be as follows:

$$T_{\text{ei}}(\omega) = (\text{TF})_{\text{eis}}(S_s + Q_{T,s}) + \frac{(U_{\text{eo}} T_o)}{Y_{\text{ei}}} \qquad [23\text{d}]$$

where

$$(\text{TF})_{\text{eis}} = \frac{1}{\left(\dfrac{Y_{\text{wall}}}{U_L} + 1\right) U_{\text{eo}}} \qquad [23\text{e}]$$

and

$$Y_{\text{ei}} = U_{\text{eo}} + \frac{Y_{\text{wall}} U_{\text{es}}}{Y_{\text{wall}} + U_{\text{es}}} \qquad [23\text{f}]$$

The transfer function $(\text{TF})_{\text{eis}}$ determines the effect of the primary source S_s, while Y_{ei} is the total room admittance as seen from the port formed by the T_{ei} node and reference node.

3.11.2.1.3(ii) Source models

Steady-state periodic conditions are assumed in computing the room temperature swing (difference between maximum and minimum) in T_{ei} or T_s over a particular day. The period is assumed to be 1 day, implying that the day in question has been preceded by identical days. Although deviations from the 1-day periodic assumption (e.g., previous day overcast and current day clear) would cause errors in the 'mean' value of T_{ei} for the day considered, the variation of the waveform of T_{ei} about its mean should not be affected, and therefore, the difference between its maximum and minimum points should be close to the actual swing. Another option would have been to include the effect of the previous day, that is, to assume a 2-day periodicity; the present method can be readily generalized to include such a model. Note that because of the 1-day periodic assumption, weather input is needed only for the particular day in question.

Fourier series models are required for the sources S_s, T_{eo}, and T_o, in order to obtain the time domain solution for T_s and T_{ei} under periodic conditions. For equatorial-facing windows (e.g., south-facing in the northern hemisphere), the primary source S_s can be closely modeled over the daytime as a half sinusoid. The constraints on the half sinusoid are chosen to satisfy two conditions: first, that it have an integrated energy equal to the actual solar radiation H_a absorbed in the room over the day, and second, that it must start at sunrise and terminate at sunset. Thus, S_s for a single day is defined by

$$S_s = 0, \quad \text{for } |t| \le t_s$$

and

$$S_s = \left(\frac{\pi H_a}{t_s}\right) \cos\left(\frac{\pi t}{2 t_s}\right), \quad \text{for } |t| > t_s \qquad [24\text{a}]$$

where t is the time measured from the solar noon (t is negative in the morning, positive in the afternoon), and t_s is the value of t at sunset. This expression for S_s can be approximated by the following truncated Fourier series:

$$S_s = q_0 + \sum_n q_n \cos(\omega_n t) \qquad [24b]$$

where

$$\omega_n = \frac{2\pi n}{t_d}, \quad q_0 = \frac{H_a}{t_d} \quad \text{and} \quad q_n = H_a f_n \qquad [24c]$$

and f_n being given by

$$f_n = \frac{\sin\left[\pi\frac{t_d + 4t_s n}{2t_d}\right]}{(t_d + 4t_s n)} + \frac{\sin\left[\pi\frac{t_d - 4t_s n}{2t_d}\right]}{(t_d - 4t_s n)} \qquad [24d]$$

As can be seen, the relative magnitude of the harmonics is determined completely by the day length $2t_s$. The number of harmonics necessary to model S_s was found to increase with a decrease in the day length because of the more abrupt increase in the absorbed radiation at sunrise and its more rapid decrease at sunset. For windows that are not south-facing, the Fourier coefficients can be determined by direct numerical integration of the instantaneous absorbed irradiation. Various methods can be used for determining the total daily irradiation absorbed H_a. Either real weather may be employed, which is cumbersome, or instead the daily clearness index may be used to generate values of the hourly clearness index.

The variation of the ambient temperature T_o was modeled by a single sinusoid, with maximum at 3.00 p.m. and minimum at 3.00 a.m. (solar times). Thus, if T_{om} is the daily average of T_o, and ΔT_o the daily range of T_o then

$$T_o = T_{om} + \left(\frac{\Delta T_o}{2}\right)\cos\left(\omega_1 t - \frac{\pi}{4}\right) \qquad [25]$$

The model does not distinguish between the differing orientations of the exterior wall surfaces, and hence, it is not possible to accurately model the effect of fluctuations in the solar radiation absorbed by the wall exterior surfaces. A sensitivity analysis showed that the effect of this absorbed solar radiation on the temperature swing is small, provided there is at least a medium amount of insulation (about 5 RSI) behind the mass. Thus, the sol-air temperature T_{eo} can be modeled as equivalent to T_o.

3.11.2.1.3(iii) Periodic solution

The time domain solution for the representative temperature T_{ei} is obtained after substituting the source models in eqn [26] and evaluating magnitudes and phase angles for the complex transfer functions. Since the variable of interest here is fluctuations, the mean source terms can be ignored. The following solution is obtained for the variation of T_{ei} about its mean T_{eim}:

$$T_{ei}(t) - T_{eim} = \left(\frac{\Delta T_o U_{eo}}{2Y_{ei1}}\right)\cos(\omega_1 t - \varphi_{ei1}\tfrac{\pi}{4}) + \frac{\Delta T_o Y_{seo1}(\text{TF})_{eis1}}{2\cos(\omega_1 t + \varphi_{eis1} + \varphi_{seo1}\tfrac{\pi}{4})} + \sum_{n=1}^N (\text{TF})_{eisn} q_n \cos(\omega_n t + \varphi_{eisn}) \qquad [26]$$

where $(\text{TF})_{eisn}$ and φ_{eisn} are the magnitude and phase, respectively, of $(\text{TF})_{eis}$ for $\omega = \omega_n$. Similar definitions apply to Y_{ei1} and φ_{ei1}, and Y_{seo1} and φ_{seo1}. The variation in T_s is given by

$$T_s(t) - T_{sm} = \left(\frac{\Delta T_o U_L}{2Y_{s1}}\right)\cos(\omega_1 - \varphi_{s1}{}^{-(\pi/4)}) + \frac{\Delta T_{eo} Y_{seo1}}{(2Y_{s1})\cos(\omega_1 + \varphi_{s1} + \varphi_{seo1}{}^{-(\pi/4)})} + \sum_{n=1}^N \frac{q_n}{Y_{sn}\cos(\omega_n t + \varphi_{sn})} \qquad [27]$$

The swings in T_s and T_{ei} can be determined by differentiating the appropriate equation, finding the two zeroes corresponding to the times at which the maximum and minimum temperatures occur, and then substituting these times back into the original equation.

3.11.2.1.3(iv) Approximate design method for temperature swings

For a well-insulated room with massive walls, the maximum temperature swings can be estimated with the following approximation that adjusts the response to the first (fundamental) harmonic to include higher harmonic effects:

$$\text{Temperature swing} = 2F_h \frac{|q_1|}{|Y_{wall}|} \qquad [28]$$

where the magnitude of the first harmonic of solar gains $|q_1|$ is estimated from eqn [24a].

$F_h = 1.12$ is a factor to approximate for the effect of higher harmonics, and $|Y_{wall}|$ may be estimated by

$$|Y_{wall}| = |Ak\gamma| \times |\tanh(\gamma x)| = Ak\left(\frac{2\pi}{P\alpha}\right)^{1/2}\left[\frac{\cosh X - \cos X}{\cosh X + \cos X}\right]^{1/2} \qquad [29a]$$

with

$$X = 2L\left(\frac{\pi}{(P\alpha)}\right)^{1/2} \quad [29b]$$

The phase angle of Y_{wall} is given by

$$\text{Phase}(Y_{wall}) = 45° + \tan^{-1}\left(\frac{\sin X}{\sinh X}\right) \quad [29c]$$

Note that the first term (45°) in eqn [29c] corresponds to the phase angle for $k\gamma$, and it is equivalent to a time lead of 3 h (15° are equivalent to 1 h for a period of 24 h).

3.11.2.1.3(v) Detailed frequency domain zone model and building transfer functions

Building heat exchanges may be represented by a thermal network, and transfer functions are obtained by performing an energy balance at all nodes in the Laplace domain. Both lumped and distributed elements can be considered with this approach. Simple models, as in the previous section which do not represent in detail infrared radiation heat exchanges between room interior surfaces, can usually be solved analytically.

The thermal network model for a typical room over a basement (**Figure 18**), with one window and convective auxiliary heating, is depicted in **Figure 19**. The thermally massive walls are modeled by a two-port distributed element, while the room air and lightweight room contents are modeled by a lumped thermal capacitance. Although this capacitance has no effect on load calculations because of the relatively low frequencies involved, it is important to include it for short-term (high frequency) control studies. Each two-port element represents the equivalent two-port for each wall, obtained after multiplying the cascade matrices for each massive and nonmassive layer. The resistances connecting node 1 (room air) to the interior surfaces represent convective conductances given by

$$U1j = A(j) \times \text{hc}(j) \quad [30a]$$

The radiation conductances interconnecting room interior surface nodes 2–8 are given by

$$Uij = A(i)\sigma 4T_m^3 F^*_{ij} \quad [30b]$$

where σ is the Stefan–Boltzman constant and $4T_m^3$ is a linearization factor that is based on an estimated mean temperature, T_m. The radiation exchange factors $F^*(i,j)$ between the pair of surfaces under consideration (i and j) are determined from the radiation view factors, F_{ij} (also denoted by $F(i,j)$) and the radiative properties of the room surfaces as follows:

$$F^*(i,j) = \frac{m(i,j)\varepsilon_i\varepsilon_j}{\rho_i} \quad [30c]$$

where $[m] = [M]^{-1}$; the elements of matrix $[M]$ are given by $M(I, j) - \rho_i F(i,j)$, with $I(i, j) = 1$ if $i = j$; otherwise, $I(i,j) = 0$ (identity matrix).

The energy balances at the room interior nodes for both models are readily obtained after replacing each wall with its Norton equivalent subnetwork, which consists of an equivalent heat source Q_{sc} and a self-admittance Y_{eq}, thereby eliminating all exterior

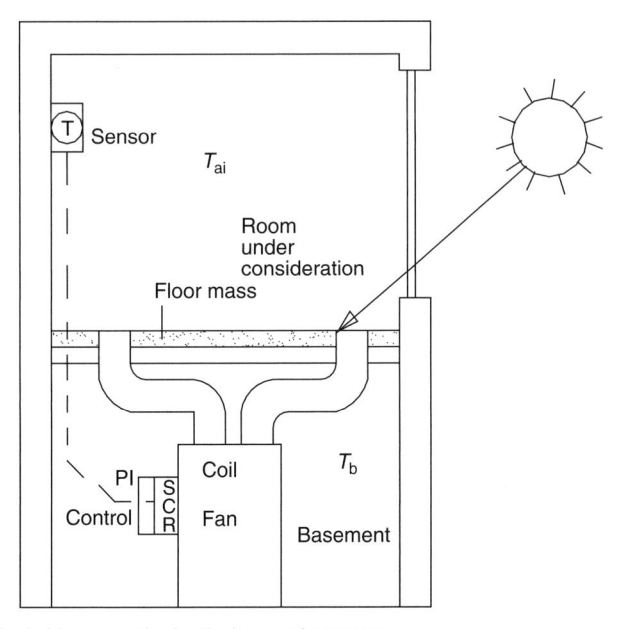

Figure 18 Schematic of one zone (heated by convective heating) over a basement.

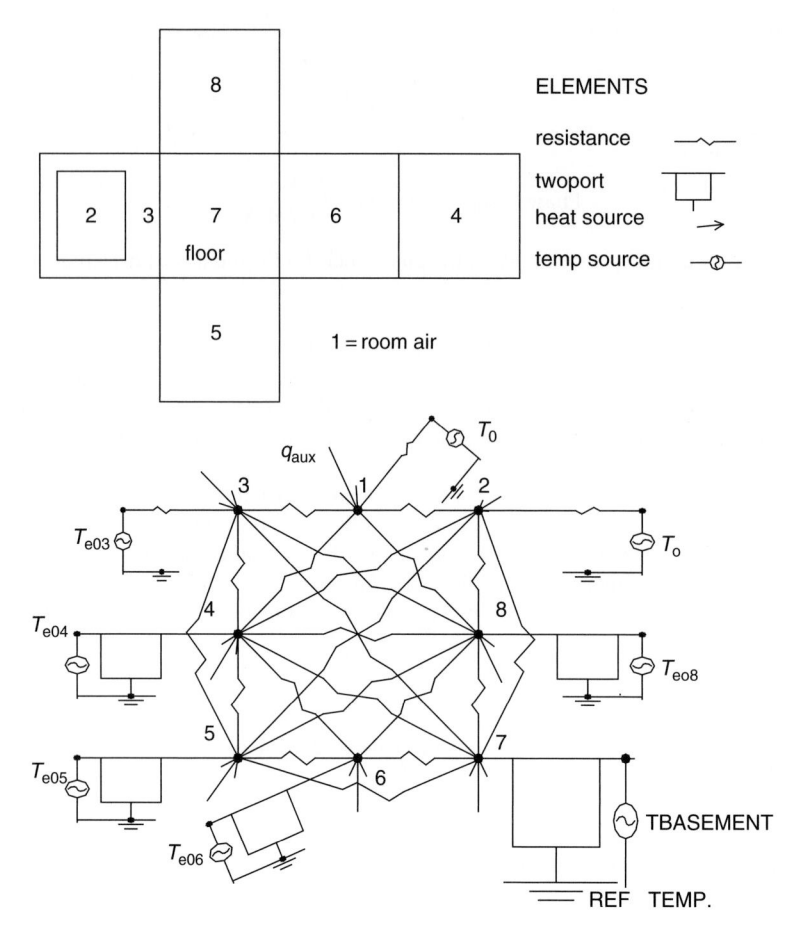

Figure 19 Detailed thermal network model of zone in **Figure 18** (node 1, room air; nodes 2–8, room interior surfaces).

nodes without discretizing the massive elements. The equivalent source Q_{sc} is equal to the wall transfer admittance times an external specified temperature. For the floor with self-admittance Y_{fs} and transfer admittance Y_{ft}, $Q_{sc} = -T_b Y_{ft}$ (the negative sign is because of the sign convention used).

The energy balance for the model (with summations ΣU_{iJ} over $J = 1$–8) is as follows:

$$\begin{bmatrix} sC_a + \Sigma U1J + U_{inf} & -U12 & -U13 & -U14 & -U15 & -U16 & -U17 & -U18 \\ -U12 & Y_{2s} + \Sigma U2J & -U23 & -U24 & -U25 & -U26 & -U27 & -U28 \\ -U13 & -U23 & Y_{3s} + \Sigma U3J & -U34 & -U35 & -U36 & -U37 & -U38 \\ -U14 & -U24 & -U34 & Y_{4s} + \Sigma U4J & -U45 & -U46 & -U47 & -U48 \\ -U15 & -U25 & -U35 & -U45 & Y_{5s} + \Sigma U5J & -U56 & -U57 & -U58 \\ -U16 & -U26 & -U36 & -U46 & -U56 & Y_{6s} + \Sigma U6J & -U67 & -U68 \\ -U17 & -U27 & -U37 & -U47 & -U57 & -U67 & Y_{7s} + \Sigma U7J & -U78 \\ -U18 & -U28 & -U38 & -U48 & -U58 & -U68 & -U78 & Y_{8s} + \Sigma U8J \end{bmatrix} \begin{bmatrix} T_1 \\ T_2 \\ T_3 \\ T_4 \\ T_5 \\ T_6 \\ T_7 \\ T_8 \end{bmatrix} = \begin{bmatrix} Q_1 \\ Q_2 \\ Q_3 \\ Q_4 \\ Q_5 \\ Q_6 \\ Q_7 \\ Q_8 \end{bmatrix}$$

[31a]

or

$$[Y]_{N \times N} \{T\}_N = \{Q\}_N$$

where $[Y]$ is the admittance matrix, $\{T\}$ is the temperatures vector, and $\{Q\}$ is the source vector. The solution for $\{T\}$ in the frequency domain is obtained by

$$[Z]\{Q\} = \{T\} \qquad [31b]$$

where $[Z] = [Y]^{-1}$.

The elements of the admittance matrix may be obtained by inspection from the topology of the network. The diagonal entry $Y(i,i)$ is equal to the sum of the component admittances connected to node i. Off-diagonal entry $Y(i,j)$ is the sum of component admittances/conductances connected between nodes i and j, multiplied by -1. The heat source vector element $Q(i)$ is the sum of the heat sources connected to node j (positive if directed to the node). As can be seen, for thermal networks the admittance matrix has certain important characteristics: (1) it is symmetric, with all off-diagonal elements $Y(i,j)$ being real and equal to – (conductance U_{ij}), and (2) all capacitances and all self-admittances appear in the diagonal entries, which are consequently complex. The transfer functions of interest are the elements of the inverse of [Y], that is, the impedance transfer functions $Z(i,j)$. The temperature of node I for each frequency is given by

$$T(I) = \sum_{J=1}^{N} Z(I,J) Q(J) \qquad [31c]$$

For room air temperature, I is set equal to 1 in the above equation, which is determined for each frequency (harmonic) of interest. The functions $Z(I,J)$ are determined at specific frequencies ($s = j\omega_n$) by inverting the admittance matrix [Y]. The operative temperature, T_e, is a scalar function of nodal temperatures $\{T(1) \ldots T(8)\}$.

Building transfer functions generally provide the response of interest – heat flow or temperature for unit heat input or unit temperature change at a node in the thermal network. The most important transfer function required in the present method is the impedance transfer function:

$$Z(I,J) = \frac{T(I)}{Q(J)} \qquad [32]$$

which represents the temperature change for node I due to unit heat input at node J for a given frequency. Thus, for heat input $Q(J)$ the room temperature change $\Delta T(1)$ (1 = room air node) is equal to

$$\Delta T(1) = Z(1,J) \times Q(J) \qquad [33]$$

It is often useful to determine a transfer function not only for individual room temperatures but also for an effective room temperature such as the operative temperature [3]. The operative temperature is defined as the uniform temperature of an enclosure in which an occupant would exchange the same amount of heat by radiation plus convection as in the actual nonuniform environment. The operative temperature is given by

$$T_e = \frac{h_r T_{mr} + h_c T_{ai}}{h_r + h_c} \qquad [34a]$$

where T_{ai} is the air temperature, T_{mr} is the mean radiant temperature, and h_r and h_c are radiative and convective coefficients, respectively, for a person or object (sensor). The operative temperature transfer functions $X(I)$ are given by

$$X(I) = \frac{T_e}{Q(I)} \qquad [34b]$$

and represent the effect of a source $Q(I)$ acting at node I on the operative temperature.

3.11.2.1.3(vi) Analysis of building transfer functions

Substantial insight into building thermal behavior may be obtained by studying the magnitude and phase angle of the important transfer functions. Consider, for example, the transfer functions Z11 and Z17 in the detailed model (Z11 and Z12, respectively, in the simple model); these represent the effects of heat sources at node 1 (room air) and 7 (floor), respectively, on the temperature of node 1 (in both cases all other sources set to zero):

$$Z11(s) = \frac{T1(s)}{Q1(s)} \qquad [35a]$$

$$Z17(s) = \frac{T1(s)}{Q1(s)} \qquad [35b]$$

The magnitude of $Z17(j\omega)$ may be used to determine the approximate room temperature swings due to solar radiation absorbed at the floor surface as follows.

If S7 represents solar radiation absorbed at the floor interior surface and $^3S7(j\omega 1)^3$ represents the magnitude of its fundamental harmonic, the approximate temperature swing amplitude is given by $^3Z17(j\omega 1)^3 \times {}^3S7(j\omega 1)^3$. Perhaps a more significant result is the time delay between the peak of $S(t)$ (noon for south-facing windows) and the resulting peak of the room temperature; this is approximately equal to φ_{17}/ω_1 (seconds), where φ_{17} is the phase angle of Z17 ($\varphi_{17} = \tan^{-1} Im(Z17)/Re(Z17)$).

3.11.2.1.3(vi)(a) Results The room considered in the example has dimensions 7.3 m wide by 2.4 m high and the north–south depth is 6.7 m. The south-facing double-glazed window area is 11.1 m^2. The thermal mass on the floor is 4 cm-thick concrete with thermal conductivity equal to 1.8 W m^{-2} K^{-1}, density 2242 kg m^{-3}, and specific heat capacity 840 J kg^{-1} K^{-1}. The interior lining on the vertical walls and on the ceiling is a 13 mm-thick gypsum board. The insulation is 3.5 RSI on the vertical walls, 7.4 RSI on the ceiling, and 1 RSI on the floor, which connects to a basement.

Figures 20 and **21** depict the magnitude and phase variation (Bode plots) for Z11 and Z17, respectively, in the case of a carpeted floor and concrete floor, respectively, showing actual discrete frequency responses and fitted third-order transfer functions. **Figure 5** shows the Nyquist plot, that is, imaginary versus real components, for Z11 of the room with a concrete floor and for Z17 of the room with the carpeted floor. **Figure 20** shows that the room response can be approximately separated into a short-term dynamics

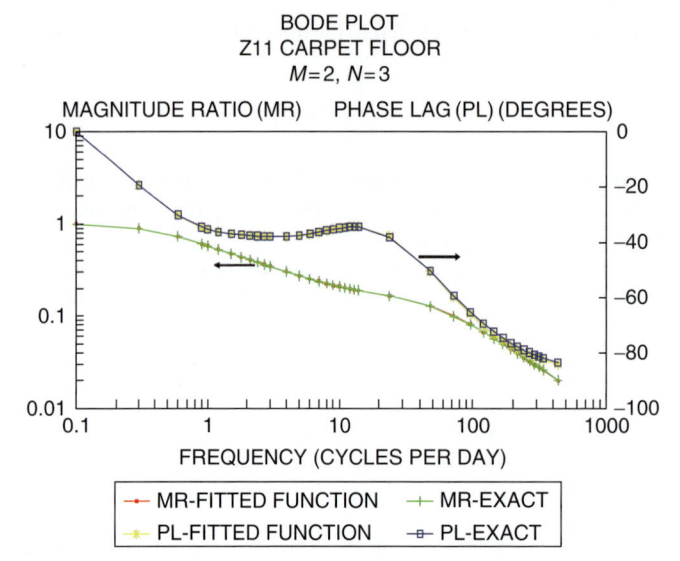

Figure 20 Transfer function plots (magnitude and phase) for Z11 (fitted third-order transfer functions also shown).

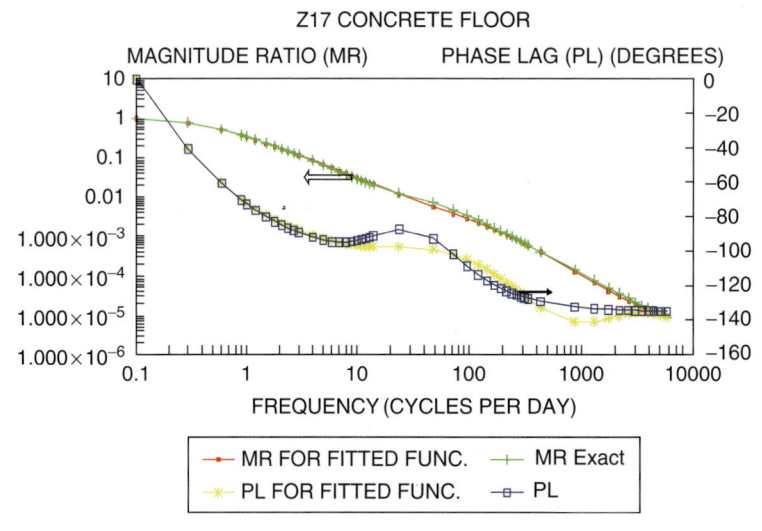

Figure 21 Transfer function plots (magnitude and phase) for Z17 (fitted third-order transfer functions also shown).

high-frequency range and a low-frequency range; in the high-frequency short-term dynamics region, the room air thermal capacitance is significant, and the difference between Z11 for the concrete floor and the carpeted one is small in both phase and magnitude, that is, the effect of thermal mass is minimal in this region. The separation between short-term and long-term building thermal dynamics begins at frequencies of approximately 35 cycles per day or periods of 41 min. The separation is also indicated in **Figure 5(a)** by the Nyquist plot of Z11; the small cusp is associated with the short-term dynamics, which is the frequency range within which the room air (and furniture, etc.) thermal capacity is important. Simulations by the authors with different constructions showed similar results for Z11, which represents the effects of convective heat gains or losses. Short-term dynamics are particularly important for feedback control studies. For lower frequencies such as one cycle per day, the magnitude and phase of Z11 and Z17 is a strong function of room construction, and there is a significant difference between the response of the massive (concrete) construction and the nonmassive (carpet) one.

An example of a third-order fitted function for Z17 obtained with the above technique is given in **Figure 21**. As can be seen, this third-order fit is good in both magnitude and phase, the error being typically less than 2%. The fitted Laplace transfer function for Z17 is

$$Z17\,(s) = \frac{0.008\,04 + 10.5\,s + 55.2\,s^2 - 10.5\,s^3}{1 + 4.01 \times 10^4\,s + 6.64 \times 10^7\,s^2 + 2.63 \times 10^9\,s^3}$$

3.11.2.1.3(vii) Heating/cooling load and room temperature calculation

Heating/cooling load and associated room temperature calculations are performed with the same building transfer functions employed in frequency response and thermal control studies. These computations are performed by means of discrete Fourier series.

The building transfer functions are calculated at discrete frequencies ($s = j\omega_n$), and a discrete Fourier transform (DFT) of the weather data is performed. For example, convective auxiliary heating is given by

$$Q(1) = q_{\text{aux}} + q_{\text{int}} + q_{\text{eq}} \qquad [36]$$

where q_{int} represents the convective portion of internal gains and q_{eq} is an equivalent source representing heat flow due to infiltration and is given by $U_{\text{inf}}T_o$. Therefore, by substituting eqn [36] in eqn [31c] and assuming that the room air temperature $T(1)$ is specified, the auxiliary heating/cooling power q_{aux} may be determined at each frequency of interest as

$$q_{\text{aux}}(j\omega) = \frac{\left\{T(1) - Z(1,1)[q_{\text{int}} + U_{\text{inf}}T_o] - \sum_{J=2}^{N} Z(1,J)Q(J)\right\}}{Z(1,1)} \qquad [37]$$

where all quantities are evaluated as complex numbers for $s = j\omega$ (N = number of nodes). Each source or specified temperature is represented by a discrete Fourier series (DFT), and the time domain variation of q_{aux} is obtained through an inverse discrete Fourier transform (IDFT). For design day analysis, five to nine harmonics are usually adequate. These are the harmonics necessary for adequate representation of the inputs, that is, heat sources such as absorbed solar radiation, internal gains, and ambient temperature T_o. One advantage of this approach over more commonly used methods is that the superposition principle is applied directly. Therefore, effects of various inputs may be studied separately, or a passive analysis ($q_{\text{aux}} = 0$) can be easily performed – in this case eqn [31c] is directly applied. Note that the air temperature $T(1)$ in eqn [37] can be a profile, that is, it may vary with time. Thus, optimum set-point profile variations may be determined to optimize solar gain utilization. The discrete Fourier series approach is described in more detail by Athienitis and Sanatmouris [1], including a model for a proportional control source in the thermal network and a technique for modeling time-varying parameters, such as a conductance representing infiltration based on the substitution network theorem.

3.11.2.1.3(viii) Discrete Fourier series method for simulation

Steady-periodic conditions are usually assumed; for example, if the simulation is to be performed for a week, it is assumed that all previous weeks have been identical to the week considered. The steps needed for a periodic steady-state solution are as follows:

1. Select the number N of harmonics to perform the analysis. If n represents a harmonic number and P is the time length of the simulation or analysis (e.g., a day or a week), then a harmonic's frequency ω_n is equal to $2\pi n/P$.
2. Obtain the appropriate discrete Fourier series representations for the sources. An arbitrary source $M(t)$ is represented by a complex Fourier series (IDFT) of the form

$$M(t) = \sum_{n=-N}^{N} m_n(j\omega_n) \exp(j\omega_n t) \qquad [38a]$$

the complex coefficients $m_n(j\omega_n)$ being determined numerically by a DFT:

$$\begin{array}{c} K \\ m_n \\ k=1 \end{array} = \frac{[\Sigma M(t_k)\exp(-j\omega_n t_k)]}{P} \qquad [38b]$$

where $M(t_k)$ is the value of M at time t_k corresponding to point k (for a total of K values over the time length P). The number of harmonics N cannot exceed $K/2$.
3. Determine the discrete frequency response $Z(j\omega_n)$ of the output of interest to unit input at each node. The periodic response to each source is obtained by superposition of the output harmonics using complex (phasor) multiplication. The total response to more than one input is determined by a double summation for all inputs $Q(J)$ and all frequencies of interest ω_n. For example, for the room air temperature $T1(t)$ is obtained by

$$T1(t) = \sum_{n=-N}^{N} \left\{ \sum_{J=1}^{8} Z(1,J,j\omega_n)Q_n(J,j\omega_n) \exp(j\omega_n t) \right\} \qquad [38c]$$

3.11.3 PV/T Systems and Building-Integrated Photovoltaic/Thermal (BIPV/T) Systems

3.11.3.1 Integration of Solar Technologies into the Building Envelope and BIPV/T

Integration improves the cost-effectiveness by having the PV panels provide additional functions, which involve active solar heating and daylighting (see **Figures 22** and **23** for two Canadian examples of a near net-zero energy house and a University building in Montreal with a BIPV/T façade). The following are some recognized methods of beneficial integration:

Figure 22 EcoTerra home and its BIPV/T modular roof. (a) EcoTerra™ home with fully BIPV/T system (top roof). (b) Construction of BIPV/T roof module. (c) BIPV/T roof module delivered on-site for assembly of house.

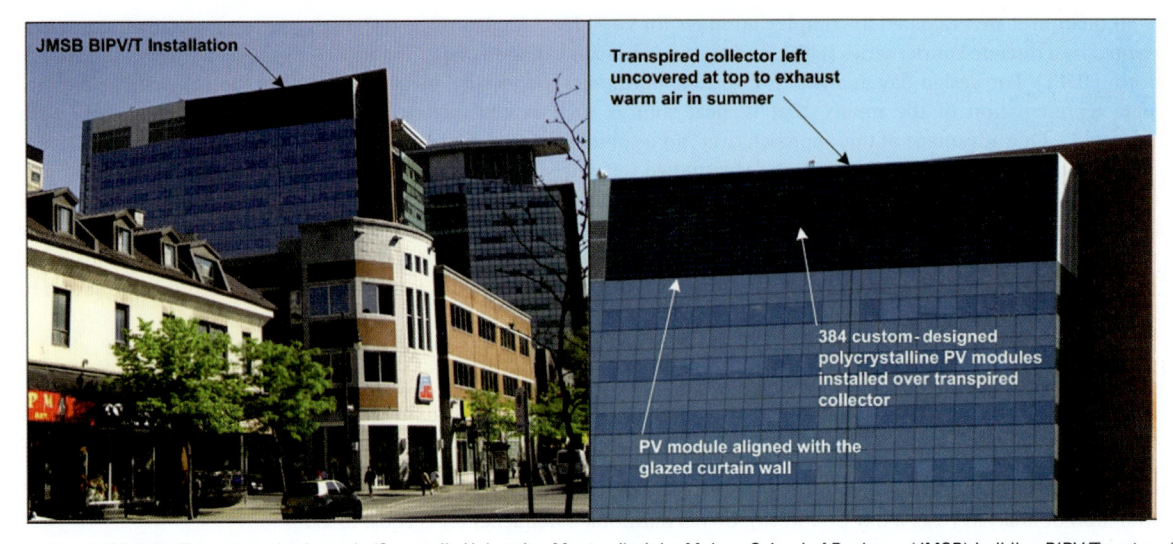

Figure 23 JMSB BIPV/T façade and schematic (Concordia University, Montreal). John Molson School of Business (JMSB) building BIPV/T system (top right section of façade) and schematic illustrating the system concept: 70% of the transpired collector cladding area (288 m^2) is covered by specially designed PV modules; the system generates up to about 25 kW electricity and 75 kW of thermal energy used to directly heat ventilation air [7].

1. *Integrating the PV panels into the building envelope (BIPV).* This strategy could involve, for example, replacing roof shingles or wall cladding with PV panels. It has significant advantages over the more usual 'add-on' strategy. Not only does it eliminate an extra component (e.g., roof asphalt shingles), but it also eliminates penetrations of a preexisting envelope that are required in order to attach the panel to the building. (It is understood that the components replaced are not windows, as this is covered by Method 3, below.) Architectural and aesthetic integration is a major requirement in this type of BIPV system. Not only can this strategy lead to much higher levels of overall performance, but it can also provide enhanced durability: one International Energy Agency (IEA) study [8] found that PV systems can last 50 years, whereas curtain wall components such as sealed glazing units may only last 25 years.
2. *Integrating heat collection functions into the PV panel (BIPV/T).* PV panels typically convert from about 6% to 18% of the incident solar energy to electrical energy, and the remaining solar energy (normally lost as heat to the outdoor environment) is available to be captured as useful heat. In this strategy, a coolant fluid, such as water or air, is circulated next to the panel, extracting useful heat. The coolant also serves to lower the temperature of the panel; this is beneficial, because panel efficiency increases at lower panel temperatures. This strategy can be adopted in either in an open-loop or closed-loop configuration. In one open-loop configuration, outdoor air is passed under PV panels, and the recovered heat can be used for space heating, preheating of ventilation air, or heating DHW – either directly or through a heat pump.
3. *Integrating light transmission functions into the PV panel (BIPV/L).* This strategy uses special PV panels (semitransparent PV windows) that transmit sunlight. As was the case for the previous strategy, this strategy draws on the fact that only a fraction of the incident solar energy is converted to electricity, and the remainder can be used for other purposes – in this case for useful light, thereby saving on the energy that electrical lights would otherwise draw. Thin-film PV cells that let some sunlight through are commercially available for this purpose. A major challenge is limiting the temperature rise of the windows and controlling the impact of the associated heat gains during times when building cooling is required. Compared with normal windows, these windows have a reduced light transmission and can therefore function as shading devices.

Appropriate modeling of building-integrated solar energy systems (thermal, electric, hybrid, daylighting) is essential for the designing of high-performance solar buildings. These systems will play a major role in achieving the net-zero energy goal and need to be carefully selected, modeled, and sized for an accurate design. Different simulation tools include different technologies and simulate building-fabric energy transfer with different levels of detail. They also utilize different techniques to model the transient response of buildings and their systems to changes in internal and external thermal loads.

At the early stage of the design, a simplified software tool may provide enough accuracy to size a BIPV or a solar thermal system as it provides monthly estimates of energy generated. However, a BIPV/T system that generates both electricity and heat requires estimation of the heat recovered and its potential uses – heating ventilation air, heating water, or space heating (directly or through a heat pump). To properly simulate these systems, tools characterized by a high-integrity representation of the dynamic and connected processes are required.

3.11.3.2 A Simplified Open-Loop PV/T Model

A simplified model for a PV/T façade or roof with the exterior layer being PV panels is described below to calculate the PV temperature and the heat recovered.

Consider a façade with PV panels as the exterior layer; this façade may be represented by the thermal network model shown in **Figure 24**.

The mean air temperature T_{ma} is determined from a differential analysis that finds the air temperature as a function of vertical distance x. It is assumed that the air speed is constant, that is, air is drawn into the window by a fan in the HVAC system fresh air intake. The actual air temperature $T(x)$ is then used to determine the T_{ma}. This is then employed to find the correct values of T_{pv} and T_b, which are used to fine-tune the calculations. Considering an element dx in the vertical direction, gives the following:

$$M \times c \times \rho \times dT = (W \times dx \times h(T_{pv} - T)) + (W \times dx \times h(T_b - T)) \qquad [39a]$$

where M = flow rate = $V \times A$ (V is average velocity and A is cross-sectional area) and W is the width of façade. Note that the convective coefficient h is an average for both cavity surfaces (in reality it will generally be higher on the hotter surface).

Note that this simple model assumes an equal convective heat transfer coefficient h for both cavity surfaces. The following ordinary differential equation is obtained:

$$a \frac{d}{dx} T + 2T = T_b + T_{pv} \qquad [39b]$$

with $a = (M \times c \times \rho)/(W \times h)$

An exponential variation is obtained for the air temperature as follows:

$$T(x) = \frac{T_{pv} + T_b}{2} + \left[T_o - \frac{T_b + T_{pv}}{2} \right] e^{\frac{-x \cdot 2}{a}} \qquad [39c]$$

The PV and back panel temperatures are obtained as

$$T_b = \frac{T_{ma} \times U_b + T_R \times U_3 + T_{pv} \times U_r}{U_3 + U_b + U_r} \qquad [39d]$$

$$T_{pv} = \frac{U_o \times T_o + U_a \times T_{ma} + U_r \times T_b + S_{pv}}{U_o + U_a + U_r} \qquad [39e]$$

where U represents conductance between the various nodes ($U_o = Ah_o$, $U_r = Ah_r$, $U_a = U_b = Ah$, and U_3 is negligible).

3.11.3.3 Transient and Steady-State Models for Open-Loop Air-Based BIPV/T Systems

BIPV/T systems produce thermal and electrical energy, and have lower effective system costs than do stand-alone PV systems. The BIPV/T system absorbs solar energy on the top surface, which includes the PV panels and generates electricity while also heating air

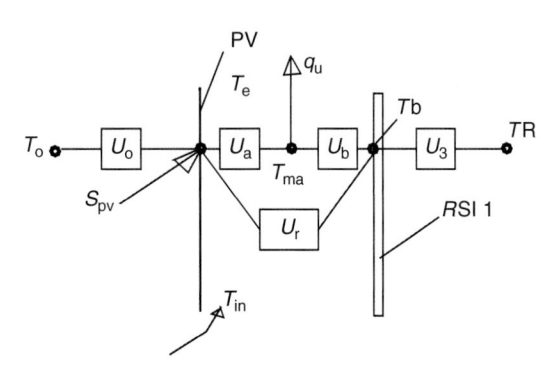

Figure 24 Thermal network model of façade with exterior PV (assuming isothermal surfaces); node b indicates the back panel interior surface (assumed to be an insulating layer with a thermal resistance of RSI 1).

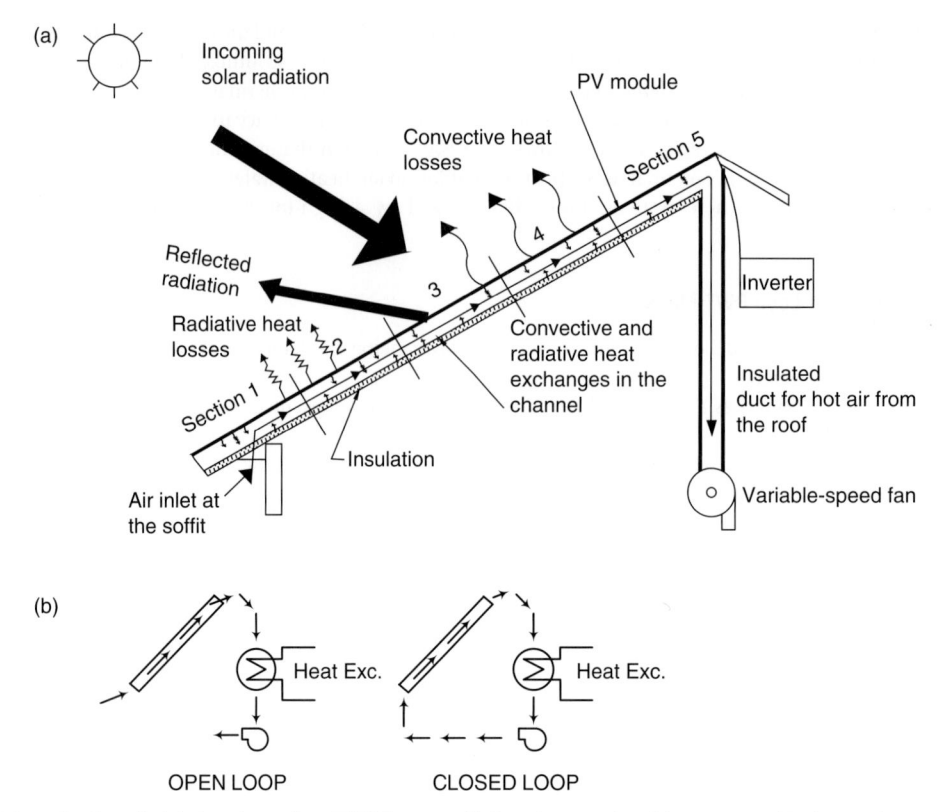

Figure 25 (a) Schematic of a typical air-based open-loop BIPV/T system. (b) Open-loop vs. closed-loop systems (the heat exchanger may be eliminated in the open-loop configuration for solar heating of fresh air used for ventilation).

flowing in a channel between the top surface and an insulated attic layer (**Figure 25(a)**). The PV modules replace cladding or roofing elements of the building envelope. Open-loop air-based BIPV/T systems supply solar-heated air that can be used either for ventilation, direct space heating, heating through a heat exchanger, or as a source for a heat pump (**Figure 25(b)**).

Accurate convective heat transfer coefficients are essential for solving the energy balance equations used for lumped parameter network modeling of these systems. This is necessary to quantify the thermal and electrical energy production, which in turn provides adequate means for sizing associated equipment, such as heat exchangers and electrical inverters. The PV module temperatures obtained by solving the energy balance equations for the PV modules are useful in designing the array layout in order to maximize total energy production. The forced convection increases the heat transfer rate from the PV modules, lowering their temperature and thus increasing their electrical conversion efficiency. Monocrystalline and polycrystalline silicon-based PV modules have typical solar energy conversion efficiencies (η_{PV}) around 5–18% and have negative maximum power point efficiency temperature coefficients, β_{mp}, between $-0.04\%\,°C^{-1}$ and $-0.08\%\,°C^{-1}$. The heat transfer coefficients are also important for the development of control algorithms for the control of the airflow that cools the panels so as to obtain a desired outlet air temperature suitable for the specific application.

Air-based BIPV/T systems are usually installed in an open-loop configuration (**Figure 25**) to avoid excessively high temperatures of the PV module; outdoor air is used to cool the PV modules by convection (commonly, forced convection). The heated air is used to provide thermal energy to one or more functions in the building before being exhausted to the exterior. Open-loop air systems are normally preferred over closed-loop air systems as the latter would likely lead to overheating of the PV module (reducing its durability and possibly causing delamination) unless fins are built into the PV design. King et al. [9] reported that delamination is more common and more severe in hot and humid climates, sometimes occurring after less than 5 years of exposure. Also, open-loop systems allow for the potential use of preheated fresh air for ventilation. Since BIPV/T systems have lower inlet temperatures than those in the case of closed-loop systems, the former system normally operates with higher thermal efficiencies, although its air exit temperatures are lower.

BIPV/T systems contain several features that need to be addressed such as heating asymmetry and a relatively complex geometry. Mathematical models of different levels of complexity, emphasizing different phenomena, have been developed over the years. This section presents two models bringing together some of the ideas presented in previous works by the authors, and the most relevant findings obtained from measurements at the experimental facilities and demonstration projects of the Canadian Solar Buildings Research Network [7, 10]. The models could readily be adapted as a design tool for air-based open-loop BIPV/T systems.

Mathematical models for the particular case of forced-convection open-loop BIPV/T systems have been developed by Clarke et al. [11], Eicker and Fux [12], Bazilian et al. [13], Bazilian and Prasad [14], Eicker [15], and Bloem [16]. Models for air-hybrid PV/T collectors – not necessarily installed as a building component – have been developed by several researchers. Examples include the work of Garg and Adhikari [17] (hybrid solar air collectors) and Hegazy [18] (four configurations of hybrid PV/T systems).

Models of naturally ventilated BIPV systems have also been studied by several researchers. Candanedo [19] provides an extensive review of these studies. For example, Yang et al. [20] developed a numerical model for a naturally ventilated PV roof and façade system. Brinkworth et al. [21] presented a model for a naturally ventilated PV roof installation. A model of a PV/T air façade was developed in TRNSYS and presented by Bosanac et al. [22]. Mittelman et al. [23] developed a naturally ventilated model where Nusselt numbers are also reported.

At Concordia University, different BIPV/T numerical models have been developed both for research on these systems and as design tools for demonstration projects. These models include the works by Charron [24], Charron and Athienitis [25, 26], Athienitis et al. [27], Liao [28], Liao et al. [29], Pantic et al. [30], Candanedo and Athienitis [31], and Chen et al. [10].

The aforementioned models, based on energy balances in control volumes, have used different levels of complexity to model the energy interactions between the surfaces. Some of the most relevant differences in approach are presented below. The majority of the models have relied on a steady-state approach, neglecting the thermal capacitance effects of the PV module. In contrast, Ito et al. [32] developed a fully explicit finite-difference model for a solar air collector. The authors found that the transient model is useful to account for the effects of rapid changes (e.g., variable cloudiness, wind speed fluctuations), and therefore, it can be useful for the development of robust control algorithms for the control of flow rate.

3.11.3.3.1 Air temperature variation within the control volume

The simplest approach uses a linear approximation to model the air temperature variation within the control volume [33]. In this case, the average air temperature inside the control volume is the arithmetic mean of the inlet and outlet temperatures. However, most recent investigations use an exponential air temperature variation, which is the exact solution if the temperatures of the surrounding surfaces are assumed to be uniform inside the control volume. The average air temperature (used for energy balances) is calculated as: $T_{avg} = \int T dx / \Delta x$.

3.11.3.3.2 Radiative heat transfer

Most investigations have used the mean temperature of the surrounding surfaces (T_m) to calculate a linearization factor ($4\sigma T_m^3$), as this facilitates the solution of the equations. The radiative heat transfer coefficient h_r is then given by $4\sigma T_m^3 ((1/\varepsilon_1) + (1/\varepsilon_2) - 1)$, assuming a view factor of 1 between the plates. The radiation exchange difference calculated by using this coefficient, assuming two plates at 350 K and 273 K, is about 1.5% underestimated from the exact value given by the equation

$$h_r = \frac{\sigma(T2^4 - T1^4)}{\frac{1}{\varepsilon_1} + \frac{1}{\varepsilon_2} - 1} \quad [40]$$

The majority of models assume, often without stating it explicitly, that the view factor between the two surfaces of interest is close to 1. This assumption is not always accurate. Charron [24] took view factor calculations for radiative heat transfer modeling into account.

As explained above, heat transfer in a BIPV/T system has several particularities due to the asymmetric heating (i.e., heat transfer occurs mainly through one side of the BIPV/T channel) and the more complex geometry. However, most researchers have used Nusselt number correlations developed for pipes and ducts with uniform boundary conditions for a given cross section, such as the classic correlation by Dittus and Boelter [34], and the Pethukov equation [13, 15]. These correlations tend to underestimate convective heat transfer coefficients because several heat transfer enhancing factors are not taken into account, such as the presence of the framing structure and surface imperfections (which act as turbulence promoters) and developing flow conditions at the inlet.

The determination of heat loss to the surroundings has been carried out through many different approaches. The McAdams formula reported by Duffie and Beckman [35], developed in the 1950s, combines radiation and convection into one coefficient. The McAdams formula has often been used [32, 33]. This approach is satisfactory for glazed collectors, since the addition of the glass layer significantly increases the insulation, and the effect of the exterior heat transfer coefficients becomes less important. Most researchers separate exterior heat losses into two components: convection to the exterior air and radiation to a representative sky temperature. The convective heat transfer correlations by Test et al. [36] and Sharples and Charlesworth [37] were developed for a roof-mounted flat-plate collector and are preferable to the McAdams formula. Both correlations have been used in modeling BIPV/T systems [10]. The model by Berdahl and Martin [38] presented a simplified calculation for a representative sky temperature, which can be used to calculate radiative heat transfer losses.

'Moisture' has an important effect on the physical characteristics of the fluid, in particular on the effective specific heat of the air, accounting for a 1–4% increase with respect to the specific heat of dry air. This effect is less significant under cold winter conditions.

3.11.3.3.3 Inlet air temperature effects

In BIPV/T systems, the inlet air temperature is sometimes slightly higher than the exterior air temperature. This is especially true in BIPV/T roofs, where the inlet air has been warmed by thermal energy released by the building's façade. However, few works have considered this effect in BIPV/T modeling [39].

3.11.3.3.3(i) Electrical efficiency modeling

Many BIPV/T investigations account for the effect of the PV modules' temperature on their electrical efficiency with a very simple linear model [30].

A common approach has been to linearize all the equations and solve the resulting linear system by matrix inversion. Since the system of equations is relatively robust, it can be solved by the simple method of assuming guess values and iterating until a convergence criterion is met. When the effects of thermal inertia have been considered, a transient method such as the fully explicit finite-difference method has been used.

The focus of this section is a BIPV/T system with outdoor air as the cooling fluid. The channel is smooth and has an aspect ratio (width-to-height) of 10. **Figure 26** presents a thermal network schematic of a typical BIPV/T system.

For the particular BIPV/T design studied here, an amorphous PV module is mounted on a metal roof sheet. The amorphous PV module is formed from different layers. These are from top to bottom, TEFZEL (an encapsulant layer), antireflective coating, amorphous silicon, a backing substrate, TEFZEL, adhesive, and a stainless steel layer to where it was pasted. R_{Tefzel} represents the thermal resistance of the PV module encapsulant and R_{mix} represents the thermal resistance of the backing substrate and the adhesive combined with the metal roof sheet where it is mounted; h_{ct} and h_{cb} represent the convective heat transfer coefficients from the top and bottom surfaces to the bulk air temperature (T_b) node, respectively. T_{plate} and T_{ins} represent the temperatures of the plate and the insulation used to compute the radiation and convective heat transfer coefficients. R_{ins} is the thermal resistance of the insulation.

A set of energy balance equations corresponding to the control volume in **Figure 26** are given below for the top surface of the PV module, the middle of the PV module, the interior surface of the metal plate, air node, and the surface of the insulation facing the cavity:

$$\frac{T_{\text{PV}_{\text{MID}}} - T_{\text{PV}_{\text{TOP}}}}{R_{\text{Tefzel}}} - \varepsilon_1 \sigma \left(T^4_{\text{PV}_{\text{TOP}}} - T^4_{\text{sky}} \right) - (T_{\text{PV}_{\text{TOP}}} - T_o)h_o = 0 \quad [41]$$

$$\alpha(\theta)G - P_{\text{elect}} - \frac{(T_{\text{PV}_{\text{MID}}} - T_{\text{PV}_{\text{TOP}}})}{R_{\text{Tefzel}}} - \frac{(T_{\text{PV}_{\text{MID}}} - T_{\text{plate}})}{R_{\text{Mix}}} = 0 \quad [42]$$

$$\frac{T_{\text{PV}_{\text{MID}}} - T_{\text{plate}}}{R_{\text{Mix}}} - q_{\text{rad}} - (T_{\text{plate}} - T_b)h_{ct} = 0 \quad [43]$$

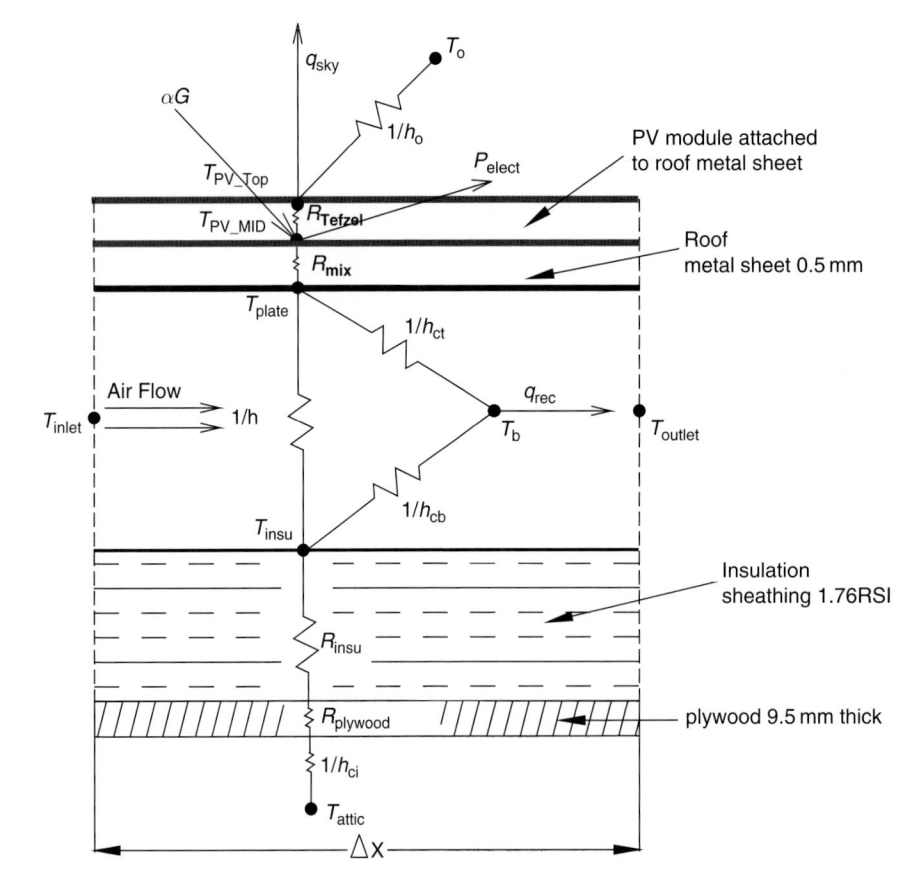

Figure 26 BIPV/T thermal network model showing the interior convective heat transfer coefficients h_{ct} and h_{cb} (the configuration shown corresponds to an experimental prototype studied by Candanedo *et al.* [31]).

$$(T_{plate} - T_b)h_{ct} + (T_{insu} - T_b)h_{cb} = q_{rec} \quad [44]$$

$$q_{rad} - (T_{insu} - T_b)h_{cb} - \frac{T_{insu} - T_{attic}}{R_{ins} + R_{plywood} + \frac{1}{h_{ci}}} = 0 \quad [45]$$

$$q_{rad} = \sigma F_{plate,insu} \left(\frac{1}{\varepsilon_2} + \frac{1}{\varepsilon_3} - 1\right)^{-1} \left(T_{plate}^4 - T_{insu}^4\right) \quad [46]$$

$$\eta_{PV} = \eta_{STC} + \beta_{mp}(T_{PV_{MID}} - 25°) \quad [47]$$

$$P_{elect} = \eta_{PV} G \quad [48]$$

$$T_{oulet} = T_{inlet} + \frac{A_{CV} q_{rec}}{\dot{m} c_p} \quad [49]$$

The bulk fluid temperature is given by

$$T_b = \frac{1}{\Delta x} \int_0^{\Delta x} \left(\frac{h_{ct} T_{plate} + h_{cb} T_{insu}}{h_{ct} + h_{cb}} + e^{-\frac{W_{PV}(h_{ct} + h_{cb})}{\dot{m} c_p} x}\right) dx \quad [50]$$

In the system of equations above, there are 10 unknowns: $T_{PV_{TOP}}, T_{PV_{MID}}, T_{plate}, T_{insu}, T_b, q_{rad}, \eta_{PV}, P_{elect}, T_{outlet}$, and q_{rec}. The rest of the variables (solar radiation, exterior temperature, mass flow rates, material properties, etc.) are known inputs. Several necessary parameters and variables are calculated as follows:

- The view factor $F_{plate,insu}$ is calculated as a function of a geometric parameter.
- The absorptance α of the exposed PV surface is corrected as a function of the angle of incidence of beam solar radiation, as described by King *et al.* [40]. The effect of the angle of incidence is significant during the early morning hours and late afternoon hours. For these models, a correction curve developed specifically for the amorphous PV laminate, calculated according to the procedure described by King *et al.* [40] and available at the Sandia National Laboratories database [41], was used.
- The sky temperature employed to calculate radiative heat losses to the exterior is obtained with the following formula [35]:

$$T_{sky} = T_a\left(0.711 + 0.005\,6 T_{dp} + 0.000\,073 T_{dp}^2 + 0.013\cos\left(\frac{\pi t}{12}\right)\right) \quad [51]$$

- The exterior convective heat transfer correlation is obtained using different correlations to compare their effects into the results. These are the correlations by Test *et al.* [36], Sharples and Charlesworth [37], and McAdams [42] as a function of the wind speed in m s^{-1}:

$$\begin{aligned} h_o &= 8.55 + 2.56 V_{wind} \\ h_o &= 11.9 + 2.2 V_{wind} \\ h_o &= 5.7 + 3.8 V_{wind} \end{aligned} \quad [52]$$

The interior convective heat transfer coefficients (h$_{ct}$ and h$_{cb}$) are calculated as average values for the entire channel, according to the correlations below [19]. The average Nusselt number coefficients for the top and the bottom surfaces were calculated from the local distributions and graphed as a function of the Reynolds number (forced convection).

For the top surface, for $250 \leq Re \leq 7500$:

$$Nu_{top} = 0.052 Re^{0.78} Pr^{0.4}$$

and for the bottom surface, for $800 \leq Re \leq 7100$:

$$Nu_{bottom} = 1.017 Re^{0.471} Pr^{0.4} \quad [53]$$

In the present case, because the bottom surface is insulated, the heat gain by long-wave radiation from the top heated surface is approximately equal to the heat transfer to the air by convection, thus resulting in a small temperature differential between the bottom surface and the air.

The Nusselt number distribution (local heat transfer coefficients) for the developing length x has been calculated for the whole length of the BIPV/T system (39 D_h) for the top surface. They are expressed by the following formulas.

For the laminar region, $250 \leq Re \leq 2400$:

$$Nu_{top}(x) = 0.039 Re^{0.78} Pr^{0.4} e^{-x/(20 \cdot D_h)} + 0.034 Re^{0.78} Pr^{0.4} \quad [54a]$$

For the turbulent region, $2400 < Re \leq 7100$:

$$Nu_{top}(x) = 0.012 Re^{0.78} Pr^{0.4} e^{-x/(9.09 \cdot D_h)} + 0.049 Re^{0.78} Pr^{0.4} \quad [54b]$$

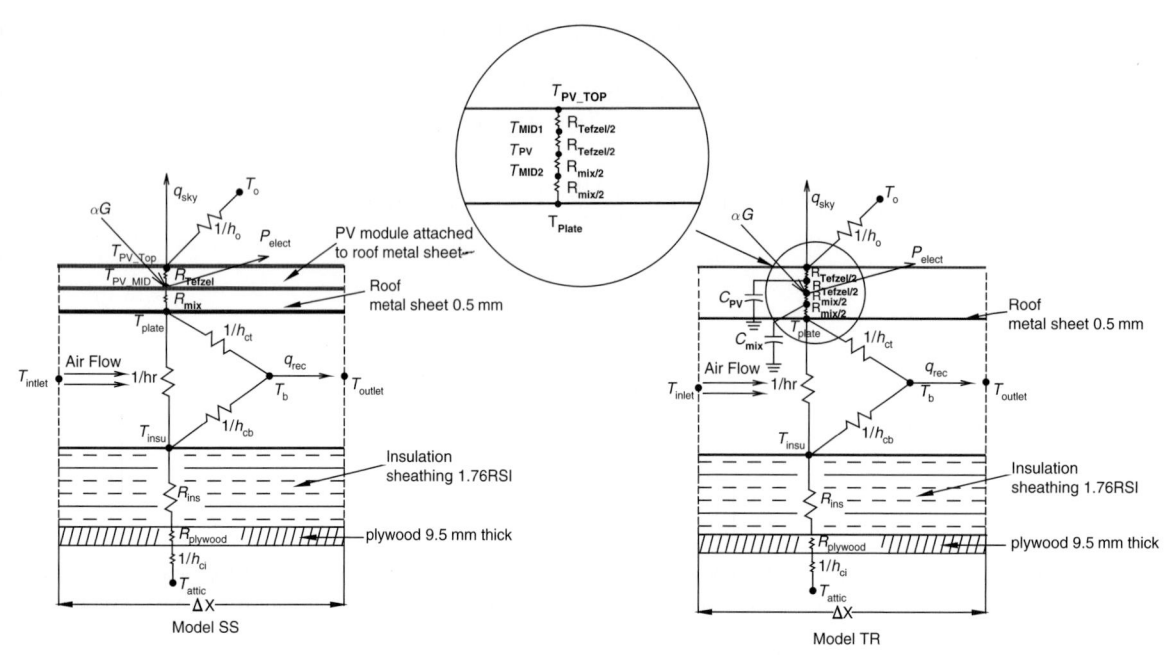

Figure 27 Models studied: Model SS (steady state) and Model TR (transient).

Both correlations represent the convective heat transfer distribution up to the maximum length (about 3 m) of the analyzed BIPV/T system. The last term in the Nusselt number distribution for the turbulent region ($0.049\, Re^{0.78}\, Pr^{0.4}$) represents the fully developed values. For the laminar region, the last term represents the Nusselt number for the maximum length. It is expected that for larger lengths, the Nusselt number will tend to keep decreasing.

The two models (steady state and transient) considered here are shown schematically in **Figure 27**. The thermal resistance associated with the film coefficient under the insulation and plywood has been neglected due to its low value compared with the thermal resistance of the insulation. The two models are identical except in one respect: the steady-state model does not consider the thermal capacitance of the PV panel (making it a steady-state model), while the transient model takes into account the thermal inertia (capacitance) of the PV panels. In a dynamic simulation, the solution of the equations of the steady-state model is independent of previous conditions. In contrast, at every time step, the transient model requires the solution of the previous time step with a fully explicit finite-difference scheme. The programming environment MATLAB® was used to numerically find the solution of both models.

As mentioned above, the transient model includes the thermal capacitance of the PV module. In this case, a fully explicit scheme has been used (the temperatures for the current time step depend only on the temperatures of the previous time step). The second equation below corresponds to the energy balance in a node associated with a midlayer of the PV module. This node has a capacitance per unit area of $1800\, J\, K^{-1} m^{-2}$, obtained from estimates of material properties. Capacitances are included only in the top part of PV module, since it is exposed to rapidly changing weather conditions, including wind and irradiance, whereas the bottom of the channel is insulated. The equations corresponding to the transient model are as follows:

$$\frac{T_{MID1,i+1} - T_{PV_{TOP},i}}{R_{Tefzel}/2} - \varepsilon_1 \sigma \left(T^4_{PV_{TOP},i+1} - T^4_{sky,i+1} \right) - (T_{PV_{TOP},i+1} - T_{o,i+1}) h_o = 0 \qquad [55]$$

$$T_{MID,i+1} = T_{MID1,i} + \frac{\Delta t}{C_{PV}} \left(\frac{T_{PV_{TOP},i} - T_{MID1,i}}{R_{Tefzel}/2} + \frac{T_{PV,1} - T_{MID1,i}}{R_{Tefzel}/2} \right) \qquad [56]$$

$$T_{PV,i+1} = \frac{\left(\dfrac{T_{MID1,i}}{R_{Tefzel}/2} + \dfrac{T_{MID2,i}}{R_{Mix}/2} + 0.96 K \tau \alpha_b (\theta)_i (\tau \alpha)_n I_{T,i} - P_{elec,i} \right)}{\dfrac{1}{R_{Tefzel}/2} + \dfrac{1}{R_{Mix}/2}} \qquad [57]$$

$$T_{MID2,i+1} = T_{MID2,i} + \frac{\Delta t}{C_{PV}} \left(\frac{T_{PV,i} - T_{MID2,i}}{R_{Mix}/2} + \frac{T_{Plate,i} - T_{MID2,i}}{R_{Mix}/2} \right) \qquad [58]$$

$$q_{rec,i+1} = (T_{plate,i} - T_b) h_{ct} + (T_{insu} - T_b) h_{cb} \qquad [59]$$

$$T_{\text{insu},i+1} = \frac{T_{b,i}h_{cb} + \dfrac{T_{\text{attic},i}}{R_{\text{ins}} + R_{\text{plywood}} + 1/h_{ci}} + q_{\text{rad},i}}{h_{cb} + \dfrac{1}{R_{\text{ins}} + R_{\text{plywood}} + 1/h_{ci}}} \quad [60]$$

$$q_{\text{rad},i+1} = \sigma F_{\text{plate,insu}} \left(\frac{1}{\varepsilon_2} + \frac{1}{\varepsilon_3} - 1\right)^{-1} \left(T_{\text{plate},i}^4 - T_{\text{insu},i}^4\right) \quad [61]$$

$$\eta_{\text{PV},i+1} = \eta_{\text{STC}} + \beta_{\text{mp}}(T_{\text{PV},i} - 25°\text{C}) \quad [62]$$

$$P_{\text{elect},i+1} = \eta_{\text{PV},i} I_{T,i} \quad [63]$$

$$T_{\text{outlet},i+1} = T_{\text{inlet},i} + \frac{A_{cv} q_{\text{rec},i}}{\dot{m}_i c_{p\text{-air}_i}} \quad [64]$$

$$T_{b,i+1} = \frac{1}{\Delta x} \int_0^{\Delta x} \left(\frac{h_{ct} T_{\text{plate},i} + h_{cb} T_{\text{insu},i}}{h_{ct} + h_{cb}} + \left(T_{\text{inlet},i} - \frac{h_{ct} T_{\text{plate},i} + h_{cb} T_{\text{insu},i}}{h_{ct} + h_{cb}}\right) e^{-\frac{W_{\text{PV}}(h_{ct} + h_{cb})}{\dot{m}_i c_{p\_\text{air}_i}} x} \right) dx \quad [65]$$

The magnitudes corresponding to the time step $i+1$ are written as a function of the magnitudes of the previous time step (i). In the equations above, the solution for $T_{\text{PV}_{\text{TOP}},i+1}$ is found numerically with the MATLAB® function *fzero*, as the rest of the parameters are known as inputs or the result of the previous time step. The function *fzero* uses a 'combination of bisection, secant, and inverse quadratic interpolation methods' [43]. Corrections corresponding to incidence angle, specific heat, view factor, and heat transfer coefficients were also applied for the transient model. In both the steady-state and transient models, the channel can be divided into an arbitrary number of control volumes. The inlet conditions of a control volume correspond to the outlet conditions of the previous control volume; local averaged heat transfer coefficients should be used in this case.

The transient and steady-state models were applied with input measurements (solar radiation, exterior temperature, wind speed, and channel flow rate) corresponding to 17 February 2009 in Montreal for a BIPV/T prototype. During this day, the flow rate in the channel was changed manually several times. **Figure 28(a)** shows the measured average air speed inside the channel and the estimated interior heat transfer coefficients (**Figure 28(b)**). The wind speed was measured during this interval as well. The correlations by Test *et al.* [36], Sharples and Charlesworth [37], and McAdams [42] were used to estimate the exterior heat transfer coefficient (**Figure 28(b)**).

In both the steady-state and transient models, four control volumes were used. Results corresponding to the average temperature of the top of the channel (**Figure 29(a)**) and the outlet temperature of the air (**Figure 29(b)**) are presented. The time step used for the transient model was 1 s. The output of both models is compared with thermocouple measurements taken at intervals of 1 min. Exterior air temperature and solar radiation measurements are presented as well. In general, there is a reasonably good agreement between both models and the experimental results. Perhaps the most relevant difference between the models is that the temperature fluctuations predicted by the transient model are much smaller than those predicted by the steady-state model. In this respect, the transient model (which includes the capacitive effect) is more accurate than the steady-state model. The presence of the capacitance considerably stabilizes the temperatures in the PV module, and reduces the effect of the varying wind speed (and its associated heat transfer coefficient) and solar radiation changes.

The effect of the exterior convective correlation on the average temperature of the top of the channel can be observed in **Figure 29**. In general, the McAdams correlation overpredicts the temperature of the top of the channel. The correlations of Test *el al.* and Sharples and Charlesworth give better estimations of the average temperature of the bottom PV surface. Although the Sharples

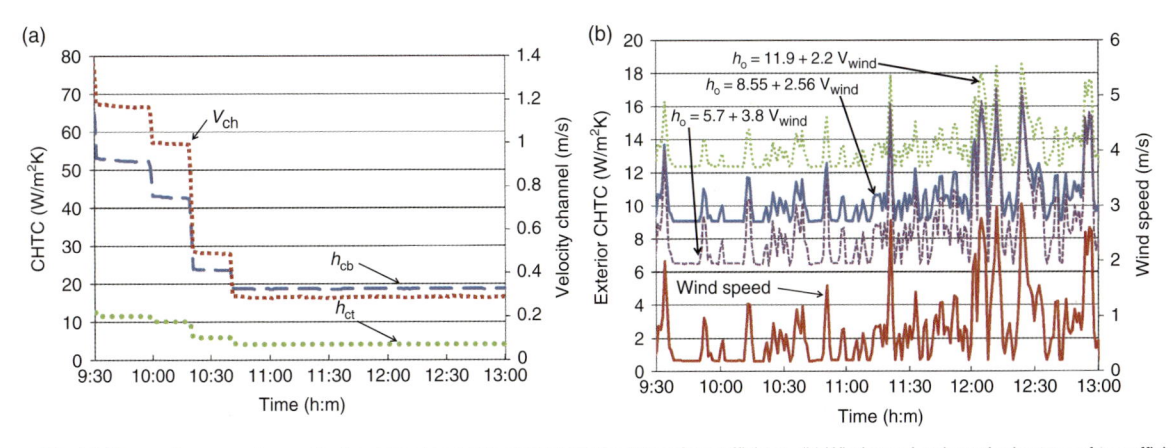

Figure 28 (a) Measured average air speed in the channel and estimated interior heat transfer coefficients. (b) Wind speed and exterior heat transfer coefficient.

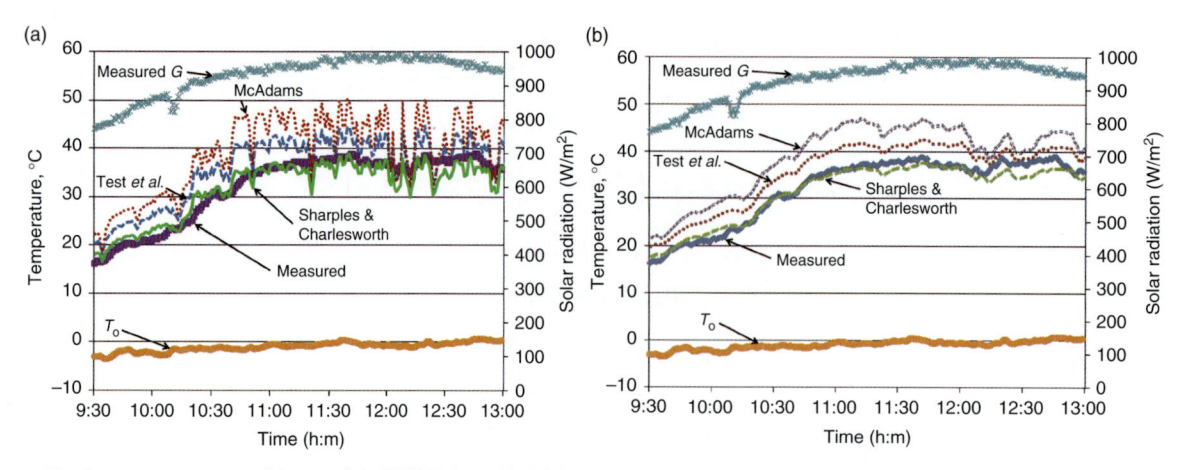

Figure 29 Average temperature of the top of the BIPV/T channel in (a) the steady-state model and (b) the transient model. G, solar radiation incident on collector; T_o, exterior air temperatures.

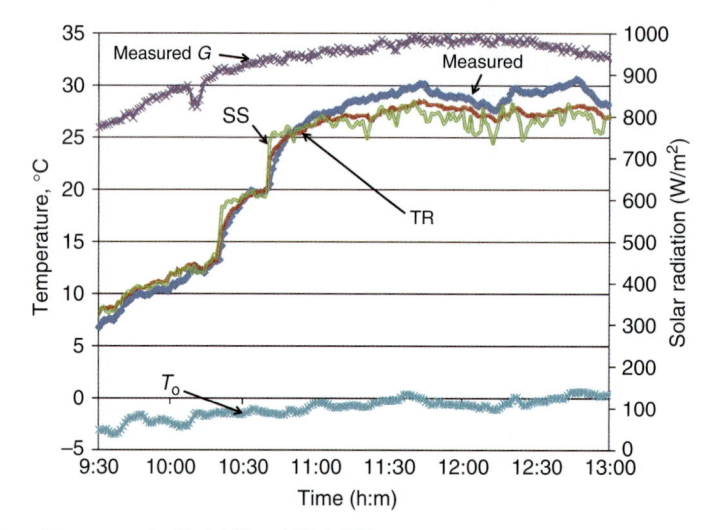

Figure 30 Outlet air temperatures (measurements, Model SS and Model TR).

and Charlesworth correlation gives better results, for high wind velocities, it seems to overestimate the exterior heat transfer coefficient (h_o) value.

The predicted outlet air temperature obtained with the Sharples and Charlesworth correlation with the SS and TR models is plotted in **Figure 30**. The transient model with Test *et al.* correlation practically mirrors the measured curve with an offset of a few degrees, which becomes very small between 12.00 p.m. and 1.00 p.m. Interestingly, this is the time when the highest wind speed values were recorded (about 1.5 vs. 0.5 m s^{-1} earlier in the day). This result suggests that the Test *et al.* correlation underpredicts h_o at low wind speeds. This can be attributed to local natural convection effects (not considered in most correlations) that may become the dominant factor at low wind speeds.

3.11.3.4 Heat Removal Factor and Thermal Efficiency for Open-Loop BIPV/T Systems

Considering a BIPV/T system as a solar thermal collector, a modified form of the Hottel-Whillier-Bliss equation that includes the electricity output can be written as

$$Q_u = F_R A_c (\alpha G - P_{elect} - U_L(T_i - T_a)) \quad [66]$$

In this case, U_L represents the heat loss coefficient (W m^{-2} K^{-1}) from the air in the BIPV/T channel to the ambient air. Neglecting the heat loss through the bottom of the BIPV/T channel, there follows:

$$U_L = ((h_o + h_r)^{-1} + R_{PV})^{-1} \quad [67]$$

Ordinary solar collectors are often designed with a glazing cover and an absorber plate to prevent heat losses, and their U_L value depends mainly on geometric parameters and the materials used; the influence of convective and radiative coefficients is small. In contrast, in this BIPV/T channel, U_L undergoes significant changes with changes in the convective and radiative coefficients. The heat removal factor (F_R) can be determined as

$$F_R = \frac{Q_U}{A_c(\alpha G - P_{elect} - U_L(T_i - T_a))} \qquad [68]$$

By dividing eqn [68] with the solar radiation times the area (GA_c) and substituting $P_{elect} = \eta_{PV}G$, the following expression for thermal efficiency is obtained:

$$\eta_{Th} = F_R\left(\alpha - \eta_{PV} - U_L\frac{T_i - T_a}{G}\right) \qquad [69]$$

Figure 31 shows the heat removal factor calculated with eqn [68] (assuming that the R_{PV} value is 0.01 RSI) for 17 February 2009, and the thermal efficiency calculated simply as $\eta_{Th} = \dot{m}c_p\Delta T/GA_c$. As expected, the efficiency is much higher when the flow rates inside the channel are higher (e.g., during the time period 9.30–10.30 a.m. in the figure as a result of the higher heat transfer coefficients).

3.11.4 Near-Optimal Design of Low-Energy Solar Homes

The passive solar design of the 272 m² two-storey solar home in Brossard, a suburb of Montreal, was optimized while taking into account user needs and priorities as well as aesthetics. Its BIPV/T roof is currently unique. The house was designed to provide superior comfort and abundant daylight, and to optimize solar energy utilization. It was custom designed by the owner in collaboration with the builder and his architect. It is expected that its annual energy consumption will be lower than that of an average Advanced House. Initial data of performance for the first 11 months confirm this. The major features of the house are the following:

1. Direct-gain passive solar design that emphasizes utilization of distributed thermal mass in the south-facing part of the ground floor; close to R2000 standard levels of insulation.
2. A grid-connected BIPV/T system (1904 W peak capacity).
3. A two-stage ground-source heat pump (2.2 ton) with electronically commutated fan used to heat/cool air in the house – the primary heating/cooling system.
4. A secondary floor heating system integrated in the floor mass of the direct-gain zone.
5. A two-zone air distribution system controlled by a multizone programmable thermostat.

A major characteristic of the house is the attempt to optimize form – mainly the south façade, the aspect ratio, and the solar roof. A rule of thumb of passive solar design is that the aspect ratio (south-facing façade width divided by the north–south depth) is about 1.2–1.3. Of course, this can only be achieved if the lot has a good orientation and is not too narrow. Two-storey home designs are more suitable for passive solar design because they provide a large south-facing façade, optimal roof slopes (35°–50°), and occupy less land. Emphasis was placed on architectural and aesthetic integration of the BIPV/T system; the heat recovered from the roof is utilized for DHW preheating, and heated air from the roof is used to heat the garage and part of the basement. The direct-gain

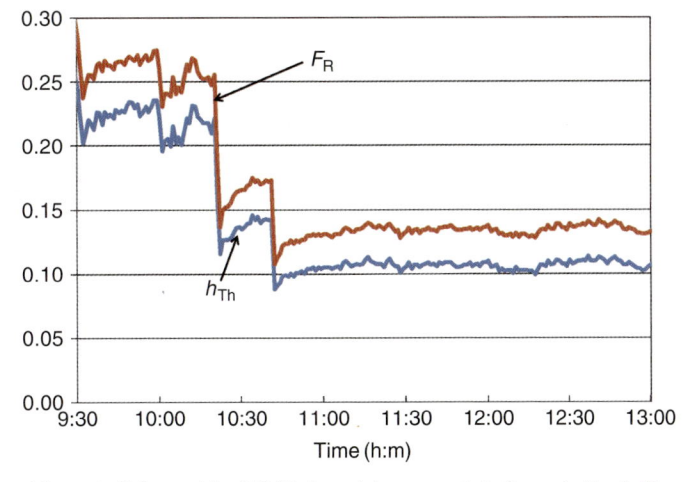

Figure 31 Heat removal factor and thermal efficiency of the BIPV/T channel (corresponds to flow velocities in **Figure 28**).

system is the major solar energy capture and utilization system of the house. To optimize this system, one must size all windows carefully in conjunction with distributed thermal mass.

3.11.4.1 Envelope and Passive Solar Design

The lot for the particular house was acquired in a new development area with particular attention to its orientation – almost perfectly due south in its backyard. The house was built after the neighboring houses by a builder who has a full-time architect on staff and who worked closely with the author/owner to customize and optimize the design. The following procedure was followed in the design:

1. The two-storey option (so-called cottage style in Quebec) was adopted as the basis for the design.
2. Several preliminary floor plan layouts were generated such that the second floor would contain four bedrooms, while the kitchen–dining–family room area, as the main direct-gain zone facing south, would be on the ground floor. On the second floor, the bedroom areas and locations were allocated based on personal preferences of the family of four. The final plan of the ground floor is shown in **Figure 32**(a).
3. The ceiling height of the ground floor was set at 3 m to enhance daylight penetration, as well as for aesthetic reasons and general well-being. The height of 3 m allowed daylight to penetrate directly up to the back wall of the direct-gain zone. Thermal mass was located on the floor of the direct-gain zone (equivalent to about 8 cm of concrete) and on a vertical wall as

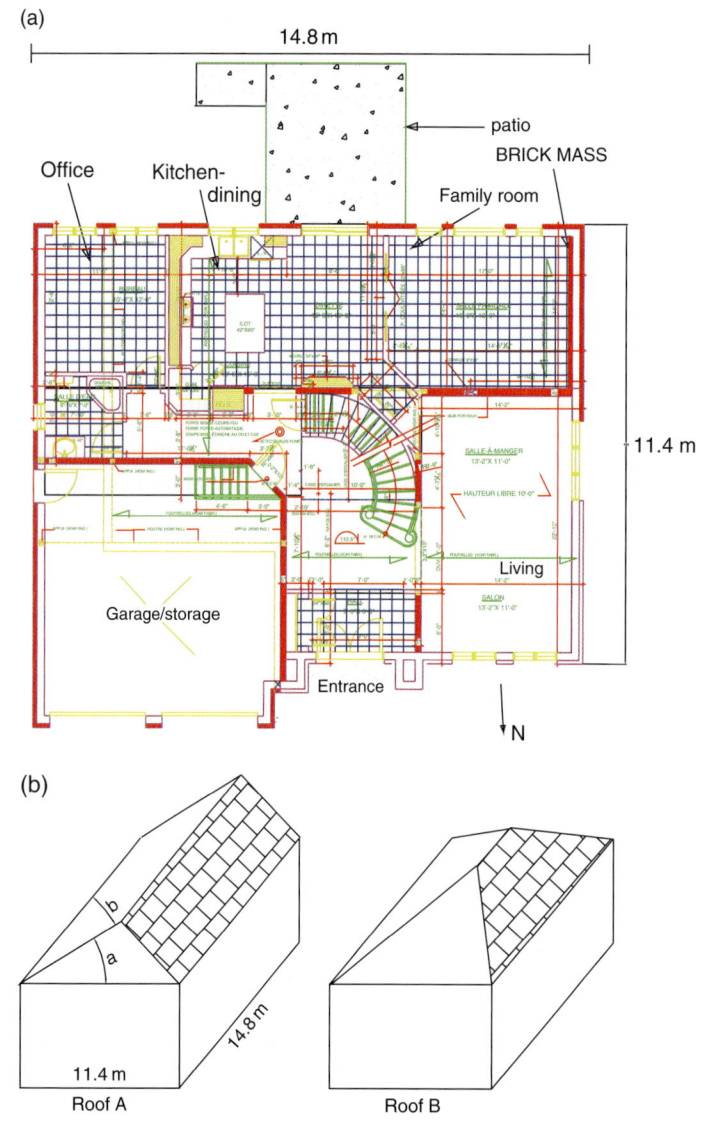

Figure 32 (a) Ground floor plan of selected option (direct-gain zone is the south part). (b) Schematic of two options considered for the roof.

interior brick. Daylight penetration to the back wall allowed direct solar gains to fully illuminate the floor in January when the sun is near its lowest altitude and the coldest temperatures are typically experienced. On the second floor, ceiling height is 2.4 m as usual.
4. The owner (Athienitis), working with the architect–builder, refined the design, adding some architectural features and developed two alternative designs for the south-facing roof shown in schematic form in **Figure 32(b)**.

A key element of the design is the selection of the floor plan of the ground floor. This resulted in an aspect ratio of 14.8 m/11.4 m = 1.3, which is ideal for passive solar design. In achieving the desired ratio of 1.2–1.3, one must generally consider several constraints, including the following:

1. A minimum distance on each side from adjacent lots (about 1.5 m).
2. Desired floor area.
3. Need to reduce costs by having as compact a design as possible.

A few rules of thumb contribute to an efficient design. For example, areas that are not frequently used, such as the guest living room and the garage, can be located in the north side of the ground floor. These areas are in general at a lower temperature most of the time than the rest of the house. Once a floor plan is selected according to user needs and passive solar design principles, there are many possible roof shapes that can fit the plans. During a solar optimization process, the designer should select the form that will accommodate the solar systems such as BIPV/T and solar thermal systems while resulting in an overall cost-effective system. In the present example, two possible roof forms for the same floor plan were considered as shown schematically in **Figure 32(b)**. Both had a slope of 40°, which is considered near-optimal for the Montreal area (latitude 45°N). Roof A may have more south-facing roof area (shaded) than roof B but uses more material (both can be considered as instances of one design with different angles *a* and *b*). If the attic space is partly useful space then this fact has to be considered also. The question of which shape is more appropriate from a solar energy utilization point of view is complex and depends on a number of factors such as the following:

- Integration of solar technologies such as BIPV/T systems that form the outer layer of the roof.
- Cost of the BIPV systems and their installation.
- Aesthetic and architectural integration issues.

The roof form/shape problem cannot be simply one of maximization of solar energy collection and utilization because other practical considerations have to be taken into account such as construction cost, aesthetics, snow accumulation and melting, and natural ventilation/cooling. In some cases, practical considerations such as preventing rain penetration and shedding snow may override small differences in solar energy collection such as the difference in solar energy incident on a roof for two slope angles that differ by 10°. In selecting a roof design, it was decided to cover an entire roof surface so as to achieve architectural, aesthetic, and functional integration. BIPV panels were used to form a continuous cover over the south-facing roof surface to reduce the risk of water penetration and have a robust water-shedding surface. For the particular case studied, option B provided a roof area of about 54 m², which was more than adequate for the installation of an approximately 2 kW PV system composed of amorphous silicon laminates attached to a metal roof. **Figure 33** shows the final design adopted for the roof together with the south-facing façade, and **Table 2** summarizes major characteristics of the solar façade and roof of the house.

The south-facing window area is 30% of the south façade area for the two floors and 41% for the ground floor. **Figure 33** shows the two main façades of the house and the interior of the family room with thermal mass on the floor and interior brick wall. The thermal resistance of the roof is RSI 8; that of the walls, RSI 4.4; and the average resistance of the basement walls is RSI 3.

3.11.4.1.1 HVAC and renewable energy systems

The key renewable generation system is a 1904 W BIPV/T (with heat recovery), which can also typically produce 4–8 kW of heat at 200 l s^{-1} of airflow. The PV array is composed of 10 Unisolar amorphous silicon 136 W laminates plus eight 68 W laminates integrated on the standing seam metal roof. The size of the PV array was chosen to cover one complete surface for improved appeal while taking into account budget limitations. Air is drawn from inlets in the plywood layer of the roof in the soffits and heated as it flows up in the cavity under the PV panels. A typical detail is shown in **Figure 34**. Typically, the inlet air is hotter than the ambient temperature by about 5–10 °C from being heated by the south-facing wall (except when windy). The flow velocity of the air under the PV panel will vary from a minimum of 0.5 m s^{-1} to a maximum of about 1 m s^{-1}, and the outlet air temperature T_{air} will typically be from 15 °C to 30 °C higher than the ambient air temperature T_o. The cavity under the panels has vertical furring 1 × 3″ for airflow between them and horizontal straps to attach the metal. The solar PV panels are thin rolls pasted on the metal before placing the metal on the roof. The wires of the PV panels enter the attic under the ridge panel at the top of the roof. A schematic of the energy systems is shown in **Figure 35**. The key features of the energy system are the following:

- The 2.2 ton two-stage geothermal water–air heat pump (120 m deep borehole) with a 10 kW auxiliary electric heating coil (normally off); it is connected to a two-zone air distribution system (heat recovery ventilation system connected to the return) designed to optimize distribution of passive solar gains when heating is not required and the electronically commutated motor fan operates at low speed.

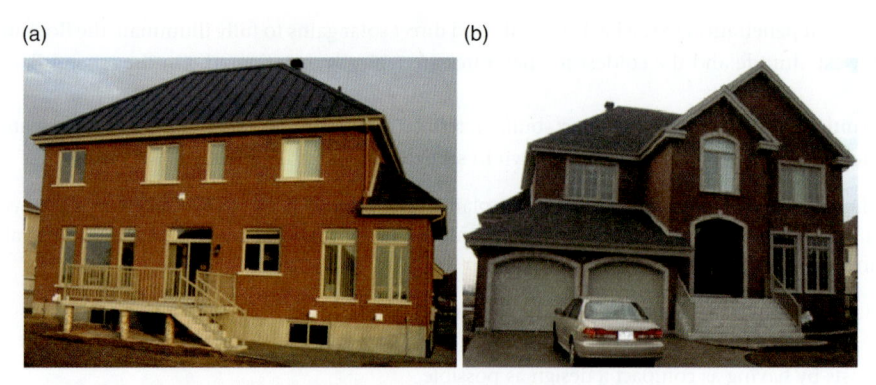

Figure 33 (a) Final design adopted for BIPV/T roof (option B) and south façade. (b) North façade.

Table 2 Major solar façade and roof characteristics

South-facing window area as % of first floor area	14%
South-facing window area as % of south façade area (over two floors)	30%
First floor south-facing window area as % of first floor façade (10′ high)	41%
South-facing total window area as % of total house floor area (2 floors)	8.7%
Non-south-facing window area as % of total house floor area	6.4%
South-facing roof area (PV coverage = 56% or 30.3 m^2); (slop 40°)	53.9 m^2
South-facing roof area as % of first floor area (excluding garage)	40%
Window-type (south-facing, first floor), double-glazed: Low-e (hard) argon, vinyl frame with thermal breaks	
Window-type (non-south-facing, first floor), double-glazed: Low-e (soft) argon, vinyl frame with thermal breaks	

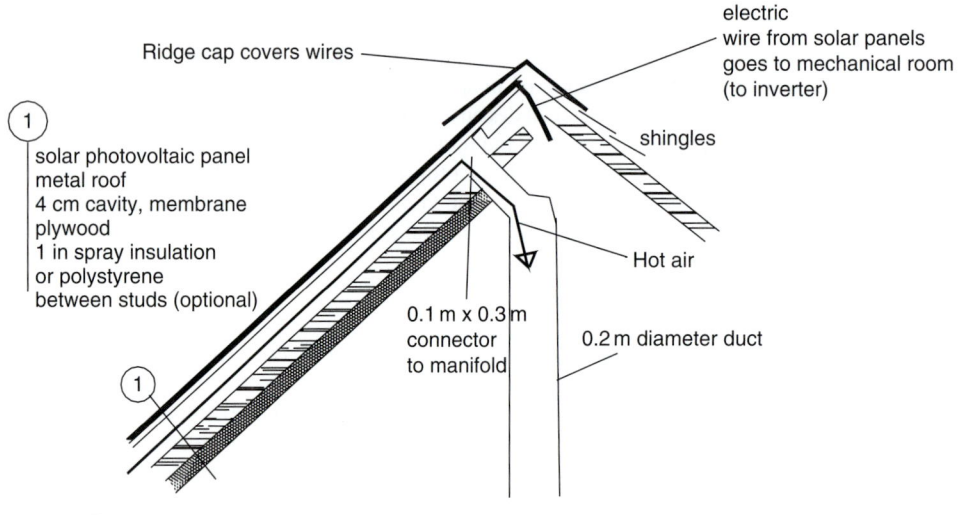

Figure 34 Detail of BIPV/T roof.

- The duct from the BIPV/T modules on the roof brings hot air to the mechanical room to heat water (or supplies fresh air).
- Two 272 l water tanks connected in series; the low-temperature water in the preheat tank is heated through an air–water heat exchanger by the BIPV/T air and the heat pump desuperheater. It then enters the high-temperature (60 °C) DHW tank.

The forced air system has two zones controlled by motorized dampers – the ground floor plus the basement (zone 1) and the second floor (zone 2). Substantial thermal mass was located in the south-facing direct-gain zone of the first floor with about 8 cm of concrete plus ceramic tiles and an interior brick wall in the family room. Hydronic floor heating was also implemented

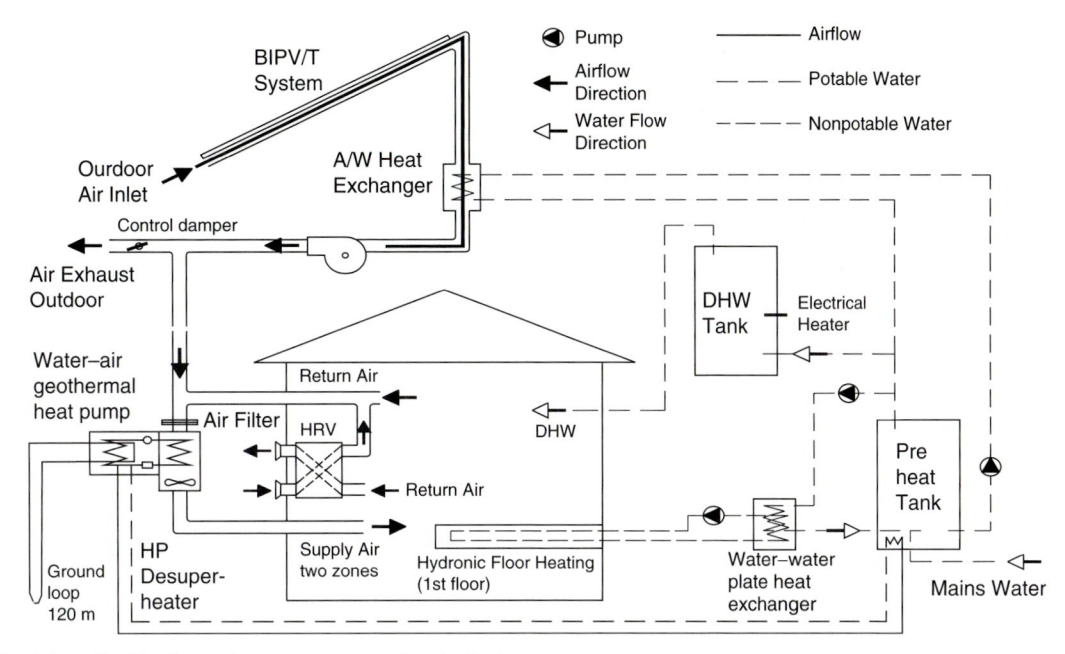

Figure 35 Schematic of heating and energy recovery system for the house.

in the direct-gain area as three subzones. This is an auxiliary heating system used on very cold days using water from the preheat tank as a heat source (the electric element in the tank is switched on only during these periods). The thermal mass in the floor serves as both storage for passive solar gains and for floor heating. In both cases, a surface temperature of 25 °C is typically achieved.

The design flow rate of the BIPV/T roof and estimates of air temperature rise were selected using a five-section model of the roof as shown in **Figure 36(a)**. Details of the model have been reported by Charron and Athienitis [25]. Improved estimates of the heat transfer coefficients in the cavity were used. The PV area was about 30 m² while the active thermal area was approximately 40 m², with the flow area narrowing toward the ridge cap under which the header collector duct was located. A typical increase in the air temperature with distance in the BIPV/T cavity is shown in **Figure 36(b)** for a clear March day. In practice, the air temperature rise will be in the range 15–30 °C for a flow rate of about 200 l s^{-1}. It should be noted that an open-loop air system is utilized for the BIPV/T system as opposed to a closed-loop one to avoid overheating the PV panels. The fan energy consumption is of the order of 1–1.6 kWh, while the useful thermal energy is typically in the range 10–25 kWh.

The windows on the south façade were carefully sized in conjunction with thermal mass to avoid overheating as described by Athienitis [44], by using custom transient thermal network models. A six-node three-capacitance thermal network model was employed to analyze the house and optimize window–mass ratio. A typical temperature variation in the direct-gain zone is shown in **Figure 37**. In general, the direct-gain zone is expected to experience a temperature swing of 5–6 °C associated with solar gains on

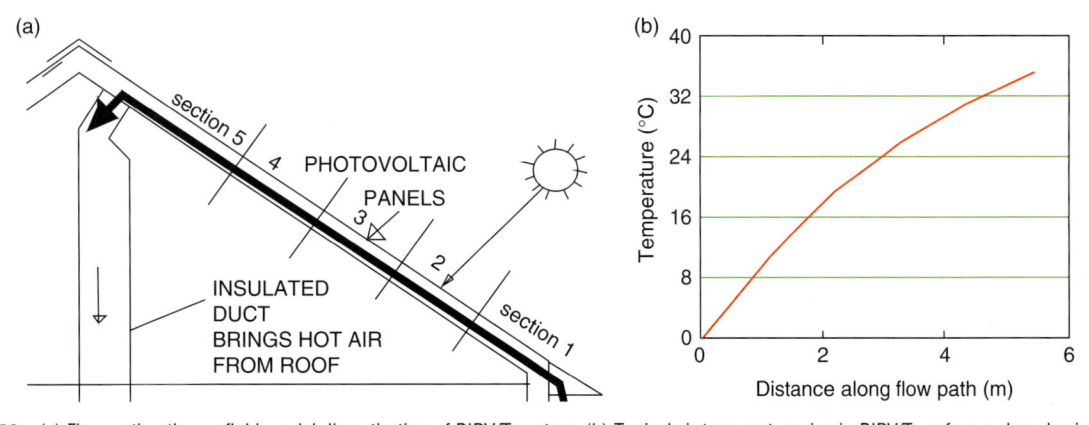

Figure 36 (a) Five-section thermofluid model discretization of BIPV/T system. (b) Typical air temperature rise in BIPV/T roof on a clear day in March (ambient temperature, 0 °C) at solar noon.

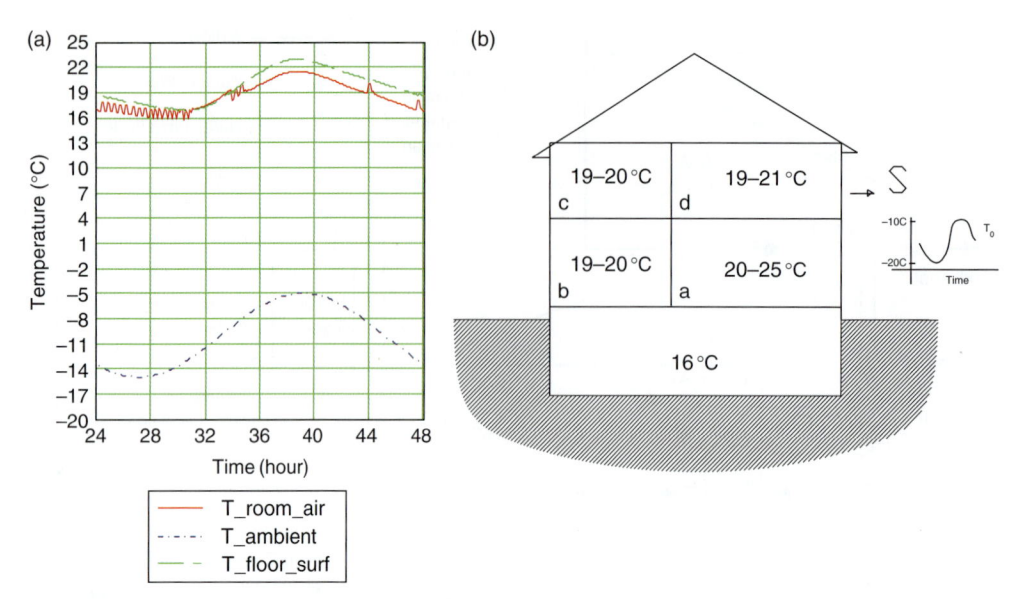

Figure 37 (a) Typical temperature profile on a cold sunny day in February (room air, outdoor air, and floor surface in direct-gain zone). (b) Measured temperature distribution on a clear cold day in February with heating system off during the daytime.

clear days in January–March. The house was occupied in early May 2006, and the BIPV/T system was operational toward the end of May 2006.

The results presented below are only indicative of the performance of the house. Some work still remains to be done, such as activating the hot air flow from the BIPV/T system to the garage and basement. The annual energy consumption without these measures is about 16 000–17 000 kWh, including the basement and garage. Completion of the additional work in the basement and garage is expected to reduce energy consumption by about 2500 kWh, while the addition of a PV/T or solar thermal overhang over the first floor south windows will reduce hot water and space heating consumption by another 2000 kWh.

Figure 37 shows a typical temperature distribution on a cold clear day in February in the early morning and in the afternoon. The direct-gain zone *a* rises from 20 °C to 25 °C, while other parts of the house are at 4–5 °C lower with the fan continuously on (at low speed, 200 l s^{-1}). The PV system was connected to the grid in January 2007 under the net metering program of Hydro-Quebec. On a clear day in March, it typically generates about 11–12 kWh. The electricity generated by the BIPV system is about 2350 kWh yr^{-1} for a slope of 40°. It is expected that in the long term the system will produce about 2300–2400 kWh yr^{-1} (based on simulations) and 4000–6000 kWh of useful thermal energy. This house would be expected to achieve net-zero energy consumption in Montreal with the addition of another 3 kW of BIPV/T connected to an air-to-water heat pump and the use of triple-glazed windows with a thermal resistance of about 1 RSI.

3.11.4.2 Overview of the Design of Two Net-Zero Energy Solar Homes

Two houses were recently designed for the Montreal area under the EQuilibrium™ demonstration program. The EcoTerra™ home was built by a prefabricated home manufacturer, Alouette Homes, while the other one is a custom-designed house, Alstonvale Home. The 'EcoTerra' is similar to the low-energy home described in the previous section, with the exception that it also has the option of passing BIPV/T-heated air through a hollow core floor in the basement as shown in **Figure 38**. The 140 m^2 house has a 2.84 kW PV system and is expected to have a net annual energy consumption of 4000–6000 kWh. The house was built as a prefabricated home in four modules in the factory and was assembled on the concrete basement structure in a few hours. A major innovation was the construction of the BIPV/T roof as a complete subsystem (with ducting and PV system installed) – as one module in the factory (**Figure 39**).

As shown in the schematic in **Figure 38(a)**, the solar-heated air from the BIPV/T roof is brought via an insulated duct with a variable-speed fan to the mechanical room in the basement where it is used for the following three applications in order of priority: for clothes drying (running the dryer in fan mode), DHW heating through an air–water heat exchanger, or heating a hollow core floor slab. The airflow rate in the BIPV/T system can be controlled to achieve the desired temperature. Research is underway to optimize the control algorithm. The main heating system of the house is a geothermal air-to-water heat pump, which also has a desuperheater to preheat DHW.

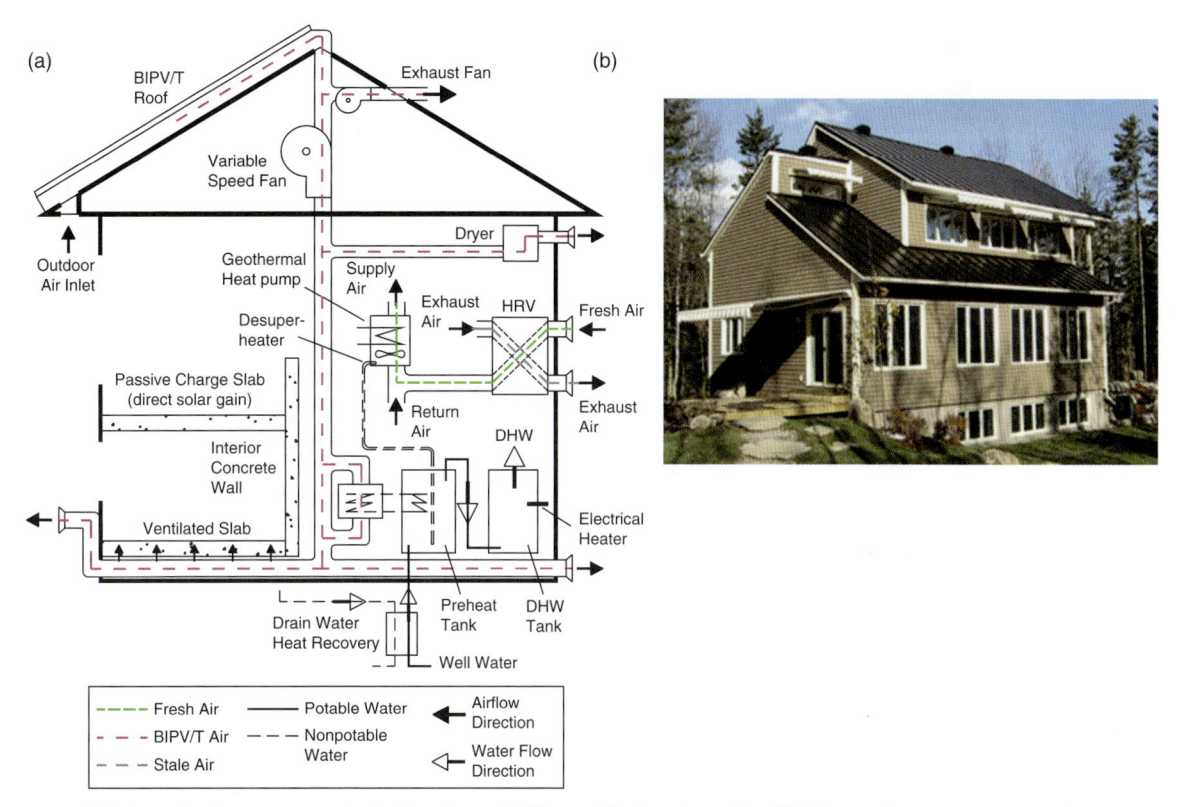

Modeling and Simulation of Passive and Active Solar Thermal Systems 395

Figure 38 (a) Schematic of energy system for EcoTerra home. (b) Photo of EcoTerra home (the BIPV/T system is on the top section of the metal roof).

Figure 39 Construction of the BIVP/T roof section in factory: (a) top view of roof section before installation of metal roof, (b) ducting for heat recovery from roof, (c) foam spray insulation applied to ducting, (d) BIPV/T module delivered on-site for assembly.

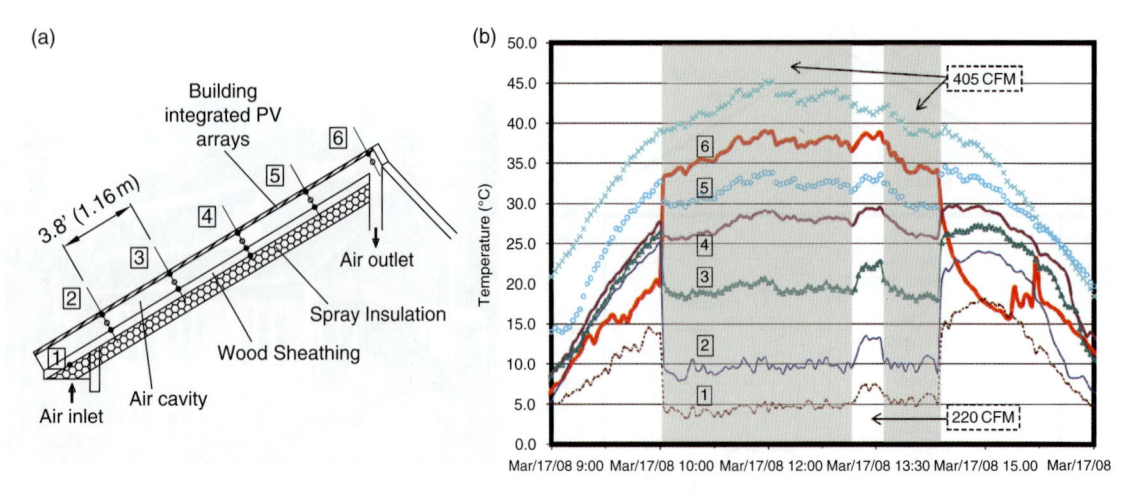

Figure 40 Measured data for the BIPV/T system of the EcoTerra home: (a) points of measurement on the roof and (b) measured temperatures of air flowing in the BIPV/T cavity.

The EcoTerra home was commissioned in early 2009 and occupied in August 2009. Detailed results on its various systems are presented elsewhere [45]. **Figure 40** shows some measured results for the BIPV/T roof. The temperature of the air flowing in the BIPV/T system as a function of distance along the flow path (total about 6 m) is shown over a day. As can be seen, a temperature rise of about 35–40 °C over the ambient is achieved for a flow rate of 405 cfm (191 l s^{-1}). During this time, a peak of about 2.8 kW of electricity is produced at solar noon, while close to 8 kW of heat is recovered. On similar days, the airflow rate was increased to about 290 l s^{-1}, and the heat recovered was close to 12 kW.

The 'Alstonvale house' [46] was designed to be an energy-positive house with an 8.4 kW BIPV/T system. The PV array was expected to be enough to achieve net-zero energy consumption and also to charge an electric car for local transportation. The heated BIPV/T air, which can reach temperatures as high as 90 °C, was planned to be utilized as a source for an air–water heat exchanger and a two-stage heat pump used to heat a large storage tank of water (about 4500 l) that supplies hot water to a floor heating system built into a concrete slab that also serves as direct-gain passive solar storage mass (**Figure 41(a)**).

An auxiliary ground loop is utilized to supplement the primary solar source, which is expected to provide up to about 22 kW of useful heat. **Figure 41** shows the (1) the basic energy concept of the house, (2) the temperature distribution in the BIPV/T system, and (3) a recent photo. This BIPV/T system has an air collector with clear glazing after the PV layer to achieve higher temperatures than the previous two houses. While it also has a small geothermal auxiliary heating system, it relies on an all-solar design philosophy to capture enough solar heat on a clear day that will sustain the house for 1–2 more days of cold weather (−20 °C).

3.11.5 Active Solar Systems

The proper sizing of the components of a solar system is a complex problem, which includes both predictable (performance characteristics of the collector and other components) and unpredictable (weather data) parameters. In this section, various design methods are presented, as well as an overview of the simulation techniques and programs suitable for active solar heating and cooling systems. The design methods presented include the f-chart, utilizability Φ, and the $\overline{\Phi}$, f – chart method. The f-chart is based on the correlation of the results of a large number of simulations in terms of easily calculated dimensionless variables. The utilizability method is used in cases where the collector operating temperature is known or can be estimated and for which critical radiation levels can be established. The utilizability method is based on the analysis of hourly weather data to obtain the fraction of the total monthly radiation that is above a critical level. The $\overline{\Phi}$, f-chart method is a combination of the utilizability and f-chart methods and is applied in systems where the energy supplied to a load is above a minimum useful temperature, and the temperature of this energy supply has no effect on the performance of the load system as long as it is greater than the minimum temperature. For more detailed results, modeling and simulation is used. In recent years, because of increases in the computational speed of personal computers, annual simulations are replacing design methods. Design methods, however, are much faster; therefore, they are still useful in early design studies. The software programs described briefly in this chapter include the f-chart TRNSYS, and WATSUN.

3.11.6 The f-Chart Method

A relatively easy way of estimating the annual thermal performance of active solar heating systems with a liquid or air working fluid and a minimum temperature of energy delivery near 20 °C is the f-chart method. It should be noted however that only standard

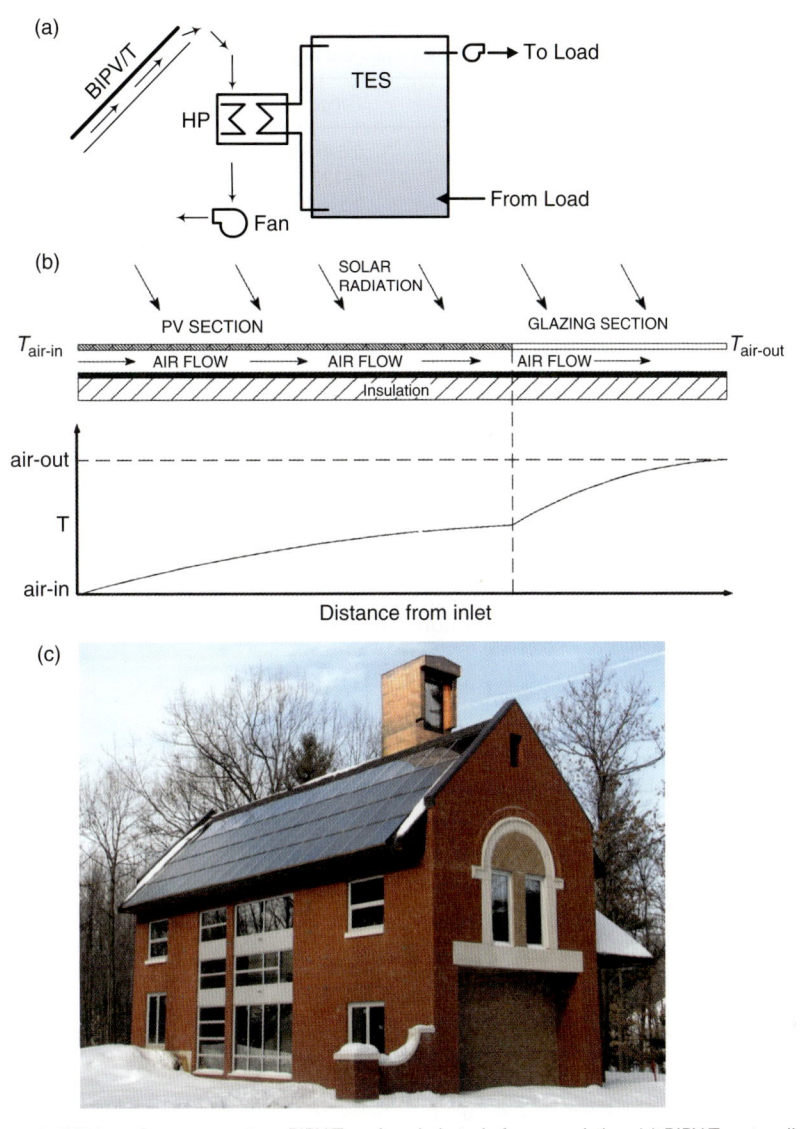

Figure 41 Schematic concept of Alstonvale energy system, BIPV/T roof, and photo before completion. (a) BIPV/T system linked to air-to-water heat pump. (b) BIPV/T system in the Alstonvale net-zero house with typical temperature rise curve (actual surface inclined 45° from the horizontal). (c) Alstonvale house (photo taken in March 2010) near completion.

system configurations can be evaluated by this method, but these are the most common in residential applications. The f-chart method gives the fraction of the total heating load that can be supplied by the solar system, called the 'solar fraction'. If the energy required for a fuel-only system or the energy required to cover the load is L, the auxiliary energy for a solar system is L_{AUX}, and the solar energy delivered is Q_S, then

$$L = L_{AUX} + Q_S \qquad [70]$$

For a month i, the fractional reduction of energy when a solar system is used, that is, the solar fraction, f, is given by the ratio

$$f = \frac{L_i - L_{AUX,i}}{L_i} = \frac{Q_{S,i}}{L_i} \qquad [71]$$

The f-chart method was developed by Klein *et al.* [47, 48] and Beckman *et al.* [49]. The method is a correlation of the results of many hundreds of thermal performance simulations of solar heating systems performed with TRNSYS, in which the simulation conditions were varied over specific ranges of parameters of practical system designs (**Table 3**) [47, 48]. In this method, the primary design variable is collector area, while secondary variables are storage capacity, collector type, load and collector heat exchanger size, and fluid flow rate. The resulting correlations give the fraction of the monthly load supplied by solar energy, f, as a function of two dimensionless parameters:

Table 3 Range of design variables used in developing f-charts for liquid and air systems

Parameter	Range
$(\tau\alpha)_n$	0.6–0.9
$F'_R A_c$	5–120 m²
U_L	2.1–8.3 W m⁻²·°C⁻¹
β (collector slope)	30–90°
$(UA)_h$	83.3–666.6 W °C⁻¹

From Klein SA, Beckman WA, and Duffie JA (1976) A design procedure for solar heating systems. *Solar Energy* 18(2): 113–127 [47]; Klein SA, Beckman WA, and Duffie JA (1977) A design procedure for solar air heating systems. *Solar Energy* 19(6): 509–512 [48].

- The ratio of collector losses to heating load, and
- The ratio of absorbed solar radiation to heating load.

Heating load includes both space heating and hot water loads. The f-chart has been developed for three standard system configurations, liquid and air systems for space and water heating and systems for service hot water only.

The solar energy delivered, Q_S, can be obtained by integrating over a time period Δt the useful energy collected by a solar collector system. Thus, from the definition of the solar fraction, f, from eqn [71], there follows:

$$f = \frac{Q_S}{L} = \frac{1}{L}\int_{\Delta t} Q_u^+ dt \qquad [72]$$

where L is the total heating load during the integration period (MJ).

Q_u is obtained by the following relation [50]:

$$Q_u = A_c F_R [G_t(\tau\alpha) - U_L(T_i - T_a)] \qquad [73]$$

where F_R is the heat removal factor, which represents the ratio of the actual useful energy gain that would result if the collector absorbing surface had been at the local fluid temperature, given by [50]

$$F_R = \frac{\dot{m}c_p}{A_c U_L}\left(1 - \exp\left[\frac{-U_L F' A_c}{\dot{m}c_p}\right]\right) \qquad [74]$$

By replacing G_t, the total incident radiation, by H_t, the total (beam and diffuse) insolation over a day, eqn [72], can be written as

$$f = \frac{A_c F'_R}{L}\int_{\Delta t}[H_t(\tau\alpha) - U_L(T_s - T_a)]dt \qquad [75]$$

It should be noted that F_R in eqn [73] is replaced by F_R' for use in eqn [75] to account for the presence of a heat exchanger in the solar collection network as is explained subsequently.

The last term of eqn [75] can be multiplied and divided by the term $(T_{ref} - T_a)$, where T_{ref} is a reference temperature chosen to be 100 °C, so the following equation can be obtained:

$$f = \frac{A_c F'_R}{L}\int_{\Delta t}\left[H_t(\tau\alpha) - U_L(T_{ref} - T_a)\frac{(T_s - T_a)}{(T_{ref} - T_a)}\right]dt \qquad [76]$$

It should be noted that the storage tank temperature T_s is a complicated function of H_t, L, and T_a; therefore, the integration of eqn [76] cannot be explicitly evaluated. This equation, however, suggests that an empirical correlation can be found, on a monthly basis, between the f factor and the two dimensionless groups mentioned above, as follows:

$$X = \frac{A_c F'_R U_L}{L}\int_{\Delta t}(T_{ref} - \overline{T}_a)dt = \frac{A_c F'_R U_L}{L}(T_{ref} - \overline{T}_a)\Delta t \qquad [77]$$

$$Y = \frac{A_c F'_R}{L}\int_{\Delta t}H_t(\tau\alpha)dt = \frac{A_c F'_R}{L}(\overline{\tau\alpha})\overline{H}_t N \qquad [78]$$

where L is the monthly heating load or demand (MJ), N is the number of days in a month, $\overline{T}_a$ is monthly average ambient temperature (°C), $\overline{H}_t$ is monthly average daily total radiation on the tilted collector surface (MJ m⁻²), and $(\overline{\tau\alpha})$ is monthly average value of $(\tau\alpha)$, which is equal to the monthly average value of absorbed solar radiation, given by

$$(\overline{\tau\alpha}) = \frac{\overline{S}}{\overline{H}_t} \qquad [79]$$

For calculations of the dimensionless parameters X and Y, eqns [77] and [78] are usually rearranged to use the factors $F_R U_L$ and $F_R (\tau\alpha)_n$, which are readily available from standard collector tests and become

$$X = F_R U_L \frac{F'_R}{F_R}\left(T_{\text{ref}} - \overline{T}_a\right)\Delta t \frac{A_c}{L} \qquad [80]$$

$$Y = F_R (\tau\alpha)_n \frac{F'_R}{F_R}\left[\frac{(\overline{\tau\alpha})}{(\tau\alpha)_n}\right]\overline{H}_t N \frac{A_c}{L} \qquad [81]$$

The dimensionless parameters X and Y have some physical significance. Parameter X represents the ratio of the total energy loss from the reference collector to the total heating load or demand (L) during period Δt, whereas parameter Y represents the ratio of the total absorbed solar energy to the total heating load or demand (L) during the same period.

The ratio F'_R/F_R in eqns [80] and [81] is used to correct the collector performance, errors in which occur because the heat exchanger causes the collector side of the system to operate at a higher temperature than a similar system without a heat exchanger and is given by [50]

$$\frac{F'_R}{F_R} = \left[1 + \frac{A_c F_R U_L}{(\dot{m}c_p)_c}\left(\frac{(\dot{m}c_p)_c}{\varepsilon(\dot{m}c_p)_{\min}} - 1\right)\right]^{-1} \qquad [82]$$

For a given collector orientation, the value of the factor $(\overline{\tau\alpha})/(\tau\alpha)_n$ varies slightly from month to month. For collectors tilted and facing the equator with a slope equal to latitude plus 15°, Klein [51] found that the factor is equal to 0.96 for a one-cover collector and 0.94 for a two-covers collector for the whole heating season (winter months). From eqn [79] for $(\overline{\tau\alpha})$, the following is obtained:

$$\frac{(\overline{\tau\alpha})}{(\tau\alpha)_n} = \frac{\overline{S}}{\overline{H}_t (\tau\alpha)_n} \qquad [83]$$

If the isotropic model is used, $\overline{S}$ is given by [50]

$$\overline{S} = \overline{H}_B \overline{R}_B (\overline{\tau\alpha})_B + \overline{H}_D (\overline{\tau\alpha})_D \left(\frac{1+\cos(\beta)}{2}\right) + \overline{H}\rho_G (\overline{\tau\alpha})_G \left(\frac{1-\cos(\beta)}{2}\right) \qquad [84]$$

Substitution of eqn [84] into [83] gives

$$\frac{(\overline{\tau\alpha})}{(\tau\alpha)_n} = \frac{\overline{H}_B \overline{R}_B}{\overline{H}_t}\frac{(\overline{\tau\alpha})_B}{(\tau\alpha)_n} + \frac{\overline{H}_D}{\overline{H}_t}\frac{(\overline{\tau\alpha})_D}{(\tau\alpha)_n}\left(\frac{1+\cos(\beta)}{2}\right) + \frac{\overline{H}\rho_G}{\overline{H}_t}\frac{(\overline{\tau\alpha})_G}{(\tau\alpha)_n}\left(\frac{1-\cos(\beta)}{2}\right) \qquad [85]$$

The term $\overline{R}_B$ is the ratio of the monthly average beam radiation on a tilted surface to that on a horizontal surface, called the monthly mean beam radiation tilt factor. Actually, this is a complicated function of the atmospheric transmittance; but according to Liu and Jordan [52], it can be estimated by the ratio of extraterrestrial radiation on the tilted surface to that on a horizontal surface for the month. For surfaces facing directly toward the equator, this is given by

$$\overline{R}_B = \frac{\cos(L-\beta)\cos(\delta)\sin(h'_{ss}) + \left(\frac{\pi}{180}\right)h'_{ss}\sin(L-\beta)\sin(\delta)}{\cos(L)\cos(\delta)\sin(h_{ss}) + \left(\frac{\pi}{180}\right)h_{ss}\sin(L)\sin(\delta)} \qquad [86a]$$

where h'_{ss} is sunset hour angle on the tilted surface (degrees) given by

$$h'_{ss} = \min\{h_{ss}, \cos^{-1}[-\tan(L-\beta)\tan(\delta)]\} \qquad [86b]$$

It should be noted that for the southern hemisphere, the term $(L-\beta)$ of eqns [86a] and [86b] changes to $(L+\beta)$.

In eqn [85], the $(\overline{\tau\alpha})/(\tau\alpha)_n$ ratios can be obtained from the following equation:

For single cover

$$\frac{(\overline{\tau\alpha})}{(\tau\alpha)_n} = -8.7\times 10^{-8}\theta^4 + 1.03\times 10^{-5}\theta^3 - 0.000\,476\,2\theta^2 + 0.008\,51\theta + 0.949\,67 \qquad [87a]$$

For two covers

$$\frac{(\overline{\tau\alpha})}{(\tau\alpha)_n} = -5.05\times 10^{-8}\theta^4 + 3.578\times 10^{-6}\theta^3 - 8.777\times 10^{-5}\theta^2 - 1.836\times 10^{-6}\theta + 1.0042 \qquad [87b]$$

Equations [87a] and [87b] are for one and two sheets of glass, respectively, with refractive index equal to 1.526. The various components of $(\overline{\tau\alpha})/(\tau\alpha)_n$, that is, the beam, diffuse, and ground-reflected components, are obtained from this equation by using the appropriate mean incidence angle. For the beam component at the effective angle of incidence $\overline{\theta}_b$, also called mean incidence

Table 4 Recommended average day for each month

	Average day of the month		
Month	Date	Day	δ (°)
January	17	17	−20.92
February	16	47	−12.95
March	16	75	−2.42
April	15	105	9.41
May	15	135	18.79
June	11	162	23.09
July	17	198	21.18
August	16	228	13.45
September	15	258	2.22
October	15	288	−9.60
November	14	318	−18.91
December	10	344	−23.05

δ is the declination angle for the day shown.

angle for beam radiation, can be obtained from the original figures of Klein [53], and for surfaces facing directly toward the equator, it can be approximated as the incidence angle at 2.5 h from solar noon on an average day of the month (**Table 4**).

For the diffuse and ground-reflected components, effective incidence angles can be used at various inclination angles β from eqns [88] and [89]:

$$\theta_{e,D} = 59.68 - 0.1388\beta + 0.001\,497\beta^2 \qquad [88]$$

$$\theta_{e,G} = 90 - 0.5788\beta + 0.002\,693\beta^2 \qquad [89]$$

As indicated above, f-chart is used to estimate the monthly solar fraction, f_i, and the energy contribution for the month is the product of f_i and monthly load (heating and hot water), L_i. To find the fraction of the annual load supplied by the solar system, F, the sum of the monthly energy contributions is divided by the annual load, given by

$$F = \frac{\sum f_i L_i}{\sum L_i} \qquad [90]$$

The method can be used to simulate standard solar water and air systems configurations and solar systems used only for hot water production. These are examined separately in the following sections.

It should be noted that although the method primarily depends on values obtained from charts, hence its name, here only equations are given. The charts can be found from the original References 47–49 or from References 35 and 50. Alternatively, the appropriate charts can be constructed easily on any spreadsheet program, or such a program can be used directly to obtain the required values easily and more accurately without having to perform a large number of hand calculations.

3.11.6.1 Performance and Design of Liquid-Based Solar Heating Systems

The f-chart for liquid-based systems has been developed for the standard liquid-based solar system (**Figure 42**). The typical liquid-based system (**Figure 42**) requires an antifreeze solution in the collector loop and water as the storage medium. A water-to-water load heat exchanger is used to transfer heat from the storage tank to the DHW system. The method can be used to design and optimize a solar heating system.

The fraction f of the monthly total load supplied by a standard liquid-based solar system given as a function of the two dimensionless parameters, X and Y, can be obtained from the following equation [47]:

$$f = 1.029Y - 0.065X - 0.245Y^2 + 0.0018X^2 + 0.0215Y^3 \qquad [91]$$

This equation applies for $0 < Y < 3$ and $0 < X < 18$.

Equation [91] is a simple estimation of the solar fraction on a monthly basis as a function of the system design and local weather conditions. The annual value can be obtained by adding up the monthly values using eqn [90]. In a solar system design, the economic optimum collector area needs to be determined, so the annual load fraction corresponding to different collector areas is required. Therefore, the present method can easily be used for these estimations.

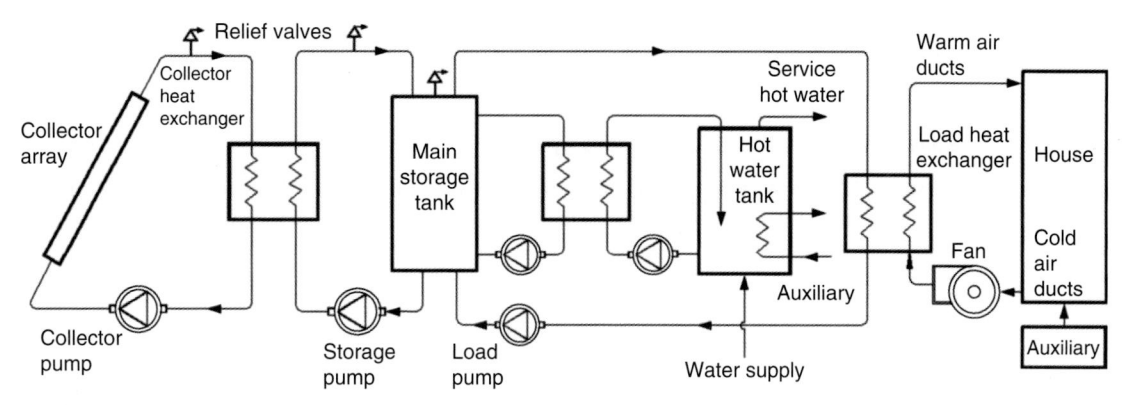

Figure 42 Schematic diagram of the standard liquid-based solar heating system.

Attention is required to the fact that the f-chart was developed using standard nominal values of storage capacity per unit of collector area, collector liquid flow rate per unit of collector area, and load heat exchanger size relative to space heating load. Therefore, the use of the f-chart method requires the application of various corrections if the system characteristics of the particular system configuration used differ from the standard ones. These corrections are analyzed in the following sections.

3.11.6.1.1 Storage capacity correction

The annual performance of liquid-based solar systems is insensitive to the storage capacity as long as this is more than 50 l of water per square meter of collector area. For the f value estimated with eqn [91], a standard storage capacity of 75 l of stored water per square meter of collector area was considered. Other storage capacities can be used by correcting the factor X with a storage size correction factor [49]:

$$\frac{X_c}{X} = \left(\frac{M_{w,a}}{M_{w,s}}\right)^{-0.25} \quad \text{for } 0.5 \leq \left(\frac{M_{w,a}}{M_{w,s}}\right) \leq 4.0 \text{ or } 37.5 \leq M_{w,a} \leq 300 \, l \, m^{-2} \quad [92]$$

where $M_{w,a}$ is the actual storage capacity per square meter of collector area $(l\,m^{-2})$ and $M_{w,s}$ is the standard storage capacity per square meter of collector area $(75\,l\,m^{-2})$.

3.11.6.1.2 Collector flow rate correction

The f value estimated with eqn [91] was obtained for a collector with an antifreeze solution flow rate of $0.015\,l\,s^{-1}\cdot m^{-2}$. A lower flow rate can reduce energy collection rate significantly, especially if the low flow rate leads to fluid boiling and relief of pressure through the relief valve, with a consequent loss of heat. The product of mass flow rate and specific heat of fluid flowing through the collector strongly affects the performance of the solar system; however, the value used in practice is not lower than the value used for the f-chart development. Besides, since an increase in collector flow rate beyond the nominal value has a small effect on the system performance, it is safe to assume that eqn [91] is applicable for all practical collector flow rates.

3.11.6.1.3 Load heat exchanger size correction

The size of the load heat exchanger also strongly affects the performance of the solar system. This is because the rate of heat transfer across the load heat exchanger directly influences the temperature of the storage tank, which consequently affects the collector inlet temperature and thus collector efficiency. Usually, in order to ensure a low operation temperature of a solar heating system, an air distribution system is used; thus, the system should include a heat exchanger to transfer the heat from the hot water to the air. Therefore, as the heat exchanger is reduced in size, the storage tank temperature must increase to supply the same amount of heat energy, resulting in higher collector inlet temperatures and thus lower collector performance. In order to account for the load heat exchanger size, a new dimensionless parameter is specified, called Z, given by [49]

$$Z = \frac{\varepsilon_L (\dot{m}c_p)_{min}}{(UA)_L} \quad [93]$$

where ε_L is effectiveness of the load heat exchanger, $(\dot{m}c_p)_{min}$ is minimum mass flow rate-specific heat product of heat exchanger $(W\,K^{-1})$, and $(UA)_L$ is building loss coefficient and area product used in degree-day space heating load model $(W\,K^{-1})$.

In eqn [93], when one side of the heat exchanger is water and the other is air, the minimum capacitance rate is always that of the air side of the heat exchanger due to the lower C_p. System performance is asymptotically dependent on the value of Z, and for Z greater than 10, the performance is the same as for an infinitely large value of Z. In fact the reduction in performance due to a small size load heat exchanger is significant for values of Z lower than 1. A value of $Z = 2$ was used for the development of f-chart, whereas practical values of Z are between 1 and 3. The performance of systems having other values of Z can be estimated by multiplying the dimensionless parameter Y by the following correction factor:

$$\frac{Y_c}{Y} = 0.39 + 0.65 \exp\left(-\frac{0.139}{Z}\right) \quad \text{for } 0.5 \leq Z \leq 50 \qquad [94]$$

3.11.6.2 Performance and Design of Air-Based Solar Heating Systems

Similar to liquid-based systems, Klein *et al.* [48] developed a design procedure for air-based systems. The f-chart for air-based systems was developed for the standard solar air-based system (**Figure 43**), which uses a pebble-bed storage unit. As can be seen, the energy required for the DHW system is provided through the air-to-water heat exchanger. During summertime, when heating is not required, it is preferable not to store heat in the pebble bed, so a bypass is usually used, which allows the use of the air collectors for water heating only.

The fraction f of the monthly total load supplied by a standard air-based solar system (**Figure 43**) is also given as a function of the two dimensionless parameters, X and Y, and can be obtained from the following eqn [48]:

$$f = 1.040Y - 0.065X - 0.159Y^2 + 0.00187X^2 - 0.0095Y^3 \qquad [95]$$

Again, this equation applies for $0 < Y < 3$ and $0 < X < 18$.

Air systems require two correction factors, one for the pebble-bed storage size and one for the airflow rate, which affects the stratification in the pebble bed. There is no need for load heat exchangers in air systems, and care must be taken to use the collector performance parameters $F_R U_L$ and $F_R(\tau\alpha)_n$ determined at the same airflow rate as used in the actual installation; otherwise, a correction factor may need to be used [50].

3.11.6.2.1 Pebble-bed storage size correction

For air systems, a standard storage capacity of $0.25 \, \text{m}^3$ of pebbles per square meter of collector area was considered. This value corresponds to $350 \, \text{kJ m}^{-2} \cdot {}^\circ\text{C}^{-1}$ for typical void fractions and rock properties. Although the performance of air-based systems is not strongly affected by the storage capacity (as in liquid-based systems), other storage capacities can be used by modifying the factor X by a storage size correction factor X_c given by [48]

$$\frac{X_c}{X} = \left(\frac{M_{b,a}}{M_{b,s}}\right)^{-0.30} \quad \text{for } 0.5 \leq \left(\frac{M_{b,a}}{M_{b,s}}\right) \leq 4.0 \text{ or } 0.125 \leq M_{b,a} \leq 1.0 \qquad [96]$$

where $M_{b,a}$ is the actual pebble storage capacity per square meter of collector area ($\text{m}^3 \, \text{m}^{-2}$) and $M_{b,s}$ is the standard storage capacity per square meter of collector area ($0.25 \, \text{m}^3 \, \text{m}^{-2}$).

3.11.6.2.2 Airflow rate correction

The standard collector flow rate is $10 \, \text{l s}^{-1}$ of air per square meter of collector area, and air-based heating systems must also be corrected for the flow rate if a different value is used. An increased airflow rate tends to increase solar collector performance by improving F_R, but tends to decrease system performance because the pebble-bed thermal stratification is reduced. The performance of systems having other collector flow rates can be estimated by using appropriate values of F_R and Y, and then modifying the value of X by a collector airflow rate correction factor X_c to account for the degree of stratification in the pebble bed [48]:

$$\frac{X_c}{X} = \left(\frac{\dot{m}_a}{\dot{m}_s}\right)^{0.28} \quad \text{for } 0.5 \leq \left(\frac{\dot{m}_a}{\dot{m}_s}\right) \leq 2.0 \text{ or } 5 \leq \dot{m}_a \leq 20 \qquad [97]$$

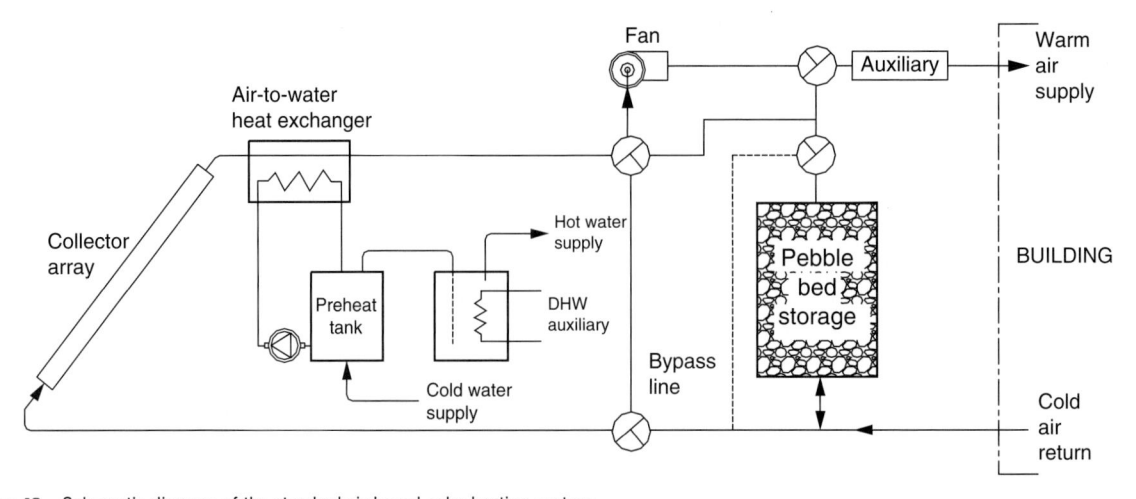

Figure 43 Schematic diagram of the standard air-based solar heating system.

where $\dot{m}_a$ is the actual collector flow rate per square meter of collector area ($l\,s^{-1}$-m^{-2}) and $\dot{m}_s$ is the standard collector flow rate per square meter of collector area ($10\,l\,s^{-1}$-m^{-2}).

As can be understood from above, if in a solar system both airflow rate and storage size are different from the standard ones, two corrections must be done on the dimensionless parameter X, and the final X value to be used should be the uncorrected value multiplied by the two correction factors obtained from eqns [96] and [97].

3.11.6.3 Performance and Design of Solar Service Water Systems

The solar contribution for liquid-based systems given by eqn [91] can also be used to estimate the performance of systems producing solar service water heating only. The system configuration is shown in **Figure 44**. Although a liquid-based system is shown, air or water collectors can be used with the appropriate heat exchanger to transfer heat to the preheat storage tank. Hot water from the preheat storage tank is then fed to a water heater, where its temperature can be increased to the required temperature if needed. A tempering valve may also be used to maintain the supply temperature below a maximum temperature, but this mixing is usually done at the point of use by the user.

In this case, the performance of the solar water heating system is affected by the mains water temperature T_m and the minimum acceptable hot water temperature T_w. Both affect the average system operating temperature and thus the collector energy losses. Thus, the parameter X, which as was seen before accounts for the collector energy losses, needs to be corrected. The additional correction factor for the parameter X is given by [49]

$$\frac{X_c}{X} = \frac{11.6 \times 1.18 T_w + 3.86 T_m - 2.32 \overline{T}_a}{100 - \overline{T}_a} \quad [98]$$

where T_m is the mains water temperature (°C), T_w is minimum acceptable hot water temperature (°C), and $\overline{T}_a$ is monthly average ambient temperature (°C).

The correction factor given in eqn [98] is based on the assumption that the solar preheat tank is well insulated. It should also be noted that tank losses from the auxiliary tank are not included in the f-chart correlations. Therefore, the load should also include the losses from the auxiliary tank, and these can be estimated from the heat loss coefficient and tank area (UA) on the basis of the assumption that the entire tank is at the minimum acceptable hot water temperature, T_w.

The system performance is also based on the storage capacity of $75\,l\,m^{-2}$ of the collector aperture area and on a typical hot water load profile, with other consumption profiles producing only small effects on the system performance. For different storage capacities, the correction given by eqn [92] can be used.

3.11.6.4 General Remarks

The f-chart design method is used to estimate quickly the long-term performance of solar systems of standard configurations. The input data needed are:

- The monthly average radiation and temperature
- The monthly load required to heat a building and provide hot water
- The collector performance parameters obtained from standard collector tests.

There are a number of general assumptions made for the development of the f-chart method such as:

- The systems are well-built
- System configuration and control are close to the ones considered in the development of the method
- Flow rate in the collectors is uniform.

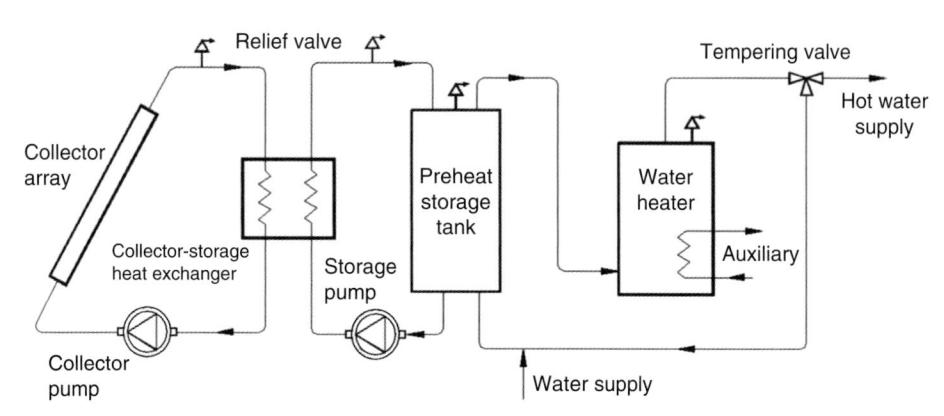

Figure 44 Schematic diagram of the standard of water heating system configuration.

If a system differs considerably from these conditions, then the f-chart method will not give accurate results.

The f-chart can be used as a design tool for residential space and domestic water heating systems of standard configuration in which the minimum temperature at the load is near 20 °C, and energy above this temperature value is useful. The f-chart method should not be used for the design of systems that require minimum temperatures that are substantially different from this minimum value. For example, it cannot be used for solar air-conditioning systems using absorption chillers, for which the minimum load temperature is 80–90 °C.

It should also be noted that because of the nature of the input data used, there are a number of uncertainties in the results obtained by the f-chart method. The first is related to the nature of the meteorological data used, especially when horizontal radiation data are converted into radiation falling on the collector surface, which is usually inclined. This is due to the fact that average weather data are used, which may differ considerably from real values, and that all days were considered symmetrical about solar noon. The second uncertainty is related to the fact that solar systems are assumed to be well-built and to have well-insulated storage tanks and no leaks in the systems, which is not valid because most air systems leak to some extent, leading to a degraded performance. Additionally, all liquid storage tanks are assumed to be fully mixed, which is not very correct, as all tanks show some degree of stratification. This however leads to conservative long-term performance predictions as the collector inlet temperature is overestimated. The final uncertainty is related to the building and hot water loads, which strongly depend on the variable weather conditions and on the habits of the occupants.

Despite these limitations, the f-chart method is a handy method that can be used for the easy and quick design of residential-type solar heating systems. When the system under study satisfies the main assumptions made in the development of the method, quite accurate results are obtained. Additionally, the method can be used in a programmable calculator or a computer to give results very quickly.

3.11.7 Utilizability Method

Due to its limitations, the f-chart method cannot be used for systems in which the minimum temperature supplied to a load is not near 20 °C. Most of the systems that cannot be simulated with f-chart however can be modeled with the utilizability method or its enhancements, presented in this section.

The utilizability method is a design technique used for the calculation of long-term thermal collector performance for certain types of systems. Initially originated by Whillier [54] and called the Φ-curve method, it is based on solar radiation statistics and the necessary calculations that have to be done at hourly intervals about solar noon each month. Subsequently, the method was generalized to be used for any time of year and geographic location by Liu and Jordan [55]. The generalized Φ curves of Liu and Jordan, generated from daily data, enable the calculation of utilizability curves for any location and tilt, by knowing only the clearness index, K_T. Subsequently, Klein [56] and Collares-Pereira and Rabl [57] eliminated the necessity of hourly calculations and introduced the monthly average daily utilizability, $\overline{\Phi}$, which reduced the complexity of the original method and improved the utility of the method.

Here again, only equations are given and not the actual graphs, which can be obtained from the original sources or by using a spreadsheet program to plot the equations as in f-chart.

3.11.7.1 Hourly Utilizability

The utilizability method is based on the notion that only radiation that is above a critical or threshold intensity is useful. Therefore, the utilizability Φ is defined as the fraction of insolation incident on a collector's surface that is above a given threshold or critical value.

A solar collector can give useful heat only if solar radiation is above a critical level, given by

$$G_{tc} = \frac{F_R U_L (T_i - T_a)}{F_R (\tau \alpha)} \quad [99]$$

This is the radiation level at which the absorbed solar radiation and loss terms are equal. It is obtained from the standard collector equation given in eqn [73], for $Q_u = 0$ and solving for G_t, now called G_{tc}, the critical incident total radiation. Similarly, hourly values of total radiation can be used with symbols I_t and I_{tc}.

When radiation is incident on the tilted surface of a collector, the utilizable energy for any hour is $(I_t - I_{tc})^+$. The + sign indicates that the utilizable energy can only be positive or zero. The fraction of the total energy for the hour that is above the critical level is called the hourly utilizability and is given by

$$\Phi_h = \frac{(I_t - I_{tc})^+}{I_t} \quad [100]$$

It should be noted that utilizability can also be defined in terms of rates, using the irradiance on tilted surface G_t and its critical value G_{tc}, but as radiation data are usually available on an hourly basis, the hourly values are preferred. This is also in agreement with the basis of the concept used for the development of the method.

The utilizability for a single hour is not a very useful quantity, whereas utilizability for a particular hour of a month having N days in which the average radiation for the hour is $\bar{I}_t$ is very useful. This is given by

$$\Phi = \frac{1}{N} \sum_{1}^{N} \frac{(I_t - I_{tc})^+}{\bar{I}_t} \qquad [101]$$

The average utilizable energy for the month is $N\bar{I}_t\Phi$. These calculations can be done for all hours of the month with the results added up to get the utilizable energy of the month. Another parameter required in these calculations is the dimensionless critical radiation level defined as

$$X_c = \frac{I_{tc}}{\bar{I}_t} \qquad [102]$$

For each hour, the monthly average hourly radiation incident on the collector is given by [50]

$$\bar{I}_t = (\bar{H}r - \bar{H}_D r_d)R_B + \bar{H}_D r_d \left(\frac{1 + \cos(\beta)}{2}\right) + \bar{H}r\rho_G \left(\frac{1 - \cos(\beta)}{2}\right) \qquad [103]$$

By dividing by $\bar{H}$ and considering the definition of the monthly average clearness index, $\bar{K}_T$, defined as the ratio of the monthly average total insolation on a terrestrial horizontal surface to the monthly average daily total insolation on an extraterrestrial horizontal surface, $\bar{H}/\bar{H}_o$:

$$\bar{I}_t = \bar{K}_T \bar{H}_o \left[\left(r - \frac{\bar{H}_D}{\bar{H}} r_d\right)R_B + \frac{\bar{H}_D}{\bar{H}} r_d \left(\frac{1 + \cos(\beta)}{2}\right) + r\rho_G \left(\frac{1 - \cos(\beta)}{2}\right) \right] \qquad [104]$$

The ratios r and r_d can be estimated by the Collares-Pereira and Rabl [58] and Liu and Jordan [52] correlations given in the following equations:

Liu and Jordan [52] correlation for r_d (ratio of hourly diffuse radiation to daily diffuse radiation) is given by

$$r_d = \left(\frac{\pi}{24}\right) \frac{\cos(h) - \cos(h_{ss})}{\sin(h_{ss}) - \left(\frac{2\pi h_{ss}}{360}\right)\cos(h_{ss})} \qquad [105]$$

Collares-Pereira and Rabl [58] correlation for r (ratio of hourly total radiation to daily total radiation) is given by

$$r = \frac{\pi}{24}(a + \beta\cos(h)) \frac{\cos(h) - \cos(h_{ss})}{\sin(h_{ss}) - \left(\frac{2\pi h_{ss}}{360}\right)\cos(h_{ss})} = \frac{\pi}{24}(a + \beta\cos(h))r \qquad [106a]$$

$$\text{where } a = 0.409 + 0.5016 \sin(h_{ss} - 60) \qquad [106b]$$

$$\beta = 0.6609 - 0.4767 \sin(h_{ss} - 60) \qquad [106c]$$

where h_{ss} is the sunset hour angle (degrees), obtained from $\cos(h_{ss}) = -\tan(L)\tan(\delta)$, where L is the local latitude and δ is the declination, and h is the hour angle (degrees) at the midpoint of each hour (degrees).

Liu and Jordan [55] constructed a set of Φ curves for various values of $\bar{K}_T$. With these curves, it is possible to predict the utilizable energy at a constant critical level by knowing only the long-term average radiation. Finally, Clark et al. [59] developed a simple procedure to estimate the generalized Φ functions given by

$$\Phi = \begin{cases} 0 & \text{if } X_c \geq X_m \\ \left(1 - \frac{X_c}{X_m}\right)^2 & \text{if } X_m = 2 \\ \left| |g| - \left[g^2 + (1 + 2g)\left(1 - \frac{X_c}{X_m}\right)^2\right]^{1/2} \right| & \text{otherwise} \end{cases} \qquad [107a]$$

where

$$g = \frac{X_m - 1}{2 - X_m} \qquad [107b]$$

$$X_m = 1.85 + 0.169 \frac{\bar{R}_h}{\bar{k}_T^2} + 0.0696 \frac{\cos(\beta)}{\bar{k}_T^2} - 0.981 \frac{\bar{k}_T}{\cos^2(\delta)} \qquad [107c]$$

The monthly average hourly clearness index, $\bar{k}_T$, is given by

$$\bar{k}_T = \frac{\bar{I}}{\bar{I}_o} \qquad [108]$$

and can be estimated using eqns [105] and [106] as

$$\bar{k}_T = \frac{\bar{I}}{\bar{I}^\circ} = \frac{r}{r_d}\bar{K}_T = \frac{r}{r_d}\frac{\bar{H}}{\bar{H}_o} = [\alpha + \beta\cos(h)]\bar{K}_T \qquad [109]$$

The parameters α and β can be estimated from eqns [106b] and [106c], respectively. The monthly average daily total insolation on an extraterrestrial horizontal surface $\bar{H}^\circ$ can be estimated from

$$H_o = \frac{24 \times 3600 G_{sc}}{\pi}\left[1 + 0.033\cos\left(\frac{360N}{365}\right)\right]\left(\cos(L)\cos(\delta)\sin(h_{ss}) + \left(\frac{\pi h_{ss}}{180}\right)\sin(L)\sin(\delta)\right) \qquad [110]$$

where h_{ss} is the sunset hour in degrees. The unit of eqn [110] is $J\,m^{-2}$.

The ratio of monthly average hourly radiation on a tilted surface to that on a horizontal surface, $\bar{R}_h$, is given by

$$\bar{R}_h = \frac{\bar{I}_t}{\bar{I}} = \frac{\bar{I}_t}{r\bar{H}} \qquad [111]$$

The hourly utilizability is used to obtain values every hour, which means that three to six hourly calculations are required per month if hour pairs are used (morning hours similar to afternoon hours with respect to solar noon). For surfaces having an azimuth angle equal to zero, that is, those facing the equator, the monthly average daily utilizability, $\bar{\Phi}$, presented in the following section, can be used, which is a simpler way of calculating the useful energy as hour pairs can be used. However, for surfaces that have a certain azimuth angle or for processes that have critical radiation levels that vary consistently during the days of a month, the hourly Φ curves need to be used.

3.11.7.2 Daily Utilizability

It is clear from the hourly utilizability method that a large amount of calculations are required in order to use the Φ curves. For this reason, Klein [56] developed the monthly average daily utilizability $\bar{\Phi}$ concept. This is defined as the sum over all hours and days of a month of the radiation falling on a titled surface that is above a given threshold or critical value, which is similar to the one used in the Φ method, divided by the monthly radiation. In equation form, it is given by

$$\bar{\Phi} = \sum_{days}\sum_{hours}\frac{(I_t - I_{tc})^+}{N\bar{H}_t} \qquad [112]$$

The monthly utilizable energy is then equal to the product $N\bar{H}_t\bar{\Phi}$. The value of $\bar{\Phi}$ for a month depends on the distribution of hourly values of radiation in that month. Klein [56] assumed that all days are symmetrical about solar noon, which means that $\bar{\Phi}$ depends on the distribution of daily total radiation, that is, the relative frequency of occurrence of below average, average, and above average daily radiation values. Because of this assumption, any departure from this symmetry within days leads to increased values of $\bar{\Phi}$, which means that the $\bar{\Phi}$ calculated will give conservative results.

Klein developed the correlations of $\bar{\Phi}$ as a function of $\bar{K}_T$, a dimensionless critical radiation level $\bar{X}_c$ and a geometric factor $\bar{R}/R_n$. The $\bar{R}$ parameter is the monthly ratio of radiation on a tilted surface to that on a horizontal surface $\bar{H}_t/\bar{H}$, given by

$$\bar{R} = \frac{\bar{H}_t}{\bar{H}} = \left(1 - \frac{\bar{H}_D}{\bar{H}}\right)\bar{R}_B + \frac{\bar{H}_D}{\bar{H}}\left(\frac{1+\cos(\beta)}{2}\right) + \rho_G\left(\frac{1-\cos(\beta)}{2}\right) \qquad [113]$$

where $\bar{H}_t$ is the monthly average daily total radiation on a tilted surface and $\bar{R}_B$ is the monthly mean beam radiation tilt factor given by eqn [86a].

For the hour centered about noon, the ratio of radiation on a tilted surface to that on a horizontal surface for an average day of the month, R_n, is given by

$$R_n = \left(\frac{I_t}{I}\right)_n = \left(1 - \frac{r_{d,n}H_D}{r_n H}\right)R_{B,n} + \left(\frac{r_{d,n}H_D}{r_n H}\right)\left(\frac{1+\cos(\beta)}{2}\right) + \rho_G\left(\frac{1-\cos(\beta)}{2}\right) \qquad [114]$$

where $r_{d,n}$ and r_n are obtained from eqns [105] and [106], respectively, at solar noon ($h = 0°$). It should be noted that R_n is calculated for a day that has a total radiation equal to the monthly average daily total radiation, that is, a day for which $H = \bar{H}$. The term H_D/H is given from Erbs et al. [60] as

For $h_{ss} \leq 81.4°$

$$\frac{H_D}{H} = \begin{cases} 1.0 - 0.2727K_T + 2.4495K_T^2 - 11.9514K_T^3 + 9.3879K_T^4 & \text{for } K_T < 0.715 \\ 0.143 & \text{for } K_T \geq 0.715 \end{cases} \qquad [115a]$$

For $h_{ss} > 81.4°$

$$\frac{H_D}{H} = \begin{cases} 1.0 + 0.2832K_T - 2.5557K_T^2 + 0.8448K_T^3 & \text{for } K_T < 0.722 \\ 0.175 & \text{for } K_T \geq 0.722 \end{cases} \qquad [115b]$$

Another parameter required is the monthly average critical radiation level $\overline{X}_c$, defined as the ratio of the critical radiation level to the noon radiation level on a day of the month in which the radiation is the same as the monthly average. In equation form, it is given by

$$\overline{X}_c = \frac{I_{tc}}{r_n R_n \overline{H}} \qquad [116]$$

The procedure followed by Klein [56] is for a given $\overline{K}_T$ and a set of days is established that have the correct long-term average distribution of K_T values. The radiation in each of the days in a sequence is divided into hours, and these hourly values of radiation are used to find the total hourly radiation on a tilted surface, I_t. Subsequently, critical radiation levels are subtracted from the I_t values and summed as shown in eqn [112] to get the $\overline{\Phi}$ values. The $\overline{\Phi}$ curves calculated in this manner can be obtained from graphs or from the flowing relation:

$$\overline{\Phi} = \exp\left\{\left[A + B\left(\frac{R_n}{\overline{R}}\right)\right]\left[\overline{X}_c + C\overline{X}_c^{\,2}\right]\right\} \qquad [117a]$$

where

$$A = 2.943 - 9.271\overline{K}_T + 4.031\overline{K}_T^{\,2} \qquad [117b]$$

$$B = -4.345 + 8.853\overline{K}_T - 3.602\overline{K}_T^{\,2} \qquad [117c]$$

$$C = -0.170 - 0.306\overline{K}_T + 2.936\overline{K}_T^{\,2} \qquad [117d]$$

Both the Φ and $\overline{\Phi}$ concepts can be applied in a variety of designs such as heating systems and passive heated buildings, where the unutilizable energy (excess energy) that cannot be stored in the building mass can be estimated.

3.11.7.3 Design of Active Systems with Utilizability Methods

The method can be developed for an hourly or daily basis as shown in the following sections.

3.11.7.3.1 Hourly utilizability

Another way of defining utilizability is that it is the fraction of incident solar radiation that can be converted into useful heat. It is the fraction utilized by an ideal collector that has no optical losses and a heat removal factor of unity, that is, $F_R(\tau\alpha) = 1$, operating at a fixed temperature difference between the inlet and the ambient temperatures. As can be understood, the utilizability of this collector is lower than 1 since thermal losses always exist.

The equation that relates the rate of useful energy collection by a flat-plate solar collector Q_u to the design parameters of the collector and meteorological conditions has been reported by Hottel and Whillier [61]. This equation is given by eqn [73] and can be expressed in terms of the hourly radiation incident on the collector plane, I_t, as

$$Q_u = A_c F_R \left[I_t(\tau\alpha) - U_L(T_i - T_a)\right]^+ \qquad [118]$$

where A_c is collector area (m^2), F_R is collector heat removal factor, I_t is total radiation incident on the collector surface per unit area (kJ m^{-2}), $(\tau\alpha)$ is effective transmittance–absorptance product, U_L is energy loss coefficient (kJ m^{-2}·K^{-1}), T_i is inlet collector fluid temperature (°C), and T_a is ambient temperature (°C).

As was seen before, the radiation level must exceed a critical value before useful output is produced. This critical level is found by setting Q_u in eqn [118] to zero. This is given in eqn [99], but in terms of the hourly radiation incident on the collector plane is given by

$$I_{tc} = \frac{F_R U_L(T_i - T_a)}{F_R(\tau\alpha)} \qquad [119]$$

Therefore, the useful energy gain can be written in terms of the critical radiation level as

$$Q_u = A_c F_R(\tau\alpha)(I_t - I_{tc})^+ \qquad [120]$$

The + sign in eqns [118] and [120] and in the following equations indicates that only positive values of I_{tc} should be considered. By considering that the critical radiation level is constant for a particular hour of the month having N days, the monthly average hourly output for this hour is

$$\overline{Q}_u = \frac{A_c F_R(\tau\alpha)}{N} \sum_N (I_t - I_{tc})^+ \qquad [121]$$

By considering that the monthly average radiation for this particular hour is $\overline{I}_t$, the average useful output can be expressed by

$$\overline{Q}_u = A_c F_R(\tau\alpha)\overline{I}_t \Phi \qquad [122]$$

where Φ is given by eqn [101].

This can be estimated from eqn [107] given earlier for the dimensionless critical radiation level X_c, given by eqn [102], which can be written in terms of the collector parameters, using eqn [119], as

$$X_c = \frac{I_{tc}}{\bar{I}_t} = \frac{F_R U_L (T_i - T_a)}{F_R (\tau\alpha)_n \frac{(\tau\alpha)}{(\tau\alpha)_n} \bar{I}_t} \quad [123]$$

where $(\tau\alpha)/(\tau\alpha)_n$ can be determined for the mean day of the month (**Table 4**) and the appropriate hour angle, and can be estimated with the incidence angle modifier equation obtained from the performance testing of the collector [50].

If Φ is known, the utilizable energy is $\bar{I}_t \Phi$. The hourly utilizability is used to estimate the output of processes that have a critical radiation level, X_c, that changes considerably during the day because of collector inlet temperature variation.

Although the utilizability method is a very powerful tool, caution is required for possible wrong use. Due to finite storage capacity, the critical level of collector inlet temperature for liquid-based domestic solar heating systems varies considerably during the month; therefore, the Φ curves method cannot be applied directly. Exceptions to this are air heating systems during winter, where the inlet air temperature to the collector is the return air from the house, and systems with seasonal storage, where due to its size, the storage tank temperature shows small variations during the month [50].

3.11.7.3.2 Daily utilizability

As mentioned in Section 3.11.7.2, the use of Φ curves involves a large number of calculations. Klein [56] and Collares-Pereira and Rabl [58, 62] simplified the calculations for systems for which it is possible to use a critical radiation level for all hours of the month.

Daily utilizability is defined as the ratio of the sum, over all hours and all days of a month, of the radiation on a tilted surface that is above a critical level to the monthly radiation, given in eqn [112]. The critical level I_{tc} is similar to eqn [119], but in this case, the monthly average $(\tau\alpha)$ product must be used and the inlet and ambient temperatures are representative temperatures for the month:

$$I_{tc} = \frac{F_R U_L (T_i - \bar{T}_a)}{F_R (\tau\alpha)_n \frac{(\overline{\tau\alpha})}{(\tau\alpha)_n}} \quad [124]$$

In eqn [124], the term $(\overline{\tau\alpha})/(\tau\alpha)_n$ can be estimated with eqn [85]. The monthly average critical radiation ratio is the ratio of the critical radiation level, I_{tc}, to the noon radiation level for a day on which the total radiation for the day is the same as the monthly average [50]. In equation form, this is given as

$$\bar{X}_c = \frac{I_{tc}}{r_n R_n \bar{H}} = \frac{\frac{F_R U_L (T_i - \bar{T}_a)}{F_R (\overline{\tau\alpha})}}{r_n R_n \bar{K}_T \bar{H}_o} \quad [125]$$

The monthly average daily useful energy gain is then given by

$$\bar{Q}_u = A_c F_R (\overline{\tau\alpha}) \bar{H}_t \bar{\Phi} \quad [126]$$

Finally, the daily utilizability can be obtained from eqn [117].

Even though monthly average daily utilizability reduces greatly the complexity of the method, quite a lot of calculations can still be required, especially when monthly average hourly calculations need to be estimated.

It should be noted that the majority of the methods described so far for computing solar energy utilizability have been derived for North-American data based on clearness index, which is the parameter used to indicate dependence on the climate. Carvalho and Bourges [63] applied some of these methods to European and African locations. By comparing the results obtained with values from long-term measurements, they found that these methods can give acceptable results when the actual monthly average daily irradiation on the considered surface is known.

3.11.8 The $\bar{\Phi}$, f-Chart Method

The utilizability design concept is useful when the collector operates at a known critical radiation level during a specific month. In actual systems however, the collectors are connected to a storage tank, and thus, the monthly sequence of weather and load-time distributions cause a changeable storage tank temperature, which leads to a variable critical radiation level. The f-chart has been developed to overcome the restriction of a constant critical level but is only applicable to systems delivering a load near 20 °C.

The utilizability concept described in the previous section has been combined with the f-chart by Klein and Beckman [64] to produce the $\bar{\Phi}$, f-chart design method for closed-loop solar energy systems (**Figure 45**). In this system, the storage tank is assumed to be pressurized or filled with a liquid of high boiling point so that no energy dumping occurs through the relief valve, and the auxiliary heater is in parallel with the solar system as shown. The new method is not restricted to loads at 20 °C. In these systems, the energy supplied to the load must be above a specified minimum useful temperature, T_{min} (not necessarily 20 °C), and it must be used at a constant thermal efficiency or coefficient of performance so that the load on the solar system can be estimated. The return temperature from the load is always at or above T_{min}. This method cannot be applied to a heat pump or heat engine because their

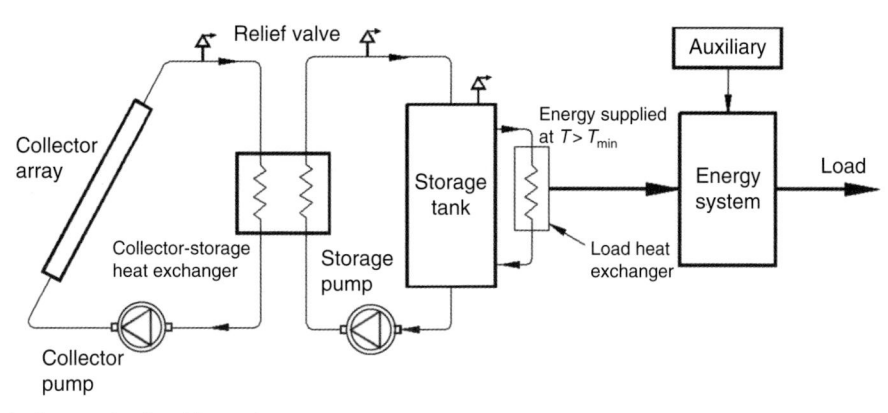

Figure 45 Schematic diagram of a closed-loop solar energy system.

performance varies with the temperature level of supplied energy. It is very useful, however, for absorption refrigerators, industrial process heating, and space heating systems [50].

The maximum monthly average daily energy that can be delivered from the system shown in **Figure 45** is given by

$$\sum \overline{Q}_u = A_c F_R (\overline{\tau \alpha}) \overline{H}_t \overline{\Phi}_{max} \qquad [127]$$

This is the same as eqn [126] except that $\overline{\Phi}$ is replaced with $\overline{\Phi}_{max}$, which is defined as the maximum daily utilizability estimated from the minimum monthly average critical radiation ratio, given by

$$\overline{X}_{c,min} = \frac{\frac{F_R U_L (T_{min} - \overline{T}_a)}{F_R (\overline{\tau \alpha})}}{r_n R_n \overline{K}_T \overline{H}_o} \qquad [128]$$

Klein and Beckman [64] correlated the results of many detailed simulations of the system shown in **Figure 45**, for various storage size–collector area ratios, with two dimensionless variables. These variables are similar to the ones used in the f-chart but are not the same. In this method, the f-chart dimensionless parameter Y is replaced by $\overline{\Phi}_{max} Y$, given by

$$\overline{\Phi}_{max} Y = \overline{\Phi}_{max} \frac{A_c F_R (\overline{\tau \alpha}) N \overline{H}_t}{L} \qquad [129]$$

and the f-chart dimensionless parameter X is replaced by a modified dimensionless variable X', given by

$$X' = \frac{A_c F_R U_L (100) \Delta t}{L} \qquad [130]$$

In fact, the modification in the dimensionless variable X given in eqn [77] is that the parameter $(T_{ref} - \overline{T}_a)$ is replaced with an empirical constant 100 and F_R is used instead of F_R'.

The $\overline{\Phi}$, f-charts can be obtained from actual charts or from the following analytical eqn [64]:

$$f = \overline{\Phi}_{max} Y - 0.015 [\exp(3.85 f) - 1][1 - \exp(-0.15 X')] R_s^{0.76} \qquad [131]$$

where R_s is the ratio of standard storage heat capacity per unit of collector area of $350 \, kJ \, m^{-2} - °C^{-1}$ to the actual storage capacity given by [64]

$$R_s = \frac{350}{\frac{M c_p}{A_c}} \qquad [132]$$

where M is the actual mass of storage capacity (kg).

Since f is included in both sides of eqn [131], it must be estimated by trial and error. Because actual $\overline{\Phi}$, f-charts are given for various storage capacities and the user has to interpolate, the use of eqn [131] is preferred. The $\overline{\Phi}$, f-chart method is used in the same way as the f-chart method. The values of $\overline{\Phi}_{max}$, Y, and X' need to be calculated from the long-term radiation data for the particular location and load patterns. As in the case of the f-chart method, fL is the average monthly contribution of the solar system, and the monthly values can be summed and divided by the total annual load to obtain the annual fraction F.

It should be noted that the $\overline{\Phi}$, f-chart method overestimates the monthly solar fraction, f. This is due to assumptions made that no losses occur from the storage tank and that the heat exchanger is 100% efficient. These assumptions require certain corrections, which are presented in the following subsections.

3.11.8.1 Storage Tank Losses Correction

The rate of energy lost from the storage tank to the environment, which is considered to be at temperature T_{env}, is given by

$$\dot{Q}_{st} = (UA)_s(T_s - T_{env}) \quad [133]$$

By integrating eqn [133], the storage tank losses for the month can be obtained. This is done by considering that $(UA)_s$ and T_{env} are constant for the month

$$Q_{st} = (UA)_s(\overline{T}_s - T_{env})\Delta t \quad [134]$$

where $\overline{T}_s$ is the monthly average storage tank temperature (°C).

The total load on the solar system is the actual load plus the storage tank losses, although the storage tanks are usually well insulated, and therefore, the storage tank losses are small. Generally, the tank temperature rarely drops below the minimum temperature. Finally, the fraction of the total load supplied by solar energy, including storage tank losses, is given by

$$f_{TL} = \frac{L_s + Q_{st}}{L_u + Q_{st}} \quad [135]$$

where L_s is the solar energy supplied to the load (GJ) and L_u is the useful load (GJ).

Therefore, first Q_{st} is estimated, and then f_{TL} is obtained from the $\overline{\Phi}$, f-charts as usual. The solar fraction f can also be represented by L_s/L_u, that is, the ratio of solar energy supplied to the load to the useful load, by using eqn [135]:

$$f = f_{TL}\left(1 + \frac{Q_{st}}{L_u}\right) - \frac{Q_{st}}{L_u} \quad [136]$$

Storage tank losses are estimated by assuming that the tank remains at T_{min} during the month, or that the average tank temperature is equal to the monthly average collector inlet temperature, $\overline{T}_i$, which is estimated by the $\overline{\Phi}$ chart method. Finally, once f_{TL} is known, the average daily utilizability is given by [64]

$$\overline{\Phi} = \frac{f_{TL}}{Y} \quad [137]$$

For the estimation of tank losses by using eqn [134], Klein and Beckman [64] recommend the use of the mean of T_{min} and $\overline{T}_i$. The process is iterative, that is, $\overline{T}_s$ is assumed and is used to estimate Q_{st}. From this, the f_{TL} is estimated with the $\overline{\Phi}$, f-charts; subsequently, $\overline{\Phi}$ is estimated from eqn [137], and $\overline{X}_c$ is obtained from the $\overline{\Phi}$ charts. The temperature $\overline{T}_i$ can then be estimated by correcting the originally assumed value with the ratio of the new and original value of X_c. Subsequently, the new average tank temperature is estimated as the mean of $\overline{T}_s$ and $\overline{T}_i$. This new value of $\overline{T}_s$ is compared with the initially assumed value, and a new iteration is carried out if necessary. Finally, eqn [136] is used to estimate the solar fraction f.

3.11.8.2 Heat Exchanger Correction

As the heat exchanger adds a thermal resistance between the tank and the load, it increases the storage tank temperature. The presence of a heat exchanger leads to a reduction in the useful energy collection, as higher collector inlet temperatures are present, and the storage tank losses are increased. The average increase in tank temperature that is necessary to supply the required energy load is given by [64]

$$\Delta T = \frac{fL/\Delta t_L}{\varepsilon_L C_{min}} \quad [138]$$

where Δt_L is the number of seconds during a month for which the load is required (s), ε_L is the effectiveness of the load heat exchanger, and C_{min} is the minimum capacitance of the two fluid streams in the heat exchanger (W °C^{-1}).

Finally, the temperature difference found by eqn [138] is added to T_{min} to find the monthly average critical radiation from eqn [128].

3.11.9 Modeling and Simulation of Solar Energy Systems

Although the simple methods described so far have been proved to be quite accurate and can be carried out with hand calculations, the most accurate way to estimate the performance of solar processes is with detailed simulation.

The initial step in modeling a system is the derivation of a structure to be used to represent the system. However, the structure that represents the system should not be confused with the real system, as this will always be an imperfect copy of reality; nevertheless, the system structure will foster an understanding of the real system. In this process, system boundaries consistent with the problem being analyzed need to be established first. This is done by specifying the items, processes, and effects that are internal and external to the system.

Two basic types of methods – simplified and detailed – are generally considered. Simplified analysis methods have the advantages of fast computational speed, low cost, rapid turnaround (which is especially important during iterative design phases), and easy use by persons with little technical experience. Their disadvantages include limited flexibility for design optimization, lack of control over assumptions, and a limited selection of systems that can be analyzed [50]. If the system application under consideration, configuration, or load characteristics is significantly nonstandard, a detailed computer simulation may be required to achieve accurate results.

Computer modeling of thermal systems presents many advantages, the most important of which are the following [50]:

1. Elimination of the expense of building prototypes.
2. Organization of complex systems in an understandable format.
3. Provision of thorough understanding of system operation and component interactions.
4. Possible optimization of system components.
5. Estimation of the amount of energy delivered from the system.
6. Provision of temperature variations of the system.
7. Estimation of the effects of design variable changes on system performance by using the same weather conditions.

Simulations can provide valuable information on the long-term performance of solar systems and can provide information on transient system performance. These simulations include variations in temperature, which may reach values above the degradability limit (e.g., of selective coating) and boiling of water with consequent heat dumping through the relief valve. Usually, detailed models and fine time steps specified by the user require intensive calculations, which increase the time required to compute the results.

There are a number of programs that were developed over the years for the modeling and simulation of solar systems. Some of the most popular ones – F-chart, TRNSYS, and WATSUN – are described briefly in this section.

3.11.9.1 The F-Chart Program

Although the f-chart method presented in Section 3.11.6 is simple in concept, the required calculations are tedious, particularly with respect to the manipulation of radiation data. The use of computers greatly reduces the effort required. The program F-chart [65], which is provided by the developers of TRNSYS, is very easy to use and gives predictions very quickly. As in the basic method, the model is accurate only for solar heating systems of a type comparable to the model assumed in the development of the f-chart.

The F-chart program is written in BASIC. It can be used to estimate the long-term performance of solar systems that use flat-plate, evacuated-tube collectors, compound parabolic concentrators, and one- or two-axis tracking concentrating collectors. Additionally, the program includes the design of other solar systems like a swimming pool heating system that provides estimates of the energy losses from the swimming pool. The solar energy systems that can be handled by the program are as follows:

- Pebble-bed storage space and domestic water heating systems
- Water storage space and domestic water heating systems
- Active collection with building storage space heating systems
- Direct-gain passive systems
- Collector-storage wall passive systems
- Swimming pool heating systems
- General heating system such as process heating systems
- Integral collector-storage domestic water heating systems

The F-chart program can also perform economic analysis of the systems. The program, however, does not provide the flexibility of detailed simulations and performance investigations as TRNSYS does.

3.11.9.2 The TRNSYS Simulation Program

TRNSYS, the transient systems simulation program that has been commercially available since 1975, was developed by the international cooperation between the United States, France, and Germany. This program, currently in version 17, was originally developed at the University of Wisconsin by the members of the Solar Energy Laboratory and written in FORTRAN. TRNSYS remains one of the most flexible energy simulation software packages, which facilitates the addition of mathematical models and add-on components, and has multizone building model capability and the ability to interface with other simulation programs. The program was originally developed for use in solar energy applications but has now been extended to include a large variety of thermal and other processes such as hydrogen production, PVs, and many others. The program consists of many subroutines that model subsystem components. The mathematical models for the subsystem components are given in terms of their ordinary differential or algebraic equations. With a program such as TRNSYS, which has the capability of interconnecting system components in any desired manner, solving differential equations and facilitating information output, the entire problem of system simulation reduces to a problem of identifying all the components that form the particular system and formulating a general mathematical description of each [66]. Users can also create their own programs, which are no longer required to be recompiled together with all other program subroutines but can just be created as a dynamic link library (DLL) file with any FORTRAN compiler and put in a specified directory.

Each component has a unique TYPE number, which relates the component to a subroutine, that is, the model of that component. The UNIT number is used to identify each component (which can be used more than once). Although two or more system components can have the same TYPE number, each must have a unique UNIT number. Once all the components of the system have been identified and as the mathematical description of each component is available, it is necessary to construct an information flow diagram for the system. The purpose of the information flow diagram is to facilitate identification of the components and the flow of information between them. Each component requires a number of constant PARAMETERS and time-dependent INPUTS, and produces time-dependent OUTPUTS. An information flow diagram shows the manner in which all system components are interconnected. A given OUTPUT may be used as an INPUT to any number of other components. Generally, simulations require some components that are not ordinarily considered as part of the system. Such components are utility subroutines and output-producing devices.

TRNSYS subsystem components include solar collectors, auxiliary heaters, heating and cooling loads, differential controllers, thermostats, pumps, pebble-bed storage, hot water cylinders, relief valves, heat pumps, and many more. Some of the main ones are shown in **Table 5** [67]. There are also components for processing radiation data, performing integrations, and handling input and output. Time steps down to 1/1000 h (3.6 s) can be used. Additionally, the program can read actual weather and other data, which makes it very flexible.

In addition to the main TRNSYS components, an engineering consulting company specializing in the modeling and analysis of innovative energy systems and buildings, called Thermal Energy System Specialists (TESS), developed libraries of components for

Table 5 Main components in standard library of TRNSYS 17

Building loads and structures
    Energy/degree-hour house
    Roof and attic
    Detailed zone
    Overhang and wingwall shading
    Thermal storage wall
    Attached sunspace
    Detailed multizone building
Controller components
    Differential controllers
    Three-stage room thermostat
    Proportional-integral-derivative (PID) controller
    Microprocessor controller
Collectors
    Flat-plate collector
    Performance map solar collector
    Evacuated-tube solar collector
    Compound parabolic collector
Electrical components
    Regulators and inverters
    Photovoltaic array
    Photovoltaic–thermal collector
    Wind energy conversion system
    Diesel engine generator set
    Power conditioning
    Lead–acid battery
Heat exchangers
    Constant effectiveness heat exchanger
    Counter flow heat exchanger
    Cross-flow heat exchanger
    Parallel-flow heat exchanger
    Shell and tube heat exchanger
    Waste heat recovery
HVAC equipment
    Auxiliary heater
    Dual-source heat pump
    Cooling towers
    Single-effect absorption chiller
Hydronics
    Pump
    Fan
    Pipe

(Continued)

Table 5 (Continued)

    Duct
    Pressure relief valve
Output devices
    Printer
    Online plotter
    Histogram plotter
    Simulation summary
Physical phenomena
    Solar radiation processor
    Collector array shading
    Psychrometrics
    Weather data generator
    Refrigerant properties
    Undisturbed ground temperature profile
Thermal storage
    Stratified fluid storage tank
    Rock-bed thermal storage
    Variable volume tank
Utility components
    Data file reader
    Quantity integrator
    Calling Excel
    Calling Energy Equation Solver (EES)
    Calling MATLAB
Weather data reading
    Standard format files
    User format files

use in TRNSYS. The TESS libraries, currently in version 3, provide a large variety of components on loads and structures, thermal storage, ground coupling, geothermal, optimization, collectors, HVAC, utility, controls, and many more. The German research institute (DLR) also developed a TRNSYS model library for solar thermal electric components (STEC). The library includes models of all the components required to model a solar electricity generation system.

TRNSYS used to be a nonuser-friendly program; however, the two latest versions of the program (since version 16) operate in a graphic interface environment called the 'simulation studio' developed by Center Scientifique at Technique du Batiment (CSTB) from France. In this environment, icons of components are dragged and dropped in the working project area from a list and connected together according to the real system configuration. This is done in a way similar to the way piping and control wires are connecting the real system components. Each icon represents the detailed program of each component and requires a set of inputs (from other components or data files) and a set of constant parameters, which are specified by the user. Each component gives a set of output parameters, which can be plotted, saved in a file, or used as input in other components. Therefore, the procedure is to identify the components required, drag and drop them in the working project area, and connect them together to form the model of the system to be simulated. Subsequently, parameters and inputs need to be introduced by the user. Additionally, by double-clicking with the mouse on the lines connecting the various components, the user can specify which outputs of one component are inputs to the other. The project area must also contain a weather processing component, printers, and plotters through which the output data are viewed and/or saved to data files, if this is required by the user. The model diagram of a solar water heating system, which includes two plotters to visually see the running output of the system and two printers to record the produced output, is shown in **Figure 46**.

More details about the TRNSYS program can be found in the program manual and in Reference 68. There are numerous applications of the program in the literature.

A characteristic change made to version 17, compared with version 16, is the new simulation studio which can create colored connection loops to enable easy interpretation of the system in the simulation. Additionally, for complex projects with numerous connections and components, it allows the user to focus exclusively on one component and its connections, making the identification of any errors easy. Equations in the new version can be written as lines of code in a single editor window as text, which saves time for users who implement many equations in a simulation.

3.11.9.3 WATSUN Simulation Program

The WATSUN program simulates only active solar systems. It was developed originally by the WATSUN Simulation Laboratory of the University of Waterloo, Canada, in the early 1970s and subsequently in the 1980s [69]. The program complexity fills the gap

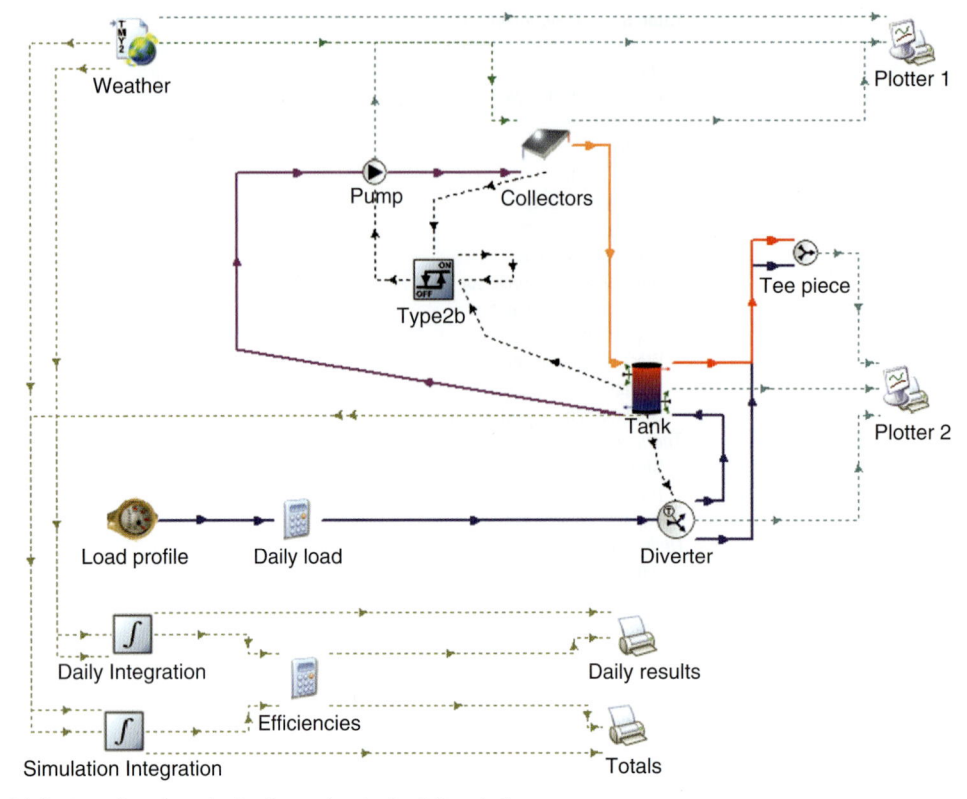

Figure 46 Model diagram of a solar water heating system in simulation studio.

between the simple tools used for quick assessments and the more complete, full simulation programs that provide more flexibility but are harder to use. The complete list of systems that can be simulated by the original program is as follows:

- DHW systems with stratified storage tanks or without storage and heat exchangers
- Phase-change system for water boiling
- Sun Switch system, stratified tank with heater
- Swimming pool heating system (indoor/outdoor)
- Industrial process heat system-reclaim before or after the collector, with and without storage
- Variable volume tank-base system
- Space heating system for one-room building.

Recently, Natural Resources Canada (NRCan) developed a new version of the program called WATSUN 2009 [70]. This new version is also used for the design and simulation of active solar systems and is freely available from the NRCan website [70]. Both versions of the program focus on the hourly simulation of solar energy systems and use similar equations for the modeling of basic components; however, the new program was rewritten from scratch, in C++, using object-oriented techniques.

The program currently models two different kinds of systems: water heating systems with and without storage. The latter actually covers a variety of system configurations in which the heat exchanger can be omitted, the auxiliary tank/heater can be replaced with an online heater, and the preheat tank can be either fully mixed or stratified.

Simple entry tables are used where the main parameters of the system (collector size, collector performance equation, tank size, etc.) can be entered easily. The program simulates the interactions between the system and its environment by using an hourly time step. However, the program can sometimes break down when sub-hourly intervals are required by the numerical solver, usually when ON/OFF controllers change state.

WATSUN is a ready-made program that the user can learn and operate easily. It combines collection, storage, and load information provided by the user with hourly weather data for a specific location and calculates the system state every hour. The output of the program provides information necessary for long-term performance calculations. The program models each component of the system, such as collector, pipes, tanks, and so on, individually and provides globally convergent methods to calculate their state.

As was seen above, WATSUN uses hourly weather data on solar radiation on the horizontal plane, dry-bulb ambient temperature, and in the case of unglazed collectors, wind speed. At the moment, WATSUN TMY files and comma or blank-delimited ASCII files are recognized by the program.

The system is an assembly of solar collectors, storage tanks, and load devices that the user wants to assess. The WATSUN simulation interacts with the user through a series of files. Such a file includes a collection of information, labeled and placed in a specific location. Files are also used by the program to input and output information. There is however one input file defined by the user, called the simulation data file, which includes all the system input data supplied by the user.

The file is made up of data blocks that contain groups of related parameters. The simulation data file controls also the simulation. The parameters in this file specify the simulation period, weather data, and output options. The simulation data file also contains information about the physical characteristics of the collector, storage device(s), heat exchangers, and load.

When the simulation is finished, the program produces three output files: a listing file, an hourly data file, and a monthly data file. The outputs of the program include a summary of the simulation and a file containing simulation results summed by month. The energy balance of the system on a monthly basis includes solar gains, energy delivered, auxiliary energy, and parasitic gains from pumps. This file can be readily imported into a spreadsheet program for further analysis and plotting of graphs. WATSUN gives also the option to output data on a sub-hourly basis, which enables the user to analyze the result of the simulation in greater detail and facilitates comparison with monitored data when these are available.

Another use of WATSUN is the simulation of active solar systems for which monitored data are available. This can be done either for validation purposes or to identify areas of improvement for the system. For this purpose, WATSUN allows the user to enter monitored data from a separate file called the 'alternate input file'. Monitored climatic data, energy collected, and other data can be read from the alternate input file and override the values normally used in the program. The program can also print out strategic variables (such as collector temperature and temperature of water delivered to the load) on an hourly basis for comparison with monitored values.

The program was validated against the TRNSYS program by Thevenard [71] by using several test cases. These program-to-program comparisons were very satisfactory and gave prediction differences in yearly energy delivered of less than 1.2% for all configurations tested.

3.11.10 Limitations of Simulations

Simulations are powerful tools for solar systems design and offer, as was seen above, a number of advantages; there are, however, limits to their use. For example, it is easy to make mistakes, such as assume wrong constants or parameters and neglect important performance factors. As in all other engineering calculations, a high level of skill and scientific judgment is required in order to produce accurate and useful results [66].

Generally, in simulations, it is very difficult to represent in detail some of the phenomena taking place in real systems. Additionally, practical problems cannot be easily modeled or accounted for, for example, bad system installation, plugged pipes, leaks, problematic operation of controllers, scale on heat exchanger surfaces, and poor insulation of collectors and other equipment. Simulation programs deal only with the thermal behavior of the processes; however, mechanical and hydraulic considerations can also affect the performance of solar systems.

It should be noted that there is no replacement to carefully executed experiments. Additionally, a combination of system simulation and physical experiments can lead to a better understanding of how processes or systems work. These can reveal whether or not current theory is adequate and where difficulties are present in the design or operation of the systems. In conclusion, simulations are powerful tools that can be used for the modeling, design, and prediction of performance and for the research and development of solar systems. They must, however, be used with care.

References

[1] Athienitis AK and Santamouris M (2002) *Thermal Analysis and Design of Passive Solar Buildings*. London, UK: James & James.
[2] ASHRAE (2005) *ASHRAE Handbook – Fundamentals*. Atlanta, GA: American Society of Heating, Refrigerating, and Air-Conditioning Engineers, Inc.
[3] Carslaw HS and Jaeger JC (1959) *Conduction of Heat in Solids*, 2nd edn. London, UK: Oxford University Press.
[4] CIBSE (2006) *CIBSE Guide A, Environmental Design*. London, UK: Chartered Institution of Building Services Engineers.
[5] Athienitis AK, Sullivan HF, and Hollands KGT (1987) Discrete Fourier series models for building auxiliary energy loads based on network formulation techniques. *Solar Energy* 39(3): 203–210.
[6] Athienitis AK (1994) *Building Thermal Analysis, Mathcad Electronic Book*. Boston, MA: Mathsoft.
[7] Athienitis AK, Bambara J, O'Neill B, and Faille J (2011) A prototype photovoltaic/thermal system integrated with transpired collector. *Solar Energy* 85: 139–153.
[8] IEA (2002) Reliability study of grid connected PV systems. *Report IEA-PVPS T7-08: 2002*. International Energy Agency. Freiburg, Germany
[9] King DL, Quintana JA, Kratochvil JA, *et al.* (2000) Photovoltaic module performance and durability following long-term exposure. *Progress in Photovoltaics* 8: 241–256.
[10] Chen Y, Athienitis AK, and Galal K (2010) Modeling, design and thermal performance of a BIPV/T system thermally coupled with a ventilated concrete slab in a low energy solar house: Part 1, BIPV/T system and house energy concept. *Solar Energy* 84(11): 1892–1907.
[11] Clarke JA, Johnstone C, and Kelly N (1997) The simulation of photovoltaic integrated building façades. *Proceedings of IBPSA*. Prague, Czech Republic, 8-10 September.
[12] Eicker U and Fux V (2000) Heating and cooling potential of combined photovoltaic solar air collector façades. *European Photovoltaic Solar Energy Conference*. Glasgow, UK, May 2000, pp. 1836–1839.
[13] Bazilian M, Groenhout NK, and Prasad D (2001) Simplified numerical modelling and simulation of a photovoltaic heat recovery system. *17th European Photovoltaic Solar Energy Conference*. Munich, Germany, 22–26 October, pp. 2387–2390.
[14] Bazilian MD and Prasad D (2002) Modelling of a photovoltaic heat recovery system and its role in a design decision support tool for building professionals. *Renewable Energy* 27: 57–68.

[15] Eicker U (2003) *Solar Technologies for Buildings*. West Sussex, UK: John Wiley & Sons.
[16] Bloem JJ (2008) Evaluation of a PV integrated building application in a well controlled outdoor test environment. *Building and Environment* 43: 205–216.
[17] Garg HP and Adhikari RS (1997) Conventional hybrid photovoltaic/thermal (PV/T) air heating collectors: Steady-state simulation. *Renewable Energy* 11: 363–385.
[18] Hegazy AA (2000) Comparative study of the performance of four photovoltaic/thermal solar air collectors. *Energy Conversion and Management* 41: 861–881.
[19] Candanedo LM (2010) Modelling and Evaluation of the Performance of Building-Integrated Open Loop Air-based Photovoltaic/Thermal Systems. PhD Thesis, Building Engineering, Concordia University.
[20] Yang HX, Marshall RH, and Brinkworth BJ (1996) Validated simulation for thermal regulation of photovoltaic structures. *Photovoltaic Specialists Conference, Conference Record of the Twenty-Fifth IEEE*. Washington, DC, USA, 13–17 May.
[21] Brinkworth BJ, Marshall RH, and Ibarahim Z (2000) A validated model of naturally ventilated PV cladding. *Solar Energy* 69: 67–81.
[22] Bosanac M, Sorensen B, Katic I, et al. (2003) Photovoltaic thermal solar collectors and their potential in Denmark, *Final Report, EEP project 17 13/00-0014*, pp. 1–114. http://www.solenergi.dk/rapporter/pvtpotentialindenmark.pdf (accessed 23 December 2011).
[23] Mittelman G, Alshare A, and Davidson JH (2009) A model and heat transfer correlation for rooftop integrated photovoltaics with a passive air cooling channel. *Solar Energy* 83: 1150–1160.
[24] Charron R (2004) One- and Two-Dimensional Modelling of Ventilated Façades with Integrated Photovoltaics. MASc Thesis, Building Engineering, Concordia University.
[25] Charron R and Athienitis AK (2006) Optimization of the performance of double façades with integrated photovoltaic panels and motorized blinds. *Solar Energy* 80: 482–491.
[26] Charron R and Athienitis AK (2006) A two dimensional model of a double façade with integrated photovoltaic panels. *Journal of Solar Energy Engineering, American Society of Mechanical Engineers* 128: 160–167.
[27] Athienitis AK, Poissant Y, Collins M, and Liao L (2005) Experimental and numerical results for a building-integrated photovoltaics test facility. *Conference Record of the Thirty-First IEEE Photovoltaic Specialists Conference*, pp. 1718–1721. Lake Buena Vista, FL, USA, 03–07 January.
[28] Liao L (2005) Numerical and Experimental Investigation of Building-Integrated Photovoltaic-Thermal Systems. MASc Thesis, Building, Civil and Environmental Engineering, Concordia University.
[29] Liao L, Athienitis AK, Candanedo L, et al. (2007) Numerical and experimental study of heat transfer in a BIVP-thermal system. *Journal of Solar Energy Engineering, American Society of Mechanical Engineers* 129: 423–430.
[30] Pantic S, Candanedo L, and Athienitis AK (2010) Modeling of energy performance of a house with three configurations of building-integrated photovoltaic/thermal systems. *Energy and Buildings* 42: 1779–1789.
[31] Candanedo LM and Athienitis AK (2011) Convective heat transfer coefficients in a building-integrated photovoltaic/thermal system. *Journal of Solar Energy Engineering, American Society of Mechanical Engineers* 133(2): 14p.
[32] Ito S, Kashima M, and Miura N (2006) Flow control and unsteady-state analysis on thermal performance of solar air collectors. *Journal of Solar Energy Engineering, American Society of Mechanical Engineers* 128: 354–359.
[33] Han J, Lu L, and Yang H (2010) Numerical evaluation of the mixed convective heat transfer in a double-pane window integrated with see-through a-Si PV cells with low-e coatings. *Applied Energy* 87: 3431–3437.
[34] Dittus FW and Boelter LMK (1930) Heat transfer in automobile radiators of the tubular type. *University of California Publications on Engineering, Berkeley, CA* 2(13): 443–461.
[35] Duffie JA and Beckman WA (2006) *Solar Engineering of Thermal Processes*. Hoboken, NJ: Wiley.
[36] Test FL, Lessmann RC, and Johary A (1981) Heat transfer during wind flow over rectangular bodies in the natural environmental. *Transactions of the American Society of Mechanical Engineers, Journal of Heat Transfer* 103: 262–267.
[37] Sharples S and Charlesworth PS (1998) Full-scale measurements of wind-induced convective heat transfer from a roof-mounted flat plate solar collector. *Solar Energy* 62: 69–77.
[38] Berdahl P and Martin M (1984) Emissivity of clear skies. *Solar Energy* 32: 663–664.
[39] Saelens D, Roels S, and Hens H (2004) The inlet temperature as a boundary condition for multiple-skin facade modelling. *Energy and Buildings* 36: 825–835.
[40] King DL, Kratochvil JA, and Boyson WE (1997) Measuring solar spectral and angle-of-incidence effects on photovoltaic modules and solar irradiance sensors. *26th IEEE Photovoltaic Specialists Conference*. Anaheim, CA, USA, 29 September-03 October 1997, p. 5.
[41] Sandia National Laboratories (2006) Database of Photovoltaic Module Performance Parameters.
[42] McAdams WH (1954) *Heat Transmission*. New York: McGraw-Hill.
[43] MathWorks I (2010) *MATLAB R2008b User Guide*. Massachusetts, MA: Natick.
[44] Athienitis AK (2008) Design of advanced solar homes aimed at net-zero annual energy consumption in Canada. *ISES-AP – 3rd International Solar Energy Society Conference – Asia Pacific Region*. Sydney, NSW, Australia, 25–28 November.
[45] Chen Y, Athienitis AK, and Galal K (2010) Modeling, design and thermal performance of a BIPV/T system thermally coupled with a ventilated concrete slab in a low energy solar house: Part 1, BIPV/T system and house energy concept. *Solar Energy* 84(11): 1892–1907.
[46] Candanedo J and Athienitis AK (2010) A simulation study of anticipatory control strategies in a net zero energy solar house. *American Society of Heating, Refrigerating and Air-Conditioning Engineers Transactions* 116(1): 246–259.
[47] Klein SA, Beckman WA, and Duffie JA (1976) A design procedure for solar heating systems. *Solar Energy* 18(2): 113–127.
[48] Klein SA, Beckman WA, and Duffie JA (1977) A design procedure for solar air heating systems. *Solar Energy* 19(6): 509–512.
[49] Beckman WA, Klein SA, and Duffie JA (1977) *Solar Heating Design by the f-Chart Method*. New York: Wiley-Interscience.
[50] Kalogirou S (2009) *Solar Energy Engineering: Processes and Systems*. Academic Press, Amsterdam: Elsevier Science, ISBN: 978-0-12-374501-9.
[51] Klein SA (1976) A Design Procedure for Solar Heating Systems. PhD Thesis, Chemical Engineering, University of Wisconsin.
[52] Liu BYH and Jordan RC (1977) Availability of solar energy for flat plate solar heat collectors. In: Liu BYH and Jordan RC (eds.) *Application of Solar Energy for Heating and Cooling of Buildings*. Atlanta, GA: ASHRAE.
[53] Klein SA (1979) Calculation of monthly-average transmittance-absorptance product. *Solar Energy* 23(6): 547–551.
[54] Whillier A (1953) Solar Energy Collection and Its Utilization for House Heating. PhD Thesis, Mechanical Engineering, MIT.
[55] Liu BYH and Jordan RC (1963) The long-term average performance of flat-plate solar energy collectors. *Solar Energy* 7(2): 53–74.
[56] Klein SA (1978) Calculation of flat-plate collector utilizability. *Solar Energy* 21(5): 393–402.
[57] Collares-Pereira M and Rabl A (1979) Derivation of method for predicting long term average energy delivery of solar collectors. *Solar Energy* 23(3): 223–233.
[58] Collares-Pereira M and Rabl A (1979) The average distribution of solar radiation-correlations between diffuse and hemispherical and between daily and hourly insolation values. *Solar Energy* 22(2): 155–164.
[59] Clark DR, Klein SA, and Beckman WA (1983) Algorithm for evaluating the hourly radiation utilizability function. *Journal of Solar Energy Engineering, American Society of Mechanical Engineers* 105: 281–287.
[60] Erbs DG, Klein SA, and Duffie JA (1982) Estimation of diffuse radiation fraction for hourly, daily and monthly average global radiation. *Solar Energy* 28(4): 293–302.
[61] Hottel HC and Whillier A (1955) Evaluation of flat plate collector performance. *Transactions of the Conference on the Use of Solar Energy*. vol. 2, Part I, p. 74. Tucson, AZ: University of Arizona Press.
[62] Collares-Pereira M and Rabl A (1979) Simple procedure for predicting long term average performance of nonconcentrating and concentrating solar collectors. *Solar Energy* 23(3): 235–253.
[63] Carvalho MJ and Bourges B (1985) Application of utilizability computation methods to Europe and Africa. *Intersol 85, Proceedings of the 9th Biennial Congress ISES*. vol. 4, pp. 2439–2448. Montreal, Canada, 23–29 June.

[64] Klein SA and Beckman WA (1979) A general design method for closed-loop solar energy systems. *Solar Energy* 22(3): 269–282.
[65] Klein SA and Beckman WA (2005) *FChart Users Manual*. Madison, WI: University of Wisconsin.
[66] Kalogirou S (2004) Solar thermal collectors and applications. *Progress in Energy and Combustion Science* 30(3): 231–295.
[67] Klein SA, Beckman WA, Mitchell JW, *et al.* (2010) *TRNSYS Version 17 Program Manual*. Madison, WI: Solar Energy Laboratory, University of Wisconsin.
[68] Beckman WA (1998) Modern computing methods in solar energy analysis. *Proceedings of Eurosun'98 on CD-ROM*. Portoroz, Slovenia, 14–17 September.
[69] WATSUN (1996) *WATSUN Users Manual and Program Documentation*, vol. 13.3, Canada: WATSUN Simulation Laboratory, University of Waterloo.
[70] NRCan (2008) Natural Resources Canada, WATSUN 2008. http://canmetenergy.nrcan.gc.ca/eng/software_tools/watsun.html (accessed 22 December 2011).
[71] Thevenard D (2008) A simple tool for the simulation of active solar systems: WATSUN Reborn. *Proceedings of the 3rd Solar Buildings Conference*, Fredericton, NB 20–22 August, pp. 189–196.

3.12 Solar Hot Water Heating Systems

G Faninger, University of Klagenfurt, Klagenfurt, Austria; Vienna University of Technology, Vienna, Austria

© 2012 Elsevier Ltd. All rights reserved.

3.12.1	Toward a Sustainable Energy System	419
3.12.1.1	Solar Heat – Renewable Energy Source with High Potential	419
3.12.1.2	Solar Water Heating	420
3.12.1.3	Solar Energy for Developing Countries	422
3.12.1.4	Market Introduction and Market Deployment of Solar Thermal Systems	422
3.12.1.5	Solar Heat Worldwide	423
3.12.1.5.1	Distribution by application	423
3.12.2	Technologies for Solar Hot Water Systems	425
3.12.2.1	Components and Concepts	426
3.12.2.1.1	Solar DHW systems with natural circulation	426
3.12.2.1.2	Solar DHW systems with forced circulation	426
3.12.2.2	Solar Thermal Collectors	426
3.12.2.2.1	High-performance flat-plate collectors	429
3.12.2.2.2	Properties of collectors	430
3.12.2.2.3	Integration of solar collectors	430
3.12.2.2.4	New developments in the collector sector	431
3.12.2.3	The Collector Circuit	431
3.12.2.3.1	Drain-back system	433
3.12.2.4	Thermal Storage	434
3.12.2.4.1	Water storage technology	434
3.12.2.4.2	Advanced heat storage technologies	435
3.12.2.5	Decentralized and Centralized Solar Thermal Systems	435
3.12.2.6	Auxiliary Heat Sources	436
3.12.2.7	Hygienic Aspects of Solar Hot Water Heaters	437
3.12.3	Design Principles of Solar Thermal Systems	438
3.12.3.1	Meteorological Conditions and Simulation Tools	438
3.12.3.2	The Solar System	440
3.12.3.3	Collector Orientation and Inclination	441
3.12.3.4	Solar DHW Systems for Households and Single-Family Houses	442
3.12.3.5	Solar DHW Systems for Apartment Houses	443
3.12.3.6	Solar-Combined Heating Systems	444
3.12.4	Summary and Conclusion	445
References		446

3.12.1 Toward a Sustainable Energy System

3.12.1.1 Solar Heat – Renewable Energy Source with High Potential

The facts of our present energy supply – limited fossil resources, instability by political influence on the oil and gas markets, and greenhouse gas emission from fossil energy resources – are serious arguments for creating a new energy system. The main resources for a *future sustainable energy* system will be renewable sources. And, solar thermal technologies have the potential for a high contribution to the future energy supply.

The 'solar source' for solar thermal systems is immense and inexhaustible. The environmental and economic benefits are substantial.

Today, solar thermal systems are regarded as a well-established, low-tech-technology with an enormous potential for energy production. 'Solar thermal technologies' for low- to medium-temperature applications can be used all over the world – cold to hot climates. A large variety of solar thermal components and systems, mostly for residential applications, are available in the market. The products are reliable and have a high technical standard in the low-temperature regime (below 150 °C).

There has been a rapid market growth in recent years for small solar hot water systems in countries moving toward partly automatic or semiautomatic fabrication of solar thermal components.

Solar thermal systems in larger buildings – multifamily houses and apartment blocks – as well as in district heating plants are now emerging in the market. The use of solar hot water systems in larger buildings and centralized solar thermal systems has the advantage of lower specific investment costs, and thus, the heat production costs can be reduced in comparison with small, decentralized systems. The possibilities for a central hot water preparation in multifamily buildings are used increasingly in the market nowadays.

The component for the conversion of solar energy into heat is the collector – either nonconcentrating or concentrating. Collector working temperatures of about 60–80 °C, with conversion efficiency from 40% to 60%, can be achieved with flat-plate collectors, which are typically used for hot water solar systems. The properties of this type of collectors are well known today and thus manufactured in many parts of the world. In countries with solar radiation $\geq 1800\,\mathrm{kWh\,m^{-2}\,yr^{-1}}$, it is advantageous to use solar systems for domestic hot water (DHW) preparation as compact system with flat-plate collectors based on the thermosiphon principle. Synthetic absorbers are preferred to metal absorbers not only for cost reasons but also due to lower corrosion potential.

Solar heating and cooling (SHC) technologies include solar water heating, solar space heating and cooling, using active technologies and passive system designs, daylighting, and agricultural and industrial process heating. The use of solar energy in housing presents remarkable advantages as follows: requires less energy; causes less adverse environmental impacts, for example, CO_2; provides open sunlight; improves building esthetics; and provides a new medium for architectural expression.

While solar water heating and solar space heating have been in the market for decades, new approaches for solar thermal applications (e.g., for cooling and process heating) are now emerging in the market. Solar-assisted cooling is an extremely promising technology as peak cooling requirement coincides with peak solar radiation. Small-scale solar cooling systems are now commercially available.

Figure 1 illustrates the market development from solar thermal technologies.

3.12.1.2 Solar Water Heating

Today, DHW preparation with solar energy is standard in many countries. In the area of building renovation, solar hot water preparation is attractive to increase the efficiency of heating systems. Especially, ineffective heating systems for hot water preparation outside the heating season have been replaced by solar hot water preparation. Thus, pollutant emissions through heating (wood, coal, and oil boilers) could be reduced, and at the same time, a high comfort in hot water preparation could be reached.

Solar hot water preparation in high-performance houses is sensible. In such houses, the energy needed to heat domestic water can equal or even exceed the energy needed for space heating, since the latter has been so far reduced by insulation and heat recovery. In Europe, about 50% of the new detached and row houses and about 15% of apartment houses are designed on this concept.

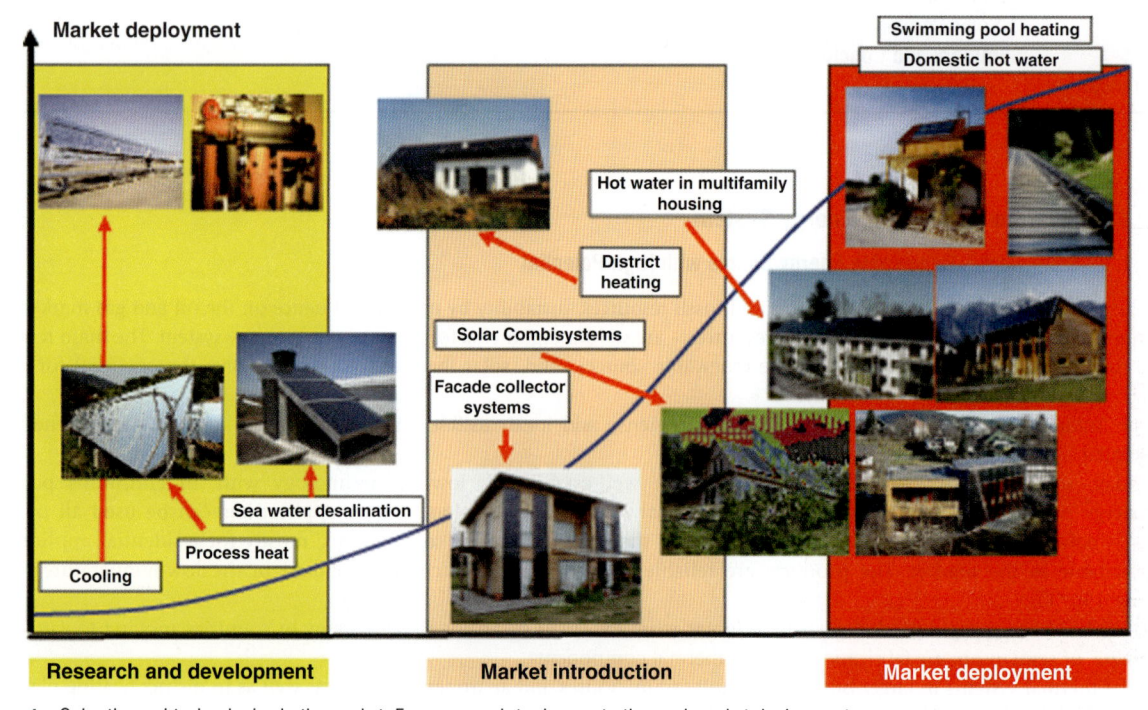

Figure 1 Solar thermal technologies in the market: From research to demonstration and market deployment.

Further, demand for heating domestic water is a 12-month energy demand, including the high insulation during the summer months. Using a solar system is therefore an effective way to reduce the total primary energy demand. Increasingly, the market for solar water heating systems also includes systems that provide, in addition to hot water preparation, space heating in winter, called 'Solar Combisystems'.

For hot water heating in transition countries, such as China and India, and also in countries without space heating systems (e.g., Greece, Cyprus, and Malta), direct electricity is used. Large amount of electricity is necessary to meet the hot water requirements in domestic, institutional, and commercial sectors resulting in peak load and load shedding to the shortage of power supply. With solar hot water systems, the electricity demand as well as the peak load can be reduced remarkably (**Figure 2**).

Figure 2 Solar hot water systems to replace electricity demand and to reduce peak load.

Figure 3 Solar heat for developing countries.

3.12.1.3 Solar Energy for Developing Countries

The utilization of solar energy is considered to be promising in developing countries with suitable meteorological conditions. Also, the potential for decentralized (stand-alone) energy systems is huge in developing countries. Therefore, the use of solar energy for heat and electricity production is the first step for economic development (**Figure 3**).

It appears essential to promote the development, testing, demonstration, and market introduction of solar technologies in developing countries with the support of industrialized countries. Many joint projects were initiated since 1980, with the governmental support of OECD-Member States, the World Bank, UNIDO, and other organizations.

3.12.1.4 Market Introduction and Market Deployment of Solar Thermal Systems

As a result of the first oil price crisis, the market introduction of solar hot water systems started in most of the industrialized countries in 1976 with the aim of consumers to reduce the dependency from oil imports (First Solar Boom). From 1980 until the mid-1990s, the solar market development was not stable. Initially, the collectors and systems were offered by small companies, but due to missing guidance information for design and construction, the consumers were not always satisfied. The market deployment decreased, but through new firms and better-educated installers and available experiences on the market, the amount of installed collectors and systems increased again in late 1970s (Second Solar Boom). The situation on the solar thermal market for Austria is illustrated in **Figure 4**. Favorable applications were the separation of hot water preparation in households from firewood heating systems in small communities, especially outside the heating season. With the decrease of oil price at the beginning of 1980, the solar market decreased again. In this period, 'self-built' solar heating systems were organized, primarily for solar projects for personal use, and were offered in the market. Through these private activities, the interest for solar systems was pushed and industry was motivated for more attention and new activities (**Figure 5**). From early 1990s onward, larger solar firms were found, and the industrial production was based on national standards, guidance for energy-efficient design, construction, and operation. With the increase of industrial produced

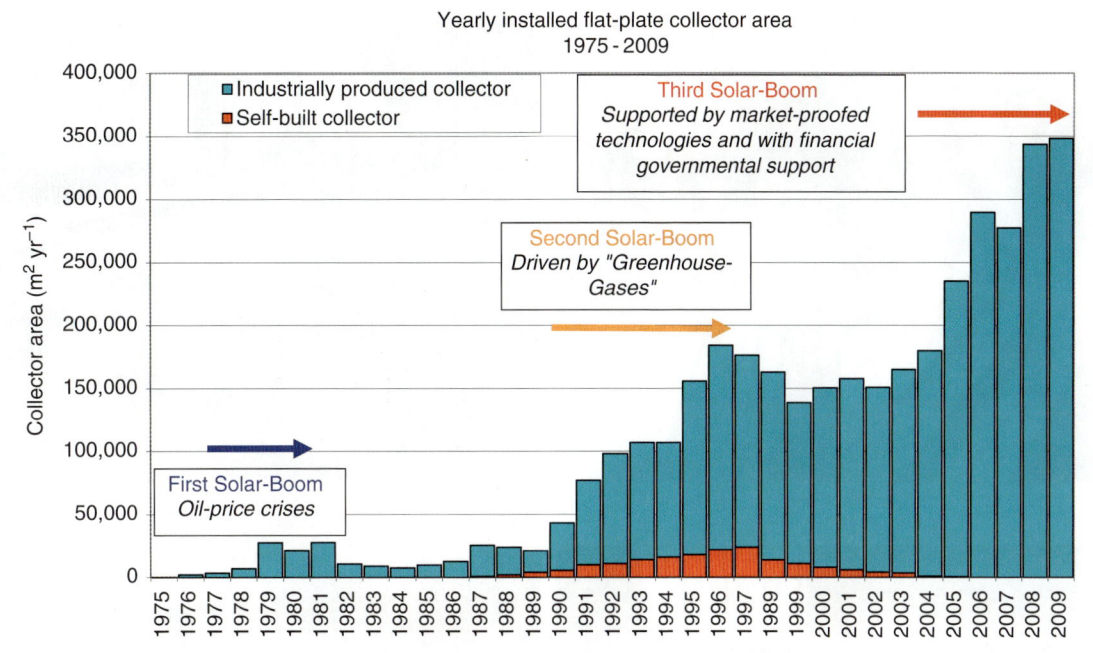

Figure 4 Market deployment of solar thermal collectors in Austria.

collectors, the production of self-built collectors and systems was focused to 'social' projects – to involve unemployed young people as well as handicapped persons with the aim to open perspectives for the job market. The products are used in social projects.

More attention for 'greenhouse gases' and their potential for climate change were given – both in policy and by consumers – and this supported the solar market remarkably at the end of 1990s (Third Solar Boom). Today, solar hot water systems are well designed, using materials with an expected lifetime of more than 25 years; the price for installed systems is acceptable; and the results are satisfying the consumers. Also, financial support by the governments has influenced the increase of annual growth rates.

3.12.1.5 Solar Heat Worldwide

Installed solar thermal capacity grew by 9% around the world in 2007. Solar thermal power output reached 88 845 GWh, resulting in the avoidance of 39.3 million tons of CO_2 emissions. At the end of 2007, the installed solar thermal capacity worldwide equaled 146.8 GW_{th} or 209.7 million square meters. The breakdown by collector type is as follows: 120.5 GW_{th} for flat-plate and evacuated-tube collectors, 25.1 GW_{th} for unglazed plastic collectors, and 1.2 GW_{th} for air collectors (**Figure 6**) [1, 2].

3.12.1.5.1 Distribution by application

The use of solar thermal energy varies greatly by country. In China and Taiwan (80.8 GW_{th}), Europe (15.9 GW_{th}), and Japan (4.9 GW_{th}), plants with flat-plate and evacuated-tube collectors are mainly used to prepare hot water and to provide space heating, while in North America (the United States and Canada), swimming pool heating is still the dominant application with an installed capacity of 19.8 GW_{th} of unglazed plastic collectors. It should be noted that there is a growing unglazed solar air heating market in Canada and the United States aside from pool heating. Unglazed collectors are also used for commercial and industrial building ventilation, air heating, and agricultural applications. Europe has the most sophisticated market for different solar thermal applications. It includes systems for hot water preparation, plants for space heating of single-family and multifamily houses and hotels, large-scale plants for district heating, as well as a growing number of systems for air conditioning, cooling, and industrial applications.

From the worldwide collectors capacity in operation (2007), 50% are evacuated-tube collectors, 32% flat-plate collectors, 17% unglazed collectors, and 1% air collectors (mainly from the 'SolarWall' type). The main markets for evacuated-tube collectors are in China, while most flat-plate collectors are found in Europe. In the United States and Australia, unglazed collectors are dominating. But in recent years, the worldwide market for new installed glazed collectors has been significantly growing, in Europe with growth rates near and above 100% compared to the capacity installed in 2006.

Figure 5 Development of collector production and installation.

The already installed capacity of solar thermal heat is considerably higher than the installed capacity of the other renewable sources. The total energy yield of solar thermal heating systems comes in second place behind solid biomass, but it is higher than the energy yield of wind and photovoltaic (PV) power.

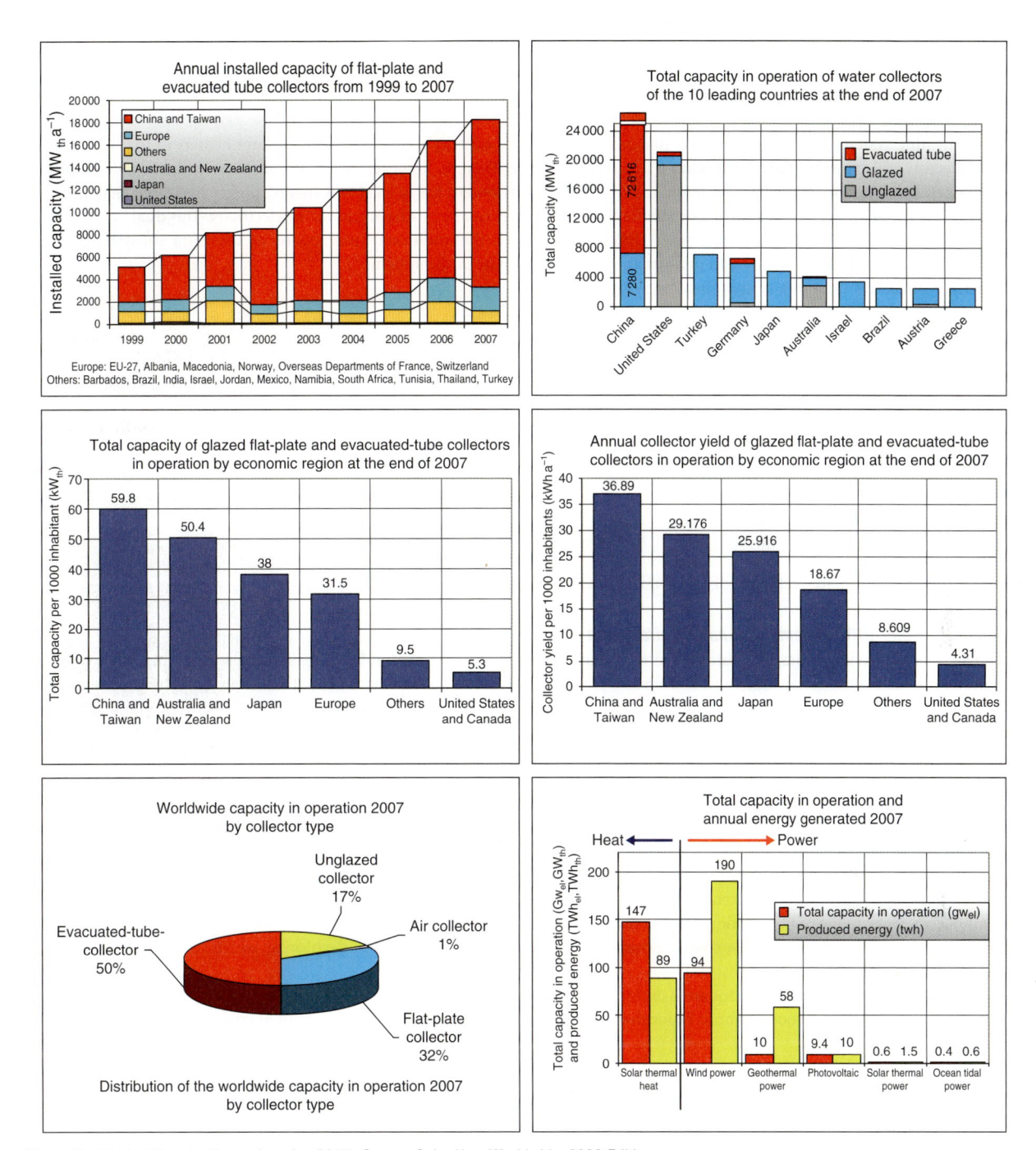

Figure 6 Worldwide solar thermal market 2007. *Source*: Solar Heat Worldwide, 2009 Edition.

To find a more detailed analysis on the market penetration of solar thermal technology in the 49 documented countries representing more than 85% of the solar thermal market, see http://www.iea-shc.org [1].

3.12.2 Technologies for Solar Hot Water Systems

The key applications for solar thermal technologies are those that require low-temperature heat, such as for swimming pools, for DHW and space heating, drying processes, and process heating in the low- to medium-temperature range.

Solar water heating, including pool heating, has been commercially available for over 30 years, and can be considered a mature technology. Active solar space heating, while commercially available for almost as long, significantly lags behind solar water heating in the market due to its relatively higher costs as well as special requirements for utilization (only low-energy buildings with low-temperature heat distribution). But in recent years, systems that combine water and space heating, called Solar Combisystems, have emerged in the market and show great promise for further market success [3, 4].

Solar heating systems for combined DHW preparation and space heating are similar to solar water heaters in that they use the same collectors and transport the heat produced to a storage device. There is, however, one major difference; the installed collector area is generally larger for Solar Combisystems, and in addition, this system has at least two energy sources to supply heat: the solar collectors and the auxiliary energy source. The auxiliary energy sources can be biomass, gas, oil, or electricity. This dual system makes Solar Combisystems more complex than solar DHW systems with the additional interactions of the extra subsystems. These interactions profoundly affect the overall performance of the solar part of the system.

Figure 7 illustrates examples of solar heating systems.

3.12.2.1 Components and Concepts

The components of a solar DHW system are collector, storage, collector cycle, heat exchanger, auxiliary heat source, and regulation.

Solar systems for DHW system are fairly simple and manufactured and marketed today in developed as well as in developing countries.

Two different principles for solar DHW systems are used:

1. Systems with natural circulation
2. Systems with forced circulation.

Figure 8 shows the principal schemes of solar water heating systems.

3.12.2.1.1 Solar DHW systems with natural circulation

Solar DHW systems with natural circulation (thermosiphon systems) are most favorable in areas with a mean annual sum of global radiation on a horizontal surface above 1800 kWh m^{-2} yr^{-1}. Thermosiphon systems can work satisfactorily only if the storage tank is mounted above the collector and if the collector warms up enough to establish a density difference between the water in the collector and the water in the storage tank. The density difference is a function of the temperature difference, and therefore, the flow rate is a function of the useful gain of the collector that produces the temperature difference. The systems are self-adjusting with increasing gain leading to increasing collector flow rates (**Figure 8**).

The efficiency of heating systems during summer months could be improved by larger storage volumes or by hot water extraction during the day. If a constant water temperature is needed at any time, a backup heating system must be incorporated in the system.

Due to the meteorological condition in most of developing countries – solar radiation ≥1800 kWh m^{-2} yr^{-1} – solar hot water systems according to the thermosiphon principle are suitable for domestic use and can be manufactured at a reasonable price. Because of the high lime and salt content of the tap water, special attention has to be paid to possible calcification and corrosion. The rubber absorber made of polymeric materials (e.g., ethylene propylene diene monomer (EPDM)) turned out to be useful. It is recommended to use glass material for covering purpose, because plastic covers tend to decolorize, which results in a reduction of the solar radiation absorbed.

Solar hot water systems with collector areas exceeding 10 m^2 should be supplied with forced circulation. It should be possible to mount the collectors on flat roofs without expensive auxiliary structures, which reduces investment costs and improves economic application considerably.

3.12.2.1.2 Solar DHW systems with forced circulation

Solar DHW systems with forced circulation are the common concepts in areas with moderate and cold climates. The components of a compact solar DHW system with forced circulation – for a household/single-family house – are shown in **Figure 9**.

3.12.2.2 Solar Thermal Collectors

Collectors are the component for the conversion of solar energy into low- and high-temperature heat. 'Nonconcentrating' collectors fully utilize the global radiation but 'concentrating collectors' use only the direct beam component of the radiation by concentrating irradiation on the absorber, thus increasing the intensity of radiation on the absorber. Concentrating collector systems are the preferred technology in regions with more than 2500 annual sunshine hours (**Figure 10**).

The simplest design of a nonconcentrating collector is the 'flat-plate collector'. The properties of this collector are well known. As absorbers, black painted metal (copper, aluminum, or steel) or plastic plates are used and in order to reduce the useful heat losses – which increase with rising temperatures – transparent covers are placed on the collectors and appropriate insulation is provided at the back side of the absorber (**Figure 11**). With this type of collector, temperatures up to 80 °C with conversion efficiency of about 40–60% can be achieved. Applications of this type of collector are swimming pool heating, water heaters, agricultural drying, desalination, and space heating.

Figure 7 Examples for solar thermal systems for low- to medium-heat production.

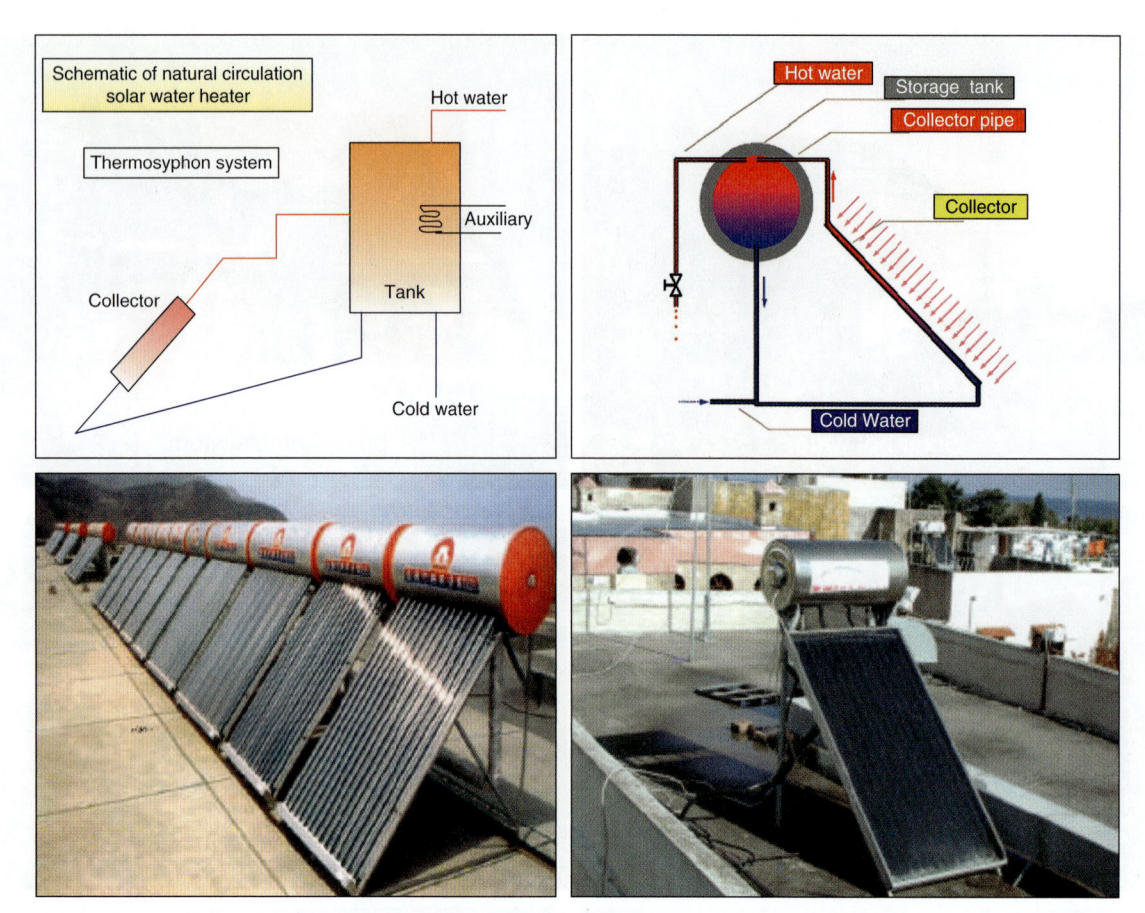

Figure 8 Solar domestic hot water (DHW) systems with natural circulation.

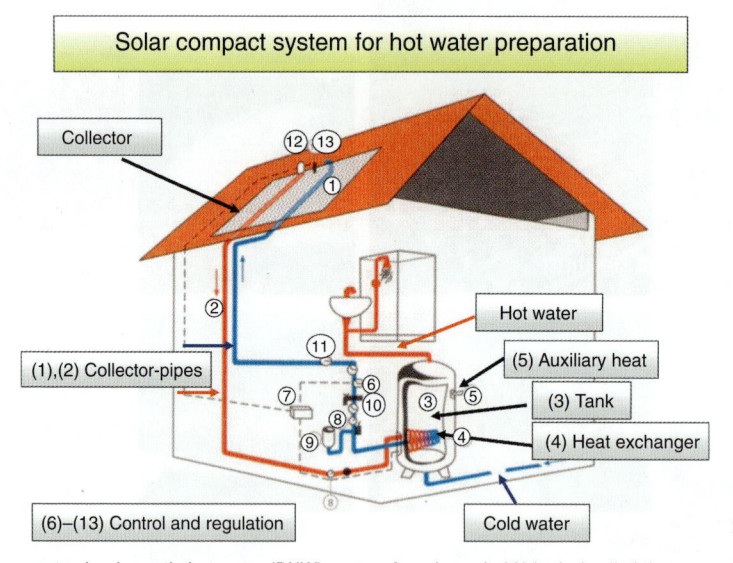

Figure 9 Components of a compact solar domestic hot water (DHW) system for a household/single-family house.

For temperatures above 100 °C, advanced designs, like some 'evacuated-tube collectors', have been developed. To obtain fluid temperatures above 150 °C, 'concentrating solar collector' systems must be used. The concentrator (a mirror or lens) is normally equipped with a tracking device that follows the sun. The absorber in this system is located close to the geometric focus of the concentrator to intercept most of the incident direct radiation. In general, there are two types of concentrators: (1) the linear focusing concentrator and (2) the point focusing concentrator. In summary, the type of collector to be used

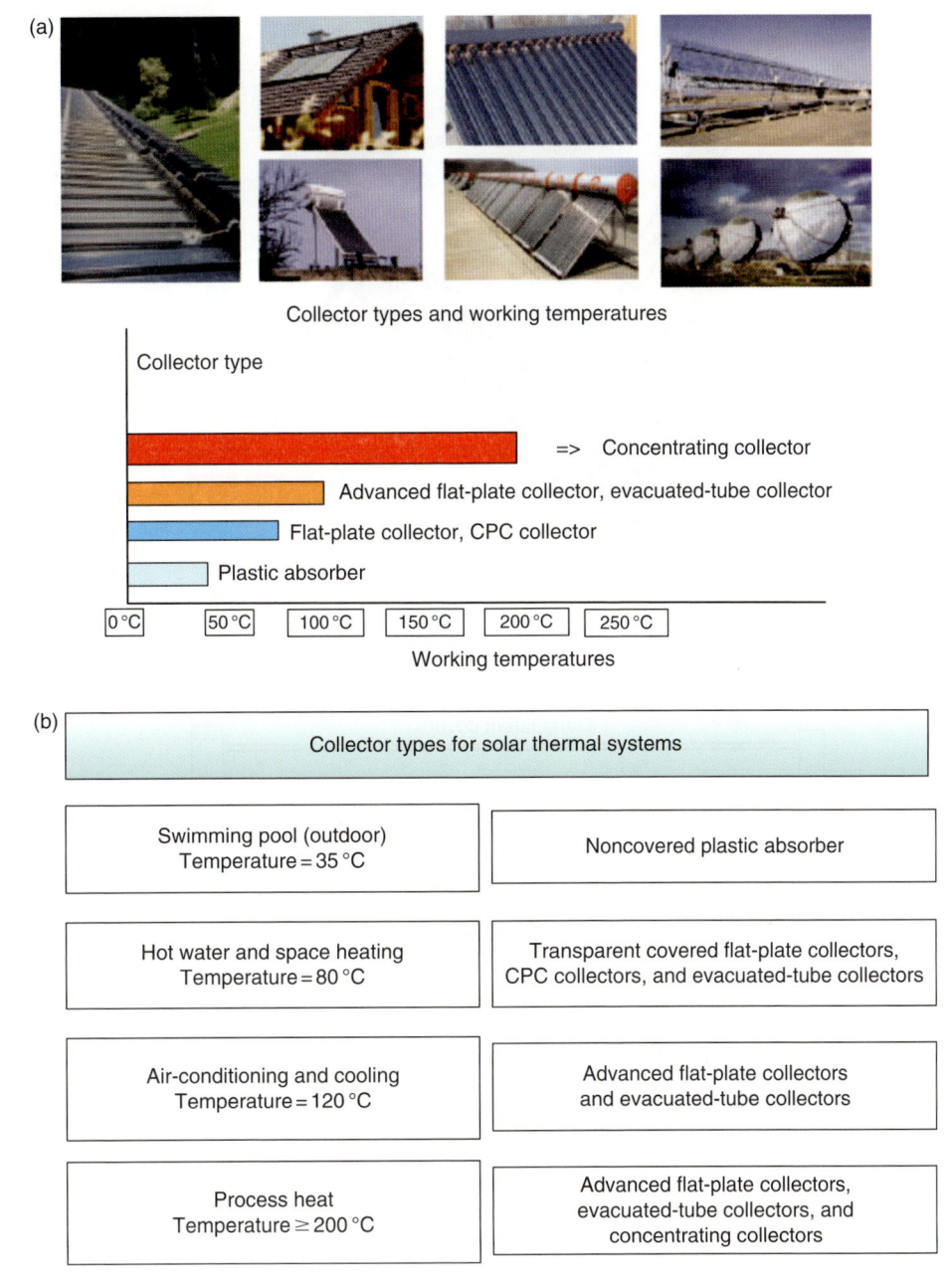

Figure 10 Collector types for low- to medium-temperature applications. (a) Collector types and working temperatures and (b) collector types for solar systems.

depends on the application and the desired temperature. For DHW preparation, flat-plate collectors with selective coating are the most cost-effective solution. For higher temperatures (above 80 °C) and lower solar radiation, evacuated-tube collectors would be the better choice.

3.12.2.2.1 High-performance flat-plate collectors

A high-performance flat-plate collector is characterized by a superior absorber and glazing. The absorber should have a coating with a high solar absorptive black painting (>95%) and low heat emissive selective coating (<5%). The glazing should be antireflection treated and consist of a low iron glass type to maximize solar radiation transmitted to the absorber. Such flat-plate collectors can easily achieve outlet temperatures of 80 °C with a conversion efficiency of about 50–60%.

Evacuated-tube collectors achieve superior performance because the vacuum surrounding the absorber drastically cuts heat losses to the ambient. Outlet temperatures above 100 °C are easily achieved with a higher conversion efficiency compared with a flat-plate collector. The inside-facing underside of the glass pipe has a reflective coating to irradiate the absorber from beneath. Thus,

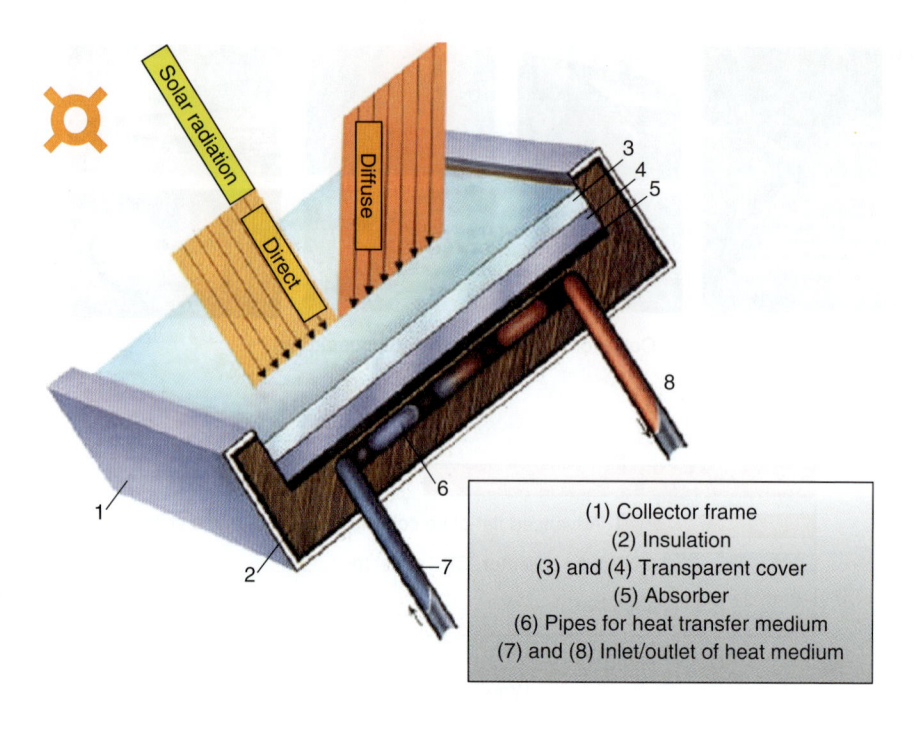

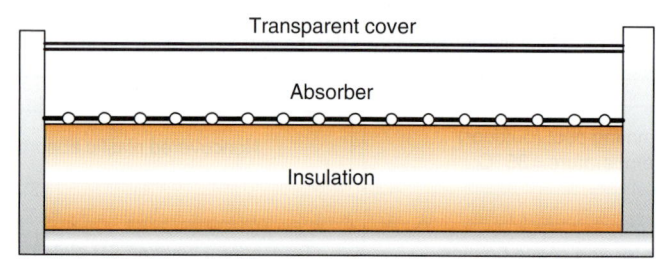

Figure 11 Design of a flat-plate collector.

(1) Collector frame
(2) Insulation
(3) and (4) Transparent cover
(5) Absorber
(6) Pipes for heat transfer medium
(7) and (8) Inlet/outlet of heat medium

vacuum collectors have the further advantage of not having any given slope for optimal performance. The glass pipes can simply be rotated to the optimal incident angle for the application. For this reason, they can be mounted on a south facade or roof.

3.12.2.2.2 Properties of collectors

Collector can be characterized by means of two experimentally determined constants:

1. Conversion factor: The collector efficiency when the ambient air temperature equals the collector temperature.
2. Heat loss coefficient: The mean heat loss of the collector per aperture area for a measured temperature difference between the collector and the ambient air temperature in $W\,m^{-2}\,K^{-1}$.

These collector constants are determined under exactly defined conditions (global radiation intensity, angle of incidence, air temperature, wind velocity, etc.). The performance of different collector types and applications are shown in **Figure 12**. The efficiencies are given for the values: temperature difference between the collector and ambient divided by the solar radiation. Logically, as the collector gets hotter, the efficiency falls off. For heating of high-performance houses, selective coated collectors or vacuum pipe collectors are a good choice.

3.12.2.2.3 Integration of solar collectors

It is beneficial to integrate solar collectors into the building envelope for esthetic and economical reasons, and when doing so, it is essential to take into consideration the architectural rules and local building traditions. Building-integrated collectors are illustrated in **Figure 13**. Facade collectors are used in urban buildings, where sufficient suitable and oriented roof for the installation of solar collectors is not available. A collector element directly integrated in the facade presents both solar collection and heat insulation of the building envelope. The advantages of facade-integrated collectors are cost savings as a result of joint use of building components, replacement of the conventional facade, and the collectors suitable for both new and existing buildings.

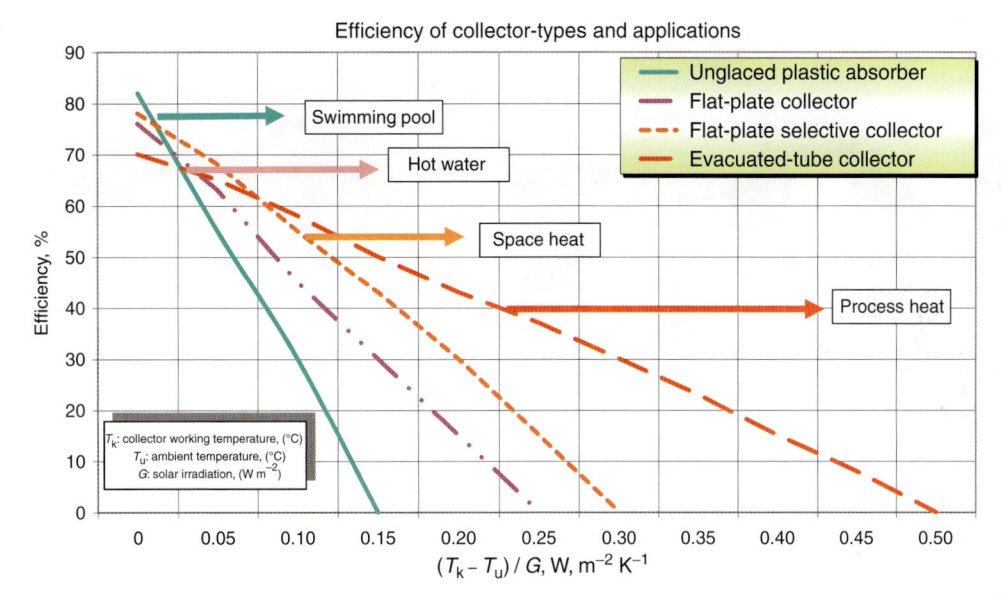

Figure 12 Efficiencies of different collector types under different conditions and appropriate uses. T_k, Collector working temperature (°C); T_u, ambient temperature (°C); G, solar irradiation (W m^{-2}).

For roof installations, where the systems deliver heat over the whole year, the optimal tilt angle (northern hemisphere) is between 30° and 75°. The orientation can be between 30° east and 45° west. Facade-integrated collector is far from optimum in all locations (see Section 3.12.3.3). However, it performs better in winter by low sun angles. When there is snow cover, it receives an extra portion of ground-reflected solar radiation. Roof collectors with too little slope, by contrast, will have zero output when covered by snow. A big limitation of facade collectors is, however, that by low sun angles, neighboring buildings and trees will cast shadows on the collector surface.

3.12.2.2.4 New developments in the collector sector

The objective of new developments in the collector sector is the cost reduction as well as durability and reliability of novel design of solar thermal systems. Polymer engineering and science offers great potential for new products and applications, which simultaneously fulfill the technological and environmental objectives as well as social needs. The full potential of polymeric materials can only be used when several product functions are integrated into a single component in a fundamentally new design. These goals will be achieved by either less expensive materials or less expensive manufacturing processes.

The most common nowadays is the use of copper absorbers for flat-plate solar collectors. The copper content in conventional flat-plate collectors varies between 2 and 6 kg m^{-2}. Taking into account the copper used in piping and heat exchangers/heat stores, 5 kg m^{-2} collector may be a good estimate. Each square meter of collector delivers about 300 kWh heat per year. Hence, 1 MWh per year corresponds to 16.5 kg copper. Thus, to increase the annual world production of solar heat to 1% of the present human energy consumption, an installation of 22 million tons of copper absorbers is required. The annual production of copper worldwide is approximately 15 million tons. The need for new materials is obvious. Aluminum, steel, and other metallic materials will be used more. Polymeric materials have to be considered as an alternative.

The major advantages in using polymeric materials are low material cost in general (there also exist very expensive high-performance polymers), low weight, and low manufacturing costs. The latter property is perhaps the most important factor when choosing polymeric materials for a specific application. Using polymers, at least in large-scale production, complex integrated structures can be manufactured in a single step through, for example, injection molding or extrusion.

The objective of the project 'Polymeric Materials for Solar Thermal Applications' (Task 39) of the Solar Heating and Cooling (SHC) Programme is the assessment of the applicability and the cost-reduction potential by using polymeric materials and polymer-based novel designs of suitable solar thermal systems and to promote increased confidence in the use of these products by developing and applying appropriate methods for assessment of durability and reliability.

3.12.2.3 The Collector Circuit

The durability and reliability of solar water collector systems are influenced by the behavior of the collector circuit/loop. The collector circuit usually has an antifreeze–water mixture as the heat transfer fluid. A heat exchanger is therefore required for heat transfer to the store. Exceptions are systems that use the drain-back (**Figure 14**). With drain-back systems, both overheating and freezing of fluid in the solar collector loop can be protected.

Figure 13 Building-integrated solar collectors: Roof and facade.

The input to the collector should always be as cold as possible, in order to keep its efficiency high. Therefore, the connecting tube to the collector is mounted at the bottom of the store, where the coldest water is.

For so-called 'high-flow' systems with flow rate in the collector circuit of approximately $50 \, l \, h^{-1} \, m^{-2}$ of collector area, the temperature rise in the collector is on the order of $10 \, °C$. The input into the store for these high-flow systems should be near the bottom of the store, and the store is heated slowly from the bottom to the top.

For so-called 'low-flow' systems with a specific collector flow rate of $10–15 \, l \, h^{-1} \, m^{-2}$ of collector area, the temperature rise in the collector is on the order of $40–50 \, °C$. The input to the store for low-flow systems should be higher up than that of the high-flow systems, the best height depending on the flow rate and system design. It can be advantageous to use a stratifying unit to make sure

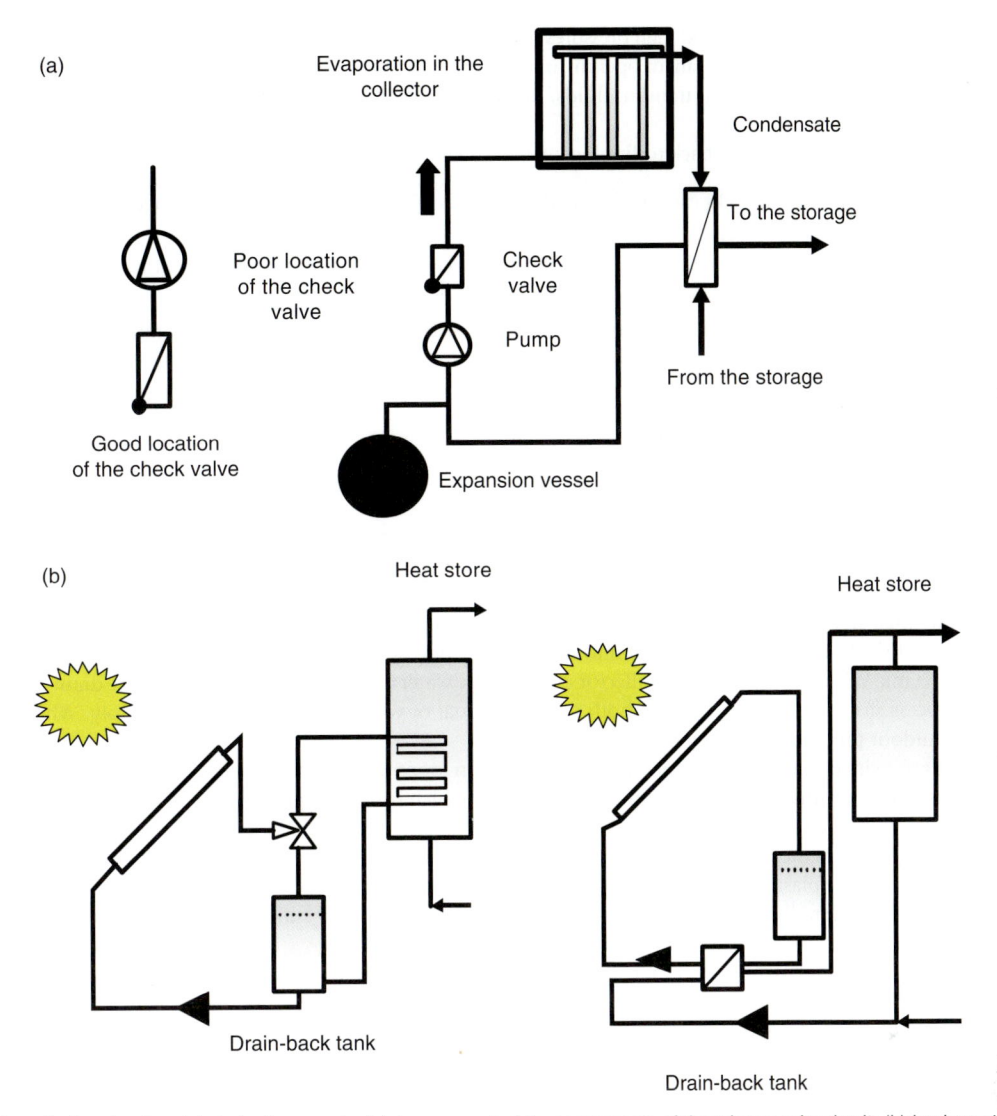

Figure 14 The collector circuit and drain-back concepts. (a) Arrangement of the components of the primary solar circuit; (b) implementation of the drain-back concept when the collector and the heat store are at the same level.

that the heat from the collector goes to the right level in the store. Low flow should not, in general, be used with internal heat exchangers, as these cannot fully use the high-temperature built up in the collector, and the resulting temperature in the store is much lower as the water in the store gets mixed rapidly. Moderate flows can be used, but in this case, the internal heat exchanger should have a greater vertical extent than when using high flows.

3.12.2.3.1 Drain-back system

In 'drain-back systems', the collector is drained of fluid when it is not in operation (see **Figure 14**). The heat transfer fluid is removed from the collector each time the collector pump stops. This method is used for protection from both frost and overheating. Another method of overheating protection involves keeping the collector circuit pump in operation and dumping heat in the ground or some other heat sink. Some systems even cool the store at night so that the risk for overheating the next day is reduced. A system design that can withstand high pressures (up to 9 bar) in the collector circuit enables the fluid to remain in the collector at all times. However, this approach can lead to rapid deterioration in the glycol and is not to be recommended for systems with stagnation temperatures over 140 °C.

Drain-back technology provides an interesting alternative for overheating protection of fluid in the solar collector loop and also prevents the heat transfer fluid from freezing. When the collector circuit is not running, the circulation can operate using plain water without (antifreeze) additives due to drain-back of the collector fluid. This system concept is based on draining the water from the tilted collector and outdoor collector pipes using gravitational force and replacing the liquid with air from the top. By replacing water in the collector with air, ice cannot be formed and damage is, therefore, avoided. The water also drains back if the heat store is fully charged, thereby avoiding boiling of water and high pressures inside the system. When using polymer materials in the collector circuit, both stopping the pump in time and a permanent opening in the collector loop to the atmosphere are needed to avoid overpressure.

In comparison with the use of heat transfer fluids, drain-back technology using water features both advantages and disadvantages.

Following are the advantages of drain-back technology using water:

- Water does not face the aging drawbacks exhibited by collector fluids with additives, such as a change in material properties and possible corrosion of the collector loop.
- Heat transfer properties of water, that is, both heat capacity and viscosity, are better than those of other heat transfer fluids.
- Water is much cheaper than all other collector fluids and easily available.
- The collector circuit generally does not face high overpressures, possibly leading to additional guarantee for safety.
- The level of maintenance for drain-back systems is lower.

The disadvantages of drain-back systems are as follows:

- less flexibility in the choice of the solar collector and
- special attention for drain-back collector loop design and installation.

The implementation of the drain-back concept in solar heating systems is simple and inexpensive; draining a solar collector requires special qualities in hydraulic design. The major feature is that all of the water must run down to the level of the drain-back storage part of the system when the pump stops. This requirement means that every pipe from the top of the solar collector loop to the drain-back volume must slope downward. When the collector loop is in operation, the drain-back volume is filled with air. This volume can be part of the heat stored or integrated into the collector side heat exchanger within the store or it can be designed as external drain-back tank. When the pump in the collector circuit stops, water drains from the collector to the drain-back volume due to gravity. This process stops when water levels in both pipes are equal or when the collector loop is empty. When complete, the collector and all outdoor pipes must be fully filled with air.

Drain-back collector circuits can be implemented as closed or open loops to the environment. Closed loops are commonly used in collector circuits that can withstand pressures up to at least 3 bar, which usually requires metal absorbers and pipes. After some time, the metal absorbs the oxygen in the circuit and no further corrosion occurs. Open loops are applied in systems with plastic materials. Pressures higher than the hydrostatic level should be avoided as combination of high temperature and pressure may cause weeping and may damage the plastic materials. The properties of the collector have to withstand stagnation temperatures with no fluid (empty) without deterioration, thermal shock when the collector is hot and suddenly fed with cold water, and repeated thermal cycling.

The conditions for good emptying behavior of collectors in the event of stagnation can be achieved by the simple repositioning of the check valve in relation to the expansion vessel as shown in **Figure 14**.

Different implementations of the drain-back systems were analyzed in the framework of IEA-SHC Programme, Task 26 Solar Combisystems [4].

3.12.2.4 Thermal Storage

A heating system needs thermal storage when there is a mismatch between thermal energy supply and energy demand, for example, when intermittent energy sources are utilized. The need for thermal storage in solar hot water systems is often short term. In such instances, water is a very efficient storage medium. Water storages are sensible heat energy storages with the advantage of being relatively inexpensive, but the energy density is low and decreases during the storage time [5–7].

3.12.2.4.1 Water storage technology

The 'hot water tank' is one of the best known thermal energy storage technologies. The hot water tank serves to bridge sunless periods in the case of solar hot water and combined heating system, to increase the system efficiency in combination with cogeneration systems, and to shave the peak in electricity demand and improve the efficiency of electricity supply in the case of an electrically heated hot water tank.

Water storage tank technology is mature and reliable. Sensible heat storage in water is still unbeaten regarding simplicity and cost. In refined systems, the inlet–outlet heights in the tank can vary according to the supply and storage temperatures. Three types of water storage concepts are in the market: (1) bivalent storage, (2) tank-in-tank storage, and (3) stratified storage (**Figure 15**).

Thermally stratified water tanks can improve the annual system efficiency by 20% and more.

'Short-term storage' for solar hot water systems typically has a storage volume between 1.5 and 2.0 times of the daily hot water demand. Even with short-term storage, generous insulation of the tank is essential. For short-term and mid-term storages, one- and two-storage concepts are used (see Section 3.12.3.2).

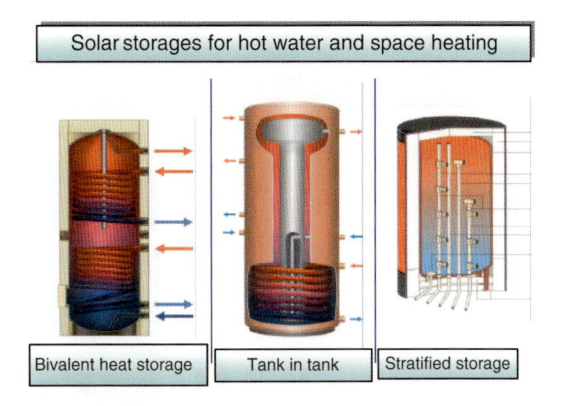

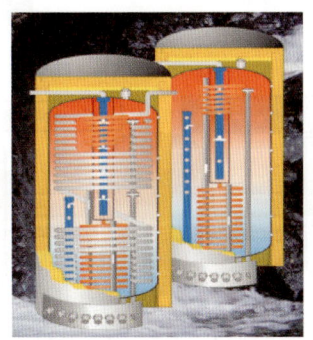

Figure 15 Concepts for water storage technology.

'Mid-term storage' for solar-combined heating systems and solar-supported district heating should cover the heat demand for 3–5 days. For detached and row single-family low-energy houses, a storage volume of about 800–1500 l will be suitable.

'Seasonal storage' is one means to achieve a high annual share of solar heat in northern latitudes. A realistic target to provide a heat capacity of 6 months in existing housing or 4 months in low-energy housing is provided.

Mid-term and seasonal storages are used in solar heating plants (district heating).

3.12.2.4.2 Advanced heat storage technologies

For a widespread market deployment of solar thermal systems, it is necessary to store heat efficiently for longer periods of time in order to reach high solar fractions, and therefore efficient and cost-effective compact storage technologies with high heat capacity are needed. Advanced storage technologies, such as concepts with a phase-change material or with thermochemical materials, are still in the research and development stage (**Figure 16**). Latent heat storage uses the principle of the change of phase of a material named the storage medium. The physical principle of latent storage is a reaction of phase change. The storage capacity of the storage medium is equal to the phase-change latent heat at the phase-change temperature + sensible heat stored over the whole temperature range of the process.

Storage systems based on chemical reactions can achieve much higher energy density than storage systems based on sensible heat or even latent heat, but are not yet commercially viable. The storage systems based on chemical reactions have negligible losses whereas sensible heat storage system dissipates the stored heat to the environment and needs to be insulated strongly if the storage period will be long.

3.12.2.5 Decentralized and Centralized Solar Thermal Systems

Solar heating systems may distinguish between a 'decentralized' and a 'centralized' approach. In a decentralized approach, the storage and collectors are placed within the individual houses like in an ordinary active solar heating system but of a larger size. In the centralized concepts, these components are centrally situated, that is, all solar heat is collected in one storage unit, from which the heat is distributed to the houses.

Figure 17 illustrates the schematics of solar-supported heating plants.

For central solar thermal systems – for example, for apartment housing – the concept of the heat distribution network is of high importance. For solar-supported heating systems, four- and two-pipe networks are used. Based on experimental data, two-pipe

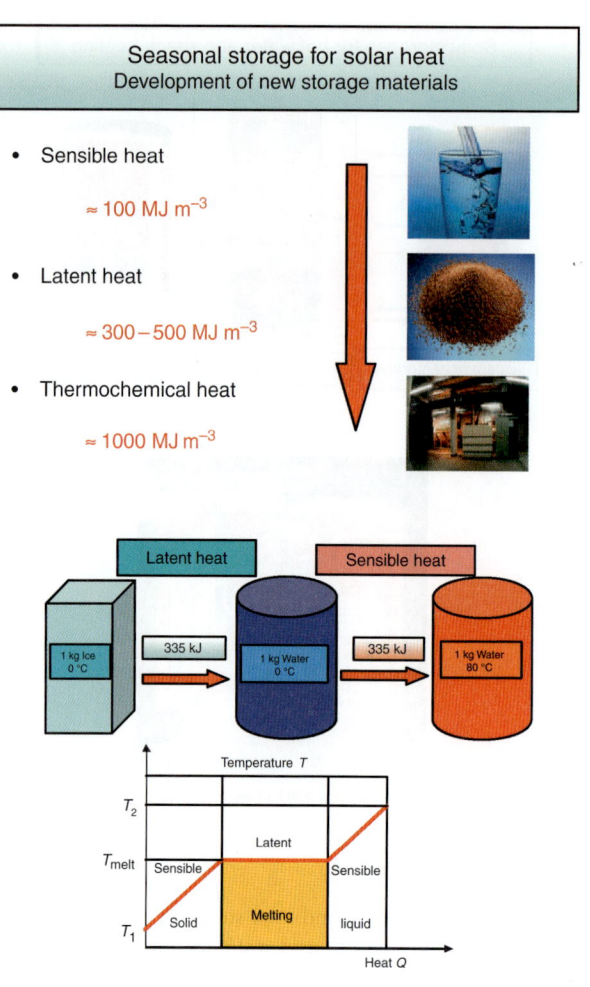

Figure 16 Advanced heat storage technologies in development.

networks have obvious advantages over four-pipe networks when it comes to the plant efficiency and utilization of the solar system. Two-pipe networks can be operated in combination with decentralized heat exchangers or decentralized boilers in the row houses. With individual storages, it is possible to operate the network at different temperatures: lower temperature for space heating (about 40 °C) and higher temperature for hot water preparation (about 65–70 °C). Therefore, the heat losses in the network can be reduced compared to a network with heat exchangers, which is operated on the highest temperature all the time. On the other hand, the investment costs for decentralized storages are higher than those for heat exchangers.

The major advantage of having a centralized system is the reduced unit costs and heat losses from the storage. In general, a centralized system may make better use of the economy of scale (unit prices decrease with the size) than a decentralized one.

The solar unit costs decrease sharply up to approximately 100 m^2, as can be seen in **Figure 18**. This translates to lower kilowatt-hour costs for the solar heat, as illustrated in the example of Austria.

On the other hand, the heat losses in the pipes of the heat distribution net have to be considered. The relatively high losses in small district heating systems mainly through the pipes in summer are caused by the lower heat consumption during the summer months.

Smaller systems could be found in countries with moderate climate for multifamily housing and heating systems in communities. The aim of such systems is to cover the hot water demand outside the heating season. Larger district heating plants will be found in Denmark and Sweden.

3.12.2.6 Auxiliary Heat Sources

In DHW compact systems for households, mainly electricity is used as the auxiliary heat source. Otherwise solar hot water systems are combined with fossil or biomass boilers or heat pumps for space heating, mainly during the heating season. The hot water preparation outside the heating season should be covered up to 100% by solar. This goal is also for Solar Combisystems, with combined hot water preparation and space heating. For example, with a combined solar–biomass heating system the contribution to the heat demand of a building (space heat and hot water) is covered 100% by renewable energy.

Natural gas is mainly used as backup system in gas district heating.

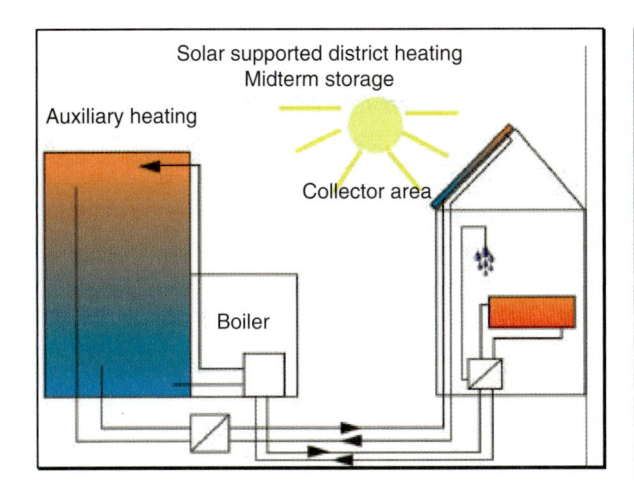

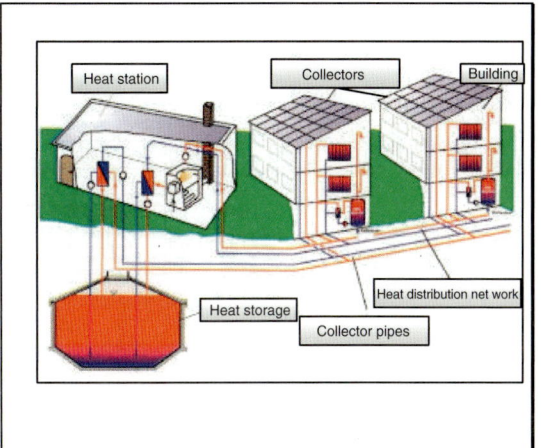

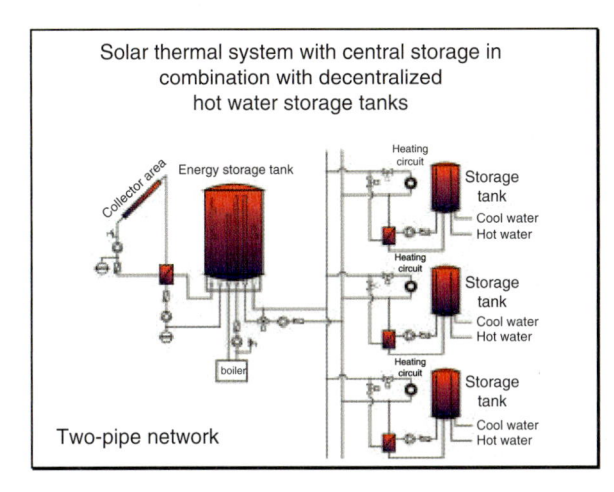

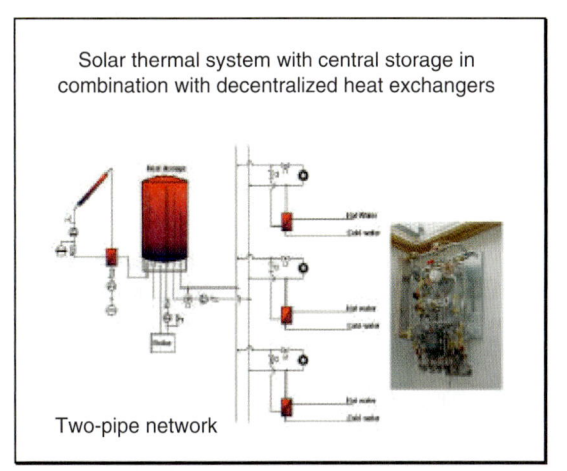

Figure 17 Schematic diagrams for district heating plants and examples for small district heating in Austria.

3.12.2.7 Hygienic Aspects of Solar Hot Water Heaters

In some active solar system configurations, the storage tank contains drinking water. There is then the risk of the so-called Legionnaires' disease, *Legionella* pneumonia. It is caused by *Legionella*, or rod-shaped, mobile, aerobic bacteria that occur naturally in surface water and groundwater. They begin to propagate at temperatures between 20 and 50 °C, with optimum growth occurring between 30 and 40 °C. Above 60 °C, they die off quickly. A long residence time in water at favorable temperatures may result in high concentrations of *Legionella*. Stagnant water in pipes or in parts of an installation that have not been flushed is a breeding ground for these bacteria.

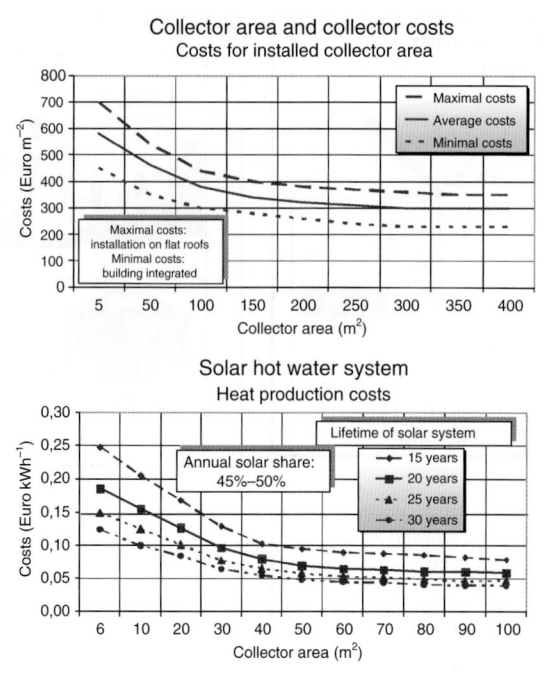

Figure 18 Economic aspects of solar water heating systems.

To prevent the growth of *Legionella*, the water temperature should be either below 25 °C or above 50 °C. Disinfecting a contaminated system can be done by flushing it, then heating the water to 60 °C for 20 min. In general, solar thermal systems for hot water preparation are backed up by an auxiliary heating system to achieve temperatures above 50 °C. In this manner, the risk of *Legionella*-contaminated water can be minimized.

A distinction is made between small and large systems. Small systems are considered to have a very low risk and need no special attention. Small systems are installations in one- or two-family houses, or installations with volume <400 l and with <3 l in pipes between the heater outlet and draw-off point. Large systems should be designed so that they can be heated up to 60 °C in a frequency prescribed by the building/sanitary code.

3.12.3 Design Principles of Solar Thermal Systems

The economic efficiency of solar heating systems depends mainly on its design. Thus, the optimal design of all components of the system – collector, storage, tanks, pumps, control mechanism, and piping – as well as the design of collector area and storage volume as a function of the daily/hourly hot water demand is essential.

3.12.3.1 Meteorological Conditions and Simulation Tools

The useful heat output of a collector system depends also on the influencing meteorological quantities at the location, as well as on the structure of consumption.

Meteorological data from all parts of the world are used to simulate solar energy systems. For many regions, the measured data may only be applied within a 50 km radius of the collection station. This makes it necessary to interpolate parameters between stations. Through existing data sets, for example, Meteonorm, it is possible to simulate solar energy systems in all parts of the world on a consistent basis. The interpolation errors are within the variations of climate from 1 year to the next [8].

Figure 19 shows the annual global solar radiation, and Figure 20 shows the absorbed solar radiation on tilted surface for different orientations and tilt angles for south-facing collectors in three climates.

There are several computer programs (simulation tools) in the market for the thermal performance calculation of solar heating systems: for example, Polysun, TSOL, and SHWwin [9–11]. All are transient simulation programs with time steps of a few minutes and feature database support for components and systems. The assurance of results from simulations is depending from the input data, also considering the site conditions, the system design, and the application, for example, required heat demand. Proved simulation tools will allow the pre-design of solar thermal systems in an easy and short way. For simple hot water systems – compact systems – no extra simulation work will be necessary. For more complicated systems – hot water systems for apartment housing, settlements, commercial buildings, as well as Solar Combisystems – additional detailed simulation is recommended, in combination with a sensibility analysis: 'energy-economic design'.

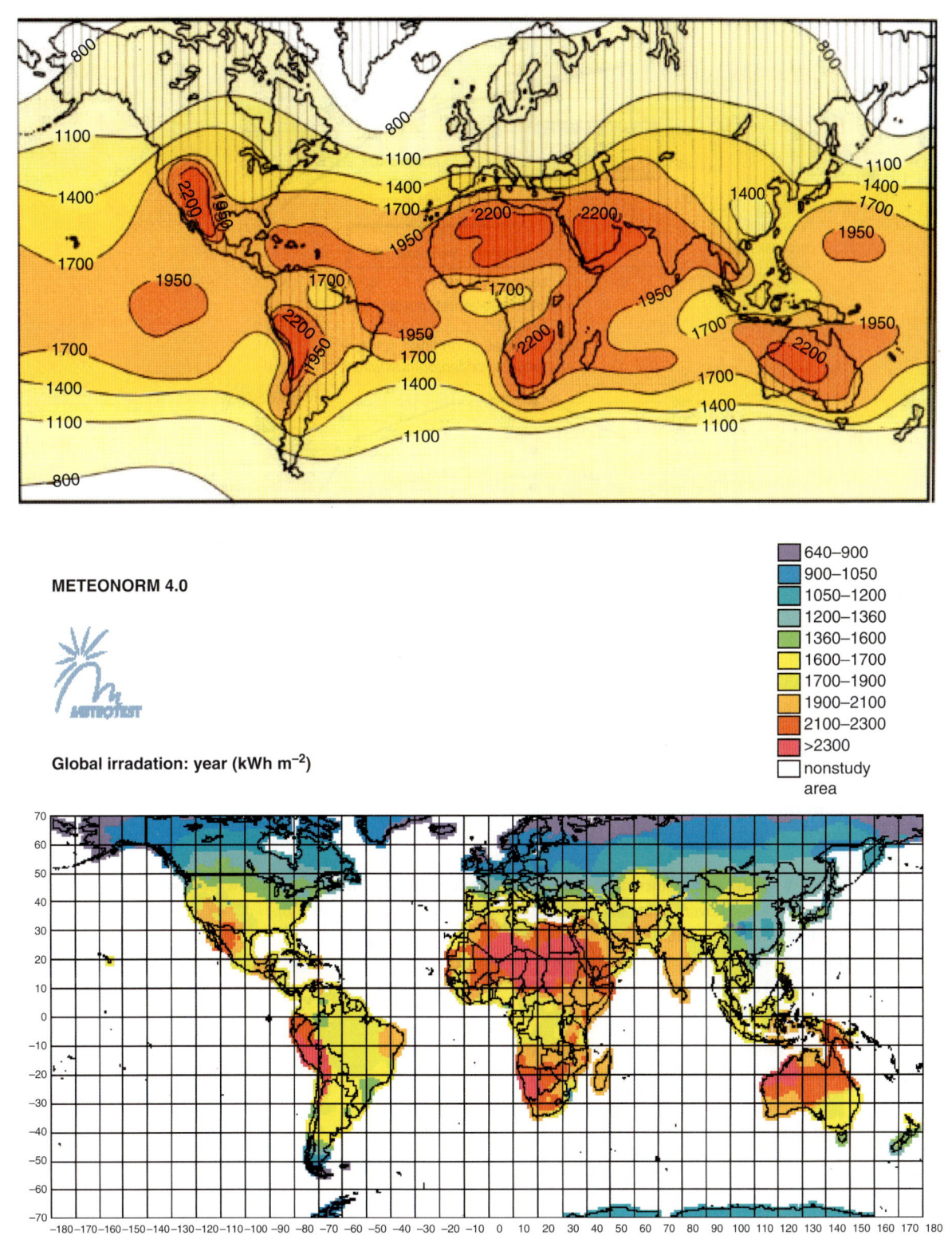

Figure 19 Global annual solar radiation (kWh m^{-2} yr^{-1}).

The main influencing factors to the output – heat production on daily, monthly, and annual basis – are the following:

- Meteorological conditions on site: availability of absorbed solar radiation on collector area (shading, dust, and snow on collector surface) and ground reflection of solar radiation (*albedo*).

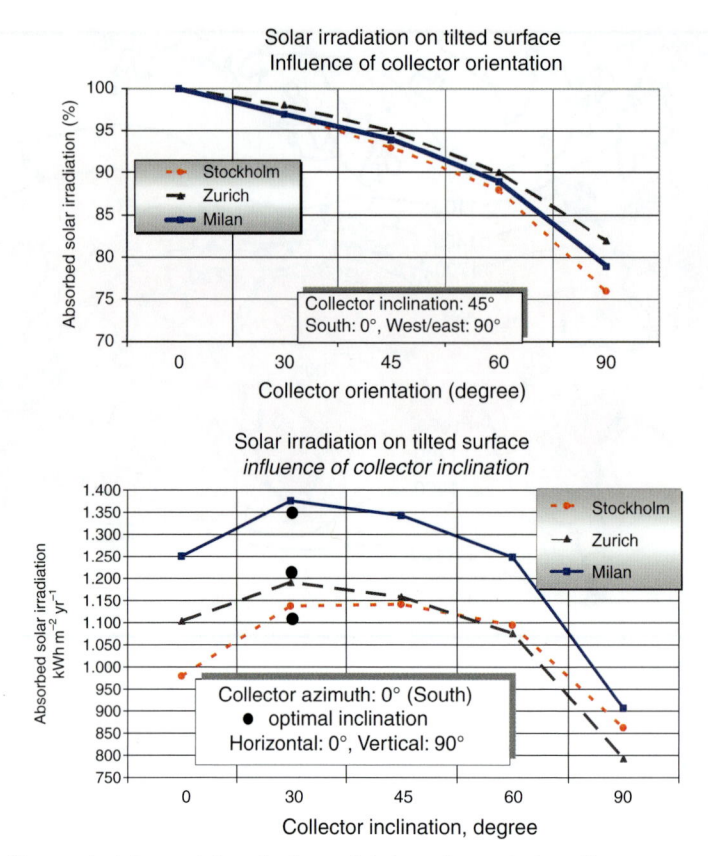

Figure 20 Solar radiation for different orientations and tilt angles for south-facing collectors in three climates.

- Heat demand: day profiles on hourly basis, week profiles on daily basis, and month profiles on weekly basis.
- Water temperature: collector inlet and outlet temperatures.
- Collector: collector characteristics (conversion factor and heat loss coefficient), depending on type and product, and connection of collectors.
- Collector loop: pipes' length and diameter, insulation, heat exchanger, high-flow systems, low-flow systems, and drain-back systems (protection from both overheating and freezing of fluid in the solar collector loop).
- Collector size, inclination, and orientation.
- Storage: amount of stores, volume, and combination of two and more stores; height and length; insulation; loading and discharging strategy; and ambient temperature.
- System integration, including regulation.

Figure 21 illustrates the program structure of simulation tools.

SHWwin is used for the following simulations.

3.12.3.2 The Solar System

For the system efficiency, the 'heat management philosophy' is important: priority is given to the load (DHW or space heating) with the lowest temperature level, so that the solar collector works with the highest efficiency. Thus, the implementation of thermal storage in a solar system and its volume, depending on storage capacity and the application, is of great importance for the efficiency and the solar share of a heating system.

The storage concept comprises the strategies – which are adjusted to the particular design of the collector area – for loading and discharging as well as for additional heating (**Figure 22**). Typical and practically proved storage concepts for solar thermal systems are 'one-storage' and 'multistorage' systems adjusted to loading and discharging strategies with collector characteristics and the heat demand. Thermally stratified water tank represents an ideal thermal storage: The inlet–outlet levels can be changed and may be considered as an advanced solar system for DHW and space heating concept. This type of storage will improve the annual solar system efficiency by about 20% and more.

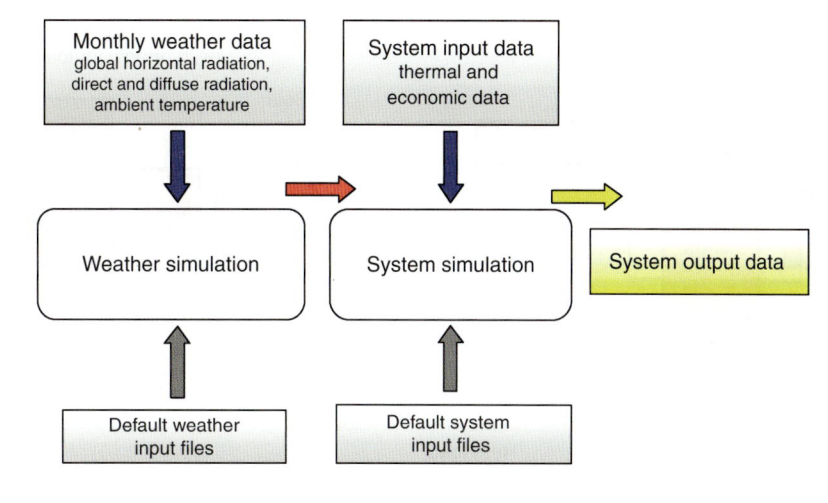

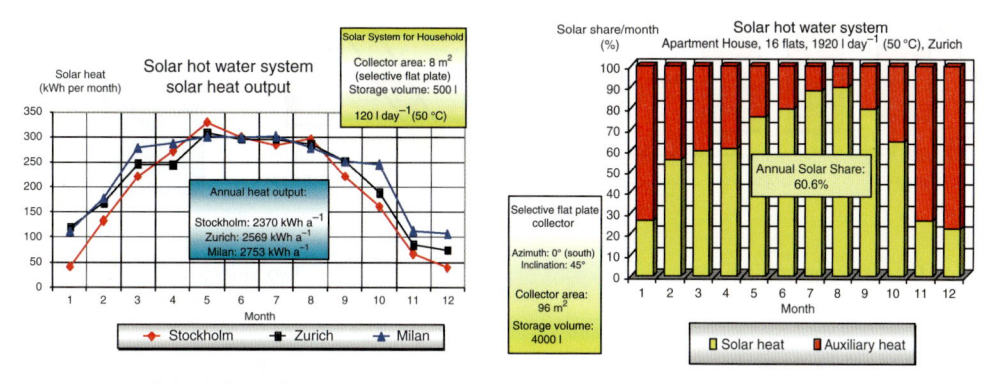

Figure 21 Program structure of simulation tools.

Two-storage solar DHW systems are typically used in apartment houses and Solar Combisystems: buffer store and separate hot water store.

To reduce the heat losses of the heat distribution system in larger buildings with more consumers, a combination of buffer storage and decentralized stores as well as decentralized heat exchangers may be a more efficient and cost-effective solution (see **Figure 17**).

Summarizing, the 'one-storage concept' will be the best solution for solar DHW systems for households and single-family houses, the 'multistorage concept' for apartment houses, and the 'two-storage concept' as well as the 'stratified storage concept' for combined hot water and space heating systems.

3.12.3.3 Collector Orientation and Inclination

The design of a solar heating system has to consider the meteorological conditions on site.

The intensity of the solar radiation on a flat surface is higher when it is tilted toward the sun. The maximum intensity occurs when the flat surface is perpendicular to the sun's rays. Two-axis tracking of absorbers may thus maximize the energy gain at the expense of technical complexity. For fixed absorber surfaces, the energy gain is a function of the slope angle (0° = horizontal, 90° = vertical) and the azimuth angle (0° = south, −90° = east, +90° = west, and 180° = north). The distribution of the annual incident energy on a tilted surface as a function of slope and azimuth angle has to be considered within the installation as well as integration of solar thermal collectors in building envelope. The absorbed solar radiation on tilted surface is shown in **Figure 20** for different orientations and tilt angles for south-facing collectors in three climates.

Collector orientation is best between 30° east and 45° west. Compared with tilted collector areas, the absorbed solar radiation on facade collectors is reduced by about 25–30% as an average. The difference during the heating season is smaller. From the energetic point of view, facade-integrated collectors are acceptable in solar-combined heating systems with an oversized collector area for hot water preparation outside the heating season.

Nevertheless, the distribution of the annual incident energy on a tilted surface gives some freedom on choosing acceptable surfaces for collection of solar energy.

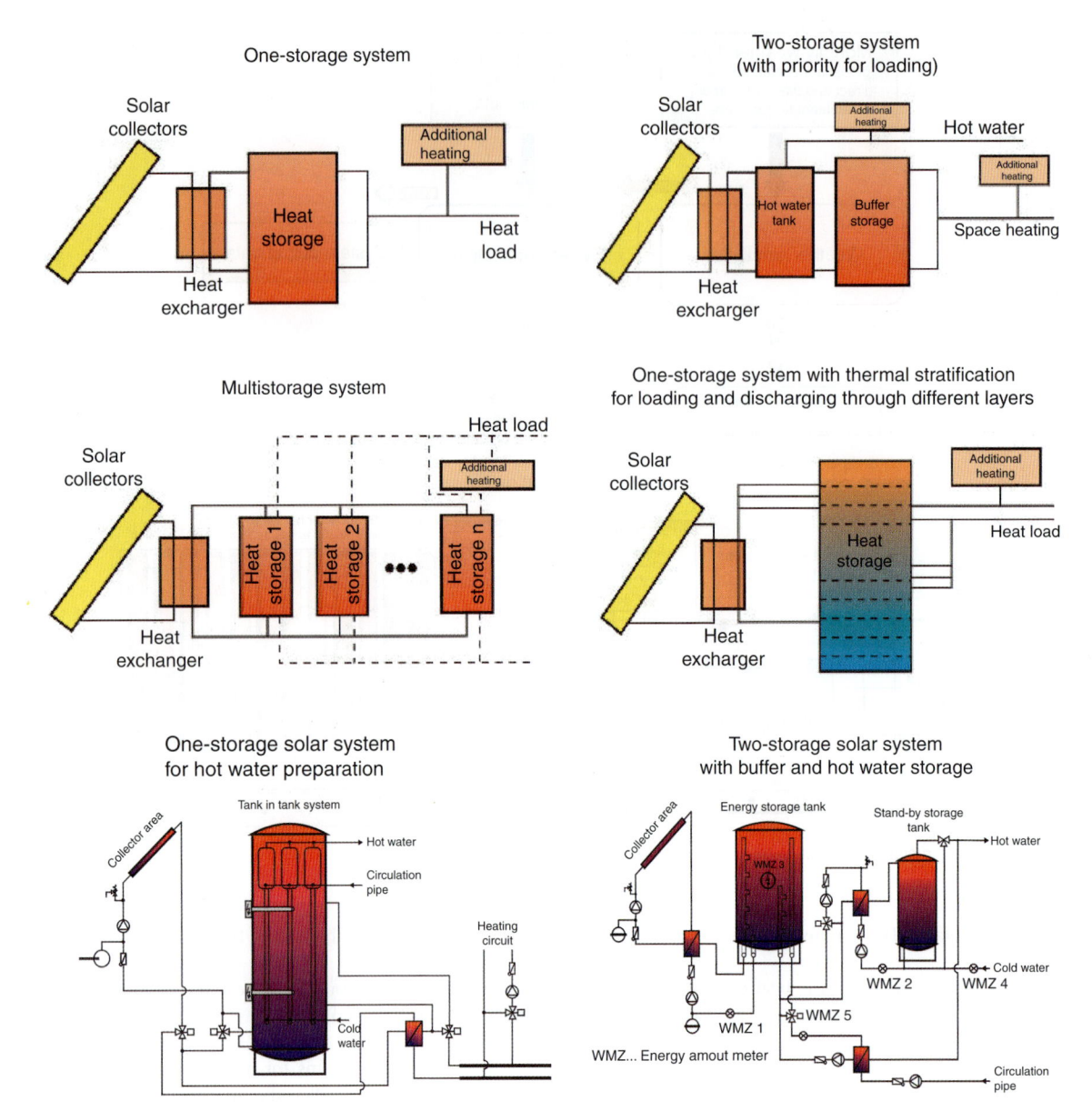

Figure 22 Hydraulic principle schematics for solar heating systems.

For roof installations, where the systems deliver heat over the whole year, the optimal tilt angle (northern hemisphere) is between 30° and 75°. The orientation can be between 30° east and 45° west. As can be seen, a 90° tilt, or facade-integrated collector, is far from optimum in all locations.

3.12.3.4 Solar DHW Systems for Households and Single-Family Houses

In solar systems for hot water preparation, flat-plate collectors of different designs (nonevacuated- and evacuated-tube collectors with and without selective coating) are used. Flat-plate collectors with selective coating – today the standard – may be in many cases the most cost-effective solution. For higher temperatures (above 80 °C), evacuated-tube collectors would be more successful.

Solar hot water preparation is nearly similar in all climates during the summer period. **Figure 23** illustrates the global radiation and the heat output of solar DHW systems for households in the three reference climates: cold (Stockholm), temperate (Zurich), and mild (Milan). The difference in the annual solar heat output between cold and mild climates amounts to 14%. The influence of collector type, collector inclination and orientation, collector size, and storage volume to the annual solar share is illustrated in **Figure 23**.

The design of a solar hot water system should be oriented on the hot water demand outside the heating season. Under the typical meteorological conditions in temperate climates, the annual solar share for hot water preparation – considering also economical

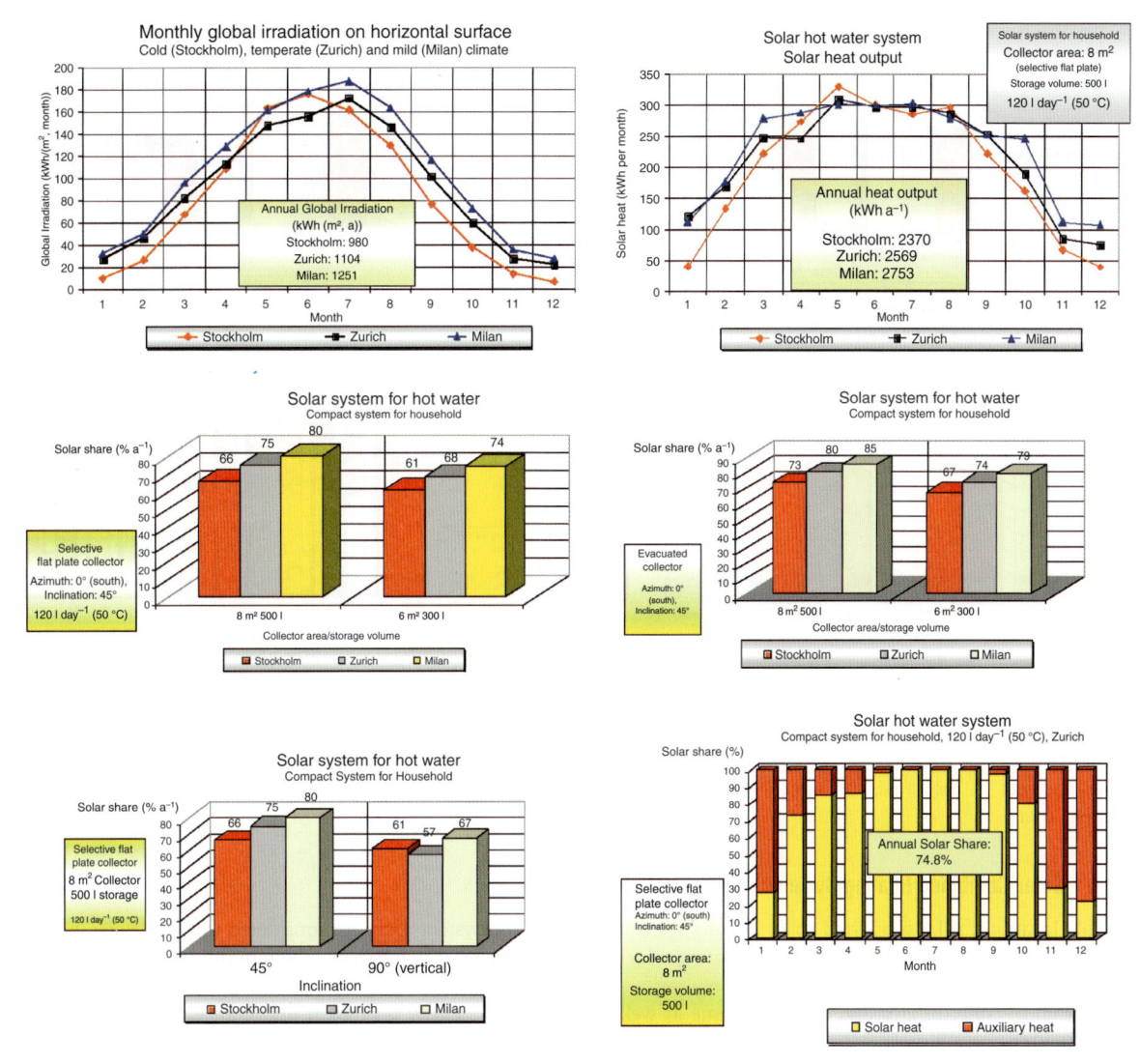

Figure 23 Design of solar domestic hot water (DHW) system for a household in three reference climates.

aspects and in dependence on the daily hot water demand – should be in the range of about 60–70%, and during the summer period, the solar share would be about 70–90%.

Facade collectors reduce the annual solar share by 5% (cold climate), 18% (temperate climate), and 13% (mild climate), compared with roof-integrated collector (45°).

For the economy and energy efficiency, the tank should be from 1.5 to 2.0 times greater than the daily hot water demand, and the collector area between 1 and 2 m² per occupant. Typically, designs for solar hot water systems in households are 3 m² per 300 l for up to three persons and 8 m² per 500 l for four to five persons.

3.12.3.5 Solar DHW Systems for Apartment Houses

The influence of collector type, storage size, and collector orientation is illustrated in **Figure 24**. Also, the monthly solar share of a solar DHW system for an apartment block, 96 m² of flat-plate collector supplying a 4000 l storage tank in moderate climate (demand 1920 l day^{-1} at 50 °C), is shown [5]. In apartment houses, the annual solar share for hot water preparation will generally be below 50% due to lack of space on the roof for the installation of collectors. The use of solar hot water systems in an apartment house has the advantage of lower specific investment costs, and thus, the heat production costs can be reduced in comparison with small, decentralized systems. The possibilities for a central hot water preparation in apartment houses are used increasingly in the market nowadays. Surprisingly, within a large range, the size of the tank relative to the collector area is not a major factor affecting system performance. This is evident in the example of an apartment block shown in **Figure 24**. Doubling the tank size increases the solar share by <15%. More important is avoiding the mixing of the hot water at the top of the tank with cooler water at the bottom, the insulation of the tank, and the avoidance of thermal bridges, for

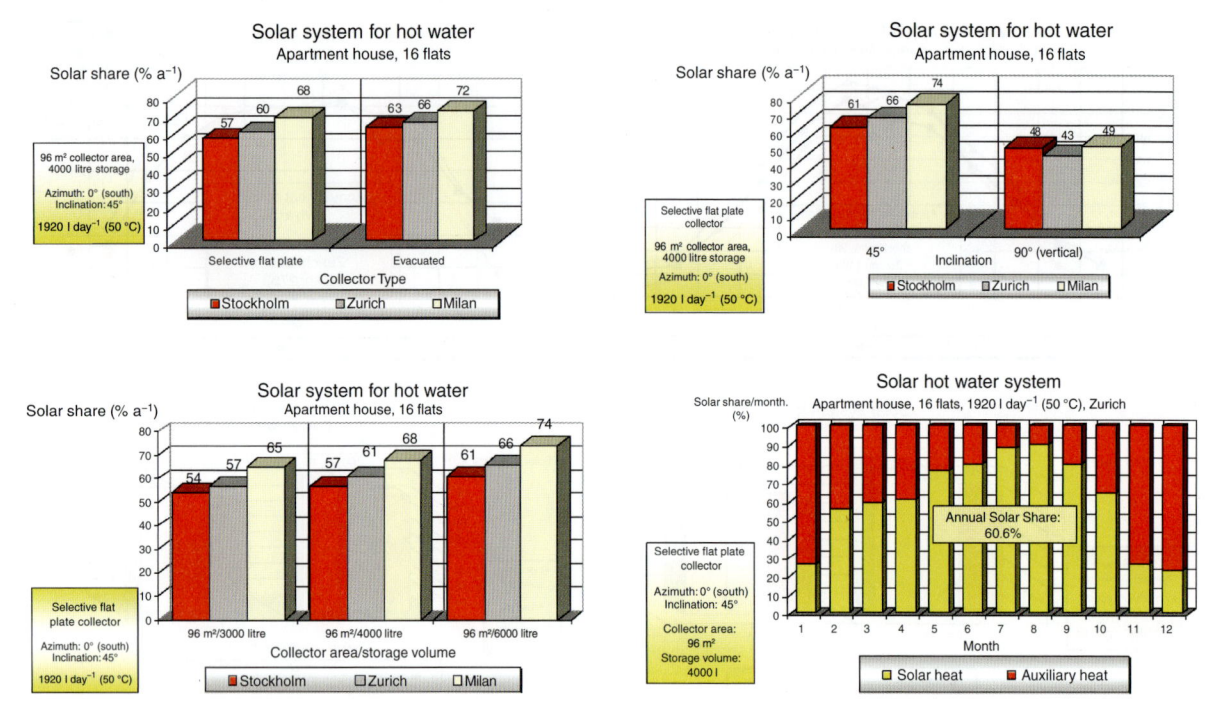

Figure 24 Design of solar domestic hot water (DHW) system for an apartment house in three reference climates.

example, the feet of the tank. The size of the tank should not be oversized because that would increase heat losses and investment costs.

3.12.3.6 Solar-Combined Heating Systems

At suitable locations, solar-supported space heating systems (Solar Combisystems) can be considered for low-energy buildings, mainly detached and row housing. Efficient operating solar-combined heating systems require high building insulation as well as low-temperature heat distribution.

The design of collector area and storage volume as well as the storage strategy is of great importance. If the solar system is combined with a space heating system and some solar heat is used for heating purposes, the collector area as well as the storage volume has to be increased. In this case, there exists some unused solar heat in the period without space heating demand. An efficient use of solar heat can be reached if an additional heat demand exists during the summer period. Typical examples are the operation of an outdoor swimming pool or the heating up of soil by operating a solar-supported ground-coupled heat pump system. In cold climates, solar heat will provide better living environment also during the summer months.

The results of different designs of Solar Combisystems for low-energy and passive houses are shown in **Figures 25** and **26**: influence of collector type, collector size, and storage size for cold, temperate, and mild climates; monthly performance of a Solar Combisystem in the Zurich reference temperate climate: detached house with 16 m^2 per 50 m^2 of collector per floor area tilted at 45° and supplying a 2000 l per 5000 l storage tank [5].

If the contribution of solar energy for the heating of residential buildings is over 40%, then the collector area and the storage volume have to be increased. Here storage for several days is not sufficient any longer; solar energy for the heating period has to be provided by seasonal heat storage during the summer months. For a solar coverage of >80% for space heating and hot water preparation for single-family house, collector areas of 80–100 m^2 and a storage volume of 80–130 m^3 are necessary. It will be difficult to realize these demands because of high costs.

Many configurations of Solar Combisystems and backup systems have been tried. From 1975 to 1985, these systems were custom engineered. Through a cooperation of the IEA-SHC Task 26: Solar Combisystems (http://www.iea-shc.org/task26/index.html), existing designs have been analyzed and optimized, and a valuable design handbook is produced. Today, solar companies offering simple and economical systems often carry out system design as part of their service. Components of Solar Combisystems are factory assembled in compact units, making the on-site work of the installer easier and assuring better reliability.

Currently, installed systems demonstrate that solar space heating is possible even in northern locations. However, solar irradiation from September to October and March to May can make a useful contribution during the beginning and end of the heating season. Especially in northern countries as well as in alpine areas, some heating in the summer period will increase living comfort.

For solar-supported heating systems, a combination with a biomass burner or a heat pump are interesting solutions. With a 'combined solar–biomass heating system', the contribution to the heat need of a building (space heat and hot water) is covered to

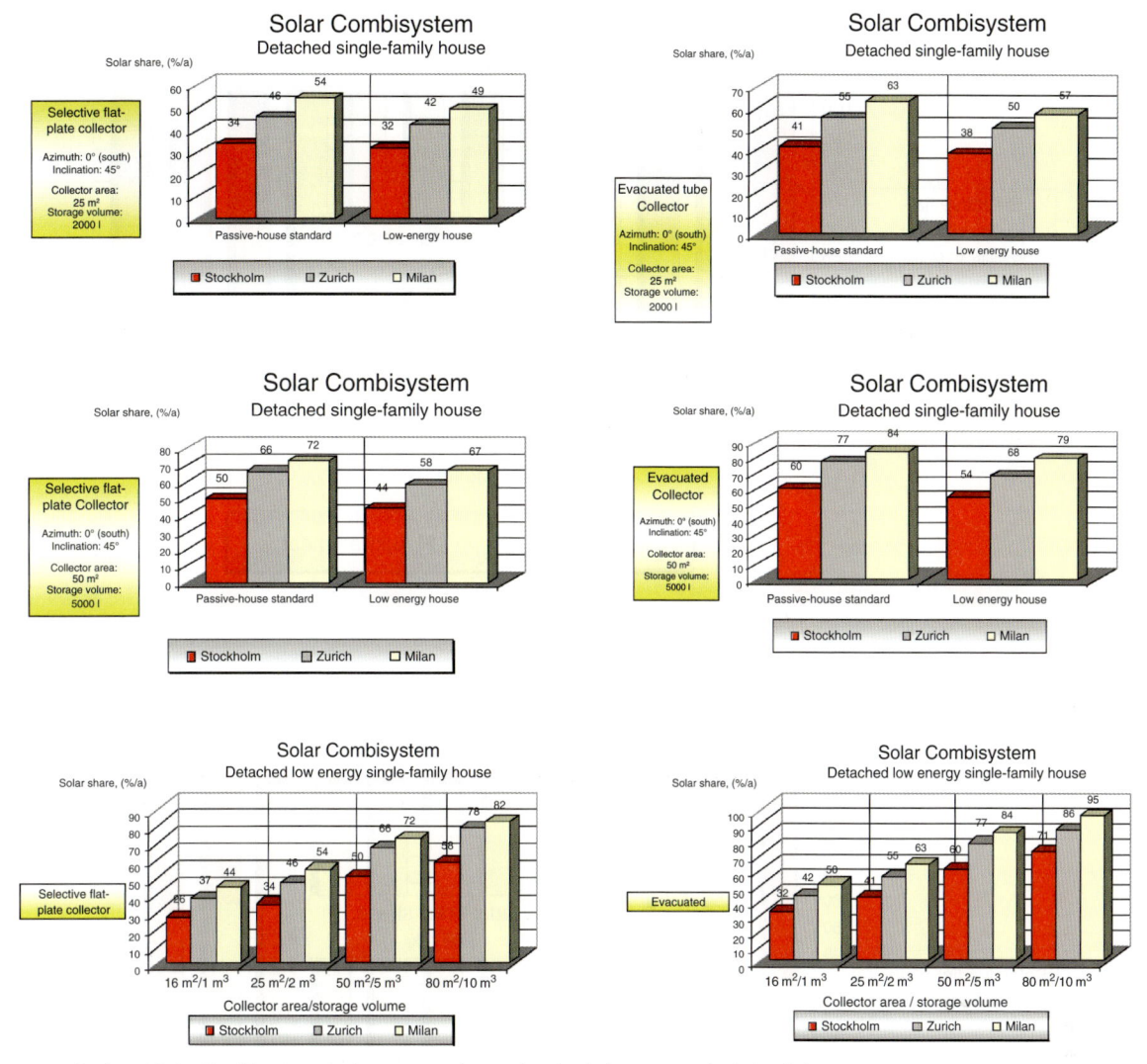

Figure 25   Design of Solar Combisystems for hot water and space heating in low-energy single-family houses.

100% by renewable energy sources. With a combined solar–heat pump system, the heat pump is primarily used for space heating during the heating period and the solar installation primarily for hot water preparation during the summer months. Considering energy–economic aspects, the annual solar share for heat production (hot water and space heating) ranges from 20% to 60% per year, depending on climate and building envelope standard.

3.12.4 Summary and Conclusion

In summary, the areas for solar thermal applications are many. The key reasons for utilization are as follows: the energy need for heating and cooling, for crop drying, and for process heating is large and growing; the solar resource is large and inexhaustible; the environmental and the economic benefits are substantial; and solar thermal technologies are essential components of a sustainable energy future.

Today, solar thermal systems are regarded as a well-established low-tech technology. Solar thermal technologies for low- to medium-temperature applications can be used all over the world: cold to hot climates.

Solar thermal energy can cover a substantial part of the energy use (worldwide, OECD, and Europe) in a cost-effective and sustainable way. Any long-term vision for economic development must include solar thermal technologies to save finite energy sources and to build up an industry of strategic importance. Necessary is the willingness for the transition from fossil fuels to renewable sources and, therefore, also to solar heat.

It may be estimated that about 30–40% of the worldwide heat demand could be covered by solar produced heat, and in OECD/Europe about 20% of the demand for heat supply. Based on these data, solar heat could provide in the long term (2050) up to 60–100 EJ yr^{-1} worldwide and to 10–20 EJ yr^{-1} in OECD-Member States. The vision of the IEA-SHC Programme and affiliated solar

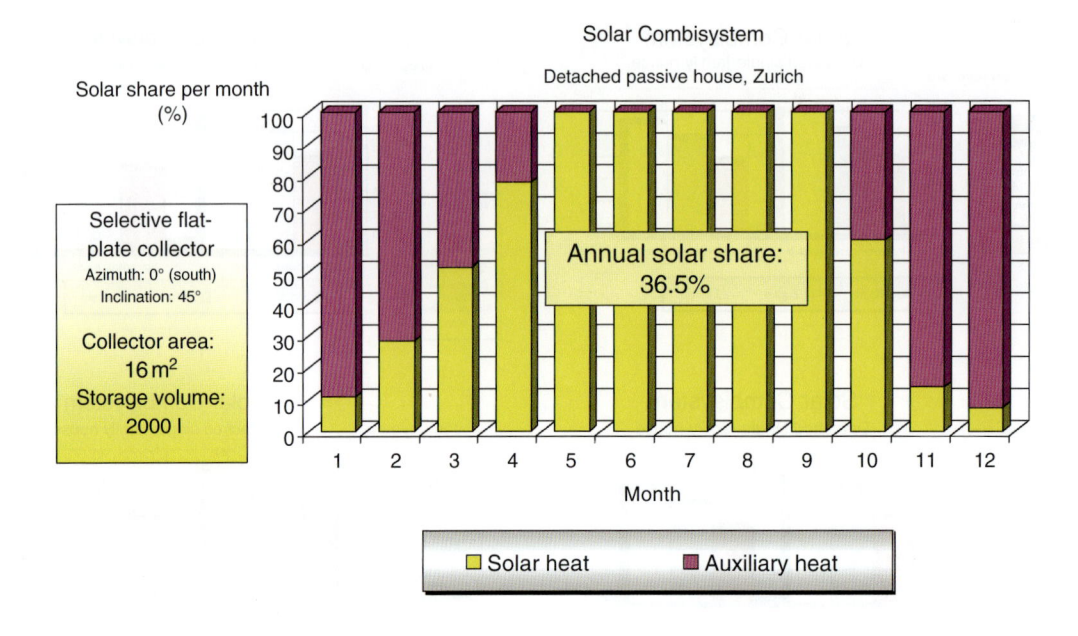

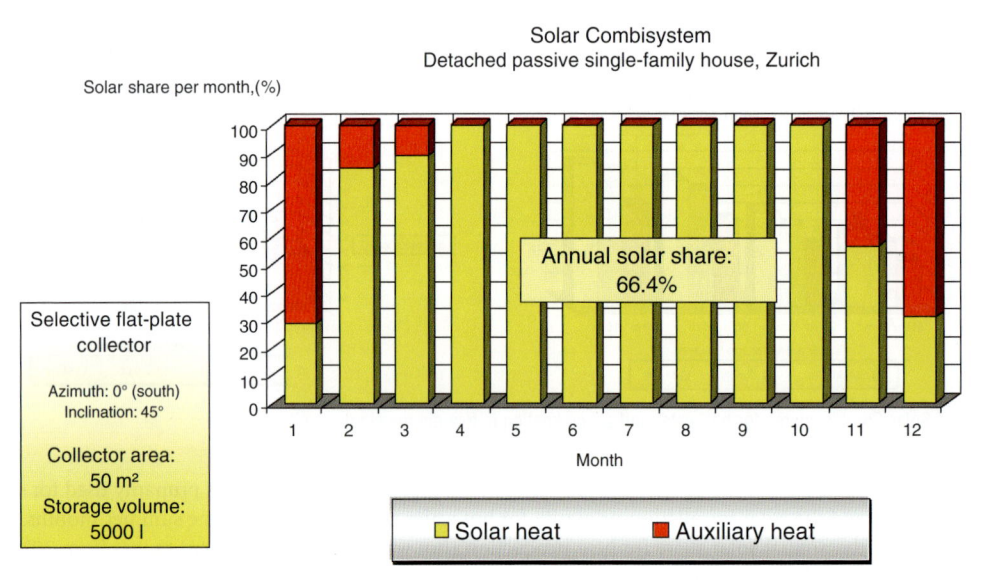

Figure 26 Solar Combisystem for hot water and space heating in low-energy single-family houses monthly and annual solar share.

associations is that solar thermal systems will provide 10–15% of the total energy demand in OECD countries by 2025 and up to 50% of low-temperature heating and cooling demand by 2030. By collaborating with others – primarily with developing countries – the IEA-SHC Programme hopes to increase awareness of solar thermal energy's potential to contribute significantly to the future supply of energy worldwide.

References

[1] IEA-Solar Heating and Cooling Programme. http://www.iea-shc.org.
[2] Weiss W et al. (2010) Solar Heat Worldwide: Edition 2009. IEA-Solar Heating and Cooling Programme.
[3] Weiss W et al. (2003) Solar Heating Systems for Houses – A Design Handbook for Solar Combisystems, ISBN 1 902916 46 8. London: James & James (Science Publishers) Ltd., http://www.jxj.com
[4] Weiss W et al. (2003) IEA-SHC-Task 26 'Solar Combisystems' homepages: http://www.solenergi.dk/task26/downloads.html.
[5] Faninger G (2004) Active solar heating: Water. In Hastings R and Wall M (eds) Sustainable. Sustainable Solar Housing: Exemplary Buildings and Technologies, ISBN-13: 978-1-84407-326-9, pp. 175–181. London; Sterling, VA: EARTHSCAN.

[6] Faninger G (2004) Thermal storage. *Sustainable Solar Housing: Exemplary Buildings and Technologies*, ISBN-13: 978-1-84407-326-9, pp. 215–219. London; Sterling, VA: EARTHSCAN.
[7] Faninger G (2004) Latent heat storage. *Sustainable Solar Housing: Exemplary Buildings and Technologies*, ISBN-13: 978-1-84407-326-9, pp. 220–222. London; Sterling, VA: EARTHSCAN.
[8] Meteonorm: METEOTEST, Fabrikstrasse 14, CH-3012 Bern, office@meteotest.ch, http://www.meteotest.ch.
[9] Polysun: Institut für Solartechnik SPF, Hochschule für Technik Rapperswil HSR, Oberseestrasse 10, CH-8640 Rapperswil, spf@solarenergy.ch, http://www.solarenergy.ch.
[10] TSOL: Dr. Valentin EnergieSoftware GmbH, Stralauer Platz 33-34, D-10243 Berlin, mailto:info@valentin.de, http://www.valentin.de.
[11] SHWwin: 'Zur Auslegung von Brauchwasseranlagen, Teilsolare Raumheizung, Nahwärmenetze'. Institut für Wärmetechnik, TU Graz (Only German version available, free download from Internet: http://wt.tu-graz.ac.at).

3.13 Solar Space Heating and Cooling Systems

SA Kalogirou and GA Florides, Cyprus University of Technology, Limassol, Cyprus

© 2012 Elsevier Ltd. All rights reserved.

3.13.1	**Active Systems**	449
3.13.1.1	Direct Circulation Systems	449
3.13.1.2	Indirect Water Heating Systems	450
3.13.1.3	Air–Water Heating Systems	452
3.13.2	**Space Heating and Service Hot Water**	453
3.13.2.1	Air Systems	455
3.13.2.2	Water Systems	456
3.13.2.3	Location of Auxiliary Source	458
3.13.2.4	Heat Pump Systems	459
3.13.3	**Solar Cooling**	460
3.13.3.1	Solar Sorption Cooling	461
3.13.3.2	Solar-Mechanical Systems	462
3.13.3.3	Solar-Related Air Conditioning	462
3.13.3.4	Adsorption Units	463
3.13.3.5	Absorption Units	464
3.13.3.6	Lithium–Water Absorption Systems	465
3.13.3.6.1	Thermodynamic analysis	466
3.13.3.6.2	Design of single-effect LiBr–H_2O absorption systems	470
3.13.3.7	Ammonia–Water Absorption Systems	471
3.13.3.8	Solar Cooling with Absorption Refrigeration	472
3.13.4	**Heat Storage Systems**	473
3.13.4.1	Air Systems Thermal Storage	474
3.13.4.2	Liquid Systems Thermal Storage	474
3.13.5	**Module and Array Design**	475
3.13.5.1	Module Design	475
3.13.5.2	Array Design	475
3.13.5.3	Heat Exchangers	477
3.13.6	**Differential Temperature Controller**	478
References		479

3.13.1 Active Systems

Active solar systems are the systems in which water or a heat transfer fluid is pumped through the collectors. These systems can be used for both water heating and space heating and cooling. In this section the use of the systems as solar water heating systems in general is presented, and in the next sections their use for space heating and cooling is described.

Active systems are more difficult to retrofit in houses, especially in cases where there is no basement, because space is required for the additional equipment, like the hot water cylinder [1]. Five types of systems belong to this category: the direct circulation systems, indirect water heating systems, air systems, heat pump systems, and pool heating systems.

According to Duff [2], the flow in the collector loop should be in the range of 0.2–0.4 l min^{-1} m^{-2} of collector aperture area. The result of low flow rate is a reduction of the collector efficiency due to higher collector temperature rise for a given inlet temperature. For example, for a reduction of flow rate from 0.9 to 0.3 l min^{-1} m^{-2}, the efficiency is reduced by about 6%. However due to the reduction of the inlet temperature to the collectors the loss of collector efficiency. The pumps required for most of these active systems are of the low static head centrifugal types (also called circulators), which for small domestic applications consume 30–50 W of electrical power.

3.13.1.1 Direct Circulation Systems

A schematic diagram of a direct circulation system is shown in **Figure 1**. In this system, a pump is used to circulate potable water from the storage tank to the collectors when there is enough available solar energy to increase its temperature and then return the heated water back to the storage tank until it is needed. Since a pump is used to circulate the water, the collectors can be mounted either above or below the storage tank. In these systems, usually a single storage tank equipped with an auxiliary water heater is used but two-tank storage systems can also be used. An important feature of this configuration is the spring-loaded check valve, which is used to prevent the reverse thermosyphon circulation energy losses when the pump is not running.

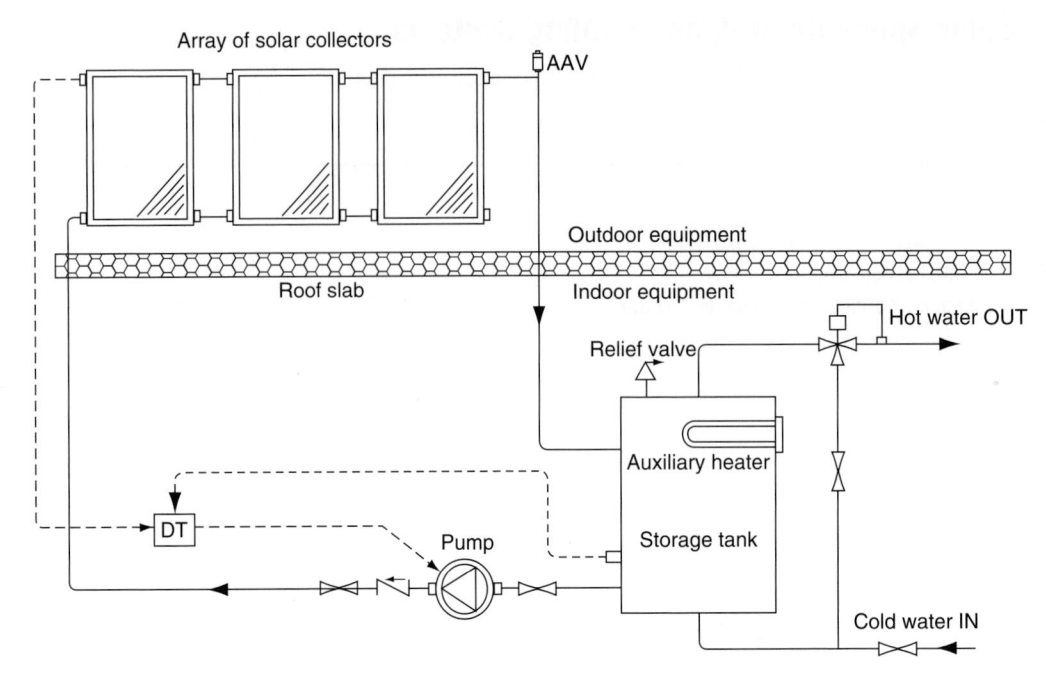

Figure 1 Direct circulation system. AAV, automatic air vent; DT, differential thermostat.

Direct circulation systems are supplied with water from a cold water storage tank or are directly connected to city water mains. Pressure-reducing valves and pressure relief valves are required, however, when the city water pressure is greater than the working pressure of the collectors. Direct water heating systems should not be used in areas where the water is extremely hard or acidic because scale (calcium) deposits may clog or corrode the collectors.

Direct circulation systems can be used in areas where freezing is not frequent. For extreme weather conditions, freeze protection is usually provided by recirculating warm water from the storage tank spending some heat to protect the system. A special thermostat is used in this case to activate the pump when temperature decreases below a certain value. Such recirculation freeze protection should only be used for locations where freezing seldom occurs (a few times a year) since stored heat is lost in the process. A disadvantage of this system is that in case of power failure the pump will not work and the system could freeze. In such a case, a dump valve can be installed at the bottom of the collectors to provide additional protection [1].

The drain-down system is a variation of the direct circulation system and is also used for freeze protection (**Figure 2**). In this case, potable water is pumped from the storage tank to the collector array where it is heated. When a freezing condition or a power failure occurs, the system drains automatically by isolating the collector array and exterior piping from the makeup water supply with the normally closed (NC) valve. Draining then is accomplished with the use of the two normally open (NO) valves as shown in **Figure 2**. It should be noted that the solar collectors and associated piping must be carefully sloped to drain the collector's exterior piping when circulation stops. The check valve, shown on the top of the collectors in **Figure 2**, allows air to fill the collectors and piping during draining and to escape during fill-up.

3.13.1.2 Indirect Water Heating Systems

A schematic diagram of an indirect water heating system is shown in **Figure 3**. In this system, a heat transfer fluid is circulated through the closed collector loop to a heat exchanger, by which the potable water is heated. The most commonly used heat transfer fluids are water/ethylene glycol solutions. Other heat transfer fluids such as silicone oils and refrigerants can also be used. When fluids that are nonpotable or toxic are used, double-wall heat exchangers should be used; this can be done in practice by two heat exchangers installed in series. The heat exchanger can be enclosed in the storage tank. It can also be placed around the tank mantle or externally (see **Figure 4**). Protection devices such as an expansion tank and a pressure relief valve are required to relieve increased pressures in the collector loop, and additional over-temperature protection may be needed to prevent the collector heat transfer fluid from decomposing or becoming corrosive.

In areas where extended freezing temperatures are observed, water/ethylene glycol solutions are used to avoid freezing. These systems are more expensive to construct and operate, as the solution should be checked every year and changed every few years, depending on the solution quality and system temperatures [1].

Typical collector configurations include the internal heat exchanger shown in **Figure 3**, the external heat exchanger shown in **Figure 4(a)**, and the mantle heat exchanger shown in **Figure 4(b)**.

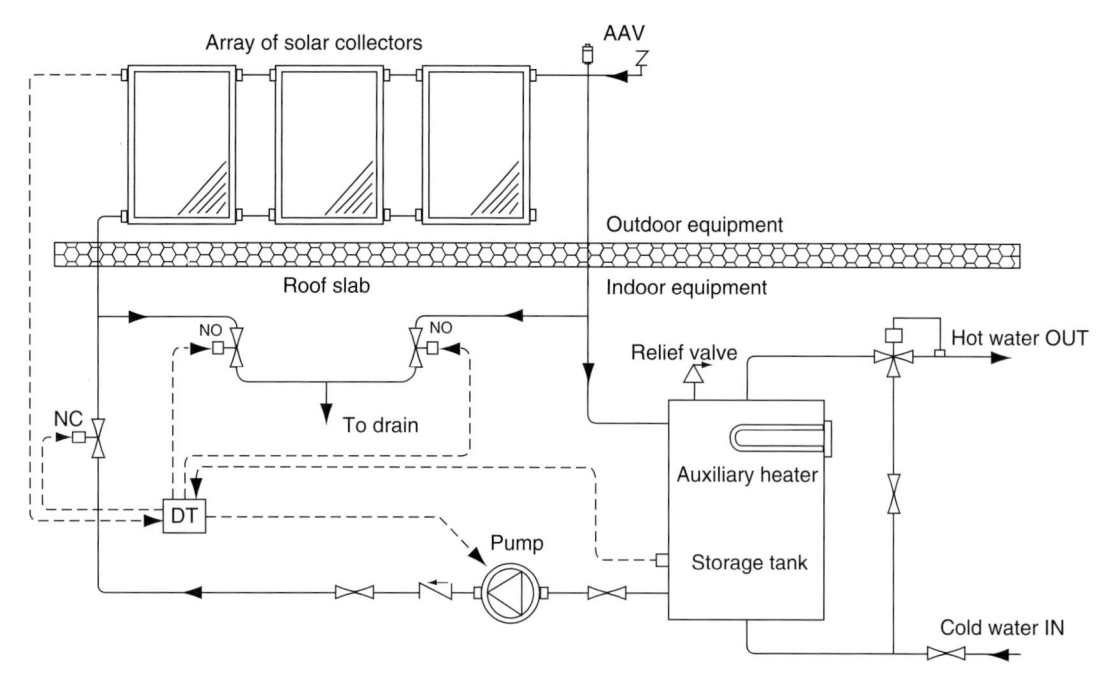

Figure 2 Drain-down system. NC, normally closed; NO, normally open.

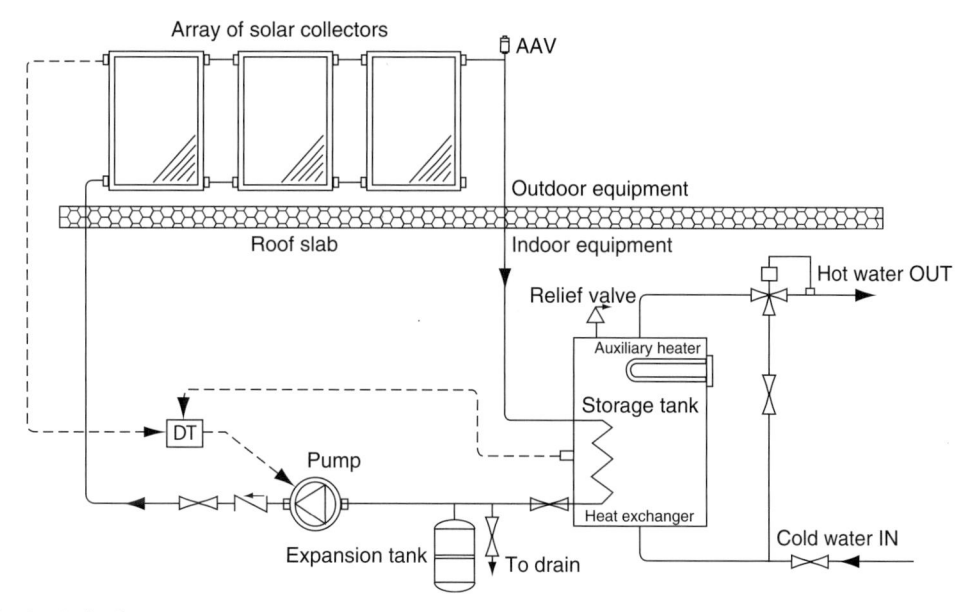

Figure 3 Indirect water heating system.

The most widely used size for the storage tank is $50 \, l \, m^{-2}$ of collector aperture area, but as a general rule the tank size should be between 35 and $70 \, l \, m^{-2}$ of collector aperture area.

For freeze protection, a variation of indirect water heating system is used called the drain-back system. This system circulates water through the closed collector loop to a heat exchanger, to heat the potable water. Circulation continues as long as solar energy is available. When the circulation pump stops, the collector fluid drains by gravity to a drain-back tank. If the system is pressurized, the tank serves also as an expansion tank when the system is operating and in this case it must be protected with a temperature and pressure relief valve. In the case of an unpressurized system (**Figure 5**), the tank is open and vented to the atmosphere. The second pipe directed from the collectors to the top of the drain-back tank is to allow air to fill the collectors during drain-back.

As the collector loop is isolated from the potable water, no valves are needed to actuate draining, and scaling is not a problem; however, the collector array and exterior piping must be adequately sloped to drain completely. Freeze protection is inherent

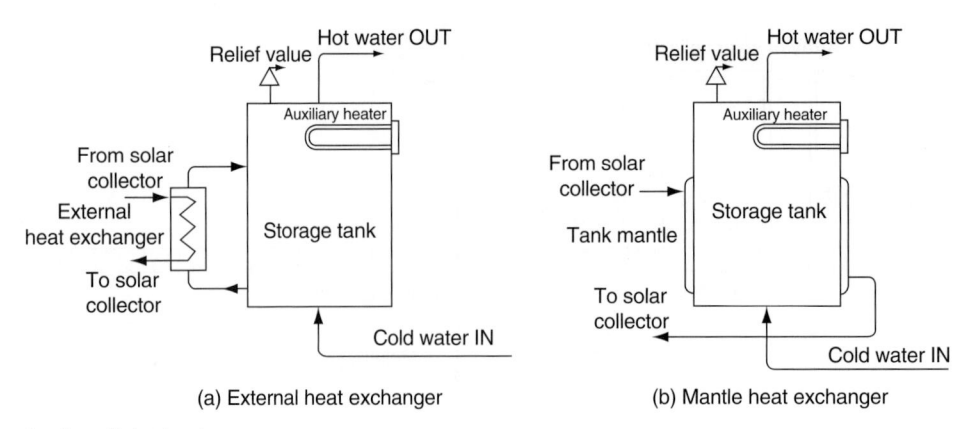

Figure 4 External and mantle heat exchangers.

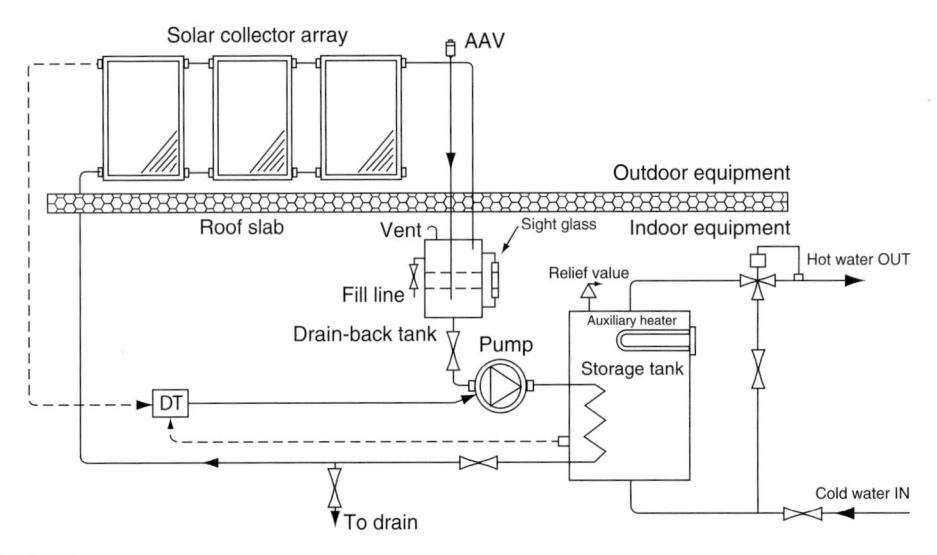

Figure 5 Drain-back system.

with the drain-back system because the collectors and the piping above the roof are empty whenever the pump is not running. A disadvantage of this system is that a pump with high static lift capability is required to fill the collector when the system starts up [1].

In drain-back systems, there is a possibility that the collectors will be drained during periods of insolation; it is therefore important to select collectors that can withstand prolonged periods of stagnation (no fluid) conditions. Such a case can occur when there is no load to meet and the storage tank reaches such a temperature that would not allow the differential thermostat to switch on the solar pump.

An alternative design to the one shown in **Figure 5**, which is suitable for small systems, is to have an open system (without a heat exchanger) and drain the water directly in the storage tank.

3.13.1.3 Air–Water Heating Systems

Air systems are indirect water heating systems because air is circulated through air collectors and via ductworks is directed to an air-to-water heat exchanger. In the heat exchanger, heat is transferred to the potable water, which is also circulated through the heat exchanger and returned to the storage tank. **Figure 6** shows a schematic diagram of a double storage tank system. This type of system is the most common one, because air systems are generally used for preheating domestic hot water and thus a separate tank with an auxiliary heater is needed for increasing the temperature of the water to the required level.

The advantages of this system are that air does not need to be protected from freezing or boiling, is noncorrosive, does not suffer from heat transfer fluid degradation, and is free. In addition, the system is more cost effective as no safety values and expansion vessel are required. The disadvantages are that air handling equipment (ducts and fans) need more space than piping and pumps, air leaks are difficult to detect, and parasitic power consumption (electricity used to drive the fans) is generally higher than that of liquid systems [1].

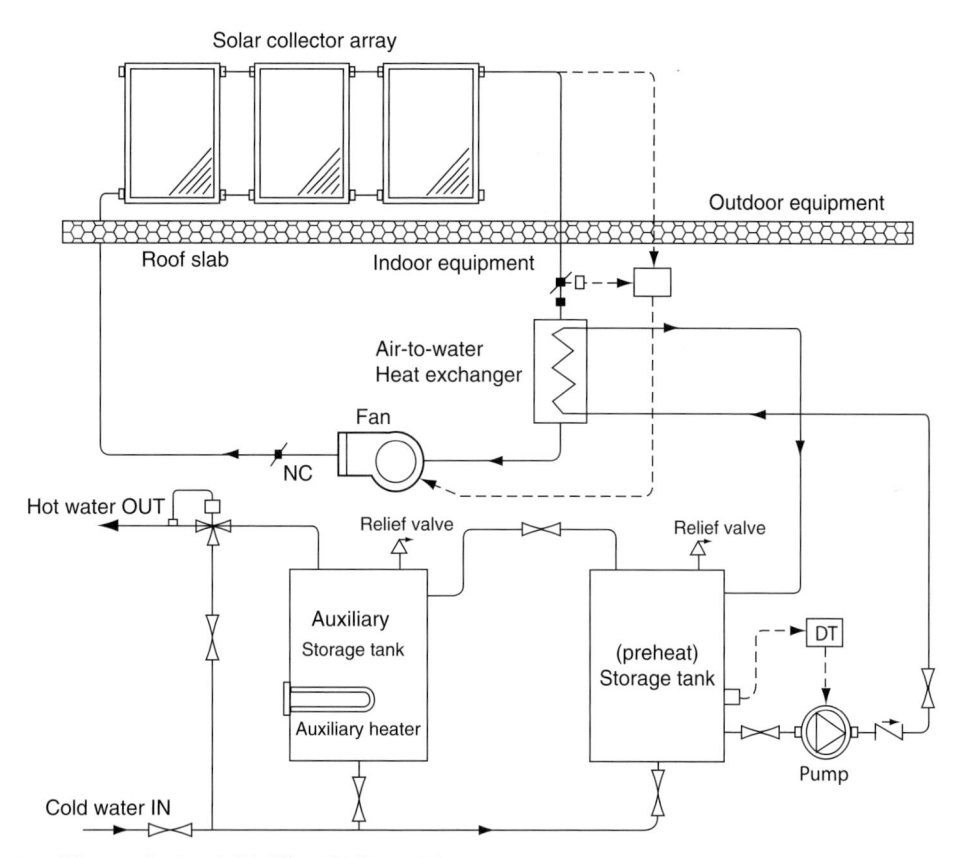

Figure 6 Air system. NC, normally closed. DT, differential thermostat.

3.13.2 Space Heating and Service Hot Water

Space heating systems are very similar to active water heating systems. The same design principles apply to both systems as described in the previous section and are therefore not repeated. The most common heat transfer fluids are water, water and antifreeze mixtures, and air. Although it is technically possible to construct a solar heating or cooling system that can satisfy fully the design load of a building, such a system would not be viable since it would be oversized most of the time. The size of the solar system is usually determined by a life-cycle cost analysis.

Active solar space systems use collectors to heat a fluid, storage units to store solar energy until needed, and distribution equipment to provide the solar energy to the heated spaces in a controlled manner. In addition, a complete system utilizes pumps or fans for transferring the energy to the storage or to the load, which require a continuous availability of nonrenewable energy, generally in the form of electricity.

The load can be space cooling, heating, or a combination with hot water supply. When it is combined with conventional heating equipment, solar heating provides the same levels of comfort, temperature stability, and reliability as conventional systems.

In solar systems, the collectors during daytime absorb solar energy, which is stored using a suitable fluid. When heat is required in the building, it is taken from the storage. The control of the solar system is exercised by differential temperature controllers (DTCs), described in Section 3.13.6. In locations where freezing conditions may occur, a low-temperature sensor is installed on the collector, which activates the solar pump when a preset temperature is reached. This process wastes some stored heat, but it prevents costly damages to the solar collectors. Alternatively, the systems described in the previous section, such as the drain-down and drain-back systems, can be used depending on whether the system is closed or open.

Solar cooling of buildings is an attractive idea as the cooling loads and availability of solar radiation are in phase. In addition, the combination of solar cooling and heating greatly improves the use factors of collectors as compared to heating alone. Solar air conditioning can be accomplished mainly by two types of systems: absorption and adsorption (desiccant) cycles. Some of these cycles are also used in solar refrigeration systems. It should be noted that the same solar collector array is used for both space heating and cooling systems when both are present.

A review of the various solar heating and cooling systems is presented by Hahne [3], and a review of solar and low-energy cooling technologies is presented by Florides et al. [4].

The solar systems usually have five basic modes of operation [1], depending on the existing conditions of the system at a particular time:

1. When solar energy is available and heat is not required in the building, solar energy is added to the storage.
2. When solar energy is available and heat is required in the building, solar energy is used to supply the building load demand.
3. When solar energy is not available, heat is required in the building, and the storage unit has stored energy, the stored energy is used to supply the building load demand.
4. When solar energy is not available, heat is required in the building, and the storage unit has been depleted, auxiliary energy is used to supply the building load demand.
5. When the storage unit is fully heated, there are no loads to meet and the collector is absorbing heat, solar energy is discarded.

The last mode is achieved through the operation of pressure relief valves. In the case of air collectors where the stagnant temperature is not detrimental to the collector materials, the flow of air is turned off and the collector temperature rises until the absorbed energy is dissipated to the environment by thermal losses.

In addition to the operation modes outlined above, the solar system may also provide domestic hot water. The operation of the system is usually controlled by thermostats. So depending on the load of each service, that is, heating, cooling, or hot water, the thermostat controlling the operation mode gives the signal to operate a pump when needed, provided that the collector temperature is higher than that of the storage. By using the thermostats, it is possible to combine modes, that is, to operate in more than one mode at a time. Some kinds of systems do not allow direct heating from the solar collectors to building but always transfer heat from the collectors to the storage whenever this is available and from the storage to the load whenever this is needed.

In Europe, solar heating systems for combined space and water heating are known as combisystems and the storage tanks of these systems are called combistores. Many of these combistores have one or more heat exchangers immersed directly in the storage fluid. The immersed heat exchangers are used for various functions such as charging via solar collectors or a boiler and discharging for domestic hot water and space heating.

For combisystems, the heat store is the key component, since it is used as a short-term store for solar energy and as a buffer store for the fuel or wood boiler. The storage medium used in solar combistores is usually the water of the space heating loop and not the tap water used in conventional solar domestic hot water stores. The tap water is heated up on demand by passing it through a heat exchanger, which can be placed either inside or outside the tank containing the water of the heating loop. When the heat exchanger is in direct contact with the storage medium, the temperature of the tap water at the start of the draw-off is identical to that of the water inside the store. The tap water volume inside the heat exchanger can vary from a few liters, for immersed heat exchangers, to several hundred liters for a tank-in-tank store.

Three typical combistores are shown in **Figure 7**. In the first type (**Figure 7(a)**), an immersed heat exchanger mounted on the whole inside surface of the mantle and top of the store is used. In the second type (**Figure 7(b)**), the water is heated with the natural circulation (thermosyphoning) heat exchanger that is mounted in the upper part of the store. The third case (**Figure 7(c)**) is called the tank-in-tank type. In this type, a conical hot water vessel is placed inside the main tank and its bottom part is almost reaching the bottom of the store. Typical heat exchanger tap water volumes for the three tank types are 15, 10, and 150–200 l, respectively [5].

In the initial stages of design of a solar space heating system, a number of factors need to be considered. Among the first ones are whether the system would be direct or indirect and whether a different fluid will be used in the solar system and the heat delivery system. Generally speaking, the designer must be aware that the presence of a heat exchanger in a system imposes a reduction of 5–10% in the effective energy delivered to the system. This is usually translated as an extra percentage of collector area to allow the system to deliver the same quantity of energy as a system without a heat exchanger.

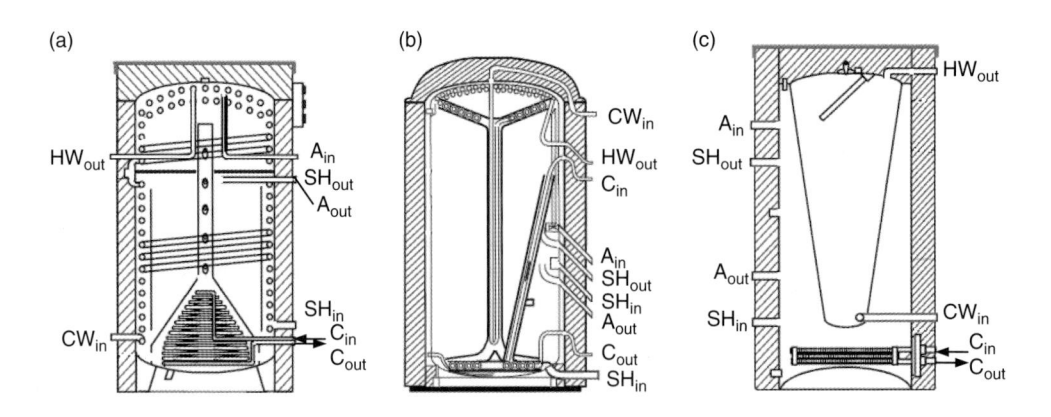

Figure 7 Schematic of three typical combistores: (a) immersed heat exchanger, (b) natural circulation heat exchanger, and (c) tank-in-tank heat exchanger. A, auxiliary; C, collector; CW, cold water; HW, hot water; SH, space heating. Adapted from Druck H and Hahne E (1998) Test and comparison of hot water stores for solar combisystems. *Proceedings of EuroSun98 – The Second ISES-Europe Solar Congress on CD-ROM.* Portoroz, Slovenia.

Another important parameter to consider is the time matching of the load and the solar energy input. The energy requirements of a building are not constant over the annual seasonal cycle. For the Northern Hemisphere, heating requirements start at about October, and the maximum heating load is during January or February. The heating season ends at about the end of April. Depending on the latitude, cooling requirements start in May, the maximum is about the end of July, and the cooling season ends at about the end of September. The domestic hot water requirements are almost constant throughout the year with some small variations due to changes in water supply temperature. Although it is possible to design a system that could cover the total thermal load requirements of a building, a very large collector area and storage would be required. Therefore, such a system would not be economically viable, as the system would, for most time of the year, collect energy that would not be possible to use.

Since the load is not constant but varies throughout the year, a space heating system would be inoperative during many months of the year. This could create overheating problems in the solar collectors during summertime. To avoid it, a solar space heating system needs to be combined with solar space cooling so as to fully utilize the system throughout the year. Solar heating systems are examined in this section, whereas solar cooling systems are examined in Section 3.13.3.

A space heating system can use either air or liquid collectors, but the energy delivery system may use the same medium or a different one. Usually air systems use air for all the processes, that is, collection, storage, and delivery. Liquid systems use water or water and antifreeze solution for collection, water for storage, and finally, water (e.g., floor heating system) or air (e.g., water-to-air heat exchanger and air handling unit) for the heat delivery process.

There are many variations of systems used for both solar space heating and service hot water production. The basic configuration is similar to that of the solar water heating systems outlined in Section 3.13.1. When used for both solar space heating and hot water production, these systems have independent control of the solar collector–storage and storage–auxiliary load loops. This allows solar-heated water to be added to the storage at the same time that hot water is removed from it to meet the building loads. Usually, a bypass is provided around the storage tank, which can be of considerable size, to avoid heating it with auxiliary energy.

3.13.2.1 Air Systems

A schematic of a basic solar air heating system, with a pebble bed storage unit and an auxiliary heating source, is shown in **Figure 8**. In this case, the various operation modes are achieved by the use of the dampers shown. Usually, in air systems, it is not practical to have simultaneous addition and removal of energy from the storage. If the energy supplied from the collector or the storage is not adequate to meet the load, auxiliary energy can be used to top up the air temperature to cover the building load. When there is no sunshine and the storage tank is completely depleted, it is also possible to bypass the collector and the storage unit and use the auxiliary alone to provide the required heat (**Figure 8**). A more detailed schematic of an air space heating system incorporating a subsystem for the supply of domestic hot water is shown in **Figure 9**. For the heating of water, an air-to-water heat exchanger is used with a preheat tank as shown. Details of controls are also shown in **Figure 9**. Furthermore, the system can use air collectors with a hydronic space heating system in an arrangement similar to that of the water heating air system described in Section 3.13.1.3 and shown in **Figure 6**.

Further to the advantages of using air as a heat transfer fluid, outlined in Section 3.13.1.3, another advantage is the high degree of stratification that occurs in the pebble bed, which leads to lower collector inlet temperatures. In addition, the working fluid is air and warm air heating systems are common in the building services industry. Control equipment are also readily available and can be obtained from the building services industry.

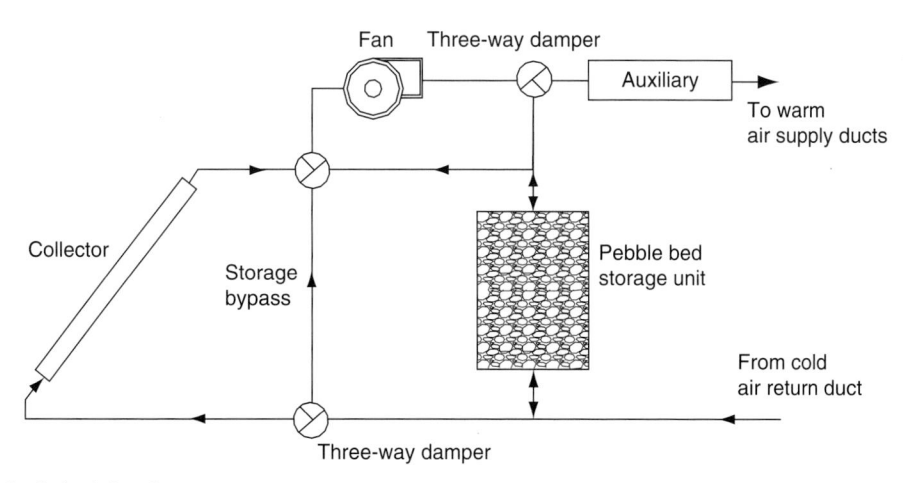

Figure 8 Schematic of a basic hot air system.

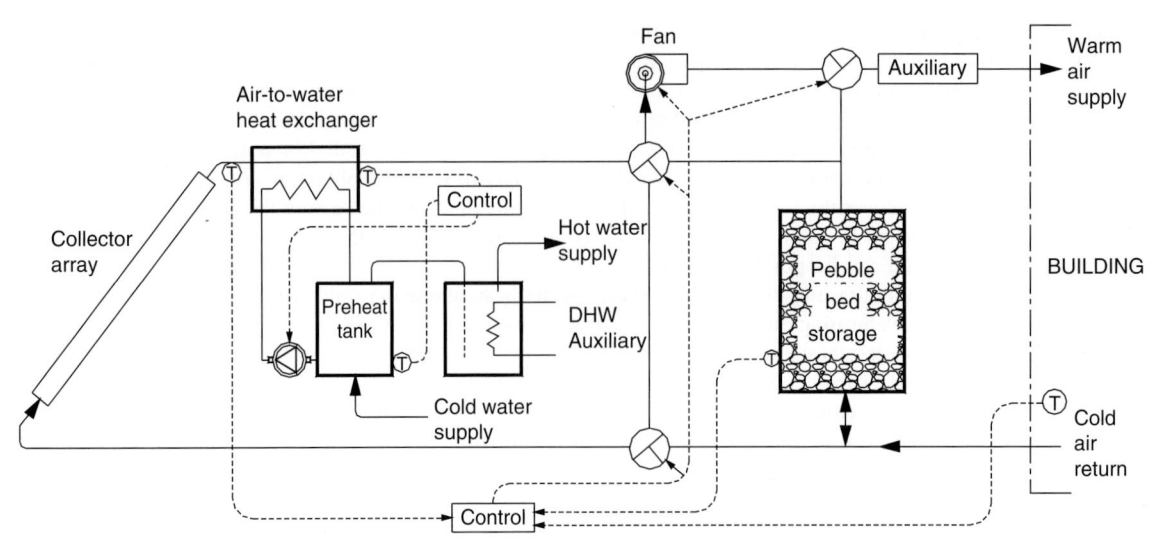

Figure 9 Detailed schematic of a solar air heating system. DHW, domestic hot water.

Further to the disadvantages of air systems analyzed in Section 3.13.1.3, additional disadvantages are the difficulty of adding solar air conditioning to the systems, the higher storage cost, and noisier operation. Another disadvantage is that air collectors are operated at lower fluid capacitance rates and thus with lower values of F_R than the liquid heating collectors.

Usually, air heating collectors used in space heating systems are operated at fixed airflow rates; therefore, the outlet temperature varies through the day. It is also possible to operate the collectors at a fixed outlet temperature by varying the flow rate. When flow rates are low, however, they result in reduced F_R and therefore reduced collector performance.

3.13.2.2 Water Systems

There are many variations of systems, which can be used for both solar space heating and domestic hot water production. The basic configurations are similar to those of the solar water heating systems outlined in Sections 3.13.1.1 and 3.13.1.2. When the systems are used for both space and hot water production, solar-heated water can be added to storage at the same time that hot water is removed from the storage to meet building loads. To accomplish this, the systems allow independent control of the solar collector–storage loop and the storage–auxiliary load loop. Usually, a bypass is provided around the storage tank, which can be of considerable size, to avoid heating it with auxiliary energy.

A schematic diagram of a solar space heating and hot water system is shown in **Figure 10**. Control of the solar heating system is based on two thermostats: the collector–storage temperature differential, and the room temperature. The collector operates with a differential thermostat as explained in Section 3.13.6. When the room thermostat senses a low temperature, the load pump is activated, drawing heated water from the main storage tank to meet the demand. If the energy stored in the tank cannot meet the load demand, the thermostat activates the auxiliary heater to supply the extra need. Usually, whenever the storage tank is depleted, the controllers actuate the three-way valves, shown in **Figure 10**, and direct all the flow through the auxiliary heater.

The solar heating system design shown in **Figure 10** is suitable for use in nonfreezing climates. To use such a system in locations where freezing may occur, provisions for complete and dependable drainage of the collector must be made. This can be done with

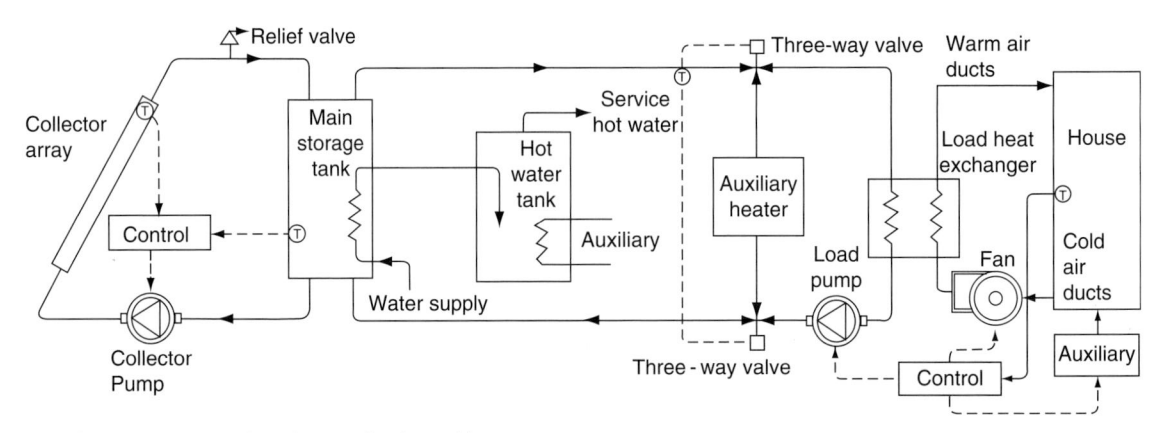

Figure 10 Schematic diagram of a solar space heating and hot water system.

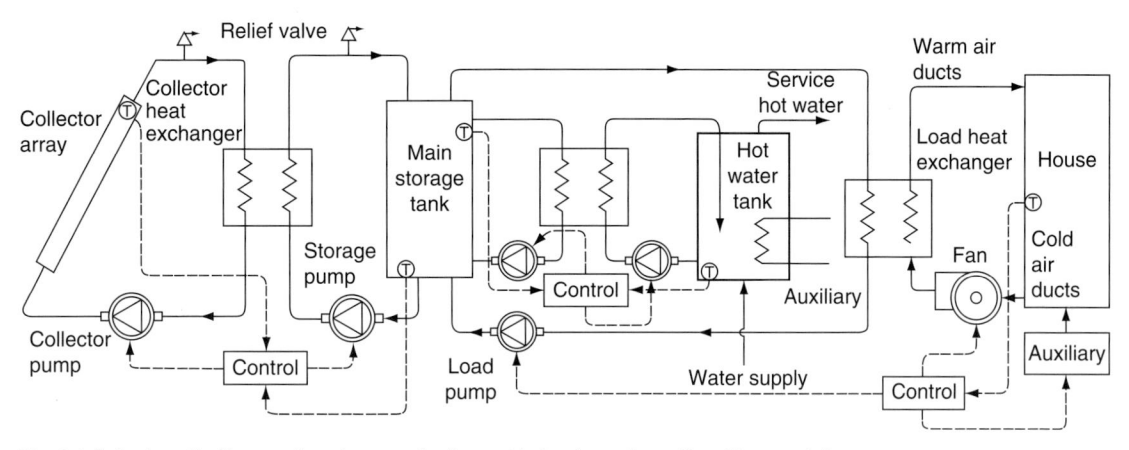

Figure 11 Detailed schematic diagram of a solar space heating and hot water system with antifreeze solution.

an automatic discharge valve, activated by the ambient air temperature, and an air vent that drains the collector water to waste. Alternatively, a drain-back system can be used in which the collector water is drained back to the storage whenever the solar pump stops. When this system drains, air enters the collector through a vent.

If the climate is characterized by frequent subfreezing temperatures, positive freeze protection with the use of an antifreeze solution in a closed collector loop is necessary. A detailed schematic of such a liquid-based system is shown in **Figure 11**. A collector heat exchanger is used between the collector and the storage tank, which allows the use of antifreeze solutions in the collector circuit. The most usual solutions are water and glycol. Relief valves are also required for dumping excess energy when overheating occurs. To 'top up' the energy available from the solar system, auxiliary energy is required. It should be noted that the connections to the storage tank should be done in such a way as to enhance stratification, that is, cold streams to be connected at the bottom and hot streams at the top. In this way, cooler water/fluid is supplied to the collectors that maintain the best possible efficiency. In this type of systems, the auxiliary is never used directly in the solar storage tank.

The use of a heat exchanger between the collector heat transfer fluid and the storage water imposes a temperature differential across the two sides, leading to a lower storage tank temperature. This has a negative impact on system performance; however, this system design is preferred in climates with frequent freezing conditions to avoid the danger of malfunction in a self-draining system.

A load heat exchanger is also required, as shown in **Figure 11**, to transfer energy from the storage tank to the heated spaces. This must be adequately sized to avoid excessive decrease in temperature with a corresponding increase in the tank and collector temperatures.

The advantages of liquid heating systems are the high collector F_R, the small storage volume requirement, and the relatively easy combination with an absorption air conditioner for cooling (see Section 3.13.3.5).

The thermal analysis of these systems is similar to that of the water heating systems. When both space heating and hot water needs are considered, then the rate of the energy removed from the storage tank to the load is Q_{ls}, that is, the space load supplied by solar energy through the load heat exchanger. The energy balance equation, which neglects stratification in the storage tank, is

$$(Mc_p)_s \frac{dT_s}{dt} = Q_u - Q_{ls} - Q_{lw} - Q_{tl} \quad [1]$$

M is the mass of stored water. c_p the specific heat of storage media (water), t is time, Q_{lw} the domestic water heating load supplied through the domestic water heat exchanger (kJ), Q_u the useful energy collected given by eqn [26], and Q_{tl} the energy lost from the storage tank given by an equation similar to eqn [2] but having T_s instead of T_R and UA of the storage tank, shown in Section 3.13.5.3.

The space heating load, Q_{hl}, can be estimated from the following equation (positive values only):

$$Q_{hl} = (UA)_l (T_R - T_a)^+ \quad [2]$$

where $(UA)_l$ is the space loss coefficient and area product.

The maximum rate of heat transferred across the load heat exchanger, $Q_{le(max)}$, is given by

$$Q_{le(max)} = \varepsilon_l (\dot{m}c_p)_a (T_s - T_R) \quad [3]$$

where ε_l is the load heat exchanger effectiveness, $(\dot{m}c_p)_a$ the air loop mass flow rate and specific heat product (W K^{-1}), and T_s the storage tank temperature (°C).

It should be noted that in eqn [3] the air side of the water-to-air heat exchanger is considered to be the minimum as the c_p of air (~1.05 kJ kg^{-1} °C^{-1}) is much lower than the c_p of water (~4.18 kJ kg^{-1} °C^{-1}).

The space load, Q_{ls}, is then given by (positive values only)

$$Q_{ls} = \left[\min\left(Q_{le(max)}, Q_{hl}\right)\right]^+ \quad [4]$$

The domestic water heating load, Q_w, can be estimated from

$$Q_w = (\dot{m}c_p)_w (T_w - T_{mu}) \quad [5]$$

where $(\dot{m}c_p)_w$ is the domestic water mass flow rate and specific heat product (W K^{-1}), T_w the required hot water temperature (usually 60 °C), and T_{mu} the makeup water temperature from mains (°C).

The domestic water heating load supplied by solar energy through the domestic water heat exchanger, Q_{lw}, of effectiveness ε_w can be estimated from

$$Q_{lw} = \varepsilon_w (\dot{m}c_p)_w (T_s - T_{mu}) \quad [6]$$

Finally, the auxiliary energy required, Q_{aux}, to cover the domestic water heating and space loads is given by (positive values only)

$$Q_{aux} = (Q_{hl} + Q_{aux,w} - Q_{tl} - Q_{ls})^+ \quad [7]$$

where the auxiliary energy required to cover the domestic water heating load, $Q_{aux,w}$, is given by (positive values only)

$$Q_{aux,w} = (\dot{m}c_p)_w (T_w - T_s)^+ \quad [8]$$

In all cases where a heat exchanger is used, there is a loss that can be estimated according to eqn [33] indicated in Section 3.13.5.3.

3.13.2.3 Location of Auxiliary Source

One important consideration concerning the storage tank is the decision for the best location of the auxiliary energy input. This is especially important in the case of solar space heating systems as bigger amounts of auxiliary energy are usually required and storage tank sizes are larger. For the maximum utilization of the energy supplied by the auxiliary source, its location should be at the load and not at the storage. The supply of auxiliary energy at the storage will undoubtedly increase the temperature of the fluid entering the collector, resulting in lower collector efficiency. When a water-based solar system is used in conjunction with a warm air space heating system, the most economical means of auxiliary energy supply is by the use of a fossil fuel-fired boiler. In case of bad weather, the boiler can take over the entire heating load.

When a water-based solar system is used in conjunction with a water space heating system or to supply the heated water to an absorption air-conditioning unit, the auxiliary heater can be located in the storage–load loop, either in series or in parallel with the storage, as illustrated in **Figure 12**. When auxiliary energy is used to boost the temperature of solar-heated water (**Figure 12(a)**),

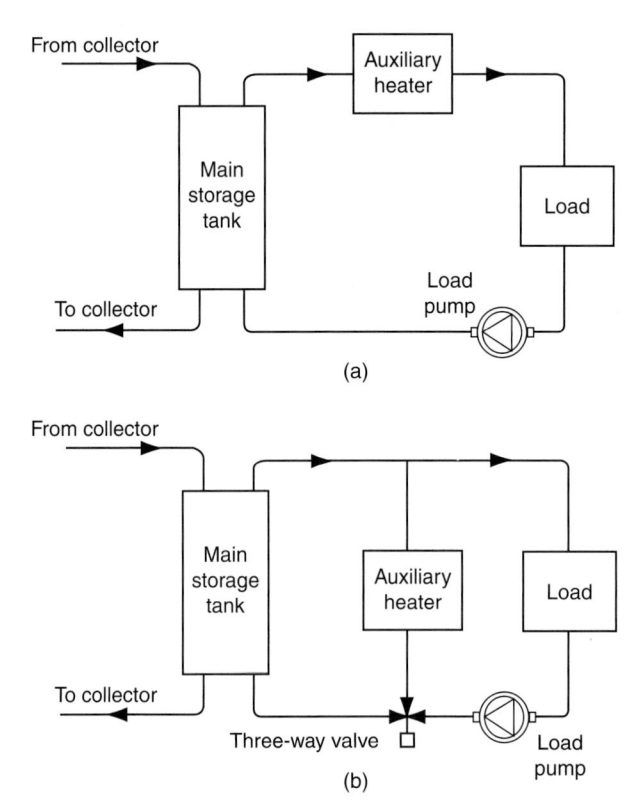

Figure 12 Auxiliary energy supply in water-based systems: (a) in series with load and (b) parallel with load.

maximum utilization of stored solar energy is achieved when the source is in series with the load. This way of connecting the auxiliary supply, however, also has the tendency of boosting the storage tank temperature because water returning from the load may be at a higher temperature than the storage. Increasing the storage temperature by auxiliary energy has the undesirable effect of lowering the collector effectiveness. This, however, depends on the operating temperature of the heating system. Therefore, a low-temperature system is required. This can be achieved with a water-to-air heat exchanger either centrally with an air handling unit or in a distributed way with individual fan coil units in each room. This system has the advantage of being connected easily with a space cooling system as for example with an absorption system (see Section 3.13.3.5). By using this type of system, solar energy can be used more effectively; with a high-temperature system, the hot water storage remains at high temperature, thus solar collectors work at lower efficiency.

Another possibility is to use underfloor heating or an all-water system employing the traditional heating radiators. In the latter case, provisions need to be made during the design stage to operate the system at low temperature, which implies the use of radiators of bigger size. Such a system is also suitable for retrofit applications.

Figure 12(b) illustrates an arrangement where it is possible to isolate the auxiliary heating circuit from the storage. Solar-heated storage water is used exclusively to meet the load demand when its temperature is adequate. When the storage temperature decreases below the required level, circulation through the storage tank is discontinued and hot water from the auxiliary heater is used exclusively to meet space heating. In this way of connecting the auxiliary supply, the undesirable increase of storage water temperature by auxiliary energy is avoided. However, it has the disadvantage that stored solar energy at lower temperature is not fully utilized and this energy may be lost from the storage (through jacket losses). To extract as much energy as possible from the storage tank, the same requirements for a low-temperature system should apply here as well.

3.13.2.4 Heat Pump Systems

Active solar energy systems can also be combined with heat pumps for domestic water heating and/or space heating. In residential heating, the solar system can be used in parallel with a heat pump, which supplies auxiliary energy when the sun is not available. In addition, for domestic water systems requiring high water temperatures, a heat pump can be placed in series with the solar storage tank.

A heat pump is a device that uses mechanical energy to pump heat from a low-temperature sink to a higher temperature one. Heat pumps are usually vapor-compression refrigeration machines, where the evaporator can take heat into the system at low temperature and the condenser can reject heat from the system at high temperature. In the heating mode, a heat pump delivers thermal energy from the condenser for space heating and can be combined with solar heating. In the cooling mode, the evaporator extracts heat from the air to be conditioned and rejects heat from the condenser to the atmosphere with solar energy not contributing to the energy for cooling. The performance characteristics of an integral-type solar-assisted heat pump are given by Huang and Chyng [6].

Electrically driven heat pump heating systems have two advantages compared to electric resistance heating or expensive fuels. The first advantage is that the heat pump's coefficient of performance (COP) is high enough to yield 9–15 MJ of heat for each kilowatt-hour of energy supplied to the compressor, which saves on purchase of energy; and the second advantage is that they can be used for air conditioning in the summer. Water-to-air heat pumps, which use solar-heated water from the storage tank as the evaporator energy source, are an alternative auxiliary heat source. Use of water in the system, however, involves freezing problems, which need to be taken into consideration.

Heat pumps have been used in combination with solar systems in residential and commercial applications. The additional complexity imposed from such a system and extra cost are offset by the high COP and the lower operating temperature of the collector subsystem. A schematic of a common residential-type heat pump system is shown in **Figure 13**.

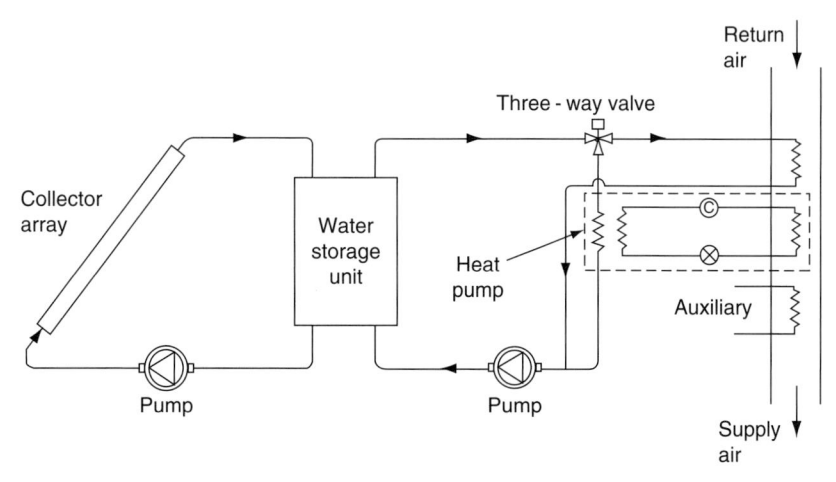

Figure 13 Schematic diagram of a domestic water-to-air heat pump system (series arrangement).

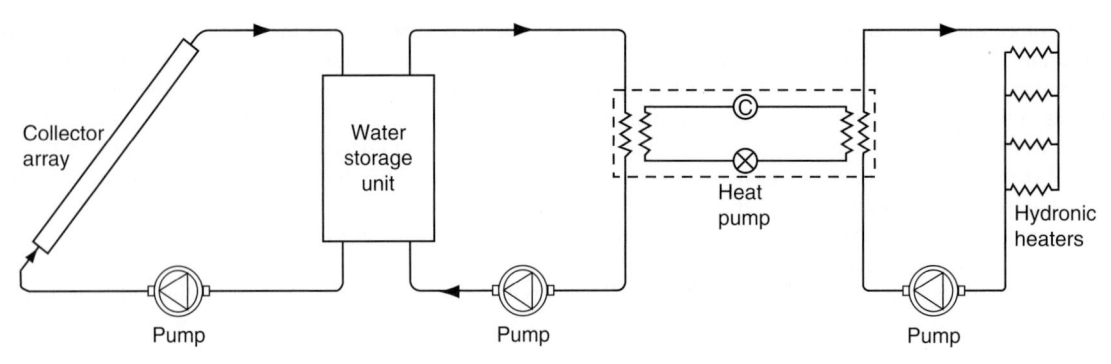

Figure 14 Schematic diagram of a domestic water-to-water heat pump system (parallel arrangement).

The arrangement in **Figure 13** is a series configuration and the heat pump evaporator is supplied with energy from the solar system. As can be seen, energy from the storage unit is directly supplied to the building when the temperature of the water in the storage tank is high. When the storage tank temperature cannot satisfy the load, the heat pump is operated and in doing so it benefits from the relatively high temperature of the solar system, which is higher than the ambient, thus increasing the heat pump's COP. A parallel arrangement is also possible where the heat pump serves as an independent auxiliary energy source for the solar system as shown in **Figure 14**. In this case, a water-to-water heat pump is used.

The series configuration is usually preferred to the parallel one as it allows all the collected solar power to be used, leaving the tank at low temperature. This allows the solar system to work more effectively the next day. In addition, the heat pump performance is higher with high evaporator temperatures. An added advantage of this system is that the solar system is conventional using liquid collectors and a water storage tank. A dual-source heat pump can also be used in which another form of renewable energy, such as a pellets boiler, can be used when the storage tank is completely depleted. In such a case, a control system switches to the use of the hotter source providing the best heat pump COP. Another possible design is to use an air solar heating system and an air-to-air heat pump.

3.13.3 Solar Cooling

The quest to accomplish a safe and comfortable environment has always been one of the main preoccupations of the human race. In ancient times, people used the experience gained over many years to utilize the available resources in the best possible way to achieve adequate living conditions. Central heating was pioneered by the Romans using double floors and passing the fumes of a fire through the floor cavity. Also in Roman times windows were covered for the first time with materials such as mica or glass. Thus, light was admitted in the house without letting in wind and rain [7]. The Iraqis, on the other hand, utilized the prevailing wind to take advantage of the night cool air and provide a cooler environment during the day [8]. In addition, running water was used to provide some evaporative cooling.

As late as the 1960s though, house comfort conditions were only for the few. From then onward, central air-conditioning systems became common in many countries due to the development of mechanical refrigeration and the rise of the standard of living. The oil crisis of the 1970s stimulated intensive research aimed at reducing energy costs. Also, global warming and ozone depletion and the escalating costs of fossil fuels, over the past few years, have forced governments and engineering bodies to reexamine the whole approach of building design and control. Energy conservation in the sense of fuel saving is also of great importance.

During recent years, research aimed at the development of technologies that can offer reductions in energy consumption, peak electrical demand, and energy costs without lowering the desired level of comfort conditions has intensified. Alternative cooling technologies are being developed that can be applied to residential and commercial buildings, in a wide range of weather conditions. These include night cooling with ventilation, evaporative cooling, desiccant cooling, slab cooling, and other cooling strategies. The design of buildings using low-energy cooling technologies, however, presents difficulties and requires advanced modeling and control techniques to ensure efficient operation.

Another method that can be used to reduce the energy consumption is ground cooling. This is based on the heat-loss dissipation from a building to the ground, which during the summer has a lower temperature than the ambient. This dissipation can be achieved either by direct contact of an important part of the building envelope with the ground or by blowing air into the building that has first been passed through an earth-to-air heat exchanger [9].

The role of designers and architects is very important, especially with respect to solar energy control, the utilization of thermal mass, and natural ventilation of buildings. In effective solar energy control, summer heat gains must be reduced while winter solar heat gains must be maximized. This can be achieved by proper orientation and shape of the building, the use of shading devices, and the selection of proper construction materials. Thermal mass, especially in hot climates with diurnal variation of ambient temperatures exceeding 10 °C, can be used to reduce the instantaneous high cooling loads, reduce energy consumption, and attenuate indoor temperature swings. Correct ventilation can enhance the roles of both solar energy control and thermal mass.

Reconsideration of the building structure, the readjustment of capital cost allocations, that is, investing in energy conservation measures that may have a significant influence on thermal loads, and improvements in equipment and maintenance can minimize the energy expenditure and improve thermal comfort.

In intermediate seasons in hot dry climates, processes such as evaporative cooling can offer energy conservation opportunities. However, in summertime, due to the high temperatures low-energy cooling technologies alone cannot satisfy the total cooling demand of domestic dwellings. For this reason, active cooling systems are required. Vapor-compression cooling systems are usually used, powered by electricity, which is expensive and whose production depends mainly on fossil fuel. In such climates, one of the sources abundantly available is solar energy, which could be used to power an active solar cooling system based on the absorption cycle. The problem with solar absorption machines is that they are expensive compared to vapor-compression machines and until recently they were not readily available in the small capacity range applicable to domestic cooling applications. Reducing the use of conventional vapor-compression air-conditioning systems will also reduce their effect on both global warming and ozone layer depletion.

The integration of the building envelope with an absorption system should offer better control of the internal environment. Two basic types of absorption units are available: ammonia–water (NH_3–H_2O) and lithium bromide–water (LiBr–H_2O) units. The latter are more suitable for solar applications since their operating (generator) temperature is lower and thus more readily obtainable with low-cost solar collectors [10].

Solar cooling of buildings is an attractive idea as the cooling loads and availability of solar radiation are in phase. In addition, the combination of solar cooling and heating greatly improves the use factors of collectors compared to heating alone. Solar air conditioning can be accomplished by three types of systems: absorption cycles, adsorption (desiccant) cycles, and solar-mechanical processes. Some of these cycles are also used in solar refrigeration systems and are described in the following sections.

Solar cooling can be considered for two related processes: to provide refrigeration for food and medicine preservation and to provide comfort cooling. Solar refrigeration systems usually operate at intermittent cycles and produce much lower temperatures (ice) than in air conditioning. When the same cycles are used for space cooling, they operate on continuous cycles. The cycles used for solar refrigeration are absorption and adsorption. During the cooling portion of the cycles, the refrigerant is evaporated and reabsorbed. In these systems, the absorber and generator are separate vessels. The generator can be an integral part of the collector, with refrigerant-absorbent solution in the tubes of the collector circulated by a combination of a thermosyphon and a vapor lift pump.

There are many options available that enable the integration of solar energy into the process of 'cold' production. Solar refrigeration can be accomplished by using either a thermal energy source supplied from a solar collector or electricity supplied from photovoltaics. This can be achieved by using either thermal adsorption or absorption units or conventional vapor-compression refrigeration equipment powered from photovoltaics. Solar refrigeration is used mainly to cool vaccine stores in areas with no mains electricity.

Photovoltaic refrigeration, although uses standard refrigeration equipment, which is an advantage, has not achieved widespread use because of the low efficiency and high cost of the photovoltaic cells. As photovoltaic-operated vapor-compression systems do not differ in operation from the mains-powered systems, these are not covered in this chapter and details are given only on the solar adsorption and absorption units with more emphasis on the latter.

Solar cooling is more attractive for southern countries of the Northern Hemisphere and northern countries of the Southern Hemisphere. Solar cooling systems are particularly applicable to large applications (e.g., commercial buildings) that have high cooling loads during large periods of the year. Such systems in combination with solar heating can make more efficient use of solar collectors, which would be idle during the cooling season. Generally, however, there is less experience with solar cooling than with solar heating systems.

Solar cooling systems can be classified into three categories: solar sorption cooling, solar-mechanical systems, and solar-related systems [4].

3.13.3.1 Solar Sorption Cooling

Sorbents are materials that have an ability to attract and hold other gases or liquids. This characteristic makes them very useful in chemical separation processes. Desiccants are sorbents that have a particular affinity for water. The process of attracting and holding moisture is described as either absorption or adsorption, depending on whether the desiccant undergoes a chemical change as it takes on moisture. Absorption changes the desiccant, as for example the table salt, which changes from a solid to a liquid as it absorbs moisture. Adsorption, on the other hand, does not change the desiccant except by the addition of the weight of water vapor, similar in some ways to a sponge soaking up water [11].

Compared to an ordinary cooling cycle, the basic idea of an absorption system is to avoid compression work. This is done by using a suitable working pair. The working pair consists of a refrigerant and a solution that can absorb the refrigerant.

Absorption systems are similar to vapor-compression air-conditioning systems but differ in the pressurization stage. In general, an evaporating refrigerant is absorbed by an absorbent on the low-pressure side. Combinations include LiBr–H_2O, where water vapor is the refrigerant, and NH_3–H_2O systems, where ammonia is the refrigerant [12].

Adsorption cooling is the other group of sorption air conditioners that utilizes an agent (the adsorbent) to adsorb the moisture from the air (or dry any other gas or liquid) and then uses the evaporative cooling effect to produce cooling. Solar energy can be used to regenerate the drying agent. Solid adsorbents include silica gels, zeolites, synthetic zeolites, activated alumina, carbons, and synthetic polymers [11]. Liquid adsorbents can be triethylene glycol solutions of lithium chloride and lithium bromide solutions.

These systems are explained in more detail in separate sections further on.

3.13.3.2 Solar-Mechanical Systems

These systems utilize a solar-powered prime mover to drive a conventional air-conditioning system. This can be done by converting solar energy into electricity by means of photovoltaic devices and then utilize an electric motor to drive a vapor compressor. The photovoltaic panels, however, have a low field efficiency of about 10–15%, depending on the type of cells used, which result in low overall efficiencies for the system.

The solar-powered prime mover can also be a Rankine engine. In a typical system, energy from the collector is stored, then transferred to a heat exchanger, and finally energy is used to drive the heat engine. The heat engine drives a vapor compressor, which produces a cooling effect at the evaporator. As shown in **Figure 15**, the efficiency of the solar collector decreases as the operating temperature increases, whereas the efficiency of the heat engine of the system increases as the operating temperature increases. The two efficiencies meet at a point (A in **Figure 15**) giving an optimum operating temperature for steady-state operation. The combined system has overall efficiencies between 17% and 23%.

Due to the diurnal cycle, both the cooling load and the storage tank temperature vary through the day. Therefore, designing such a system presents appreciable difficulties. When a Rankine heat engine is coupled with a constant-speed air conditioner, the output of the engine seldom matches the input required by the air conditioner. Therefore, auxiliary energy must be supplied when the engine output is less than that required, or otherwise, excess energy may be used to produce electricity for other purposes.

3.13.3.3 Solar-Related Air Conditioning

Some components of systems installed for the purpose of heating a building can also be used to cool it but without the direct use of solar energy. Examples of these systems can be heat pumps, rock bed regenerator, and alternative cooling technologies or passive systems. Heat pumps were examined in Section 3.13.2.4. The other two methods are briefly introduced here.

1. *Rock bed regenerator.* Rock beds (or pebble beds) storage units of solar air heating systems can be night-cooled during summer to store 'cold' for use the following day. This can be accomplished by passing outside air during the night when the temperature and humidity are low through an optional evaporative cooler, through the pebble bed, and to the exhaust. During the day, the building can be cooled by passing room air through the pebble bed. A number of applications using pebble beds for solar energy storage are given by Hastings [13]. For such systems, airflow rates should be kept to a minimum so as to minimize fan power requirements without affecting the performance of the pebble bed. Therefore, an optimization process should be followed as part of the design.
2. *Alternative cooling technologies or passive systems.* Passive cooling is based on the transfer of heat by natural means from a building to environmental sinks, such as clear skies, the atmosphere, the ground, and water. The transfer of heat can be by radiation, naturally occurring wind, airflow due to temperature differences, conduction to the ground, or conduction and convection to bodies of water. It is usually up to the designer to select the most appropriate type of technology for each application. The options depend on the climate type.

Adsorption and absorption systems are explained in more detail below.

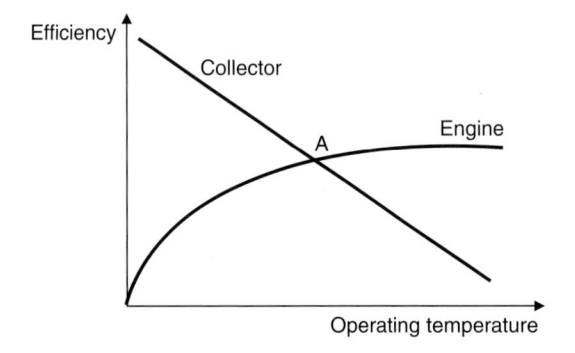

Figure 15 Collector and power cycle efficiencies as a function of operating temperature.

3.13.3.4 Adsorption Units

Porous solids, called adsorbents, can physically and reversibly adsorb large volumes of vapor, called the adsorbate. Although this phenomenon, called solar adsorption, was recognized in the nineteenth century, its practical application in the field of refrigeration is relatively recent. The concentration of adsorbate vapors in a solid adsorbent is a function of the temperature of the pair, that is, the mixture of adsorbent and adsorbate, and the vapor pressure of the adsorbate. The dependence of adsorbate concentration on temperature, under constant pressure conditions, makes it possible to adsorb or desorb the adsorbate by varying the temperature of the mixture. This forms the basis of the application of this phenomenon in the solar-powered intermittent vapor sorption refrigeration cycle.

An adsorbent–refrigerant working pair for a solar refrigerator requires the following characteristics:

1. a refrigerant with a large latent heat of evaporation,
2. a working pair with high thermodynamic efficiency,
3. a small heat of desorption under the envisaged operating pressure and temperature conditions, and
4. a low thermal capacity.

H_2O-NH_3 has been the most widely used sorption refrigeration pair and research has been undertaken to utilize the pair for solar-operated refrigerators. The efficiency of such systems is limited by the condensing temperature, which cannot be lowered without the introduction of advanced and expensive technology. For example, cooling towers or desiccant beds have to be used to produce cold water to condensate ammonia at lower pressure. Among the other disadvantages inherent in using water and ammonia as the working pair are the heavy-gauge pipe and vessel walls required to withstand the high pressure, the corrosiveness of ammonia, and the problem of rectification, that is, removing water vapor from ammonia during generation. A number of different solid adsorption working pairs, such as zeolite–water, zeolite–methanol, and activated carbon–methanol, have been studied to find the one that performed better. The activated carbon–methanol working pair was found to perform the best [14].

Many cycles have been proposed for adsorption cooling and refrigeration [15]. The principle of operation of a typical system is indicated in **Figure 16**. The process followed at points from 1 to 9 of **Figure 16** is traced on the psychrometric chart depicted in **Figure 17**. Ambient air is heated and dried by a dehumidifier from point 1 to 2, regeneratively cooled by exhaust air from

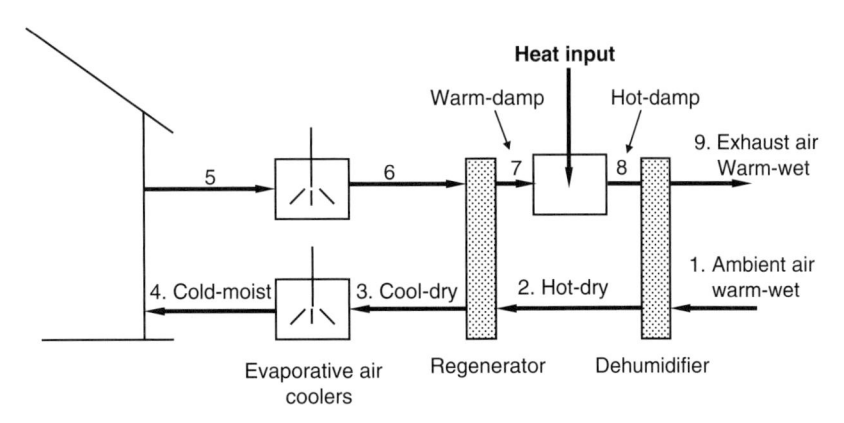

Figure 16 Schematic of a solar adsorption system.

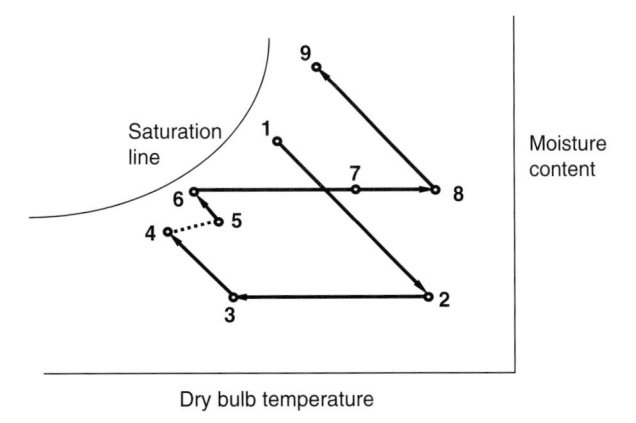

Figure 17 Psychrometric diagram of a solar adsorption process.

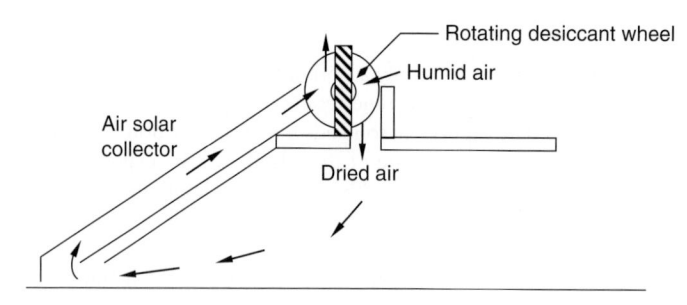

Figure 18 Solar adsorption cooling system.

point 2 to 3, evaporatively cooled from point 3 to 4, and introduced into the building. Exhaust air from the building is evaporatively cooled from point 5 to 6, heated to point 7 by the energy removed from the supply air in the regenerator, heated by solar or other source to point 8, and then passed through the dehumidifier where it regenerates the desiccant.

The selection of the adsorbing agent depends on the size of the moisture load and application.

Rotary solid desiccant systems are the most common for continuous removal of moisture from the air. The desiccant wheel rotates through two separate air streams. In the first stream, the process air is dehumidified by adsorption, which does not change the physical characteristics of the desiccant, while in the second stream, the reactivation or regeneration air, which is first heated, dries the desiccant. A schematic of a possible solar-powered adsorption system is illustrated in **Figure 18**.

When the drying agent is a liquid, such as triethylene glycol, the agent is sprayed into an absorber where it picks up moisture from the air inside the building. Then it is pumped through a sensible heat exchanger to a separation column where it is sprayed into a stream of solar-heated air. The high-temperature air removes water from the glycol, which then returns to the heat exchanger and the absorber. Heat exchangers are provided to recover sensible heat, maximize the temperature in the separator, and minimize the temperature in the absorber. This type of cycle is marketed commercially and used in hospitals and large installations [16].

The energy performance of these systems depends on the system configuration, geometries of dehumidifiers, properties of adsorbent agent, and other factors, but generally the COP of this technology is around 1.0. It should be noted, however, that in hot/dry climates the desiccant part of the system may not be required.

Because complete physical property data are available for only a few potential working pairs, the optimum performance remains unknown at the moment. In addition, the operating conditions of a solar-powered refrigerator, that is, generator and condenser temperature, vary with its geographical location [14].

The development of three solar/biomass adsorption air-conditioning refrigeration systems is presented by Critoph [17]. All systems use active carbon–ammonia adsorption cycles and the principle of operation and performance prediction of the systems are given.

Thorpe [18] presented an adsorption heat pump system that uses ammonia with granular active adsorbate. A high COP is achieved and the cycle is suitable for the use of heat from high-temperature (150–200 °C) solar collectors for air conditioning.

3.13.3.5 Absorption Units

Absorption is the process of attracting and holding moisture by substances called desiccants. Desiccants are sorbents (i.e., materials that have an ability to attract and hold other gases or liquids) that have a particular affinity for water. During absorption, the desiccant undergoes a chemical change as it takes on moisture; an example we have seen before is table salt, which changes from a solid to a liquid as it absorbs moisture. The characteristic of the binding of desiccants to moisture makes them very useful in chemical separation processes [11].

Absorption machines are thermally activated and they do not require high input shaft power. Therefore, where power is unavailable or expensive, or where there is waste, geothermal, or solar heat available, absorption machines could provide reliable and quiet cooling. Absorption systems are similar to vapor-compression air-conditioning systems but differ in the pressurization stage. In general, an absorbent, on the low-pressure side, absorbs an evaporating refrigerant. The most usual combinations of fluids include $LiBr–H_2O$, where water vapor is the refrigerant, and $NH_3–H_2O$ systems, where ammonia is the refrigerant.

Absorption refrigeration system is based on extensive development and experience in the early years of the refrigeration industry, in particular for ice production. From the beginning, its development has been linked to periods of high energy prices. Recently, however, there has been a great resurgence of interest in this technology not only because of the rise in the energy prices but also mainly due to the social and scientific awareness about the environmental degradation, which is related to the energy generation.

The pressurization is achieved by dissolving the refrigerant in the absorbent, in the absorber section (**Figure 19**). Subsequently, the solution is pumped to a high pressure with an ordinary liquid pump. The addition of heat in the generator is used to separate the low-boiling refrigerant from the solution. In this way, the refrigerant vapor is compressed without the need of large amounts of mechanical energy that the vapor-compression air-conditioning systems demand.

The remainder of the system consists of a condenser, expansion valve, and evaporator, which function in a similar way as in a vapor-compression air-conditioning system.

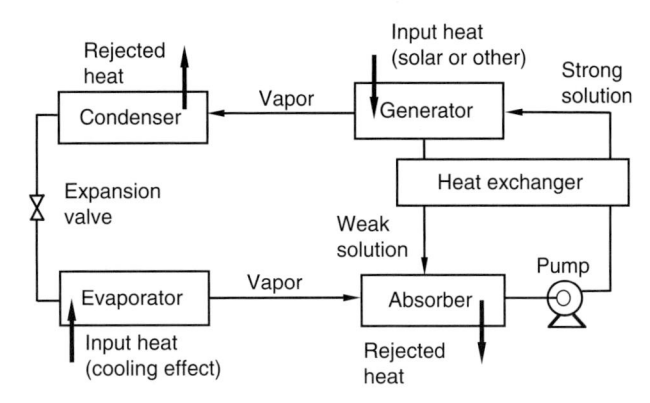

Figure 19 Basic principle of the absorption air-conditioning system.

3.13.3.6 Lithium–Water Absorption Systems

The LiBr–H$_2$O system operates at a generator temperature in the range of 70–95 °C with water used as a coolant in the absorber and condenser and has COP higher than that of the NH$_3$–H$_2$O systems. The COP of this system is between 0.6 and 0.8. A disadvantage of the LiBr–H$_2$O systems is that their evaporator cannot operate at temperatures much below 5 °C since the refrigerant is water vapor. Commercially available absorption chillers for air-conditioning applications usually operate with a solution of LiBr in water and use steam or hot water as the heat source. In the market, two types of chillers are available, the single- and the double-effect chillers.

The single-effect absorption chiller is mainly used for building cooling loads, where chilled water is required at 6–7 °C. The COP will vary to a small extent with the heat source and the cooling water temperatures. Single-effect chillers can operate with hot water temperature ranging from about 70 to 150 °C when water is pressurized [19].

The double-effect absorption chiller has two stages of generation to separate the refrigerant from the absorbent. Thus, the temperature of the heat source needed to drive the high-stage generator is essentially higher than that needed for the single-effect machine and is in the range of 155–205 °C. Double-effect chillers have a higher COP of about 0.9–1.2 [20]. Although double-effect chillers are more efficient than the single-effect machines, they are obviously more expensive to purchase. However, every individual application must be considered on its own merits since the resulting savings in the capital cost of the single-effect units can largely offset the extra capital cost of the double-effect chiller.

The Carrier Corporation pioneered LiBr absorption chiller technology in the United States, with early single-effect machines introduced around 1945. Due to the success of the product, soon other companies joined the production. The absorption business thrived until 1975. Then the generally held belief that natural gas supplies were lessening led to US government regulations prohibiting the use of gas in new constructions and together with the low cost of electricity led to the declination of the absorption refrigeration market [21]. Today, the major factor influencing the decision on the type of system to install for a particular application is the economic trade-off between the different cooling technologies. Absorption chillers typically cost less to operate, but they cost more to purchase than vapor-compression units. The payback period depends strongly on the relative cost of fuel and electricity assuming that the operating cost for the needed heat is less than the operating cost for electricity.

The technology was exported to Japan from the United States early in the 1960s, and the Japanese manufacturers set a research and development program to improve further the absorption systems. The program led to the introduction of the direct-fired double-effect machines with improved thermal performance.

Today, gas-fired absorption chillers deliver 50% of commercial space cooling load worldwide but less than 5% in the United States, where electricity-driven vapor-compression machines carry the majority of the load [21].

Many researchers have developed solar-assisted absorption refrigeration systems. Most of them have been produced as experimental units and computer codes were written to simulate the systems. Some of these designs are presented here.

Hammad and Audi [22] described the performance of a nonstorage, continuous, solar-operated absorption refrigeration cycle. The maximum ideal COP of the system was determined to be equal to 1.6, while the peak actual COP was determined to be equal to 0.55.

Haim *et al.* [23] performed a simulation and analysis of two open-cycle absorption systems. Both systems comprise a closed absorber and evaporator as in conventional single-stage chillers. The open part of the cycle is the regenerator, used to reconcentrate the absorber solution by means of solar energy. The analysis was performed with a computer code developed for modular simulation of absorption systems under varying cycle configurations (open- and closed-cycle systems) and with different working fluids. Based on the specified design features, the code calculates the operating parameters in each system. The results indicate that there is a definite performance advantage of the direct regeneration system over the indirect one.

Hawlader *et al.* [24] developed a LiBr absorption cooling system using an 11 × 11 m collector/regenerator unit. They also have developed a computer model, which they validated against real experimental values with good agreement. The experimental results showed a regeneration efficiency varying between 38% and 67% and the corresponding cooling capacities ranged from 31 to 72 kW.

Ghaddar et al. [25] presented the modeling and simulation of a solar absorption system for Beirut. The results showed that, for each ton of refrigeration, it is required to have a minimum collector area of 23.3 m^2 with an optimum water storage capacity ranging from 1000 to 1500 l for the system to operate solely on solar energy for about 7 h day^{-1}. The monthly solar fraction of total energy use in cooling is determined as a function of solar collector area and storage tank capacity. The economic analysis performed showed that the solar cooling system is marginally competitive only when it is combined with domestic water heating.

Erhard and Hahne [26] simulated and tested a solar-powered absorption cooling machine. The main part of the device is an absorber/desorber unit, which is mounted inside a concentrating solar collector. Results obtained from field tests are discussed and compared with the results obtained from a simulation program developed for this purpose.

Hammad and Zurigat [27] described the performance of a 1.5 ton solar cooling unit. The unit comprises a 14 m^2 flat-plate solar collector system and five shell-and-tube heat exchangers. The unit was tested in April and May in Jordan. The maximum value obtained for actual COP was 0.85.

Zinian and Ning [28] described a solar absorption air-conditioning system that uses an array of 2160 evacuated tubular collectors of total aperture area of 540 m^2 and a LiBr absorption chiller. Thermal efficiencies of the collector array are 40% for space cooling, 35% for space heating, and 50% for domestic water heating. It was found that the cooling efficiency of the entire system is around 20%.

Finally, Ameel et al. [29] gave performance predictions of alternative low-cost absorbents for open-cycle absorption using a number of absorbents. The most promising of the absorbents considered was a mixture of two elements, lithium chloride and zinc chloride. The estimated capacities per unit absorber area were 50–70% less than those of LiBr systems.

A new family of integrated compound parabolic collector (ICPC) designs was developed by Winston et al. [30], which allows a simple manufacturing approach to be used and solves many of the operational problems of previous ICPC designs. A low concentration ratio is used that requires no tracking together with an off-the-shelf 20 ton double-effect LiBr direct-fired absorption chiller, modified to work with hot water. The new ICPC design with the double-effect chiller was able to produce cooling energy for the building using a collector field that was about half the size of that required for a more conventional collector and chiller.

A method to design, construct, and evaluate the performance of a single-stage LiBr–H$_2$O absorption machine is presented by Florides et al. [19]. In this, the necessary heat and mass transfer relations and appropriate equations describing the properties of the working fluids are specified. Information on designing the heat exchangers of the LiBr–H$_2$O absorption unit is also presented. Single-pass vertical tube heat exchangers have been used for the absorber and the evaporator. The solution heat exchanger was designed as a single-pass annulus heat exchanger. The condenser and the generator were designed using horizontal tube heat exchangers. Another valuable source of LiBr–H$_2$O system properties is with program EES (Engineering Equation Solver), which can also be used to solve the equations required to design such a system [31].

If power generation efficiency is considered, the thermodynamic efficiency of absorption cooling is very similar to that of the electrically driven compression refrigeration system; the benefits of the solar systems, however, are very obvious when environmental pollution is considered. This is accounted for by the total equivalent warming impact (TEWI) of the system. As proved by Florides et al. [32] in a study of domestic size systems, the TEWI of the absorption system was 1.2 times smaller than that of the conventional system.

3.13.3.6.1 Thermodynamic analysis

Compared to an ordinary cooling cycle, the basic idea of an absorption system is to avoid compression work. This is done by using a suitable working pair. The working pair consists of a refrigerant and a solution that can absorb the refrigerant. A more detailed schematic of the LiBr–H$_2$O absorption system is shown in **Figure 20** [33], whereas a schematic presentation of a pressure–temperature diagram is illustrated in **Figure 21**.

The main components of an absorption refrigeration system are the generator, absorber, condenser, and evaporator. In the model shown in **Figure 20**, Q_G is the heat input rate from the heat source to the generator; Q_C and Q_A are the heat rejection rates from the condenser and the absorber to the heat sinks, respectively; and Q_E is the heat input rate from the cooling load to the evaporator. At point 1, the solution is rich in refrigerant and a pump (1–2) forces the liquid to the generator after passing it through a heat exchanger. The temperature of the solution in the heat exchanger is increased (2–3).

In the generator, thermal energy is added and the refrigerant boils off the solution. The refrigerant vapor (7) flows to the condenser, where heat is rejected as the refrigerant condenses. The condensed liquid (8) flows through a flow restrictor to the evaporator (9). In the evaporator, the heat from the load evaporates the refrigerant, which flows back to the absorber (10). A small portion of the refrigerant leaves the evaporator as liquid spillover (11). At the generator exit (4), the steam consists of absorbent–refrigerant solution, which is cooled in the heat exchanger. From points 6 to 1, the solution absorbs refrigerant vapor from the evaporator and rejects heat through a heat exchanger. This procedure can also be presented in a Duhring chart (**Figure 22**). This chart is a pressure–temperature graph where diagonal lines represent constant LiBr mass fraction, with the pure water line at the left.

For the thermodynamic analysis of the absorption system, the principles of mass conservation and the first and second laws of thermodynamics apply to each component of the system. Each component can be treated as a control volume with inlet and outlet streams, heat transfer, and work interactions. Mass conservation includes the mass balance of each material of the solution in the system. The governing equations of mass conservation for every kind of material for a steady-state and steady-flow system are the following [34]:

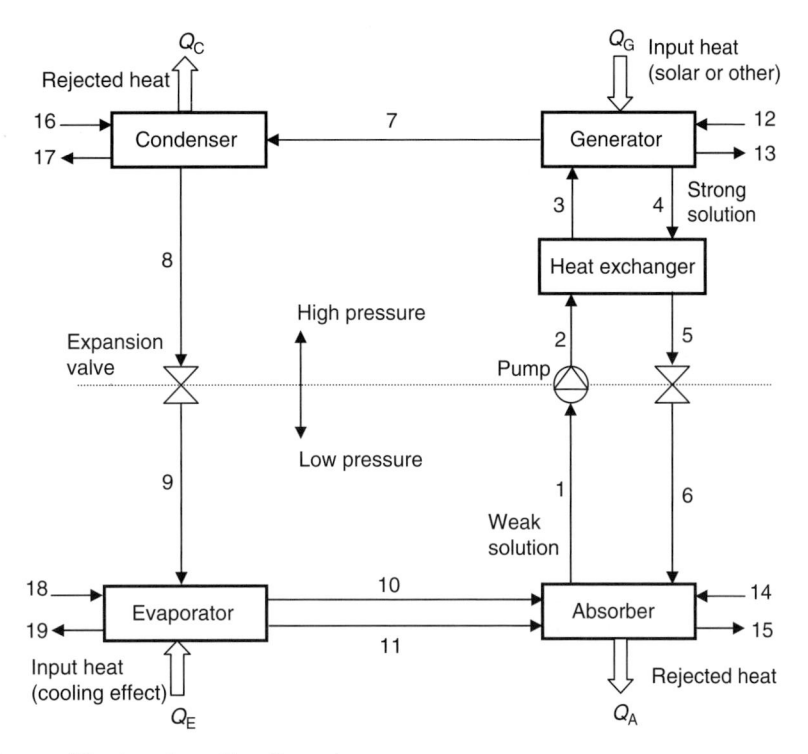

Figure 20 Schematic diagram of the absorption refrigeration system.

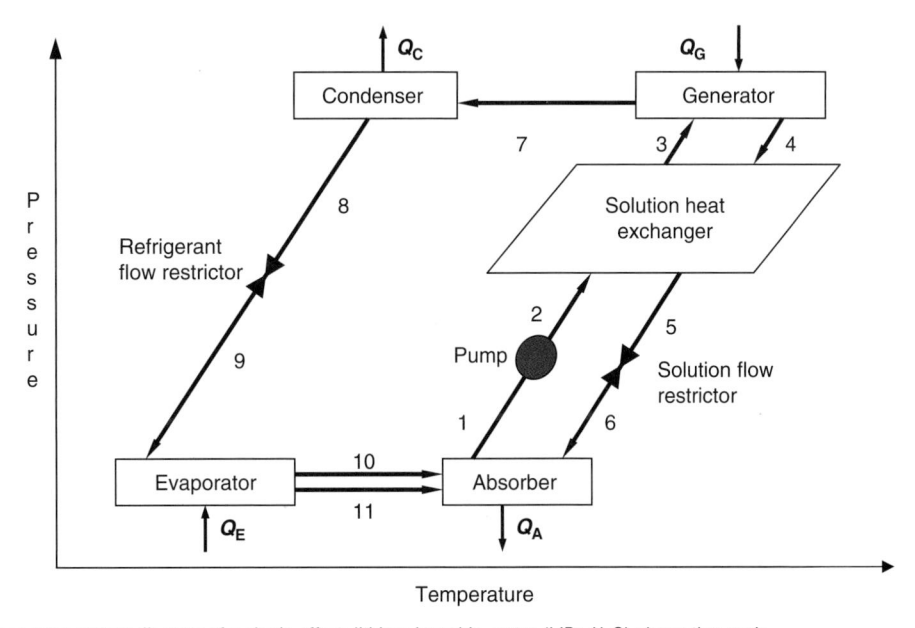

Figure 21 Pressure–temperature diagram of a single-effect, lithium bromide–water (LiBr–H$_2$O) absorption cycle.

$$\sum \dot{m}_i - \sum \dot{m}_o = 0 \qquad [9]$$

$$\sum (\dot{m}x)_i - \sum (\dot{m}x)_o = 0 \qquad [10]$$

where $\dot{m}$ is the mass flow rate and x the mass concentration of LiBr in the solution. The first law of thermodynamics yields the energy balance of each component of the absorption system as follows:

$$\sum (\dot{m}h)_i - \sum (\dot{m}h)_o + \left[\sum Q_i - \sum Q_o\right] + W = 0 \qquad [11]$$

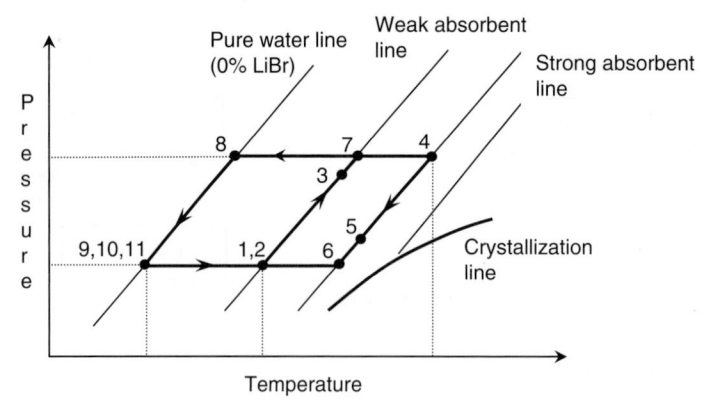

Figure 22 Duhring chart of the water–lithium bromide (H$_2$O–LiBr) absorption cycle.

Table 1 Energy and mass balance equations of absorption system components

System components	Mass balance equations	Energy balance equations
Pump	$\dot{m}_1 = \dot{m}_2,\ x_1 = x_2$	$w = \dot{m}_2 h_2 - \dot{m}_1 h_1$
Solution heat exchanger	$\dot{m}_2 = \dot{m}_3,\ x_2 = x_3$ $\dot{m}_4 = \dot{m}_5,\ x_4 = x_5$	$\dot{m}_2 h_2 + \dot{m}_4 h_4 = \dot{m}_3 h_3 + \dot{m}_5 h_5$
Solution expansion valve	$\dot{m}_5 = \dot{m}_6,\ x_5 = x_6$	$h_5 = h_6$
Absorber	$\dot{m}_1 = \dot{m}_6 + \dot{m}_{10} + \dot{m}_{11}$ $\dot{m}_1 x_1 = \dot{m}_6 x_6 + \dot{m}_{10} x_{10} + \dot{m}_{11} x_{11}$	$Q_A = \dot{m}_6 h_6 + \dot{m}_{10} h_{10} + \dot{m}_{11} h_{11} - \dot{m}_1 h_1$
Generator	$\dot{m}_3 = \dot{m}_4 + \dot{m}_7$ $\dot{m}_3 x_3 = \dot{m}_4 x_4 + \dot{m}_7 x_7$	$Q_G = \dot{m}_4 h_4 + \dot{m}_7 h_7 - \dot{m}_3 h_3$
Condenser	$\dot{m}_7 = \dot{m}_8,\ x_7 = x_8$	$Q_C = \dot{m}_7 h_7 - \dot{m}_8 h_8$
Refrigerant expansion valve	$\dot{m}_8 = \dot{m}_9,\ x_8 = x_9$	$h_8 = h_9$
Evaporator	$\dot{m}_9 = \dot{m}_{10} + \dot{m}_{11},\ x_9 = x_{10}$	$Q_E = \dot{m}_{10} h_{10} + \dot{m}_{11} h_{11} - \dot{m}_9 h_9$

An overall energy balance of the absorption system requires that the sum of the generator, evaporator, condenser, and absorber heat transfer must be zero. If it is assumed that the system is in steady state and that the pump is operating and environmental heat losses are neglected, the energy balance can be written as

$$Q_C + Q_A = Q_G + Q_E \quad [12]$$

The energy, mass concentrations, and mass balance equations of the various components of an absorption system are given in **Table 1** [33].

In addition to the above equations, the solution heat exchanger effectiveness is also required and is obtained from [34]

$$\varepsilon_{SHx} = \frac{T_4 - T_5}{T_4 - T_2} \quad [13]$$

The absorption system shown in **Figure 20** provides chilled water for cooling applications. Furthermore, the system can also supply hot water for heating applications by circulating the working fluids. The difference in the operation between the two applications is the operating temperature and pressure levels in the system. The useful output energy of the system for heating applications is the sum of the heat rejected from the absorber and the condenser, while the input energy is supplied to the generator. The useful output energy of the system for the cooling applications is the heat that is extracted from the environment from the evaporator, while the input energy is supplied to the generator [34, 35].

The cooling COP of the absorption system is defined as the heat load in the evaporator per unit of heat load in the generator and can be written as [34, 36]

$$COP_{cooling} = \frac{Q_E}{Q_G} = \frac{\dot{m}_{10} h_{10} + \dot{m}_{11} h_{11} - \dot{m}_9 h_9}{\dot{m}_4 h_4 + \dot{m}_7 h_7 - \dot{m}_3 h_3} = \frac{\dot{m}_{18}(h_{18} - h_{19})}{\dot{m}_{12}(h_{12} - h_{13})} \quad [14]$$

where h is the specific enthalpy of working fluid at each corresponding state point (kJ kg^{-1}).

The heating COP of the absorption system is the ratio of the combined heating capacity, obtained from the absorber and condenser, to the heat added to the generator, and can be written as [34, 36]

$$COP_{heating} = \frac{Q_C + Q_A}{Q_G} = \frac{(\dot{m}_7 h_7 - \dot{m}_8 h_8) + (\dot{m}_6 h_6 + \dot{m}_{10} h_{10} + \dot{m}_{11} h_{11} - \dot{m}_1 h_1)}{\dot{m}_4 h_4 + \dot{m}_7 h_7 - \dot{m}_3 h_3} = \frac{\dot{m}_{16}(h_{17} - h_{16}) + \dot{m}_{14}(h_{15} - h_{14})}{\dot{m}_{12}(h_{12} - h_{13})} \quad [15]$$

Therefore, from eqn [12] the COP for heating can also be written as

$$\text{COP}_{\text{heating}} = \frac{Q_G + Q_E}{Q_G} = 1 + \frac{Q_E}{Q_G} = 1 + \text{COP}_{\text{cooling}} \quad [16]$$

Equation [16] shows that the heating COP is in all cases greater than the cooling COP.

Exergy analysis can be used to calculate the system performance. This analysis is a combination of the first and second laws of thermodynamics and exergy is defined as the maximum amount of work potential of a material or an energy stream, in relation to the surrounding environment [33]. The exergy of a fluid stream can be defined as [37, 38]

$$\varepsilon = (h - h_o) - T_o(s - s_o) \quad [17]$$

where ε is the specific exergy of the fluid at temperature T (kJ kg^{-1}).

The terms h and s are the enthalpy and entropy of the fluid, whereas h_o and s_o are the enthalpy and entropy of the fluid at environmental temperature T_o (in all cases absolute temperature is used in Kelvin).

The availability loss in each component is calculated by

$$\Delta E = \sum \dot{m}_i E_i - \sum \dot{m}_o E_o - \left[\sum Q\left(1 - \frac{T_o}{T}\right)_i - \sum Q\left(1 - \frac{T_o}{T}\right)_o\right] + \sum W \quad [18]$$

where ΔE is the lost exergy or irreversibility that occurred in the process (kW).

The first two terms on the right-hand side of eqn [18] are the exergy of the inlet and outlet streams of the control volume. The third and fourth terms are the exergy associated with the heat transferred from the source maintained at a temperature T. The last term is the exergy of mechanical work added to the control volume. This term is negligible for absorption systems as the solution pump has very low power requirements.

The equivalent availability flow balance of the system is shown in **Figure 23** [39]. The total exergy loss of the absorption system is the sum of the exergy loss in each component and can be written as [40]

$$\Delta E_T = \Delta E_1 + \Delta E_2 + \Delta E_3 + \Delta E_4 + \Delta E_5 + \Delta E_6 \quad [19]$$

The second-law efficiency of the absorption system is measured by the exergetic efficiency, η_{ex}, which is defined as the ratio of the useful exergy gained from a system to that supplied to the system. Therefore, the exergetic efficiency of the absorption system for cooling is the ratio of the chilled water exergy at the evaporator to the exergy of the heat source at the generator and can be written as [40, 41]

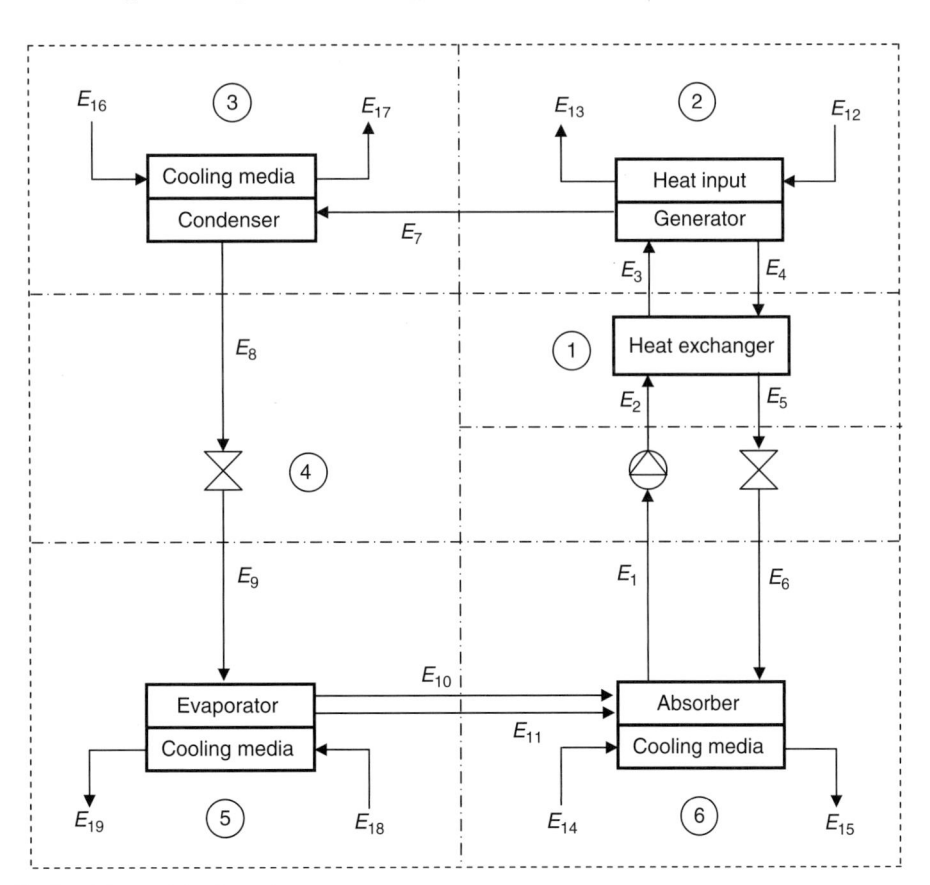

Figure 23 Availability flow balance of the absorption system.

$$\eta_{ex,\,cooling} = \frac{\dot{m}_{18}(E_{18} - E_{19})}{\dot{m}_{12}(E_{12} - E_{13})} \qquad [20]$$

The exergetic efficiency of the absorption systems for heating is the ratio of the combined supply of hot water exergy at the absorber and condenser to the exergy of the heat source at the generator and can be written as [42, 43]

$$\eta_{ex,\,heating} = \frac{\dot{m}_{16}(E_{17} - E_{16}) + \dot{m}_{14}(E_{15} - E_{14})}{\dot{m}_{12}(E_{12} - E_{13})} \qquad [21]$$

3.13.3.6.2 Design of single-effect LiBr–H₂O absorption systems

To perform estimations of equipment sizing and performance evaluation of a single-effect H$_2$O–LiBr absorption cooler, basic assumptions and input values must be considered. With reference to **Figures 20–22**, usually the following assumptions are made:

1. The steady-state refrigerant is pure water.
2. There are no pressure changes except through the flow restrictors and the pump.
3. At points 1, 4, 8, and 11, there is only saturated liquid.
4. At point 10, there is only saturated vapor.
5. Flow restrictors are adiabatic.
6. The pump is isentropic.
7. There are no jacket heat losses.

A small 1 kW unit was designed and constructed by the authors [19]. To design such a system, the design (or input) parameters are required to be specified. These parameters for the 1 kW unit are listed in **Table 2**.

To estimate the energy, mass concentrations, and mass balance of a LiBr–H$_2$O system, the equations of **Table 1** can be used. Some details are given in the following paragraphs so that the reader will understand the procedure required to design such a system.

Since in the evaporator, the refrigerant is saturated water vapor and the temperature (T_{10}) is 6 °C, the saturation pressure at point 10 is 0.934 6 kPa (from steam tables) and the enthalpy is 2511.8 kJ kg^{-1}. Since at point 11 the refrigerant is saturated liquid, its enthalpy is 23.45 kJ kg^{-1}. The enthalpy at point 9 is determined from the throttling process applied to the refrigerant flow restrictor, which yields that $h_9 = h_8$. To determine h_8 the pressure at this point must be determined. Since at point 4 the solution mass fraction is 60% LiBr and the temperature at the saturated state is assumed to be 75 °C, the LiBr–H$_2$O charts (see Reference 11) give a saturation pressure of 4.82 kPa and $h_4 = 183.2$ kJ kg^{-1}. Considering that the pressure at point 4 is the same as at point 8 then $h_8 = h_9 = 131.0$ kJ kg^{-1} (steam tables). Once the enthalpy values at all ports connected to the evaporator are known, mass and energy balances, given in **Table 1**, can be applied to give the mass flow of the refrigerant and the evaporator heat transfer rate.

The heat transfer rate in the absorber can be determined from the enthalpy values at each of the connected state points. At point 1, the enthalpy is determined from the input mass fraction (55%) and the assumption that the state is saturated liquid at the same pressure as the evaporator (0.934 6 kPa). The enthalpy value at point 6 is determined from the throttling model which gives $h_6 = h_5$.

The enthalpy at point 5 is not known but can be determined from the energy balance on the solution heat exchanger, assuming an adiabatic shell as follows:

$$\dot{m}_2 h_2 + \dot{m}_4 h_4 = \dot{m}_3 h_3 + \dot{m}_5 h_5 \qquad [22]$$

The temperature at point 3 is an input value (55 °C) and since the mass fraction for points 1–3 is the same, the enthalpy at this point is determined as 124.7 kJ kg^{-1}. Actually, the state at point 3 may be subcooled liquid. However, at the conditions of interest, the pressure has an insignificant effect on the enthalpy of the subcooled liquid and the saturated value at the same temperature and mass fraction can be an adequate approximation.

Table 2 Design parameters for the single-effect water–lithium bromide absorption cooler

Parameter	Symbol	Value
Capacity	$\dot{Q}_E$	1.0 kW
Evaporator temperature	T_{10}	6 °C
Generator solution exit temperature	T_4	75 °C
Weak solution mass fraction	x_1	55% LiBr
Strong solution mass fraction	x_4	60% LiBr
Solution heat exchanger exit temperature	T_3	55 °C
Generator (desorber) vapor exit temperature	T_7	70 °C
Liquid carryover from evaporator	$\dot{m}_{11}$	$0.025\dot{m}_{10}$

The enthalpy at point 2 can be determined from the equation for the pump given in Table 1 or from an isentropic pump model. The minimum work input (w) can therefore be obtained from

$$w = \dot{m}_1 v_1 (p_2 - p_1) \quad [23]$$

In eqn [23] it is assumed that the specific volume (v, m^3 kg^{-1}) of the liquid solution does not change appreciably from point 1 to 2. The specific volume of the liquid solution can be obtained from a curve fit of the density [44] and noting that $v = 1/\rho$:

$$\rho = 1145.36 + 470.84x + 1374.79x^2 - (0.333\,393 + 0.571\,749x)(273 + T) \quad [24]$$

This equation is valid for $0 < T < 200\,°C$ and $20\% < x < 65\%$.

The temperature at point 5 can be determined from the enthalpy value. The enthalpy at point 7 can be determined since the temperature at this point is an input value. In general, the state at point 7 will be superheated water vapor and the enthalpy can be determined once the pressure and temperature are known.

A summary of the conditions at various parts of the unit is given in Table 3; the point numbers are as shown in Figure 20.

3.13.3.7 Ammonia–Water Absorption Systems

Contrary to compression refrigeration machines, which need high-quality electric energy to run, NH$_3$–H$_2$O absorption refrigeration machines use low-quality thermal energy. Moreover, as the temperature of the heat source does not usually need to be so high (80–170 °C), the waste heat from many processes can be used to power absorption refrigeration machines. In addition, NH$_3$–H$_2$O refrigeration systems use natural substances as working fluids, which do not cause ozone depletion. For all these reasons, this technology has been classified as environmentally friendly [34, 35].

The NH$_3$–H$_2$O system is more complicated than the LiBr–H$_2$O system, since it needs a rectifying column that assures that no water vapor enters the evaporator where it could freeze. The NH$_3$–H$_2$O system requires generator temperatures in the range of 125–170 °C with air-cooled absorber and condenser and 80–120 °C when water cooling is used. These temperatures cannot be obtained with flat-plate collectors. The COP, which is defined as the ratio of the cooling effect to the heat input, is between 0.6 and 0.7.

The single-stage NH$_3$–H$_2$O absorption refrigeration system cycle consists of four main components, namely, the condenser, evaporator, absorber, and generator, as shown in Figure 24. Other auxiliary components include expansion valves, pump, rectifier, and heat exchanger. Low-pressure weak solution is pumped from the absorber to the generator through the solution heat exchanger operating at high pressure. The generator separates the binary solution of water and ammonia by causing the ammonia to vaporize and the rectifier purifies the ammonia vapor. High-pressure ammonia gas is passed through the expansion valve to the evaporator as low-pressure liquid ammonia. The high-pressure transport fluid (water) from the generator is returned to the absorber through the solution heat exchanger and the expansion valve. The low-pressure liquid ammonia in the evaporator is used to cool the space to be refrigerated. During the cooling process, the liquid ammonia vaporizes and the transport fluid (water) absorbs the vapor to form a strong ammonia solution in the absorber [11, 34].

In some cases, a condensate precooler is used to evaporate a significant amount of liquid phase. This is in fact a heat exchanger located before the expansion valve in which the low-pressure refrigerant vapor is passing to remove some of the heat of the

Table 3 LiBr–H$_2$O absorption refrigeration system calculations based on a generator temperature of 75 °C and a solution heat exchanger exit temperature of 55 °C

Point	h (kJ kg^{-1})	$\dot{m}$ (kg s^{-1})	P (kPa)	T (°C)	%LiBr (x)	Remarks
1	83	0.005 17	0.93	34.9	55	
2	83	0.005 17	4.82	34.9	55	
3	124.7	0.005 17	4.82	55	55	Subcooled liquid
4	183.2	0.004 74	4.82	75	60	
5	137.8	0.004 74	4.82	51.5	60	
6	137.8	0.004 74	0.93	44.5	60	
7	2612.2	0.000 431	4.82	70	0	Superheated steam
8	131.0	0.000 431	4.82	31.5	0	Saturated liquid
9	131.0	0.000 431	0.93	6	0	
10	2511.8	0.000 421	0.93	6	0	Saturated vapor
11	23.45	0.000 011	0.93	6	0	Saturated liquid

Description	Symbol	Value (kW)
Capacity (evaporator output power)	$\dot{Q}_E$	1.0
Absorber heat, rejected to the environment	$\dot{Q}_A$	1.28
Heat input to the generator	$\dot{Q}_G$	1.35
Condenser heat, rejected to the environment	$\dot{Q}_C$	1.07
Coefficient of performance	COP	0.74

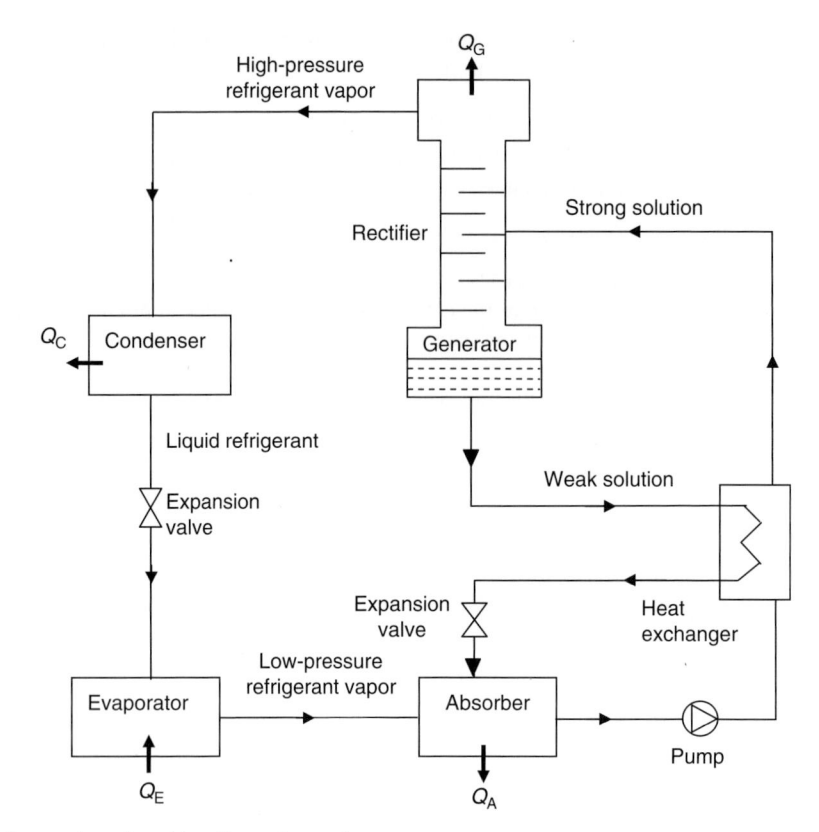

Figure 24 Schematic of ammonia–water refrigeration system cycle.

high-pressure and relatively high-temperature (~40 °C) ammonia. Therefore, some liquid is evaporating and the vapor stream is heated, so there is additional cooling capacity available to further subcool the liquid stream, which increases the COP.

3.13.3.8 Solar Cooling with Absorption Refrigeration

The greatest disadvantage of the solar heating system is that a large number of collectors need to be shaded or disconnected during summertime to reduce overheating. A way to avoid this problem and increase the viability of the solar system is to use a combination of space heating and cooling and domestic hot water production system.

This is economically viable when the same collector is used for both space heating and cooling. Flat-plate solar collectors are commonly used in solar space heating. Good quality flat-plate collectors can attain temperatures suitable for LiBr–H_2O absorption systems. Another alternative is to use evacuated tube collectors, which can give higher temperatures. With these collectors, NH_3–H_2O systems, which need higher temperatures to operate, can also be used.

A schematic diagram of a solar-operated absorption refrigeration system is shown in **Figure 25**. The refrigeration cycle is the same as that described in Section 3.13.3.5. The difference between this system and the traditional fossil fuel-fired unit is that the energy supplied to the generator is from the solar collectors. Due to the intermittent nature of available solar energy, a hot water storage tank is needed; thus, the collected energy is stored in the tank and used as energy source in the generator to heat the strong solution when needed. When the storage tank temperature is low, the auxiliary heater is used to reach the required generator temperature. Again here the same auxiliary heater of the space heating system can be used, at a different set temperature. If the storage tank is completely depleted, the storage is bypassed to avoid wasting auxiliary energy, which is used to meet the heating load of the generator. As in the case of space heating, the auxiliary heater can be arranged in parallel or in series with the storage tank. A collector heat exchanger can also be used to keep the collector fluid separated from the storage tank water (indirect system).

It should be noted that the operating temperature range of the hot water supplied to the generator of a LiBr–H_2O absorption refrigeration system is from 70 to 95 °C. The lower temperature limit is imposed from the fact that hot water must be at a temperature sufficiently high (at least 70 °C) to be effective for boiling the water off the solution in the generator. Also, the temperature of the concentrated LiBr solution returning to the absorber must be high enough to prevent crystallization of the LiBr. An unpressurized water storage tank system is usually used in a solar system; thus, an upper limit of about 95 °C is allowable to prevent water from boiling. For this type of systems, the optimum generator temperature was found to be 93 °C [19].

Since in an absorption–refrigeration cycle heat must be rejected from the absorber and the condenser, a cooling water system is needed. Perhaps the most effective way of providing cooling water is to use a cooling tower as shown in **Figure 25**. Since the

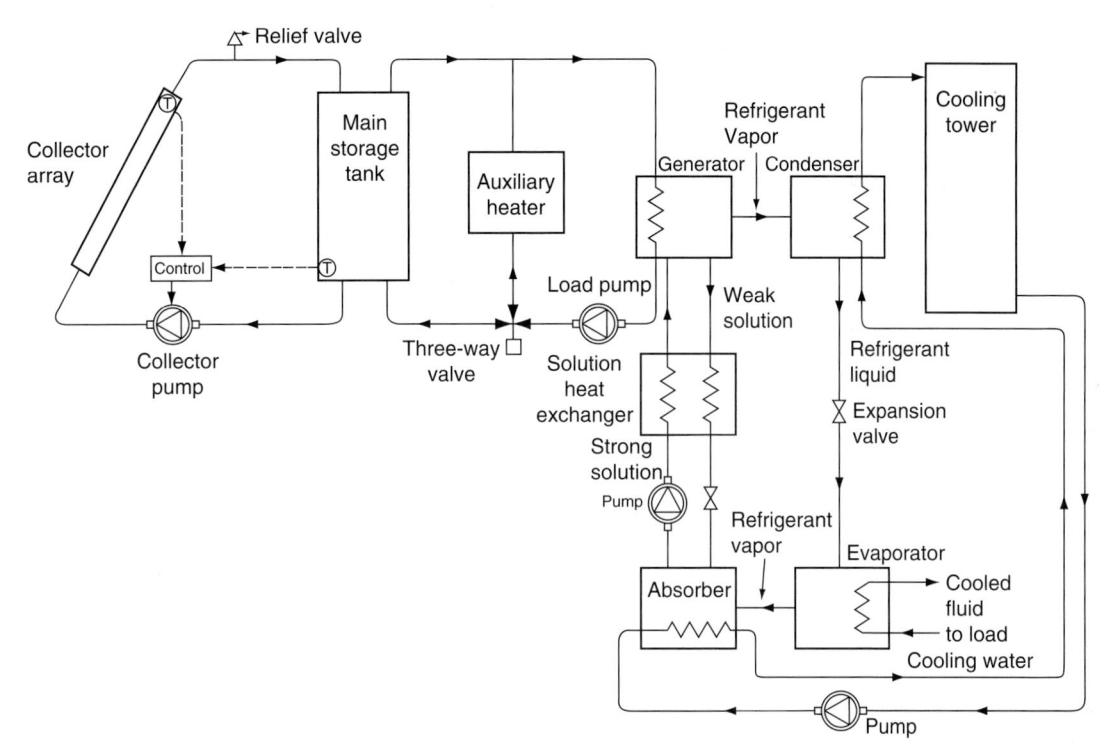

Figure 25 Schematic diagram of a solar-operated absorption refrigeration system.

absorber requires a lower temperature than the condenser, the cool water from the cooling tower is first passed to the absorber and then to the condenser. It should be noted that the use of a cooling tower in a small residential system is problematic with respect to both space and maintenance requirements; thus, whenever possible water drawn from a well can be used.

A variation of the basic system shown in **Figure 25** is to eliminate the hot storage tank and the auxiliary heater and to supply the solar-heated fluid directly to the generator of the absorption unit. The advantage of this arrangement is that higher temperatures are obtained on sunny days, which increase the performance of the generator. A disadvantage is the lack of stored energy to produce cooling during evenings, on cloudy days, and when there is not enough solar energy to meet the load. To minimize the intermittent effects of this arrangement (due to the absence of hot water storage), cold storage can be used. One way of doing this is to use the absorption machine to produce chilled water, which is then stored for cooling purposes [45]. Such a solution would have the advantage of low-rate tank heat gains (actually a loss in this case) because of the smaller temperature difference between the chilled water and its surroundings. An added disadvantage, however, is that the temperature range of a cool storage is small in comparison with that of a hot storage; thus, for the same amount of energy, a larger storage volume is needed for chilled water storage than for hot water storage. As solar heating systems always use a storage tank, the arrangement shown in **Figure 25** is preferred.

3.13.4 Heat Storage Systems

Thermal storage is one of the main parts of a solar heating, cooling, and power generating system. As for approximately one-half of the year any location is in darkness, heat storage is necessary if the solar system will operate continuously. For some applications, such as swimming pool heating, daytime air heating, and irrigation pumping, intermittent operation is acceptable, but most other uses require operating at night or when the sun is hidden behind clouds.

Usually the design and selection of the thermal storage equipment is one of the most neglected elements of the solar energy systems. It should be realized, however, that the energy storage system has an enormous influence on the overall system cost, performance, and reliability. Furthermore, the design of the storage system affects the other basic elements such as the collector loop and the thermal distribution system.

A storage tank in a solar system has several functions, the most important of which are as follows:

- improvement of the utilization of collected solar energy by providing thermal capacitance to alleviate the solar availability/load mismatch and to improve system response to sudden peak loads or loss of solar input; and
- improvement of system efficiency by preventing the array heat transfer fluid from quickly reaching high temperatures, which will lower the collector efficiency.

Generally, solar energy can be stored in liquids, solids, or phase-change materials (PCMs). Water is the most frequently used storage medium for liquid systems, irrespective of the fact that the collector loop may be using water, oils, water/glycol mixtures, or any other heat transfer medium. This is because water is inexpensive and nontoxic and it has a high storage capacity, based on both weight and volume. In addition, as a liquid it is easy to transport using conventional pumps and plumbing. For service water heating applications and most building space heating, water is normally contained in some type of tank, which is usually circular. Air systems typically store heat in rocks or pebbles, but sometimes the structural mass of the building is used.

An important consideration is that the temperature of the fluid delivered to the load should be appropriate for the intended application. The lower the temperature of the fluid supplied to the collectors, the higher will be the efficiency of the collectors.

The location of the storage tank should also be given careful consideration. The best location is indoors, where thermal losses are minimal and weather deterioration is not a factor. If the tank cannot be installed inside the building, then it is located outside above the ground or on the roof. Such a storage tank should have a good insulation and a good outside protection of the insulation. The storage tank should also be located as close as possible to the collector arrays so as to avoid long pipe runs.

3.13.4.1 Air Systems Thermal Storage

The most common storage media for air collectors are rocks. Other possible media include PCM, water, and the inherent building mass. Gravel is widely used as a storage medium because it is abundant and relatively inexpensive.

In cases where large interior temperature swings can be tolerated, the inherent structure of the building may be sufficient for thermal storage. Loads requiring no storage are usually the most cost-effective applications of air collectors and heated air from the collectors can be distributed directly to the space. Generally, storage may be eliminated in cases where the array output seldom exceeds the thermal demand [46].

The main requirements for gravel storage are good insulation, low air leakage, and low pressure drop. Many different designs can fulfill these requirements. The container is usually constructed from concrete, masonry, wood, or a combination of these materials. Airflow can be vertical or horizontal. A schematic diagram of a vertical flow bed is shown in **Figure 26**. In this arrangement, the solar-heated air enters at the top and exits from the bottom. This tank can work as effectively as a horizontal flow bed. In these systems, it is important to heat the bed with the hot airflow in one direction and to retrieve the heat with airflow in the opposite direction. In this way, pebble beds perform as effective counterflow heat exchangers.

The size of rocks for pebble beds ranges from 35 to 100 mm in diameter, depending on airflow, bed geometry, and desired pressure drop. The volume of the rock needed depends on the fraction of collector output that must be stored. For residential systems, storage volume is typically in the range of 0.15–0.3 m^3 per square meter of collector area. For large systems, pebble beds can be quite large but their large mass and volume may lead to location problems [1].

Water can also be used as a storage medium for air collectors through the use of a conventional water-to-air heat exchanger to transfer heat from the air to the water in the storage tank. This option has two advantages:

1. Water storage is compatible with hydronic heating systems.
2. It allows relative compactness, as the required storage water volume is roughly one-third of the pebble bed's volume.

3.13.4.2 Liquid Systems Thermal Storage

Two types of water storage for liquid systems are available: pressurized and unpressurized. Other differentiations include the use of an external or internal heat exchanger and the use of a single or multiple tank configurations. Water may be stored in copper, galvanized metal, or concrete tanks. However, every type of storage vessel must be well insulated and large tanks must also be provided with internal access for maintenance.

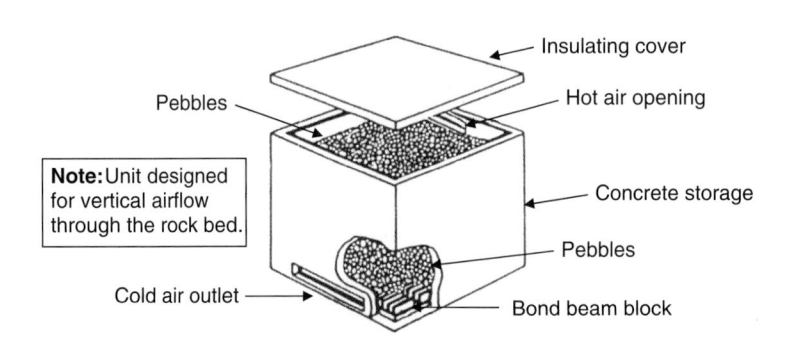

Figure 26 Vertical flow packed rock bed.

Pressurized systems are open to the city mains water supply. Pressurized storage is preferred for small service water heating systems. Typical storage size is about 40–80 l per square meter of collector area. With pressurized storage, the heat exchanger is always located on the collector side of the tank. Either internal or external heat exchanger configurations can be used.

For small systems, an internal heat exchanger/tank arrangement is usually used, which has the added advantage of preventing the water side of the heat exchanger from freezing. However, the energy required to maintain the water above freezing is extracted from the storage; thus, the overall system performance is decreased. With this system, a bypass can be arranged to divert cold fluid around the heat exchanger until it has been heated to an acceptable level of about 25 °C [46]. When the heat transfer fluid is warmed to this level, it can enter the heat exchanger without causing freezing or extraction of heat from storage. If necessary, this arrangement can also be used with internal heat exchangers to improve performance.

For systems with sizes greater than about 30 m^3, unpressurized storage is usually more cost effective than pressurized storage. This system, however, can also be used in small domestic flat-plate collector systems and in this case the makeup water is usually supplied from a cold water storage tank located on top of the hot water cylinder.

Unpressurized storage for water and space heating can be combined with pressurized city water supply. This implies the use of a heat exchanger on the load side of the tank so as to isolate the high-pressure mains potable water loop from the low-pressure collector loop.

Stratification is the collection of hot water to the top of the storage tank and cold water to the bottom. This improves the performance of the tank as hotter water is available for use and colder water is supplied to the collectors, which enables the collector to operate at higher efficiency.

Another category of hot water stores is the so-called solar combistores. These are used mainly in Europe for combined domestic hot water preparation and space heating. Further details on these are provided in Section 3.13.2, and for more information on thermal storage in general *see* Section 3.13.1.

3.13.5 Module and Array Design

3.13.5.1 Module Design

Most commercial and industrial systems require a large number of collectors to satisfy the heating demand. Connecting the collectors with just one set of manifolds makes it difficult to ensure drainability and low pressure drop. It is also difficult to balance the flow and have the same flow rate through all collectors. A module is a group of collectors, which can be grouped into parallel flow and combined series–parallel flow. Parallel flow is the most frequently used because it is inherently balanced, has low pressure drop, and can be drained easily. The external and internal manifolds are the two most popular collector header designs and are illustrated in **Figure 27**.

The external manifold collector has a small header pipe diameter because it carries the flow of only one collector. Thus, each collector is connected individually to the manifold piping, which is not part of the collector panel. The internal manifold collector incorporates several collectors with large headers, which can be placed side by side to form a continuous supply and return manifold, so the manifold piping is integral with each collector. The number of collectors that can be connected depends on the size of the header.

External manifold collectors are generally more suitable for small systems. Internal manifolding is preferred for large systems because it offers a number of advantages. These are cost savings as the system avoids the use of extra pipes (and fittings), which need to be insulated and properly supported, and the elimination of heat losses associated with external manifolding, which increases the thermal performance of the system.

3.13.5.2 Array Design

An array usually includes many individual groups of collectors, called modules, to provide the necessary flow characteristics. To maintain balanced flow, an array or field of collectors should be built from identical modules. There are basically two types of systems that can be used: the direct return and the reverse return. In the direct return, shown in **Figure 28**, balancing valves are needed to ensure uniform flow through the modules. The balancing valves must be connected at the module outlet to provide the flow resistance necessary to ensure filling of all modules on pump start-up. Whenever possible, modules must be connected in a reverse-return mode as shown in **Figure 29**. The reverse return ensures that the array is self-balanced as all collectors operate with the

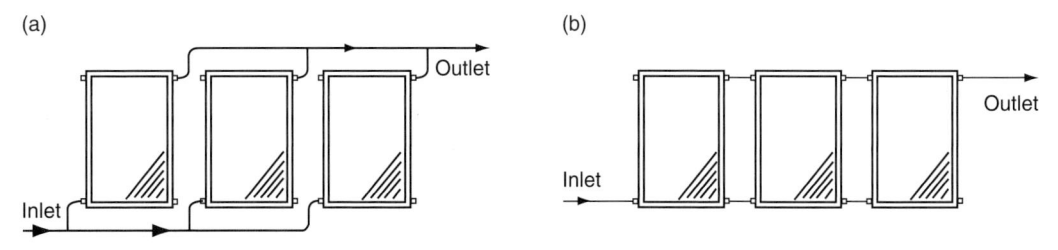

Figure 27 Collector manifolding arrangements for parallel flow modules: (a) external manifolding and (b) internal manifolding.

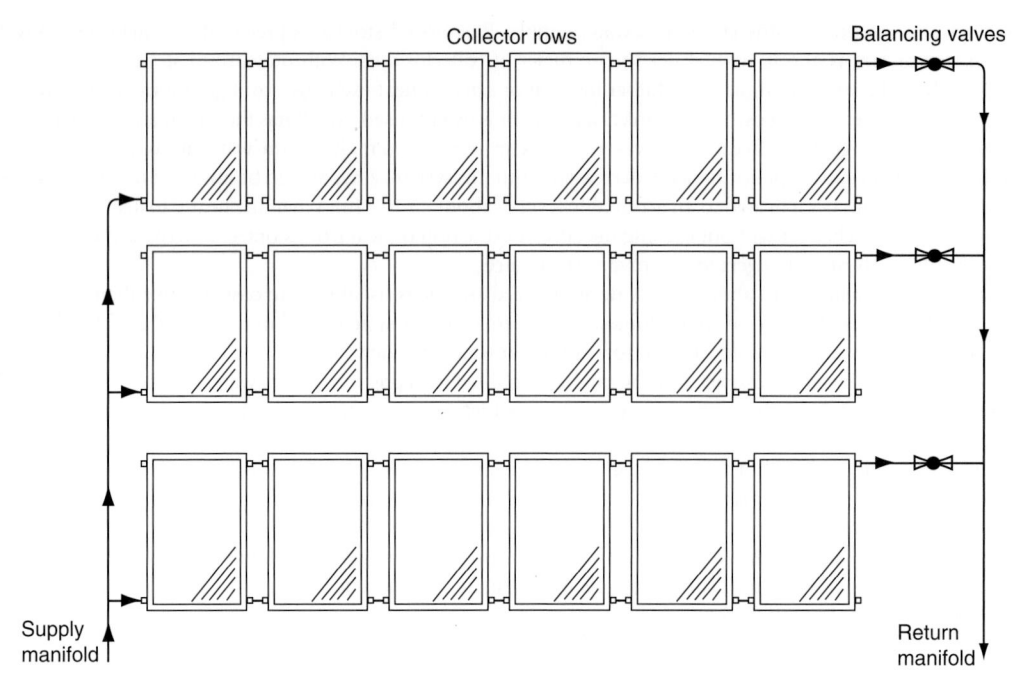

Figure 28 Direct-return array piping.

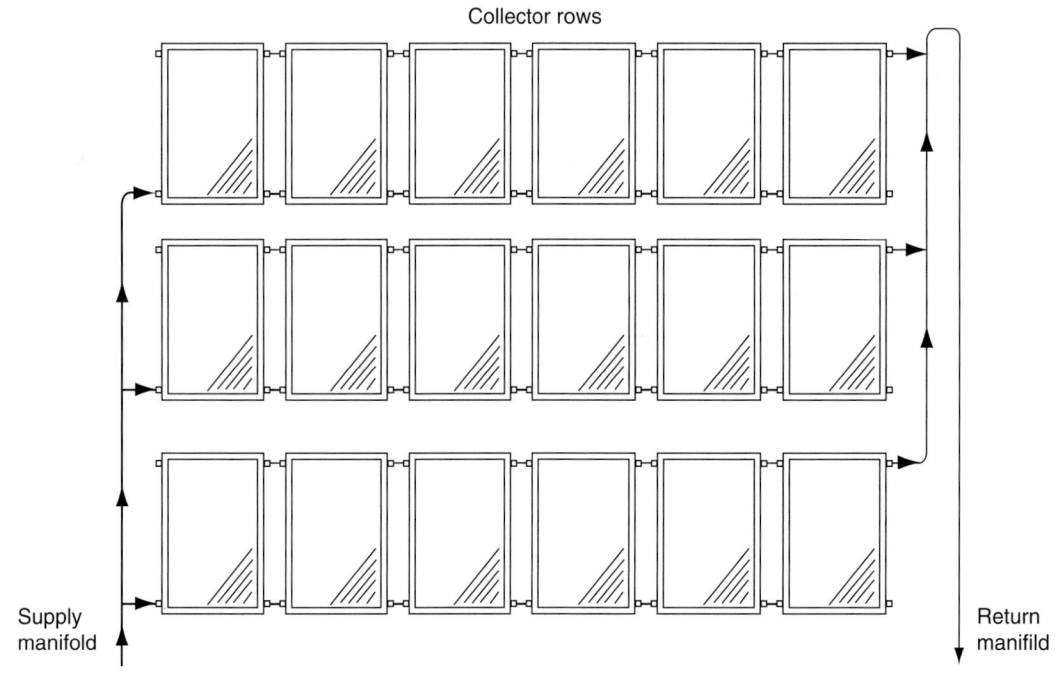

Figure 29 Reverse-return array piping.

same pressure drop. With proper design, an array can drain, which is an essential requirement for drain-back and drain-down freeze protection. For this to be possible, piping to and from the collectors must be sloped properly. Typically, piping and collectors must slope to drain with an inclination of 20 mm per linear meter [46].

The external and internal manifold collectors have different mounting and plumbing considerations. A module with externally manifolded collectors can be mounted horizontally, as shown in **Figure 30(a)**. In this case, the lower header must be pitched as shown. The slope of the upper header can be either horizontal or pitched toward the collectors so that it can drain through the collectors.

Arrays with internal manifolds are a little more difficult to design and install. For these collectors to drain, the entire bank must be tilted, as shown in **Figure 30(b)**. Reverse return always implies an extra pipe run, which is more difficult to drain, so sometimes in this case it is more convenient to use direct return.

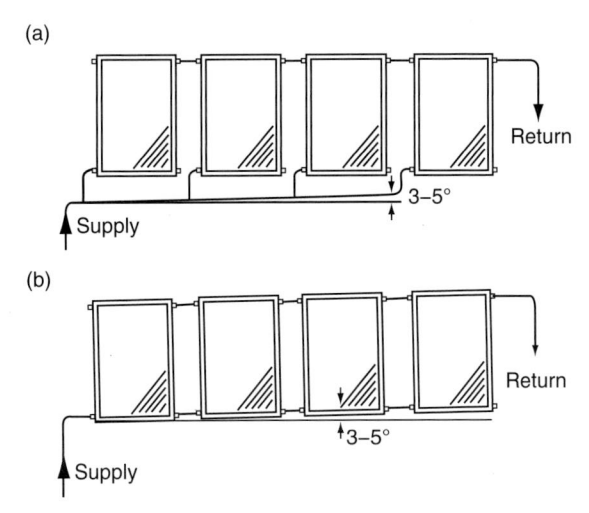

Figure 30 Mounting for drain-back collector modules: (a) external manifold and (b) internal manifold.

3.13.5.3 Heat Exchangers

The function of a heat exchanger is to transfer heat from one fluid to another. In closed solar systems, it also isolates circuits operating at different pressures and separates fluids that should not be mixed. As mentioned earlier, heat exchangers for solar applications may be placed either inside or outside the storage tank. The selection of a heat exchanger involves considerations of performance (with respect to heat exchange area), guaranteed fluid separation (double-wall construction), physical size and configuration (sometimes may be a serious problem in internal heat exchangers), pressure drop caused (influence energy consumption), and serviceability (provide access for cleaning and scale removal).

The factors that should be considered when selecting an external heat exchanger for a system protected by a nonfreezing fluid that is exposed to extreme cold are the possibility of freeze-up of the water side of the heat exchanger and the performance loss due to extraction of heat from storage to heat the low-temperature fluid.

The combination of a solar collector and a heat exchanger performs exactly like a collector alone with a reduced F_R. A collector heat exchanger arrangement is shown in **Figure 31**. Therefore, with the nomenclature used in **Figure 31** the useful energy collected can be obtained from

$$Q_u = (\dot{m}c_p)_c (T_{co} - T_{ci})^+ \quad [25]$$

$$Q_u = A_c F_R [G_t(\tau\alpha)_n - U_L(T_{ci} - T_a)]^+ \quad [26]$$

The plus sign indicates that only positive values should be considered.

The heat exchanger performance is expressed in terms of its effectiveness. By neglecting any piping losses, the collector energy gain transferred to the storage fluid across the heat exchanger is given by

$$Q_{Hx} = Q_u = \varepsilon(\dot{m}c_p)_{min}(T_{co} - T_i) \quad [27]$$

where $(\dot{m}c_p)_{min}$ is the smaller of the fluid capacitance rates of the collector and tank sides of the heat exchanger (W °C^{-1}), T_{co} the hot (collector loop) stream inlet temperature (°C), and T_i the cold (storage) stream inlet temperature (°C).

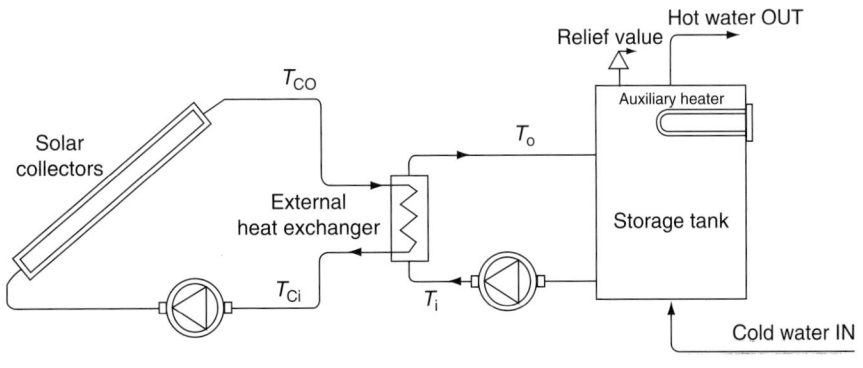

Figure 31 Schematic diagram of a liquid system with an external heat exchanger between the solar collectors and storage tank.

The effectiveness, ε, is the ratio between the heat actually transferred and the maximum heat that could be transferred for given flow and fluid inlet temperature conditions. The effectiveness is relatively insensitive to temperature, but it is a strong function of the heat exchanger design. A designer must decide what heat exchanger effectiveness is required for the specific application. The effectiveness for a counterflow heat exchanger is given by

$$\text{if } C \neq 1 \quad \varepsilon = \frac{1 - e^{-NTU(1-C)}}{1 - Ce^{-NTU(1-C)}} \quad [28]$$

$$\text{if } C = 1 \quad \varepsilon = \frac{NTU}{1 + NTU} \quad [29]$$

where NTU is the number of transfer units given by

$$NTU = \frac{UA}{(\dot{m}c_p)_{min}} \quad [30]$$

And the dimensionless capacitance rate, C, is given by

$$C = \frac{(\dot{m}c_p)_{min}}{(\dot{m}c_p)_{max}} \quad [31]$$

For heat exchangers located in the collector loop, the minimum flow usually occurs on the collector side rather than on the tank side.

Solving eqn [25] for T_{ci} and substituting into eqn [26] gives

$$Q_u = \left[1 - \frac{A_c F_R U_L}{(\dot{m}c_p)_c}\right]^{-1} \{A_c F_R [G_t(\tau\alpha)_n - U_L(T_{co} - T_a)]\} \quad [32]$$

Solving eqn [27] for T_{co} and substituting into eqn [32] gives

$$Q_u = A_c F_R' [G_t(\tau\alpha)_n - U_L(T_i - T_a)] \quad [33]$$

In eqn [33], the modified collector heat removal factor takes into account the presence of the heat exchanger and is given by

$$\frac{F_R'}{F_R} = \left[1 + \frac{A_c F_R U_L}{(\dot{m}c_p)_c}\left(\frac{(\dot{m}c_p)_c}{\varepsilon(\dot{m}c_p)_{min}} - 1\right)\right]^{-1} \quad [34]$$

In fact, the factor F_R'/F_R is the reduction in the collector performance, which occurs because the heat exchanger causes the collector side of the system to operate at higher temperature than a similar system without a heat exchanger. This can also be viewed as the increase of collector area required to have the same performance as a system without a heat exchanger.

3.13.6 Differential Temperature Controller

As was seen in the previous sections of this chapter, the control system should be capable of handling all possible system operating modes, such as heat collection, heat rejection, power failure, freeze protection, and auxiliary heating. The basis of solar energy system control is the differential temperature controller (DTC). This is simply a fixed temperature difference thermostat with hysteresis. The DTC is a comparing controller with at least two temperature sensors that controls one or more devices. Typically, one of the sensors is located at the topside of the solar collector array and the second at the storage tank as shown in **Figure 32**. Most other controls used in solar energy systems are similar to those used for building services systems.

The DTC monitors the temperature difference between the collectors and the storage tank. When the temperature of the solar collectors exceeds that of the storage by the predetermined amount (usually 4–11 °C), the DTC switches the circulating pump ON. When the temperature of the solar collectors decreases to 2–5 °C above the storage temperature, the DTC stops the pump. Instead of directly controlling the solar pump, the DTC can operate indirectly through a control relay to operate one or more pumps and possibly perform other control functions such as the actuation of control valves.

The differential temperature set point of the controller may be fixed or adjustable. If the controller set point is fixed, the selected controller should correspond to the requirements of the solar system. An adjustable differential set point makes the controller more flexible and allows it to be adjusted to the specific system or specific condition of the solar system. The optimum differential ON set point is difficult to calculate because of the changing variables and conditions. Typically, the ON set point is 5–9 °C above the OFF set point. The optimum ON set point is a balance between optimum energy collection and the avoidance of short starts and stops of the pump. The optimum OFF temperature differential should be the minimum possible, which depends on whether there is a heat exchanger between the collectors and the storage.

Frequent starts and stops of the pump (called short cycling) must be minimized because it can lead to premature pump failure. Short cycling depends on how quickly and how often the solar collector sensor temperature exceeds the ON set point and decreases below the OFF set point. This is influenced by the insolation intensity, the pump flow rate, the solar collector thermal mass, the

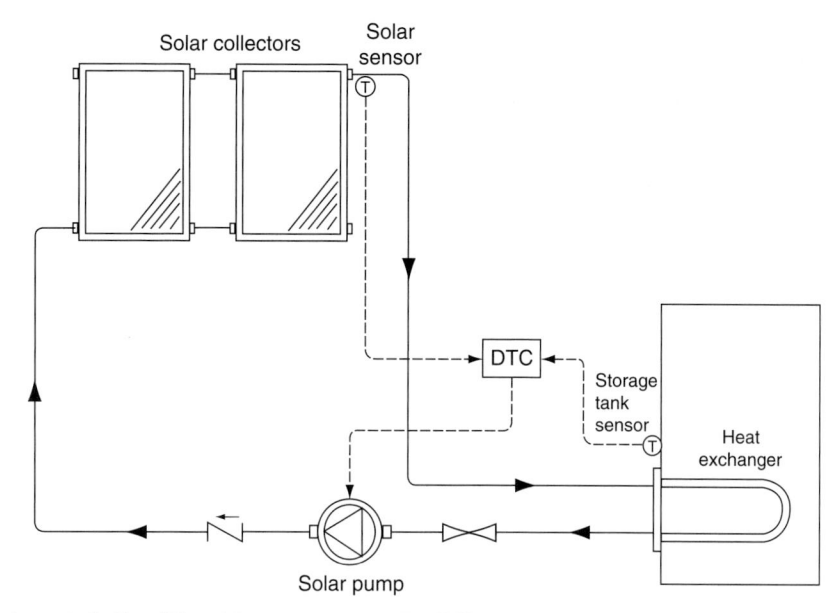

Figure 32 Basic collector control with a differential temperature controller (DTC).

response of the sensor, and the temperature of the fluid entering the collector. The most common method of avoiding short cycling is the use of wide temperature difference between the ON and OFF set points. This, however, will lead to the requirement of a lot of insolation to switch the pump ON, which will lose energy in the collector and may never reach the ON set point in periods of low insolation. Therefore, the guidelines given below must be followed for deciding the correct setting.

If the system does not have a heat exchanger, a range of 1–4 °C is acceptable for the OFF set point. If the system incorporates a heat exchanger, a higher differential temperature set point is used so as to have an effective heat transfer. The minimum or OFF temperature differential is the point at which the cost for pumping the energy is equal to the cost of the energy being pumped in which case the heat lost in the piping should also be considered. For systems with heat exchangers, the OFF set point is generally between 3 and 6 °C.

In closed-loop systems, a second temperature sensor may be used in the tank above the heat exchanger to switch the pump between low and high speed and hence provide some control of the return temperature to the tank heat exchanger.

References

[1] Kalogirou S (2009) *Solar Energy Engineering: Processes and Systems*. New York, NY: Academic Press, Elsevier Science. ISBN: 978-0-12-374501-9.
[2] Duff WS (1996) *Advanced solar domestic hot water systems. International Energy Agency, Task 14, Final Report*. USA: Colorado State University.
[3] Hahne E (1996) Solar heating and cooling. *Proceedings of Eurosun'96*, vol. 1, pp. 3–19. Freiburg, Germany.
[4] Florides G, Tassou S, Kalogirou S, and Wrobel L (2002) Review of solar and low energy cooling technologies for buildings. *Renewable and Sustainable Energy Reviews* 6(6): 557–572.
[5] Druck H and Hahne E (1998) Test and comparison of hot water stores for solar combisystems. *Proceedings of EuroSun98 – The Second ISES-Europe Solar Congress on CD-ROM*. Portoroz, Slovenia.
[6] Huang BJ and Chyng JP (2001) Performance characteristics of integral type solar-assisted heat pump. *Solar Energy* 71(6): 403–414.
[7] Kreider JF and Rabl A (1994) *Heating and Cooling of Buildings – Design for Efficiency* ch. 1, pp. 1–21. Singapore: McGraw-Hill, Book Co.
[8] Winwood R, Benstead R, and Edwards R (1997) Advanced fabric energy storage. *Building Services Engineering Research and Technology* 18(1): 1–6.
[9] Argiriou A (1997) Ground cooling. In: Santamouris M and Asimakopoulos D (eds.) *Passive Cooling of Buildings*, pp. 360–403. London: James & James (Science Publishers) Ltd.
[10] Florides G, Kalogirou S, Tassou S, and Wrobel L (2001) Modelling and simulation of an absorption solar cooling system for Cyprus. *Solar Energy* 72(1): 43–51.
[11] ASHRAE (2005) *Handbook of Fundamentals*. Atlanta, GA: ASHRAE.
[12] Keith EH, Radermacher R, and Klein SA (1996) *Absorption Chillers and Heat Pumps* ch. 1, pp. 1–5. Boca Raton, FL: CRS Press.
[13] Hastings SR (1999) *Solar Air Systems – Built Examples*. London: James & James.
[14] Norton B (1992) *Solar Energy Thermal Technology*. London: Springer-Verlag.
[15] Dieng AO and Wang RZ (2001) Literature review on solar adsorption technologies for ice making and air conditioning purposes and recent development in solar technology. *Renewable and Sustainable Energy Reviews* 5(4): 313–342.
[16] Duffie JA and Beckman WA (1991) *Solar Engineering of Thermal Processes*, 2nd edn. New York, NY: John Wiley & Sons.
[17] Critoph RE (2002) Development of three solar/biomass adsorption air conditioning refrigeration systems. *Proceedings of the World Renewable Energy Congress VII on CD-ROM*. Cologne, Germany.
[18] Thorpe R (2002) Progress towards a highly regenerative adsorption cycle for solar thermal powered air conditioning. *Proceedings of the World Renewable Energy Congress VII on CD-ROM*. Cologne, Germany.
[19] Florides G, Kalogirou S, Tassou S, and Wrobel L (2003) Design and construction of a lithium bromide–water absorption machine. *Energy Conversion and Management* 44(15): 2483–2508.
[20] Dorgan CB, Leight SP, and Dorgan CE (1995) *Application Guide for Absorption Cooling/Refrigeration Using Recovered Heat*. Atlanta, GA: ASHRAE.

[21] Keith EH (1995) Design challenges in absorption chillers. *Mechanical Engineering – CIME* 117(10): 80–84.
[22] Hammad MA and Audi MS (1992) Performance of a solar LiBr–water absorption refrigeration system. *Renewable Energy* 2(3): 275–282.
[23] Haim I, Grossman G, and Shavit A (1992) Simulation and analysis of open cycle absorption systems for solar cooling. *Solar Energy* 49(6): 515–534.
[24] Hawlader MNA, Noval KS, and Wood BD (1993) Unglazed collector/regenerator performance for a solar assisted open cycle absorption cooling system. *Solar Energy* 50(1): 59–73.
[25] Ghaddar NK, Shihab M, and Bdeir F (1997) Modelling and simulation of solar absorption system performance in Beirut. *Renewable Energy* 10(4): 539–558.
[26] Erhard A and Hahne E (1997) Test and simulation of a solar-powered absorption cooling machine. *Solar Energy* 59(4–6): 155–162.
[27] Hammad M and Zurigat Y (1998) Performance of a second generation solar cooling unit. *Solar Energy* 62(2): 79–84.
[28] Zinian HE and Ning Z (1999) A solar absorption air-conditioning plant using heat-pipe evacuated tubular collectors. *Proceedings of ISES Solar World Congress on CD-ROM*. Jerusalem, Israel.
[29] Ameel TA, Gee KG, and Wood BD (1995) Performance predictions of alternative, low cost absorbents for open-cycle absorption solar cooling. *Solar Energy* 54(2): 65–73.
[30] Winston R, O'Gallagher J, Duff W, *et al* (1999) Demonstration of a new type of ICPC in a double-effect absorption cooling system. *Proceedings of ISES Solar World Congress on CD-ROM*. Jerusalem, Israel.
[31] Klein SA (1992) Engineering Equation Solver. http://www.fchart.com (accessed March 2011).
[32] Florides G, Kalogirou S, Tassou S, and Wrobel L (2002) Modelling, simulation and warming impact assessment of a domestic-size absorption solar cooling system. *Applied Thermal Engineering* 22(12): 1313–1325.
[33] Kizilkan O, Sencan A, and Kalogirou SA (2007) Thermoeconomic optimization of a LiBr absorption refrigeration system. *Chemical Engineering and Processing* 46(12): 1376–1384.
[34] Herold KE, Radermacher R, and Klein SA (1996) *Absorption Chillers and Heat Pumps*. Boca Raton, FL: CRC Press.
[35] Alefeld G and Radermacher R (1994) *Heat Conversion Systems*. Boca Raton, FL: CRC Press.
[36] Tozer RM and James RW (1997) Fundamental thermodynamics of ideal absorption cycles. *International Journal of Refrigeration* 20(2): 120–135.
[37] Kotas TJ (1985) *The Exergy Method of Thermal Plant Analysis*. Great Britain: Anchor Brendon Ltd.
[38] Ishida M and Ji J (1999) Graphical exergy study on single state absorption heat transformer. *Applied Thermal Engineering* 19(11): 1191–1206.
[39] Sencan A, Yakut KA, and Kalogirou SA (2005) Exergy analysis of LiBr/water absorption systems. *Renewable Energy* 30(5): 645–657.
[40] Talbi MM and Agnew B (2000) Exergy analysis: an absorption refrigerator using lithium bromide and water as working fluids. *Applied Thermal Engineering* 20(7): 619–630.
[41] Izquerdo M, Vega M, Lecuona A, and Rodriguez P (2000) Entropy generated and exergy destroyed in lithium bromide thermal compressors driven by the exhaust gases of an engine. *International Journal of Energy Research* 24: 1123–1140.
[42] Lee SF and Sherif SA (2001) Thermodynamic analysis of a lithium bromide/water absorption system for cooling and heating applications. *International Journal of Energy Research* 25: 1019–1031.
[43] Çengel YA and Boles MA (1994) *Thermodynamics: An Engineering Approach*. New York, NY: McGraw-Hill.
[44] Lee RJ, DiGuilio RM, Jeter SM, and Teja AS (1990) Properties of lithium bromide–water solutions at high temperatures and concentration. II. Density and viscosity. *ASHRAE Transactions* 96: 709–728.
[45] Hsieh JS (1986) *Solar Energy Engineering*. New Jersey: Prentice-Hall Inc.
[46] ASHRAE (2004) *Handbook of Systems and Equipment*. Atlanta, GA: ASHRAE.

3.14 Solar Cooling and Refrigeration Systems

GG Maidment and A Paurine, London South Bank University, London, UK

© 2012 Elsevier Ltd. All rights reserved.

3.14.1	Introduction	481
3.14.2	Solar-Powered Cooling	481
3.14.3	Need for Solar-Powered Cooling	481
3.14.4	Solar-Powered Cooling Technologies	482
3.14.4.1	Desiccant Cooling System	482
3.14.4.2	Solid Desiccant	483
3.14.4.3	Liquid Desiccant	483
3.14.4.4	Absorption Systems	484
3.14.4.5	Adsorption Systems	486
3.14.4.6	Ejector Systems	489
3.14.4.7	Photovoltaic–Compression Systems	489
3.14.5	Relative Comparison of Solar Cooling Technologies	490
3.14.5.1	Solar Coefficient of Performance	490
5.14.5.2	Capital Cost Comparison	491
5.14.5.3	Life-Cycle Cost Comparison	491
3.14.6	Application of Solar Cooling System	492
3.14.7	Integration with Solar Hot Water and Solar Tthermal Systems for Cost-Effectiveness	492
5.14.8	Conclusions	493
References		493

3.14.1 Introduction

Thermally driven cooling offers a more sustainable and low-energy solution for refrigeration and air-conditioning applications. For most cooling applications, there is a coincidence between peak solar gain and peak cooling demand. By using solar thermal energy to drive a cooling cycle, it is possible to produce cooling virtually coincident with the demand for cold, and thus solar-powered cooling is a potential technology for domestic, commercial, and industrial buildings. The coincidence of cooling with demand is shown in **Figure 1**.

This chapter presents an overview of the state-of-the-art of solar cooling. It describes the general theory, the technologies, and their relative performance and applications. Several competing technologies for solar energy collection for sorption and vapor compression refrigeration are compared in terms of efficiency, life-cycle cost (LCC), and primary energy basis.

3.14.2 Solar-Powered Cooling

Solar cooling is a technology for converting heat collected from the sun into useful cooling into refrigeration and air-conditioning applications. Solar thermal energy is collected and used by a thermally driven cooling process, which in turn is normally used to generate chilled water or conditioned air for use in the building. A typical solar cooling scheme essentially includes three components. These include the solar collector for harnessing solar energy by converting it into heat or mechanical work, a refrigeration or air-conditioning plant for producing cooling, and a heat sink for heat rejection. A diagram of the main components of a solar cooling scheme is shown in **Figure 2**.

3.14.3 Need for Solar-Powered Cooling

Many buildings require cooling to offset heat gains. In most temperate countries, solar heat gains represent a large proportion of the overall load to the building. For the United Kingdom, according to Jones [2], for the typical hypothetical office block, the solar gain contributes between 25% and 40% of the total cooling load. Low-energy and more sustainable cooling systems have been proposed as an alternative to traditional energy-intensive methods. Interest in solar cooling systems was first shown during the energy crisis of 1970s. These systems used solar thermal energy to energize absorption cycles or light to provide electrical power from photovoltaic (PV) panels for vapor compression refrigeration cycles. As these systems utilize solar energy, they require minimal grid-derived electricity, unlike conventional vapor compression equipment. The main advantage of such systems is that they provide virtually 'free cooling' that is coincident with the occurrence of solar gains. Also, solar energy is freely available in moderate to hot climates where more than 50% of the world's population reside [3].

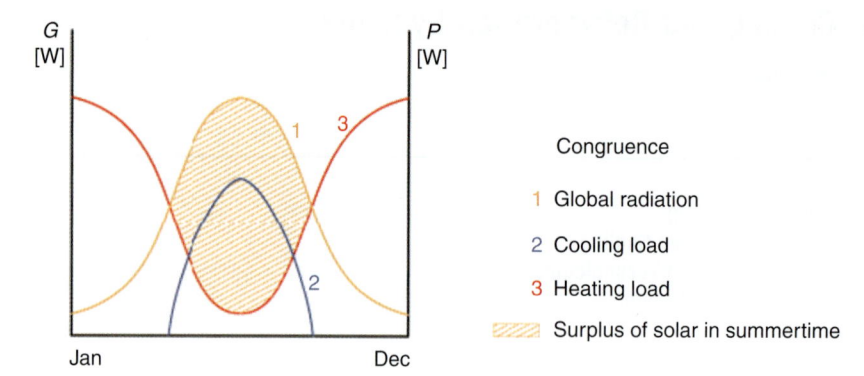

Figure 1 Relationship between incidence of solar radiation and cooling [1].

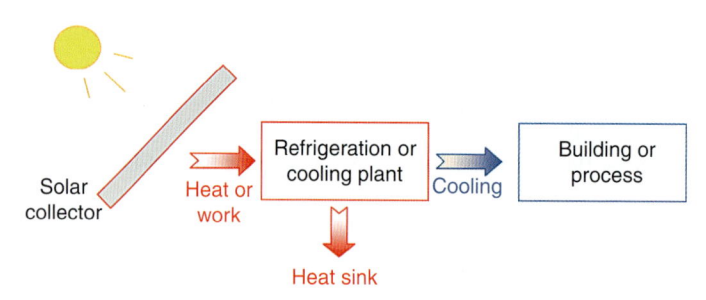

Figure 2 Scheme of a typical solar cooling.

3.14.4 Solar-Powered Cooling Technologies

There have been numerous projects worldwide relating to the systems used for converting solar thermal energy into useful cooling. These systems have included the use of flat-plates, evacuated-tube, PV, and concentrating solar collectors in combination with desiccant cooling, adsorption chillers, absorption chillers, vapor compression systems, and ejector refrigeration system.

The relative efficiency for each of these solar cooling systems is determined based on the efficiency of the collector device (η_{coll}) and the coefficient of performance (COP) of the cooling cycle. The overall system efficiency, also referred to as solar coefficient of performance (SCOP), is indicated in eqn [2].

$$\text{SCOP} = \frac{Q_u}{G_T} \times \text{COP} \qquad [1]$$

or

$$\text{SCOP} = \eta_{coll} \times \text{COP} \qquad [2]$$

where η_{coll} is collector efficiency, Q_u is the useful heat gained by the collector, and G_T is the solar insolation.

The SCOP is used because it gives a simple but combined index of system efficiency as well as capital cost. Therefore, it should be noted that the collector and heat rejection component size and cost for technologies (described below) are significantly affected by SCOP.

3.14.4.1 Desiccant Cooling System

In a desiccant cooling system, air can be passed over common solid desiccants such as zeolite or silica gel for dehumidification and to sensibly cool the air well below ambient temperature conditions in some form of evaporative cooling process. Also, liquid dessicants such as lithium or calcium chloride have been used for air dehumidification processes. In either case, the desiccant requires regeneration and this can be achieved using solar thermal energy to dry it out, in a cost-effective, low energy, and continuously repeating cycle.

A number of desiccant-based solar cooling demonstration projects have been cited in the literature reviews conducted by Lu et al. [16], Pesaran and Wipke [15], Ahmed et al. [4], and Gommed and Grossman [18]. The main advantage of desiccant-based systems when combined with solar cooling is that regeneration takes place at relatively low temperatures, a factor suited for use with solar energy.

3.14.4.2 Solid Desiccant

A range of solar air-conditioning systems utilizing solid desiccants in open-cycle configuration have been reported. The original concept was applied to the Pennington cycle. A system that produces dehumidification and cooling as modeled by Halliday et al. [12] is shown in **Figure 3**.

It should be noted that in **Figure 3** a rotating desiccant wheel containing silica gel particles is deployed to dehumidify and provide supplementary sensible cooling of incoming outside air. The desiccant wheel operates such that as a heat exchanger sensibly increases the temperature of the process air while decreasing its latent heat. The thermal effectiveness ($\varepsilon_{T,DW}$) of the desiccant wheel is given by the following expression, where notation relates to the numbering in **Figure 3**:

$$\varepsilon_{T,DW} = \frac{\dot{m}_{\text{process air}}\left(C_p(T_{8'} - T_7) + (g_8 - g_7)h_{fg}\right)}{\dot{m}_{\text{regeneration air}}(h_4 - h_3)} \quad [3]$$

where $T_{8'}$ is the temperature of process air at vapor pressure similar to that of the outside air entering the desiccant wheel and equivalent to dry bulb temperature of air leaving the desiccant wheel and g and h_{fg} are moisture content and vaporization latent heat of water, respectively.

The effectiveness of the thermal wheel can also be expressed in the terms of the vaporization latent heat rate of the adsorbed water and the regeneration input heat rate into the system. The regeneration effectiveness ($\varepsilon_{R,DW}$) of the desiccant wheel is given by the following expression:

$$\varepsilon_{R,DW} = \frac{\dot{m}_{\text{process air}}(g_8 - g_7)h_{fg}}{\dot{m}_{\text{regeneration air}}(h_4 - h_3)} \quad [4]$$

By using a perfectly designed and optimized desiccant wheel with high regeneration effectiveness, it is possible to achieve high COP with desiccant-based cooling systems.

3.14.4.3 Liquid Desiccant

Liquid-based desiccant systems are described in the literature [5] and these are reported to also clean the air and improve indoor air quality. There are some liquid desiccant cooling systems that use water–lithium chloride (LiCl–H$_2$O) and water–calcium chloride (CaCl$_2$–H$_2$O) solutions for sorption purposes. In comparison with solid desiccant cooling systems, the liquid desiccant cooling systems have higher rate of air dehumidification at the same range of driving temperatures and in that they have high energy storage capacity when used in the concentrated solutions. **Figure 4** shows a distinctive liquid desiccant solar cooling system.

The effectiveness of the liquid desiccant solar cooling can be defined based on the process and regeneration air inlets and outlets. Assuming there is minimal or no heat loss from the system described in **Figure 4**, the cooling effectiveness ($\varepsilon_{C,LD}$) of the liquid desiccant system is given by the following expression:

$$\varepsilon_{C,LD} = \frac{\dot{m}_{\text{Process Air}}(g_B - g_C)h_{fg}}{\dot{m}_{\text{Regeneration Air}}(h_E - h_D)} \quad [5]$$

where g and h_{fg} are moisture content and vaporization latent heat of water, respectively.

Alternatively, the $\varepsilon_{C,LD}$ can be defined in terms of the temperature of the salt solution in the system:

$$\varepsilon_{C,LD} = \frac{\bar{C}_{P(1-2)}(T_2 - T_1)}{\bar{C}_{P(3-2)}(T_3 - T_2)} \quad [6]$$

where $\bar{C}_{P(1-2)} \approx \bar{C}_{P(3-2)}$ is the average specific heat capacities of the salt solutions in the two heat exchangers and T is the temperature of the salt solution.

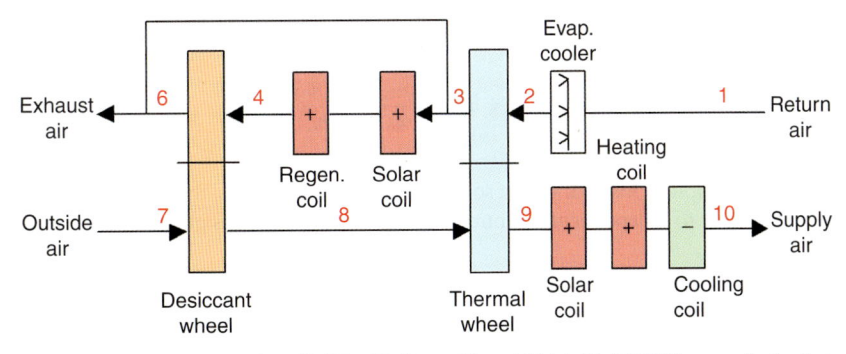

Figure 3 Solar desiccant cooling system. Developed from Halliday SP, Beggs CB, and Sleigh PA (2007) The use of solar desiccant cooling in the UK: a feasibility study. *Applied Thermal Engineering* 22: 1327–1338 [12].

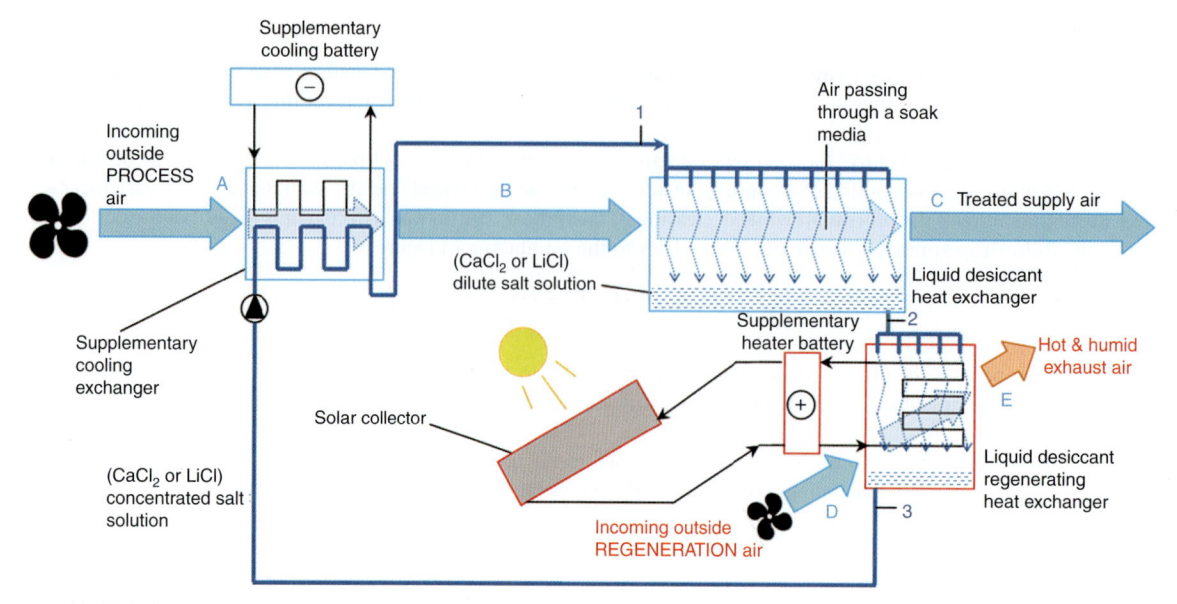

Figure 4 Liquid desiccant solar cooling system.

Therefore, eqn [5] simplifies to the following expression below:

$$\varepsilon_{C,LD} = (T_2 - T_1)(T_3 - T_2)^{-1} \quad [7]$$

The cooling effectiveness in this case is similar to relative efficiency, and therefore, the SCOP for liquid solar cooling system can be established as follows:

$$SCOP = \eta_{coll}\varepsilon_{C,LD} \quad [8]$$

where η_{coll} is solar collector efficiency.

Liquid desiccants are not popular in the supply airstream due to possible health risks such as Legionnaires' disease and the risk of desiccant droplet carryover causing corrosion in metal ducts. A number of liquid desiccant cooling systems have been developed to eliminate the use of the humidifier and desiccant in the supply airstream. One arrangement utilizes two heat exchangers, where the cooled airstream of the first indirect evaporative liquid-desiccant air-cooling heat exchanger is used in a second heat exchanger to cool a clean supply airstream without direct contact with either the cooling water or the liquid desiccants. This is shown in **Figure 5**.

Although the use of the second heat exchanger eliminates the possibility health risks and ductwork metal corrosion due to droplet carryover, it does impinge on the overall effectiveness of the cooling system. Since the liquid desiccant flowing from heat exchanger 2 (HTX 2) via pip. 5 in **Figure 5** is minimal, it does not significantly influence the performance of the regenerating heat exchanger. Therefore, the overall SCOP can be defined in terms of incoming primary outside process air (IPOPA) onto the heat exchanger 1 (HTX1) and incoming outside regeneration air (IORA) onto the liquid desiccant regenerating heat exchanger using the following expression:

$$SCOP = \eta_{coll} \frac{\varepsilon_{HTX2}\dot{m}_{IPOPA}(g_A - g_B)h_{fg}}{\dot{m}_{IORA}(h_H - h_G)} \quad [9]$$

Alternatively, this can be defined in terms of the incoming secondary outside process air (ISOPA) onto HTX 2. Since the air will not be in direct contact with the liquid desiccant, it will be sensibly cooled only, and therefore, this can be established using the following expression:

$$SCOP = \eta_{coll} \frac{\dot{m}_{ISOPA}(h_E - h_F)}{\dot{m}_{IORA}(h_H - h_G)} \quad [10]$$

where ε_{HTX2} is effectiveness of the heat exchanger.

While there are relatively few suppliers/installations of solar-based desiccant systems, they have been used extensively in certain niche applications where the ability to independently control air humidity at low levels provides additional benefits.

3.14.4.4 Absorption Systems

The absorption cycle consists of four basic components operating at two pressure conditions and uses an absorbent–refrigerant solution such as water lithium bromide (LiBr-H$_2$O) as the working fluid. These components include the evaporator, absorber, generator, and condenser as shown in **Figure 6**.

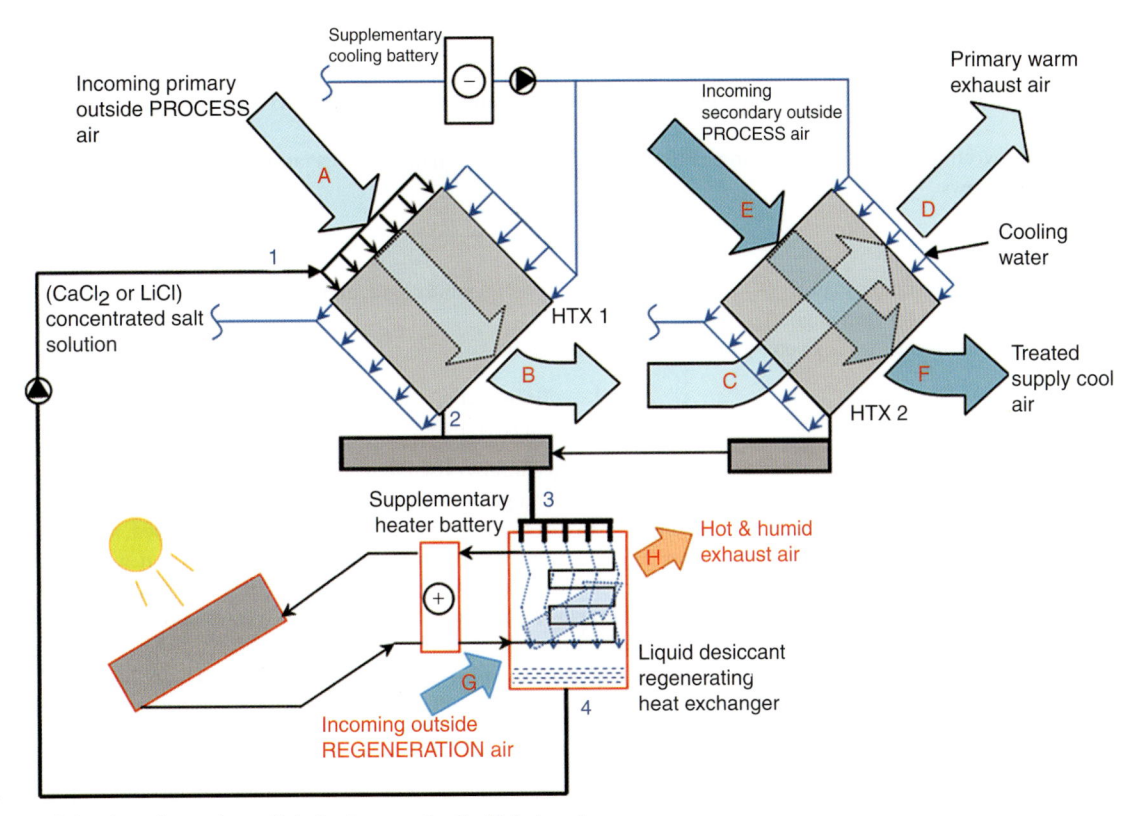

Figure 5 Solar air cooling system with indirect evaporative liquid desiccant.

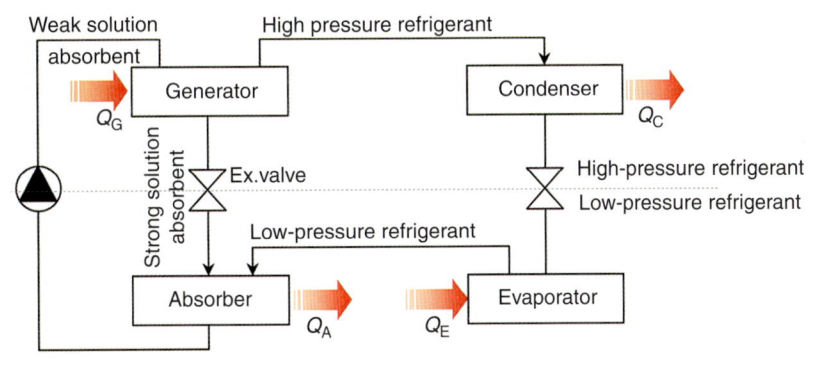

Figure 6 The basic absorption cycle.

The system works such that high-pressure liquid refrigerant flows from the condenser through an expansion device, which reduces the pressure, to the evaporator condition. The refrigerant evaporates in the evaporator, cooling the secondary air or water (cooled medium) and the resulting low-pressure vapor passes to the absorber, where it is absorbed into a strong solution absorbent.

It is necessary to continually reconcentrate the solution to maintain the low evaporation temperature required. The 'weak' solution with high percentage of refrigerant is recirculated to the generator where most of the refrigerant is boiled off and the resulting 'strong' solution is passed back to the absorber via an expansion device. The heat input into absorption chillers can be supplied via an array of solar thermal collectors.

There are many different variants of absorption chillers including half-, single-, double-, and triple-effect systems. There are also open- and closed-cycle absorption units that utilize liquid/vapor, solid/vapor, and sorbent/refrigerant combinations. The variants of solar absorption system are detailed in the paper by Syed *et al.* [6]. The main practical difference between these systems is the driving temperature required for regeneration of the solution and their relative COPs as well as capital cost and complexity. The most common cycle is the single-effect LiBr–H_2O system that requires heat at around 80 °C will typically achieve a COP of around 0.7 for a chilled water application.

The COP of a typical absorption chiller can be expressed by assuming an ideal heat engine operating in a Carnot cycle. Therefore, relation between work and heat for an ideal heat engine is given by the second law of thermodynamics:

$$\text{Carnot efficiency}: \frac{W}{Q_G} = \frac{T_h - T_s}{T_h} \qquad [11]$$

where W (kW) is the work, Q_G (kW) is the heat input rate, T_h (K) is the temperature of heat source, and T_s (K) is the temperature of heat sink.

The relation between work required and refrigeration load for an ideal mechanical refrigeration machine operating as a reverse Carnot cycle is as follows:

$$\text{Carnot efficiency}: \frac{W}{Q_s} = \frac{T_l - T_s}{T_l} \qquad [12]$$

where Q_s (kW) is the refrigeration load, T_l (K) is the temperature of refrigeration load, and T_s (K) is the temperature of heat sink (assumed to be the same as for heat engine).

The COP of the two ideal cycles is given by the following expression:

$$\text{COP} = \frac{Q_s}{Q_G} = \frac{T_l(T_h - T_s)}{T_h(T_l - T_s)} \qquad [13]$$

Absorption-type cooling is the most common type of solar cooling technology used in practice. According to a survey of pilot plants by International Energy Agency [7], small capacity machines in the range of 1–10 kW were mainly solar-energized as they can be operated with low-grade heat of temperatures below 100 °C. Most of the machines in the survey were air-cooled, and during good climatic conditions, a theoretical COP in the range of 0.7–0.75 was attained. In a more recent survey [8], it was reported that absorption technology dominated the other technologies applied in solar cooling industry, that is, it is incorporated in 67% of the installations. Moreover, it was reported that there has been growth in small-scale systems (< 20 kW), which were not really on the market a few years ago.

A number of commercial solar-powered absorption products are on the market now, such as that shown in **Figure 7** marketed by Solar Polar. This is reported to provide better integration of the components, and also offers scope to provide combined cooling and heating.

The main issues reported with the application of LiBr absorption chillers were that of mismatch between cooling load and chiller capacity for commonly used residential applications in Europe [8]. There are also spatial constraints reported in accommodating a water-cooled chiller in a typical three- to four-bed house. This problem has now been reportedly overcome with a smaller commercially available air-cooled (rotary) LiBr-H$_2$O chiller of 4.5 kW nominal cooling capacity to replace a split DX unit.

Some pictures of commercially available packaged units are shown in **Figure 8**. These are designed to be installed outside the building and piped to high-wall fan coil unit in an adjacent room. There is no external condenser circuit and the hot water cylinder tee-offs are piped directly to the chiller, hence saving cost and space.

3.14.4.5 Adsorption Systems

The adsorption cycle is similar to absorption cycle, but it uses solid sorbent rather than a liquid. The system uses an adsorption medium such as zeolite and activated carbon together with a refrigerant to achieve a cooling effect. The natural mineral zeolite has the property to attract water vapor and to incorporate it in its internal crystal lattice while releasing heat at the same time. The operation of adsorption heat pumps and refrigerators is therefore based on the ability of porous solids (the adsorbent) to adsorb vapor (the adsorbate or refrigerant) when at low temperature and to desorb it when heated. The adsorption system is a

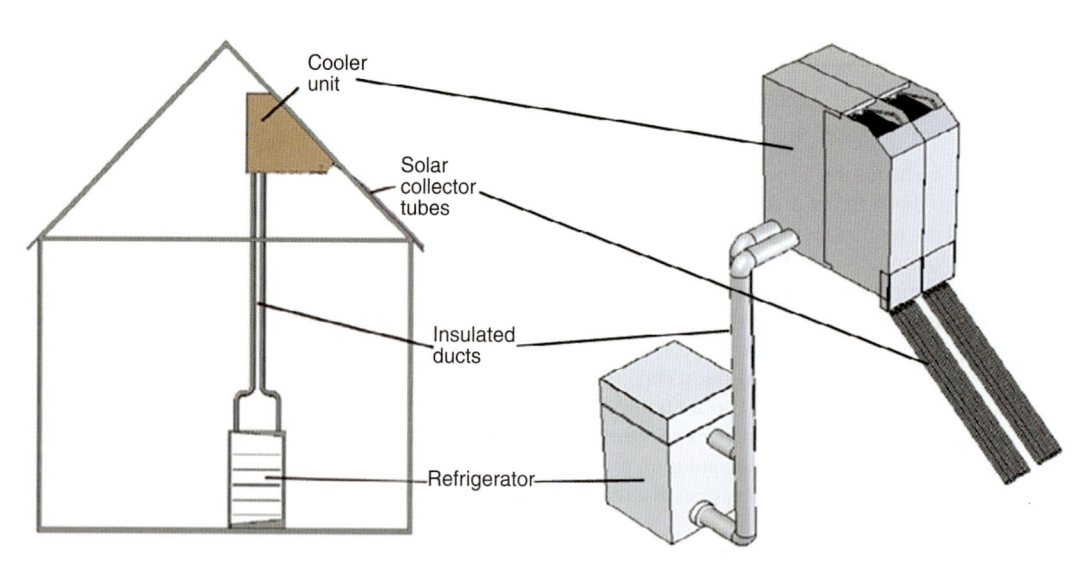

Figure 7 Solar Polar's commercial product.

Figure 8 Rotartica commercial product.

four-temperature discontinuous cycle that consists of one or several adsorbers connected to heating sources, condenser, and evaporator. **Figure** 9 below shows a single adsorbent bed intermittent adsorption cycle.

The adsorption cycle presented in **Figure** 9 consists of four stage processes that are detailed in **Figure 10**.

The processes demonstrated in **Figure 10** are as follows:

- *Process A to B.* Heating and pressurization, where the adsorbent is heated while the adsorber is closed and therefore raising the pressure from the evaporating to the condensing pressure.
- *Process B to C.* Desorption (generation) and condensation, where the adsorbent temperature continues to increase and hence inducing desorption of vapor which is then passed into condenser for condensation by rejecting heat to the environment. The heat necessary to regenerate the adsorbent is a low-grade heat source such as solar energy or waste heat.
- *Process C to D.* Cooling and depressurization, where the adsorbent releases heat while the adsorber is closed and therefore decreasing the pressure from the condensing to evaporating the pressure.
- *Process D to A.* Adsorption and evaporation, where the adsorbent temperature continues to decrease and hence inducing adsorption of vapor being vaporized in the evaporator. The heat of evaporation is drawn from the space by means cooling medium, which is usually air or water in the case of air conditioning.

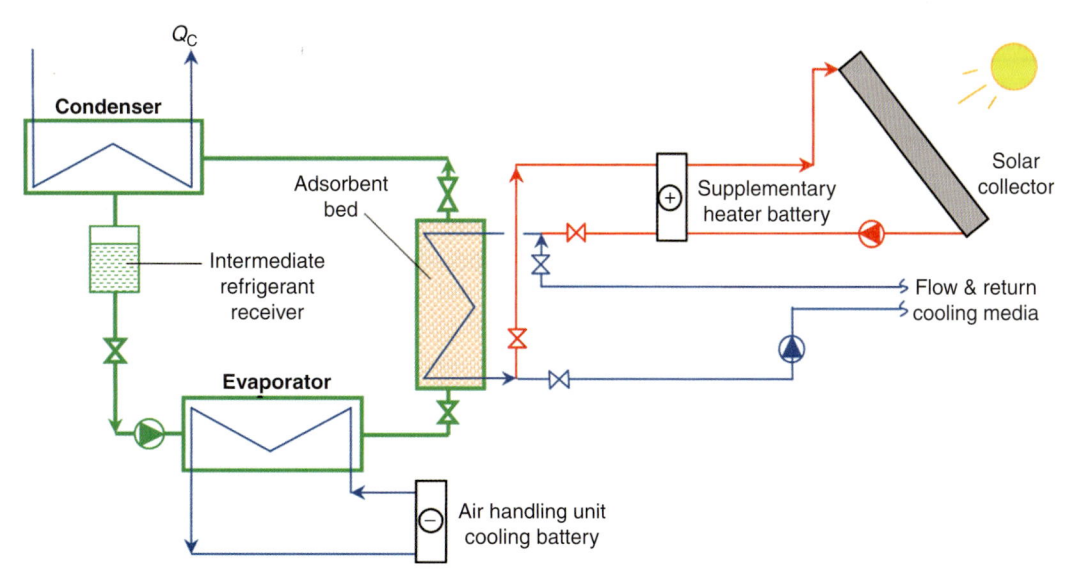

Figure 9 Schematic diagram of an intermittent adsorption cycle.

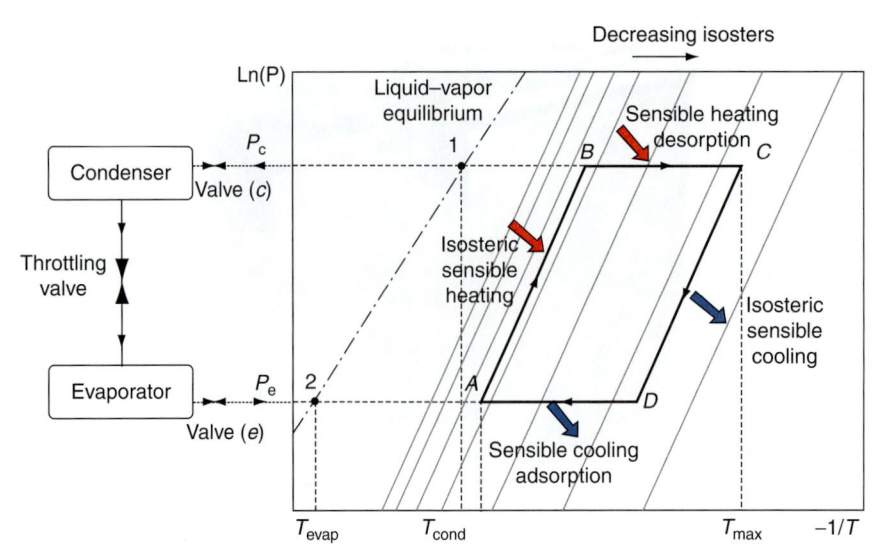

Figure 10 Clapeyron diagram for an adsorption system [9].

Although the heating and cooling provided by a single generator is discontinuous, it can be made continuous by operating two or more generators out of phase. **Figure 11** shows a schematic diagram of a typical conventional adsorption system with two adsorbers (generators).

The heating and cooling water media interchange between the two adsorbent beds and therefore ensuring the adsorption of vapor is continuous in order to maintain the cooling condition requirements.

Assuming, heat supplied to the systems in **Figures 9** and **11** is derived from solar energy, the SCOP can be established based on the two ideal Carnot cycles and this is given by the following expression:

$$\text{SCOP} = \eta_{\text{Coll}} \frac{T_{\text{evap}}(T_s - T_{\text{Cond}})}{T_s(T_{\text{evap}} - T_{\text{Cond}})} \qquad [14]$$

where $T_s > T_{\max}$ (K) is the temperature of heat source, T_{evap} (K) is the temperature of refrigeration load, and T_{Cond} (K) is the temperature of heat sink.

There are a few solar-powered adsorption systems operating. According to Solair [8], 11% of the systems installed utilize adsorption cycles.

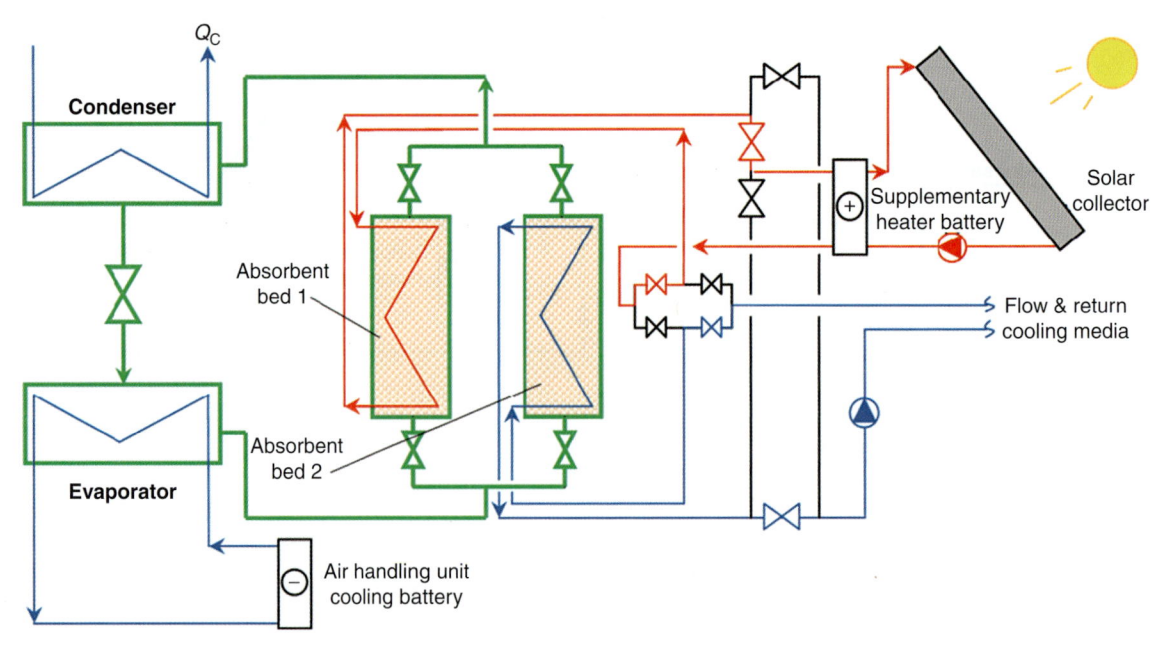

Figure 11 Schematic diagram of a continuous adsorption cycle.

3.14.4.6 Ejector Systems

An ejector cooling system (ECS) is a mechanical system utilizing the Rankine cycle and the gas dynamic effect of an ejector (a thermal compression process). The basic ejector refrigeration cycle is illustrated in **Figure 12**. The system consists of two loops, the power loop and the refrigeration loop. In the power loop, low-grade heat, Q_G, is used in a generator to evaporate high-pressure liquid refrigerant (process 1–2). The high-pressure vapor generated, known as the primary fluid, flows through the ejector where it accelerates through the nozzle. The reduction in pressure that occurs induces vapor from the evaporator, known as the secondary fluid, at point 3. The two fluids mix in the mixing chamber before entering the diffuser section where the flow decelerates and pressure recovery occurs. The mixed fluid then flows to the condenser where it is condensed rejecting heat, Q_C to the environment. A portion of the liquid exiting the condenser at point 5 is then pumped to the boiler for the completion of the power cycle. The remainder of the liquid is expanded through an expansion device and enters the evaporator of the refrigeration loop at point 6 as a mixture of liquid and vapor. The refrigerant evaporates in the evaporator producing a refrigeration effect, Q_E, and the resulting vapor is then drawn into the ejector at point 3.

The ECS is reported to compete with absorption on the grounds of simplicity, reliability, and low installation cost; however, its COP is much lower (typically 0.3 for a single-effect system).

The efficiency of the integrated cycle or SCOP for an ECS is established using the following equation:

$$\text{SCOP} = \eta_{\text{coll}} \left(\phi \frac{h_5 - h_4}{h_1 - h_6} \right) \qquad [15]$$

where $\phi = \dot{m}_e / \dot{m}_g$ (entrainment ratio), η_{coll} is collector efficiency, and h is vaporization latent heat of the refrigerant.

The SCOP of 0.25 was reported at evaporating, condensing, and generating temperatures of 8 °C, 32 °C, and 95 °C, respectively. Furthermore, Mostofizadeh and Bohne [13] reported a COP of 0.3–0.35 at evaporator, condenser, and generator operating temperatures of 4 °C, 40 °C, and 90 °C.

Huang et al. [10] have reported on the development of a solar-driven ECS of 10.5 kW cooling capacity with a 65 m² double-glazed flat-plate solar collector. Wolpert and Riffat [17] theoretically obtained a COP of 0.62 for a PTC-driven steam ejector system of 13 kW cooling capacity. The experimentally derived COP of their system operating in Loughborough, UK, was only 0.3.

3.14.4.7 Photovoltaic–Compression Systems

These systems combine PV cells with electrically driven vapor compression refrigeration systems. PV cells convert insolation to DC electricity, which is then inverted into AC to produce shaft power for an electromechanical compressor. According to Best and Pilatowski [14], these systems have strong market pull mainly due to the lower cost and higher COP of the refrigeration machine. A typical system is shown in **Figure 13**.

However, research is needed to improve the efficiency and lower the cost of PV panels. Various materials for PV cells such as cadmium sulfide (CdS), amorphous silicon (a-Si), copper indium diselenide (CuInSe$_2$), cadmium telluride (CdTe), and polycrystalline silicon have been tested. It has been established that the maximum power delivered is limited by the relatively low efficiency of the panel (<20%). Results of the Solair project have shown promise in air-conditioning and cold storage. A 1 kW (COP = 2.5–4) prototype air conditioner was built and connected to a 1.2 kW output array of PV cells activated by threshold insolation of 450 W m^{-2}. The cold storage prototype was built and tested in Spain. Results show that the operation has been satisfactory over a range of climatic conditions and a variety of foodstuffs.

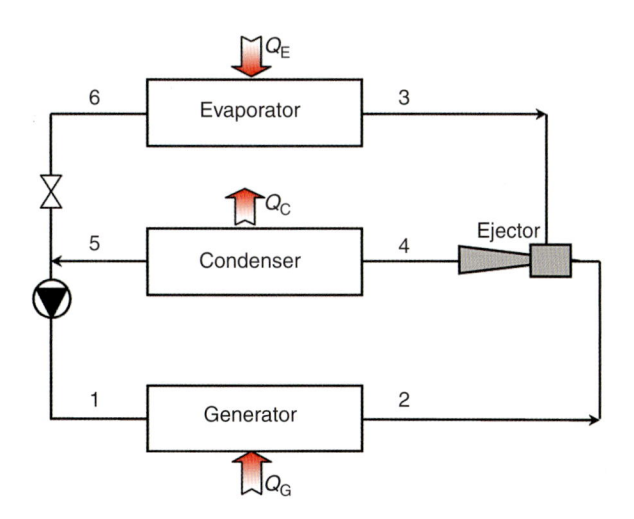

Figure 12 Basic ejector cycle.

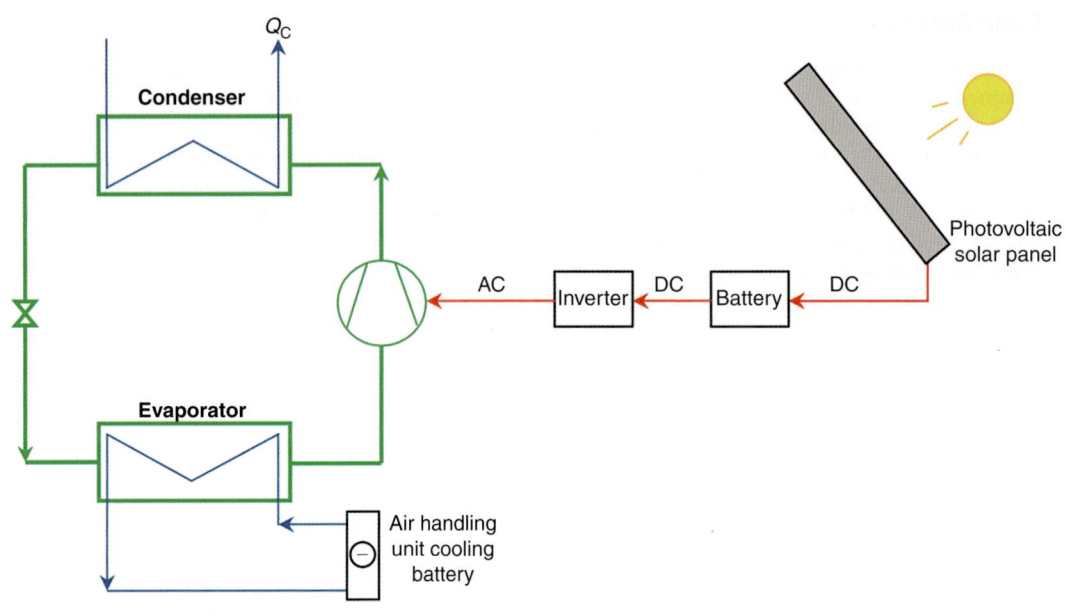

Figure 13 Typical photovoltaic vapor compression cycle.

3.14.5 Relative Comparison of Solar Cooling Technologies

The relative use of solar cooling systems will depend on their relative performance in terms of efficiency, capital cost, and LCC. Work carried out by Syed *et al.* [6] investigated these and the results of this investigation are detailed below.

3.14.5.1 Solar Coefficient of Performance

In assessing the relative efficiency of a solar cooling cycle, we are concerned with the efficiency of the cooling cycle and efficiency of the collector device itself. **Figure 14** shows the range of SCOP data reported for four competing solar cooling technologies at different application temperatures.

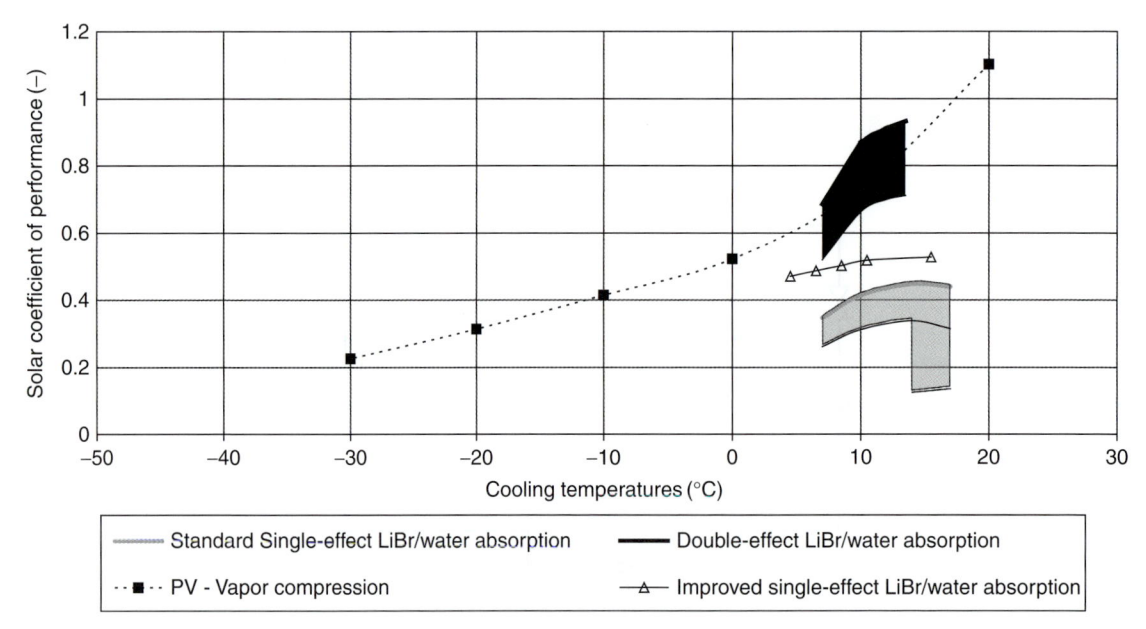

Figure 14 High-level SCOP map for a range of cooling temperatures.

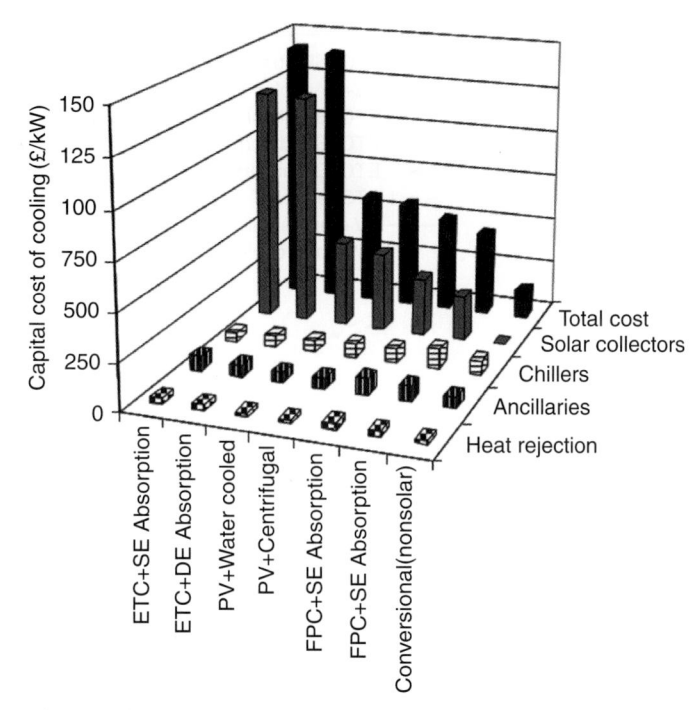

Figure 15 A comparison of the capital cost of solar cooling systems.

5.14.5.2 Capital Cost Comparison

Figure 15 subdivides the three generic families and compares the capital cost composition of solar cooling equipment normalized per kilowatt of cooling.

The following observations from **Figure 15** are noteworthy:

- The collector cost ranges from 2 to 26 times the chiller cost depending on their types and operating temperatures.
- About a sixth of the investment is required for procuring flat-plate collectors for supplying hot water at a temperature of 75 °C compared with concentrating collectors for higher temperatures. The lower capital cost system consists of flat-plate collectors and single-effect absorption chillers sized for low hot water temperatures.
- The lowest cost option is currently 3 times the cost of a conventional (nonsolar) vapor compression system.

5.14.5.3 Life-Cycle Cost Comparison

LCC depends on the SCOP as well as capital and running cost of systems. Only those systems that show lower SCOP could have better LCC if they have lower capital costs. These two have the highest SCOP; however, the options that have a marginally lower SCOP were also considered in an LCC evaluation. In practice, the SCOP will depend on the availability of solar energy and whether additional thermal energy is required. The solar fraction SOLF is sometimes used to describe the utilization of solar energy for cooling. Therefore, SOLF is described as a ratio of thermal solar energy or electrical solar energy input to total energy input (including ancillary energy). It should be noted that a solar fraction of unity is achievable if a system is energized entirely with solar energy. This is given by either of the following equations:

$$\text{SOLF}_{\text{the}} = \frac{Q_{\text{sol}}}{Q_{\text{sol}} + Q_{\text{gas}}} \quad [16]$$

$$\text{SOLF}_w = \frac{W_{\text{pv}}}{W_{\text{pv}} + W_{\text{poh}}} \quad [17]$$

where Q_{sol} is the solar thermal energy, Q_{gas} is the gas auxiliary energy, and W_{pv} is the solar electrical energy.

Therefore, the overall LCC is given by the following equation:

$$\text{LCC} = \frac{1}{Q_e}\left(Z\left(\frac{i}{1-(1+i)^{-n}}\right) + C_{\text{wg}}\left(\text{EFLH} \times W_{\text{eflh}} + \text{POH} \times W_{\text{poh}}\right) + \left(Q_g \times C_{\text{ng}}\right) + M \right) \quad [18]$$

where Z is the capital cost, Q_g is the generator load, C_{ng} is the natural gas tariff, C_{wg} is the grid electricity tariff, EFLH is the number of equivalent full load hours (EFLH), POH is the plant on hours which is typically 1.5 EFLH, W_{eflh} is the electrical

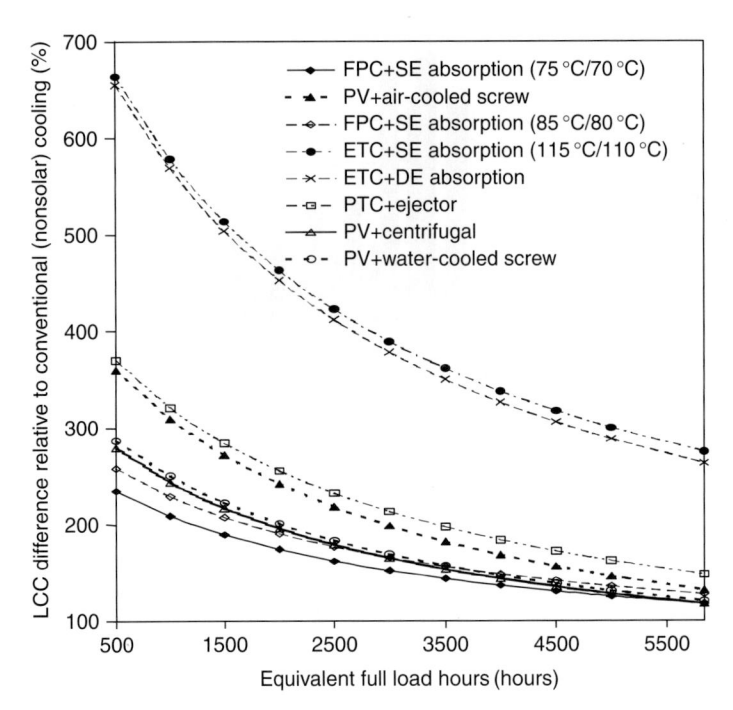

Figure 16 Annual difference in life-cycle cost between solar and nonsolar cooling systems.

energy input as shaft power to mechanical compressor, Q_e is the evaporator load, W_{poh} is the ancillary plant power, and M is the maintenance cost.

An LCC comparison was carried out to consider the combined effect of capital and running cost on system performance. It was found that due to the high capital cost of currently available solar collectors, annual LCC savings with solar cooling systems compared with the conventional system cannot yet be realized. This is indicated in **Figure 16**, which provides the difference in LCC of solar cooling systems and a conventional centrifugal vapor compression system with a base of 100% (indicating LCC equivalence) against EFLH.

As the systems are run for longer EFLH, the LCC difference diminishes due to the impact of cost of saved energy. Interestingly, this results show that the lowest capital cost option reflects the lowest LCC difference for a number of EFLH of cooling.

The result of an LCC sensitivity study has shown that solar cooling using flat-plate collectors and single-effect absorption chillers at the lowest driving temperatures could become economical if the collector capital cost is reduced [11].

3.14.6 Application of Solar Cooling System

A recent study funded by the European Union investigated the current and future potential use of the solar cooling systems in Europe. It created a database of installed systems and was able to draw some key conclusions.

There is a significant potential stated for solar cooling technology and particularly in the <20 kW capacity range. The total number of systems currently in operation in Europe is not very well known but may be estimated to 300–400 installations. Specifically, an increase in small-size solar cooling systems for residential application has been observed in southern European countries. In general, the increase of the sales rate of small-sized chillers within the last two years is promising. Absorption chillers are the thermally driven systems most present on the market in both small and large applications. Their combination with flat-plate or evacuated-tube solar collectors is quite well experienced in large systems.

Small-scale sorption chillers are now commercially available, but the market is in its infancy and there are several nontechnical barriers which can resist penetration. At the moment, the key factors are that combining solar heating and cooling needs high effort in design stage, which is not affordable for small applications, and small-scale sorption chillers are at the moment expensive due to low production numbers.

Critical to expansion is the integration with a solar heating system, and if so, it is possible for solar-powered cooling to deliver large-scale benefits.

3.14.7 Integration with Solar Hot Water and Solar Tthermal Systems for Cost-Effectiveness

A key barrier to application is the relative cost associated with the technology. However, as the solar cooling system has solar collectors, it is possible to produce heating also and therefore improving the economics of application. A typical combined system is illustrated in **Figure 17**.

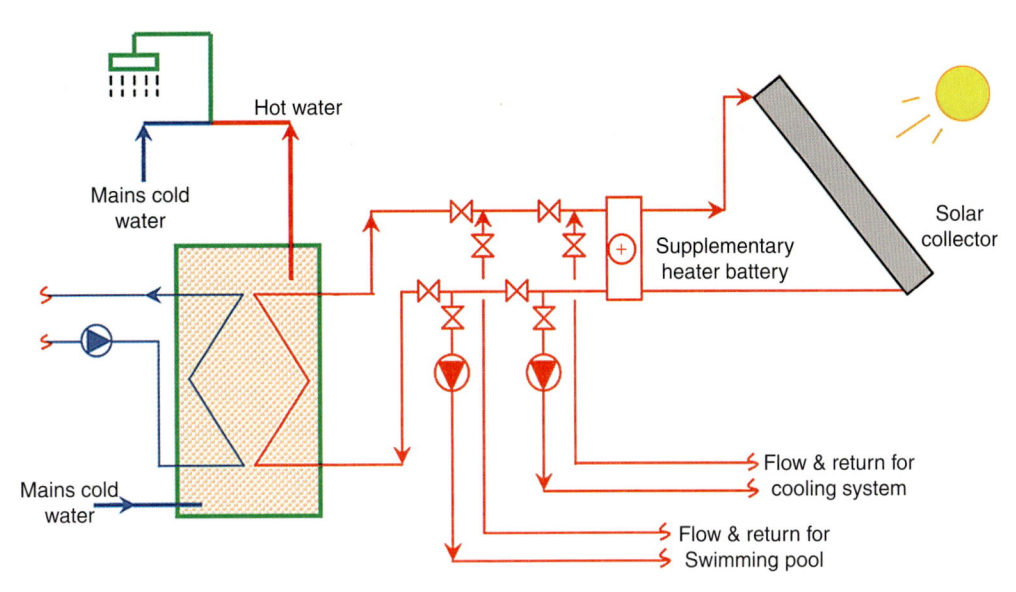

Figure 17 A schematic diagram of a combined solar cooling, heating, and hot water system.

5.14.8 Conclusions

This chapter highlights the what, how, and why solar-powered cooling could be utilized. It provides information on the current state of the solar cooling market and the relative performance of different technologies. Specifically, the benefits of solar-powered cooling are as follows:

- Enables the usage of the surplus solar heat during the summer
- No overheating of the solar system during the summer
- Simultaneity of solar heat supply and cooling demand
- Minimum operating costs for cooling, heating, and for domestic hot water
- Using solar heat as a renewable energy source
- Independency from fossil fuels.

To fully realize these potential benefits, some significant developments in terms of cost minimization, value engineering, and integration of systems are required.

References

[1] SOLARNEXT (2011) http://www.solarnext.eu/eng/sol/solarcooling.shtml (accessed 12 October).
[2] Jones WP (1997) *Air-Conditioning Applications and Design*, 2nd edn. London, UK: Edward Arnold.
[3] Gutkowsky KM and Ryduchowski KW (1986) Solar absorption system for air-conditioning. *International Journal of Refrigeration* 9: 39.
[4] Ahmed CSK, Gandhidasan P, and Al-Farayedhi AA (1997) Simulation of a hybrid liquid desiccant based air-conditioning system. *Applied Thermal Engineering* 17(2): 125–134.
[5] Dieckmann J, Roth K, and Brodrick J (2008) *Liquid Desiccant Air Conditioners. ASHRAE Journal*, October 2008. American Society of Heating, Refrigerating and Air-Conditioning Engineers, Inc.
[6] Syed A, Maidment GG, Tozer R, and Missenden J (2005) Optimal solar cooling systems. *Proceedings of the Institute of Refrigeration*, London.
[7] International Energy Agency (IEA) (2002) Solar assisted air-conditioning of buildings. *Task 25*. http://www.iea-shc.org/task25/ (accessed 12 September 2011).
[8] SOLAIR (2009) Survey of Available Technical Solutions and Successful Running Systems. www.solar-project.eu/uploads/media/SOLAIR_survey_cross_country_update.pdf (accessed 7 December 2011).
[9] Hassan HZ, Mohamad AA, and Bennacer R (2011) Simulation of an adsorption solar cooling system. *Energy* 36(1): 530–537.
[10] Huang BJ, Chang JM, Petrenko VA, and Zhuk KB (1998) A solar ejector cooling system using R141b. *Solar Energy* 64(4–6): 223–226.
[11] Syed A, Maidment G, Tozer R, and Missenden J (2002) A study of the economic perspectives of solar air-conditioning schemes. *CIBSE National Technical Conference*, part 2. 24 September. London, UK: Royal College of Physicians.
[12] Halliday SP, Beggs CB, and Sleigh PA (2007) The use of solar desiccant cooling in the UK: a feasibility study. *Applied Thermal Engineering* 22: 1327–1338.
[13] Mostofizadeh and Bohne (2001) Theoretical and experimental investigation of a two-phase/two-component ejector for cold production. *Proceedings of the 2nd International Heat Powered Cycles Conference*, Paris, pp. 217–224.
[14] Best R and Pilatowsky I (1998) Solar assisted cooling with sorption systems: status of the research in Mexico and Latin America. *International Journal of Refrigeration* 21(2): 150–159.
[15] Pesaran AA and Wipke K (1994) Use of unglazed transpired solar collectors for desiccant cooling. *Solar Energy* 52: 419–427.

[16] Lu SM, Shy RJ, Yan WJ, and Chung TW (1995) Development and experimental validation of novel solar desiccant-dehumidification refrigeration systems. *Energy* 20(8): 751–757.
[17] Wolpert and Riffat (2002) 13 kW cooling hybrid/gas ejector air-conditioning system. *Proceedings of the 1st International Conference on Sustainable Energy Technologies, Porto,* Portugal, pp. RHP 51/70–53/70.
[18] Gommed K and Grossman G (2007) Experimental investigation of a liquid desiccant system for solar cooling and dehumidification. *Solar Energy* 81: 131–138.

3.15 Solar-Assisted Heat Pumps

DA Chwieduk, Warsaw University of Technology, Warsaw, Poland

© 2012 Elsevier Ltd. All rights reserved.

3.15.1	Introduction to the Concept of Solar-Assisted Heat Pumps	495
3.15.2	Heat Pump Fundamentals	495
3.15.2.1	Principles of Heat Pump Operation	495
3.15.2.2	Thermodynamic Cycles	497
3.15.2.3	Classification of Heat Pumps	501
3.15.2.4	Renewable Heat Sources	502
3.15.3	Solar-Assisted Heat Pump System	506
3.15.3.1	Classification, Configurations, and Functions	506
3.15.3.2	Direct Solar-Assisted Heat Pump Systems	507
3.15.3.3	Series Solar-Assisted Heat Pump Systems	508
3.15.3.4	Parallel Solar-Assisted Heat Pump	511
3.15.3.5	Dual-Source Solar-Assisted Heat Pump	516
3.15.3.6	Other Configurations	517
3.15.4	Solar-Assisted Heat Pump System with Seasonal Storage	519
3.15.4.1	Fundamental Options of Seasonal Energy Storage	519
3.15.4.2	Classification and Evaluation of Seasonal Ground Storage	521
3.15.4.3	Heat and Mass Transfer in the Ground Store, General Consideration	524
3.15.4.4	Applications	525
References		527

3.15.1 Introduction to the Concept of Solar-Assisted Heat Pumps

There are some limitations on the use of solar radiation for heating purposes, mainly because of its stochastic and intermittent character. There are changes in solar radiation availability in the long term, that is, over a year, and also in the short term, that is, over a day. When solar energy is used for space heating, the time and peak values of available solar radiation are quite opposite to the time and peak values of space heating demand. This is especially true in high-latitude countries, where in winter the solar radiation level is low and the duration of solar irradiation is short, and consequently there is a cold climate and long heating season with high heating demands.

In many high-latitude regions, heating of buildings is a major component of the total energy used in the building sector. Usually 'traditional' solar active heating systems alone cannot provide all the heating needs. There are different options to solve this problem. One of them is to couple a solar heating system with a heat pump in one combined heating system, as can take place in a small- or medium-scale application, that is, in single-family houses and multifamily or public buildings, respectively. This type of a heating system is called a solar-assisted heat pump (SAHP) system. Another option is to use the seasonal solar energy storage in the form of sensible heat of a large storage volume. Usually the temperature of the heat stored is too low to be used directly for heating. The low-temperature heat stored can be converted into higher temperature heat by applying a heat pump. In this way also a heat pump is incorporated into the heating system. Such heating systems can be used for medium- or large-scale applications, that is, in multifamily or public buildings, or blocks of buildings (i.e., in communes and small city districts), respectively. In the case of medium-scale applications, the heating system is termed a solar-assisted heat pump system with seasonal storage (SAHPSS) system, and a common example is a solar-assisted heat pump system with ground storage (SAHPGS). In the case of large-scale applications, such a system is called a central solar heating plant with seasonal storage (CSHPSS). There are a variety of underground thermal energy storage (UTES) system configurations and modes of operation. Solar collectors and a heat pump are the major system components.

This chapter describes the concept, classification, and operation of SAHP systems, including systems with seasonal storage. For better understanding of the idea of SAHP system operation and application, the fundamentals of heat pumps are initially presented. Heat pumps applied in SAHP systems are vapor compression heat pumps, and this type of heat pumps are described and analyzed.

3.15.2 Heat Pump Fundamentals

3.15.2.1 Principles of Heat Pump Operation

Heat pumps, refrigerators, and heat engines are heat machines. Their operation is based on thermodynamic processes that are governed by the first and second laws of thermodynamics [1, 2]. Heat pumps and refrigerators operate in reversed cycles compared with heat engines. The processes and energy flows are in the opposite direction to those in the power cycles of heat engines, as presented schematically in **Figure 1**.

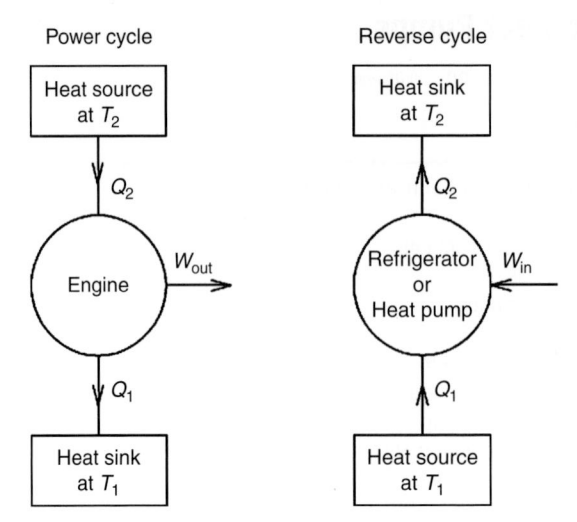

Figure 1 Concept of power cycle for a heat engine and reverse cycle for a refrigerator or a heat pump.

A heat engine's function is to generate work using a heat source. In a heat engine, the high-temperature T_2 heat source is used giving the heat input Q_2 to get the energy output in the form of work W. However, there is an amount of heat Q_1 at lower temperature T_1 that must be removed to the heat sink to fulfill the first law of thermodynamics. The first law of thermodynamics is the conservation of energy law, and can be written (see **Figure 1**) as follows:

$$Q_2 = |W| + |Q_1| \qquad [1]$$

Unlike a heat engine, a heat pump's function is to lift a certain quantity of heat Q_1 from a heat source at a lower temperature level T_1 to a heat sink at higher temperature T_2. However, to fulfill the first law of thermodynamics, the upgrading of heat must be done by the work W that is supplied to the machine. Following this and **Figure 1**, it can be seen that the amount of heat Q_2 to the heat sink is the sum of heat Q_1 extracted from the heat source and the amount of work W required in the process, and the first law of thermodynamics, described by eqn [1], is accomplished.

As it has been already mentioned, a heat pump is used to supply heat Q_2 at high temperature T_2. Conversely, a refrigerator is used to extract heat Q_1 at low temperature T_1. It means that a refrigerator's function is to cool down a given heat source extracting a certain quantity of heat Q_1 from this source (at lower temperature T_1). In a refrigerator, as in a heat pump, to fulfill the first law of thermodynamics, to extract the heat from the heat source the work W must be supplied to drive the cycle and heat must be removed at a higher temperature. In practice, the functions of both heat pump and refrigerator can be combined in one machine, when both heating and cooling are required simultaneously. For example, such situations can be found at a sport center where some chillers are used to cool an ice skating area and at the same time they also provide heat for hot water for swimming pools, operating like a heat pump.

The efficiency of a heat engine, a refrigerator, and a heat pump is defined using the first law of thermodynamics. In the case of a heat pump and refrigerator, efficiency is measured by the coefficient of performance (COP), which is the ratio of the energy that is used for heating (at the heat sink) or for cooling (at the heat source) to the work that has to be supplied to drive the cycle. The efficiency of a heat engine, a refrigerator, and a heat pump can be expressed by eqns [2a], [2b], and [2c], respectively, in the following way:

$$\eta = \frac{W}{Q_2} = \frac{Q_2 - |Q_1|}{Q_2} = 1 - \frac{|Q_1|}{Q_2} \qquad [2a]$$

$$\text{COP}_r = \frac{|Q_1|}{|W|} = \frac{|Q_1|}{Q_2 - |Q_1|} = \frac{Q_2 - |W|}{|W|} = \left|\frac{Q_2}{W}\right| - 1 \qquad [2b]$$

$$\text{COP}_{hp} = \frac{Q_2}{|W|} = \frac{Q_2}{Q_2 - |Q_1|} \qquad [2c]$$

It can be seen from eqn [2a] that the efficiency of the heat engine is always lower than 1, and the COP of a refrigerator (eqn [2b]) is one less than that of a heat pump (eqn [2c]).

Summarizing, a heat engine is a machine generating work from the heat that is provided to the process and rejecting some amount of the heat at a lower temperature. Conversely, a heat pump is a machine that lifts a certain quantity of heat from a lower temperature level to a higher temperature level using the work provided to the machine. A refrigerator is a machine that extracts a certain quantity of heat from a lower temperature level and transfers it to a higher temperature level also using work provided to the machine.

According to the second law of thermodynamics, heat cannot flow from a lower to a higher temperature without the expenditure of energy. This law for the reversible cycle can be expressed by the following equation:

$$\sum \frac{Q_i}{T_i} = 0 \qquad [3a]$$

Taking into account eqn [3a] and referring to the nomenclature used before, the following can be written:

$$\frac{Q_1}{T_1} - \frac{Q_2}{T_2} = 0 \qquad [3b]$$

Referring to eqn [1], eqn [3b] can be rewritten in the following way:

$$\frac{Q_1}{T_1} - \frac{Q_1 + W}{T_2} = 0 \qquad [4]$$

After rearranging the terms, it is as follows:

$$\frac{Q_1}{T_1} - \frac{Q_1}{T_2} - \frac{W}{T_2} = 0 \qquad [5]$$

Because $T_2 > T_1$, the difference between the first and the second term of eqn [5] is larger than zero, and the work input must be sufficiently big to make the sum to be equal to 0. Thus, there is a minimum work that is required for the machine, that is, the heat pump, to operate reversibly. For the vapor compression heat pumps considered, the work supplied is in the form of mechanical energy provided by electrical energy to drive the heat pump compressor. There are other types of heat pumps, where the energy required to drive the system is supplied in the form of heat, and these are sorption heat pumps (not analyzed in this chapter).

3.15.2.2 Thermodynamic Cycles

In principle, to achieve the reversible cycle in a heat pump, a condensable fluid must realize a reversed Carnot cycle. This allows heat to be input and output at a constant temperature by means of boiling and condensation. This meets the requirement that all heat transfer to and from the system must be reversible. The Carnot cycle [1–4] for a heat pump in a temperature–entropy diagram is shown in **Figure 2** on the left and the main components of a heat pump based on the Carnot cycle are shown on the right.

The following processes presented and numbered in **Figure 2** take place:

1–2 Isentropic compression. Two-phase liquid–gas of the working fluid from the evaporator flows into the compressor and is compressed to the required level of pressure and temperature.

2–3 Constant pressure and temperature heat rejection – condensation. Vapor of the working fluid at high pressure and temperature flows from the compressor to the condenser. At constant pressure and temperature, the working fluid condenses giving up the heat (latent heat – condensation heat) to the sink, for example, space heating medium that provides the heat required by the space heating demand.

3–4 Isentropic expansion. Liquid of the working fluid from the condenser flows into the ideal expansion device (at high pressure and temperature) and is expanded to the required level of pressure and temperature to close the reversible cycle.

4–1 Constant pressure heat absorption (evaporation). The two-phase liquid–gas working fluid at low pressure and temperature flows from the expansion valve to the evaporator. At constant pressure and temperature, the working fluid evaporates, because of the existing temperature gradient between working fluid and the low-temperature heat source. Then the process repeats.

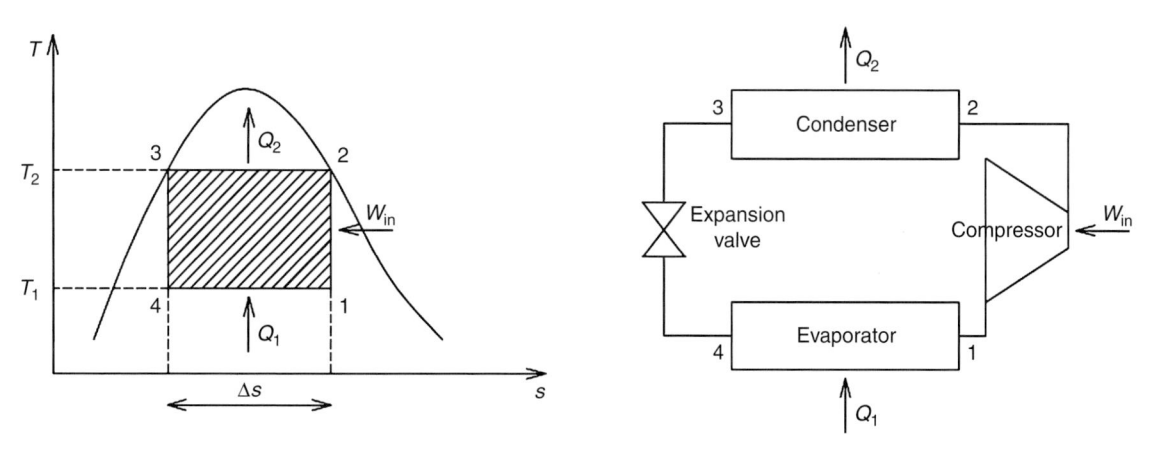

Figure 2 The Carnot cycle for a heat pump and schematic concept of a vapor compression heat pump.

The ideal reversed Carnot cycle is realized between heat source and heat sink that have constant temperature, that is, T_1 = const and T_2 = const. The transition process between these two states (lines) is adiabatic, and can be written in the following way:

$$\frac{dQ}{T} = dS = 0 \qquad [6]$$

Equation [6] is true for only reversible adiabatic processes and then S = const. Analyzing **Figure 2** it can be seen that two processes are adiabatic: 1–2 compression and 3–4 expansion. Because of the equity of entropy differences, $S_4 - S_1 = S_3 - S_2$, the efficiency of the Carnot cycle for a heat engine (eqn [2]) is as follows:

$$\eta = \frac{|W|}{Q_2} = 1 - \frac{|Q_1|}{Q_2} = 1 - \frac{T_1(S_4 - S_1)}{T_2(S_3 - S_2)} = 1 - \frac{T_1}{T_2} \qquad [7a]$$

The same can be written for the efficiency (i.e., COP) of a refrigerator and a heat pump operating in reversible adiabatic processes 1–2 and 3–4 (**Figure 2**), and according to eqns [2b] and [2c] respectively, it is as follows:

$$COP_r = \frac{|Q_1|}{Q_2 - |Q_1|} = \frac{T_1 \Delta S}{(T_2 - T_1)\Delta S} = \frac{T_1}{(T_2 - T_1)} \qquad [7b]$$

$$COP_{hp} = \frac{|Q_2|}{|Q_2| - Q_1} = \frac{T_2 \Delta S}{(T_2 - T_1)\Delta S} = \frac{T_2}{(T_2 - T_1)} \qquad [7c]$$

The work W that is necessary to drive the machine is equal to the area limited by lines 1–2, 2–3, 3–4, and 4–1, which represent all ongoing processes, as shown in **Figure 2**. The Carnot cycle has the maximum possible COP between any two temperature levels T_2 and T_1 and is used as an ideal cycle for comparison with practical ones. From eqns [7b] and [7c], it is clear that the COP is the biggest when the temperature difference between T_2 and T_1 is the smallest (the work W – the matched area – is the smallest). It means that the operation of a heat pump and refrigerator is most efficient when the temperature of a heat source is as close as possible to the temperature of a heat sink. This is very important for the practical selection of heat sources and heat sinks.

The main components of a heat pump specified below are responsible for processes presented and numbered in **Figure 2**:

1–2 Compressor.
2–3 Condenser.
3–4 Theoretically it could be a turbine; however, a Carnot cycle is impractical for power generation, therefore it is expansion valve (and in practice a throttle).
4–1 Evaporator.

To determine the COP of an ideal Carnot cycle heat pump, eqn [7c] can be used. For example, if outside air at 0 °C (273 K) is a heat source and the air inside the house at 20 °C (293 K) is a heat sink, then the COP of the heat pump considered is equal to 14.65. In practice, it is not possible and a real machine would have a COP much smaller, of about 3–4, as is described in the following paragraphs. In reality, a Carnot cycle cannot easily be used for a heat pump (or refrigeration) cycle and the reversed Rankine, Perkins/Elmer, or Linde cycles are used, all being vapor compression cycles [3, 4]. **Figure 3** presents the basic vapor compression cycle for heat pumping in a temperature–entropy diagram.

The following processes presented and numbered in **Figure 3** take place:

1'–2' Isentropic compression. Saturated dry vapor (of the working fluid) at low pressure flows from the evaporator into the compressor and is compressed to the required level of pressure and temperature in the superheating vapor region.

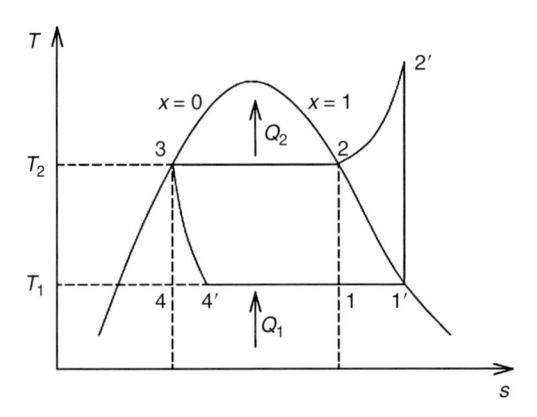

Figure 3 The vapor compression cycle for a heat pump presented in a temperature–entropy diagram.

2'-2   Isobaric heat rejection. Superheated vapor of the working fluid at high pressure and temperature flows from the compressor to the condenser. The heat rejection takes place due to temperature gradient and represents desuperheating of the vapor.

2-3   Isobaric and isothermal heat rejection – condensation. Desuperheated vapor (of the working fluid) at high pressure flows through the condenser. At constant pressure and temperature, vapor condenses giving up the heat to the sink (e.g., space heating medium). Saturated liquid leaves the condenser. There is no pressure drop in the condenser and connecting piping.

3-4'   Isenthalpic expansion. Saturated liquid (of the working fluid) from the condenser flows into the throttle (at high pressure and temperature) and is expanded to the required low pressure and temperature. Expansion losses mean that the cycle is not reversible (not isentropic expansion process).

4'-1'   Isobaric and isothermal evaporation. Two-phase mixture of the working fluid at low pressure and temperature from the throttle flows through the evaporator. At constant pressure and temperature, the working fluid evaporates, taking heat from the low-temperature heat source. There is no pressure drop in the evaporator and connecting piping.

Comparing the evaporation process of this cycle and the Carnot cycle, it is evident that now the end of the evaporation process is exactly on the saturation line (point 1'). It must be underlined that in reality stopping evaporation at just the right dryness fraction, as it is in the Carnot cycle, is very difficult. In addition, real compressors might be damaged because of compressing two-phase mixtures (saturated liquid and vapor) to a saturated vapor state.

In practice, to ensure that the evaporation is really completed and there is only one-phase fluid (saturated vapor) at the compressor inlet, a small amount of superheat (typically a few degrees) is transferred to the vapor just after leaving the evaporator. This is shown in **Figure 4** in the T–S diagram where state 1" (beginning of 'suction') is slightly superheated.

Using a throttle in the place of an ideal expansion device means that the expansion process is not reversible. There is saturated liquid leaving the condenser which flows into the throttle. However, the reduction in pressure in the throttle causes some of the liquid to boil and a two-phase mixture is formed. As a result, the temperature of the working fluid drops. The whole process is isenthalpic, because the enthalpy of the stream of fluid is the same before and after the throttle. However, two phase mixture leaving the throttle contains liquid with lower enthalpy than the fluid before throttle and vapor with higher enthalpy than the fluid before throttle. This means that the working fluid enters the evaporator at point 4' not 4 and the entropy of expansion process in the throttle increases and the process is irreversible.

Entropy difference at the heat source is not equal to that of the sink, the former being bigger than the latter. At such cycle, the work input W to the device must be bigger than that for the Carnot cycle (the rectangular area matched in **Figure 2**). As a consequence, the vapor compression COP is reduced in comparison with a Carnot cycle working between the same temperature limits, and can be written as follows:

$$\text{COP}_{hp} = \frac{|Q_2|}{|Q_2| - Q_1} = \frac{T_2 \Delta S_{2-3}}{(T_2 - T_1)\Delta S_{4'-1}} = \frac{T_2}{(T_2 - T_1)} \frac{\Delta S_{2-3}}{\Delta S_{4'-1}} = \text{COP}_{hpCar}\eta_{hpCar} < \text{COP}_{hpCar} \quad [8]$$

As mentioned above, to ensure complete evaporation, the quantity of heat absorbed from the heat source is increased (evaporation ends at point 1" not at 1 for the Carnot cycle, or 1' for the Linde cycle), as shown in **Figure 4**. This effect of slightly overheating the dry vapor before it enters the compressor results in an increase in the refrigeration effect, which is positive for a refrigerator, but not for a heat pump.

The vapor compression cycle is very often presented as the $\ln(p)$–h diagram. An example of such diagram for the vapor compression cycle is shown in **Figure 5**.

In **Figure 5**, most of the same state points are presented in the $\ln(p)$–h diagram as before (see **Figure 4**). However, there is an extra point 2''', which represents the state of the desuperheated vapor after the compression, which in reality is not an isentropic process. The points in **Figure 5** represent the following processes:

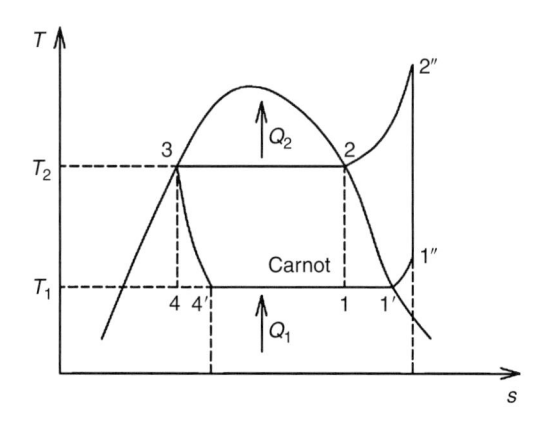

Figure 4 T–S diagram of the ideal vapor compression with the beginning of 'suction' slightly superheated.

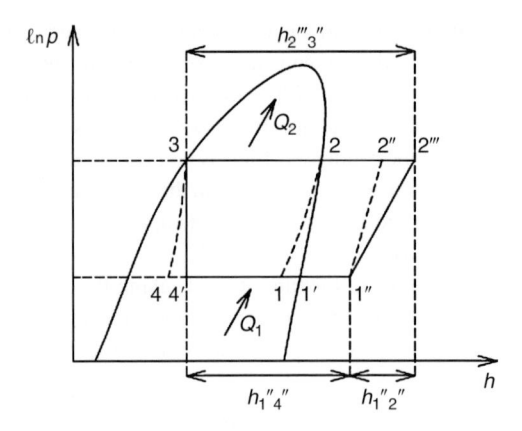

Figure 5 The vapor compression cycle presented in a ln(p)–h diagram.

1″–2‴ Nonisentropic compression in the superheating vapor region, 1″–2″ isentropic compression, dotted line.
2‴–2 Isobaric heat rejection representing the desuperheating of the vapor.
2–3 Isobaric and isothermal heat rejection – condensation.
3–4′ Isenthalpic expansion.
4′–1′ Isobaric and isothermal evaporation.

Analyzing the ln(p)–h diagram, it can be seen that

$q_1 = h_{1″} - h_{4′} = h_{1″4′}$ – isobaric evaporation ($w = 0$);
$q_2 = h_3 - h_{2‴} = -h_{2‴3}$ – isobaric condensation ($w = 0$);
$w_{in} = h_{1″} - h_{2‴} = -h_{1″2‴}$ – adiabatic compression process ($q = 0$).

It is very convenient to use the ln(p)–h diagram to determine the COP of a heat pump, because the COPs are simple ratios of length (enthalpies) in the ln(p)–h diagram, as presented in **Figure 5**. A COP of a refrigerator and a heat pump (referring to eqns [2b] and [2c], respectively) can be expressed as a function of enthalpy. The enthalpies of different refrigerants as functions of pressure and temperature can be found in the literature (e.g., in tables and charts [5]). Thus, the COP of a refrigerator and a heat pump, using the diagram in **Figure 5**, can be expressed as follows:

$$\text{COP}_r = -\frac{h_{1″4″}}{h_{1″2‴}} \quad [9a]$$

$$\text{COP}_{hp} = \frac{h_{2‴3}}{h_{1″2‴}} \quad [9b]$$

The COP of a heat pump described by eqn [9b] is higher than the real one and there are many reasons for this. First, in practice, liquid leaving a condenser is often subcooled to ensure that only the liquid phase of the working fluid enters the throttle. Therefore, apart from the so-called 'superheat horn region' (see **Figures 3** and **4**), there is a 'subcooled region' outside the saturated line (point 3 is moved into the liquid region, to the left). This makes the input work W to drive the machine bigger than for a Carnot cycle, as indicated by the increased area enclosed by the cycle in a T–S diagram, and as a consequence the COP is smaller. It must be also underlined that in real heat exchangers there is a temperature difference between evaporating working fluid and a heat source (e.g., about 10 °C) and between condensing working fluid and a sink (e.g., 5 °C). It makes the temperature difference in a vapor compression heat pump between a heat source and a heat sink bigger than that in an ideal Carnot cycle heat pump, and makes the COP smaller. Another reason for the reduction in COP is the nonideal compression process. Compressors operate with a certain isentropic efficiency and in addition electric motors driving a compressor operate with an efficiency less than one. Therefore, in practice, COP drops to 3–4.

It should be mentioned that nowadays some compressor heat pumps can offer apart from the heating an additional function by being able to cool buildings. There are two main different methods for cooling with a heat pump. In the first method, a heat pump can operate in a reversible cycle, so in summer it operates like a refrigerator (the fundamentals have been described in the beginning of this chapter). In the second method, the so-called direct 'natural cooling' takes place. It means that a heat pump is switched off, except for the control unit and the circulation pumps. The 'natural cooling' is applied in ground and underground water heat pumps when the brine of underground heat exchangers or the groundwater system absorbs the heat from the heating circuit (e.g., floor heating system) in a building and transfers it to the heat source medium in the ground. This method can also be considered as thermal regeneration of the ground heat source (cooled during heating season and heated during summer).

One of the most important issues of heat pumps is requirements for refrigerants. Refrigerants should have low pressures (all subcritical) at heat exchange temperatures. They must be nontoxic, not flammable, and nonpolluting, that is, environmentally safe. Considering their influence on the environment, the following indexes are usually used:

- ODP – ozone depletion potential;
- GWP – global warming potential;
- TEWI – total equivalent warming impact (for the whole system).

It is also required that the refrigerant's density is high for low-volume flow rate and thus a smaller compressor, piping diameter, and heat exchangers can be used. In the past, the most popular refrigerant for domestic and light commercial heat pumps was R22. Nowadays, it has been replaced mainly by R 134a (a hydrofluorocarbon (HFC)). However, there are a number of new (and old) refrigerants such as other HFCs, propane and butane mixtures, ammonia, or carbon dioxide. Another important issue is the selection of a heat source suitable for heating demands and the type of heat pump as described below.

3.15.2.3 Classification of Heat Pumps

As has been described in previous paragraphs, the general principle of a heat pump operation is to extract heat from a low-temperature heat source and to transfer it to a heat sink at a higher temperature. The useful energy output must be significantly greater than additional energy required to drive a heat pump to achieve a real reduction in primary energy use. Heat pumps can use renewable energy or waste heat as a heat source. Energy extracted from these sources is converted into useful heat in the low-temperature range. This low-temperature heat can be applied with high efficiency, for example, for space heating and domestic hot water (DHW) [6].

A number of different classifications of heat pumps can be made; the main one is according to the form of energy that is used to drive them. In this case, the following types are considered:

- mechanically driven, that is, compressor heat pumps;
- thermally driven, that is, sorption heat pumps.

In this chapter, the mechanically driven compressor heat pumps are considered. Among compressor heat pumps, we can list

- electrical heat pumps in which the compressor is driven by electricity (e.g., by an electric motor);
- heat pumps in which the compressor is driven by an internal combustion engine; these heat pumps operate with natural gas, diesel, or biofuel (rapeseed oil).

The heat pumps considered can be classified according to the type of the end user as follows:

- domestic heat pumps for small- and large-scale application used for space heating and DHW;
- domestic heat pumps for small- and large-scale application used for space heating, cooling, and DHW; these heat pumps can work depending on the season of the year (winter and summer) in heating or cooling mode, which means that a heat pump function can be reversed;
- light commercial heat pumps for different heating purposes (applied in offices, schools, hotels, hospitals, public buildings);
- heat pumps with dehumidification function (for swimming pools; for drying of vegetables, fruits, plants, etc.);
- large commercial and industrial heat pumps (for town districts and towns, industrial applications). These mainly use waste heat sources. The sources of waste heat can be sewage, exhaust gases, or technological waste heat in air, water, and vapor.

Classification can also be made according to the heat pump's construction. There are two fundamental options:

- compact or unitary heat pump – all the components are in one compact unit, there is a heat exchanger between a heat pump evaporator and a heat source, and between a heat pump condenser and a heat sink. Usually the heat source is outside the building heated; however, when the waste heat is used it could be also inside a building;
- split heat pumps – the components are split (divided) usually into two units: one of them is located in a separate room or outside a building. Usually an evaporator or a condenser can be located directly at the heat source or at the heat sink, respectively. It means that evaporation and/or condensation take part directly at a heat source or at a heat sink. When the evaporator is located directly at a heat source, such systems are also called direct expansion.

The other way of classification can be done in accordance with the role of a heat pump in a heating system, and it is as follows:

- monovalent heat pump – it operates throughout the year in monovalent mode providing all heating requirements by itself;
- bivalent or hybrid heat pump – to provide all heating requirements it has to operate in conjunction with another heating device or system.

Heat pumps can also be classified according to the type of a heat source medium, which can be generally air, water, and brine (antifreeze mixture). They can use waste or renewable energy heat sources. Renewable energy sources are mainly used for domestic and light commercial (including swimming pools) applications. The renewable energy sources are as follows:

- ambient air;
- ground (soil);
- geothermal water;
- surface water;
- solar radiation.

Another way of heat pump classification is according to the type of heat sink medium, Water and air are the two main heating mediums depending on the type of heating system. Sometimes, heat pumps are named (classified) according to the type of heat source and heat sink medium in the following way:

- air–air;
- air–water;
- water–air;
- water–water;
- ground–water, or brine–water;
- ground–air, or brine–air;
- solar–water (SAHP-w);
- solar–air (SAHP-a).

However, it can be mentioned that the last four types are also called in general ground source heat pumps and solar (solar-assisted) heat pumps (the last two) respectively. Selection of a heat source suitable for a heat sink and for a given heating demand is very important and influences considerably the heat pump operation and in turn its performance (COP).

3.15.2.4 Renewable Heat Sources

Generally, when heat pumps are considered for effective use, the following characteristic features of a heat source are taken into account [6]:

- good availability;
- coherency between the source and the user;
- high thermal capacity;
- constant in time and of relatively high temperature;
- natural energy equilibrium of the source (environment) and its physical characteristics are not affected by heat extraction;
- high purity (to avoid corrosion);
- no pollution, damage to environment, and other ecological issues;
- low cost of heat extraction.

Renewable energy heat sources are described below and their characteristic features that have been just mentioned are analyzed briefly. The simplified idea of utilizing different renewable energy sources for a heat pump at a single-family house is presented in **Figure 6**.

Considering availability of heat sources ambient air is the best. Unfortunately, it is not coherent with space heating demand. When space heating demand is the highest, the air temperature is the lowest. The temperature of ambient air is not constant in time and it can fluctuate very rapidly. Ambient air (heat source) heat pumps operate usually with a COP of about 3. When the temperature of ambient air is just above 0 °C, then the problem with ice formation on the evaporator surface can occur. This surface ice effect causes worse heat transfer conditions and together with the low ambient air temperature they result in low thermal performance of a heat pump, that is, low COP. Nowadays, these possible problems are overcome by applying regular automatic defrosting (the high-temperature working fluid from the compressor, instead of flowing into the condenser, is recirculated into the evaporator). Modern air–water heat pumps can operate down to an outside temperature of −15 °C. However, then their COP is much lower than 3 and they no longer can meet the heating demand completely. Air heat pumps operate in bivalent (dual) mode using an auxiliary heater in times of low outside temperature. Usually, this bivalent mode is monoenergetic mode, that is, electric heater is used. The heating water is preheated by the heat pump, to the selected flow temperature, and then an electric heating cartridge is used to provide auxiliary peak heat. It should be mentioned that an air–water heat exchanger must circulate a large volume of air (e.g., 3000–4000 m^3 h^{-1}). As a consequence, they can generate a lot of noise. Air heat pumps can be constructed and installed as compact heat pumps and in this case air supply duct is used to supply outside air to the heat pump evaporator inside the building and exhaust air duct is used to take off the air used. In this case, a problem with noise generation is very likely. Therefore, the split construction is used very often, and the intake and outtake of air and evaporator are located outside the building, and other heat pump elements inside the building.

There are also heat pumps utilizing exhausted air as a heat source. They are applied mainly in buildings with very low energy demand, for example, in passive buildings, where they are coupled with domestic ventilation system with heat recuperation. The

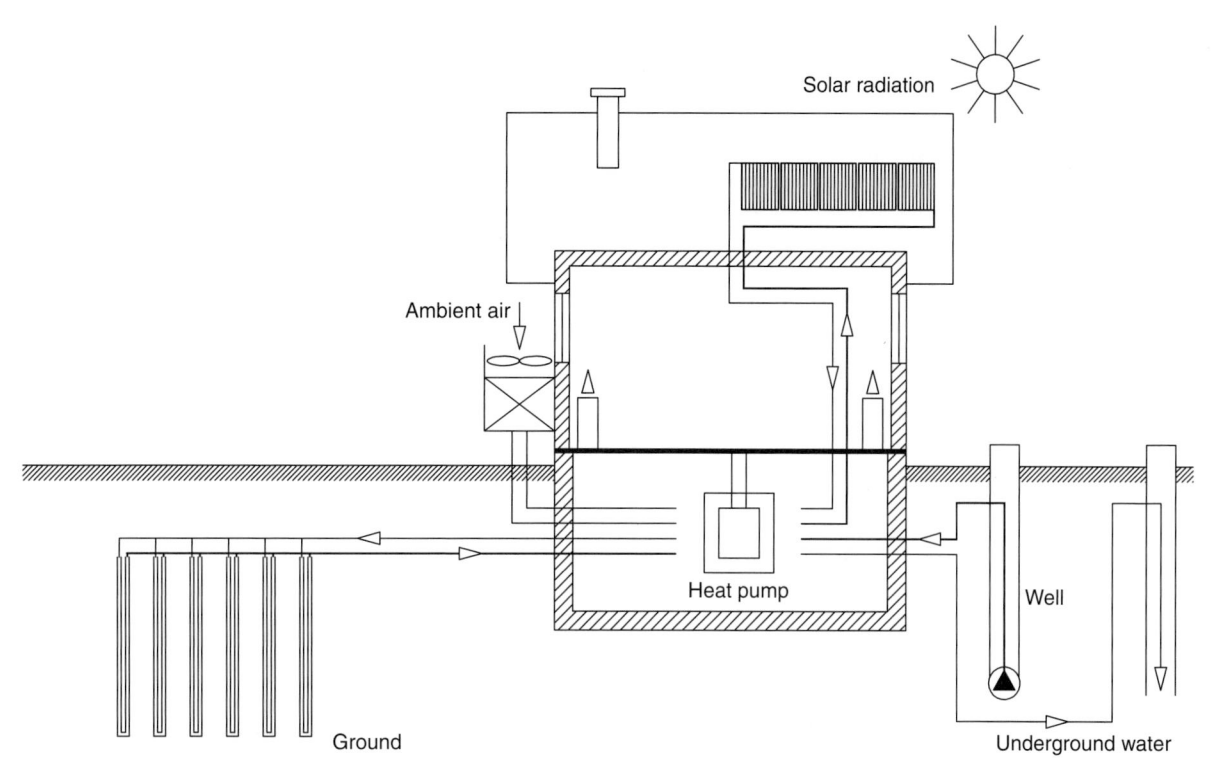

Figure 6 Idea of utilizing different renewable energy sources for a heat pump at a single-family house.

part of heat of air extracted from a building from the ventilation system that cannot be recovered in a direct way (in a recuperative heat exchanger) is used as a heat source for an integral exhaust air–water heat pump. This type of a heat pump can also be used in other so-called 'low-energy buildings', but it cannot operate only in monovalent mode and an electrical supplementary heater is usually used to provide the additional auxiliary heating energy required to meet the total heat demand.

The main advantages of air heat pumps, apart from very good availability of a heat source, are the following:

- heat extraction from outside air does not disturb the natural energy equilibrium of a heat source (environment) and its physical characteristics;
- high purity;
- there is no pollution because of extraction and exhaustion of air cooled, and no damage to the environment;
- there are very low costs of heat extraction, the lowest among all types of renewable energy source heat pumps, and the method of heat extraction is the simplest one.

However, the main disadvantage, that is, no coherency between a heat source and a heat sink (space heating demand), causes the operation of a heat pump with low COP, and as a consequence a higher amount of electricity is used to drive the air heat pump than that required, for example, for the ground source one.

The ground constitutes a suitable heat source for a heat pump considering small-scale low-temperature heating systems [7]. The seasonal temperature fluctuations are much smaller than those of the ambient air even at small depths. Ground at small depth is under the influence of solar radiation, rain, melt snow (water), and other environmental factors. At a depth of 2 m, underground temperatures range from 2 to 13 °C during the heating season (in most European countries). With the increase of ground depth down to 10 m the temperature becomes nearly constant throughout the whole year and is approximately equal to the annual mean outside (ambient) air temperature [8]. With the further increase of depth, the ground temperature increases but relatively very slowly. The influence of geothermal energy is weak even at a depth of 50 or 100 m [9]. The energy flowing from deeper layers upward represents only $0.063-0.1\,\mathrm{W\,m^{-2}}$.

Energy stored in a natural way in the ground medium is extracted by means of large-area horizontal plastic pipework buried underground or longer length plastic tubes set into drilled vertical ducts or bore holes [7, 10]. Heat exchangers are installed in an area next to the building. In horizontal heat exchanger systems, the plastic pipes (e.g., polyurethane (PE)) are buried underground at a depth of between 1.2 and 1.5 m. Individual pipe runs (loops) are usually limited to a length of 100 m. If the length of pipe runs is too big, then there is pressure drop in piping and as a consequence the required pump capacity would be too great. All loops have to be of the same length, because the pressure drop must be the same to achieve identical flow conditions in every pipe run. As a consequence all heat exchanger loops can extract heat evenly from the ground medium. Usually, heat extracted from the ground is transferred via water and antifreeze mixture (brine) to an evaporator of a heat pump. Because of the liquid used, these heat pumps are called brine/water heat pump (brine in the primary and water in the secondary (heating) circuit). In the ground outside the building or just directly inside the building, there is a header duct with a brine distribution that consists of two brine distributors, flow and return, where the pipe ends come together. Return and flow headers are installed slightly higher than piping (venting). It is important that each loop is able to be shut off separately. A circulation pump circulates the brine through the pipes that extract the heat stored underground. The heat extraction from the ground varies from $10\,W\,m^{-2}$ (in the case of underground areas of dry sandy soil) to $35\,W\,m^{-2}$ (in the case of ground with groundwater ways).

In central European countries, the freezing zone in the soil is 1 m and in some regions 1.5 m deep. More to the north (high-latitude countries) the freezing depth is bigger. This makes it preferable to use vertical ground heat exchangers rather than horizontal ones [6]. Heat is extracted from the ground by vertical ground heat exchangers that are mainly in the form of U tubes (so-called ground ducts or probes), double U tubes (so-called duplex probes), or concentric tubes (popular in the past, not at present). These tubes are coupled with a heat pump evaporator similar to the horizontal heat exchanger system. Water and antifreeze mixture (brine) circulate in pipes and the pipe ends come together in a header duct with a brine distribution (with flow and return distributors) located outside or inside the building. If a header duct is located outside the building, it is recommended to insulate the underground collector pipes (flow and return). The location of heat exchanger tubes can vary, and they can be set into the ground in rectangular, hexagonal, or cylindrical configuration. The distance between vertical tubes depends on the thermal and hydrological characteristics of the ground. Usually, this distance can be at least about 4 m for single U tubes and 5 m for double U tubes. Possible heat flux extraction for vertical ground probes depends on the type of the ground [7] and it can be at a level of $20\,W\,m^{-1}$ of a tube length for dry sediment with relatively low thermal conductivity (lower than $1.5\,W\,m^{-1}\,K^{-1}$) or even $70\,W\,m^{-1}$ (of a tube length) for solid rock with high thermal conductivity (higher than $3\,W\,m^{-1}\,K^{-1}$). In the case of ground formed by gravel and sand with waterways, the specific heat extraction for double U tube can be about $55-65\,W\,m^{-1}$, and for moist clay and loam about $40\,W\,m^{-1}$. Under standard hydrological conditions, an average possible heat flux extraction (so-called probe capacity) of $50\,W\,m^{-1}$ probe length can be expected (according to Reference [11]).

The most important advantage of a ground heat pump, especially with vertical heat exchangers, is the fact that heating of a building can be accomplished in a monovalent mode of operation. Of course, at the end of the heating season, due to heat extraction the ground medium is cooled down. However, because of the natural heat and mass processes, that is, influence of ambient environment from the top, undisturbed ground surrounding the sides, and geothermal energy from the bottom, the ground can come back to its initial thermal balance. This way, in an annual cycle, the natural thermal state of the ground source cannot be disturbed. When bigger heat demand is expected, then it is very good to apply artificial charging of the soil, for example, by solar energy [12] (as described in Section 3.15.4), to ensure return to initial undisturbed thermal conditions. Of course, when heating requirements of a building are rather small, then it is quite sufficient to apply ground heat pumps, using the ground as a natural heat source without artificial charging of the ground medium.

Ground source heat pumps can use the earth in direct or indirect mode. In direct mode, heat exchangers buried horizontally or set vertically in the ground constitute the evaporator coils (evaporation process takes place just in the ground medium). When ground heat exchangers constitute separated closed loops or pipe runs and are coupled with a heat pump evaporator located inside a building, then a heat pump uses the ground in indirect mode. It means that heat exchange between the ground body and working fluid in the heat pump evaporator (refrigerant) is accomplished through an additional medium. In this case, a heat carrier fluid (brine), as an additional medium, circulates in the ground heat exchangers.

The possibility of utilizing ground as a heat source varies from place to place and depends mainly on local geology and size of system. To design a system it is good to make a general review of a place proposed for location and positioning of the ground system and to estimate heat demand and its distribution in time. Having made this preliminary study on ground source potential and heating needs, the selection of the type and configuration of the ground heat pump can be made. In most ground heat pump systems for small-scale applications, only very rough analysis is needed. This analysis becomes more complicated when the size of the system, that is, heat demand, is bigger. It is very useful to know the geological and hydrogeological characteristics of the ground. As a result, the thermal behavior of a ground system can be predicted more easily. Geological and hydrological conditions are not so important in the case of small-scale ground-coupled heat pump systems. When a high level of underground water (waterways) exists, then it is a great advantage for a ground system. Heat from the surrounding undisturbed ground body at a higher temperature is transferred more quickly to the ducts and probes of a ground system. In the case of small systems, very often there is not much area available to install the system; therefore an analysis of disposition and arrangements of the system components, especially tubes of ground heat exchangers, is needed.

As mentioned before, vertical ground heat exchanger systems are more recommended than horizontal coils, especially in high-latitude countries. The main reasons are as follows:

- Heat extraction conditions are better deeper in the ground than just approximately 1 m below the earth surface, especially when freezing phenomena develop. Deeper in the ground the temperature is higher (than just below the earth surface), and a heat pump uses the heat source of the higher temperature and operates in better thermal conditions. As a consequence, the COP is higher (it can be at a level of 4–4.5), and hence a smaller amount of electricity is used to drive the heat pump.
- Problem with ice formation on the evaporator surface (of a heat pump) does not occur; there is no need for defrosting. The heating mode can be more predictable and stable.
- The operation of a heat pump can be accomplished in a monovalent mode, as the heat pump is the only heating device providing all heating requirements.

- If a part of heat exchanger tubes or one of them does not operate in an effective way or it is just out of order, this situation does not require to stop operation of the whole system (vertical tubes of heat exchangers are connected in parallel), as the other part of the system can overtake all heating requirements.
- They do not need a large area of ground surface.
- No excavation is needed (excavation can cause devastation of a big land (garden) area).
- They do not affect the plants growing and other gardening.
- Maintenance of the system, including makeover, is more simple and convenient for the user.

It should be added that nowadays drilling methods used to insert vertical tubes into the ground are well developed and prices are being continuously decreased. Currently, the costs of borehole drilling including pipe inserting and working fluid infilling can lie between 30 and 50 € m^{-1}. Depending on the technology used for given ground conditions and advancement of equipment applied, the drilling is usually done at a depth of 50–100 m, sometimes to 150 or even 200 m [13].

Nowadays, the majority of heat pumps that are installed are ground source heat pumps, mainly because the ground is available everywhere (however, the available ground surface can be different), and temperature and thermal capacity are predictable and they are relatively constant in time of a month or longer. This makes ground source heat pumps very attractive for end users because they can operate in monovalent mode and their efficiency is relatively high. Usually COP for ground source heat pumps with vertical heat exchangers is about 4–4.5 and for heat pumps with horizontal heat exchangers it is 3–4. To summarize, to design and select a ground source heat pump, there is a need to estimate the expected heating load and its nature, including demand level and its distribution in time, and expected temperature range, which can be different for space heating and DHW, and for any other use. Apart from the specific heating requirements, a heat pump has to be selected according to its operation and thermal characteristics, ground thermal conditions, and expected efficiency of the ground source, including type and size of ground heat exchangers and their location and configuration.

When analyzing geothermal water as a heat source, one should consider the deep geothermal energy resources (more than 1000 m deep) (are not dealt with in this chapter) and shallow geothermal energy sources (from a few meters to a few hundred meters). Ground water at considerable depth (aquifers) and shallow geothermal water are very interesting solutions for direct heating or for heating via a heat pump (depending on water temperature and heat flux that are carried by them). However, there are two main problems: high drilling and operating costs and very often poor water quality, for example, corrosive salt content.

Shallow geothermal water can be used with good efficiency if geohydrological conditions, including purity of water, are good enough to be used for heating purposes. Most groundwater at depths of about 10 m is available at constant and relatively high temperature. This constant temperature of between 7 and 12 °C (in central Europe) is maintained at a depth of several meters below the earth surface. Groundwater is extracted through a supply well via a suction pump and transported to the evaporator of the water/water heat pump. Subsequently, the cooled down water is returned via a return well. This must be done in such a way as to not disturb water flows, and especially depletion of groundwater layers should be avoided. A special regulation should be imposed to keep the necessary distance between a supply and return well. Usually it cannot be smaller than 5 m (this is the minimum distance for small-scale applications). The purity of water is also very important. Therefore usually there is an intermediate circuit heat exchanger that separates the water circuit of the supply and return wells from the evaporator circuit. This type of heat pump system is suggested for small- to medium-scale applications. However, groundwater heat sources can also be used at a larger scale, for example, when aquifers, groundwater reservoirs, are used as a heat source or for storage.

Surface water constitutes a heat source that cannot be used in every location and is mostly used in medium-scale applications. The temperature of surface water is strongly dependent on ambient temperature fluctuations; therefore, its possible application for heating purposes is limited in some climatic conditions. The average river temperature in the coldest months can be about 0 °C, and the average lake temperature, which depends mainly on the depth of the lake, is even lower [14]. For these heat sources, detailed analysis of the given location must be carried out. In winter, surface ice formation can occur very easily. However, with the increase of depth, the dependence on ambient air temperature decreases. Therefore, some systems of this type have two intakes of water. One of them is located at the surface of water and this is for the use in spring, summer, and autumn. The other intake is located deep in the water, much below the freezing depth and this is for the use in winter.

Surface water as a heat source for a heat pump is not used very often nowadays. This heat source has too many disadvantages to be popular. The availability is not very good, because it is limited to few locations. Coherency between the source and the user is rather poor, because it is strictly connected with ambient air temperature. When space heating demand is high, the surface water temperature is low, because the ambient air temperature is very low. The thermal capacity is quite big but the heat extraction can disturb the natural state of the source, especially in winter when freezing of water can develop very quickly, and the heat cannot be extracted. In addition, the costs of heat extraction are usually significant. Surface water (heat source) heat pumps have COP at different levels in time, the averaged COP for the whole year's operation can be about 3 to 3.5.

Solar energy is available during the daytime, but at different levels depending on geographical latitude, time of the day, and season of the year. 'Solar energy supply' and 'solar energy heating demand' are quite opposite in time. When energy is needed for space heating purposes, the time and peak values of heat demand are quite opposite to the time and peak values of available solar radiation. However, a heat pump is a device that makes the application of solar energy for heating quite effective, as is considered in detail in the following section.

Nowadays, the most popular heat sources for residential and commercial heat pumps are ambient air and ground. Solar energy as a heat source is not used so often. However, recently ground source heat pumps have become increasingly popular and solar collectors have been used more often not only for DHW, but also for space heating (combi systems) or even cooling (combi plus systems). It means that heat pumps and solar collectors 'come together' quite often in modern heating and cooling systems to provide all thermal energy needs. In this way, they constitute combined solar thermal and heat pump systems, termed SAHP systems. SAHP systems are planned and installed with different levels of complexity, using different components, and are applied for different heating and even cooling needs.

3.15.3 Solar-Assisted Heat Pump System

3.15.3.1 Classification, Configurations, and Functions

The intermittent character of solar radiation and the strong dependence of the irradiation level on time of the day and season of the year make it necessary to store the solar energy and necessitate combining solar heating systems with other heating device to fulfill all heating requirements. One such device is a heat pump. Combining solar thermal systems with heat pumps is especially popular in modern low-energy buildings, because such heating systems can supply all the heating demand and no auxiliary conventional heating is needed. A heat pump replaces the burner or other conventional device or system used for space heating. In summer when solar irradiation is high, a solar thermal system can provide nearly all heating demand for DHW use. Combining a heat pump with solar thermal into one heating system can contribute significantly to the reduction of fossil fuel usage and as a result in reduction in the running costs of a heating system. The other very important advantage is that such combination allows in most cases that the system operates in a monovalent mode, that is, not requiring any auxiliary heating device and as a result reduces fossil energy consumption. The reduction of fossil fuel consumption is not only because of substituting the fuel (from fossil to renewable) but also due to better operation conditions of a heat pump, which results in higher COP and in consequence in reduced electricity demand (to drive the heat pump).

Nowadays, there are a variety of concepts of solar thermal and heat pump system combinations but there are not enough proven results to state definitely which one is the best. Classification of SAHP systems is usually made because of the configuration of the system; mainly it is connected with the role of solar collectors and a heat pump for heating and the mutual interaction between them. Traditional classification of SAHP systems is according to the heat source of a heat pump and its connection to the solar thermal part of the system, mainly solar collectors [15, 16]. Based on that, the following categories can be classified: parallel, series, and dual-source SAHP systems. In a parallel system, a heat pump uses a heat source other than collected solar energy and solar energy is supplied directly to the heating system or is stored in a storage tank. The solar collectors and the heat pump are generally independent and can operate in parallel mode. In a series SAHP system, solar energy directly from solar collectors or storage is used as a heat source for a heat pump. The heat pump is dependent on the solar collector operation. In a dual-source SAHP system, a heat pump can use two heat sources. Collected and stored solar energy is one of the heat sources and the other renewable heat source is usually ground or air. The heat pump is only partly dependent on solar collector operation.

There are three main functions of heating systems under consideration. They are as follows: water heating (DHW), space heating, and space cooling. The SAHP system can provide all these three energy needs or two or only one of them. Nowadays, the monofunction systems (only for hot water or only for space heating) are used very rarely. Usually multifunction systems are used. They supply heat for hot water preparation (DHW) and for space heating. Some such systems can also be used for cooling. The cooling mode is mainly achieved via a heat pump or directly (see Section 3.15.2.2).

In the last decades of the past century, solar thermal systems were used only for hot water preparation. Therefore in that time, SAHP systems were offered and installed with 'traditional' solar thermal part only for water heating for DHW system and with a heat pump for space heating [15–19]. The concept of such system represents the idea of parallel SAHP system [17], where the solar thermal part for DHW was independent of the heat pump that was used only for space heating and it was based on a renewable heat source other than solar heat source. In those days, because of the technology available and applied, the heat pumps were used mainly for space heating due to the requirement to operate in relatively stable conditions (space heating demand is needed continuously in winter and it is relatively constant during a day and night or even over a longer time span). DHW use is characterized by high fluctuation of heating demand during a day. Without appropriate storage and automatic control (daily automatic timetable of hot water use), there would be sudden changes (increase) in a short time in the temperature level and the quantity of heat required for heating needs. With the increase of the temperature difference between the heat source and heat sink (DHW system), and the increase of heat needed, the COP of a heat pump decreases. Nowadays, construction of heat pumps and storage has been improved, automatic control is well developed, and heat pumps are used for all heating functions with high efficiency. At present, there are many different configurations of SAHP systems. The main components and loops of these systems can operate alternatively in series or in parallel mode; some have also extra function called active regeneration of the heat source (mainly ground and groundwater).

Usually, a heat source is used in an indirect way to supply heat to the evaporator of a heat pump. It means that the heat source and the evaporator are integrated through an intermediate heat exchanger loop. This loop transfers the solar energy collected or another renewable energy extracted from the environment to the refrigerant loop of a heat pump. Sometimes, more intermediate loops and elements are used, for example, when a working fluid circulates between solar collectors and a heat exchanger in a storage tank, and then there is another heat exchanger in the storage connected with a heat pump evaporator. Of course, every heat exchanger has a certain effectiveness, that influences (reduces) the final share of solar energy used. Sometimes, the source of heat for the heat pump is used in a direct way. It means that a solar collector and a heat pump evaporator are integrated into one unit. The evaporator is also the solar collector where direct evaporation of refrigerant takes place. The heat output of a heat pump condenser can also be used in a direct way when the condenser is located directly in the space to be heated or in an indirect way through an intermediate heat exchanger loop.

Liquid (water or antifreeze mixture) and air solar collectors can be used in SAHP systems. The heat pump can also be of different type, for example, water–water, water–air, air–air, air–water, or brine–water. In the case of air collectors, a storage tank is not always used, because they can provide heat directly to a heat pump evaporator. When liquid solar collectors are used, they are always coupled with a storage tank. Storage is a very important component of the heating system and it integrates all the other components [20]. Storage tanks can contain intermediate heat exchanger loops or loops with direct evaporation or condensation. Improvement of the thermal performance of storage and reduction in storage volume can be achieved through utilization of not only specific heat of the storage medium but also the latent heat gained during a phase change process (melting phenomena) of the medium. For this, the storage tank can be filled with phase change materials (PCMs) that melt at a given temperature [21–23].

In operation, SAHPs can have high, low, or even zero interaction between the heat pump and solar collectors. A heat pump and solar collectors can be coupled very strongly and solar energy can be even used for active regeneration of a heat source of a heat pump, as is applied in the case of ground and groundwater heat sources. However, it shall be mentioned that the systematic classification of SAHP systems is still an open issue. The interest in SAHP systems is growing, as evidenced by many new investments as well as many new research tasks (e.g., International Energy Agency (IEA) Task 44 'Solar and Heat Pump Systems', and IEA Solar Heating and Cooling Program) [24].

3.15.3.2 Direct Solar-Assisted Heat Pump Systems

In a direct SAHP system, solar energy is used directly to heat the working fluid of a heat pump, that is, a refrigerant. A solar collector and a heat pump evaporator constitute one integrated unit. Two types of solar collectors are used: unglazed solar collectors (bare solar collector) and regular glazed solar collector with one cover. In this system, the working fluid of the heat pump, a refrigerant, flows through an integrated solar collector-evaporator. Due to solar radiation incident on the integrated unit and the direct effect of the ambient surroundings, the refrigerant undergoes a phase change from liquid to vapor, so the evaporation process takes place at the location of the heat source, usually located on the roof of the building. The refrigerant is directly evaporated in an integrated solar collector-evaporator. Such system is called a direct expansion solar-assisted heat pump system (DX SAHP). This system represents also a split configuration.

The main advantage of a DX SAHP system is the elimination of the intermediate heat exchanger that is required for standard SAHP systems with a closed loop of collector working fluid (antifreeze mixture), which makes the construction of the system simpler. This also improves the thermal performance of the system only if it operates under appropriate weather conditions [25–27]. A very important issue for DX SAHP system operation is the selection of a suitable refrigerant and it seems to be one of the main problems for the widespread use of such systems [25]. Another very crucial and critical issue is the sizing of the collector–evaporator panels. The thermal capacity of solar collectors (also evaporators) collecting solar energy should be matched to the heat pumping capacity of the compressor. A collector–evaporator temperature can fluctuate rapidly. The flexible operation of the direct SAHP system can be maintained by using compressor capacity modulation (a variable speed compressor). The refrigerant, especially during phase change from liquid to vapor during the evaporation process, should operate in relatively stable conditions. However, in a direct SAHP system, the temperature level can change rapidly in a short time, that is, during a few hours of a day, and over a longer span of time. There are also huge differences in the temperature of working fluid in winter and summer; for example, in summer a refrigerant should evaporate at a temperature of 30 °C and in winter at a temperature of –20 °C. Of course, it is possible to find places (countries) with not so huge differences in temperature throughout the year. The idea of DX SAHP is presented in Figure 7 on the left side and the T–S diagram representing the ongoing vapor compression cycle on the right side.

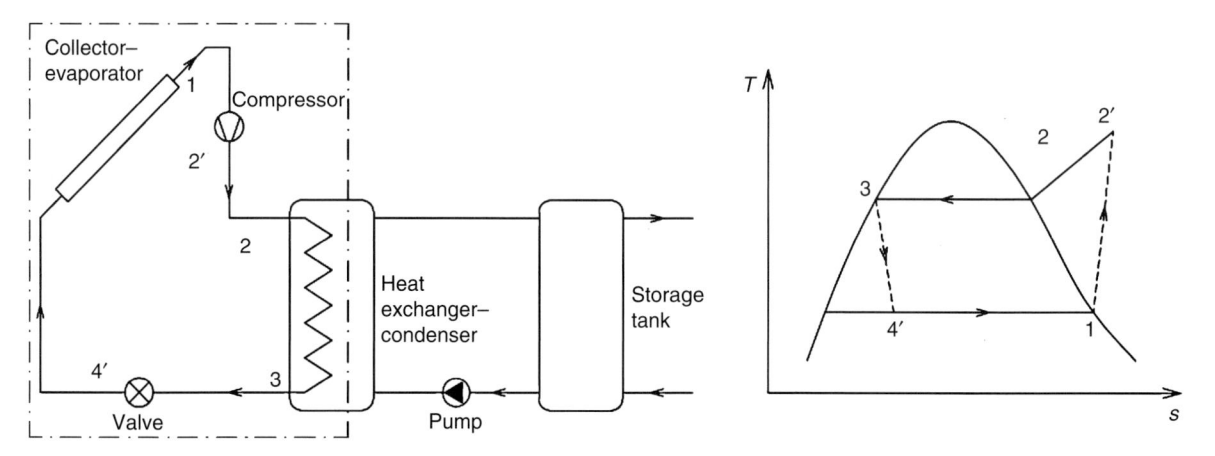

Figure 7 The idea of DX SAHP and T–S diagram for the vapor compression cycle.

The following processes presented and numbered in **Figure 7** take place:

1'–2' Nonisentropic compression. Slightly superheated refrigerant vapor (working fluid) at low pressure flows from the solar collector–evaporator into the mechanical compressor and is compressed to the required level of pressure and temperature.
2'–2 Isobaric heat rejection. Superheated vapor of the working fluid at high pressure and temperature flows from the compressor to the heat exchanger-condenser. The heat rejection takes place due to temperature gradient and represents the desuperheating of the vapor.
2–3 Isobaric and isothermal heat rejection – condensation. Desuperheated vapor at high pressure flows through the heat exchanger–condenser. Vapor condenses giving up the heat to the sink, that is, water flowing to a storage tank (then from storage to space heating circuit).
3–4' Isenthalpic expansion. Saturated (or slightly subcooled) refrigerant liquid from the condenser flows into the thermostatic expansion valve (throttle) and is expanded to low pressure and temperature (nonisentropic expansion process).
4'–1' Isobaric and isothermal evaporation at the solar collector–evaporator due to solar radiation incident on the solar collector–evaporator. Saturated liquid/vapor mixture at low pressure and temperature from the thermostatic expansion valve flows through the evaporator. Under solar radiation the working fluid evaporates and at low pressure flows to the compressor, and the cycle repeats.

A collector–evaporator is under the influence of the ambient surroundings, that is, solar radiation and ambient temperature. The energy gain causes an increase in the enthalpy of the refrigerant and it can evaporate. The energy balance of a solar collector–evaporator under steady-state conditions can be written as follows:

$$\dot{m}(h_{1'} - h_{4'}) = F'A_c[G_s(\tau\alpha) - U_L(T_f - T_a)] \qquad [10]$$

The term on the left-hand side of eqn [10] represents the energy gained by the working fluid (refrigerant) during evaporation (m is the mass flow rate, h is the enthalpy of the working fluid according to the state points in **Figure 7**) and it is equal to the solar energy gained by the solar collector–evaporator, represented by the term on the right-hand side, that is, the useful energy Q_u gained from solar collectors (F' is the efficiency of solar collectors, A_c the surface area of solar collectors, G_s the solar irradiation, U_L the averaged loss coefficient). It can be assumed that the working fluid temperature T_f in a collector remains constant at the saturation value at constant saturation pressure (frictional pressure drop is neglected). Equation [10] can also be used in a quasistationary model of solar collector–evaporator operation. During a day it is possible to observe that one quasistationary state follows the other. At every quasistationary state temperature of the ambient air T_a and the working fluid temperature T_f of evaporation in a colleter, and solar irradiance G_s are stable, but they are different than in the following state.

With the development of new technologies there are some novel ideas to integrate the DX SAHP system with other innovative technologies. One of them is to replace the solar thermal collector–evaporator by PV/T (photovoltaic/thermal) collector–evaporator. Some experimental studies on photovoltaic SAHP systems have been performed recently [28]. PV/T collector–evaporator converts some portion of solar energy into electricity and some into heat. Heat is absorbed by the refrigerant circulating in a heat pump loop and the refrigerant evaporates directly in a PV/T collector–evaporator. The system also consists of the standard air evaporator, which is used when there is no or not enough solar radiation available (both evaporators are connected in parallel). There are also two condensers, air cooled and water cooled (also connected in parallel). The water-cooled condenser is used for space heating and DHW and the air-cooled condenser is used only for space heating. There is a variable-frequency compressor and an electronic expansion valve in the system. With changes in the frequency of the compressor, the input power to drive the compressor also changes. To meet the changes in the operating frequency of the compressor, the expansion valve adjusts its position automatically. The PV DX SAHP system generates heat and electricity; therefore, it is proposed to use a comprehensive coefficient of thermal and electrical performance COP$_{p/t}$ which is defined in the following way [28]:

$$\text{COP}_{p/t} = \frac{Q_\text{heat} + W_p/\eta_\text{power}}{W} \qquad [11]$$

In eqn [11], W corresponds to work input of a heat pump compressor and W_p is the output power of the PV panels. The PV output power is transformed into equivalent thermal power, taking into account the average standard electricity generation efficiency (η_power).

The idea of application of direct SAHP systems was presented many years ago [29], and from time to time some researchers call for the comeback of this technology [25–28]. However, up to now, this technology has not become popular. There are some advantages of direct SAHP systems, but perhaps disadvantages, with the main one being uncertainty of their operation in unstable weather conditions, are so strong that they limit significantly the interest in the implementation of these systems in practice.

3.15.3.3 Series Solar-Assisted Heat Pump Systems

A series SAHP system could be just called a solar heat pump, because solar energy is the only heat source used for the heat pump. In most series SAHP systems, there are two main modes of system operation (it could also have auxiliary heating, and then it can be considered as a third mode of operation):

- solar direct heating – if the temperature of heat collected or stored (depending on the system configuration) is high enough, then solar energy is used directly for heating;
- solar indirect heating via a heat pump – if the temperature of heat collected or stored is too low for direct heating, then a heat pump is used to meet the heating demand, that is, solar energy converted into useful heat is used as a heat source for a heat pump.

It should be mentioned that in the middle- and high-latitude countries, mainly liquid solar collectors are used (flat plate or vacuum tube) with the antifreeze mixture circulating in a collector loop and a storage tank, with water as a storage medium. A storage tank is a central component of the heating system. Storage of heat improves the thermal performance of a system and increases its reliability [20, 30]. The location of a storage tank can differ depending on the system configuration, which influences the mode of operation. To improve the ability to store heat, PCMs can be used (the storage tank is filled with PCM) and then heat storage takes place due to both the specific and latent heat of the water and PCM storage medium [21–23]. In low- and middle-latitude countries, liquid, mainly water, or air solar collectors are used.

In the case of air collectors, they are usually applied for space heating of a building, mainly by passive operation, and they are usually integrated with the south façade of a building. The outdoor (ambient) air circulates in spaces or channels within the solar collectors' south facade. The air collectors can also be used actively when fans are used for forced circulation of the air or when they (collectors) assist the evaporator of an air–air or air–water heat pump. If the solar air collectors of a solar passive system are used to supply space heating directly very often in winter even in a warm climate (like the Mediterranean), they do not operate all the time, because of too low ambient temperature and too low solar irradiation level [31]. However, if these collectors are used to supply outside air heated by solar radiation as a heat source for a heat pump, then they can be used all year long and there is no need to use any other heating device. This type of series SAHP systems can operate in a hybrid mode, that is, they are based on passive (collectors)–active (heat pump) operation at the same time. If a heat pump is used only for space heating, it can be an air–air heat pump. However, if it is used for a few functions, mainly space heating and cooling and DHW, then the air–water heat pump can be used, and space heating and cooling can be accomplished, for example, by fan coils.

The idea of series SAHP systems with solar collectors was introduced at the end of the 1970s [18]. An example of a traditional series SAHP is presented in **Figure 8**. The numbers given in the figure are for the main components of the system. In the series SAHP system, the heat carrier working fluid (water or antifreeze mixture) circulates in a solar collector loop and transfers heat collected by solar collectors to a heat exchanger in the storage tank. There is another heat exchanger in the storage tank that couples this storage tank with a DHW storage tank and/or with the heating circuit of a building or with a heat pump evaporator. It means that the DHW system is theoretically independent of the space heating and the DHW storage tank is equipped with an auxiliary heater. Heating of the building can be accomplished directly from the storage tank or via a heat pump. The heat carrier fluid, which is usually water, transfers heat from the storage tank to the heat pump evaporator. Heat pump refrigerant takes heat out of the water, which after being cooled down comes back to the storage tank. Heat from a heat pump condenser is extracted by the working fluid of a heating circuit to provide heat to the building. Depending on the type of heating system, water or air is used as the space heating fluid.

To describe the operation of the standard SAHP system presented in **Figure 8**, the energy balance of the storage in unsteady state can be represented as

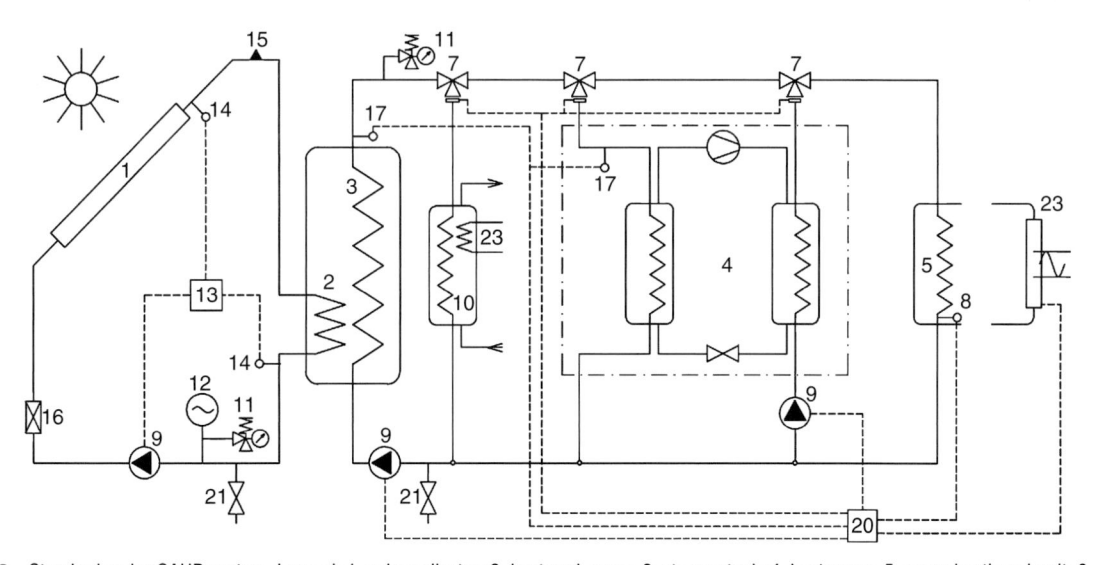

Figure 8 Standard series SAHP system. Legend: 1, solar collector; 2, heat exchanger; 3, storage tank; 4, heat pump. 5, space heating circuit; 6, ground heat exchanger; 7, three-way control valve; 8, temperature sensor; 9, circulating pump. 10, DHW storage tank; 11, safety valve; 12, expansion tank; 13, solar control; 14, temperature sensor in a collector loop. 15, bleed; 16, nonreturn valve; 17, temperature sensor; 18, temperature sensor in a ground loop. 19, circulating pump in a ground loop. 20, control; 21, cold water supply; 22, main storage tank; 23, auxiliary heater.

$$(Vc\rho)\frac{dT_s}{dt} = Q_u(t) - Q_{loss}(t) - Q_{hd}(t) - Q_{hp}(t) - Q_{DHWd}(t) \quad [12]$$

The term on the left-hand side of eqn [12] expresses the storage capacity of a storage medium in a tank ($Vc\rho$ (J K^{-1})) and the fluctuation of storage temperature T_s in time caused by (terms on the right-hand side) useful solar energy gains Q_u supplied by solar collectors, which is reduced because of the heat losses from the storage Q_{loss} (with high-quality thermal insulation of the tank, the losses can be neglected) and the heat used directly for space heating purposes Q_{hd} and for DHW heating demand Q_{DHWd} (heat supplied to a DHW tank) and because of heat supplied to a heat pump evaporator Q_{hp}. The storage temperature T_s in eqn [12] refers to storage with full mixing of storage medium (water) or can be treated as the averaged value if there is stratification effect in the storage tank.

The main modes of operation of the series SAHP system under consideration (the heat losses from the storage are neglected, $Q_{loss} = 0$) are as follows:

- Solar DHW heating: Heat stored in the storage tank is transferred to the DHW tank. When temperature T_{sDHW} of stored heat in the DHW tank is high enough, that is, if $T_{sDHW} > T_{DHWmin}$, then all DHW load is supplied from the DHW tank, $Q_{DHWd} = Q_{DHW}$, and the auxiliary heater is turned off, so $Q_{aux} = 0$. When the temperature of water in the DHW tank is too low, $T_{sDHW} < T_{DHWlimit}$, then the auxiliary heater is on and supplies the rest (auxiliary) of heat, thus $Q_{DHW} = Q_{DHWd} + Q_{aux}$. When the temperature of water in the DHW tank is below the minimum level, $T_{sDHW} < T_{DHWmin}$, then the auxiliary heater is on and supplies all DHW demand, $Q_{DHW} = Q_{aux}$. Depending on the solar radiation level and the difference between the temperature of solar collectors and the main storage, the solar collector loop can operate or not.
- Solar direct heating of the building, when solar energy is used directly for heating the building: When temperature T_s of stored heat is high enough, that is, if $T_s > T_{smin}$, then $Q_{hd} = Q_{heat}$ and the heat pump is turned off, so $Q_{hp} = 0$; depending on solar irradiation and the difference between the temperature of solar collectors and storage, the solar collector loop can operate ($Q_u > 0$) or not ($Q_u = 0$).
- Solar indirect heating of the building via the heat pump: When the temperature of collected or stored heat is too low for direct heating, that is, if $T_s \leq T_{smin}$, then the heat pump is used and supplies heat to meet space heating demand. Taking into account eqn [2c], the heat extracted out of the storage tank as a heat source of the heat pump is equal to

$$Q_{hp}(t) = Q_{heat}(t)\left(1 - \frac{1}{COP_{hp}(t)}\right) \quad [13]$$

and heat supplied to a building is extracted from the heat pump condenser, so $Q_{hpcon} = Q_{heat}$ and $Q_{hd} = 0$, and $Q_u > 0$ or $Q_u = 0$, depending on whether solar collectors operate or not.
- Solar indirect heating of a building via a heat pump and auxiliary heating: When the heat pump is used to supply heat but it cannot provide all heating requirements (e.g., there is a limit for the lowest COP value), then the auxiliary heater is used to supply the rest of the space heating demand, and $Q_{hpcon} + Q_{aux} = Q_{heat}$.

The COP of a heat pump is given in general form by eqn [2c]. However, the COP is also applied to determine the thermal performance of the whole SAHP system. The COP of the whole SAHP system is defined as the ratio of the total heat received to the total work input to the heating system. Thus, in the case of a series SAHP system used only for heating a building, the COP can be expressed in the following way:

$$COP = \frac{Q_{heat}}{W_{total}} = \frac{Q_{hd} + Q_{hpcon}}{W_{total}} = \frac{m_c C_p[(T_{sout} - T_{sin}) + (T_{conout} - T_{conin})]}{W + W_{pumpSd} + W_{pumpShp} + W_{heat}} \quad [14]$$

The numerator of eqn [14] represents the quantity of heating energy at the heat sink, that is, Q_{heat}, that is supplied by the solar system directly Q_{hd} (T_{sout} is the supply temperature at the outlet of the storage and T_{sin} is the return temperature at the inlet of the storage tank) and by a heat pump from the heat pump condenser Q_{hpcon} to the heating circuit (water or air of specific heat C_p and mass flow rate m_c; T_{conout} and T_{conin} are the temperature at the outlet and inlet of the condenser, respectively). The denominator represents the total work input into the SAHP system, that is, not only the work input W needed to drive the compressor of a heat pump, but also the work input W_{pumpSd} for the circulating pumps of the solar heating system (without DHW part) during direct heating mode, the work input $W_{pumpShp}$ for the circulating pumps of the solar heating system (without DHW part) during heating via a heat pump, and the work input W_{heat} for the circulating pumps of water heating circuit in a building or for fans in the case of the air heating system.

The COP of the series SAHP system under consideration can be also written taking into account the auxiliary heating; then, the numerator of eqn [14] represents the quantity of all heating energy supplied to the building $Q_{heattotal}$, that is, by the solar system directly Q_{hd}, by the heat pump from the heat pump condenser Q_{hpcon}, and by the auxiliary heater Q_{aux}. The denominator represents the total work input including the work input W_{aux} for auxiliary electric heater and eqn [14] takes the following form:

$$COP = \frac{Q_{heattotal}}{W_{total}} = \frac{Q_{hd} + Q_{hpcon} + Q_{aux}}{W + W_{pumpSd} + W_{pumpShp} + W_{heat} + W_{aux}} \quad [15]$$

The COP given by eqns [14] and [15] should be applied only for the space heating system of the SAHP system considered. This is due to the fact that a heat pump is coupled directly with a solar thermal system only for space heating needs. The DHW heating system constitutes in some way an independent solar thermal system with its own auxiliary heater. The DHW system operates in parallel to the SAHP space heating system. Therefore, even if there is a common storage tank for both systems (in result there is some interaction between the two systems), in the case under consideration it is better not to include operation of the DHW solar heating system in the determination of the COP of the series SAHP system.

In one of the very simple forms of a series SAHP system, the solar energy collected by the solar collectors is used only as a heat source for the heat pump and there is no other mode of operation, so there is no direct supply of solar energy (collected by solar collectors) to the heating system [32]. In such system, there are two storage tanks: a low-temperature storage tank and a high-temperature storage tank. The low-temperature storage tank is located between a solar collector loop and a heat pump evaporator and the high-temperature storage tank between a heat pump condenser and a space heating circuit in a building. This idea was also checked experimentally [33]. A heat pump evaporator can be situated directly in a low-temperature storage tank and a heat pump condenser directly in a high-temperature storage tank. However, it is also possible to use heat exchangers in low- and high-temperature storage tanks to be coupled with a heat pump evaporator and condenser, respectively. Of course, an auxiliary peak heater can be also included in the system, for example, in a high-temperature storage tank.

There are different modifications of the series SAHP system. One of them is realized through introduction of long-term storage separate from short-term storage. However, such system is no longer a typical series SAHP system. It should be mentioned that in the past hot water preparation (DHW) used to be an independent function (from space heating) and DHW was provided by solar energy and auxiliary heater (usually electrical) in parallel to space heating, which was accomplished by the series SAHP system. Heating of a building and heating of DHW were then independent. Nowadays, hot water preparation is one of the standard functions of the SAHP system. Usually, storage (with stratification) is a central component of the heating system and space heating and DHW are supplied by a combined heating system. The automatic control system manages the heat supply to DHW and space heating or eventually to cooling or air conditioning system.

3.15.3.4 Parallel Solar-Assisted Heat Pump

A parallel SAHP system consists of a solar thermal part and a heat pump that uses a heat source other than solar energy [17]. Solar liquid (water or antifreeze mixture) collectors or solar air collectors can be used. In a solar heating system based on liquid solar collectors, solar energy can be used directly for heating purposes or through a storage tank, and an auxiliary heater can also be applied. A heat pump uses usually the ambient air or ground as an independent heat source. If solar air collectors are used, they are applied mainly for passive heating of a building, but because they cannot usually fulfill the space heating requirements in cold days (even in a warm climate) the active heating of the building is realized through air-to-air or air-to-water heat pump [31].

As it has been mentioned, in the past a solar heating system (solar collectors and storage) was responsible only for hot water heating (DHW) and a heat pump for space heating. Both systems used to operate without interaction. A standard parallel SAHP system is presented in **Figure 9**. The legend to this figure is the same as for **Figure 8**.

This system consists of conventional solar thermal part with solar liquid collectors (water or antifreeze mixture) in a closed solar collector loop and a storage tank. (If air collectors are used, they are integrated into the building façade and the solar collector loop is open.) There are also heat exchangers in a storage tank for DHW and for space heating. There is another heat exchanger in the storage tank that couples this storage with a DHW storage tank, in a similar way as a series SAHP system presented in **Figure 9**. The DHW

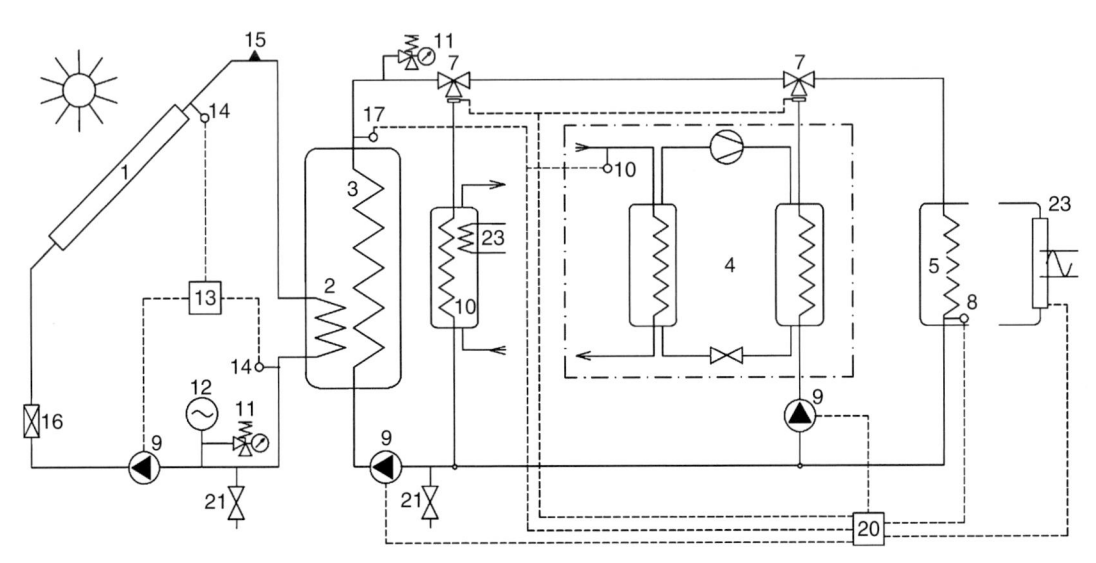

Figure 9 Standard parallel SAHP system. See **Figure 8** caption for legends.

system is theoretically independent of space heating; however, some interaction exists because of a common main storage tank. The other main component of the parallel SAHP is a conventional heat pump, which can be one of the following types: air–air, air–water, brine (water)–water, brine (water)–air. Solar energy is given priority to meet heating requirements. There is also an auxiliary heater for space heating. The main modes of the system operation are as follows:

- Solar DHW heating: Heat stored in the main storage tank is transferred to the DHW tank (description of this mode of operation is the same as for series SAHP system presented in **Figure 8**).
- Solar space heating: When temperature T_s of stored heat is high enough, that is, if $T_s > T_{smin}$, then $Q_{hd} = Q_{heat}$ and at that time a heat pump is off, $Q_{hp} = 0$; depending on solar irradiation and the difference between the temperature of solar collectors and storage, the solar collector loop can operate ($Q_u > 0$) or not ($Q_u = 0$).
- Heat pump heating: If the temperature of collected or stored heat is too low to meet heating requirements, that is, if $T_s \leq T_{smin}$, the heat pump operates using heat source other than solar energy and heat supplied to the building is extracted from the heat pump condenser, so $Q_{hpcon} = Q_{heat}$ and $Q_{hd} = 0$; depending on solar conditions and the difference between the temperature of solar collectors and storage, the solar collector loop can operate ($Q_u > 0$) and heat can be stored in a storage tank or not ($Q_u = 0$).
- Heat pump and auxiliary heating: The rule of this mode of operation is the same as for the series heat pump shown in **Figure 8**, and the only difference is in the heat source for the heat pump, which is different from solar energy. Heating load is provided by a heat pump and an auxiliary heater, and $Q_{hpcon} + Q_{aux} = Q_{heat}$.

In the parallel SAHP system, the total available energy of the system is the sum of energy gained from two different systems: solar thermal and heat pump systems. Thermal description of the two systems considered is the same as they operate as stand-alone systems. However, indirectly they influence each other, because when one heat source is used, the other is not. It means that heat is extracted from these heat sources not so quickly and during breaks in operation if they have the ability, like ground for example, they can recover slightly or retain the heat accumulated for later use. To describe solar thermal system operation including heating of DHW, the standard energy balance of the storage can be expressed in a similar way as eqn [12] in the following form:

$$(Vc\rho)\frac{dT_s}{dt} = Q_u(t) - Q_{loss}(t) - Q_{hd}(t) - Q_{DHWd}(t) \qquad [16]$$

The term on the left-hand side of eqn [16] expresses (as before) storage capacity and fluctuation of storage temperature T_s in time and that on the right-hand side gives useful solar energy Q_u supplied by solar collectors, heat losses from the storage Q_{loss}, heat provided directly to the heating circuit Q_{hd} to meet the space heating load, and heat provided to the DHW storage tank Q_{DHWd}. There is no heat supplied to a heat pump evaporator Q_{hp}.

A heat pump operates in a standard way, as conventional heat pump; therefore, the COP of the heat pump can be expressed by the standard equation [2c]. However, it is also possible to determine the COP of the whole parallel SAHP system. Then the total work input into the system must be included, so apart from the work input W to drive the compressor of the heat pump, it is necessary to add the work input W_{heat} for the circulating pump of a water heating circuit or for the fans of an air heating system in the building, and the work input W_{pump} for the circulating pumps of the solar heating system. Total heat Q_{heat} supplied to the space heating system (DHW system is not taken into account for COP determination, because theoretically it is an independent heating system) during the longer time of its operation is the sum of heat extracted directly Q_{hd} from the 'solar' storage tank and heat Q_{hpcon} supplied by the heat pump condenser and heat Q_{aux} provided by the auxiliary heater, which can be written in the following way:

$$\sum_t Q_{heat} = \sum_t Q_{hd} + \sum_t Q_{hpcon} + \sum_t Q_{aux}$$

Thus, the COP of the parallel SAHP system under consideration (see **Figure 9**) can be expressed in a similar way as the COP for the series SAHP system (see **Figure 8**) with the difference that there is a new work input W_{hp}, which represents the work needed for circulation of the working fluid at the heat source of a heat pump to extract heat out of this source. In the case of a heat pump using ambient air as the heat source, it is usually equal to zero. Referring to eqn [15], the COP of the parallel SAHP system considered above can be written as

$$\text{COP} = \frac{Q_{heattotal}}{W_{total}} = \frac{Q_{hd} + Q_{hpcon} + Q_{aux}}{W + W_{pumpSd} + W_{heat} + W_{aux} + W_{hp}} \qquad [17]$$

There are a variety of heat sources and heat sinks for a heat pump and a solar system can be based on air or liquid collectors supplying heat to air or water heating system in the building. All these varieties can be used in parallel systems; however, some of them are more popular than others. A parallel SAHP system can provide heat to the heating system where water or air is the heat carrier fluid. The solar collector loop can supply heat to the water storage tank. The heat stored can be supplied to water-to-water heat exchanger located in the water heating circuit, or to water-to-air heat exchanger located in heated (conditioned) space. The air solar collectors can also be used; they usually operate in a passive way and supply heat directly to the space. Heat pumps use renewable heat sources other than solar energy. An ambient air (heat source) heat pump can be used to supply heat to indoor air (a heat sink). In such system, 'solar' water-to-air heat exchanger and air-to-air heat pump individually provide heat for space heating in a building. It is also possible to use a ground source heat pump, which is especially popular in high-latitude countries. In such system, mostly 'solar' water-to-water heat exchanger and ground (brine)-to-water heat pump provide heat for space heating through heating circuit (floor or wall heating) in a building. An auxiliary heater and automatic control system are also included in the system.

The operating strategy for a parallel SAHP is to give priority to the solar thermal part, then to the heat pump, and eventually, as the final alternative, to the electric heater as the peak source. However, in the past, all components used to operate separately, one after the other. Nowadays, there are systems that through automatic control make it possible to supply heat at the same time from a solar thermal system and from a 'nonsolar' heat pump, and even from an auxiliary heater, to storage or to a heating system directly. If a storage tank is used for heating of a building and DHW, then because of sanitary reasons (*Legionella* bacteria) it is necessary to have periodically (e.g., once per week) the temperature of water for the DHW system above a certain level (usually 55 °C is the limit). To ensure this temperature level, sometimes all three heating components operate (solar collectors, heat pumps, electric heater). The heating circuit in a building can use water or air as the heat carrier fluid. In this modified parallel SAHP system, the following modes of operation are possible:

- Solar heating only: If temperature T_s of stored heat is high enough, that is, if $T_s > T_{smin}$, then $Q_{hd} = Q_{heat} + Q_{DHW}$, and the heat pump does not operate; depending on solar and ambient conditions, the solar collector loop can operate and useful heat Q_u from solar collectors can be transferred to the storage tank.
- Solar heating and heat pump heating in parallel: If the temperature of collected or stored heat is too low to meet total heat load, $T_s \leq T_{smin}$, but still this temperature is high enough (above a given temperature limit), $T_s > T_{slimit}$, to supply some heat $Q_{sol} = Q_{hd}$ to the heating system, the solar system operates providing part of the heating demands. At the same time, a heat pump operates using a heat source other than solar energy, and provides the rest of the heat required Q_{hpcon}, therefore $Q_{hd} + Q_{hpcon} = Q_{heat} + Q_{DHW}$.
- Heating via the heat pump. If the temperature of collected or stored heat is too low to meet heating requirements even partly, that is, if $T_s \leq T_{slimit}$, the heat pump operates using a heat source other than solar energy and provides all heating requirements $Q_{hpcon} = Q_{heat} + Q_{DHW}$; depending on solar conditions and the temperature difference between solar collectors and storage, the useful heat from solar collectors Q_u can be collected and stored.
- Heating via heat pump and auxiliary heating: If the temperature of heat collected by solar collectors or heat stored in the storage tank is too low to meet heating requirements even partly, that is, if $T_s \leq T_{slimit}$, the heat pump operates using a heat source other than solar energy and supplies Q_{hpcon} to the heating system; however, if the COP of the heat pump drops below the limit determined by the control system, then auxiliary heater is used to provide the rest of heat Q_{aux} to meet all heating requirements $Q_{hpcon} + Q_{aux} = Q_{heat} + Q_{DHW}$; depending on solar conditions and the temperature difference between solar collectors and storage, the useful heat from solar collectors Q_u can be collected and stored.
- Solar heating, heat pump heating, and auxiliary heating: This is when the peak load must be met; if it is possible, there is heat provided by solar collectors $Q_{sol} = Q_{hd}$ and the heat pump operates providing more heat Q_{hpcon}, and because it is not enough to meet all heating requirements $Q_{hd} + Q_{hpcon} < Q_{heat} + Q_{DHW}$, the auxiliary heater is turned on and it supplies the rest of the heat required Q_{aux}, therefore, $Q_u + Q_{notsol} + Q_{aux} = Q_{heat}$.

Total heat supplied to the heating system can be expressed by the same equation [16] as in the case of the standard parallel SAHP system. However, now the heat supplied for DHW needs should also be taken into account because a heat pump also accomplishes this function. Therefore, the input work (electrical energy) of the auxiliary heater for DHW should also be included as well as the other work input W_{DHW} associated with this function, for example, to drive circulating pumps of DHW circulation loop and of a regular piping network. The averaged energy performance of the parallel SAHP system for space heating and DHW, that is, the averaged COP of the whole system, can be expressed in a similar way as for the parallel SAHP system including heat provided to the DHW and the work input associated with this function. The COP takes the following form:

$$\text{COP} = \frac{Q_{heattotal}}{W_{total}} = \frac{Q_{hd} + Q_{hpcon} + Q_{haux} + Q_{auxDHW}}{W + W_{pumpSd} + W_{heat} + W_{haux} + W_{hp} + W_{DHW} + W_{auxDHW}} \quad [18a]$$

Assuming that the solar thermal and 'nonsolar' heat pump supply heat to the same heating circuit in a building with the same heat carrier fluid and referring to eqn [14], now eqn [18] of the averaged COP of the parallel SAHP system considered takes the form:

$$\text{COP} = \frac{Q_{heattotal}}{W_{total}} = \frac{Q_{hd} + Q_{hpcon} + Q_{aux}}{W_{total}} = \frac{m_c C_p[(T_{sout} - T_{sin}) + (T_{conout} - T_{conin})] + Q_{haux} + Q_{hdDHW} + Q_{hpconDHW} + Q_{auxDHW}}{W + W_{pumpSd} + W_{heat} + W_{haux} + W_{hp} + W_{DHW} + W_{auxDHW}}$$

[18b]

The formulation of Q_{hd} depends on the type of solar thermal system that is used. The work input symbols are the same as in eqn [14]. If other circulation pumps or fans are used, their work should be also included in eqns [18a] and [18b].

Nowadays, one of most typical variations of the parallel SAHP system is realized through integration of all the main components in a water storage tank with stratification. Solar collectors through a working fluid (water or antifreeze mixture) circulating in a closed loop supply useful heat Q_u to a storage tank. The heat exchanger of the solar collector loop is usually located at the lower part of the storage tank. A heat pump uses a heat source other than solar energy and supplies heat Q_{hpcon} extracted from this source also to the storage tank. In some systems, it is also possible to supply heat directly to the heating system in a building (not via storage) [13]. Usually the heat exchanger that links the heat pump condenser and store is located in the upper part of the storage tank, above the solar collector heat exchanger. Sometimes, a heat pump condenser can be put directly into a storage tank. If the storage tank is also for DHW, the inlet of cold water is located at the bottom. At the top of the tank the outlet of hot water for DHW is installed, to extract the heat Q_{hDHW} for DHW. There is another heat exchanger in the tank, below the DHW outlet, that connects the store with the heating circuit for space heating, usually low temperature, for example, floor heating circuit. The heat Q_{heat} needed for heating a building is extracted through this heat exchanger. Very often an auxiliary heater, usually an electric one, as the peak source is also integrated into the storage tank at the top. If necessary, when the temperature of the storage tank, even at the top, is too low to meet the heating requirements, the electric heater is turned on and it supplies auxiliary heat Q_{aux} to the storage tank.

Most of the modern parallel SAHP systems contain a storage tank, which is a main core component of the system that integrates all the other components. In such a configuration of the system, even if the solar thermal system and the heat pump do not have direct contact, through the common storage tank they interact with each other. There are positive effects of this interaction, because the solar thermal part and heat pump are complementary to each other. This makes the operation of the whole heating system very reliable. A parallel SAHP system can provide all heating loads and there is no need to install and use any other heating device, extra burner, or boiler. This is very convenient for the user. However, due to the fact that a heat pump and solar collectors deliver heat to the same storage medium, sometimes operation of one part of the system, usually the heat pump, limits the operation of the other one, that is, the solar collectors. For example, in winter in high-latitude countries, very rarely is the temperature of the working fluid of the solar collectors higher than the temperature of the heat carrier fluid extracting heat from the heat pump condenser. As a consequence, the heat pump operates most of the time and limits the utilization of solar energy. In addition, sometimes installers (through the automatic control system) set too high a limit for the temperature of the working fluid of the solar collectors to circulate. If this value is too high (e.g., above 40 °C) the working liquid does not circulate and supply heat to the storage tank in winter and on cloudy days, which limits significantly the operation of the solar thermal part of the system.

Figure 10 presents a scheme of modern parallel SAHP system and **Figure 11** presents the main components of the system in the indoor 'boiler room' (heat pump in the middle, combined buffer storage at the right side). This system has been operating recently. In **Figure 10** the symbols T with numbers in indexes represent main temperature sensors linked to the control. This system contains the following main components: solar collectors – flat plate with antifreeze mixture as a working fluid; a ground source heat pump with U-shaped vertical heat exchangers and antifreeze mixture as a working fluid; combined buffer storage with water as a storage medium; storage tank for DHW with peak electric heater. There is a low-temperature floor heating circuit in the building. The combined buffer storage consists of a big tank and a small one inside the big one. The solar collector loop is closed and heat is transferred through a heat exchanger to the big storage tank. The big tank is also supplied by a ground source heat pump. The small tank inside the big one is used as a buffer for the DHW. There is an inlet of cold water at the bottom and an outlet of warm water at the top. The outlet is connected to the DHW storage tank, which can be also supplied directly from the heat pump and if necessary

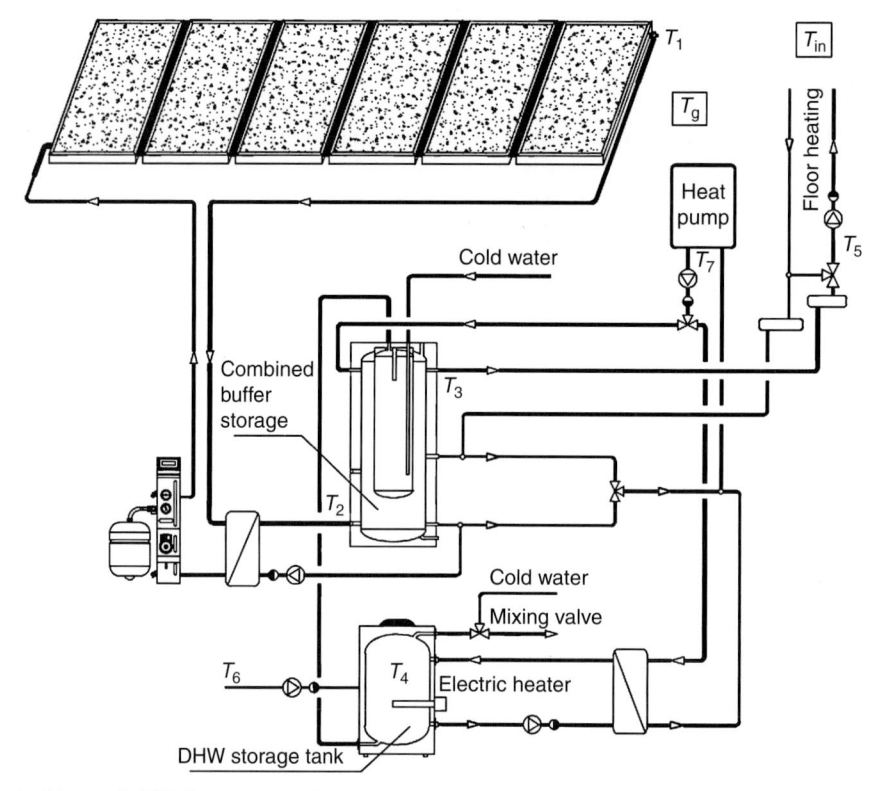

Figure 10 An example of the parallel SAHP system operating since 2010.

Figure 11 Components of the parallel SAHP system shown in **Figure 10**.

the electric heater can be on. Heating of the building is accomplished by the heat stored in the big tank of combined buffer storage. Referring to eqn [12] written for the averaged storage temperature T_s, the energy balance of the combined buffer storage in unsteady state of the system considered can be written in the following way:

$$(Vc\rho)\frac{dT_s}{dt} = Q_u(t) + Q_{hpBS}(t) - Q_{loss}(t) - Q_{hDHWBS}(t) - Q_h(t) \qquad [19]$$

In eqn [19], there is heat Q_{hpBS} supplied by the heat pump to the combined buffer storage. It can be the total heat provided by the heat pump, $Q_{hpBS} = Q_{hp}$, or only part $Q_{hpBS} = xQ_{hp}$ of that heat, if there is some quantity of heat $Q_{hpDHW} = (1-x)Q_{hp}$ provided by the heat pump to the DHW storage tank. In a given time, there can also be extraction of some water heated from the small tank to feed the DHW storage tank, $Q_{hDHWBS} = mC(T_{DHWBS} - T_{in})$. Thus the energy balance of the DHW storage tank can be written in the following way:

$$(Vc\rho)\frac{dT_{DHW}}{dt} = Q_{hDHWBS}(t) + (Q_{hp}(t) - Q_{hpBS}(t)) + Q_{auxE}(t) - Q_{loss}(t) - Q_{hDHW}(t) \qquad [20]$$

There is no inlet of cold water to the DHW storage but only outlet for direct use. Some cold water is provided to the three-way valve out of the storage tank to protect the user against too high water temperature from the DHW system.

The parallel SAHP system presented in **Figure 10** supplies heat for building heating and for a DHW system. The operation of the system is based on solar collectors and a ground source heat pump that supply heat to one or both the storage tanks. The main modes of operation of the system considered can be described in a general way as follows:

- Solar heating only: storage tanks: combined buffer and DHW storage are supplied by solar collectors; the heat pump is off and no auxiliary energy is used.
- Solar heating and peak auxiliary heating for DHW: Storage tanks are supplied by only solar collectors; the heat pump is off, for a peak load (or to protect against *Legionella* bacteria) the auxiliary electric heater is on; depending on thermal and environmental conditions, the useful heat Q_u from solar collectors can be transferred to storage tanks.
- Solar heating and heat pump heating in parallel: If the temperature of collected or stored heat is too low to meet total heat load, for DHW and space heating, the heat pump is switched on and supplies heat to one or two storage tanks; the useful solar energy can be collected and stored in the combined storage tank, if possible.
- Heating via the heat pump only: When the temperature difference between the outlet of solar collectors loop and the storage (at a given point) is below the limit value, the solar collectors do not operate, and the heat pump provides all heating requirements and supplies one or two tanks.
- Heating via the heat pump and auxiliary heating: When there is no available solar energy and the heat pump cannot provide all the heat for DHW, auxiliary electric heater is on during peak time.

The COP of the system under consideration that is applied for space heating and DHW can be expressed in a general way as follows:

$$\text{COP} = \frac{Q_{heattotal}}{W_{total}} = \frac{Q_{hd} + Q_{hpcon} + Q_{auxDHW}}{W + W_{pumpSd} + W_{heat} + W_{hp} + W_{DHW} + W_{auxDHW}} \qquad [21]$$

The equation above is written with the assumption that total heat requirements are provided by the system considered. The use of electric heater (W_{auxDHW}) is included in the total work required to accomplish all heating requirements; however, electric heater is used for only DHW. In the total work W_{DHW} there is also work required to drive circulation loop and pumps in the DHW system. Of course it is the automatic control system that is responsible for the effective operation of the system [34].

In some parallel SAHP systems, it is possible that a heat pump can supply heat directly to the heating system (usually to the storage tank as in the system presented in **Figure 10**), depending on the heating demand and temperature level of working fluid. The automatic control of the system considered can be organized in a different way and priorities could be given to different heat sources. The solar thermal collectors and the heat pump are not connected together. They can operate in alternative ways, that is, each of them at a different time, but they can also operate together, both supplying heat at the same time. The main idea of the parallel operation is to use two heat sources: solar for solar collectors and the other one (not solar) for the heat pump in a parallel way. However, as it was presented, there is interaction between operations of the main components of the system even if they are not coupled together. Perhaps such systems could be called flexible parallel SAHP systems. The modern control systems based on microprocessor techniques make it possible to apply different operation strategies for different applications and heat demand.

3.15.3.5 Dual-Source Solar-Assisted Heat Pump

In a dual-source SAHP system, there are two heat sources for a heat pump [19, 21, 35]. A heat pump is equipped with two evaporators or one evaporator but supplied by two heat sources (through two heat exchangers). One heat source is solar energy and the other source is usually air or ground or other heat source. When air solar collectors are used, then solar energy collected is transferred directly to the heat pump evaporator. When liquid solar collectors are used, then solar energy is absorbed by solar collectors and can be sent directly to the heat pump evaporator or can be stored in the form of sensible heat in the storage tank. Then heat stored can be used as heat source for the heat pump evaporator if the temperature of the storage medium (water) is high enough. If not, the heat pump can use the other heat source (usually ground or air). Solar or the other renewable heat source is used depending on which source results in a higher COP of the heat pump. It can be said that the dual-source SAHP system is in some way a combination of two systems: parallel and series. A standard dual-source SAHP system with liquid (flat plate) solar collectors is presented in **Figure 12**.

In a traditional dual-source SAHP system, presented in **Figure 12** (numbers represent the main system components and are given in the legend of **Figure 8**), the following main modes of system operation can be used:

- Solar DHW heating: Heat stored in the main storage tank is transferred to the DHW tank (description of this mode of operation is the same as for series SAHP system presented in **Figure 8**).
- Solar direct heating: When solar energy is used directly for heating, if temperature T_s of stored heat is high enough to supply heat to the heating system directly, that is, if $T_s > T_{smin}$, then $Q_{hd} = Q_{heat}$ and a heat pump does not operate, $Q_{hp} = 0$; depending on the

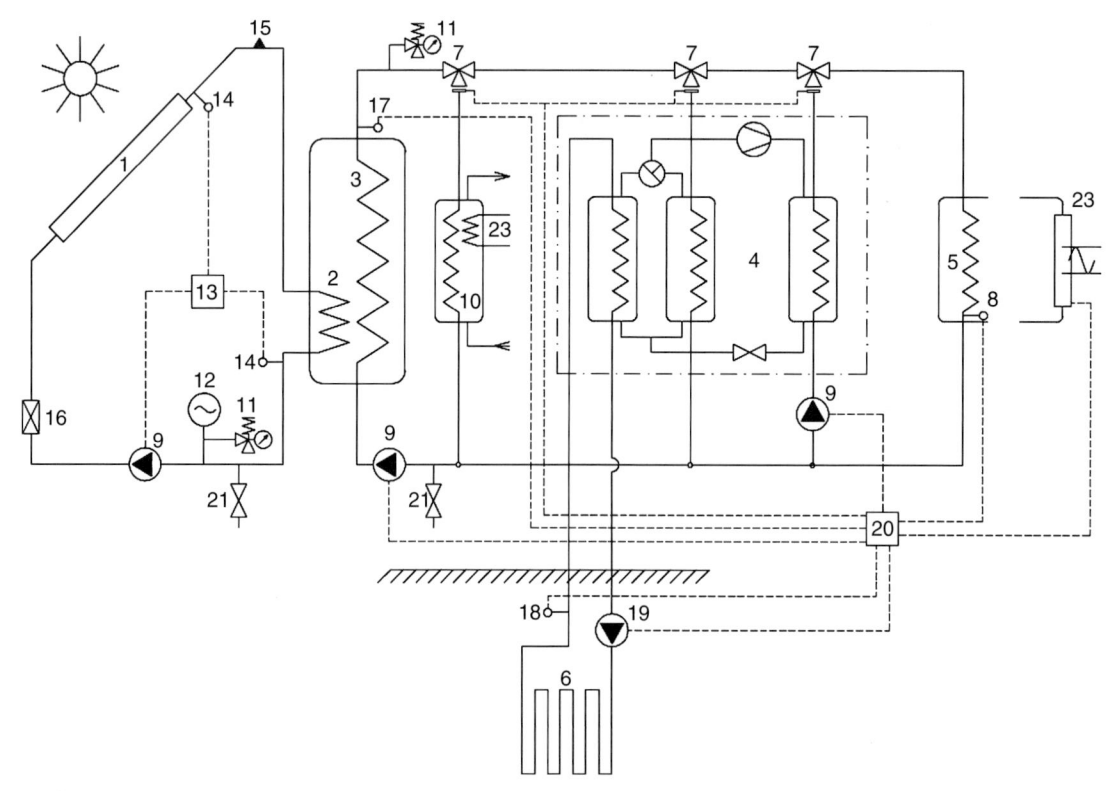

Figure 12 Standard dual-source SAHP system. See **Figure 8** caption for legends.

solar radiation level and the difference between the temperature of working fluid in solar collectors and storage medium, the solar collector loop can operate gaining useful energy ($Q_u > 0$) or not ($Q_u = 0$).

- Solar indirect heating via the heat pump: If the temperature of collected or stored heat is too low for direct heating, $T_s \leq T_{smin}$, but if it is higher than the temperature of the other heat source of the heat pump evaporator $T_s > T_{notsol}$, then the heat pump can use the heat stored to meet heating demand, so $Q_{hpcon} = Q_{heat}$ and $Q_{hd} = 0$, and $Q_u > 0$ or $Q_u = 0$, depending on whether the solar collectors operate or not; the heat Q_{hp} extracted out of the storage tank as a heat source for the heat pump can be calculated using eqn [13].
- Heating via the heat pump using the renewable energy other than solar energy: When the storage temperature T_s is too low for effective use of the heat stored as a heat source of the heat pump evaporator, and/or the temperature T_{notsol} of the other heat source is higher than the solar one, that is, $T_s \leq T_{notsol}$, then $Q_{hpnotsolcon} = Q_{heat}$, and $Q_{hd} = 0$, $Q_{hp} = 0$, and $Q_u > 0$ or $Q_u = 0$, depending on whether the solar collectors operate or not.
- Heat pump and auxiliary heating: The rule of this mode of operation is the same as for the series heat pump shown in **Figure 8**, with the only difference being that there are two heat sources for the heat pump: solar or the other renewable heat source is used depending on which source results in a higher COP of the heat pump; heating load is provided by the heat pump and an auxiliary heater, so at the heat sink it is always true that $Q_{hpcon} + Q_{aux} = Q_{heat}$.

If needed, additional modes of operation can be applied. The automatic control system is responsible for the effective operation of the system. The energy balance of the storage tank of the dual-source SAHP system presented in **Figure 12** can be described in the unsteady state in the same way as in the case of the series SAHP system, that is, by eqn [12]. The heat pump is used only for space heating; therefore, the COP of the system considered is presented without DHW function and can be written (referring to eqns [15] and [17]) in the following way:

$$\text{COP} = \frac{Q_{heattotal}}{W_{total}} = \frac{Q_{hd} + Q_{hpcon} + Q_{aux}}{W + W_{pumpSd} + W_{pumpShp} + W_{heat} + W_{aux} + W_{hp}} \quad [22]$$

When the heat pump of the dual-source SAHP system also supplies heating energy for DHW, then eqn [22] includes more terms, similar to eqn [18] or [21].

3.15.3.6 Other Configurations

Studies and experiments in the past showed that the parallel systems were much better than the series systems and slightly better than dual source [36]. However, at present, it is difficult to state definitely which system is the most effective and has the highest thermal performance; more results of the operation of different systems are needed and comparative and optimization studies are necessary. Nowadays, different strategies of operation are possible in one system due to well-developed automatic control systems and any system can be a mixture of different configurations and operate as a multifunctional system in a flexible way.

Nowadays, most heat pump systems are used for heating of buildings and DHW supply. These systems must include a hot water heater (an electric heater (booster)). The electric heater provides the auxiliary energy when there is peak demand, usually in cold winter days. Heat pumps at the small scale, for example, for single-family houses, should be designed to cover about 60–70% of the maximum designed heat load of a building, but not more, because of high investment costs. It means that a heat pump can cover nearly most, up to 90–95%, of the annual heat demand of the building. The rest is covered by the auxiliary peak electric heater included in a storage tank or in the heat pump. This construction of the heat pump makes the SAHP system configuration different from standard series or parallel systems used in the past. However, these modern heat pumps can also be coupled to a solar system in a series or parallel way. Therefore, it is difficult to classify them as 'other' configuration of the SAHP systems, but the past definitions of series, parallel, or dual-source SAHP system also do not suit them fully.

Some of the SAHP systems using the ground as a heat source for the heat pump have a function of recharging (regeneration) the ground (duct, borehole, etc.). An example of such a system is presented in **Figure 13**.

As shown in **Figure 13** (the legend is the same as for **Figure 8**), solar collectors can be connected to the return pipe from the evaporator going back to the ground. The antifreeze mixture (based on glycol) circulating into the solar collector loop can be sent to the ground heat exchanger loops. Some results show that the recharging process results in an increase of the ground temperature by only a few degrees [13]. However, these few degrees can improve much the operation of the heat pump. When solar collectors and ground heat exchangers are linked together and the same antifreeze mixture can circulate in both loops, then apart from the recharging effect it is also possible to use another mode of operation. When the temperature of the working fluid in solar collectors is higher than the temperature of the working fluid in ground heat exchangers, the antifreeze mixture can circulate first in ground heat exchangers, which behave as a preliminary heat source. Next the antifreeze mixture circulates through solar collectors gaining more heat and then it flows into the heat pump evaporator. In this way, the heat extracted from the ground is upgraded by solar energy and the heat pump operates longer in better thermal conditions (higher temperature of the heat source – ground upgraded by solar), in consequence with higher COP. This type of SAHP system is a very specific configuration and it represents a hybrid of parallel and series and dual-source SAHP system.

A solar-assisted ground storage heat pump system with latent heat energy storage [23] is another example of a rather complicated system in configuration. Its effective operation depends on automatic control systems giving possibilities of different strategies for

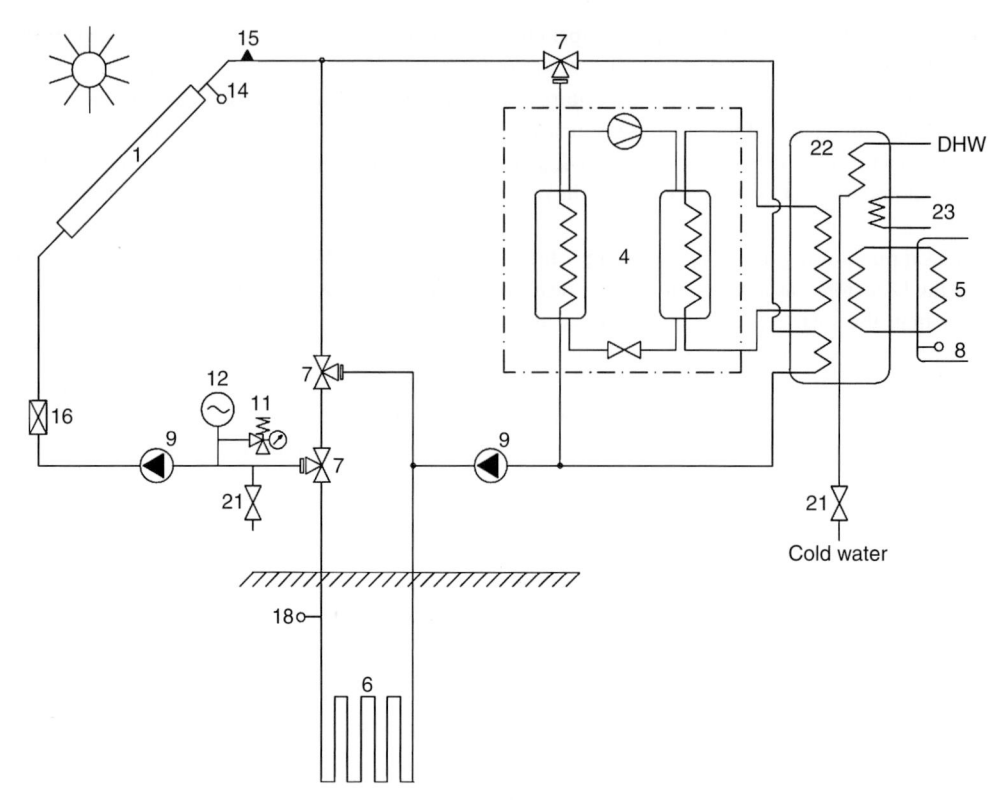

Figure 13 A combined SAHP system: hybrid of parallel–series–dual-source SAHP system. See **Figure 8** caption for legends.

operation and it is very difficult to classify this system according to traditional categories. The main components of the system are the following: solar collectors, latent heat storage with PCM material and a serpentine heat exchanger, U tube ground heat exchangers, heat pump, and a heating system in the form of fan coils. These components can operate on their own, or in cooperation with some others or with all of them. A system of valves controlled automatically play a very important role in managing the energy flow in the system. It is possible that the same fluid can flow through different loops linked together. The main modes of the system operation are as follows:

- Direct solar heating: The building is heated directly by heat gained by solar collectors and the heat pump is switched off; depending on solar and ambient conditions, the useful heat Q_u from solar collectors can be transferred to a latent heat storage with PCM material.
- Direct heating from the latent heat storage: The building is heated directly from the latent heat storage; the heat pump is switched off, and solar energy cannot be stored and used.
- Solar heating via the heat pump and storage of solar energy: Solar energy is collected by solar collectors and then stored in the form of latent heat in storage; loading and unloading of the latent heat storage tank take place all the time; the heat stored in the tank becomes the heat source of the heat pump evaporator, the process of supplying heat from the store to the heat pump evaporator can be considered as the low-temperature cycle; working fluid flows out of the evaporator and comes back to solar collectors; heat from the heat pump condenser is transferred to the fan coil system in a building, the process of supplying heat from the condenser of the heat pump to the fan coil system can be considered as the high-temperature cycle.
- Solar heating via the heat pump: Solar heat stored in a latent heat storage tank is used as a heat source of the heat pump; heat from the store is sent to the heat pump evaporator for the low-temperature loop; heat from the heat pump condenser is transferred to the fan coil system in a building in a high-temperature loop; solar energy is not collected or stored.
- Heating via the ground source heat pumps: Heat extracted by ground heat exchangers is used as a heat source for the heat pump; this constitutes the low-temperature circuit; heat from the heat pump condenser is transferred to the fan coil system in a high-temperature loop.
- Solar heating and ground heating via the heat pump in series: Working fluid circulates first in the ground heat exchangers, which preheats the working fluid, then the working fluid circulates through the solar collectors gaining more heat, and finally it flows through the heat pump evaporator and comes back to ground heat exchangers; this is the low-temperature circuit; the heat from the heat pump condenser is transferred to the fan coil system in the high-temperature circuit.
- No heating; only storing heat from solar collectors in the latent heat storage tank.
- No heating; only storing heat from solar collectors in the ground, regenerating the ground source.

This is a very brief description of SAHP system operation, which shows how complicated the configuration of the system can be and how complex are the strategies of operation of such a heating system, especially when there are multiple heat sources. The complication of the system structure makes the investment costs high but at the same time its operation is much more effective.

Apart from traditional functions such as heating or cooling, SAHP systems can be used for dehumidification including drying purposes. Some of SAHP drying systems have already been manufactured and tested [27, 37, 38]. One of the interesting examples of such systems [38] proposes the use of air solar collectors and an air heat pump operating in a parallel way. Even if these two heating systems operate in parallel, it is difficult to classify this system strictly as a parallel one. The main modes of operation of the system can explain this statement and these modes are as follows:

- Solar heating and ventilation: When solar irradiance is high enough, the ambient air is heated by solar collectors and sent to the granary to dry grains.
- Solar heating and heat pump heating and ventilation: When solar irradiance is not high enough to meet drying needs, the ambient air is heated by solar collectors and by an air heat pump, the airflow from both sources is mixed and sent to the granary to dry grains, the return air (from granary) flows to the heat pump evaporator for heat recovery.
- Heat pump heating and ventilation: When solar irradiance is very low or it is nighttime, the fans of solar collectors are off and the ambient air is heated by an air heat pump and sent to the granary to dry grains, the return air flows back to the heat pump evaporator for heat recovery.
- Heat pump dehumidification and ventilation: It is used on rainy and cloudy days. Ambient air is sent first to the heat pump evaporator to be cooled and dehumidified and then to the heat pump condenser to be heated again.

It is possible to find an example of SAHP systems that are combined with systems that produce electricity. One such system has been presented in Section 3.15.2.2 and it represents DX SAHP system with PV/T collector–evaporator [28]. The other example can be the solar-assisted geothermal heat pump coupled with small wind turbine systems for heating agricultural and residential buildings [39].

By analyzing the examples presented above it is evident how many different technologies and modification of standard categorization of SAHP system are available nowadays and how flexible are the modes of operation of these systems.

3.15.4 Solar-Assisted Heat Pump System with Seasonal Storage

3.15.4.1 Fundamental Options of Seasonal Energy Storage

Energy storage of different forms of thermal energy is a very efficient way of energy conservation. Energy storage can very much improve the efficiency of the whole thermal process and the rate of useful energy conversion. Heat supply and demand are often at quite different times.

Energy storage is widespread with many typical everyday applications. In addition to the different types of energy, the basic difference in energy storage systems is the duration of the storage period. The most common heat stores are used as short-term storage systems (e.g., hot water boilers in domestic use). The application of long-term storage is currently much less common, mostly due to economic reasons. However, there is a large amount of surplus heat in summer and surplus cold in winter, which could be stored for a longer period of time, for example, for a season, to be used when it is really needed.

In the literature [20] we can find some general and important information about requirements regarding energy storage. In combination with seasonal energy storage, solar energy can make a major contribution to heating of buildings. The incoherency of the solar radiation peak season and space heating demand creates interest in applying the ground as a seasonal storage medium of solar energy.

A seasonal storage facility can be designed in many different ways. Heat can be stored in the ground (clay, sand), in unfractured rocks, and in water [7, 40–42]. Four fundamental options for long-term solar thermal energy storage are presented in a schematic way in **Figure 14** and they are mentioned below:

- water tanks (including water pits, water–gravel, and solar ponds);
- rocks (boreholes in rocks, rock caverns, pits);
- soil storage (ducts in earth, earth coils);
- aquifers.

A water tank contains a mass of water heated by solar collectors and stored in a tank. The water tank can be located on the ground surface (see **Figure 14**, top left) or partly embedded in the ground, or fully embedded in the ground (see **Figure 14**, top right). Water tanks should have appropriate storage volume, usually a few thousand cubic meters. The water tank construction is usually of reinforced concrete. It should be insulated partly or fully depending on its position, but at least over the roof area. To ensure water tightness, the tank can be built with extra steel liners or special high-density concrete material with very low vapor permeability can be used. Water pits are usually expensive due to the cost of excavation. They need lit construction; however, it is possible to keep excavation cost low if they are built on sites with soft ground. A water–gravel pit is a pit with a watertight liner and is filled with gravel–water mixture, which forms the storage medium. This store should have thermal insulation on its top and side walls. The specific heat capacity of the mixture is lower than water; therefore, for the same amount of heat stored, the volume of the gravel–water store should be bigger (50%) than that of the water storage tank.

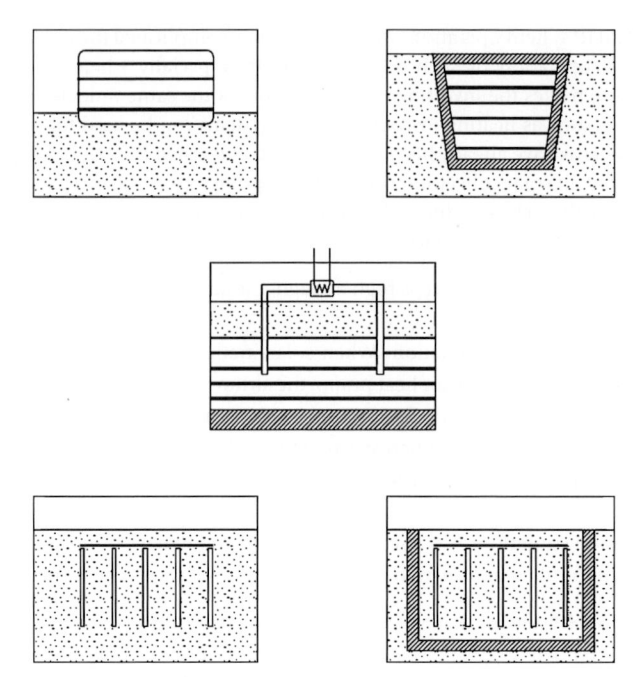

Figure 14 Basic options of long-term solar energy storage.

A solar pond is a mass of relatively shallow salty water (about one and half meter depth) used as a solar collector. Solar radiation is absorbed at the bottom of the pond. Due to the density gradient of salt water in the pond, the concentration increases with depth and convection is suppressed. The density gradient causes the temperature gradient to increase with depth. The heat stored in the lower layer can be utilized for heating purposes. Due to heat extraction, a lower convection layer exists. At the surface of the water, due to wind an upper convection layer exists. In this manner, the nonconvective layer (about 1 m thickness) between the two convection layers acts as thermal insulation.

Rocks can be used as a storage medium by excavating in rock caverns and pits, which in most cases are filled with water. But more popular is drilling in rocks making a great number of boreholes, which are filled with plastic tubes in which water flows. Rock is a very good storage medium due to high thermal conductivity and thermal capacity. The typical depth of the boreholes is from 40 to 150 m and spacing is about 4 m. When the ground surface area available for the system is limited, then the boreholes require other arrangements (e.g., increasing duct spacing as depth increases). The heat exchanger may consist of a single plastic tube in a borehole or a configuration of multiple boreholes with plastic tubes inside. In the simplest arrangements, the fluid flows down in the plastic tube and flows up in the channel, which constitutes the plastic tube and borehole wall. The fluid is extracted from the top of this channel to the heat distribution system. Such a borehole with a concentric inner tube is defined as an open system. The main advantage of this system is that heat carrier fluid is in direct contact with the surrounding rock; this provides the best heat transfer conditions. Unfortunately, the hydrogeological and geochemical conditions are not very often good for open systems. The most common type of heat exchanger is therefore a closed system. The close system composes a U-shaped loop of plastic tube in the boreholes [43]. The volume of the borehole outside the pipe contains groundwater or filling material as sand to improve the thermal contact between the plastic pipe and the borehole wall. The heat transfer conditions for closed systems are not as good as for open ones. In summer, the heat from the solar system can be transported to the rock store via a fluid circulating in the channels of the heat exchanger. This is the time the store is loaded (charged). During the heating season, when heat is needed for heating purposes, the store is unloaded (discharged). The fluid circulating in the channels of heat exchangers coupled with a heat pump is heated by the surrounding rocks. When the temperature of the circulating fluid is expected to be below 0 °C, due to heavy energy demand in winter, then an antifreeze mixture in a closed loop must be used. All systems mentioned above are systems operating in an indirect mode with a heat pump. Indirect mode of the system operation means that heat stored in rocks is transferred to the heat pump evaporator through a fluid circulating in heat exchangers, that is, a matrix of vertical pipes in boreholes. Some investigations have been made using a direct mode of the system operation, that is, direct evaporation of the working fluid of the heat pump in copper pipes in the boreholes.

Nowadays, a duct system is the most common type of ground heat storage device. The main advantage of the duct systems is the low construction cost, because of no ground excavation. However, it is very important that duct system must be designed in accordance with the geologic conditions of the site. When the geologic conditions are not checked properly, unexpected disadvantages of the system may appear. There are two basic components of a duct ground heat store:

- the geological medium, which provides the storage capacity;
- the ground heat exchanger.

In the ground storage system, the ground (soil) is used as a storage medium of sensible heat. Heat is injected or extracted from the ground by means of ground heat exchangers. The heat exchanger consists of vertical or horizontal tubes, which are inserted into the soil. What is most important, considering ground as a storage medium, is the low construction cost and the fact that heat losses from the storage are relatively small. These heat losses depend on the size and shape of the store, the average storage temperature during a cycle, and the physical and thermal properties of the ground storage medium. Heat losses from the store increase with higher temperature and higher water flow through the store. The heat loss density decreases with larger volume of the store.

In the ground (clay, sandy soil, peat) deposits, a duct system is obtained by drilling holes and inserting vertical U-shaped loops of thin plastic tubes. Heat exchangers are set into a depth of 30–100 m below the surface. The typical spacing between tubes of a ground heat exchanger is about 2 m. This distance is shorter than in rocks due to the lower thermal conductivity of the clay. The volume of the ground store must be a few times more than the volume of a water tank for the same quantity of heat to be stored. The storage volume is defined as the volume of the ground perforated by the ducts (see **Figure 14**, bottom left). The heat transport in the ground is mainly by heat conduction. The heat transfer mechanism in the ground depends on the physical and thermal properties of the ground. Typically, the ground region has a parallelepiped shape or it is a cylinder with a vertical axis. When the store is of shallow depth, a high temperature gradient between the ground surface and the upper parts of the storage exists. To avoid large heat losses from these upper parts, thermal insulation is used between heat exchangers and ground surfaces. Even when deep duct systems are applied, very often the upper part of the heat exchanger tubes is insulated. Sometimes, the land area above the store is covered with a shallow layer of soil with low thermal conductivity. When there are waterways in the vicinity of the store, with water flow more than 5 m per year, then special protection (thin foil) around the store can be set (see **Figure 14**, bottom right corner). The important advantage of the system is its modularity; therefore, it is easy to extend the store by inserting more heat exchangers, when more heat is needed because of the increasing number of houses being supplied.

An aquifer is a special hydrogeological formation; therefore, its practical application is limited to few locations. An aquifer is very often defined as a saturated permeable geologic unit, which transmits significant quantities of water under an ordinary hydraulic gradient. This geologic unit can be sediment or permeable rock capable of conducting groundwater. There are two main types of aquifers: confined and unconfined. When one layer of the aquifer is enclosed by two layers of low permeability (e.g., clay), then this layer in the middle is called confined, and the whole aquifer is called confined. Heat can be stored in aquifers by heating the ambient aquifer water. During summer or times when there is no heat demand (or heat demand is low), heat from solar collectors is injected to aquifer. Besides solar energy, waste heat from industry or power stations can be used. When the aquifer is loaded, water is extracted from the aquifer through a supply well, then is heated by solar energy or waste heat (through a heat exchanger), and as a hot medium is injected into an injection well. When the aquifer is unloaded, hot water from aquifer is taken and is used as a heat source for the heat pump evaporator. Then cooled water is rejected into the supply (cold) well.

3.15.4.2 Classification and Evaluation of Seasonal Ground Storage

Ground storage systems can be classified in many different ways. One of them is based on the type of storage medium: liquid – water; solid – rocks, ground; mixture of liquid and solid: water–gravel; aquifer; or saturated soils. The other important classification, mainly for ground systems, is made according to the temperature range of the store, as is done in the following way:

- CT – cold-temperature store – < 10 °C;
- LT – low-temperature store – 10–30 °C;
- MT – medium-temperature store – 30–50 °C;
- HT – high-temperature store – > 50 °C.

The cold store (CT) is applied to small heating systems when heat demand is not high, for example, in single-family houses and in small farm buildings. The cold store system can consist of vertical or horizontal heat exchangers using undisturbed soil as a storage medium of sensible heat. In a CT system, no artificial charging (loading) of the soil is applied. The ground is used as a natural source of energy, where natural thermal regeneration process, because of the influence of the environment, takes an important role. To meet the house heating demand, the heat exchangers are coupled with a heat pump. The CT store is usually called a ground source heat pump system and has already been described in a previous section. The temperature in a ground body and the temperature of the fluid that circulates between ground heat exchanger and the heat pump evaporator may drop below zero. Therefore, an antifreeze mixture (ethylene–glycol–water) is used. The CT systems are usually designed to operate in a monovalent mode, that is, only one source of energy (energy extracted from the ground) for the heat pump is used and heat demand is provided only by ground heat exchangers coupled with the heat pump. In monovalent CT systems, no auxiliary conventional source of energy is used.

In LT system, artificial charging of the ground is required. The low temperature range allows applying simple flat plate solar collectors, which can be roof-integrated collectors. For LT application, solar collectors do not need to have any covers, therefore unglazed collectors can be used. In most LT stores, the storage volume is created by constructing vertical channels for vertical ground heat exchangers. The spacing between the tubes depends mainly on the type of the ground. The depth of the heat exchanger depends on the size of the heating load together with technical restrictions. The LT system has to be coupled with the heat pump. Heat from the heat pump is transmitted to the heating system in a house. Both LT stores and CT systems require a low-temperature space heating system in the house. In order to obtain sufficient area for the heat exchange between heating fluid and air in the house, floor or wall heating systems are mainly used. When typical radiators are applied in low-temperature space heating systems, then the surface of these radiators must be sufficiently large, approximately two times more than in conventional high-temperature heating systems. The LT storage systems can be used for heating small houses, bigger residential and attached houses, or apartment buildings, according to the size of solar collector matrix, storage volume, and capacity of the heat pump.

In the MT storage system, during the loading period solar energy or waste heat is transferred to the ground storage body. During unloading of the ground store, heat can be transferred directly to the heating system in the building. It takes place when the temperature of the fluid circulating in the ground heat exchangers is high enough for direct space heating. In the other case, when the temperature of the store and consequently the temperature of the heat carrier fluid are too low, the heating mode is accomplished via the heat pump. For MT storage systems, solar collectors with a higher working fluid temperature can be useful. Therefore, evacuated tube solar collectors are very often applied. In some projects with MT stores (e.g., Kulavik Project, Sweden), the heat storage is divided into two regions. The first storage region is in the center of a store and is designed for storing heat at higher temperature. This region is surrounded by a region in which heat at lower temperature is stored. Heat from the central region can be used directly for the space heating system. But heat from the outer region has to be used via a heat pump. The main advantage of this system is that radial heat losses from the inner region have been withdrawn in the outer region. The distance between the heat exchanger tubes in the center region is much less (e.g., 0.5 m) than this distance in the outer region (e.g., 1.5–2.0 m). The center region and outer region ought to be situated at some distance (e.g., about 5 m). It can also be mentioned that the heat exchanger tubes in the outer region should be buried deeper than tubes in the center region (to reduce heat losses from the inner region). The MT storage system can be applied to a group of single-family houses, a group of apartment buildings and commercial buildings, that is, office buildings, school and administration buildings, and garages.

The HT storage systems are still under development. The storage of high-temperature heat would be very attractive since it allows utilizing waste heat and it is very important to transfer this high-temperature heat directly to the district heating system. Therefore, there is no need to apply a heat pump. However, an auxiliary burner ought to be used to cover, if it is necessary, the peak load. The most common types of solar collectors, which can be applied in HT systems, are high-temperature evacuated tube collectors. Considering HT stores it ought to be mentioned that these systems need a special duct technology which depends on geologic conditions. It is necessary to ensure a good thermal contact between the heat carrier fluid and the ground, a good thermal conductivity of the ground, especially in the near vicinity of the duct, also small heat losses, especially in the near vicinity of the duct, and to minimize heat losses, especially through the top. In HT stores, two main problems occur, groundwater flow and as a result heat losses and moisture migration, the latter producing a drying effect in the ground. HT stores cannot be used in small systems; heat losses in such systems would be extremely large. Therefore, HT store projects are made only for large loads, a group of apartment or commercial buildings.

The general idea of underground storage through application of vertical heat exchangers is presented in a schematic way in **Figure 15**. However, it should be underlined that the possibilities of utilizing ground as a heat source vary from place to place and depend mainly on the local geology and on the size of the system. As mentioned, usually systems of middle scale, that is, for a small group of heating systems, or large scale for district heating are considered. Planning of ground seasonal storage systems requires some preliminary study and careful design. There are places not suitable for seasonal heat storage application from a hydrogeological point of view.

To evaluate a seasonal ground store in a large-scale application, a detailed study has to be made. Thus to evaluate a project of central heating plant with seasonal storage (CHPSS), the following study steps have to be performed:

– site selection, a review of proposed sites taking into account
  • heat load and its nature,
  • land availability,
  • possibility of integration of the CHPSS to existing system,
  • site geology;

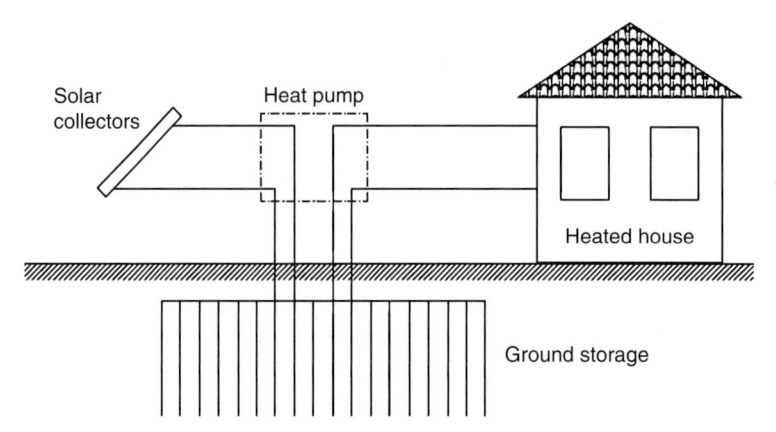

Figure 15 The idea of underground storage through application of vertical heat exchangers.

- investigation of the storage properties:
  - geological conditions,
  - hydrological conditions,
  - hydrochemical conditions (for HT systems),
  - thermal and physical properties of the store,
  - review of construction techniques suitable for the given geology;
- preliminary analysis of the system performance:
  - preliminary evaluation of mathematical model,
  - simulation study including economic analysis, using special design tools, that is, computer simulation programs;
- recommendations for the proposed system based on the simulation results.

The design of the seasonal storage system depends on whether CHPSS is planned for a new building and new heating system, or the CHPSS is expected to be integrated to existing building and heating system. If CHPSS is integrated to existing space heating system, it is good if this system is the low-temperature type. Buildings using steam for heating are not favored because they are likely to require extensive retrofitting. Sufficient land area for seasonal storage system is a very important factor. A special review study about land availability for storage, solar collectors in CSHPSS system, and other coupled equipment should be made. A suitable land area for solar collectors with good insolation conditions is required. These sites are favorable when they have got well-documented geology, for example, geological characteristics are known from geological survey maps and sometimes experimental borings are made during the construction of other buildings and plants at the chosen site. The lack of information pertinent to the geology of the sites means that the site will not be favored for the CHPSS applications. When the heating building and the land area are selected and they are found to be the potential site for the application of the CHPSS or CSHPSS project, further investigations can be made.

The storage medium should be investigated from the point of view of its geology and its physical and thermal properties. The local geology of the store is characterized by geological, geothermal, hydrogeological, and hydrochemical conditions. Hydrogeological studies are very important to estimate the water movement and the water table in the store and its surroundings. As it is known, water flow through the store leads to heat losses. Physical and thermal properties influence the thermal storage capability. Geotechnical investigation is necessary for the proper design of a system particularly when clay is used as a storage medium. Inaccurate soil properties can result in different than assumed actual performance of the system. Lessons from Groningen project [44] show how important is a detailed storage properties study. Higher heat losses and lower thermal capacity and consequently lower efficiencies in real projects are due to convective flow in saturated, especially highly permeable ground. Therefore, it is very important to take into account the geological conditions to choose suitable sites for ground store location.

In many countries, soil conditions are characterized by a high groundwater table that leads to high water movement in the store. When the effects of natural and induced convection to the surrounding can be reduced, then a higher store efficiency can be obtained. Groundwater can flow through the pores or voids in soils. The water flow depends on the permeability and the hydraulic gradient in the soil. The flow of water through the soil for the proposed storage system has to be analyzed before planning the type and size of such a system. Thermal properties of the soil, that is, thermal conductivity and volumetric heat capacity, describe the thermal storage ability [45, 46]. Thermal conductivity of any kind of rock within the water-saturated zone is higher than for the nonsaturated zone.

The thermal parameters of the store depend on the property–temperature variations of the soil medium. The dependence of heat conduction on temperature is noticeable; however, it is not as strong as dependence on density and especially on water content. As it is known, thermal parameters are influenced by the physical properties of the store such as water content, bulk density, dry density, and porosity and by the soil mechanics. The water content and porosity are very important for thermal properties of the soil, so they are important in designing the heat store. The water content is defined as the ratio of mass of water to mass of dry material.

It was found by Adolfson *et al.* [47] that water pore pressure increases with increasing temperature in the soil. This is due to the fact that water has greater coefficient of volumetric expansion than the soil solids. With the increase of temperature, water in the vicinity of the heat exchanger will move away from its tube. It can be explained by the fact that water in the soil will tend to move from a high-pressure to a low-pressure zone. The significant amount of water migrating away from the tubes may reduce the effectiveness of the heat exchange into storage. Drying conditions at the contact surface between the heat exchanger tube and the soil may occur. Air voids may take the place of the expelled water and add resistance to heat flow and consequently cause the drying conditions at the contact surface, for example, at the contact surface of heat exchanger tube and clay. Dry conditions are not expected in the store where operating temperatures are not so high, for example, for LT storage systems. The study shows that even for MT systems, the risk of significantly drying the saturated clay is very small indeed. If the ground is saturated and has a low permeability, then these sites are preferable for high-temperature storage. For soils with higher permeability, a large store volume is needed for the same store efficiency. Considering the HT seasonal storage systems, a more detailed study ought to be performed due to more complicated heat and moisture phenomena and more evident chemical processes in the storage medium.

In HT systems, apart from moisture reduction and dissolution, additional phenomena such as effects of desorption of water from clay minerals, dehydration of gypsum, and structural decomposition of specific clay minerals ought to be taken into account. To apply HT systems in the ground, very intensive and careful geological studies are needed. Geochemical, geotechnical, and hydrogeological problems in HT systems are described in the literature [48].

It can be said that sites suitable for seasonal thermal energy storage especially for HT systems should be chosen in a soil with high water content, due to the fact that porous sediment in nonsaturated conditions has poor thermal properties. If the ground is unsaturated, then it should have a high thermal conductivity.

To increase the thermal efficiency of the storage, boreholes around the heat exchanger tubes are filled with a special material, for example, quartz sand, Portland cement, bentonite, and water. It helps to keep soil (sand) around the tube moist and helps to reduce the overall thermal resistance from heat exchanger tube to the clay (sand moist has higher thermal conductivity than clay). Sand also has larger pores than clay and water can move easily in the filling material in the borehole, which results in adding a convective heat transfer contribution to the process. Application of filling material in boreholes gives better performance of the heat store and can reduce some geothermal problems in a clay heat store. However, the additional cost of applying and installing filling materials in boreholes needs to be justified by the increased performance of storage and reduction of borehole numbers.

It has to be mentioned that in the case of large-scale seasonal ground storage systems, a very careful analysis is necessary to achieve efficient performance of the operating system. It turns out that in some cases when no or very poor preliminary design studies were used, the actual overall performance of the storage systems was far away from predictions. The most common way to predict thermal performance of CHPSS or CSHPSS systems is to simulate the operation of the system and thermal behavior of each of the system components using computer models.

3.15.4.3 Heat and Mass Transfer in the Ground Store, General Consideration

Thermal processes in ground storage are characterized by rapid heat flow in the near vicinity of the duct and by relatively slow heat flow in the surrounding ground. It is proposed to analyze thermal processes in the ground in two groups [46]:

- local thermal processes around each ground heat exchanger, so-called microscale,
- global thermal processes in the storage volume and the surrounding ground, so-called macroscale.

To analyze the heat transfer phenomena and to solve the problem, it is necessary to determine the temperature field in the ground body, that is, in the near vicinity of the ground heat exchangers and in the whole storage medium and surroundings. The complete temperature field may be considered as a superposition of a global (slowly varying in time) temperature field and local temperature field with steep gradients near the duct. The theory of thermal processes and analysis of duct storage systems can be found in the literature [35, 40–51]. However, the approach given by scientists sometimes differs.

The basic concepts of heat transfer, between the heat-carrying fluid of ground heat exchanger and the surrounding ground, and the heat flow process in the storage region are described briefly in this section. At the beginning it is essential to describe the initial ground store state. Usually initial conditions are determined by the undisturbed ambient ground temperature, which increases with depth due to the geothermal heat flow.

The governing equation of heat transport in a solid body is based on the principle of energy conservation. The density of heat flow is a function of spatial coordinates and time. Taking into account Cartesian coordinates, the three components of heat flux density are $qx(x,y,z,t)$, $qy(x,y,z,t)$, and $qz(x,y,z,t)$. The energy balance equation is as follows:

$$-\nabla q = \frac{\partial \rho c_p T}{\partial t} \qquad [23]$$

where ∇ is $(\partial/\partial x, \partial/\partial y, \partial/\partial z)$. The density and specific heat of ground medium can be also functions of spatial coordinates and time.

The heat flow takes place by conduction and convection. According to Fourier's law, the conductive heat flow is proportional to the temperature gradient:

$$\vec{q}_{\text{cond}} = -\lambda \nabla T \qquad [24]$$

The ground is composed of grains of different minerals. The ground structure varies very often with spatial directions, which gives rise to anisotropic physical parameters. Anisotropic thermal conductivity in a large-scale store may have some consequences if the ground grains have a preferential orientation within the structure. Thermal anisotropy in the case of small ground samples does not affect the thermal properties of the whole ground store so much. Therefore, the averaged thermal parameters as well as averaged thermal conductivity can also be considered. In addition, by analyzing the dynamic processes of heat flow in low-temperature storage range, the thermal conduction can be assumed to have a constant value.

The convective heat transport can be represented by the following relationship:

$$\vec{q}_{\text{conv}} = (\rho c_p) \vec{q}_w (T - T_{\text{ref}}) \qquad [25]$$

where T_{ref} is an arbitrary reference temperature, which can be set to zero.

The convective heat transfer is a result of groundwater flow. This heat transport is caused by:

- regional groundwater flow – forced convection;
- buoyancy effects caused by the temperature difference between the storage region and the surrounding ground – natural convection.

The magnitude of the groundwater flow in the ground body is determined by:

- permeability of ground – intrinsic property of a porous material;
- hydraulic conductivity of ground – property of a ground material and fluid;
- local water gradient.

The groundwater flow q_w through a porous material is described by Darcy's law.

Now taking into account conductive and convective heat transfer (eqns [24] and [25]), the combined heat transfer in the ground body can be written as

$$-\nabla(\vec{q}_{cond} + \vec{q}_{conv}) = -\nabla\left[-\lambda \nabla T + (\rho c_p)_w \vec{q}_w T\right] \quad [26]$$

When it is assumed that groundwater can be treated as an incompressible fluid, then

$$\nabla \vec{q}_w = 0 \quad [27]$$

and the divergence of convective term can be written as

$$\nabla(T\vec{q}_w) = \vec{q}_w \nabla T + T \nabla \vec{q}_w = \vec{q}_w \nabla T \quad [28]$$

Additionally, when we assume an isotropic ground medium with constant thermal properties, the divergence of the heat conduction term can be written as

$$\nabla(\lambda \nabla T) = \lambda \nabla^2 T \quad [29]$$

When we assume that inner heat sources exist in the ground medium (in some models loading of store is regarded as an additional inner heat source), then the energy balance in the ground store can be written as

$$(\rho c_p)_g \frac{\partial T}{\partial t} = \lambda \nabla^2 T - (\rho c_p)_w \vec{q}_w \nabla T + q_v \quad [30]$$

To solve this equation it is necessary to determine boundary conditions. Modeling of heat transfer in the ground body is very complicated. Different numerical methods are used to solve the problem. To describe undisturbed ground temperature field and temperature distribution during loading and unloading of the ground store, different assumptions are made. The most typical models assume that heat convective transfer is neglected. This assumption can be made for low-permeability ground. In this case, the governing partial differential equation for heat transport in a solid body is an unsteady heat conduction equation, known as Fourier–Kirchhoff's equation, which takes the following form:

$$(\rho c_p)_g \frac{\partial T}{\partial t} = \lambda \nabla^2 T + q_v \quad [31]$$

In most models, axis-symmetrical thermal processes in a cylindrical storage region and a duct are considered. Then it is convenient to write eqn [31] in two-dimensional cylindrical coordinates, using radial and axial coordinates. The boundary and initial conditions are also written for the cylindrical heat transfer model.

The temperature distribution of the ground medium, during the heat extraction, depends on the total length of the tubes of ground heat exchangers (number of tubes and length of one tube) and the distance between them. When the tube number and their length are small, then the ground is cooled down significantly [37]. In a CT store system for very small number of tubes, the freezing phenomena of the ground body in the near vicinity of the heat exchanger can appear at the end of the heating season. When the tube number and their length are large enough, then the temperature of the natural ground store is relatively high all the time. That leads to more efficient operation of the heat pump.

3.15.4.4 Applications

A lot of information on energy storage problems, including seasonal storage of solar energy, and information on different applications, projects, and demonstration plants of SAHPSS including large-scale CSHPSS can be found at the website of the IEA Energy Storage Program, http://www.iea-eces.org, or at the websites of different tasks and annexes of the Energy Conservation through Energy Storage Program.

A distinguishing feature of ground systems with seasonal storage applying to large heating demand, that is, CSHPSS, is a large store with soil, water, or rock as a storage medium and a large solar collector array to charge the store. So the main components of CSHPSS are the following:

- solar collectors,
- storage system,
- distribution network for the load.

The CSHPSS systems are really very large. To justify the use of such systems, a forecast heating load of a few hundred MWh should be expected per year. Therefore, it is obvious that these systems are not practical for single-family houses and other small loads. The CSHPSS systems can be applied in large residential districts, schools, hospitals, and public or commercial facilities. The CSHPSS concept is also suitable for retrofitting existing building stock and for the integration of solar energy with other energy sources.

The Northern and Central European countries are leaders in large-scale application for seasonal storage systems. The first operational system was built in 1978 at Studsvik Laboratory, in Sweden. This system was designed to provide heat demand for an office building. In 1979, the IEA Solar Heating and Cooling Projects created a new Task VII on Central Solar Heating Plant with Seasonal Storage. This task was established to investigate the feasibility and cost-effectiveness of CSHPSS systems and to promote and assist in the establishment of this technology in the participating countries, which in alphabetic order were as follows: Austria, Canada, CEC (JRC Ispra), Denmark, Federal Republic of Germany, Finland, Italy, The Netherlands, Sweden, Switzerland, the United Kingdom, and the United States. In 1990 Task VII was finished. However, promoting the very successful results of this task's investigations led to the creation of the new Task XV on Advanced Central Solar Heating Plants in Built Environments. Later other tasks that were a kind of successors of Task XV were developed. Since the beginning of 1990, when Task VII was established, many CSHPSS systems were built and tested in many countries, mainly in Europe. Some of those projects, in some way historic projects with seasonal storage, are presented briefly below:

Kerava, Finland. The Kerava Solar Village (KSV) Project was put into operation in 1983. It was to provide heat for 44 apartments (3756 m^2 total area). The solar energy was stored in a stratified water tank (1500 m^3 volume) excavated in bedrock. Fifty-four boreholes in rocks (11 000 m^3 volume) were additionally used. The system was coupled with a heat pump. The storage capacity was found to be too small to achieve the design solar fraction.

Scarborough, Canada. The purpose of this project was to test the performance and economic feasibility of seasonal storage in aquifers. This project, completed in 1985, provided cool and heat for 30 470 m^2 Scarborough Canada Center Building, the major federal government building in the eastern part of Toronto. The Scarborough building had a cooling load greater than heating load; therefore, the aquifer was used to store cold water to be used for summer cooling. A vacuum tube solar collector array (700 m^2 area) was used for DHW demand.

Groningen, The Netherlands. Dutch CSHPSS at Groningen was put in operation in 1984. The system was designed for heating purposes (1200 MWh) of 96 houses divided into nine blocks and grouped around the seasonal duct heat store. Vacuum tube solar collectors (2400 m^2 area) were used. The storage system consisted of short-term (daily) and long-term storage. The short-term storage was a water tank (100 m^3 capacity) embedded in the center of clay seasonal storage (23 000 m^3 capacity). In the clay storage, 360 polybutylene U-shaped vertical tubes (20 m deep) were used. The system performance evaluation showed that the solar contribution of the system (628 MWh or 52% fraction) was about 15% lower than expected. This lower solar fraction was due to lower solar collector efficiency, higher storage losses through the top insulation, slightly higher minimum useful temperature in the system, and greater regional groundwater flow than expected.

Treviglio, Italy. The Treviglio Project was put in operation in 1982. The system was designed to provide heat for five apartment buildings (35 062 m^3 total heating volume). Flat plate solar collectors were used (2727 m^2 total area). Heat was transferred into the ground by 55 horizontal U-shaped pipes and 414 vertical boreholes. The total storage volume was about 43 400 m^3. The system was assisted by a heat pump. The evaluation of the system showed a very close agreement between the expected and measured solar fraction (expected 76%, real value 72%).

Sunclay, Sweden. The Sunclay Project was designed to supply low-temperature heat to a school. It was put in operation in 1980. Unglazed roof-integrated solar collectors (15 000 m^2 area) and duct store in clay (87 000 m^3 storage capacity) were coupled with a heat pump (diesel type). The annual heating requirement of the school was 1650 MWh.

Lambohov, Sweden. The CSHPSS at Lambohov was put in operation in 1980. This system used flat plate solar collectors (2900 m^2 area) and an insulated water storage volume (10 000 m^3) in bedrock to provide heat for 50 small houses (7000 m^2 total area). The annual heating demand was equal to 940 MWh.

Lyckebo, Sweden. Lyckebo was the largest and most widely known plant in Sweden. Lyckebo was put in operation in 1983. The system consisted of water storage in a rock cavern (105 000 m^3 capacity) and high-temperature flat plate solar collectors (final area 28 800 m^2). The rock cavern was not insulated. The heat losses from the cavern differed from the design study due to convection losses through the old access tunnel that was used during construction. The storage was designed to supply 100% of heating requirements for 550 houses at a temperature of 70 °C. The heat supplied to the system was approximately 8500 MWh per year.

Stuttgart University, Germany. An SAHP system with an artificial aquifer was built in 1985. This was the first project with seasonal heat storage in Germany on a large scale. The artificial aquifer gravel- and water-filled pit (1050 m^3 capacity) and unglazed solar collectors (211 m^2 area) and an electric heat pump (66 kW) were used. The system was designed to supply heat for an office building (floor area 1375 m^2) of the University Institute. The annual heat load was 150 MWh and consumption of energy for hot water was about 25 MWh. The heat distribution system was a low-temperature system (50/40 °C). Two different storage concepts combined in one store were used (artificial aquifer, man-made, that constituted primary and a secondary system: coils in gravel).

Since the 1980s, some new CSHPSS systems have been installed in other places. Some of them are not coupled with heat pumps. There is a new type of large-scale system, the so-called central solar heating plants with diurnal storage (CSHPDS). They have 'small' diurnal storage and are connected with the main heating plant, usually a conventional one, and the central district heating system. Some examples of both types of systems are listed below [52–55].

- Falkenberg, Sweden, CSHPDS in operation since 1989, collector area 5500 m^2, 1100 m^3 water tank, annual load size 30 GWh;
- Ry, Denmark, CSHP in operation since 1990, collector area 3025 m^2, directly connected to district heating, annual load size 32 GWh;
- Hamburg, Germany, CSHPSS in operation since 1996, collector area 3000 m^2, 4500 m^3 water-filled concrete tank, annual load size 1.6 GWh;
- Friedrichshafen, Germany, CSHPSS in operation since 1996, collector area 2700 m^2, 12 000 m^3 water-filled concrete tank, annual load size 2.4 GWh; in 2003 the collector area was extended to 3500 m^2, in 2004 to 4050 m^2, annual heat demand increased to 3–3.4 GWh, due to enlargement of residential area.
- Marstal, Denmark, CSHPDS in operation since 1996, collector area 18 300 m^2, 2100 m^3 water tank + 4000 m^3 sand water store + 10 000 m^3 water pit (2003), annual load size 28 GWh;
- Aeroskobing, Denmark, CSHPDS in operation since 1998, collector area 4900 m^2, 1200 m^3 water tank, annual load size 13 GWh;
- Neckarsulm, Germany, CSHPSS in operation since 1999, in 1999 collector area 2636 m^2, in 2002 extension to 5044 m^2, in 2007 next extension to 5670 m^2, in 1999 20 000 m^3 duct heat store, in 2001 store enlargement to 63 400 m^3, in 1999 annual load size 1.25 GWh, in 2007 increase to 2.8 GWh;
- Kungalv, Sweden, CSHPDS in operation since 2000, collector area 10 000 m^2, 1000 m^3 water tank, annual load size 90 GWh;
- Rise, Denmark, CSHPSS in operation since 2001, collector area 3575 m^2, 4500 m^3 water tank, annual load size 3.7 GWh;
- Steinfurt, Germany, CSHPSS (second generation) in operation since 2000, collector area 510 m^2, 1500 m^3 gravel–water, annual load size 0.325 GWh;
- Rostock, Germany, CSHPSS (second generation) in operation since 2000, collector area 1000 m^2, 20 000 m^3 aquifer, annual load size 0.497 GWh;
- Hannover, Germany, CSHPSS (second generation) in operation since 2000, collector area 1350 m^2, 2750 m^3 hot water, annual load size 0.694 GWh;
- Attenkirchen, Germany, CSHPSS (second generation) in operation since 2000, collector area 800 m^2, 500 m^3 hot + 9350 m^3 duct, annual load size 0.487 GWh.

During the last five years the next generation CSHPSS systems were realized in Germany thanks to R&D program Solartermie2000plus [56]. For example, in 2007 in Munich the new CSHPSS with 2900 m^2 of solar collectors and water tank (pit storage) of 5700 m^3 was put into operation. The annual heat demand is 2.3 GWh. In the same year the other CSHPSS in Crailsheim was realized with 7300 m^2 of solar collectors and duct ground store of 37 500 m^3 ground volume (there are also two buffer water tanks of 100 and 480 m^3). The annual heat load is 4.1 GWh. The solar fraction of the new plants is about 50%, which is really high.

Apart from the CSHPSS and CSHPDS, there are systems for combined heat and cold storage. Aquifer thermal energy storage (ATES) systems are especially good for cold storage. Such systems can be found in Sweden in Solna/Frosundavik at the SAS head office, and in Berlin in the German Parliament building and in other places. However, this technology is still not so popular at present, even though some of the systems represent high storage efficiency and solar fraction. A main obstacle for quick implementation of this technology is high investment cost.

References

[1] Cengel YA and Boles MA (2006) *Thermodynamics. An Engineering Approach*. New York: McGraw-Hill Higher Education.
[2] Holman JP (2002) *Heat Transfer*. New York: McGraw-Hill. Higher Education.
[3] Berghmans J (1983) *Heat Pump Fundamentals*. NATO Science Series E: Applied Sciences, No. 53. The Hague, The Netherlands: Martinus Nijhoff Publisher.
[4] Radermacher R and Hwang Y (2005) *Vapor Compression Heat Pumps with Refrigerant Mixes*. Boca Raton, FL: Taylor & Francis Group, LLC.
[5] American Society of Heating, Refrigerating, and Air-Conditioning Engineers, Inc. (ASHRAE) (2001) Refrigerants. In: *ASHRAE Handbook – Fundamentals*. Atlanta, GA.
[6] Chwieduk D (1996) Analysis of utilisation of renewable energies as heat sources for heat pumps in building sector. *Renewable Energy, International Journal* 1–4/SEP–DEC/1996. Oxford, UK: Pergamon, Elsevier Sciences.
[7] Schulz H and Chwieduk D (1995) *Wärme aus Sonne und Erde Energiesparende Heizungsysteme mit Erdwärmespeicher, Solarabsorber und Wärmepumpe*. Staufen bei Freiburg, Germany: Okobuch Verlag.
[8] Baggs SA (1983) Remote prediction of ground temperature in Australian soils and mapping its distribution. *Solar Energy* 30(4): 351–366.
[9] Eskilson P (1987) *Thermal Analysis of Heat Extraction Boreholes*. Lund, Sweden: Department of Mathematical Physics, University of Lund.
[10] Böswarth R (2005) *Installateur der Wärmepumpen*. EU Project. INTERREG IIIB CADSES CER^2 – Central European Regions Cluster for Energy from Renewables Network. Österreichisches Forschungs- und Prüfzentrum Arsenal GmbH (ed.) Wien, Austria.
[11] VDI Richtlinieeeee (2000) *Thermische Nutzung des Untergrundes*, VDI 4640, p.12. Norm (German Standard), Germany.
[12] Knoblich K, Rammner R, and Martin G (eds.) (1990) *Proceedings of the Workshop on Seasonal Thermal Energy Storage in Duct Systems*. Weihenstephan, Germany: Landtechnik.

[13] Kjelsson E, Hellstrom G, and Perers B (2010) Optimization of systems with the combination of ground-source heat pump and solar collectors in dwellings. *Energy* 35: 2667–2673.
[14] Brodowicz K and Dyakowski T (1990) *Pompy Ciepła*. Warszawa, Poland: PWN.
[15] Tleimat BW and Howe ED (1978) A solar assisted heat pump system for heating and cooling residence. *Solar Energy* 21(1): 45–51.
[16] Freeman TL, Mitchell JW, and Audit TE (1979) Performance of combined solar heat pump systems. *Solar Energy* 22(2): 125–135.
[17] Anderson JV, Mitchell JW, and Beckmann WA (1980) A design method for parallel solar-heat pump system. *Solar Energy* 25(2): 155–163.
[18] Terrell RE (1979) Performance and analysis of a 'series' heat pump-assisted solar heated residence in Madison, Wisconsin. *Solar Energy* 23(5) 451–453.
[19] Sakoi T, Takagi H, Terakowa K, and Ohue J (1976) Solar space heating and cooling with bi-heat source heat pump and hot water supply system. *Solar Energy* 18(6): 525–532.
[20] Duffie JA and Beckman WA (1991) *Solar Engineering of Thermal Processes*. New York: Wiley.
[21] Kaygusuz K and Ayhan T (1999) Experimental and theoretical investigation of combined solar heat pump system for residential heating. *Energy Conservation & Management* 40: 1377–1396.
[22] Comakli O, Bayramoglu M, and Kaygusuz K (1996) A thermodynamic model of a solar assisted heat pump system with energy storage. *Solar Energy* 56(6): 485–492.
[23] Han Z, Zheng M, Kong F, *et al* (2008) Numerical simulation of solar assisted ground-source heat pump heating system with latent heat energy storage in severely cold area. *Applied Thermal Engineering* 28: 1427–1436.
[24] Frank E, Haller M, Herkel S, and Ruschenburg J (2010) Systematic classification of combined solar thermal and heat pump systems. *Proceedings of the EuroSun 2010 Conference*. Graz, Austria, 29 September–1 October.
[25] Gorozabel Chata FB, Chaturvedi SK, and Almogbel A (2005) Analysis of a direct expansion solar assisted heat pump using different refrigerants. *Energy Conservation & Management* 46: 2614–2624.
[26] Kuang YH and Wang RZ (2006) Performance of multi-functional direct expansion solar assisted heat pump system. *Solar Energy* 80: 795–803.
[27] Hawlader MNA, Rahman SMA, and Jahangeer KA (2008) Performance of evaporator-collector and air collector in solar assisted heat pump dryer. *Energy Conservation & Management* 49: 1612–1619.
[28] Ji J, Pei G, Chow T, *et al.* (2008) Experimental study of photovoltaic solar assisted heat pump system. *Solar Energy* 82: 43–52.
[29] Sporn P and Ambrose ER (1955) The heat pump and solar energy. *Proceedings of the World Symposium on Applied Solar Energy*, 1–5 November, pp. 1–5. Phoenix, AZ, USA.
[30] Chwieduk D (2009) Key issues for solar thermal systems. *Renewable Energy*. London, UK: Sovereign Publication Limited.
[31] Koragiorgas M, Galatis K, Tsagouri M, *et al* (2010) Solar assisted heat pump on air collectors: A simulation tool. *Solar Energy* 84: 66–78.
[32] Zaheer-Uddin M, Rink RE, and Gourishanker VG (1987) A design criterion for a solar assisted heat pump system. *Energy* 12(5): 355–367.
[33] Kuang YH, Wang RZ, and Yu LQ (2003) Experimental study on solar assisted heat pump system for heat supply. *Energy Conservation & Management* 44: 1089–1098.
[34] www.hewalex.pl. Hewalex – solar collectors, Poland, 2006–2011 Hewalex.
[35] Chwieduk D (1994) *Słoneczne i gruntowe systemy grzewcze. Zagadnienia symulacji funkcjonowania i wydajności cieplnej*, Studia z zakresu inżynierii, Nr. 37, Komitet Inżynierii Lądowej i Wodnej PAN, Warszawa.
[36] Li H and Yang H (2010) Study on performance of solar assisted air source heat pump systems for hot water production in Hong Kong. *Applied Energy* 87: 2818–2825.
[37] Best R, Cruz JM, Gutierrez J, and Soto W (1996) Experimental results of a solar assisted heat pump rice drying system. *Proceedings of WREC*, pp. 690–694.
[38] Heifeng LI, Dai Y, Dai J, *et al.* (2010) A solar assisted heat pump drying system for grain in-store drying. *Frontiers of Energy and Power Engineering in China* 4(3): 386–391.
[39] Ozgener O (2010) Use of solar assisted geothermal heat pump and small wind turbine systems for heating agricultural and residential buildings. *Energy* 35: 262–268.
[40] Bakema G and Snijders NB (1995) *Underground Thermal Energy Storage, State of the Art 1994*. IEA Energy Storage Programme Report. Arnhem, The Netherlands: IF Technology.
[41] van Meurs GAM (1985) *Seasonal Heat Storage in the Ground*, ISBN 90 6231 1474. Pijnacker, The Netherlands: Dutch Efficiency Bureau.
[42] Sanner B (2002) A different approach to shallow geothermal energy – Underground Thermal Energy Storage (UTES). International Summer School on Direct Application on Geothermal Energy. International Geothermal Days, 7–15 October, Thessaloniki, Greece.
[43] Florides G and Kalogirou S (2007) Ground heat exchangers: A review of systems, models and applications. *Renewable Energy* 32(15): 2461–2478.
[44] Dalenback JO (1990) *IEA Technical Report: Central Solar Heating Plants with Seasonal Storage – Status Report*. Gothenburg, Sweden: Department of Building Services Engineering, Chalmers University of Technology, June 1990.
[45] Eskilson P (1987) *Thermal Analysis of Heat Extraction Boreholes*. Lund, Sweden: Department of Mathematical Physics, University of Lund.
[46] Hellstrom G (1991) *Ground Heat Storage. Thermal Analyses of Duct Systems. Theory*. Lund, Sweden: Department of Mathematical Physics, University of Lund.
[47] Adolfson A, Rydel KB, Salfors G, and Tidfors M (1985) Heat storage in clay. *Proceedings of the Eleventh International Conference on Soil Mechanics*, 12–16 August. San Francisco. CA, USA.
[48] Sanner B and Knoblich K (1990) Geochemical and geotechnical aspects of high temperature thermal energy storage in the ground. *Zeitschrift fur angewandte Geowissenschaften, Heft 9*. Knoblich K, Rammner R, and Martin G (eds.) *Proceedings of the Workshop on Seasonal Thermal Energy Storage in Duct Systems*, 19–20 June, Landtechnik Weihenstephan, Freising, Germany.
[49] Chwieduk D (1992) An analysis of vertical ground heat exchangers coupled with a heat pump for family house heating in Polish climatic conditions. *Archiwum Termodynamiki (Archives of Thermodynamics)*. Warszawa, Poland: PWN.
[50] Lund PD and Ostman MB (1985) A numerical model for seasonal storage of solar heat in the ground by vertical pipes. *Solar Energy* 34(4/5): 351–366.
[51] Wang F, Zheng M, Shao J, and Li Z (2008) Simulation of embedded heat exchangers of solar aided ground source heat pump system. *Journal of Central South University of Technology* 15: 261–266.
[52] Schmidt T, Mangold D, and Steinhagen M (2004) Central solar heating plants with seasonal storage in Germany. *Solar Energy* 76: 165–174.
[53] Nussbicker J, Mangold D, Heidemann W, and Mueller SH (2004) Solar assisted district heating system with seasonal duct heat store in Neckarsulm Amorbach (Germany). *Proceedings of Eurosun 2004 (14th International Sonnenforum)*. 20–24 June. Freiburg, Germany.
[54] Dalenback JO (2010) Take off for solar district heating in Europe. *Polska Energetyka Słoneczna* No. 1–4/2009, pp. 9–13, Polskie Towarzystwo Energetyki Słonecznej – ISES.
[55] Schmid T, Nussbicker J, and Raab S (2005) *Monitoring Results from German Central Solar Heating Plants with Seasonal Storage*. ISES 2005 Solar World Congress, August 6–12, Orlando, Florida, USA.
[56] Mangold D and Schmidt T (2006) *The New Central Solar Heating Plants with Seasonal Storage in Germany*. EuroSun 2006, 27–30 June, Glasgow, UK.

3.16 Solar Desalination

E Tzen, Centre for Renewable Energy Sources and Saving (CRES), Pikermi, Attica, Greece
G Zaragoza and D-C Alarcón Padilla, Centro de Investigaciones Energéticas Medioambientales y Tecnológicas (CIEMAT), Plataforma Solar de Almeria, Almeria, Spain

© 2012 Elsevier Ltd. All rights reserved.

3.16.1	Introduction	529
3.16.2	Solar Thermal Desalination Systems	530
3.16.3	Photovoltaics-Driven Desalination Systems	536
3.16.4	Solar Stills	541
3.16.5	Solar Humidification–Dehumidification	542
3.16.6	Solar Membrane Distillation	543
3.16.7	Technologies Selection Guidelines	546
3.16.8	Solar Desalination Applications	547
3.16.8.1	Solar Thermal MES Plant for Seawater Desalination, Abu Dhabi, UAE	547
3.16.8.2	Solar Thermal MED Plant for Seawater Desalination, Almeria, Spain	549
3.16.8.3	PV–RO Plant for Seawater Desalination, Lampedusa Island, Italy	553
3.16.8.4	PV–RO Plant for Brackish Water Desalination, Ceara, Brazil	556
3.16.8.5	PV–RO Plant for Seawater Desalination, Pozo Izquierdo, Gran Canaria Island	558
3.16.8.6	PV Water Pumping RO for Brackish Water Desalination, Saudi Arabia	558
3.16.8.7	PV–RO Brackish Water Desalination, Aqaba, Jordan	560
3.16.9	Lessons Learned	563
3.16.10	Economics	564
3.16.11	Market	564
3.16.12	Conclusions	564
References		565

Glossary

Brackish water Saline water with a salt concentration ranging from 1000 mg/l to about 25 000 mg/l total dissolved solids (TDS).
Desalination Process of removing salts from water sources.
Distillation A method of desalting water that uses heat to vaporize water and collect the condensed water.
Electrodialysis (ED) A process by which ions are transferred through membranes to a more concentrated solution as a result of using a direct current electrical potential.
Electrodialysis reversal (EDR) A variation of ED in which polarity and cell function change periodically to maintain efficient performance.
Energy recovery Possible energy saving in reverse osmosis in which the concentrate stream, under pressure, is used to drive a turbine that provides part of the feed requirement.
kWh Kilowatthours A measure of electrical usage.
Membrane In desalting, used to describe a semipermeable film. Membranes used in electrodialysis are permeable to ions of either positive or negative charge. Reverse osmosis membranes ideally allow the passage of pure water and block the passage of salts.
Performance ratio (PR) A performance rating associated with the distillation desalting process. It is defined as the number of pounds of distillate produced for each 1000 Btu of heat input, or as kg/MJ in metric.
Post-treatment The processes, such as pH adjustment and chlorination, that may be employed on the product water from a desalting unit.
Pretreatment The processes such as chlorination, clarification, coagulation, scale inhibition, acidification, and deaeration that may be employed on the feed water to a desalting unit to minimize algae growth, scaling, and corrosion.
Recovery ratio The ratio of the product flow rate to the feed water flow rate.
Reverse osmosis (RO) Method of desalination which uses pressure to move water from a concentrated solution to a dilute solution through a membrane separating two solutions.

3.16.1 Introduction

Converting seawater or brackish water into freshwater is a promising approach to overcome the insufficiency in water supply caused by population increase, agricultural and irrigation needs, industrial needs, etc. Production of freshwater using desalination technologies driven by renewable energy sources (RESs) is thought to be a viable solution to the water scarcity in remote areas characterized by lack of potable water and lack of an electricity grid. RES–desalination matching is mainly categorized as distillation desalination technologies driven by heat produced by RESs, and membrane and distillation desalination technologies driven by electricity or mechanical energy produced by RESs.

Indirect use of solar energy by means of solar thermal systems and photovoltaics (PVs) in tandem with desalination seems to be the most applicable technology. Direct use of solar energy for desalination, such as the use of solar stills, is the oldest, simplest, and most used method. **Figure 1** presents the possible combinations of solar energy technologies with desalination. The selection of the most appropriate combination is mainly site specific. Several parameters that affect the final decision are discussed in the following paragraphs.

Many applications of relatively small scale exist around the world; some of the most known are examined in this chapter. The majority of the solar desalination systems involve the use of photovoltaic-driven reverse osmosis (PV–RO) units for brackish and seawater desalination. Most of the already existing applications have been built within National or European projects and are pilot demonstration units [1].

Some of the installed units cover basic needs of the region where they have been installed, while some are no longer in operation. Nevertheless, the lessons learned from their operation have been passed on and are the guidelines for the new installations.

This chapter focuses on the state of the art of the solar desalination technologies, their current applications, the lessons learned, and the economics and market for these technologies.

3.16.2 Solar Thermal Desalination Systems

Solar energy refers to applications of solar thermal conversion and PV conversion. Solar thermal systems are usually classified according to the temperature level reached by the thermal fluid in the collector (**Figures 2** and **3**). The thermal effects produced by

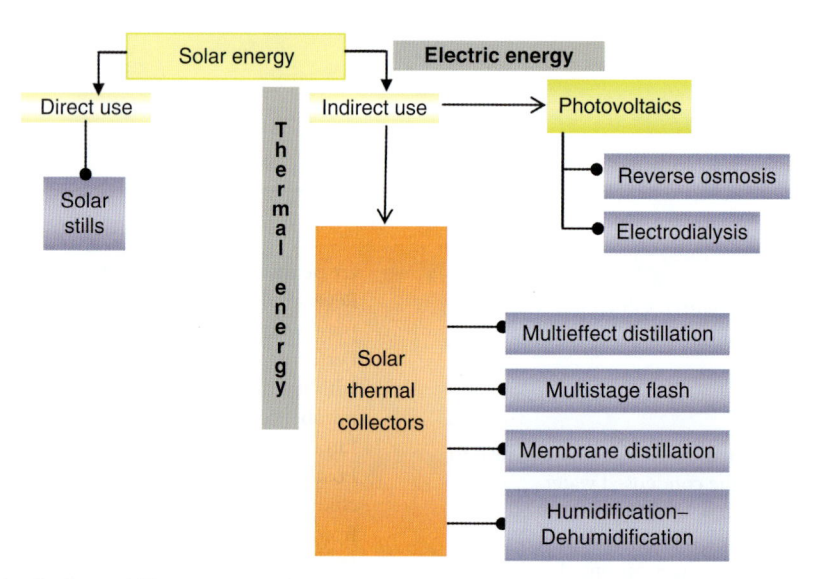

Figure 1 Solar energy–desalination matching.

Figure 2 Parabolic-trough collectors, CIEMAT PSA, Almeria, Spain.

Figure 3 Fresnel Technology, CIEMAT PSA, Almeria, Spain.

solar radiation enables Man to take direct advantage of them by using devices that collect, concentrate, and intensify the heat and transfer the thermal energy to other fluids by heating them. Depending on the design of the collector, it can provide heat for domestic applications, industrial processes, and electricity production.

There are basically two types of solar collectors:

1. Stationary or nonconcentrating
2. Concentrating.

A nonconcentrating collector has the same area for intercepting and absorbing solar radiation, whereas a sun-tracking, concentrating solar collector usually has concave reflecting surfaces to intercept and focus the sun's radiation to a smaller receiving area, thereby increasing the radiation flux. **Table 1** presents the different types of available solar collectors and their main characteristics [2].

A solar thermal energy system mainly consists of a solar collector array, a storage tank, and necessary controls (**Figure 4**). The solar collector system provides the desalination unit with the required hot steam.

Analytically, solar thermal distillation plants include a field of solar collectors, where a thermal fluid is heated. This hot fluid is used, by means of a heat exchanger, to warm up the feedwater circulating through the distillation plant. The collectors must be able to heat the thermal fluid up to medium temperatures so that after appropriate heat transfer, the water fed to the evaporator reaches temperatures between 70 and 120 °C. Temperature limits protect the distillation plant from scaling and corrosion problems.

The best known solar thermal distillation combinations are the solar multistage flash (MSF) and solar multieffect distillation (MED). Both processes are classified as phase-change or thermal processes. Distillation units routinely use designs that convert as much thermal energy as possible by interchanging the heat of condensation and heat of vaporization within the units. The major energy requirement in the distillation process is, thus, providing the heat of vaporization to the feedwater.

MSF and MED processes consist of a number of stages or effects at successively decreasing temperatures and pressures, and generally operate on the principle of reducing the vapor pressure of water within the unit to permit boiling to occur at lower temperatures, without any extra heat.

Table 1 Main types of solar collectors Reproduced from: Kalogirou S (2003) The potential of solar industrial process heat applications. *Applied Energy* 76(4): 337–361.

Motion	Collector type	Absorber type	Concentration ratio	Indicative temperature range (°C)
Stationary	Flat-plate collector (FPC)	Flat	1	30–80
	Evacuated tube collector (ETC)	Flat	1	50–200
			1–5	60–240
Single-axis tracking	Compound parabolic collector (CPC)	Tubular	5–15	60–300
	Linear Fresnel reflector (LFR)	Tubular	10–40	60–250
	Parabolic-trough collector (PTC)	Tubular	15–45	60–300
	Cylindrical-trough collector (CTC)	Tubular	10–50	60–300
Two-axes tracking	Parabolic-dish reflector (PDR)	Point	100–1000	100–500
	Heliostat field collector (HFC)	Point	100–1500	150–2000

Note: Concentration ratio is defined as the aperture area divided by the receiver/absorber area of the collector.

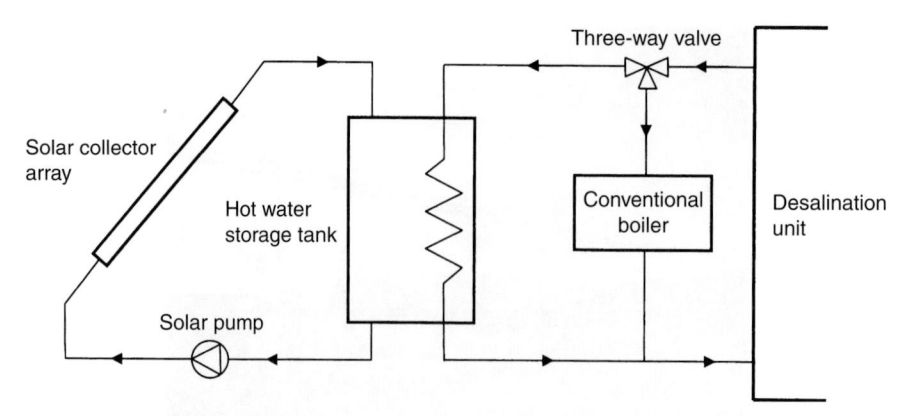

Figure 4 Typical configuration of a solar thermal desalination plant [2]. Adapted from Kalogirou S (2003) The potential of solar industrial process heat applications. *Applied Energy* 76(4): 337–361.

The MSF process is based on the generation of vapor from seawater or brine caused by a sudden pressure reduction when seawater enters an evacuated chamber [3]. The process is repeated stage by stage at successively decreasing pressures. This process requires an external steam supply, normally at a temperature between 100 and 110 °C. The maximum temperature is limited by the salt concentration to avoid scaling, and this limits the performance of the process.

There are two process arrangements for the MSF process: once-through and brine recirculation. In the brine recirculation MSF, the system is divided into the heat-rejection, the heat-recovery, and the heating sections (see **Figure 5**). Seawater is fed through the heat-rejection section that rejects thermal energy from the plant and discharges the product and brine at the lowest possible temperature [3]. The feed is then mixed with a large mass of water, which is recirculated around the plant. This water then passes through a series of heat exchangers to raise its temperature. The water then enters the solar collector array or a conventional brine heater to raise its temperature to nearly the saturation temperature at the maximum system pressure. The water then enters the first stage through an orifice and in doing so has its pressure reduced. Since the water was at the saturation temperature at high pressure, it becomes superheated and flashes into steam. The vapor produced passes through a wire mesh (demister) to remove any entrained brine droplets and then into the heat exchanger, where it condenses and drips into a distillate tray. Generally, only a small percentage of this water is converted to steam (water vapor), depending on the pressure maintained in this stage, since boiling will continue only until the water cools [5]. This process is repeated through the plant as both brine and distillate streams flash as they enter subsequent stages, which are at successively lower pressures.

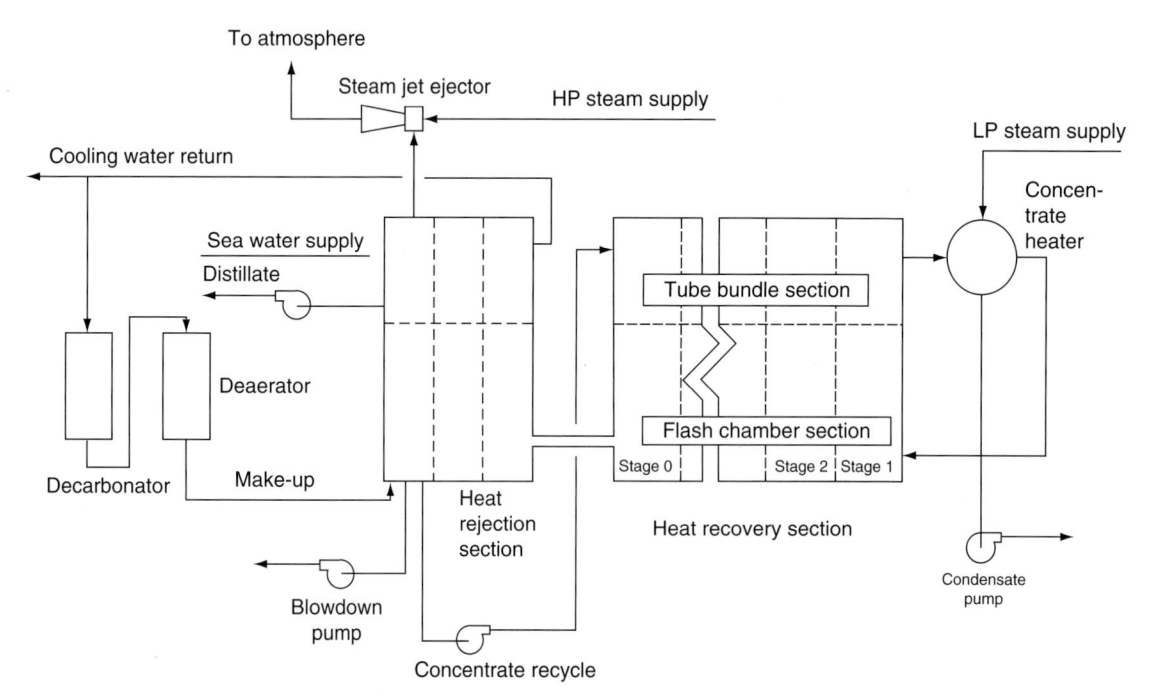

Figure 5 MSF brine recirculation schematic. Adapted from Watson IC, Morin OJ, Jr., and Henthorne L (2003) *Desalting Handbook for Planners*, 3rd edn. USA: U.S. Department of the Interior Bureau of Reclamation [4].

In MSF, the number of stages is not tied rigidly to the performance ratio (PR), which is the ratio of the distillate produced to the heat input (steam consumed, kilograms per megajoule) required from the plant. In practice, the minimum temperature must be slightly greater than the PR, while the maximum is determined by the boiling-point elevation. The minimum interstage temperature drop must exceed the boiling-point elevation for flashing to occur at a finite rate. This is advantageous because as the number of stages is increased, the terminal temperature difference over the heat exchangers increases and hence a smaller heat transfer area is required with obvious savings in plant capital cost.

MSF is the most widely used desalination process in terms of capacity. MSF plants are generally built-in units of about 4000–55 000 $m^3 day^{-1}$. Current commercial installations are designed with 10–30 stages (2 °C temperature drop per stage) [3].

The MED process takes place in a series of vessels (effects) and uses the principles of condensation and evaporation at reduced ambient pressure in the various effects. This permits the seawater feed to boil without the need for supply of additional heat beyond the first effect. In general, an effect consists of a vessel, a heat exchanger, and devices for transporting the various fluids between the effects. As with the MSF plant, the incoming brine in the MED process also passes through a series of heaters, but after passing through the last of these, instead of entering the brine heater, the feed enters the top effect, where the heating steam raises its temperature to the saturation temperature for the effect pressure. Further amounts of steam, either from a solar collector system or from a conventional boiler, are used to produce evaporation in this effect. The vapor then goes, in part, to heat the incoming feed and, in part, to provide the heat supply for the second effect, which is at a lower pressure and receives its feed from the brine of the first effect (see **Figure 6**). This process is repeated all the way through (down) the plant. The distillate also passes down the plant. Unlike the MSF plant, the PR for an MED plant is more rigidly linked to and cannot exceed a limit set by the number of effects in the plant. For instance, a plant with 13 effects might typically have a PR of 10. However, an MSF plant with a PR of 10 could have 13–35 stages depending on the design. MED plants commonly have PRs as high as 12–14 [3].

The choice and optimization of the PR and the number of effects in an MED plant is a matter of balancing the high energy costs associated with a setup with a low PR and a small number of effects against the high capital costs of a setup with a large number of effects, and large transfer surfaces in both the effects and the feed heaters. Three main arrangements have evolved for MED processes. They are based primarily on the arrangement of the heat exchanger tubing which can be as follows [4]:

- Horizontal tube arrangement
- Vertical tube arrangement
- Vertically stacked tube bundles.

MED plants are typically built-in units of 2000–20 000 $m^3 day^{-1}$. Some of the more recent plants have been built to operate with a top temperature (in the first effect) of about 70 °C, which reduces the potential for scaling of seawater within the plant [5].

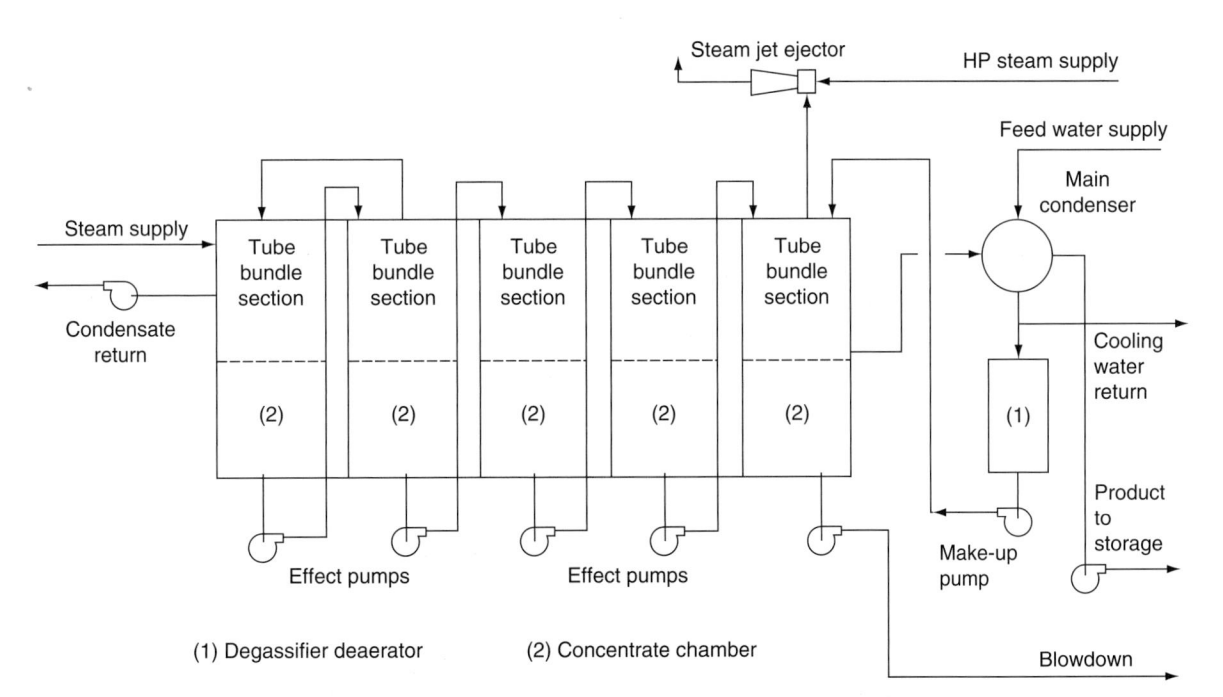

Figure 6 MED schematic [4]. Adapted from Watson IC, Morin OJ, Jr., and Henthorne L (2003) *Desalting Handbook for Planners*, 3rd edn. USA: U.S. Department of the Interior Bureau of Reclamation.

As can be concluded from the above, thermal distillation technologies are best fitted to large capacities; however, research has been done in small capacities also. Several solar thermal plants have been installed and examined around the world (see **Table 2**) [1].

An example is the MSF plant installed in 1987 in El Paso, Texas. The combination was somewhat unusual involving a 3355 m^2 solar pond and a cogeneration system, producing electricity in a Rankine cycle and water in a 24-stage MSF evaporator capable of producing 19 m^3 day^{-1}.

More reference cases can be found at San Luis de la Paz, Mexico, where a double solar field (194 m^2 flat-plate collectors plus 160 m^2 concentrating collectors) provides heat for a 10 m^3 day^{-1} MSF unit, with 10 stages. The plant was commissioned in 1980.

One more example is found in Lampedusa Island in Italy. The plant was commissioned in 1983. The MSF plant had a capacity of 7.2 m^3 day^{-1} driven by 408 m^2 solar collectors. Another solar MSF system was installed in Safat, Kuwait, in 1981. The 12-stage MSF plant had a capacity of 10 m^3 day^{-1} driven by 220 m^2 parabolic-trough solar collectors.

Concerning solar MED applications in 1981, a solar MED plant of 10 m^3 day^{-1} capacity was installed in Takeshima Island in Japan, and in the same year a 2 m^3 day^{-1} solar MED plant started its operation at the Black Sea, Bulgaria.

A very famous solar MED plant is the one in Abu Dhabi, United Arab Emirates. The system consists of 1862 m^2 evacuated-tube collectors (ETCs) and an MED plant of around 120 m^3 day^{-1} distillate water capacity. The plant has many years of satisfactory operation. The plant is discussed analytically in the following paragraphs.

Another well-known example of a solar MED plant of 3 m^3 h^{-1} water capacity and 500 m^2 compound parabolic concentrators (CPC) is located at the Plataforma Solar de Almeria (PSA), Spain, as part of the AQUASOL project (**Figure 7**). The plant is described analytically in the following paragraphs [6].

A small solar thermal MED plant was commissioned in 2002 in Muscat in the Sultanate of Oman (owned by the M/S Power System International) and was operational for a year (see **Figure 8**). The pilot MED plant was designed to produce 1 m^3 day^{-1} in 9 h

Table 2 Solar thermal desalination plants

Location	Desalination unit	Solar collector	Year of installation
Hazeg, Tunisia	0.1–0.35 m^3 h^{-1} distillation	–	1980
San Luis de la Paz, Mexico	10 m^3 day^{-1} MSF	352 m^2 FPC + PTC	1980
Lampedusa Island, Italy	7.2 m^3 day^{-1} MSF	408 m^2 low-concentration solar collectors	1983
Safat, Kuwait	10 m^3 day^{-1} MSF	220 m^2 low-concentration solar collectors	1984
Takami Island, Japan	16 m^3 day^{-1} MED	FPC	–
Abu Dhabi, UAE	80–120 m^3 day^{-1} MED	ETC	1984
Almeria, Spain	72 m^3 day^{-1} MED	PCP	1993
Almeria, Spain	24 m^3 day^{-1} MED	Parabolic concentrating	1988/1990
Almeria, Spain, AQUASOL project	30–40 l day^{-1}	6 m^2 Vacuum-tube solar collectors	1998
Al Azhar, PSA	0.2 m^3 day^{-1} MSF	FPC + PVs	1998/2000
Pozo Izquierdo, Gran Canaria, Spain, SODESA project	0.6 m^3 day^{-1}	50 m^2 solar collectors + PVs	2000
Oman	1 m^3 day^{-1} MED	5.34 m^2 VTC	2002

Figure 7 Compound parabolic collectors (CPC), CIEMAT PSA, Almeria, Spain.

Figure 8 View of the solar thermal MED unit in Oman. Adapted from Report on the Status of Autonomous Desalination Units Based on Renewable Energy Systems (2005) INCO-CT-2004-509093, Co-ordination Action for Autonomous Desalination Units Based on Renewable Energy Systems, ADU-RES Project. www.medrc.org.om

of operation during the day, using solar energy. The innovative techniques and methods used in the plant included high-temperature tubular solar collectors, scale-preventing coating, and a device for water softening. The desalination system operated at a top brine temperature of 100 °C. Water recovery reached 80–85%. The MED unit included 12 effects and 6 preheaters. The thermal energy consumption was 64 kWh m^{-3}, while the electric energy consumption was 1.4 kWh m^{-3}. The plant was tested with water salinity of 30 000–35 000 ppm total dissolved solids (TDS). The salinity of the water produced by the plant was 80–120 ppm TDS.

The solar thermal system consisted of high-temperature vacuum tubular solar collectors with mirror concentrators, a separator for steam and water separation, and a solar tracking system. The solar power plant included 16 collector panels, with an effective collector area of 5.34 m^2. The circulation flow rate through the whole collector system was 460 l h^{-1} and the maximum pressure of operation was 1.05 bar. The system's electricity demand was satisfied by 2 m^2 PV cells [6]. The project was cofinanced by the Middle East Desalination Research Center (MEDRC) in Oman.

Also, a number of small distillation plants have been installed in Tunisia: a 40–50 l h^{-1} single-effect evaporation process for brackish water desalination in Hazeg, Sfax (1986), an MED of 150–200 l day^{-1} for seawater desalination in Béni Khiar, Nabeul (2003), and a solar multiple condensation evaporation cycle (SMCEC) system of 12–30 l h^{-1} for brackish water desalination in the University of Sfax, Sfax [7].

Finally, a solar MED plant of small scale has been recently installed in Paphos, Cyprus, to cover the water needs of a public swimming pool (see **Figures 9–11**).

The one-effect MED unit desalinates seawater and has a capacity of 1 m^3 day^{-1}. The solar thermal plant consists of 110 m^2 high-efficiency selective flat-plate collectors. The MED plant operates at a temperature around 75 °C. The plant was developed within the ADIRA project [8].

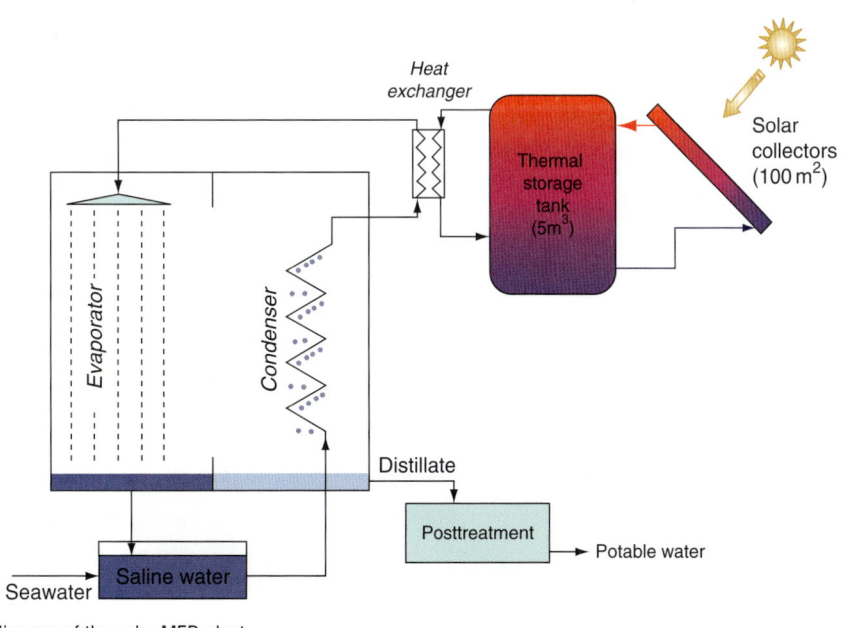

Figure 9 Schematic diagram of the solar MED plant.

Figure 10 The MED seawater desalination plant, Paphos, Cyprus.

Figure 11 The solar collector area, Paphos, Cyprus.

3.16.3 Photovoltaics-Driven Desalination Systems

PVs are specially designed semiconductor devices that convert sunlight directly into electricity. They are modular devices having long life and characterized by low maintenance requirements. The basic component of a PV system is the solar cell. Groups of cells are mounted on a glass plate and wired in series to form a PV module. Groups of modules electrically connected together form a PV array (**Figure 12**). The nominal voltage and current of an array depend on the number of modules connected in series and in parallel. PV arrays can be mounted on fixed or on sun-tracking structures to maximize the incident solar radiation on the solar cell surface. The power production capacity of a PV array is expressed in watt peak (W_p) units. A solar cell is said to be of 1 W_p power if it produces 1 W of electric power when exposed to 'peak' solar irradiance (1000 W m^{-2}) at a solar cell temperature of 25 °C [9].

Figure 12 The 4 kW$_p$ photovoltaic system, CRES, Greece.

There are various types of PV cells. The main ones are monocrystalline, polycrystalline, amorphous silicon, and other thin films. PVs can be used directly with the load, such as in water pumping and grid connected or stand-alone.

The energy production unit consists of a number of PV modules, which convert solar into direct current (DC) electricity. The most suitable desalination processes for this combination should use electricity in some form. Therefore, reverse osmosis (RO) and electrodialysis (ED) appear as the most suitable choices for coupling with PV systems.

RO is a membrane separation process in which the water from a pressurized saline solution is separated from the solutes (the dissolved material) by making it flow through a membrane. The amount of desalinated water that can be obtained (recovery ratio) ranges between 30% and 75% of the volume of the input water, depending on the initial water quality, the quality of the product needed, and the technology and membranes involved.

No heating or phase change is necessary for this separation. The major energy required for desalting is for pressurizing the feedwater (the saline feedwater is pumped into a closed vessel where it is pressurized against the membrane) (see **Figure 13**). Theoretically, the only energy requirement is to pump the feedwater at a pressure above the osmotic pressure. In practice, higher pressures must be used, typically 14–25 bar for brackish water and from 55–80 bar for seawater desalination, in order to have a sufficient amount of water pass through a unit area of membrane. **Figure 13** shows an illustration of the feed being pressurized by a high-pressure pump and which is made to flow across the membrane surface. Part of this feed passes through the membrane, where most of the dissolved solids are removed. The remainder, together with the remaining salts, is rejected at high pressure. In large plants, it is economically viable to recover the rejected brine energy with a suitable brine turbine [3]. Such systems are called energy recovery devices. The fraction of power, recovered by the power recovery device, depends on the type and efficiency of the power recovery equipment used. In general, two recent developments have helped to reduce the operating cost of RO plants in the past decade: the use of energy recovery devices and the development of more efficient membranes (operational at lower pressures). The main advantages of RO process are the modularity/compactness and the sufficient performance and reliability in all scales.

ED is an electrochemical process and a low-cost method for the desalination of brackish water. Due to the dependency of the energy consumption on the feedwater salt concentration, the ED process is not economically attractive for the desalination of seawater.

In the ED process, ions are transported through a membrane by an electric field applied across the membrane. The process utilizes a DC electric field to remove salt ions in the brackish water [3]. Saline feedwater contains dissolved salts separated into positively charged sodium and negatively charged chlorine ions. These ions will move toward an oppositely charged electrode immersed in the solution, that is, positive ions (cations) will move toward the negative electrode (cathode) and negative ions (anions) toward the positive electrode (anode). If special membranes, alternatively cation-permeable and anion-permeable, separate the electrodes, the gap between these membranes will be depleted of salts [3]. In an actual process, a large number of alternating cation and anion membranes are stacked together, separated by plastic flow spacers that allow the passage of water (**Figure 14**). The streams through alternating flow-spacers are a sequence of diluted and concentrated water which flow parallel to each other. To prevent scaling, inverters are used to reverse the polarity of the electric field in about every 20 min. As the energy requirements of the system are proportional to the water's salinity, ED is economically attractive for low concentration brackish water with TDS equal to or less than 3500 ppm.

A typical stand-alone system consists of the PV modules, the charge controller(s), the battery bank, and the inverters(s). The main advantages in the coupling of PVs with desalination units are the ability to develop small-size desalination plants, the limited maintenance cost of PVs, as well as easy transportation and installation.

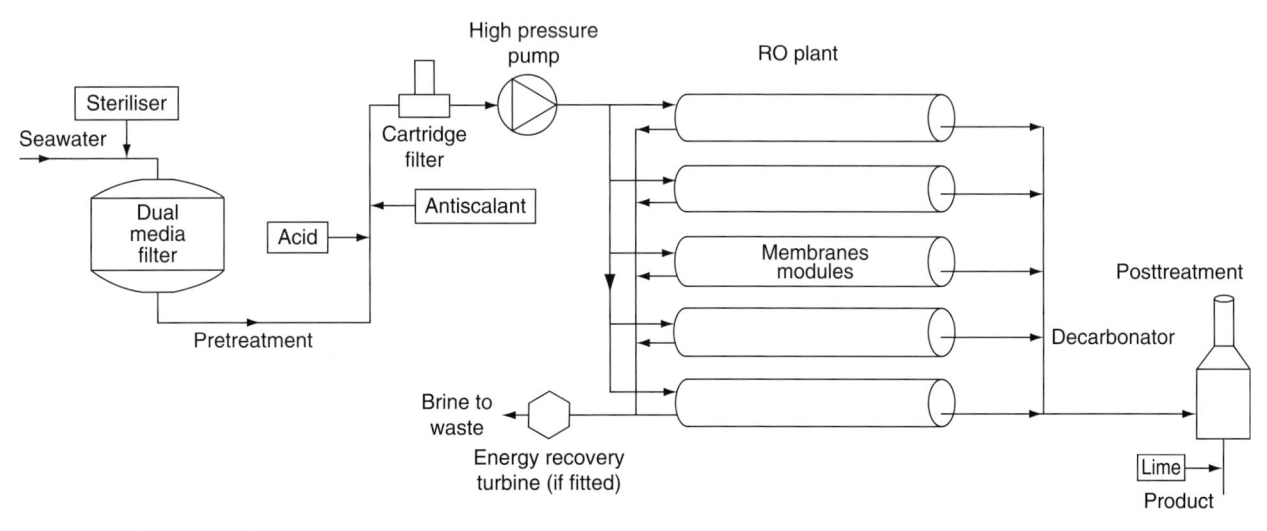

Figure 13 RO schematic [2].

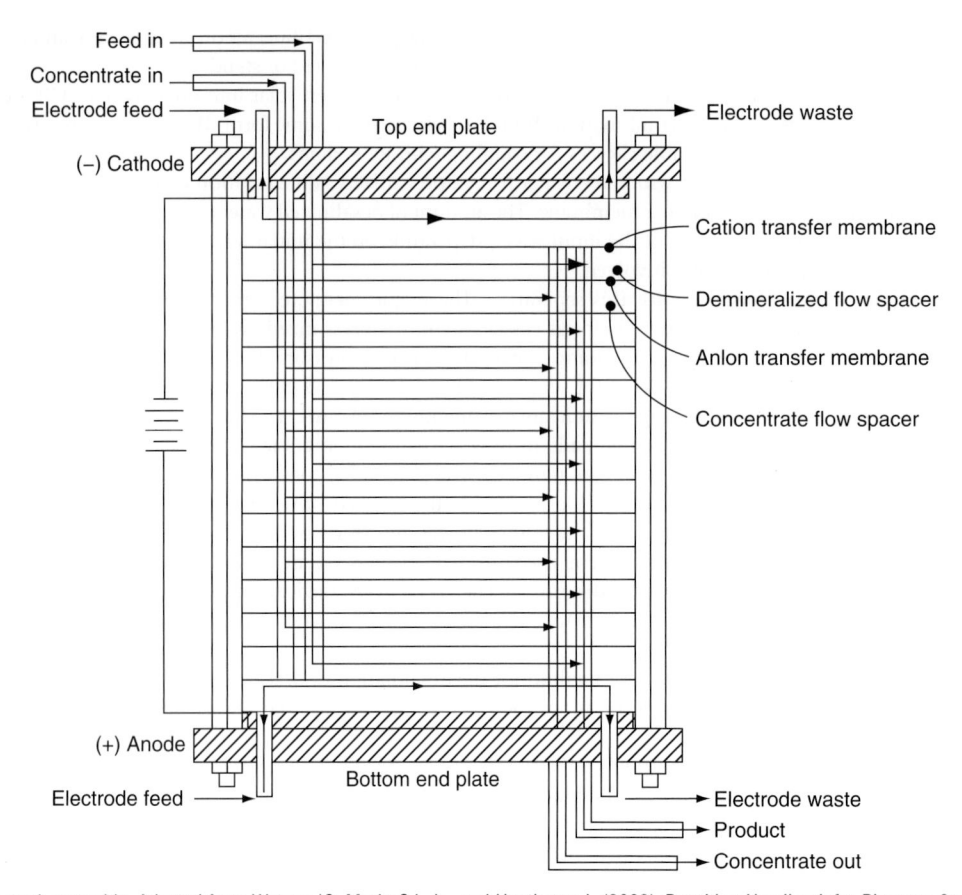

Figure 14 ED stack assembly. Adapted from Watson IC, Morin OJ, Jr., and Henthorne L (2003) *Desalting Handbook for Planners*, 3rd edn. USA: U.S. Department of the Interior Bureau of Reclamation.

RO usually uses alternating current (AC) for the pumps, which means that DC/AC inverters have to be used. Energy storage is again a matter of concern, and batteries are used for PV output power smoothing or for sustaining system operation when sufficient solar energy is not available. The typical PV–RO applications are of stand-alone type, and there exist some interesting examples. **Table 3** presents the data on the PV–RO plants that have been installed within the last two decades for seawater and brackish water desalination.

Several plants have been built during the 1980s. A brackish water desalination application was installed in 1982 in Perth, Australia. The plant consisted of 1.2 kW$_p$ PV to drive a 0.1 m^3 h^{-1} RO unit. Another such plant was installed in 1984 in Vancouver, Canada: a seawater RO unit of 1 m^3 day^{-1} product water capacity with a 4.8 kW$_p$ PV system. In 1984, a 11.2 kW$_p$ PV to drive a 5.7 m^3 day^{-1} seawater RO unit was installed in Doha, Qatar.

Another RO plant, set up in 1986, is located at El Hamrawein, at the edge of Red Sea. The PV array is rated at 19.84 kW$_p$, delivering voltage of 104 V for the pumps as main consumption plus a secondary array rated 0.64 kW$_p$ at 24 V for instruments and control. The battery storage unit has a capacity of 208 kWh and is designed for 3 days of autonomy. The RO plant has a capacity of 10 m^3 h^{-1}, operating at a pressure of 13 bar. The feedwater is brackish water having a salinity of 4400 mg l^{-1} TDS. The unit energy consumption is 0.89 kWh m^{-3}.

During 1990–2000, with technical improvements in both technologies, bigger RES desalination plants were installed to cater to water needs [11]. For RO, the development of efficient energy recovery devices and the operation of the membranes at lower pressures significantly reduced the energy requirements and obviously the power requirements of the RES power supply plants. On the other hand, the cost of PV fell dramatically.

During this period, a lot of work was done by the Instituto Tecnológico de Canarias (ITC) in Spain [12]. Several combinations of RES desalination systems such as photovoltaic–electrodialysis reversal (PV–EDR), wind–mechanical vapor compression (MVC), and PV–RO were installed and examined; one of them is presented in this chapter.

Furthermore, in order to reduce the cost and maintenance requirements, the direct coupling of PV to RO unit is examined. In most cases, the power variability from the solar source reduces the lifetime of the membranes. The Centre for Renewable Energy Systems Technology, CREST, UK, installed a 1.54 kW$_p$ PV-powered seawater RO unit without batteries. The system operates at variable flow, enabling it to make efficient use of the naturally varying solar resource, without the need of batteries. The same RO unit has also been coupled and tested with a wind turbine without any battery bank. Frequent replacement of the RO membranes is mentioned.

The electricity from PVs for desalination applications can be used for electromechanical devices such as pumps, or in a DC device for ED. ED uses DC for the electrodes at the cell stack, and hence it can use the energy supply from the PV panels without major

Table 3 PV–RO applications for seawater (SW) and brackish water (BW) desalination

Plant location	Water type	RO capacity	PV installed (Power)	Commissioning year
El Hamrawein, Egypt	BW	10 m^3 h^{-1}	~20 kW$_p$	1986
Hassi-Khebi, Algeria	BW	0.95 m^3 h^{-1}	2.6 kW$_p$	1988
University of Almeria, Spain	BW	2.5 m^3 h^{-1}	23.5 kW$_p$	1988
Lampedusa Island, Italy	SW	3 + 2 m^3 h^{-1}	100 kW$_p$	1990
Lipari Island, Italy	SW	2 m^3 h^{-1}	63 kW$_p$	1991
Sadous Riyadh Region, Saudi Arabia	BW	600 l h^{-1}	10.89 kW$_p$	1994
St. Lucie, Florida	SW	0.6 m^3 day^{-1}	2.7 kW$_p$	1995
Gillen Bore, Australia	BW	1.2 m^3 day^{-1}	4.16 kW$_p$	1996
Maagan Michael, Israel	BW	0.4 m^3 h^{-1}	3.5 kW$_p$ PV, 0.6 kW W/T +3 kW diesel	1997
Pozo Izquierdo, Gran Canaria Island, DESSOL	SW	3–4 m^3 day^{-1}	4.8 kW$_p$	1998–2000
Sadous Village, Saudi Arabia	BW	600 l h^{-1}	10.08 kW$_p$	2001
CREST, UK	SW	3 m^3 day^{-1}	2.4 kW$_p$	2001–02
CRES, Greece	SW	130 l h^{-1}	4 kW$_p$ PV, 1 kW W/T	2002
White Cliffs, New South Wales, Australia	BW	500 l day^{-1}	150 W$_p$	2003
Aqaba, Jordan	BW	3.4 m^3 h^{-1}	16.8 kW$_p$	2004
Ksar Ghilane, Tunisia ADIRA project	BW	2.1 m^3 h^{-1}	10.5 kW$_p$	2006
Benhssaine Morocco, ADIRA Project (**Figure 15**) [10]	BW	1 m^3 h^{-1}	4.8 kW$_p$	2006–07
Msaim, Morocco, ADIRA project (**Figures 16** and **17**) [10]	BW	1 m^3 h^{-1}	3.9 kW$_p$	2006–07

Figure 15 The PV–RO unit in Benhssaine, Morroco. Adapted from Mokhlisse A (2008) A new experience of fresh water supply in two rural villages in Morocco, *ADIRA Workshop on Desalination Powered by Renewable Energy*, Athens.

modifications. Yet, some kind of power conditioning is required in this case as well for a typical photovoltaic–electrodialysis (PV–ED) system design. Batteries are used for PV output power smoothing or for sustaining system operation when sufficient solar energy is not available. Furthermore, energy storage is again a matter of concern.

ED is an electrochemical process and a low-cost method for the desalination of brackish water. Due to the dependency of the energy consumption on the feedwater salt concentration, the ED process is not economically attractive for the desalination of seawater.

A small number of PV–ED plants have been installed exclusively for brackish water desalination. In the city of Tanot, in Thar Desert, Rajasthan, India, a small plant was commissioned in 1986, featuring a PV system capable of providing 450 W$_p$ in 42 cell pairs. The ED unit includes three stages, producing 1 m^3 day^{-1} water from brackish water of 5000 mg l^{-1} TDS. The unit energy consumption is 1 kWh kg^{-1} salt removed.

Another application for seawater desalination has been reported from Japan. A 25 kW$_p$ PV system was used to drive a 10 m^3 day^{-1} ED plant. The system is located at Oshima Island, Nagasaki, and has been operating since 1986. The quality of the water produced is reported to be below 400 ppm TDS.

In 1988, another ED plant was developed in Fukue City in Japan. The ED units desalinate low-concentration brackish water of 700 ppm TDS, resulting in very low energy demand. A 65 kW$_p$ PV array supplies enough energy to produce an average of 200 m^3 day^{-1}

Figure 16 The PV–RO unit in Msaim, Morocco. Adapted from Mokhlisse A (2008) A new experience of fresh water supply in two rural villages in Morocco, *ADIRA Workshop on Desalination Powered by Renewable Energy*, Athens.

Figure 17 The 1 m^3 h^{-1} RO unit, Morocco. Adapted from Mokhlisse A (2008) A new experience of fresh water supply in two rural villages in Morocco, *ADIRA Workshop on Desalination Powered by Renewable Energy*, Athens.

Figure 18 PV–EDR plant, Spencer Valley, New Mexico.

of potable water. Battery storage of 1200 Ah provides constant power. A 30 kVA inverter supplies AC power to the pumps, while the electrodes are powered by a DC bus. Due to natural fluctuations in feedwater salinity and temperature, the water production rate and energy requirements fluctuate between 130 and 370 m^3 day^{-1} and 0.6 and 1.0 kWh m^{-3}, respectively [13].

A small experimental unit was reported in Spencer Valley, New Mexico, by the Bureau of Reclamation, USA. Two separate PV arrays are used: two-tracking flat arrays, 1000 W$_p$ power, 120 V, with DC/AC inverters for pumps, plus three fixed arrays, 2.3 kW$_p$, 50 V for EDR supply (see **Figures 18** and **19**). The EDR design calls for 2.8 m^3 day^{-1} product water from a feed around 1000 mg l^{-1} TDS. Units of power consumption was 0.82 kWh m^{-3} and the reported cost was 11 065 ECU (US$ 13 500).

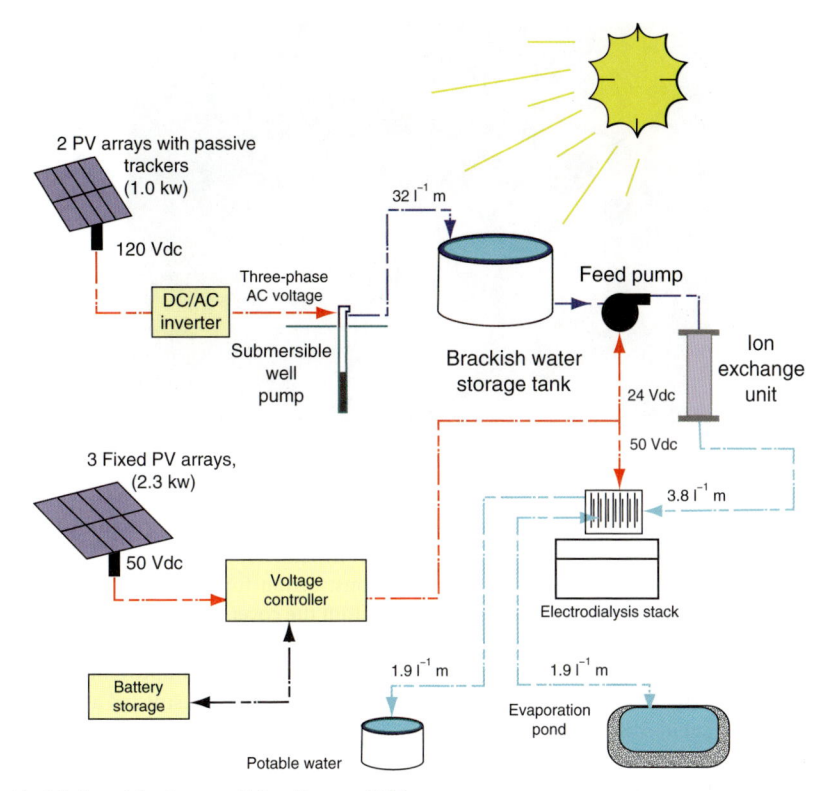

Figure 19 Schematic of installation at the Spencer Valley. Source: *NREL*.

3.16.4 Solar Stills

Solar distillation is a process in which the energy of the sun is directly used to evaporate freshwater from sea or brackish water. The process has been used for many years, usually for small-scale applications.

Solar distillation systems are classified into two groups [14] in terms of energy supply: (1) passive or conventional and (2) active solar stills. The passive solar stills use solar energy as the only source of thermal energy. In active solar stills, extra thermal energy from a solar collector or any available waste heat is directed to the solar still for faster evaporation. Humidification–dehumidification (HD) process, described in the next section, is an active solar technique.

Solar stills are the simplest devices that are used to obtain freshwater using solar energy as the sole energy supply. The basic principle of solar water distillation is simple as distillation replicates the way nature makes rain. In such systems, energy is required only to power the circulating water pumps.

A solar still consists of a shallow basin with a transparent cover designed to act as a condenser (**Figures 20** and **21**). Water in the basin is heated by the sun to produce vapor. The vapor produced by the evaporation of seawater is condensed on the cool surface of the roofs of the stills, and the condensate is collected as the product water. Well-designed units can produce around $2.5 \, l \, m^{-2} \, day^{-1}$ with a thermal efficiency of 50%. Parameters that affect the efficiency of solar stills and the amount of water

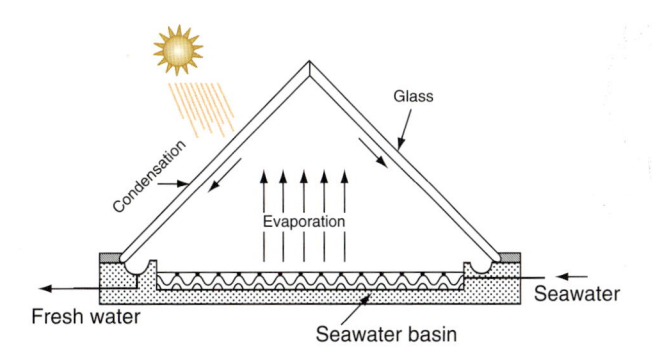

Figure 20 A simplified schematic diagram of a solar still. Source: *CRES*. Adapted from Karen TE (1997) *Desalination of Village Scale, Renewable Energy Powered Desalination*, NREL, USA [13].

Figure 21 Solar distillation plant in Kastelorizo, Greece.

desalinated are the solar potential of the specific site, the area of the still, the ambient air temperature, the feedwater temperature, insulation of the still, slope of the cover, and the depth of the water in the still.

The main advantage of the solar stills is the simplicity of their construction from locally available and low-cost materials. Maintenance of the stills involves periodic cleaning of debris and dust from the cover and checking for leakages, or removal of salt deposits.

The main development of this technology was in the 1960s and 1970s, concerning the improvement of the solar stills efficiency and the reduction of construction cost. Over this period, many distillation plants were constructed around the world. Passive solar distillation is usually suitable for small-scale applications. In remote areas where low-cost land is available and solar radiation is high, passive solar distillation can be viable.

A great number of installations have been constructed around the world in Australia, Haiti, Spain, India, United States, Mexico, Greece, etc. However, most of them are not in operation today. Several of the old plants were affected by storm damage, structure failure, sealing problems, and leakage.

One of the biggest plants was installed in 1967 in Patmos Island in Greece. The solar still had an area of $8640\,m^2$ and a product water capacity of $26\,m^3\,day^{-1}$ from seawater.

Until today, a significant number of variations aiming on the improvement of solar stills have been examined and several new plants have been installed.

Many studies discuss in detail the effect of different factors, such as solar input, ambient temperature, water depth, and wind velocity, on the performance of the still. For most cases, even under optimized operating conditions, the reported efficiency of the single-basin solar still was in the range of 30–45%, with $<5\,l\,m^{-2}$ daily freshwater production. This low efficiency is mainly due to the complete loss of latent heat of condensation of water vapor on the glass cover of the solar still [15].

Efforts have been focused for some time on recovering the latent heat of condensation. Preheating of the feedwater by passing it over the glass cover allowed only partial utilization of the latent heat, resulting in a limited increase in still production. More significant improvements in solar still design were achieved through the multiple use of the latent heat of condensation within the still. In a multiple-effect unit consisting of several cells, heat is supplied only to the first cell (effect). Water is evaporated in the second effect as it trickles over a metallic surface heated by the condensation of the vapor from the first effect. This allows the utilization of the latent heat of condensation at different levels. In the literature, an efficiency of 57% for a double-effect still has been reported while other reports indicate a production ranging up to $13\,l\,m^{-2}\,day^{-1}$. This increased productivity was achieved by using mirrors as solar reflectors to increase the solar energy received so that the operating temperature could reach 85 °C in the multieffect still. However, if the reflector area is included in the calculation, productivity is still not better than $6\,l\,m^{-2}\,day^{-1}$. Multieffect solar stills may be used for efficient production of desalinated water but only with small capacities because the condenser is an integral part of the still. The low heat and mass transfer coefficients in this type of still require operation at relatively high temperatures, and thus the use of large, expensive, metallic surfaces for evaporation and condensation [15].

3.16.5 Solar Humidification–Dehumidification

A recent modification of the solar stills is the so-called humidification–dehumidification (HD) process. The concept of HD is the collection of potable water by first humidifying an air current by contact with warm seawater and then dehumidifying by cooling. By this method, the defect (operation of distillation plants at high temperatures, around 115 °C, generates scaling problems) of high temperature used in other distillation processes is avoided and the desalination performance is an improvement over what is realized in the conventional solar stills [16].

More analytically, in the HD process, a dry airstream is enriched with vapor in a humidification unit and then the vapor is recondensed in a dehumidification unit where freshwater is collected.

These processes seem to be highly promising, first for the high efficiency, and second, for the possibility of using renewable energies to power them, such as the use of direct solar energy for desalting saline water.

Several aspects of HD have been examined in order to improve their efficiency and the amount of produced water [17, 18]. The multieffect humidification–dehumidification (MEH) process is the most efficient HD process, and extensive research has been carried out by different institutions, especially in Germany, to develop an efficient means of utilizing solar energy for water desalination [19]. Small plants based on MEH were constructed and tested in different countries. The research proves that the solar HD process has much room for improvement.

3.16.6 Solar Membrane Distillation

Membrane distillation (MD) is the youngest of the membrane separation processes that is being used to desalinate water. It was introduced commercially on small scale in the 1980s. The process combines both the use of distillation and membranes. In the process, saline water is warmed to enhance vapor production, and this vapor is exposed to a hydrophobic membrane that allows the passage of vapor, but not water (see **Figures** 22 and 23). After the vapor passes through the membrane, it is condensed on a cooler surface to produce freshwater. In the liquid form, the freshwater cannot pass back through the membrane, so it is trapped and collected as the output of the plant.

Compared to the more commercially successful processes, MD requires more space and may use a considerably large pumping energy per unit of production.

The main advantages of MD are in its simplicity and the requirement for only small temperature differentials to operate the process. Like any distillation process, its energy requirement and product water quality are independent of the feedwater quality. Because it operates at lower temperatures (50–80 °C), the feedwater can be heated by solar thermal collectors, while the electric energy required for pumping could be provided by PVs.

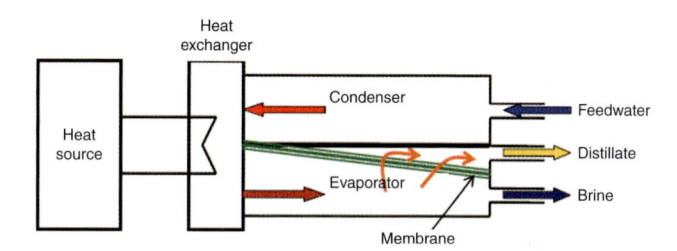

Figure 22 Membrane distillation principle. Adapted from Fath H, Elsherbiny SM, Alaa A, *et al.* (2008) PV and thermally driven small-scale, stand-alone solar desalination systems with very low maintenance needs. *Desalination* 225: 58–69.

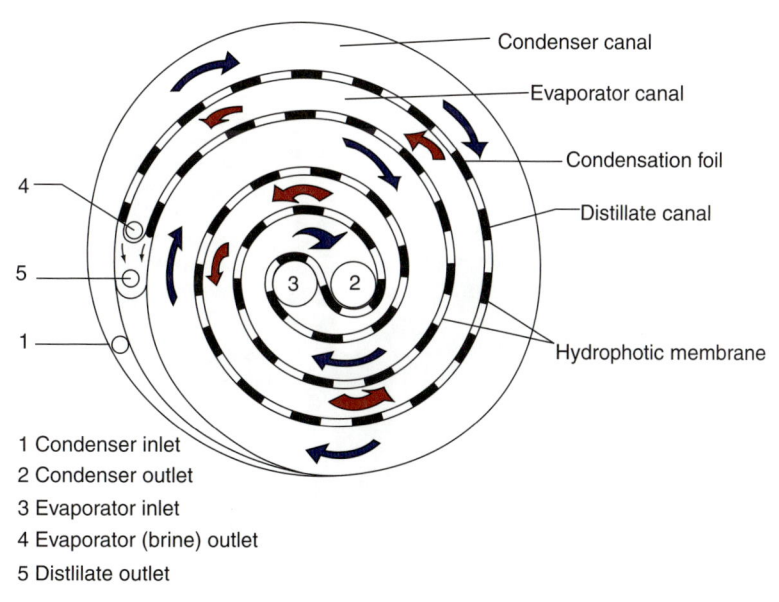

1 Condenser inlet
2 Condenser outlet
3 Evaporator inlet
4 Evaporator (brine) outlet
5 Distlilate outlet

Figure 23 Spiral wound MD module. Adapted from Fath H, Elsherbiny SM, Alaa A, *et al.* (2008) PV and thermally driven small-scale, stand-alone solar desalination systems with very low maintenance needs. *Desalination* 225: 58–69.

Typical characteristics of the process are as follows:

- Efficient and compact spiral-wound MD modules
- Recovery of the heat of condensation integrated in the module design
- No feedwater chemical pretreatment required
- Low system pressure
- Insensitivity to dry-running and fouling
- Negligible scaling problems due to process temperatures around 80 °C
- Production of pure distillate water
- Modularity.

Many pilot plants have been built and are being operated with encouraging results. During 1990s, at least two solar MD demonstration projects were built [13]. A 0.05 m^3 day^{-1} system using 3 m^2 solar collectors was built at the University of New South Wales in Australia. A calculated efficiency of 17 l day^{-1} m^{-2} of collector area is mentioned. In 1994, a solar MD plant was developed in Water Re-use Promotion Center in Tokyo, Japan. The system produces 40 l h^{-1}. Automatic controls start up the desalination system whenever sufficient sunlight is present to provide hot water from the solar collectors and electricity for pumping from the PV panels.

Furthermore, in the last decade, several solar MD systems have been installed and examined, mainly within EU projects (SODESA, MEMDIS, and SMADES). The Fraunhofer Institut, Germany, has done a lot of work on the development of MD modules and on the provision of compact solar MD units. Some of the characteristics of the MD modules developed by Fraunhofer are as follows:

- Distillate output: 10–30 l h^{-1} (80 °C evaporator inlet, 300 l h^{-1} feed flow)
- Operation temperature range: 50–85 °C
- Thermal energy demand: 90–200 kWh m^{-3}
- High water quality of the produced water: 5–50 μS cm^{-1}
- No pretreatment of the feedwater required.

The first compact solar MD system by the Fraunhofer Institut was developed in 2004. The system consists of 6 m^2 2AR-collectors (AR, antireflective) having an operating collector temperature up to 85 °C, 80 W$_p$ PV module, and one MD module with a daily water capacity of 80–150 l.

In the period 2003–06, several other solar MD plants were installed in Jordan, Gran Canaria, Egypt, and Morocco by Fraunhofer within EU projects for the desalination of seawater and tap and brackish water. The systems integrate solar, thermal, and PV energy. The desalination energy is supplied entirely by solar thermal collectors and the electrical auxiliary energy (feedwater pumping) is supplied by a PV system.

Figures 24 and **25** present the stand-alone solar MD system installed at Alexandria University, Alexandria, Egypt, in June 2005 within SMADES project [20].

The solar collector consists of three similar rectangular sections connected in series. The dimensions of each section are 2020 mm × 1020 mm × 80 mm with a total area of 2.06 m^2 and an aperture area of 1.91 m^2. The electric conductivities for feed

Figure 24 MD compact system (SMADES), Alexandria, Egypt. Adapted from Fath H, Elsherbiny SM, Alaa A, *et al.* (2008) PV and thermally driven small-scale, stand-alone solar desalination systems with very low maintenance needs. *Desalination* 225: 58–69.

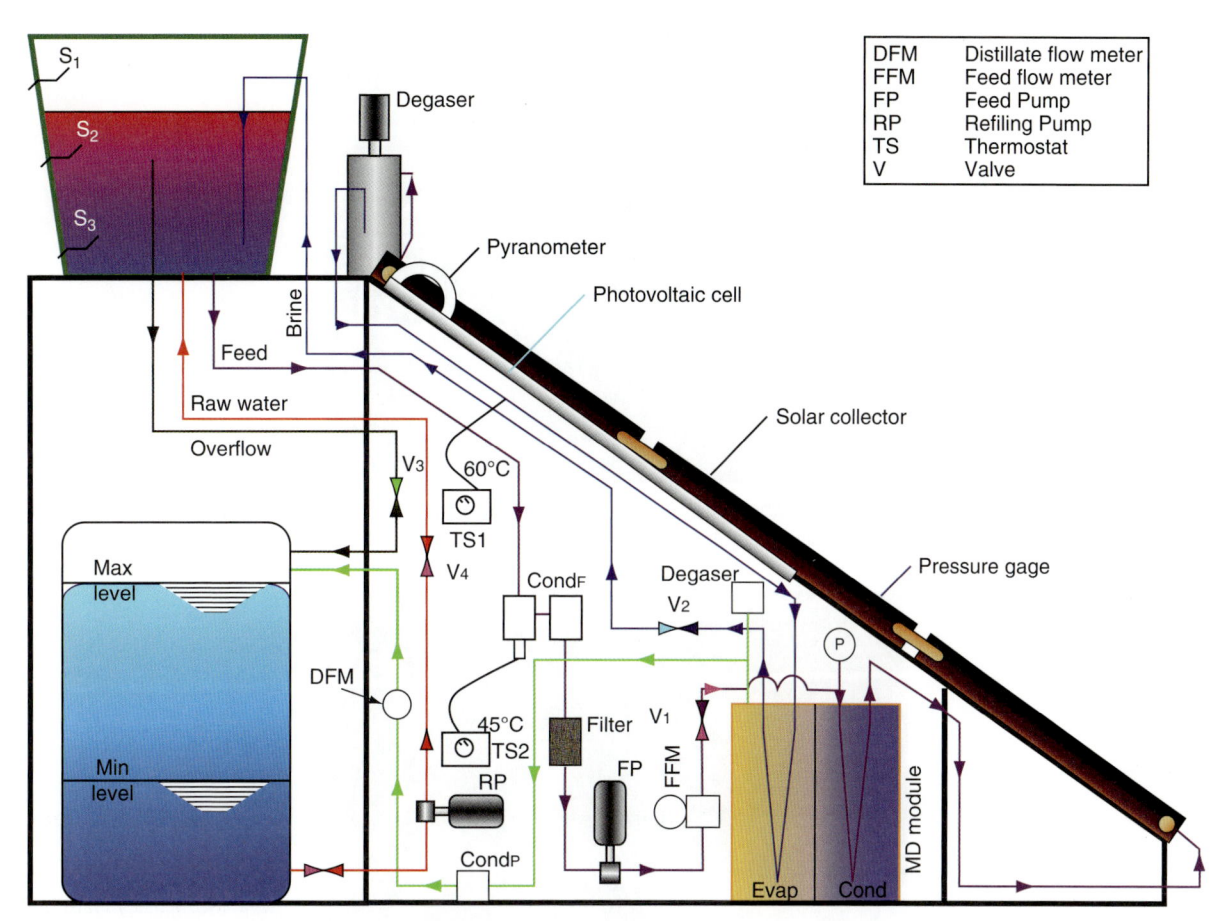

Figure 25 Flow diagram of MD compact system, Alexandria (SMADES). Adapted from Fath H, Elsherbiny SM, Alaa A, et al. (2008) PV and thermally driven small-scale, stand-alone solar desalination systems with very low maintenance needs. *Desalination* 225: 58–69.

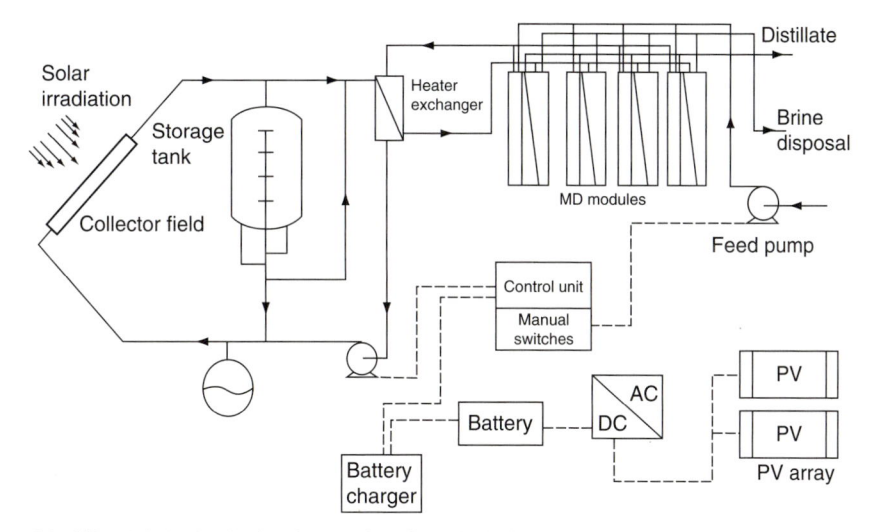

Figure 26 Flow sheet of the MD unit in Aqaba, Jordan. Adapted from Banat F, Jwaied N, Rommel M et al. (2007) Performance evaluation of the 'large SMADES' autonomous desalination solar-driven membrane distillation plant in Aqaba, Jordan. *Desalination* 217: 17–28 [21].

and distillate water are 526 and 3 µS cm^{-1}, respectively. The daily production is 64 l day^{-1} (11.2 l m^{-2} day^{-1}), while the accumulated solar energy is 41.6 kWh day^{-1} (7.25 kWh m^{-2} day^{-1}). The process works at a lower temperature of 60–80 °C [21].

At the system installed in the Marine Science Station in Aqaba, Jordan, within SMADES, the energy for the desalination process is also supplied entirely by solar thermal collectors in the form of heat at temperatures in the range of 60–80 °C (see **Figures 26** and **27**). The desalination units are improved MD modules with internal heat recovery function. The electrical auxiliary energy,

Figure 27 View of the main components of the large SMADES system in Aqaba, Jordan. Adapted from Banat F, Jwaied N, Rommel M et al. (2007) Performance evaluation of the 'large SMADES' autonomous desalination solar-driven membrane distillation plant in Aqaba, Jordan. *Desalination* 217: 17–28 [21].

Figure 28 Collector field of the SPMD system in Aqaba. Adapted from Banat F, Jwaied N, Rommel M et al. (2007) Performance evaluation of the 'large SMADES' autonomous desalination solar-driven membrane distillation plant in Aqaba, Jordan. *Desalination* 217: 17–28 [21].

which is required to drive the pumps and valves for the automatically operated systems, is supplied by PV panels. The feedwater is real seawater from the Red Sea. The seawater desalination system's primary power supply is generated by PV panels. The system supplies and stores energy according to demand. The unit is operated with untreated seawater.

The collector area is 72 m^2, the hydraulic loop of the collector field comprises a solar heat storage tank of 3 m^3 and the collector loop is separated from the seawater loop of the MD desalination modules. The effective membrane area in each MD module is 10 m^2. The system consists of four MD modules operated in parallel.

The system provides an output in the range of 2–11 l day^{-1} m^{-2} with specific energy consumption in the range of 200–300 kWh m^{-3}. The distillate is water of low TDS with conductivity in the range of 20–250 µS cm^{-1}.

Figure 28 shows the solar collectors and the PV panels on the top of the housing building, three separated collector racks each of 12 collectors and four PV modules on top.

Automatic controls start up the desalination unit whenever sufficient sunlight is present to provide hot water and electricity for pumping from the solar collectors and PV panels.

3.16.7 Technologies Selection Guidelines

Autonomous systems are developed in remote areas where no electricity grid is available. Due to the dispersed population that characterizes the South Mediterranean and Gulf areas, relatively small systems are used to cover the potable water needs in remote villages. The main desirable features for such systems are low-cost, low-maintenance requirements, simplicity of operation, as well as high reliability [9].

The decision to use an autonomous solar desalination system, as well as the selection of the most appropriate combination, depends on several parameters and is mostly site specific.

For solar desalination systems, the most important parameter concerning the power supply system is sufficient solar potential in the selected region. Other factors that should be taken into consideration and that affect the final unit cost of water and the life of the plant are the availability of land, the land cost, and the availability of technical staff and local market.

Regarding desalination, a number of basic parameters should be investigated. The first is the evaluation of the overall water resources. This should be done both in terms of quality and quantity (for brackish water resources). In inland sites, brackish water may be the only option. In these cases, care should be taken on the brine disposal output and rejecting them without polluting the local water resources.

On a coastal site, seawater is normally available. Specific guidelines are followed, in this case, during disposal of the brine disposal into the sea.

Distillation processes are used mainly for seawater desalination, while membrane processes are used for a wide range of salinity from brackish water to seawater.

Application of the ED process is preferred for brackish water desalination.

The determination of the quality of the water produced depends on the purpose of the plant, for instance, whether the plant is used for potable, agricultural, or industrial needs. Distillation processes are used for the production of distillate water, while membrane processes are used for the production of potable water. However, with an extra treatment of the distillate water, it is possible to produce potable water as well; with the use of a dual-purpose RO plant, it is possible to produce water of very low conductivity.

From the energy point of view, the main supply to the desalination plant is a large thermal input. Like all thermal processes, distillation demands a high-energy input (due to the energy required for change of phase). Besides, some auxiliary electricity is also required for pumping (electricity could be produced via PVs).

On the other hand, the solar thermal systems are so much dependent on the radiation (day/night) that some heat storage is always required. The accumulator may thus become the main subsystem of the plant, and the adopted control strategies become of particular importance.

For MSF evaporators, the PR increases with temperature so that high temperatures (up to 120 °C) are preferred. This in turn increases the risks of scaling and corrosion. MED evaporators, nowadays, operate at lower temperatures (around 70 °C) and those hazards are reduced.

Finally, the control of such evaporators must be very accurate, particularly the flash equilibration in MSF. The system is unstable in small sizes. This leads to the use of medium and large size evaporators (thousands of cubic meters per day capacity), which do not quite fit with the sizes and capacities usually applied with renewable energies, unless a huge solar field could be built, which in turn implies large ground surfaces. Therefore, the combination, solar–thermal distillation seems best suited for medium and high production capacities.

On the other hand, RO is available in a large range of sizes and water salinities. The use of energy recovery devices can considerably reduce the energy requirements. The stability of the power supply is important for the membrane's life.

ED is available also in small sizes; however, this process is mainly used for the desalination of brackish water due to the dependency of the energy consumption on the feedwater concentration.

Simplicity of operation and maintenance, as well as system automation, is a major concern.

Commercial maturity in solar desalination units is not easy to be found; however, a sufficient number of plants exist that can be validated by their examination.

3.16.8 Solar Desalination Applications

3.16.8.1 Solar Thermal MES Plant for Seawater Desalination, Abu Dhabi, UAE

The Abu Dhabi solar desalination plant is situated at the Umm Al Nar Power and Desalination Station about 20 miles east of Abu Dhabi city. The plant was commissioned in 1984. The plant was designed as a demonstration unit aimed at evaluating the technical and economic feasibility of using this type of technology to provide the remote coastal communities in UAE with freshwater. The seawater has a salinity of 55 000 ppm TDS.

A bank of evacuated-tube and flat-plate collectors with a total absorber area of 1862 m^2 is used to provide the thermal energy required by a multiple-effect stack-type evaporator having a rated capacity of 80–120 m^3 day^{-1}. The maximum daily distillate production corresponding to the optimum operating parameters was found to be 120 m^3 day^{-1} (full load) for 8 months of the year, that is, February, March, April, May, June, August, September, and October. The production level during the other months is somewhat lower, reaching its lowest value of 90 m^3 day^{-1} in December (see **Figure 29**) [22].

In order to ensure that the evaporator can run 24 h per day during sunny days, a thermally stratified heat accumulator is incorporated in the design to provide the thermal energy required during the nighttime.

The electrical energy required by the different pumps is provided from the main grid.

The bank of evacuated-tube solar collectors, whose orientation with respect to the sun has been optimized to collect the maximum amount of solar radiation, is used to heat the collector fluid (water) to a maximum temperature of about 95 °C. The effective collector–absorber area of the bank is 1862 m^2. The collector bank, which is divided into six blocks, consists of 1064 collector units, each having an effective absorber area of 1.75 m^2. Twenty-eight collector units are combined to form a single group of collectors with its own support structure. Thirty-eight such groups are arranged in U-shape to form the whole collector bank. All the groups are connected and each is provided with two isolating valves – at the group inlet and exit headers, a drain valve and an air vent. The collector efficiency ranges from 0.5 to 0.7, whereas the heat efficiency ranges from 41.4% in winter to 47.4% in summer.

A bypass line is installed between the heat collector bank and the heat accumulator tanks to allow the heat collecting water to recirculate through the collector bank if the water temperature at the discharge of the collector bank is below a set point, which can

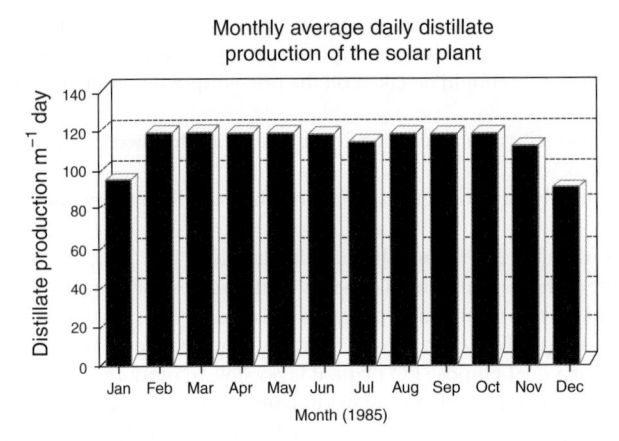

Figure 29 Monthly average water production [22].

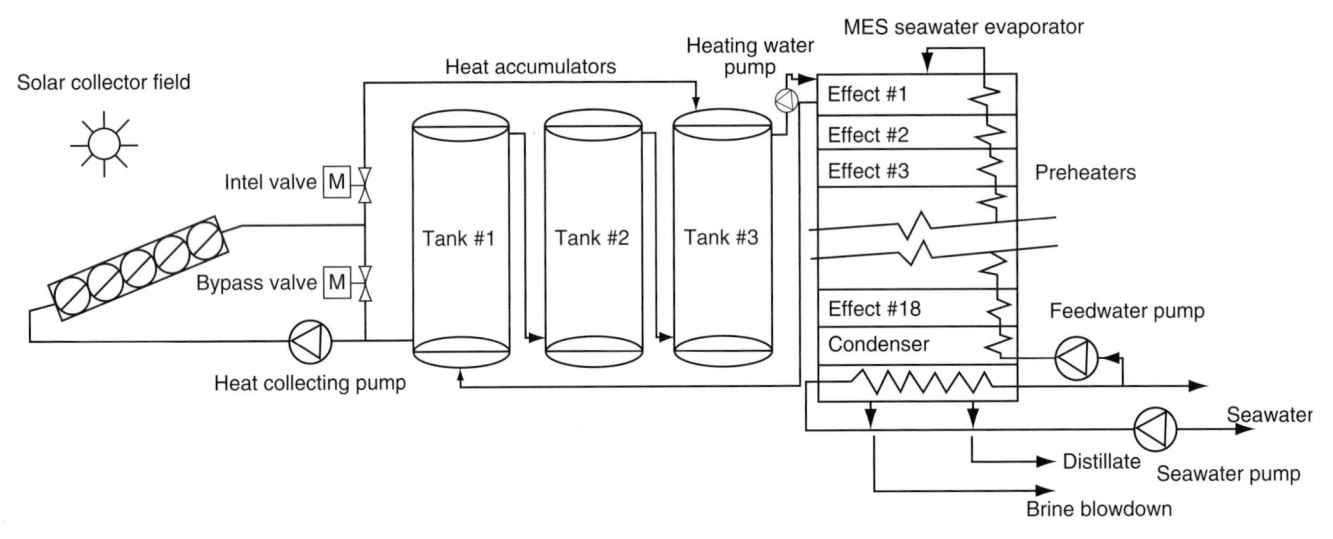

Figure 30 Solar thermal multistack evaporator plant in Abu Dhabi [23].

be adjusted manually. The heat collecting water from the collector bank is introduced at the top of the heat accumulator system (**Figure 30**).

The heat accumulator system is designed to provide thermal energy to the evaporator during its 24 h daily operation – autonomy period about 16 h. During extended overcast periods or hazy days, when sandstorms prevail, the plant may shut down due to insufficient thermal energy storage. The heat accumulator consists of three heavily insulated carbon steel tanks filled with hot water, and having a total capacity of 300 m^3. The evaporator is of the horizontal-tube, thin-film type and is designed for a rated distillate output of 120 m^3 day^{-1} from seawater. The multieffect stack-type evaporator (MES) has 18 effects stacked one on top of the other. The PR is 12.4, where the heating fluid transfers from 95 to 99 °C.

The plant has been in operation for over 16 years. After 16 years, the performance of the collector field and evaporator subsystems has not declined to any appreciable degree.

No problem has so far been encountered with any of the tube bundles; distillate conductivity has been in the range of 10–20 mS cm^{-1}. This is an indication that a correct choice of tube and tube sheet materials has been made by the manufacturer. This desalination technology has proved its reliability and flexibility for variable load operation and is worth serious consideration as a provider of freshwater in remote communities.

Table 4 provides the technical characteristics of the system [9].

Capital and operating costs, as well as the cost of the water produced by the Abu Dhabi solar desalination plant, have been calculated to assess the economic performance of the system. The capital cost figures were determined from actual prices provided by the plant manufacturer (Sasakura and Sanyo of Japan). The calculations of the water cost are based on the following economic assumptions [23]:

- Evaporator lifetime: 20 years
- Heat accumulator lifetime: 20 years
- Solar collector's lifetime: 20 years

Table 4 Technical characteristics of the Abu Dhabi plant

Site characteristics	
Annual mean solar radiation	5000 kcal (m² day)
Annual mean ambient temperature	30 °C
Average wind speed	5 m s⁻¹
MED plant	
Product water capacity	80–120 m³ day⁻¹
Design raw water salinity	55 000 ppm TDS
Product water salinity	50 ppm TDS
Performance ratio	12.4
Number of effects	18
Number of preheaters	17
Evaporator	Horizontal tube, thin-film type
Design seawater temperature	35 °C
Heating water temperature	95–99 °C
Brine blowdown temperature	43 °C
Brine blowdown salinity	1.4 Times the raw water salinity
Specific heat consumption	43.8 kcal kg⁻¹ distillate
Hours of operation	24 h day⁻¹
Solar collector field	
Solar collector type	Evacuated tube, flat plate
Total absorber area	1862 m²
Absorber area per single panel	1.75 m²
Number of collector panels	1064
System type (stand-alone grid)	Stand-alone + diesel generator
Selective coating	Absorptivity $\alpha \geq 0.91$, Emissivity $\varepsilon \leq 0.12$
Absorber area	1.75 m²
Circulation flow rate	700–1800 l h⁻¹
Maximum operating pressure	6 bar
Heat accumulator	
Type	Thermally stratified, sensible heat
Total capacity	300 m³
Number of tanks	Three cylindrical tanks in series
Accumulator fluid	Water
Tank pressure	Atmospheric pressure
Insulation type	10 cm fiber glass
Diesel generator set	50 KVA

- Interest rate: 8%
- Plant availability: 85% (7446 h yr⁻¹).

The capital costs are as follows:

- Evaporator: $299 180
- Heat accumulator: $91 304
- Solar collectors: $1 098 580.

Local fabrication and installation costs were estimated at 30% of the sum of the above three capital cost components, which results in an amount of $446 719. Marine transportation costs amounted to $102 000. Thus, the installed capital cost of the plant was $2 037 783.

The operation and maintenance (O&M) costs consist of the following main cost components: cost of chemicals (antiscalant for seawater treatment, corrosion inhibitor for collector fluid, and seawater disinfectant to inhibit bacterial growth); spare parts costs; cost of operation and maintenance personnel; and cost for electrical power consumption. Based on an average daily water production of 100 m³ day⁻¹, the unit water cost is estimated at around $7 m⁻³ of distillate.

The Abu Dhabi solar thermal MES plant has had a successful operation, proving that with an improved sizing, it is feasible to produce water of sufficient quality at a reasonable cost.

3.16.8.2 Solar Thermal MED Plant for Seawater Desalination, Almeria, Spain

The Centro de Investigaciones Energéticas Medioambientales y Tecnológicas (CIEMAT), Spain, and Deutsche Forschungsanstalt für Luft und Raumfahrt (DLR), Germany, decided in 1987 to develop an advanced solar thermal desalination system, thus initiating the so-called Solar Thermal Desalination (STD) project carried out at the PSA until 1994 [24]. The following two project phases were scheduled and executed during this period aiming to achieve specific project objectives:

- Phase I: To study the reliability and technical feasibility of solar–thermal technology application to seawater desalination.
- Phase II: To develop an optimized solar desalination system by implementing specific improvements in the system initially installed at the PSA, which could make it more competitive against conventional desalination systems.

Phase I was launched in 1988 and its evaluation was completed in 1990. During this phase, a solar desalination system was implemented at the PSA. This desalination system was composed of

1. a 14-effect MED plant,
2. a solar parabolic-trough collector field, and
3. a thermocline thermal energy storage tank.

These subsystems were interconnected as shown in **Figure 31**. The system operates with synthetic oil that is heated as it circulates through the solar collectors. The solar energy is thus converted into thermal energy in the form of sensible heat of the oil, and is then stored in the thermal storage tank. Hot oil from the storage system provides the MED plant with the required thermal energy. The desalination plant installed at PSA uses sprayed horizontal tube bundles for seawater evaporation, which must be limited to around 70 °C to reduce scale formation. The MED plant is composed of 14 cells or effects at successively decreasing temperatures and pressures from cell (1) to cell (14). **Table 5** provides the technical data of the system.

The seawater is preheated from cell to cell in the 13 preheaters. From cell (1), the seawater passes on from one cell to another by gravity before being extracted from cell (14) by the brine pump. Part of the seawater used to cool the condenser is rejected and the rest is used for the feedwater required to spray the cell (1) tube bundle. The fresh distilled water is extracted from the condenser by means of a distilled water pump (**Figure 32**).

The plant can also be fed with steam at 16–26 bar. High-pressure steam is produced in the PSA's electricity generation system to drive a small power plant. A small fraction of this steam can be used to feed the desalination plant, where it is sent to thermo-compressors, and mixed with steam produced in the fourteenth effect. This mixture is then ejected into the evaporator of the first cell to restart the desalination process. In this case, the MED plant consumption is lower. A vacuum system, composed of two ejectors (not shown in **Figure 31**) driven by seawater at 3 bar, is used to evacuate the air from the unit at

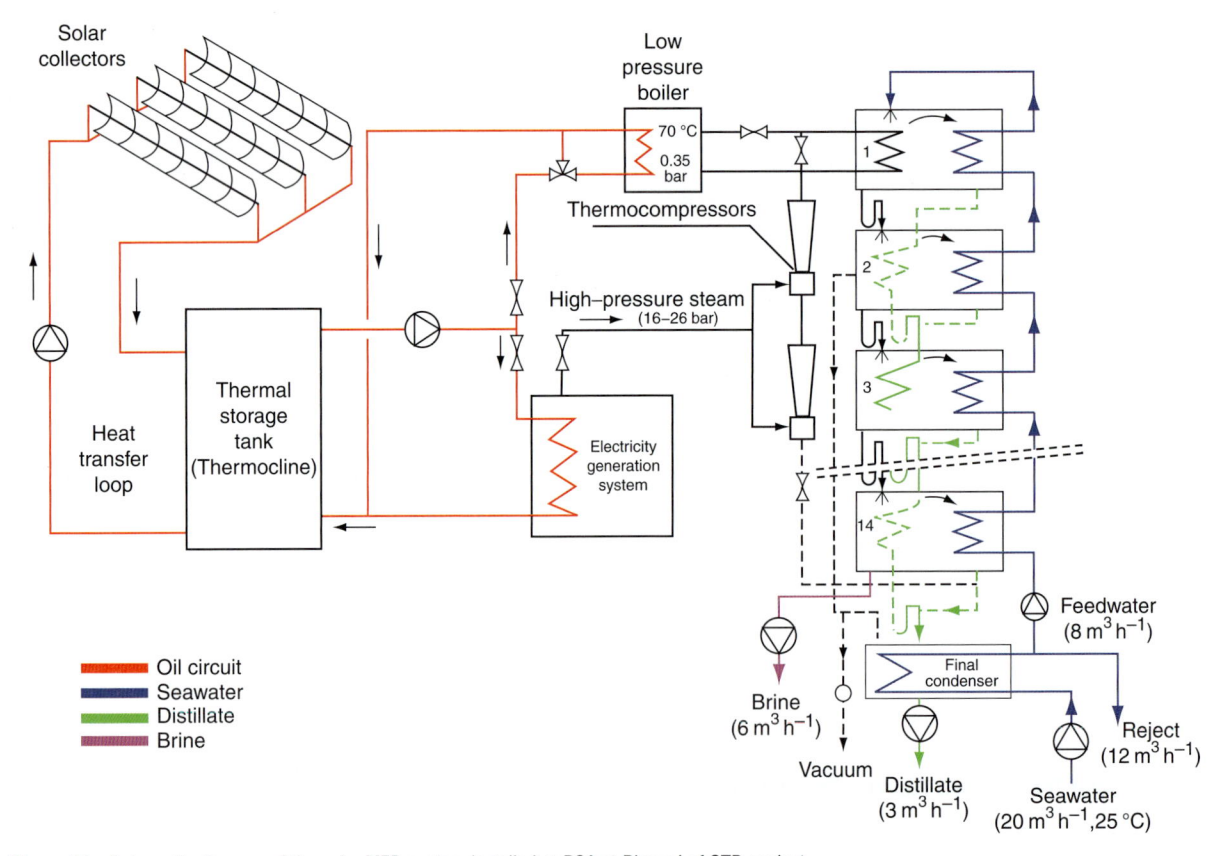

Figure 31 Schematic diagram of the solar MED system installed at PSA at Phase I of STD project.

Table 5 Technical characteristics of the Almeria plant

Nominal distillate production	3 m^3 h^{-1}
Heat source energy consumption	190 kW
Performance ratio (kilogram distillate/2300 KJ heat input)	>9
Output salinity	50 ppm TDS
Seawater flow	
At 10 °C	8 m^3 h^{-1}
At 25 °C	5 m^3 h^{-1}
Feedwater flow	8 m^3 h^{-1}
Brine reject	5 m^3 h^{-1}
Number of cells	14
Vacuum system	Hydroejectors (seawater at 3 bar)

Figure 32 View of the solar MED plant at PSA/CIEMAT.

start-up and to compensate for the small amounts of air and gases released from feedwater and from small leaks through the gaskets.

The most outstanding evaluation results obtained during Phase I were the following:

- High reliability of the system, as no major problem was observed in the coupling of the solar collector field with the MED plant.
- Low thermal inertia: it usually took 35 min to reach the nominal distillate production.
- Specific electricity consumption in the range of 3.3–5 kWh m^{-3} of distillate.
- The plant showed a PR (e.g., number of kilograms of distillate produced by 2300 kJ heat input) within the range of 9.4–10.4 when operating with low-pressure steam. PR increases up to the range of 12–14 if high-pressure steam is used to feed the plant.

From the results obtained during Phase I, it was possible to identify potential relevant improvements that could be implemented in the MED solar system to increase its efficiency and competitiveness.

This analysis concluded that

- the plant electrical demand could be reduced by replacing the initial hydroejector-based vacuum system with a steam ejector system, and
- the plant thermal demand is 50% reduced by incorporating a double-effect absorption heat pump coupled to the MED plant.

Since these improvements would considerably reduce the specific cost of distillate produced by the optimized solar MED desalination system, it was decided that the Phase II of the STD project be carried out. A schematic diagram of the improved desalination system in which an absorption heat pump was coupled to the MED plant has been shown in **Figure 33**. The heat pump delivers around 200 kW of thermal energy at ±65 °C to the MED plant. The desalination process in the plant evaporator body uses only 90 kW of the 200 kW, while the remaining 110 kW is recovered by the heat pump evaporator at 35 °C and pumped to usable temperature of 65 °C. For this, the heat pump needs 90 kW of thermal power at 180 °C. The energy consumption of the desalination system was thus reduced from 200 to 90 kW.

The improvements implemented in the desalination system (i.e., absorption heat pump and steam-ejector-based vacuum system) reduced the thermal energy consumption of the desalination system by 44%, that is, from 63 to 36 kWh m^{-3}, and electricity consumption by 12%, from 3.3 to 2.9 kWh m^{-3}.

A new R&D European project, named AQUASOL, was initiated in 2002, trying to improve the existing system at PSA. AQUASOL project objective was the development of a low-cost and more energy-efficient seawater desalination technology based on MED process with zero brine discharge. Specific proposed technological developments (new design of CPC solar collectors and a new prototype of absorption heat pump, hybridization with natural gas, and recovering of salt) were implemented to both improve the energy efficiency of the process and for process economy. The expected result was an enhanced MED technology with market possibilities and suitable to be applied in the Mediterranean area and similar locations around the world. If a fuel cost (i.e., natural gas) of € 4.5 GJ^{-1} is considered, the needed cost of solar system (considering a solar contribution of 50% to the overall system) for the achievement of the same economic competitiveness as conventional MED plant is equivalent to around € 150 m^{-2} of solar collector.

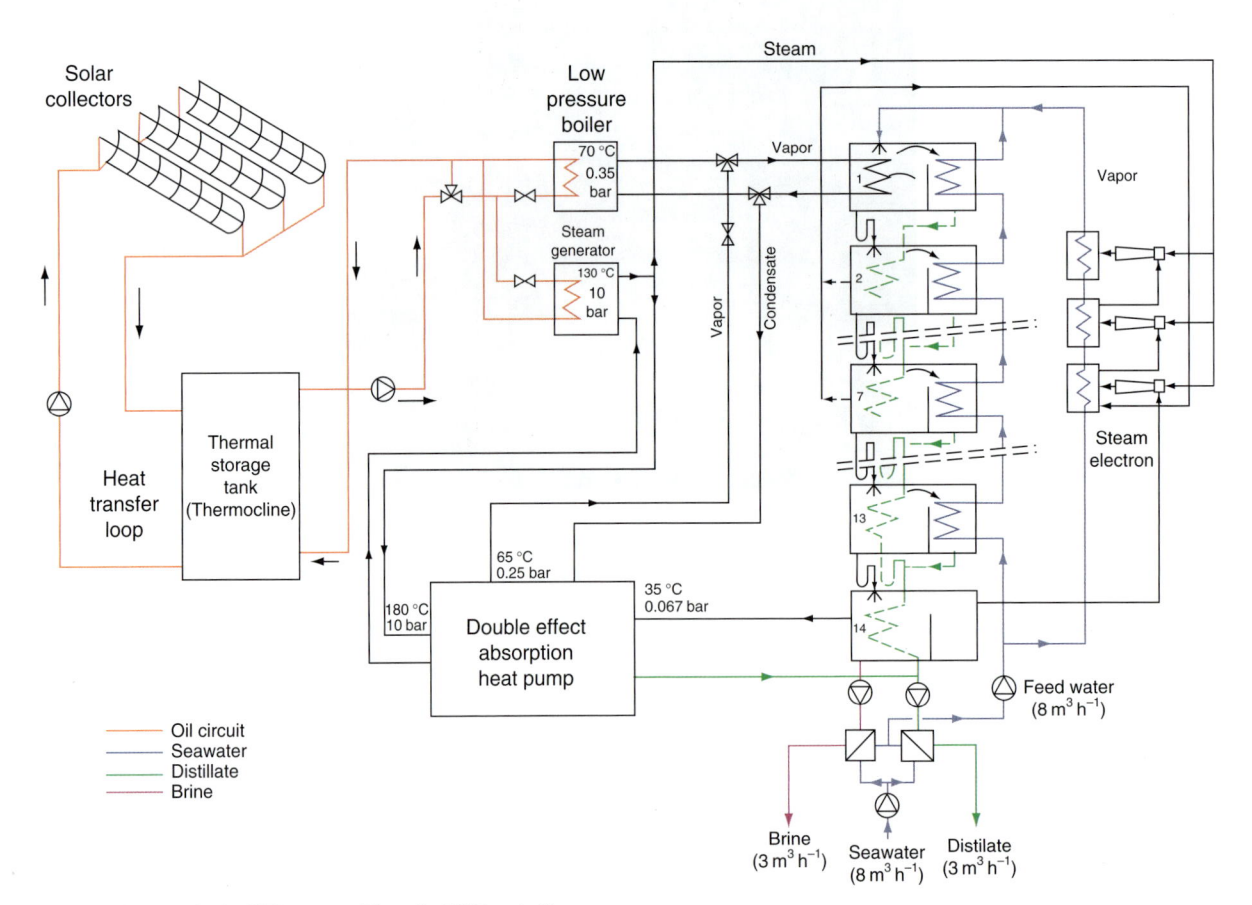

Figure 33 Improved solar MED system (Phase II of STD project).

3.16.8.3 PV–RO Plant for Seawater Desalination, Lampedusa Island, Italy

The matching of PVs with RO has a large number of applications due to the modularity, efficiency, and simplicity of the combination. The largest and most known stand-alone PV–RO seawater plant was installed in 1990 in Lampedusa Island in Italy (**Figure 34**). The plant is characterized by successful operation providing freshwater at a reasonable cost. The RO unit consists of two units with a total water production capacity of $5\,m^3\,h^{-1}$. The power supply system consists of $100\,kW_p$ PV arrays, $2 \times 2000\,Ah$ at $220\,V$ (DC) – $880\,kWh$ batteries and inverters [9].

The system was sized to provide $5\,m^3\,h^{-1}$ of desalinated water for 3 days of 8 h operation on three consecutive nonsunny days (**Figure 35**). The original plant was powered by a $100\,kW$ PV system. Having run as a demonstration plant for 5 years and shown that the unit can perform satisfactorily as an autonomous system, it was decided in 1995 to modify the system and incorporate it into the island grid. This allows the RO plant to be run continuously at full output, which makes better use of this capital resource. The PV system is then used to reduce the consumption of diesel fuel.

The pretreatment of the desalination system consists of addition of chemicals to prevent colloidal and alkaline scaling and passing of the feedwater through cartridge filters (5, 20 µm) before entering the high-pressure pump (**Figure 36**).

The high-pressure pump is a piston pump, which includes an energy recovery system, recovering 15–20% of the consumed energy. The energy requirements of the RO plant (including the energy recovery system) are of the order of $5.5\,kWh\,m^{-3}$ of produced water.

Both units have similar layout, with freshwater flow of $3\,m^3\,h^{-1}$ for the first unit (three pumps, three permeators) and $2\,m^3\,h^{-1}$ for the second unit (two pumps, two permeators). The module arrangement of each unit is of one stage, operating with seawater. Spiral wound permeators are used.

The salt content of the produced water is <500 ppm, in compliance with World Health Organization (WHO) specifications for drinking water. In **Table 6**, the technical data of the RO unit, as well as of the power supply system, are presented.

The power supply system consists of a $100\,kW$ PV array, a battery bank with storage capacity of $2 \times 2000\,Ah$ at $220\,V$ (DC), and two sinusoidal inverters in order to convert the DC from the battery bank to AC for the desalination unit (**Figure 37**). The inverters have been sized to allow easy starting of the 22 kW motors.

The cost of the system is analyzed as follows:

Equipment	Cost	
PV array	10 000	ECU (kW_p)
Batteries	125	ECU (kWh)
RO unit	19 000	ECU (m^3h)
O&M cost		
Staff (one employee)	20 000	ECU (year)
Energy	0.7	ECU (m^3)
Chemicals	0.1	ECU (m^3)
Membrane replacement	0.25	ECU (m^3)
Spares	0.05	ECU (m^3)
Electricity production cost	0.7	ECU (kWh)
Total water cost	6.5	ECU (m^3)

Figure 34 The PV plant in Lampedusa, Italy. Adapted from Morris R (1999) *Renewable Energy Powered Desalination Systems in the Mediterranean Region*. France: United Nations Educational, Scientific and Cultural Organization [25].

Figure 35 The RO unit of Lampedusa plant. Adapted from Morris R (1999) *Renewable Energy Powered Desalination Systems in the Mediterranean Region*. France: United Nations Educational, Scientific and Cultural Organization.

Figure 36 The high-pressure pump of the RO unit. Adapted from Morris R (1999) *Renewable Energy Powered Desalination Systems in the Mediterranean Region*. France: United Nations Educational, Scientific and Cultural Organization [25].

The Lampedusa PV–RO plant has had a successful operation for more than 5 years, proving that with an improved sizing and without any incentive, it is feasible to produce and sell water at prices definitely lower than from other water sources, like water transportation. The need for energy recovery devices optimization and lower maintenance requirements of the pumps have been considered as issues for improvement.

Table 6 Technical data of the Lampedusa plant [9]

RO unit technical data

Product water capacity	$3 + 2\,m^3\,h^{-1}$
Feedwater type	Seawater
Product water concentration	<500 ppm
Recovery ratio	~30%
Nominal pressure	55 bar (actual)
Membranes type	Spiral wound
Number of membranes	2 membranes / vessel
Number of permeators / vessels	3 + 2 vessels
Energy consumption	5.5–6 kWh m^{-3}
Installed power	22 + 15 kW
Hours of operation	8
Operation	Automatic
Module arrangement	One stage

PSS technical data

Nominal / installed power	100 kW$_p$ PV
PV global efficiency	81%
Average wind speed	6 m s^{-1}
System type (stand-alone/grid)	Stand-alone with network back-up

Power supply system

Number of modules	2272 36 MS/C
Number of cells/module	36–5″ mono square
Encapsulant	Double glass
Array voltage at maximum power	264 V
V_{oc}	336 V
Strings	142 of 16 modules each
Subfields	2 × 15 strings, 8 × 14 strings

Battery characteristics

Type of battery	Lead–acid
Capacity	2 × 2000 Ah at 220 V (DC) – 880 kWh
Maximum battery discharge	50%
Battery efficiency	80%
Type of connection	In parallel
Sizing	Capable to assure 3 days of consecutive backup of 8 h each
Nominal voltage	220 V
Inverter character	One inverter for each plant
Inlet voltage	22 V DC (20.0 minimum–27.0 maximum)
Outlet voltage	380 / 220 V AC
Wave shape	Sinusoidal
Capability	To allow easy starting of 22 kW motors

Figure 37 The battery storage bank, Lampedusa, Italy. Adapted from Morris R (1999) *Renewable Energy Powered Desalination Systems in the Mediterranean Region*. France: United Nations Educational, Scientific and Cultural Organization [25].

3.16.8.4 PV–RO Plant for Brackish Water Desalination, Ceara, Brazil

The PV–RO plant was installed in the community of Coité-Pedreiras, in the state of Ceará, northeast region of Brazil in 2000. The selected community has a population of about 150 families. The main water source of the village was a well with a salinity of 1200 ppm TDS. The region is characterized by a high yearly solar potential of about 2000 kWh m^{-2} yr^{-1}. The project was financed by the Banco do Nordeste and CNPq and developed by the Departamento de Engenharia EléctricaUniversidade Federal de Ceará (DEE-UFC) in cooperation with Agência Reguladora de Serviços Públicos Delegados do Estada do Ceará (ARCE) and Instituto Federal de Educação, Ciência e Tecnologia do Ceará (CEFET) in Brazil [26].

The aim of the project was to investigate the coupling of the two technologies RO and PVs for brackish water desalination, considering two strategies: the first concerns the use of a DC motor, and second, the use of a three-phase induction motor. Through the analysis of the stored data, the second option was chosen as the better alternative [6].

The plant consists of 20 PV modules of 55 W each, totally 1.1 kW, eight batteries of 12 V, 100 Ah, and a charge controller. The RO unit has a water capacity of 250 l h^{-1}. The pressure of operation of the RO unit is around 8 bar working at a recovery ratio of 27% (**Figure 38**).

The plant is equipped with sensors for measuring the following:

- Global solar radiation
- Ambient temperature
- Module temperature
- Wind speed
- Water flow
- Direct voltage of the PVs and batteries
- DC of the PVs and batteries.

In the first case, the power from PVs drives only the high-pressure pump of the RO unit, which is the main load. The grid drives the booster pump. The DC motor used at the RO unit has a nominal power of 750 W and a nominal voltage of 24 V. The specific electricity consumption was 4.7 kWh m^{-3}.

Due to damage of the brushes of the motor and the lack of suitable brushes or suitable pump in the local market, the motor was totally replaced by a three-phase induction motor. The three-phase induction motor was of 2 HP with a nominal voltage of 220 V (**Figure 39**). A DC–DC converter was used to elevate the voltage from 24 V (battery output) to 220 V and an inverter with a nominal power of 750 W to convert the DC to AC (**Figure 40**).

During this period of the plant's operation, the recovery ratio (the ratio of the produced water to the feedwater) and the electrical consumption showed no significant variation, and were more stable in comparison with the previous operation with the DC pump. With the use of the three-phase motor, the specific electrical consumption was reduced to about 3 kWh m^{-3}.

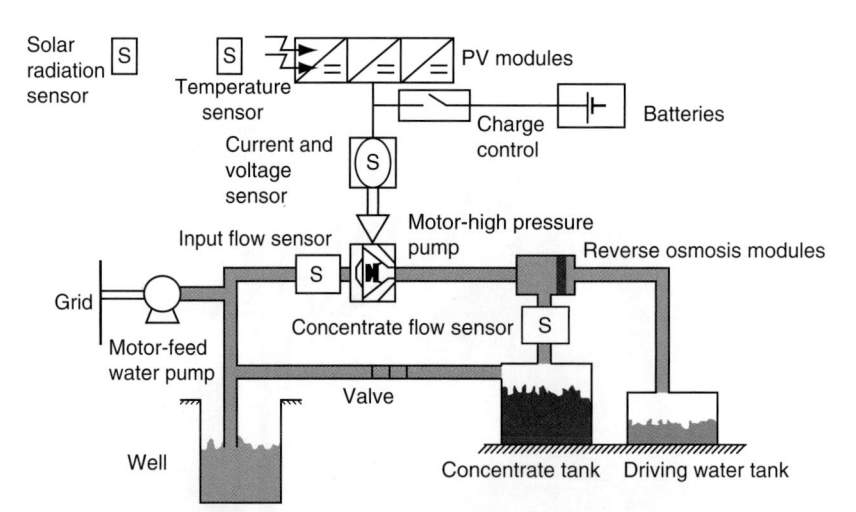

Figure 38 Configuration of the PV–RO plant, Brazil. Adapted from Report on the Status of Autonomous Desalination Units Based on Renewable Energy Systems (2005) INCO-CT-2004-509093, Co-ordination Action for Autonomous Desalination Units Based on Renewable Energy Systems, ADU-RES Project. www.adu-res.org

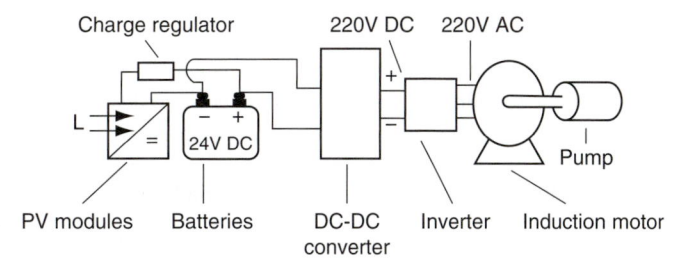

Figure 39 Electrical figure of the plant with the three-phase induction motor, Brazil. Adapted from Report on the Status of Autonomous Desalination Units Based on Renewable Energy Systems (2005) INCO-CT-2004-509093, Co-ordination Action for Autonomous Desalination Units Based on Renewable Energy Systems, ADU-RES Project. www.adu-res.org

Figure 40 The RO unit and the battery bank, Brazil. Source: *ITC, Spain*. Adapted from Report on the Status of Autonomous Desalination Units Based on Renewable Energy Systems (2005) INCO-CT-2004-509093, Co-ordination Action for Autonomous Desalination Units Based on Renewable Energy Systems, ADU-RES Project. www.adu-res.org

The cost of the PV–RO unit is as follows:

Equipment	Cost (US$)
RO	2667
PV modules (2 × 55 W_p)	7333
Batteries	405
DC/DC converter, AC/AC inverter	1267
Charge controllers (2 × 30 A)	187
Induction motor	133
Total	11 992
Battery replacement	200
Membrane replacement	283
Filters replacement	10
Labor	200
Total O&M costs	693

The unit cost of water was estimated assuming an annual interest rate of 10%, a lifetime of the plant of 20 year, and an annual drinking water production of 200 m^3. The drinking water cost is estimated to about US$ 12.7 m^{-3} (€ 10.32 m^{-3}). This can be compared to bottled water that is offered in 20 l bottles at a price of US$ 63 m^{-3} (around € 51 m^{-3}).

From the system's operation, the following conclusions could be drawn:

- Due to the hard working conditions, the DC motor is not adequate to operate in a stand-alone PV–RO plant
- With the use of the three-phase motor, the specific electrical consumption is reduced to about $3\,kWh\,m^{-3}$
- The participation of the community is of great importance for the success of a project.

3.16.8.5 PV–RO Plant for Seawater Desalination, Pozo Izquierdo, Gran Canaria Island

An autonomous PV–RO for seawater desalination was installed in 1998 in a collaboration between the Instituto Tecnológico de Canarias, Spain, and the Sola-Institute Jülich in Germany. The aim of the project was the design, installation, and optimization of a drinking water production system in coastal areas isolated from the electric grid [27].

The first version of the project was considered in 1998 and the second in 2000. The second version was carried out by ITC directly. The pilot system was installed in Pozo Izquierdo. The system consists of a seawater RO unit with a nominal production of $0.4\,m^3\,h^{-1}$. The pretreatment system consists only of two cartridge filters of 20 and $10\,\mu m$. The salinity of the produced water is <1000 ppm TDS, while the seawater salinity is of 35 500 ppm TDS. The RO unit operates at a working pressure of 55 bar and at a recovery ratio of 45%. The unit consists of two pressure vessels in parallel with six membranes each (**Figure 41**).

The total installed power of the RO unit is 3 kW and the specific energy consumption is $5.5\,kWh\,m^{-3}$.

The unit is operated automatically on an average of 9 h during summer and 7 h during wintertime. The power supply system consists of $4.8\,kW_p$ monocrystalline PV system and a battery bank of 19 kWh. The batteries are of Pb–acid type. The nominal voltage output is 48 V (24 elements in series of 2 V each). The purpose of the batteries is the stabilization of voltage and to supply power to the RO unit when energy from PV is not available. A charge controller of 75 A protects the batteries from overcharge. A pure sinusoidal inverter converts the 48 V output voltage from the batteries to 220 V for the RO unit [6].

The unit water cost of the desalination plant coupled to a solar photovoltaic field (DESSOL) system is estimated at around € $9.0\,m^{-3}$.

3.16.8.6 PV Water Pumping RO for Brackish Water Desalination, Saudi Arabia

The PV water pumping RO system, located in Sadous Riyadh Region, was the first RES desalination plant in Saudi Arabia. The system installation was completed in December 1994. The system has been in continuous operation ($24\,h\,day^{-1}$) since January 1995.

The purpose of the system was to supply sufficient potable water to satisfy the various needs of the consumers. The system was designed by the Energy Research Institute of King Abdulaziz City for Science and Technology (KACST) in collaboration with National Renewable Energy Laboratory (NREL), USA, as a result of a Saudi and US cooperation program in the field of renewable energy research [28].

The design of the plant was mainly based on the specification of the site, the depth of the well, the quality and quantity of the feedwater, water needs, and autonomy period of the plant during cloudy conditions as well as other local climatic conditions. The design is based on the selection of equipment commonly available in the local market in order to make the operation and maintenance of the system highly reliable.

The plant consists of two main separate PV systems: first, PV water pumping system, which is characterized by water being stored in two storage tanks and without battery storage, and second, PV for the operation of the RO unit, which is characterized by battery storage (see **Figure 42**). The battery storage system is used to provide the required energy to the RO unit during cloudy days and during the night, as well as to offer 5 days of autonomy to the plant.

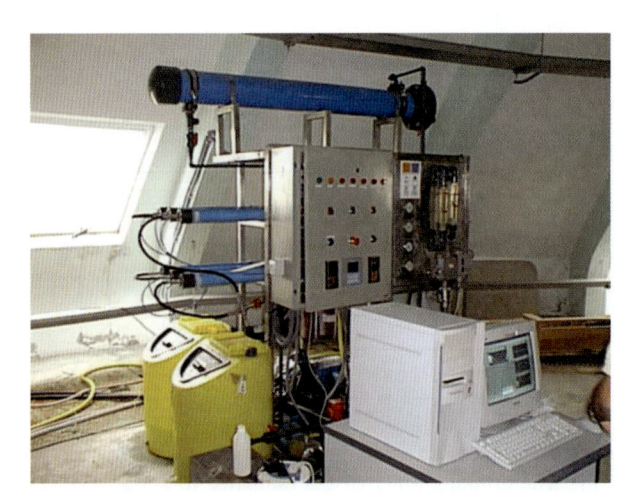

Figure 41 The RO unit of DESSOL project, Gran Canaria. Source: *ITC*.

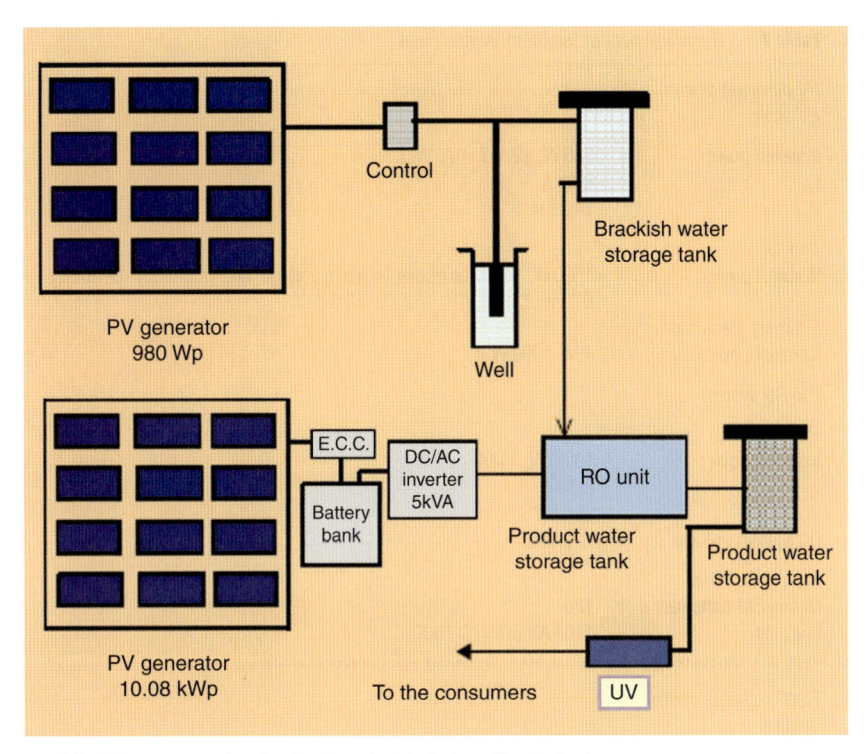

Figure 42 Block diagram of the PV water pumping desalination plant in Sadous Riyadh Region.

The total PV installed capacity is 10.89 kW$_p$, 10.08 kW$_p$ to drive the RO unit and 980 W$_p$ for water pumping. The head of the submersible pump is 50 m from the surface level and the product water capacity from the RO unit is about 600 l h^{-1}.

The PV generator is divided into seven arrays, one PV array for the water pumping and the other six for the desalination unit with adjustable tilt angle (**Table 7**).

The PV pumping system consists of a 980 PV generator, an inverter of 1500 W to convert DC to three-phase AC of variable frequency and the submersible pump. The measured efficiency of the inverter ranges from 90% to 96% for low and high irradiance, respectively. This control unit is based on a microprocessor control unit to protect the motor and the PV array, and also has various functions during operation and standby mode. The control unit has a maximum power point circuit, which converts the possible maximum power available from the PV array to the motor. In addition, the control unit can start the operation of the motor with a low value of solar radiation and adjust the flow of water according to the available insolation. Also, because of the overall system performance, efficiency must be as high as possible and the system's cost as low as possible, and there is no storage of electric energy in the system. All the energy available from the PV array is used to pump water, which is stored in two tanks. The submersible pump is around 2 kW and is installed approximately 50 m below the ground level.

Two water storage tanks of 120 and 60 m^3 capacity were used to store the feedwater (brackish water) and product water, respectively.

The PV desalination system mainly consists of the PV generator, the storage battery system, electric charge controller (ECC), the inverter, and the RO unit. The 10.08 kW$_p$ PV generator consists of six PV arrays, 840 W$_p$ each and charges two parallel battery banks, a total of 120 batteries, with a capacity of 1101 Ah each (C-100) and a 5-day storage capacity to drive the RO unit. Also, each battery is equipped with a recombinator to convert the generated gases (hydrogen and oxygen) during the charging to water.

The ECC is a DC to DC converter built in maximum power point (MPP) tracker. The plant has six microprocessor-based electronic charge controllers and is used to transfer the energy from the PV array to charge the batteries. The ECC also protects the PV generator and the battery from different hazardous conditions such as input and output reverse polarity, high and low voltage, and also provides protection in the case of overload and short circuit conditions. The rated power of the inverter is 5 kVA and it is designed to match the inductive AC load in the system. The major AC load of the inverter consists of three AC motors with a total rating of 3300 VA. The inverter is fully controlled and protected by a built-in microprocessor automatic controller to increase the reliability of the system. The average efficiency of the inverter for variable loads of 50–125% of its rated capacity is 90%.

The output power of the inverter at rated capacity has good sinusoidal wave, which corresponds to minimum total harmonic distortion. The shape of output power wave from the inverter is distorted if all the motors start at the same time. For this short duration of about 20 s, the current drawn from the inverter is at least six times more than the rated current. With a distorted power wave, the control circuit of RO unit has no reliable operation; this critical condition was solved, first, by scheduling the starting time of the motors, and second, by using a UPS (250 VA). The use of the UPS guarantees, even in case of distorted power, that the control circuit in the plant will continue to operate normally.

Table 7 Technical data of the Saudi Arabia plant

PV pumping system	
PV array	
Installed power	980 W_p (2 × 7 × 70 W_p)
I_{sc}	8.82 A
V_{oc}	149.8 V
Inverter	
Nominal power	1500 W, DC/three phase, variable voltage, and frequency (6–60 Hz)
	DC input: 120 VDC ± 20 V, 12.5 ADC
Submersible pump	
Nominal power	424–1990 W
PV–RO system	
PV array	
Installed power	10.8 kW_p (144 × 70 W_p)
I_{sc}	8.82 A
V_{oc}	256.8 V
DC system voltage	120 VDC
Storage batteries	
Number of batteries	120
Capacity	1101 Ah each (C-100)
Type of connection	(2V × 60 × in series) × 2 parallel branches
Electric charge control	
Quantity	6
Rated power	1800 W with MPP
Input	0–12 ADC, 40–25 VDC
Output	0–20 ADC, 26–250 VDC
Inverter	
Nominal power	5 kVA, sinewave
	120 VDC, 220 VAC, 60 Hz
UPS	250 VA
RO unit	
Product water capacity	600 l h^{-1}
Conversion rate	21–35%
Pressure of operation	14 bar

The RO system is operated intermittently, according to fluctuating demand for water. Typically, the unit goes through six start-up–shutdown cycles each day, staying on for 1–4 h during each cycle. The automatic control flushes the membranes after each shutdown. The RO unit produces approximately 600 l h^{-1}, converting brackish water from 5700 ppm TDS to about 170 ppm TDS, having a pressure of operation around 14 bar. The RO unit consists of a booster pump, pretreatment system, high-pressure pump, RO modules, and posttreatment including a UV sterilization system as well as the control and distribution system. Thin film composite (TFC) membranes are used. The system's recovery rate varies depending on the pressure, age of filter time elapsed since the membranes were cleaned, and temperature [6].

The major problems are related to membranes fouling and failure of some hardware. The membranes needed to be cleaned every 6 months. However, no technical problem has been referred concerning the coupling of PVs with the RO unit.

3.16.8.7 PV–RO Brackish Water Desalination, Aqaba, Jordan

A small-scale desalination unit was installed in Jordan through the project titled 'Solar Powered Desalination and Pumping Unit for Brackish Water in Jordan' under a subcontract signed between the Midwest Research Institute acting through its NREL division, Colorado, USA, and the National Energy Research Center (NERC), Amman, Jordan. The unit was installed in 2005, within the campus of the Aqaba International Industrial Estate (AIIE) to supply customers within the estate with potable water. This unit was driven by a hybrid utility/PV generator [29, 30].

The area of Aqaba is characterized by sufficient solar potential; the annual daily average of solar radiation on a horizontal surface reaches 5.5 kWh m^{-2} day^{-1}.

The raw water of the desalination unit water is classified as brackish water with a salinity not exceeding 4000 ppm TDS.

The power supply unit consists of the following (**Figure 43**):

- A PV system with a total peak power of 16.8 kW (140 silicon monocrystalline PV panels, each rated at 120 W_p). The PV generator is divided into six subarrays, with three subarrays in both of the mentioned arrays (**Figure 44**).

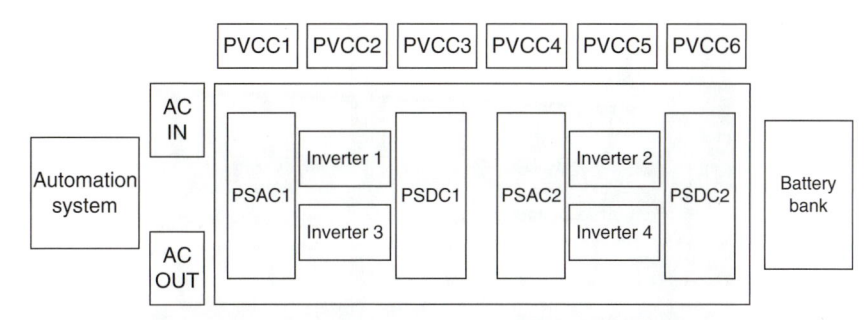

Figure 43 System components installed within the power conditioning room, Aqaba plant, Jordan [29]. Adapted from Touryan KJ Solar powered desalination and pumping unit for brackish water, *Final Report* (February 2003–2006), NREL, USA.

Figure 44 View of the PV panels and the solar pond (NERC, Jordan).

Figure 45 The charge controllers (NERC, Jordan).

- Six PV charge controllers (PVCC) to protect the batteries from overcharging (**Figure 45**).
- A battery bank with a total storage capacity of 73.44 kWh. The battery bank consists of 24 sealed lead–acid batteries, each rated at 12 V/255 Ah (**Figure 46**). The battery bank is configured as six parallel strings with four series batteries in each string to obtain the required system DC voltage (48 V). The battery bank is placed inside a power conditioning room within a special rack.
- Four pure sine-wave inverters/chargers, each rated at 220 V, 50 Hz, and 3.3 kVA (**Figure 47**).
- DC disconnect boxes (PSDC1 and PSDC2).
- AC disconnect boxes (PSAC1 and PSAC2).

Figure 46 View of the battery storage system (NERC, Jordan).

Figure 47 The four inverters of the system (NERC, Jordan).

Three-phase backup utility grid power is obtained by an AC INPUT circuit breaker and three-phase output power is obtained by an AC OUTPUT circuit breaker.

Three single-phase inverters, which are synchronized together, one master and two slaves, are installed to obtain a three-phase power supply (380 V/50 Hz), which will energize the electric loads. The three inverters are programmed to operate in the low battery transfer mode.

The system operates as a stand-alone power system, independent of the utility grid. When the system is no longer able to keep up with the power requirements of the AC load, discharging the batteries to the low battery transfer V (DC) setting, the inverters connect to the utility grid. It then feeds utility power directly to the loads and charges the batteries. When the battery voltage reaches the low battery transfer V (DC) setting, the inverters disconnect from the utility grid and once again operate the AC loads from the batteries.

The fourth inverter is programmed to work as a stand-alone inverter to operate the feed pump of the RO unit.

A backup power grid connection was obtained and connected to the system. A three-phase AC INPUT circuit breaker is used for this manner. The utility grid power is used to operate the RO system for 24 h, if needed, and operate the lighting lamps, sockets, and the air conditioning system within the power conditioning room.

The raw water of the desalination plant is pumped up by a submersible pump, which is submerged 79 m below the ground level, or 8 m below the level of the water in the well. Protection against overload, dry-running, raw water tank overflow, and phase fault for the motor that drives the pump is obtained via a special relay-based control system. The outlet of this submersible pump is connected to the raw water tank.

Basic system components of the RO unit include the sediment prefilter, high-pressure pump, RO modules, automatic membrane flushing system, and the control system (**Figures 48** and **49**).

Figure 48 View of the RO unit (NERC, Jordan).

Figure 49 Filtration of the RO unit (NERC, Jordan).

The product water capacity of the brackish water desalination RO unit is 3.4 m³ h⁻¹. The RO unit operates at a recovery ratio of 60% and a pressure of around 15 bar. The energy consumption is of 2.2 kWh m⁻³.

The concentrated water outlet of the RO unit is connected via a hose to a 600 m² brine water evaporation pond coated with a special liner to prevent penetration of brine water into ground water.

The PV–RO unit of Aqaba has a successful operation, providing good quality water to the local people.

3.16.9 Lessons Learned

Numerous solar desalination stand-alone plants have been installed, most of them for demonstration projects and consequently of small capacity. Most of the applications refer to the combination of PVs with RO technology.

The matching of the desalination process to an RES is not simple, mainly because desalination process is best suited to continuous operation. Most RESs are distinctly noncontinuous and are in fact intermittent, often on a diurnal basis. Unpredictable and nonsteady power input force the desalination unit to operate in nonoptimal conditions and this may cause operational problems [25]. Each desalination method has its problems regarding the intermittent operation, for instance, in RO, the variable operation has to cope with the sensitivity of the membranes, while in thermal processes, the variable operation may cause fouling and scaling problems. Thus, in small autonomous systems, energy storage systems such as batteries are usually used.

Besides, no technical problems in the matching of the two technologies have been encountered [25]. Proper selection of technologies, matching, optimum sizing, and selection of material, sufficient automation of the system, and local people acceptance and participation could be the base of a successful installation.

Researchers are still in the process of optimizing the combinations of the two technologies. Final success will be achieved with the development of reliable, market-available systems, which will have the capability to provide sufficient quality and quantity of water at a reasonable cost.

3.16.10 Economics

In general, the final unit water cost of RES desalination systems is site specific and depends on several parameters such as the RES potential, the feedwater quality, the availability of local market, and technical staff. However, from the already existing applications, it has been concluded that small autonomous RES desalination systems in remote areas can be competitive with other water sources such as water transportation, and bottled water, etc.

Also, it should be mentioned that over the years, the cost of water produced by seawater desalination has dropped considerably, but the cost of water produced from 'conventional' sources has risen due to the overexploitation of aquifers and the intrusion of saline water, and also to the generally increasing contamination of groundwater. Regarding the cost of solar thermal systems and PVs, there is also a fall in their cost mainly due to the high market competition.

As concluded from the already existing solar desalination plants and from the literature, the unit price cost from conventional stills is in the order of US$ $3-12\,m^{-3}$. According to Al-Hallaj [19], a conventional solar still with a product water capacity of $1\,m^3\,day^{-1}$ and a collecting surface area of $250\,m^2$ provides water at a cost of $3\,m^{-3}$. **Table 8** provides unit water costs from existing autonomous solar desalination applications for seawater and brackish water desalination.

3.16.11 Market

Although everybody recognizes the strong potential of solar energy for seawater or brackish water desalination in arid and semiarid regions due to the usual coincidence of water shortage, good solar radiation, and seawater availability, the process has not yet developed at commercial level [31]. Only few companies provide compact solar thermal distillation plants and PV–RO units, mainly of small sizes, to the market.

3.16.12 Conclusions

Among the energy sources suitable to drive desalination processes, solar energy is one of the most promising options due to the coupling of the dispersed nature and availability of solar radiation with water demand–supply requirements in many world locations [31].

The coupling of solar energy technologies with desalination processes is seen as having the potential to offer a sustainable route for increasing the supplies of potable water. The matching of solar energy with desalination does not have the capacity to solve the water crisis; however, it offers the potential of providing a sustainable source of potable water to some communities, particularly those in arid areas where there are no indigenous sources of fossil fuels. Keeping in mind the climate protection targets and strong environmental concerns, future water desalination around the world should be increasingly powered by solar and other natural resources. Such environmentally friendly systems should be potentially available at economic costs.

Table 8 Unit water costs from installed plants

Installation	Solar technology	Desalination $m^3\,hr^{-1}$	Unit water cost
SW Solar thermal MED, Almeria	500 m^2	3	€2.5–3 m^{-3}
SW PV–RO, Pojo Izquierdo	4.8 kWp PV	0.4	€9 m^{-3}
SW Solar termal plant, Abu Dhabi	1862 m^2	4	$7 m^{-3}
SW PV–RO, Lampedusa	100 kWp PV	5	ECU 6.5 m^{-3}
BW PV–RO, Brazil	1.1 kWp PV	0.250	$12.7 m^{-3}
BW PV–RO, Morocco ADIRA Project	4 kWp PV	1	€5.3 m^{-3}

References

[1] Tzen E (2008) *Renewable Energy Sources for Seawater Desalination – Present Status and Future Prospects*, ISBN 978-1-60456-567-6, *Desalination Research Progress*, pp. 145–160. New York, NY: NOVA Science Publishers.
[2] Kalogirou S (2008) *Renewable Energy Sources Used for Seawater Desalination*, ISBN 978-1-60456-567-6, *Desalination Research Progress*, pp. 67–144. New York, NY: NOVA Science Publishers.
[3] Kalogirou SA (2005) Seawater desalination using renewable energy sources. *Progress in Energy and Combustion Science* 31: 242–281.
[4] Watson IC, Henthorne L, Morin OJ, et al. (2003) *Desalting Handbook for Planners*, 3rd edn. Alexandria, VA: US Department of the Interior Bureau of Reclamation.
[5] Buros OK (1999/2000) *The ABCs of Desalting*, 2nd edn. Topsfield, MA: International Desalination Association.
[6] Report on the Status of Autonomous Desalination Units Based on Renewable Energy Systems (2005) INCO-CT-2004-509093, Co-ordination Action for Autonomous Desalination Units Based on Renewable Energy Systems, ADU-RES Project.
[7] Ben Bacha H, Bouzguenda M, Abid MS, and Maalej AY (1999) Modelling and simulation of a water desalination station with solar multiple condensation evaporation cycle technique. *Renewable Energy* 18: 349–356.
[8] Panaras G and Mathioulakis E (2008) Humidification–Dehumidification Desalination Powered by Solar Thermal Energy, National Center for Scientific Research 'DEMOKRITOS', Greece, *ADIRA Workshop on Desalination Powered by Renewable Energy*, Athens.
[9] Centre for Renewable Energy Sources (1998) *Desalination Guide Using Renewable Energies*, ISBN 960-90557-5-3. Greece: CRES.
[10] Mokhlisse A (2008) A New Experience of Fresh Water Supply in Two Rural Villages in Morocco, *Workshop on Desalination Powered by Renewable Energy* (ADS), Athens.
[11] Argaw N (2003) Renewable energy in water and wastewater treatment applications, *National Renewable Energy Laboratory*, NREL, NREL/SR-500-30383, June.
[12] Subiela JV, de la Fuente JA, Piernavieja G, et al. (2009) Canary Islands Institute of Technology (ITC) experiences in desalination with renewable energies (1996–2008). *Desalination and Water Treatment Science and Engineering* 7(1–3): 220–235.
[13] Karen TE (1997) *Desalination of Village Scale, Renewable Energy Powered Desalination*. NREL, USA.
[14] Kabeel AE and Hamed AM (2008) *Solar Still Innovation – Review Article*, ISBN 978-1-60456-567-6, *Desalination Research Progress*, pp. 275–316. New York, NY: NOVA Science Publishers.
[15] Al-Hallaj S, Mehdi Farid M, and Rahman Tamimi A (1998) Solar desalination with a humidification–dehumidification cycle: Performance of the unit. *Desalination* 120: 273–280.
[16] Abdel Dayem AM (2008) *HD Solar Water Desalination – A General Prospect*, ISBN 978-1-60456-567-6, *Desalination Research Progress*, pp. 317–327. New York, NY: NOVA Science Publishers.
[17] Hou SB (2008) Two-stage solar multi-effect humidification–dehumidification desalination process plotted from pinch analysis. *Desalination* 222: 572–578.
[18] Hou SB, Ye SQ, and Zhang HF (2005) Performance optimization of solar humidification–dehumidification desalination process using pinch technology. *Desalination* 183: 143–149.
[19] Al-Hallaj S, Parekh S, Farid MM, and Selman JR (2006) Solar desalination with humidification–dehumidification cycle: Review of economics. *Desalination* 195: 169–186.
[20] Fath H, Elsherbiny SM, Alaa A, et al. (2008) PV and thermally driven small-scale, stand-alone solar desalination systems with very low maintenance needs. *Desalination* 225: 58–69.
[21] Banat F, Jwaied N, Rommel M, et al. (2007) Performance evaluation of the 'large SMADES' autonomous desalination solar-driven membrane distillation plant in Aqaba, Jordan. *Desalination* 217: 17–28.
[22] El Nashar Ali M (1992) Optimizing the operating parameters of a solar desalination plant. *Solar Energy* 48(4): 207–213.
[23] El-Nashar Ali M (2001) Water from the Sun – Case study: The Abu Dhabi solar desalination plant. *Re-Focus* 2(2): 26–29.
[24] Blanco J, Zarza E, Alarcón D, et al. (2002) Advanced multi-effect solar desalination technology: The PSA experience. *11th International Symposium on Concentrated Solar Power and Chemical Energy Technologies*. Zurich, Switzerland, 4–6 September.
[25] Morris R (1999) *Renewable Energy Powered Desalination Systems in the Mediterranean Region*. France: United Nations Educational, Scientific and Cultural Organization.
[26] de Carvalho PCM, Freire C, Montenegro FFD, and Riffel DB (2004) The Brazilian experience with a photovoltaic powered reverse osmosis plant. *Progress in Photovoltaics: Research and Applications* 12: 373–385.
[27] Espino T, Peñate B, Piernavieja G, et al. (2003) Optimised desalination of seawater by a PV powered reverse osmosis plant for a decentralised coastal water supply. *Desalination* 156: 349–350.
[28] Alajlan SA and Smiai MS (1996) Performance and development of PV-plant for water pumping and desalination for remote area in Saudi Arabia. *Proceedings of World Renewable Energy Congress Renewable Energy, Energy Efficiency and the Environment*, vol. 1, pp. 441–446. Denver, CO, USA.
[29] Touryan K (2006) *Solar Powered Desalination and Pumping Unit for Brackish Water*. Washington, DC: National Renewable Energy Laboratory.
[30] Personal Conduct with Firas A, Batayneh S, National Energy Research Center, Amman, Jordan, 2008.
[31] Tzen E and Morris R (2003) Renewable energy sources for desalination. *Solar Energy* 75: 375–379.

3.17 Industrial and Agricultural Applications of Solar Heat

B Norton, Dublin Institute of Technology, Dublin, Ireland

© 2012 Elsevier Ltd. All rights reserved.

3.17.1	Introduction	568
3.17.2	Characteristics of Industrial and Agricultural Energy Use	568
3.17.2.1	Application Temperatures	568
3.17.2.2	Economics	569
3.17.3	Selection of Appropriate Solar Collector and Energy Storage Technologies	569
3.17.3.1	Collector Types	569
3.17.3.2	Aperture Cover Materials	570
3.17.3.3	Flat-Plate Absorbers	571
3.17.3.4	Line-Axis Collectors	571
3.17.3.5	Nonconvecting Solar Panels	572
3.17.4	System Component Layouts	573
3.17.4.1	Components	573
3.17.4.2	Generic Solar Industrial Process Heat System Layouts	573
3.17.4.3	Real Solar Industrial Process Heat Systems	575
3.17.4.4	Operational Limits	576
3.17.5	Solar Hot Water Industrial and Agricultural Process Heat System Design	577
3.17.5.1	Conceptual Distinctions	577
3.17.5.2	Design Methodologies	578
3.17.6	Solar Drying Technologies	579
3.17.6.1	Solar Drying Processes	579
3.17.6.2	Solar Dryer Types	580
3.17.6.3	Practical Issues in the Use of Solar Dryers	582
3.17.6.3.1	Analysis of solar dryers	582
3.17.7	Solar Furnaces	585
3.17.8	Greenhouses	586
3.17.8.1	Achieving a Desired Interior Microclimate	586
3.17.8.2	Greenhouse Heating and Cooling	586
3.17.9	Heating and Ventilation of Industrial and Agricultural Buildings	587
3.17.9.1	Solar Air Heating	587
3.17.9.2	Direct Solar Gain and Thermal Mass	587
3.17.10	Solar Cooking	588
3.17.10.1	Types of Solar Cooker	588
3.17.10.2	Analysis of Solar Cookers	589
3.17.11	Solar Desalination	589
3.17.11.1	Solar Desalination Systems	589
3.17.11.2	Passive Basin Stills	591
3.17.12	Solar Refrigeration	592
3.17.12.1	Types of Solar Refrigeration	592
3.17.12.2	Uses of Solar Refrigeration	592
Acknowledgments		592
References		593

Glossary

Auxiliary Heating Auxiliary heating is heat provided by non-solar sources to satisfy load requirement during periods when solar energy is unavailable or insufficient.

Desalination Desalination describes a range of process that can be used to remove dissolved and suspended material from brackish water to render it potable.

Greenhouse A greenhouse is a transparent or semi transparent building that provides a modified environment for plant growth.

Heat Store A heat store returns solar heat for use at times when solar energy is unavailable or insufficient. A heat store can use sensible heat storage via the this temperature elevation of a solid or liquid media. Alternatively the use of phase change materials allows large thermal energy to be retained as latent heat around the phase transition temperature.

Solar cooker A solar cooker uses the incident solar radiation to directly or indirectly cook food.

> **Solar dryer** Solar dryers are a range of devices that convert solar energy to heat that is employed for drying.
> **Solar fraction** The solar fraction is the energy fraction of a total energy load that is met by solar energy conversion.
> **Solar Industrial Process Heat** Solar industrial process heat involves the use of solar heated steam, water or air in manufacturing.

3.17.1 Introduction

Mankind's earliest use of solar energy was probably the drying of food crops to aid their preservation. Open sun drying of fruit, vegetables, fish and meats often improved or enhanced particular flavors and textures such that solely because of those attributes many dried products remain in culinary use today, as examples, dried seaweed, sun-dried tomatoes, raisins and dried pistachio nuts. Open sun drying is displaced increasingly by glazed solar dryers that (i) enable equilibrium moisture content to be reached sooner and (ii) avoid losses of the crop to insects and rodents.

A further agricultural application, the greenhouse extended the use of solar energy from post-harvest to crop-production. Today greenhouses are ubiquitous with a huge variety of designs providing a wide range of modified climates for plant growth. Solar energy also finds use in agriculture in solar water pumping for irrigation and in the desalination of brackish water.

Solar cooking has taken the use of solar energy in the food production chain directly to the end-user. Broader industrial uses of solar energy have also tended to be linked to food and beverage production because the temperatures required can be satisfied readily in many climates by a well-designed solar thermal system. Non-agricultural technologies such as solar furnaces have considerable potential but have had limited practical use to-date.

This chapter discusses the attributes, contexts and applications of the full range of industrial and agricultural applications of solar heat.

3.17.2 Characteristics of Industrial and Agricultural Energy Use

3.17.2.1 Application Temperatures

The use of solar energy in a thermal nondomestic application should ideally be designed, installed, and operated to meet the specific energy and temperature requirements of the particular industrial or agricultural context via an optimal combination of efficient performance, high solar fraction, low initial and running costs, robustness and durability, safety, and environmental sustainability. Industrial processes vary greatly in their required processing temperatures [1]. **Figure 1** shows the percentage of process within the particular temperature ranges used by major industrial sectors. The form of presentation in **Figure 1** allows solar collectors classified by their type of tracking to be matched to their applicability or otherwise to processes in particular sectors. The data used in **Figure 1** are for the United States in 1980. Given the uncertainties associated with continuing global shifts in primary

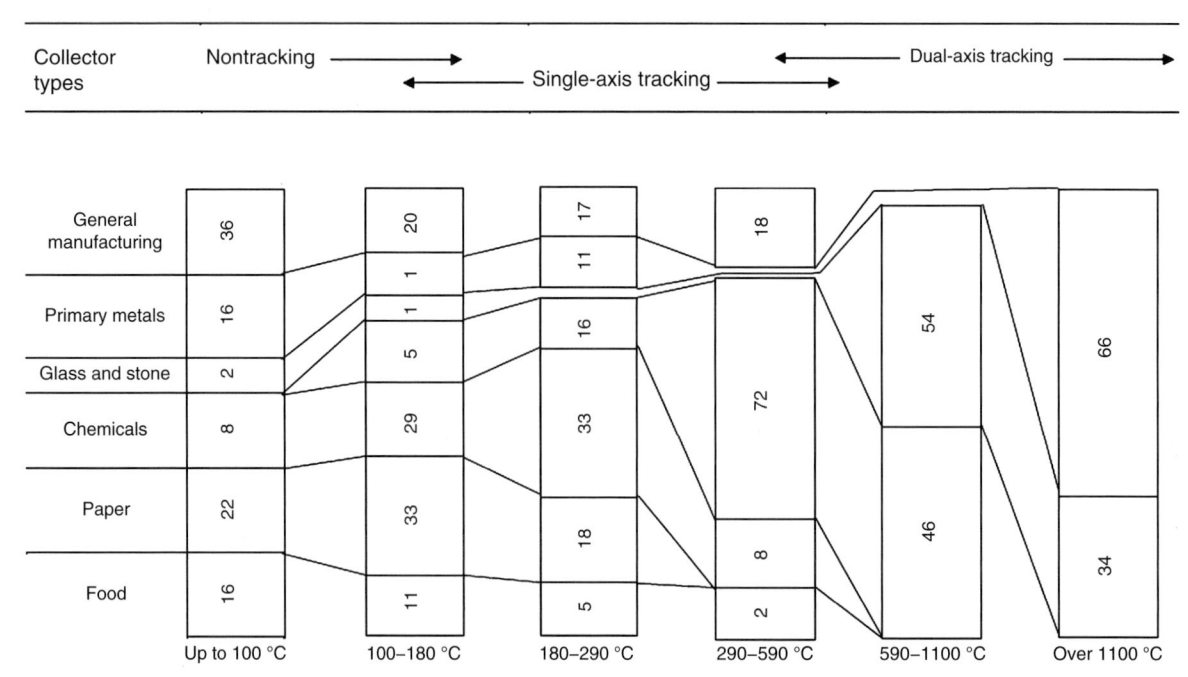

Figure 1 Processing temperatures for industrial sectors.

Table 1 Process temperatures in low- to medium-temperature solar industrial process applications

Sector	Process	Required temperature range (°C)
Food and beverages	Drying	30–90
	Washing	40–80
	Pasteurizing	80–110
	Boiling	95–105
	Sterilizing	140–150
	Heat treatment	40–60
	Preheating of feedwater to boilers	30–80
	Space heating of factories	30–100
Textiles	Washing	40–80
	Bleaching	60–100
	Dyeing	100–160
	Preheating of feedwater to boilers	30–80
	Space heating of factories	30–100
Chemicals	Boiling	95–105
	Distilling	110–300
	Ancillary processes	120–180
	Preheating of feedwater to boilers	30–80
	Space heating of factories	30–100

manufacturing capacity, the data presented in **Figure 1** are probably a reasonable illustration of the pattern of process temperatures associated with particular industry sectors that now prevails worldwide. As can be seen, nontracking collectors, of the flat-plate type (and at higher desired outlet temperature, of the evacuated-tube type) could find ready application across a broad range of sectors (except for the glass and stone processing industries) in the temperature range up to 180 °C.

A more detailed examination of low- to medium-temperature solar industrial processes is provided in **Table 1** [2].

At temperatures above 1100 °C, primary metal, glass, and stone production processes dominate and the processing temperatures necessary can only be met directly by solar energy if dual-axis tracking systems are employed to focus insolation onto a solar furnace.

3.17.2.2 Economics

At present, many solar thermal applications are viable economically when particular favorable circumstances of climate and use prevail. More would be so if, for those applications nearing economic viability, the economic externalities associated with the potential for solar energy applications to provide greenhouse gas abatement [3] were given tangible value by appropriate fiscal interventions. Most solar energy industrial and agricultural process heat applications generally employ mature technologies with a long history [4] whose engineering design is well understood [5–11]. The unreliability and irregularity of supply together with variable and often high cost of fossil fuels and electricity means that in many hot climates, particularly in remote and/or island locations, many thermal applications of solar energy in agriculture and industry are not only viable economically but are the obvious and preferred approach. The fact that they are not ubiquitous is due to two interlinked factors: (1) lack of widespread system component suppliers and associated design and installation expertise and experience and (2) the often large initial capital cost. The latter is a particular obstacle where the potential user does not have sufficient available capital and/or is unable or unwilling to borrow funds at favorable interest rates. However, often as a consequence of a diverse range of governmental market stimulation interventions internationally, the influences of such limiting behavioral, trading structure, and capital market factors are, in specific favorable contexts, now being superseded by recognition of the tangible commercial advantages of solar energy use. These include, for example, the often minimal or nonexistent recurrent outlays for fuel, leading to predictable running costs that are a hedge against inflationary energy costs adversely affecting business competitiveness.

3.17.3 Selection of Appropriate Solar Collector and Energy Storage Technologies

3.17.3.1 Collector Types

Instead of solar heat being provided by a separate and distinct solar energy collector, harnessing solar energy is often an inherent and intrinsic attribute of many agricultural systems that use solar energy, for example, greenhouses and integral solar dryers. Distinct solar energy collectors are usually employed in most industrial applications. Solar collectors can be either concentrating or flat-plate types and can be either stationary or can track solar position azimuthally (often using fairly simple sensors [12]) in either one or two axes. A classification of principal generic solar collector types is provided in **Figure 2**.

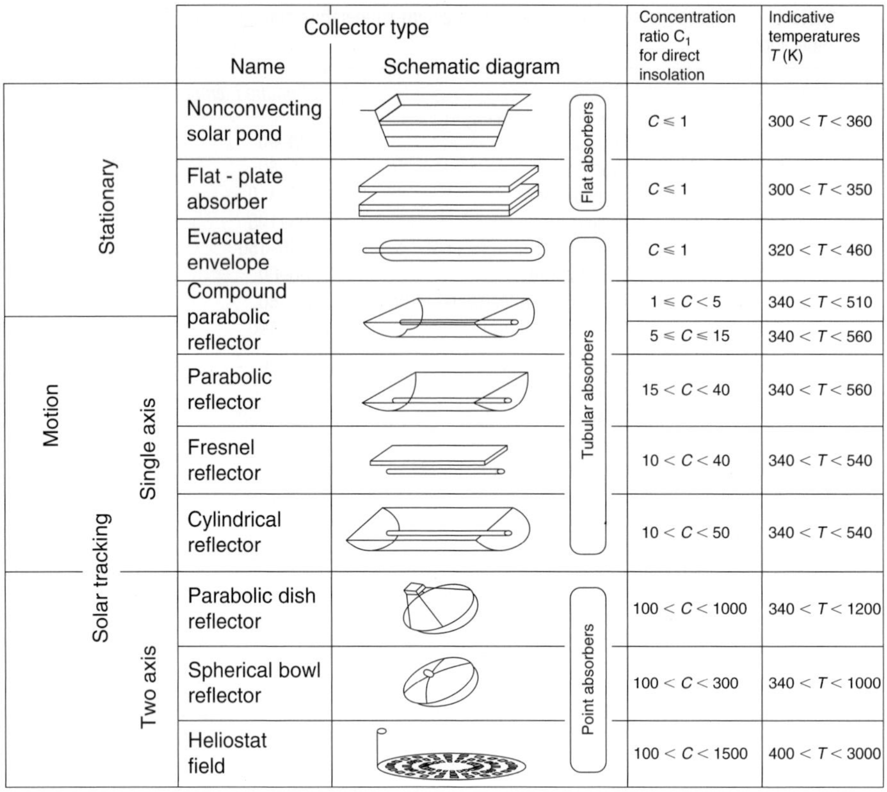

	Collector type		Concentration ratio C_1 for direct insolation	Indicative temperatures T (K)
	Name	Schematic diagram		
Stationary	Nonconvecting solar pond	Flat absorbers	$C \leq 1$	$300 < T < 360$
	Flat-plate absorber		$C \leq 1$	$300 < T < 350$
	Evacuated envelope	Tubular absorbers	$C \leq 1$	$320 < T < 460$
Motion / Single axis / Solar tracking	Compound parabolic reflector		$1 \leq C < 5$	$340 < T < 510$
			$5 \leq C \leq 15$	$340 < T < 560$
	Parabolic reflector		$15 < C < 40$	$340 < T < 560$
	Fresnel reflector		$10 < C < 40$	$340 < T < 540$
	Cylindrical reflector		$10 < C < 50$	$340 < T < 540$
Two axis	Parabolic dish reflector	Point absorbers	$100 < C < 1000$	$340 < T < 1200$
	Spherical bowl reflector		$100 < C < 300$	$340 < T < 1000$
	Heliostat field		$100 < C < 1500$	$400 < T < 3000$

Figure 2 Classification of solar collectors [8].

A flat-plate collector absorber plate gains heat from the incident insolation and transmits it to a working fluid, commonly air, water, aqueous glycol solution, or heat transfer oil. In an evacuated-tube collector, each absorber fin is enclosed in a separate cylindrical glass envelope. Evacuation of the envelope prevents convective heat loss from the absorber plate. The choice of the most appropriate collector depends on the temperature required for given applied conditions. For certain low-temperature applications, an unglazed collector may be the best option. For example, a liquid-film solar collector has been demonstrated for salt recovery from agricultural drainage water in the San Joaquin Valley in California, USA [13]. The absorber material in a flat-plate collector, in addition to having a high absorptance of the incident radiation, should also have a low emittance, provide good thermal conductivity, and be stable thermally under temperatures encountered during both operation and stagnation. It should also be durable, have low weight per unit area, and, most importantly, have a reasonably low initial installed capital cost. Apart from the last criterion, many solar collectors for agricultural applications often fail to meet these criteria as they are fabricated from materials that are readily available locally. However, the overriding factor in the choice of materials for the design of cheap and simple solar energy collectors, particularly those that heat air, is low initial cost; thus, in the actuality of practical system realization, certain ideal desired material properties will often inevitably be compromised.

3.17.3.2 Aperture Cover Materials

A good collector aperture cover material should have (1) a high transmittance for the incident insolation spectrum, (2) a low transmittance to infrared radiation in order to effectively trap re-radiated heat from the absorber, (3) for water heaters, stability at high temperatures under stagnation conditions, (4) resistance to breakage and damage, and (5) low cost. The variation of the radiative transmittance of a 'transparent' material is determined by its chemical composition, molecular structure, and method of fabrication. Glass with a low iron content is the most common aperture cover material for solar collectors. It is mostly transparent to insolation but as it is almost opaque to thermal radiation, re-radiation from the absorber plate is reduced. Improved thermal insulation of the aperture of higher temperature application solar collectors is achieved from the use of (1) multiple-glazed flat-plate solar collectors though each glass sheet increases optical losses, (2) vacuum tube solar collectors, and/or (3) increased concentration, rendering smaller the aperture area available to lose heat. Glass has high transmittance to visible light, low transmittance to infrared radiation, and stability at high temperatures [14]. However, it has a relatively high cost, low shatter resistance unless toughened, and relatively large weight per unit area, which also increases the cost of the supporting frames or structures required. This has encouraged the adoption of alternative cover materials such as plastics. However, the strength and flexibility of a plastic film normally depend on the polymer chain length: the longer the chains, the less brittle the material. There are several processes that act to break up long polymer chains that are typically several thousand monomers long. Degradation processes include

(1) thermal degradation, (2) photodegradation (both involving the migration of hydrogen atoms and the formation of free radicals, thus commonly resulting in depolymerization), (3) oxidation, also resulting in depolymerization, owing to the reaction with oxygen, especially at chain branches, and (4) mechanical degradation, owing to the mechanical breaking of chains, for example, tears, surface scratches, and repeated flexing. Although most plastic films have transmittances to visible light greater than 0.85, they exhibit very wide variations in transmittance to infrared from 0.01 for polymethyl methacrylate to 0.77 for polyethylene compared to 0.01 for glass. Some plastic materials exhibit translucent diffusion of incident direct-component insolation [15]. The major limitations of plastics are their poor physical stability at high water heating collector operating temperatures and their limited long-term durability primarily due to degradation under ultraviolet radiation. In applications that are open to the environment, condensation on the inner surface of a plastic cover reduces light transmission (when compared with glass) because of the higher angle of contact between water droplets and plastics. However, many plastics are available that have been treated chemically to overcome at least some of these shortcomings for a significant period of their use; for example, polymers containing fluorine compounds have radiation transmission properties and resistance to aging superior to those of polyethylene films. As plastics weigh typically about 10% of the same area of glass, collectors with plastic covers can be installed on roofs where extensive deployment of heavy collectors with glass apertures would exceed that particular roof's load limits.

3.17.3.3 Flat-Plate Absorbers

The plate and tubes of a flat-plate solar collector are usually made of copper or aluminum, whose high thermal conductivity ensures good heat transport to the heat transfer fluid. A high solar absorptance absorber plate surface should also, to reduce radiative losses, have a relative low emittance to thermal radiation. Such selective surfaces consist of either (1) a thin upper layer that is both highly absorbent to insolation and relatively transparent to thermal radiation; this layer is deposited on a high-reflective surface with low thermal radiation emittance, or (2) a nonselective highly absorbing material coated with a high solar transmittance and high infrared reflectance heat mirror. For example, the commonplace 'black chrome' selective surface is the result of microscopic chromium particles deposited on a metal substrate; long-wave thermal radiation is reflected by the chromium particles, but shorter wavelength insolation passes between the particles. Water heating applications in locations prone to subzero winter ambient temperatures are usually indirect systems with a closed circuit formed between the collector and a heat exchanger located in the store. To avoid winter frost damage in pipework, the heat transfer fluid used most commonly is an aqueous solution of propylene glycol with corrosion-preventing additives [16]. Propylene glycol should be used because it is less toxic than ethylene glycol.

3.17.3.4 Line-Axis Collectors

Evacuated-tube collectors use either direct flow or a heat pipe. With direct flow, the fluid in the primary loop passes through the absorber pipe. The advantage of this arrangement is that a heat exchanger is absent and thus its inefficiencies are avoided. In addition to water heating, direct flow evacuated-tube collectors can be used with heat transfer oils or for direct steam generation. When a heat pipe is used, the condensing fluid in the heat pipe relinquishes its heat to the fluid in the primary circuit via a heat exchanger. Parabolic troughs with concentration ratios ranging from 15 to 30 provide temperatures in the range of 250–400 °C, depending on a high direct component of insolation prevailing. Troughs with concentration ratios in the range 8–15 can heat fluids to output temperatures between 90 and 250 °C. The latter troughs have smaller aperture widths typically between 0.5 and 2.5 m. For aperture widths of up to 1.5 m, it is feasible to glaze the aperture as shown in **Figure 3** to (1) further reduce heat losses (though as evacuated-tube absorbers are invariably used at these temperatures, the heat retention advantage of additional glazing is minimal), (2) maintain high mirror reflectance and specularity as dust and dirt accrual is avoided, and (3) provide structural rigidity. Unfortunately, the inclusion of such an additional glazing also decreases the insolation transmitted to the collector.

For parabolic trough collectors, the whole system moves to track the sun. Alternative concentrator designs have been developed in which only either the reflector or the absorber moves to track the sun. Linear concentrating Fresnel mirror collectors employ an

Figure 3 Parabolic trough with aperture glazing.

Figure 4 Moving line-axis Fresnel reflectors focusing insolation onto a fixed absorber.

array of mirror strips each of which tracks the sun on a single axis to focus the direct component of incident insolation onto a stationary evacuated-tube absorber within a secondary concentrator as shown in **Figure 4**. As the absorber is stationary, no fluid couplings are required; this enhances reliability and reduces both initial and maintenance costs.

As the stationary absorber is the only component protruding prominently above the roof or ground level, the wind loading on the system is low. The mirror strips can be located close to each other without mutual shading, so less roof or ground space is wasted when compared with parabolic troughs that require a large spacing between each row of troughs to avoid mutual overshading. Linear concentrating Fresnel mirror collectors have been used for absorption chillers in Italy and Spain [17] and have been placed on a floating rotating base, which gives a two-axis tracking like in a system in Ras al-Khaimah in the United Arab Emirates [18].

In an alternative concept, a stationary arc section of a cylindrical mirror is used to produce a line focus that follows a circular trajectory as the solar incident angle changes. The absorber is moved to be coincident with this line focus [19, 20]. This system also makes efficient use of the available installation area but as a fluid-filled absorber is heavier than mirror strips, more energy is consumed in solar tracking than in a Fresnel mirror system. For systems where either the whole trough/absorber assembly or just the absorber tracks the sun, either flexible or coaxial couplings are required to convey the heated fluid from the absorber.

3.17.3.5 Nonconvecting Solar Panels

Nonconvecting stratified solar ponds are unitary solar energy collectors and heat stores in which part of the incident insolation absorbed is stored as heat in its lower regions [21]. A salt-gradient nonconvecting solar pond consists of three zones: (1) an upper-convecting zone (UCZ), of almost constant low salinity at close to ambient temperature and typically 0.3 m thick, is the result of evaporation, wind-induced mixing, and surface flushing; wave-suppressing surface meshes and nearby windbreaks keep the UCZ thin; (2) a nonconvecting zone (NCZ), in which a vertical salt gradient inhibits convection providing the thermal insulation that enables temperature to increase with depth; and (3) a lower-convecting zone (LCZ) of typically 20% salinity by weight at a high temperature in which heat is stored to provide interseasonal heat storage. Algae and cyanobacteria may be deposited by rain and airborne dust and thrive at the temperatures and salt concentrations prevailing in a solar pond. Both algae and cyanobacteria growth inhibit solar transmittance and the latter is toxic. To prevent algae formation, copper sulfate is added at a concentration of $1.5 \, \text{mg} \, \text{l}^{-1}$. A solar pond will only function with maintenance of the vertical salt gradient's stratification by controlling the overall salinity difference between the two convecting layers, inhibiting internal convection currents if they form in the NCZ, and limiting the total depth of the pond occupied by the UCZ. For increasingly deep ponds, the thermal capacity increases and annual variations of LCZ temperature decrease. However, the construction of deeper ponds increases both the initial capital outlay and start-up times. The unshaded site for a solar pond should be located close to a cheap source of salt and an adequate source of water, and the cost of land should be low. Nonconvecting solar ponds for industrial heat production tend to be large and so site excavations and preparations may typically account for more than 40% of the total capital cost.

3.17.4 System Component Layouts

3.17.4.1 Components

A solar energy industrial or agricultural process heat system comprises at the conceptual level a solar collector, intermediate heat storage, and a means of conveying the collected heat between these and to the application. An active system requires a pump to drive the heated fluid through the system, whereas a passive system requires no external power. The term 'integral systems' is used to describe installations where there are no distinct parts performing different functions. For example, in integral solar dryers and cookers, solar energy collection, storage, and use are concurrent in the same part of the system. Most solar hot water industrial and agricultural process heat applications are distributed systems defined as comprising a solar collector, hot water store, and connecting ducts or pipework; they may be either active or passive. The former would describe all medium- to large-scale systems. In a thermosiphon system, fluid flow is due to buoyancy forces produced by the difference in the densities of the fluid in the collector and that of the cooler fluid in the store or application chamber. The applications of thermosiphon solar hot water systems in this context are restricted to small-scale ancillary washing. The shallow solar pond is a low-cost modular, site-built, passive solar water heating system. Each module contains flat water bags on a layer of insulation or sand on the ground. In vineyards, a water-filled 'quilt' placed on the soil surface has been shown to provide effective protection against frost damage to the grapes [22].

The flow-through solar collectors in industrial process heat and agricultural applications are driven usually by a pump or fan. Operating a solar collector at a lower inlet temperature increases its efficiency since it reduces heat losses. The intermediate heat storage may also store heat generated from fossil fuels, and where this is the case, the long-term economically optimal magnitude of, and possibly the need for, the heat store has to be considered against the direct use of fossil fuels at times when there is no output from the solar energy system. The solar collector is selected usually in terms of how the predominant range of outlet temperatures is matched to that of the process heat requirement. Where, and/or at times when, the collector outlet temperature is less than that at the process inlet, additional heating is provided from a heat store or auxiliary sources. Many solar energy industrial and agricultural process applications do not include energy storage because either the diurnal heat load or its sub-daily duration is generally well matched to the available insolation or auxiliary heating may be provided more readily via the combustion of process by-products (e.g., in timber drying solar kilns, wood waste is often used for auxiliary heating). **Figures 5–12** show schematic diagrams of a range of generic process system layouts.

3.17.4.2 Generic Solar Industrial Process Heat System Layouts

The simple buoyancy-driven arrangement without recirculation shown schematically in **Figure 5** is found typically in simple cabinet dryers. The introduction of a fan, as shown in **Figure 6**, is necessary in large industrial-scale dryers to overcome the resistance to fluid flow present even when large-diameter duct work is employed. The arrangement in **Figure 6** is also used for unglazed transpired air heating solar collectors. As these provide large volumes of warmed air, they are particularly suited to applications with large air

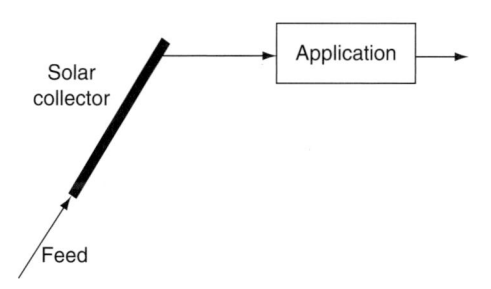

Figure 5 Buoyancy-driven system with heat stored in the application subsystem.

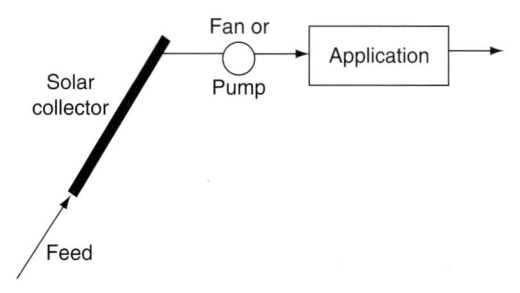

Figure 6 Forced circulation system with heat stored in the application subsystem.

574 **Applications**

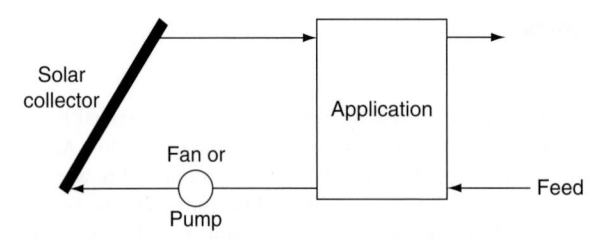

Figure 7 Forced circulation system with return recirculation of the working fluid to the collector.

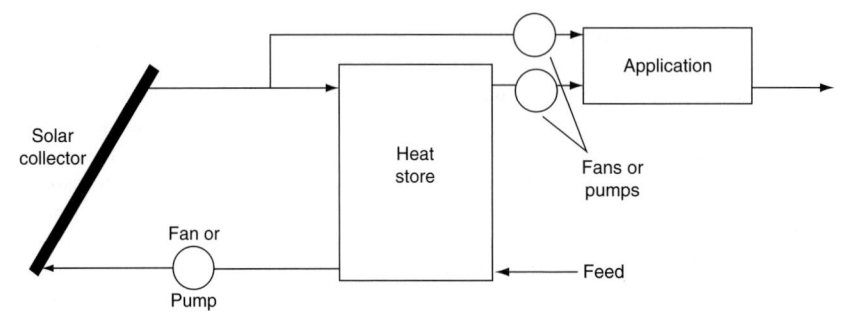

Figure 8 Forced circulation with dedicated heat storage.

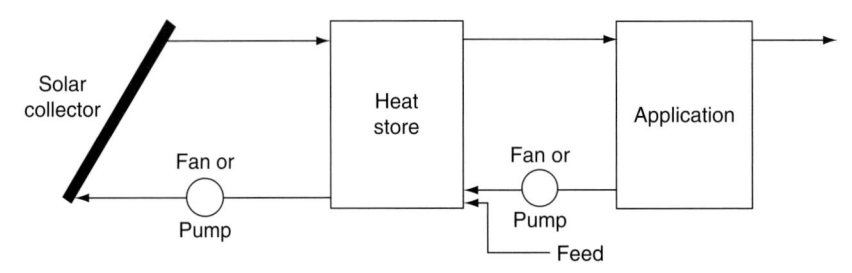

Figure 9 Forced circulation system with recirculation from the store to the collector and from the application to the store.

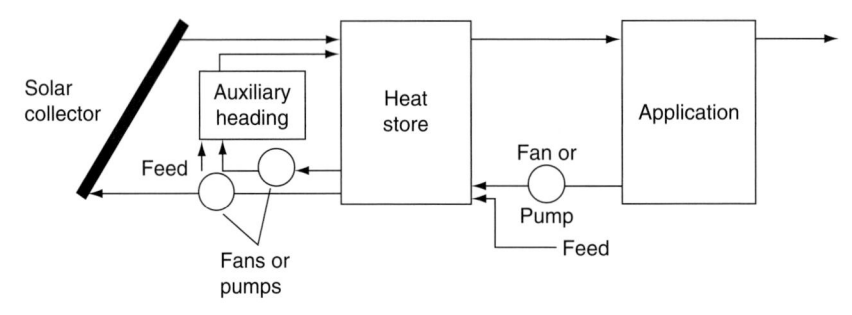

Figure 10 Forced circulation with auxiliary heating of the heat store.

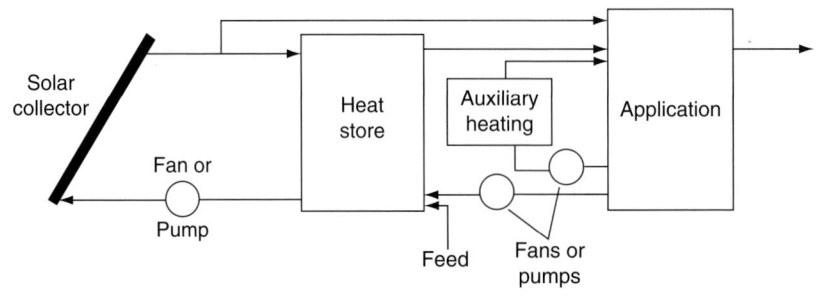

Figure 11 Forced circulation system with auxiliary heating of the application and heat storage.

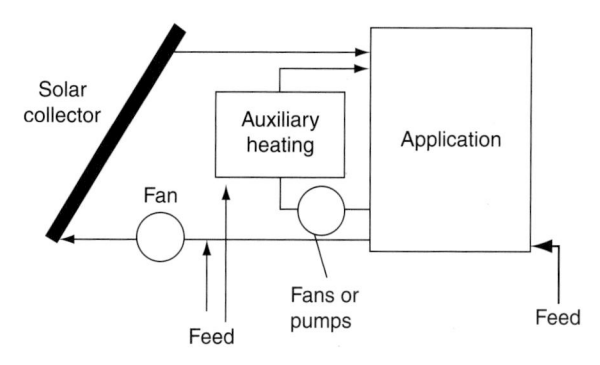

Figure 12 Forced circulation system with auxiliary heating but no dedicated heat storage.

change rates such as the space heating of paint shops. It is preferable in remote locations for the fan or pump shown in **Figures 6–12** to be powered by a photovoltaic array. The photovoltaic array provides power to the fan or pump when receiving insolation. No battery is required as the system would not be operated when there is no insolation. The use of a direct current fan or pump obviates the need for, and cost of, including a DC to AC inverter.

The arrangement illustrated in **Figure 7** may also be found in air heating applications such as drying or the heating of livestock buildings. **Figure 7** also shows the arrangement found typically in most domestic solar water heaters, and is equally applicable to similarly scaled washing and cleaning hot water demands in small enterprises. Water heating systems of the form shown in **Figures 7** and **8** will also have other critical components; these include (1) temperature sensors located at the collector inlet and outlet connected to a differential controller that activates the pump at a preset temperature difference, (2) a header tank or other mains pressure controller, (3) in an indirect system, a heat exchanger in the heat store, and (4) pressure relief and nonreturn valves. The colder replenishing fluid enters at the base of the heat store to maintain thermal stratification. Sensible heat storage media are water and for air heating systems, a rock bed or water; in the latter case, an air-to-water heat exchanger is introduced into the secondary circuit.

In the system shown in **Figure 8**, heat from the collector or the store is conveyed to the application and the fluid then rejected to the ambient environment. The arrangement in **Figure 8** would be applicable to intermittent batch processes that would take place only when sufficient fluid has been heated to the required temperature.

In many cases, the fluid may retain some heat after its use in the application. Where this is the case, as shown in **Figure 9**, some or all of the fluid is recirculated from the application to the base of the store. The proportion of fluid rejected and recirculated can be either fixed or, as is more frequent, altered over time to achieve optimal process conditions. This often requires the extensive deployment of sensors, valves, and controllers in various parts of the layout.

When solar energy is insufficient to meet a heat load either directly or via storage, auxiliary heating is required. It can be introduced into the system layout in the primary circuit as shown in **Figure 10**, often supplying an additional heat exchanger in the heat store, or for smaller hot water systems, an additional immersed electrical heating element is provided.

Auxiliary heating can also be introduced into a secondary circuit as shown in **Figure 11**. This layout is common where solar heating is retrofitted to an existing process heat system. Not all aspects of the generic layout shown will be present in particular practical examples. The facility to bypass the store so as to connect the collector directly to the application may often be omitted. This omission can lead, however, to operational inflexibility.

In the system shown in **Figure 12**, the solar heat is used when available, with auxiliary heating being used at all other times. Not all of the feed options illustrated will be present or (where they are) used in particular practical systems. Certain feed options may come into use only to maintain operation when a particular circuit is undergoing routine maintenance or inspection. The layout in **Figure 12** will arise when the life-cycle costs of providing a heat store are higher than those for auxiliary heating. This can be the case for air heating systems where rock-bed stores incur high initial cost due to their heat transfer inefficiency and scale. The layout in **Figure 12** without recirculation and auxiliary heating reduces to that shown in **Figure 6**.

3.17.4.3 Real Solar Industrial Process Heat Systems

Real system layouts for industrial processes are rarely as simple as those shown schematically in **Figures 5–12**. An illustrative example of a practical layout for a solar-heated brewing process is shown in **Figure 13**.

Relatively small-scale batch brewing is undertaken using the system shown in **Figure 13**. Double-glazed collectors of 20 m^2 feed a 1 m^3 hot water store. The brewing vessel volume of 400 l enables around 40 000 l of beer to be produced annually. The system has been in operation since June 2006. The detailed layout of another closed-loop two-tank system shown in **Figure 14** illustrates the typical locations of the valves, sensors, and drains required in practical installations. Local building codes and regulations for the installation of water heating systems will apply. In contrast, the legal requirements for the installation and operation of air heating systems are much less onerous and may be nonexistent in some jurisdictions.

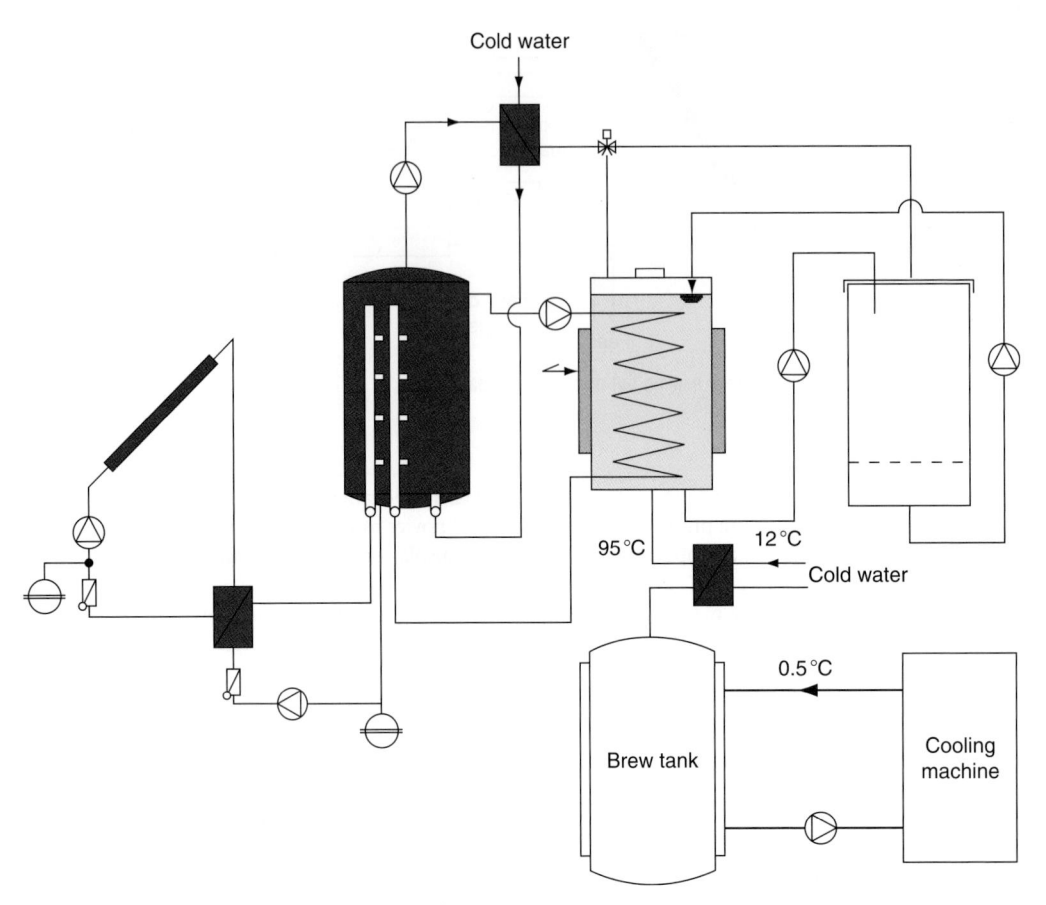

Figure 13 Layout of the Neuwirth solar-heated brewery in Austria.

3.17.4.4 Operational Limits

In solar process heat applications where sensible energy storage is present, it has tended to be both low temperature and low energy density leading to large physical size leading to high initial cost. Water is the preferred sensible heat storage media for which maintaining good outlet discharge temperatures requires thermal stratification [23]. Only occasionally have higher energy density latent or chemical energy storage systems been used: certain types of both the systems are unproven as to the resilience of their energy storage properties after many phase change or chemical reaction cycles, respectively. The use of phase change materials requires careful selection of materials to avoid rapid corrosion [24]. For processes that continue during the night or during periods of insufficient insolation, providing auxiliary heating has been frequently found to be more viable economically than providing sufficient energy storage that would enable solar fractions close to unity to be achieved. An exception is the concomitant solar energy collection and storage provided by a nonconvecting solar pond.

Auxiliary heating is also required where the magnitude and duration of the direct component are insufficient to render feasible a concentrating solar energy collector providing directly the higher application temperatures desired. Flat-plate collectors and evacuated-tube collectors will only provide the temperatures indicated in **Figure 2** when the incident insolation has reached a sufficient intensity, and for concentrating collectors the desired outlet temperature is attained only when the direct component of insolation is above a particular intensity. Thus, both the duration of solar-only operation and the range of suitable geographic locations become increasingly limited as the temperature of the application increases. These geographic limitations have been illustrated for flat-plate solar water heating in Europe [25, 26], an example of which is shown in **Figure 15**.

Figure 15 is indicative of the number of days that solar-only operation of a 45 °C batch process (e.g., washing or low-temperature drying) would be possible using system layouts similar to those shown in **Figures 8** and **9** for European locations.

Nonimaging compound parabolic trough medium-temperature solar collectors can exploit a greater part of the available diffuse insolation compared with a parabolic trough collector, although this advantage diminishes as the concentration ratio increases [5].

Many higher temperature industrial processes use steam. Direct steam generation (usually, parabolic trough) solar collectors, intended for electricity production, remove the need to include a heat transfer oil and oil-to-steam heat exchanger when generating steam from a solar thermal system. Again, system control is an important issue; however, the practical limiting factor to the diffusion of this technology is the commercial availability of absorber tubes coated with high-temperature selective surfaces. To reduce costs, the environmental impact of solar energy use in the cement industry has been examined closely. In the dry cement production process, the preliminary partial drying of materials with high moisture content is a promising use of solar energy.

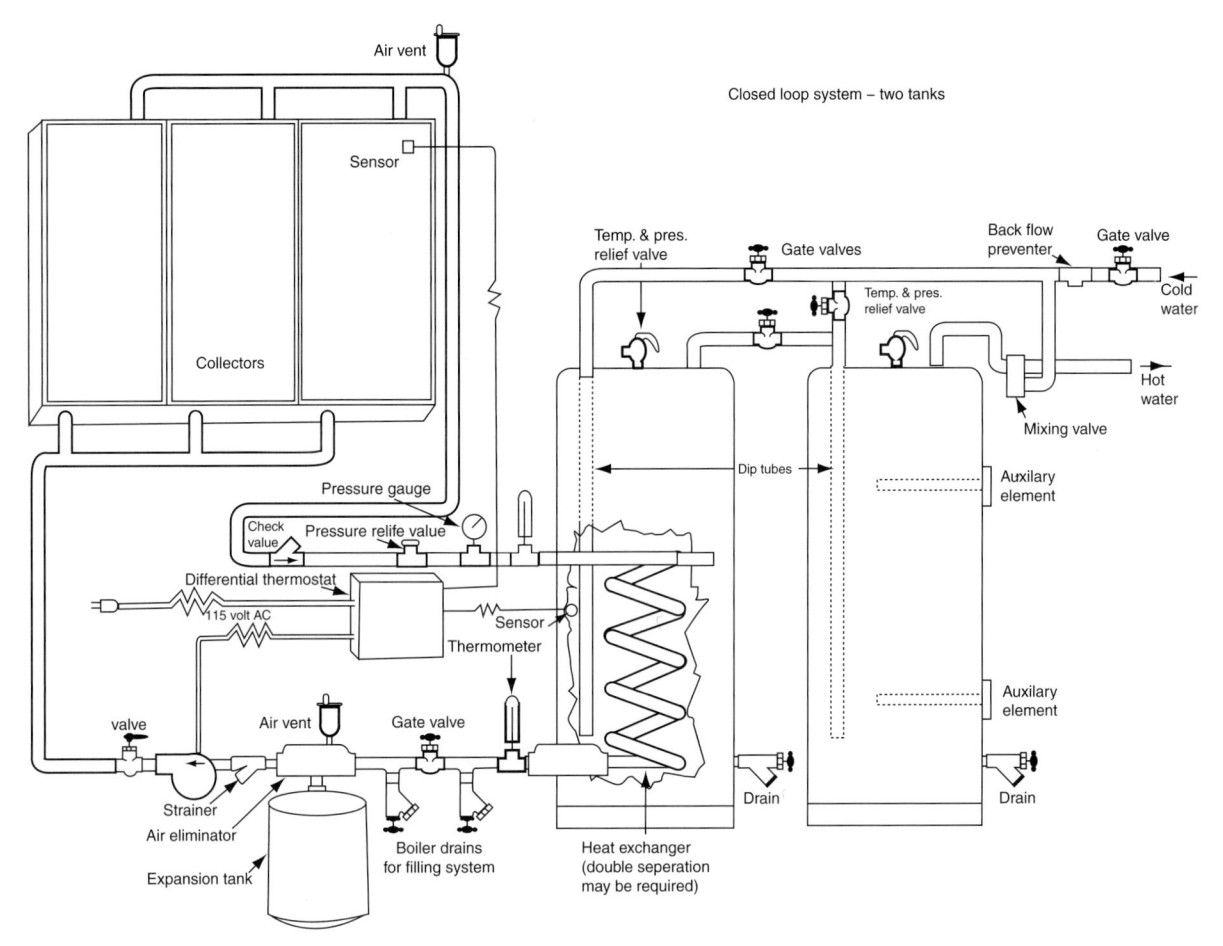

Figure 14 Detailed layout of a closed-loop two-tank system.

To obtain higher temperatures than provided solely by a solar collector, either additional auxiliary heating or thermodynamic conversion is necessary. An example of the latter is heat provided by solar collectors being used to evaporate the working fluid in the evaporator of a heat pump and transfer of heat from a colder reservoir to a warmer reservoir. During the compression, the temperature of the heat pump working fluid increases to well above the temperature provided by the solar collector. During condensation, heat is rejected at a higher temperature to an industrial process heat system or to provide space heating in a glasshouse.

3.17.5 Solar Hot Water Industrial and Agricultural Process Heat System Design

3.17.5.1 Conceptual Distinctions

Designing a process heat application that can successfully harness solar energy requires a different conceptual approach from that used typically to design systems that combust fossil fuels. Component sizing and specification together with the choice of control parameters and algorithms have to account for diurnal and annual variations in insolation as well as changes in ambient temperature, humidity, and, in certain circumstances, wind speed. Linked with this, another distinguishing aspect of solar process heating systems is that usually the system control strategy is coupled strongly to collecting the maximum input of solar energy as well as, and often more so than, to satisfying the load. Specifically, a pump or fan for circulating water or air, respectively, through the collector will be activated when a threshold value of insolation is reached that enables the collector to provide a net heat output. In many fossil fuel-heated industrial processes, the control regime seeks to reduce the heat input when the load is satisfied. In contrast, for solar energy systems, discontinuous activations of pumps or fans to maintain an order of precedence of the use of thermal energy first from solar collectors, second from heat stores, and finally from auxiliary heat inputs characterize the control regimes of many solar industrial process heat systems. With the exception of large-scale dryers of high-value products, agricultural systems generally tend to be simpler and thus easier to design, as the process conditions required are often not tightly specified.

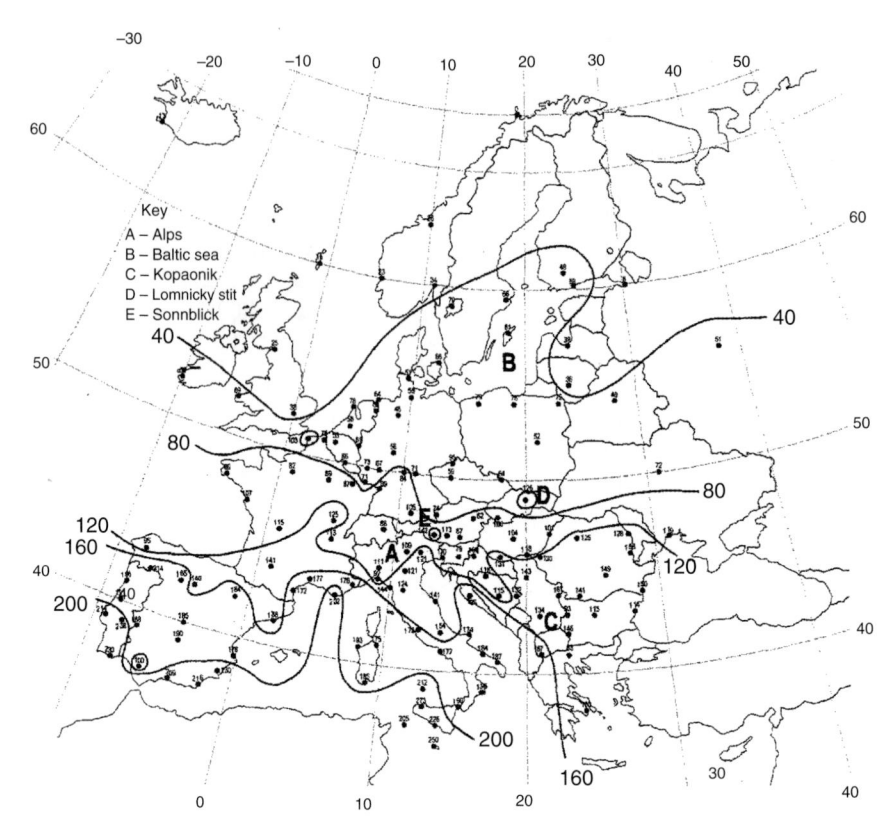

Figure 15 Contour maps of the number of days in a year for which the temperature of solar-heated water in a storage tank reaches or exceeds 45 °C for Europe [25].

3.17.5.2 Design Methodologies

A wide variety of methodologies are available for the sizing of system components and determining the optimal operating parameters to satisfy a known set of characteristics of the energy load. These methodologies can be classified as utilizability, empirical correlations, simplified analysis, semi-analytical simulation, stochastic simulation, simplified representative-day simulations, and detailed hour-by-hour simulations. Each of these will be considered individually.

Utilizability approaches are based on determining a minimum threshold insolation at which the solar heat gained by a collector corresponds to its heat losses at a particular ambient temperature. Only above this minimum insolation threshold does the collector provide a useful heat output. Utilizability is a statistical property of the location-specific variation of insolation over a given duration. For example, hourly utilizability is the fraction of hourly incident insolation that can be converted to heat by a collector with ideal heat removal and no optical losses. As all solar collectors have heat losses (otherwise, the threshold insolation would always be zero), utilizability always has a value of less than 1. Utilizability can be related to other statistical properties of diurnal and annual patterns of insolation [27–30] to produce expressions to which specific collector parameters can be attached. Generalized expressions can then be derived, for example, for the yearly total energy delivered by flat-plate collectors whose tilt angles equaled the latitude of their notional location [31]. Although this approach can certainly be useful in initial conceptual and evaluative stages of design, it has inherent limitations. The limitations include (1) the limited accuracy (or otherwise) of underlying insolation data correlations employed, (2) limited portability of design outcome to new locations as utilizability correlations apply to specific locations, particular months and hours within them, and set collector inclinations and orientation, and (3) as only solar collector output is predicted, it should only be applied to industrial and agricultural processes with interseasonal thermal storage where collector inlet temperatures are independent of the very large thermal store mass required [32]. The method has been extended to use two monthly utilizabilities corresponding to those radiation levels that give minimum and maximum operating temperatures [33].

Approaches based on the use of empirical correlations are founded on the reasonable expectation that for a given solar energy process heat system, greater insolation will lead to a larger proportion of the heat load being met by solar energy. Using extensive detailed simulations, design charts have been produced that relate a dimensionless or normalized solar energy input to a similarly parameterized output for a given system configuration, for example the 'F-chart' method [34, 35]. The main drawback of such methods is that accuracy depends on how closely the putative system layout and component specifications correspond with those of the system from which correlations were obtained.

Simplified analyses consider solely the key driving parameters of system performance assuming that all other variables are constant. For solar industrial heat loads that over the operating period have largely constant flow rates and temperatures, simplified analyses have been developed that can be employed for feasibility and initial design of industrial hot water systems with heat storage [36] and industrial steam systems [37]. Simplified analyses maintain a logical physical basis for the relationships between parameters that are largely lost in empirical correlations whose equations are of the form of polynominal curve fits.

Semi-analytical simulations use detailed numerical models. However, rather than undertaking hour-by-hour (or similarly discrete time step) calculations using insolation, ambient temperature, and load data, in this approach, sinusoidal and linear functions are usually used to describe the insolation and load, respectively, with ambient temperature either varying sinusoidally or remaining constant. This approach has largely been superseded by hour-by-hour analysis, as the computing resources required to successfully undertake hour-by-hour analysis have become widely available.

A fairly detailed analysis of a representative pressurized hot water solar industrial process system was undertaken to determine curves that define constant solar fractions on graphs of solar collector area against heat storage volume [38]. This approach has been employed to develop a system optimization tool.

In stochastic simulations, Markov chain models are produced to represent insolation, ambient temperature, and load characteristics from hour-by-hour data collected over several years for a specific location. Although long-term system behavior can be determined readily from the transition probability matrices, the method has been rarely, if ever, used in design. Representative-day simulations involve the selection of a meteorologically typical day (or days) within the operating season of the solar industrial or agricultural process heat system. A variety of simulation models may then be employed to determine the outputs of systems with differing layouts, component specifications, and control regimes.

Detailed hour-by-hour simulations are undertaken using mainly well-developed and supported software. The most commonly used solar energy system simulation software is TRNSYS [39] either in its widely available freeware form or as a kernel accessed through a proprietory graphical user interface. It includes ordinary differential and algebraic equations that describe each system component and a differential equation solver. TRNSYS has obtained this ubiquity through (1) its association with authors of one of the seminal textbooks in solar thermal applications [7], (2) its modular structure, which enables easy description of system component interactions via the matching of their respective outputs and inputs via the construction of an information flow diagram, (3) the wide range of component models available, and (4) the fact that should a model for a particular desired component be unavailable, a user can develop a program to simulate that component. The TRNSYS information flow diagram has a similar notional relationship to the actual layout of components as a process flow diagram would have in a chemical engineering process simulation [40]. When appropriate hourly insolation and ambient temperature data and a realistic description of the heat load are available, simulation tools such as TRNSYS can give very accurate predictions of the performance of solar industrial process heat systems. However, to determine the economically optimal combination of system components, many simulations are required. In reality, this use of simulation software is limited to (1) obtaining the final detailed design, (2) developing design correlations, or (3) addressing research issues in systems and components. Artificial intelligence methods have been demonstrated to successfully determine economically optimal designs for a simple, but representative, solar industrial process heat system [41].

3.17.6 Solar Drying Technologies

3.17.6.1 Solar Drying Processes

The objective in drying is to reduce the moisture content, usually that of an agricultural product, to a certain level that prevents deterioration within a duration of time regarded as the safe storage period. Drying is the dual process of (1) heat transfer to the product from the heating source and (2) mass transfer of moisture from the interior of the product to its surface and from the surface to the surrounding air. In solar drying, solar energy is used either as the sole source of the required heat or as a supplemental source, and the air flow can be generated by either forced or natural convection. The heating procedure could involve the passage of preheated air through the product, directly exposing the product to solar radiation, or often a combination of both. The major requirement is the transfer of heat to the moist product by convection and conduction from the surrounding air mass at temperatures above that of the product, by radiation mainly from the sun and/or to an extent from the surrounding hot surfaces, or by conduction from heated surfaces in contact with the product. Water starts to vaporize from the surface of the moist product, for example, crop, when the absorbed energy has increased its temperature sufficiently for the water vapor pressure of the crop moisture to exceed the vapor pressure of the surrounding air. The rate of moisture replenishment to the surface by diffusion from the interior depends largely on the nature of the product and its moisture content. If diffusion rate is slow, it becomes the limiting factor in the rate of the drying process, but if it is sufficiently rapid, the controlling factor becomes the rate of evaporation at the product surface. Both the moisture diffusion and convective mass transfer coefficients increase with temperature, although the rate will depend on how the crop is prepared for drying, that is, whether it is peeled and/or sliced. For example, large differences, particularly for convective mass coefficients, have been found between the drying kinetics of cylindrical and sliced potatoes [42]. The solar absorptance of the product is important in direct solar drying; most agricultural materials have relatively high absorptances of between 0.67 and 0.81. Heat transfer and evaporation rates must be controlled closely for an optimum combination of drying rate and acceptable final product quality.

Examples of 'open-sun' drying are shown in **Figure 16**. Although widespread, it has inherent limitations: high crop losses can ensue from inadequate drying, fungal attacks, and rodent and insect encroachment.

Figure 16 Examples of open-sun drying in Nigeria.

3.17.6.2 Solar Dryer Types

The different types of solar energy crop dryers [43] are classified taxonomically as shown in **Figure 17**.

The distinguishing features of different types of solar energy dryers are shown in **Figure 18**.

The advantages of solar dryers over traditional open-sun drying include (1) a smaller area of land in order to dry similar amounts of crop, (2) relatively high quality of dry crop, because insects and rodents are unlikely to infest it during drying, (3) shortened drying period, (4) protection from sudden rain, and (5) low capital and running costs.

Simple integral-type natural circulation solar energy dryers are cheaper to construct than distributed-type solar energy dryers of similar capacity. However, as natural circulation solar energy dryers are liable to localized overheating and show relatively slow overall drying rates, a solar chimney is often employed to provide enhanced buoyant force on the airstream [44], thereby increasing the rate at which dry air enters. Drying times to achieve safe storage moisture content for a variety of tropical crops have been shown experimentally to be reduced by over 20% when greenhouse drying with a solar chimney is compared to open-air drying under Brazilian conditions [45]. Detailed studies have been undertaken of passive solar dryers incorporating an air heating solar collector, transparent-walled drying chamber, and solar chimney [46].

Cabinet dryers are, usually, relatively small units used typically to preserve domestic quantities of fruits, vegetables, fish, and meat. Solar radiation is transmitted through the cover and is absorbed on the blackened interior surfaces as well as by the product itself. Holes located at both the upper and base of the cabinet's sides allow warmed moist air to leave and replenishing fresh air to be drawn in, respectively, under the action of buoyant forces. Shallow layers of the product are placed on perforated or mesh trays inside the enclosure. Cabinet dryers are almost invariably constructed from materials available locally. As cabinet dryers can exhibit poor air circulation, poor moist air removal results in both slow drying rates and very high internal temperatures of between 70 and

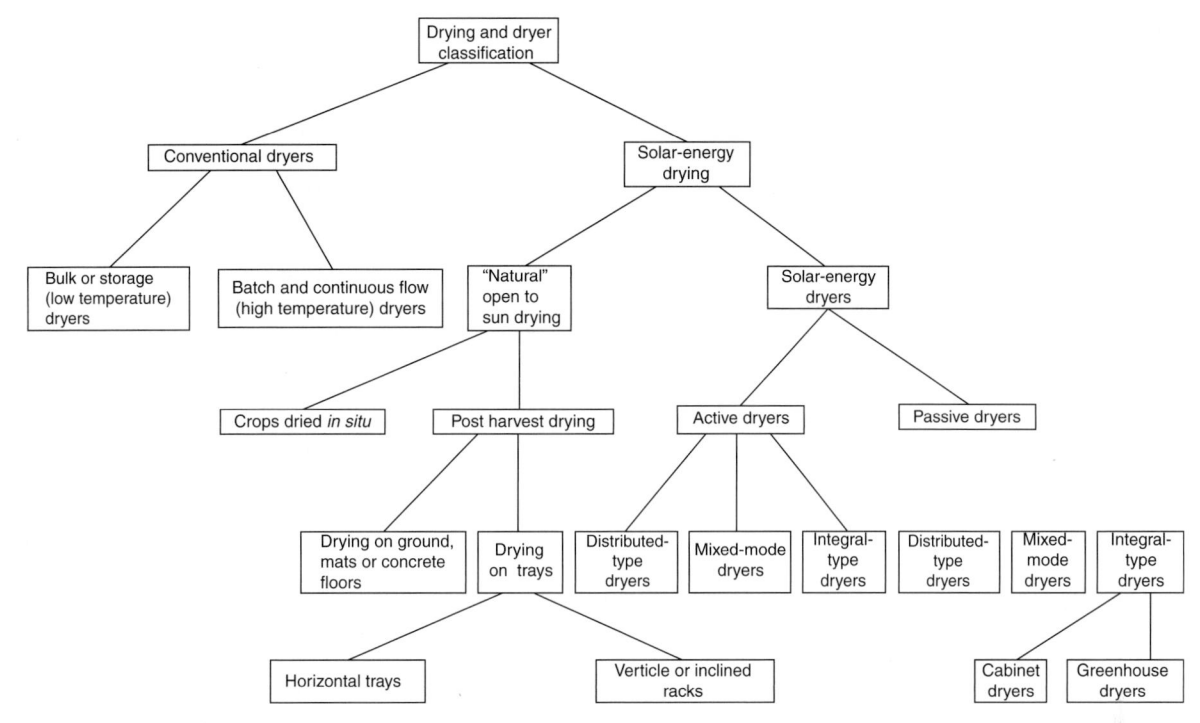

Figure 17 Taxonomy of solar energy dryers.

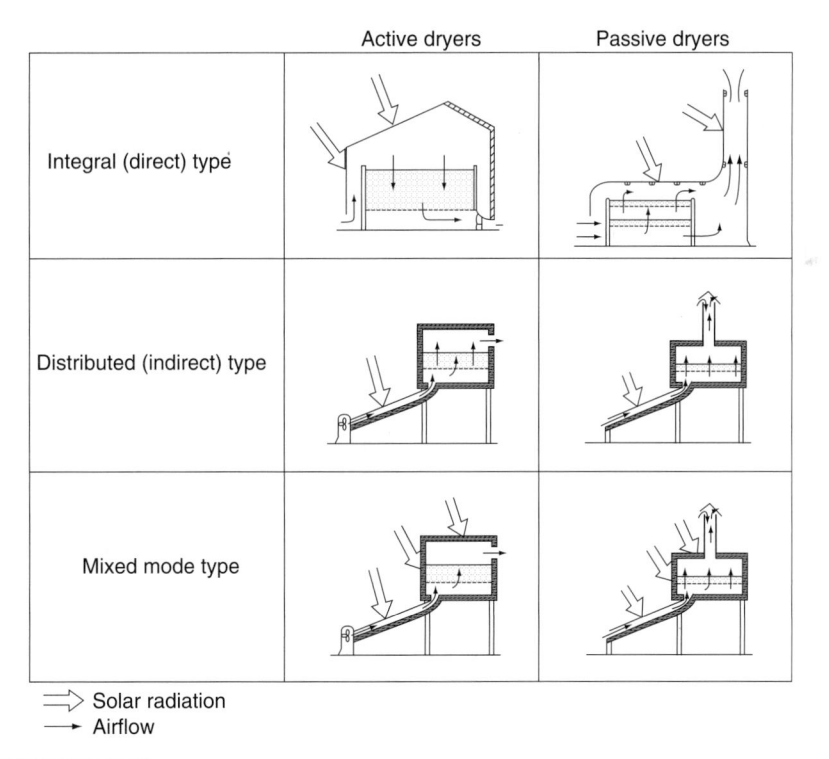

Figure 18 Features of solar energy dryers.

100 °C, which can spoil perishables, fruits and vegetables, by overheating. Relatively large air inlet and outlet ducts, so as to incur a low pressure drop, together with the addition of a solar chimney are recommended to ensure adequate air circulation.

Natural circulation solar energy greenhouse dryers are larger than most cabinet dryers and are characterized by extensive, usually plastic, glazing on their sides. Insulating panels may be drawn over the glazing at night to reduce heat losses and heat storage may also be provided; although in practice, both these features are rare. A solar greenhouse dryer is more appropriate for large-scale drying, as it gives greater control over the drying process than the solar cabinet dryer.

3.17.6.3 Practical Issues in the Use of Solar Dryers

The performance of natural circulation solar dryers can be compromised by very high ambient humidity during the wet season [47]: as can be seen in **Figure 19**, at night the 'dry' air temperature can fall below the prevailing ambient temperature.

This leads, as shown in **Figure 20**, to relatively moist air being entrained into the dryer and nocturnal reabsorption of moisture by the product.

For crops that require low safe storage moisture contents, drying times can be many days as shown in **Figure 21** depending on the dryer's operating temperature.

Direct absorption of solar radiation enhances the proper color 'ripening' of greenish fruits by allowing, during dehydration, the decomposition of residual chlorophyll. For certain varieties of grapes and dates, exposure to sunlight is considered essential for the development of the required color in the dried products. A period of exposure to sunlight of Arabica coffee is thought to give full flavor in the roasted bean. However, insolation entering a process chamber can directly (1) cause different rates of heating due to internal radiant temperature asymmetry and (2) shorten the durability of internal components due to ultraviolet exposure and overheating. For some fruits, exposure to sun reduces the vitamin content considerably. Color retention in some highly pigmented commodities can also be affected adversely by direct exposure to sunlight, although solar tunnel dryers have been used to dry, and retain color in, chillies [48]. The limited concentration of incident insolation provided by reflection from an inclined north wall (at latitude 30.56 °N) reduced drying time when drying bitter gourd slices in a greenhouse solar dryer [49]. Greenhouse dryers have employed photovoltaic-powered ventilation [50] and incorporated photovoltaic/thermal collectors [51]. A photovoltaic array has also been employed to power the fan and control systems in dryers with separate air heating solar collectors [52]. Dynamic control is essential if a crop dryer is to achieve the desired process conditions under varying insolation. In solar wood drying, it is necessary to control the interactions of insolation, ambient humidity, wood species characteristics, and variability in the initial moisture content [28, 53].

3.17.6.3.1 Analysis of solar dryers

A mathematical model elaborated here follows that developed by Janjai *et al.* [50] for predicting the performance of a greenhouse dryer. In developing the model, the following were assumed:

1. There is uniformly mixed air inside the dryer.
2. Crop drying behavior can be represented by thin-layer drying correlations.
3. Specific heat capacities of air, cover, ground, and product are constant.
4. The fraction of solar radiation lost through the north wall is negligible and absorptivity of air is negligible.
5. A time interval is employed in the numerical solution of the system of equations that ensures that constant air conditions prevail.

The rate at which energy is stored in the cover is equal to the convective heat energy transfer rate between the air inside the dryer and the cover, plus the rate of radiation heat transfer between the sky and the cover, the thermal convecture heat transfer rate between the cover and ambient air, the radiation heat transfer rate between the crop and the cover, and the rate of solar radiation absorbed by the cover. This energy balance of a greenhouse dryer cover [50] is expressed as

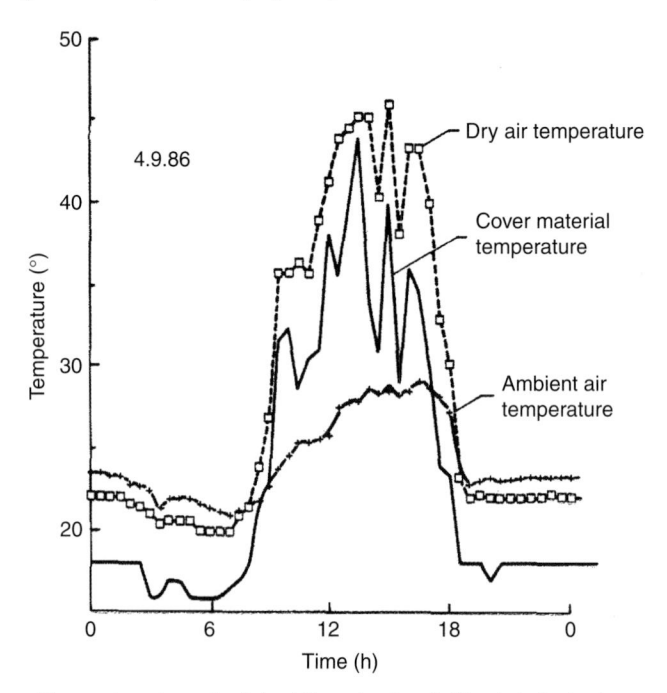

Figure 19 Typical diurnal variation of temperatures in a natural circulation solar dryer in Nigeria in September.

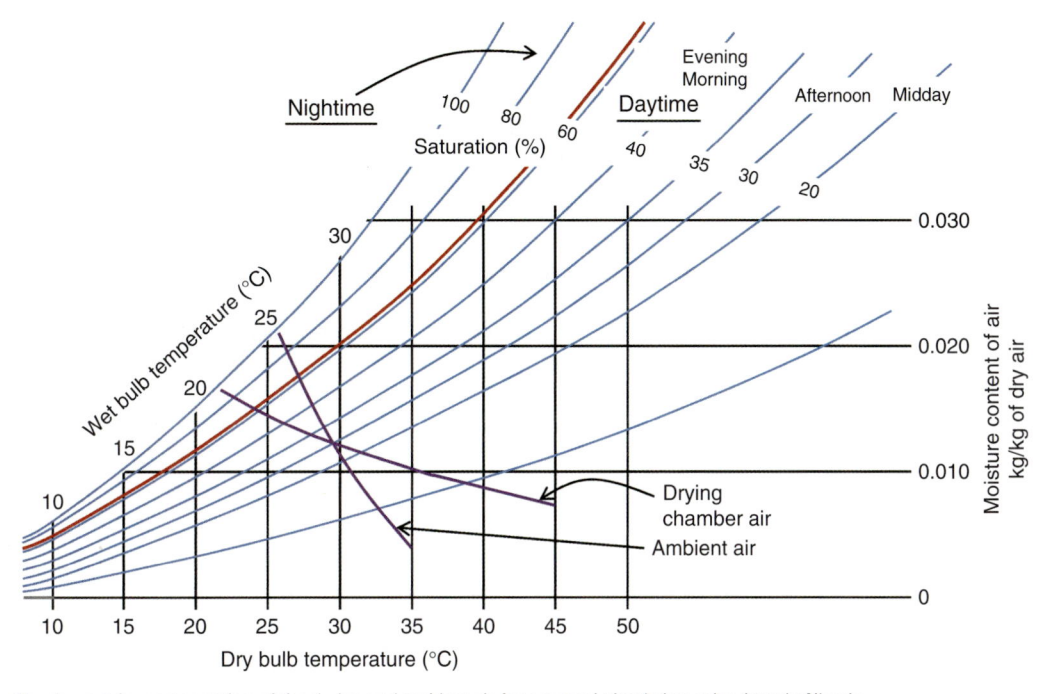

Figure 20 Psychrometric representation of the drying and ambient air for a natural circulation solar dryer in Nigeria.

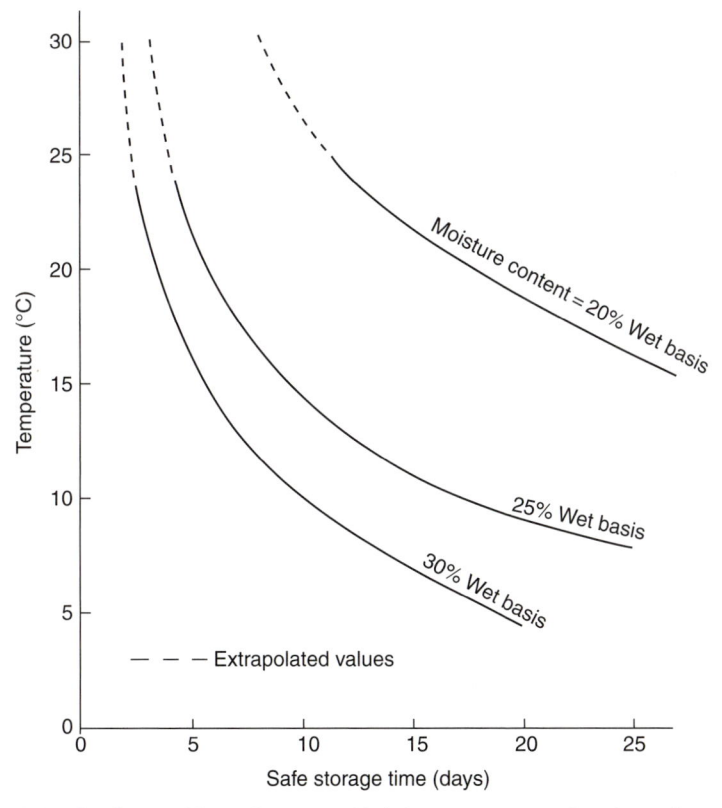

Figure 21 The variation of the drying duration to achieve safe storage with drying temperatures and product moisture contents.

$$m_c C_{pc} \frac{dT_c}{dt} = A_c h_{c,c-a}(T_a - T_c) + A_c h_{r,c-s}(T_s - T_c) + A_c h_w(T_{am} - T_c) + A_p h_{r,p-c}(T_p - T_c) + A_c \alpha_c I_t \qquad [1]$$

where C_{pc} is the specific heat capacity of the cover (J kg^{-1} K^{-1}); m_c is the mass of the cover; T_a, T_{am}, T_c, T_p, and T_s are the temperatures (K) of the internal air, ambient, cover, product, and sky, respectively; A_c and A_p are the areas (m^2) of the cover and product, respectively; h is the relevant heat transfer coefficient (W m^{-2} K^{-1}) (with radiative heat transfer coefficient, h_r, calculated by iteration for the applicable temperature range); I_t is the insolation (W m^{-2}); and α_c is the absorptance of the cover. The energy balance of the air within the layer is equal to the rates of convective heat transfer between the crop and air and floor and air, plus the sensible heat transfer from the crop to air plus the heat associated with flow of air in and out of the dryer taking account of heat loss from air in the layer to ambient and solar energy collected as in eqn [2] where m_a and C_{pa} are the mass and specific heat of air in kg and J kg^{-1} K^{-1}, respectively; M_p, ρ, A_p, D_p, T_p, and C_{pp} are the mass, density, area, depth, temperature, and specific heat capacity of the product in kg, kg m^{-3}, m^2, m, K, and J kg^{-1} K^{-1}, respectively; α_f, A_f, and T_f apply to the floor; V_{in} and V_{out} are the inlet and outlet flow rates (m^3 s^{-1}), respectively; and T_{in} and T_{out} are the corresponding temperatures (K). F_p is the fraction of insolation incident on the product and I_1 is the insolation incident.

$$\begin{aligned} m_a C_{pa} \frac{dT_a}{dt} &= A_p h_{c,p-a}(T_p - T_a) + A_f h_{c,f-a}(T_f - T_a) + A_p D_p C_{pv} \rho_p (T_p - T_a) \frac{dM_p}{dt} \\ &\quad + (\rho_a V_{out} C_{pa} T_{out} - \rho_a V_{in} C_{pa} T_{in}) + U_c A_c (T_{am} - T_a) + [(1 - F_p)(1 - \alpha_f) + (1 - \alpha_p) F_p] I_1 A_c \tau_c \end{aligned} \qquad [2]$$

The rate at which thermal energy is stored in the crop is equal to the sum of the rate, of thermal energy convective heat transferred to the crop, the rate of thermal energy received from cover by the product due to radiation, the rate of thermal energy lost from the crop due to sensible and latent heat loss from the crop, and the rate of thermal energy absorbed by the crop [50]:

$$m_p(C_{pp} + C_{pl} M_p) \frac{dT_p}{dt} = A_p h_{cp-a}(T_a - T_p) + A_p h_{r,p-c}(T_c - T_p) + A_p D_p \rho_p [L_p + C_{pv}(T_p - T_a)] \frac{dM_p}{dt} + F_p \alpha_p I_t A_c \tau_c \qquad [3]$$

where L is the latent heat of vaporization of moisture from the product (J kg^{-1}). The conductive heat flow into the floor is equal to the rate of solar radiation absorption on the floor plus the rate of conductive heat transfer between the air and the floor.

$$-k_f A_f \frac{dT_f}{dx} = (1 - F_p) \alpha_f I_1 A_c \tau_c + A_f h_{c,f-a}(T_a - T_f) \qquad [4]$$

where k_f is the thermal conductivity of the floor (W m^{-1} K^{-1}). The rate of thermal energy flow into the floor due to conduction is

$$-k_f A_f \frac{dT_f}{dx} = A_f h_{d,f-g}(T_f - T_\infty) \qquad [5]$$

where T_∞ is the temperature at a depth for which it is interseasonally invariant [54]. The rate of moisture accumulation in the air inside the dryer is equal to the rate of moisture inflow into the dryer due to entry of ambient air minus the rate of moisture outflow from the dryer due to exit of air from the dryer plus the rate of moisture removed from the crop inside the dryer; that is,

$$\rho_a V \frac{dH}{dt} = \rho_a H_{in} V_{in} - \rho_a H_{out} V_{out} + A_p D_p \rho_p \frac{dM_p}{dt} \qquad [6]$$

where H is the humidity ratio, with suffixes 'in' and 'out' referring to the dryer inlet and outlet, respectively. The radiative heat transfer coefficient from the cover to the sky ($h_{r,c-s}$) is given by [7]

$$h_{r,c-s} = \varepsilon_c \sigma (T_c^2 + T_s^2)(T_c + T_s) \qquad [7]$$

where ε_c is the emittance of the cover, σ is the Stefan–Boltzmann constant (W m^{-2} K^{-4}). Radiative heat transfer coefficient between the crop and the cover ($h_{r,p-c}$) is given by [7]

$$h_{r,p-c} = \varepsilon_p \sigma (T_p^2 + T_c^2)(T_p + T_c) \qquad [8]$$

where ε_p is the emittance of the crop. As ($h_{r,c-s}$) and ($h_{r,p-c}$) are functions of temperature, these are computed iteratively at each time during a simulation. The sky temperature (T_s) is

$$T_s = 0.552 T_{am}^{1.5} \qquad [9]$$

Convective heat transfer coefficient from the cover to ambient due to wind h_w is [7]

$$h_w = 5.7 + 3.8 V_w \qquad [10]$$

Convective heat transfer coefficient inside the solar greenhouse dryer for either the cover or product and floor (h_c) is computed from

$$h_{c,f-a} = h_{c,c-a} = h_{c,p-a} = h_c = \frac{\mathrm{Nu}\, k_a}{D_h} \qquad [11]$$

where D_h is given by

$$D_h = \frac{4WD}{2(W+D)} \quad [12]$$

where W and D are the width and height of the dryer (m), respectively, and the Nusselt number is

$$Nu = 0.0158 Re^{0.8}, \quad \text{Re is the Reynolds number,} \quad Re = \frac{D_h V_a}{\nu_a} \quad [13]$$

where V_a is the air speed in the dryer and ν_a is the kinematic viscosity of air. The overall heat loss coefficient from the greenhouse dryer cover (U_c) is computed from

$$U_c = \frac{k_c}{\delta_c} \quad [14]$$

where k_c and δ_c are the thermal conductivity (W m^{-1} K^{-1}) and the thickness (m) of the cover, respectively.

Thin-layer drying correlations are obtained for particular crops by determining experimentally the best fit to an equation of the form

$$\frac{M(t) - M_e}{M_o - M_1} = X \exp(-Yt^Z) \quad [15]$$

where $M(t)$, M_o, and M_e are the moisture contents (as percentage of dry bulb) at time t, originally, and at equilibrium respectively. X, Y, and Z are constants. Different values for X, Y, and Z are found for different crops and often for different methods of crop preparation before drying. For example, for peeled longan (in a single layer), the following thin-layer drying correlation has been obtained [50]:

$$\frac{M - M_e}{M_o - M_e} = \exp(A_1 t^{B_1}) \quad [16]$$

where

$$A_1 = -0.213\,788 + 0.010\,164\,0T - 0.001\,37 \text{rh}$$

$$B_1 = 1.108\,816 - 0.000\,521\,0T - 0.000\,061 \text{rh}$$

where T is the air temperature in °C and rh is the relative humidity expressed as a percentage.

For banana, the thin-layer drying correlation

$$\frac{M - M_e}{M_o - M_e} = A_2 \exp\left(-B_2^t\right) \quad [17]$$

has been obtained [55] where

$$A_2 = 1.503\,574 + 0.005\,054\,55\text{rh} - 0.013\,27T - 0.000\,214\,17\text{rh}^2 + 0.000\,094T^2$$

$$B_2 = 0.187\,4 + 0.001\,93\text{rh} - 0.006\,35T - 0.000\,079\,78\text{rh}^2 + 0.000\,81T^2$$

Similarly, empirically derived equations have been determined experimentally for equilibrium moisture content (M_e, %db) of crops; for peeled longan [50], this is

$$a_w = \frac{1}{1 + \left[\dfrac{b_o + b_1 T}{M_e}\right]^{b_2}} \quad [18]$$

where a_w is the water activity, $b_o = 79.9826$, $b_1 = -0.8277$, and $b_2 = 2.1867$, and for banana this is [55]

$$M_e = 74.660\,23 = 1.144\,253T + 37.072\,24a_w + 0.001\,166T^2 + 51.553\,74a_w^2 \quad [19]$$

3.17.7 Solar Furnaces

Solar materials processing involves effecting the chemical conversion of materials by their direct exposure to concentrated solar energy. Solar furnaces can reach higher temperatures (up to 3800 °C) than combustion or electric furnaces and avoid product contamination from the carbon electrodes of the latter. A diverse range of approaches are being researched for applications related to high-added-value products such as fullerenes, large carbon molecules with major potential commercial applications in

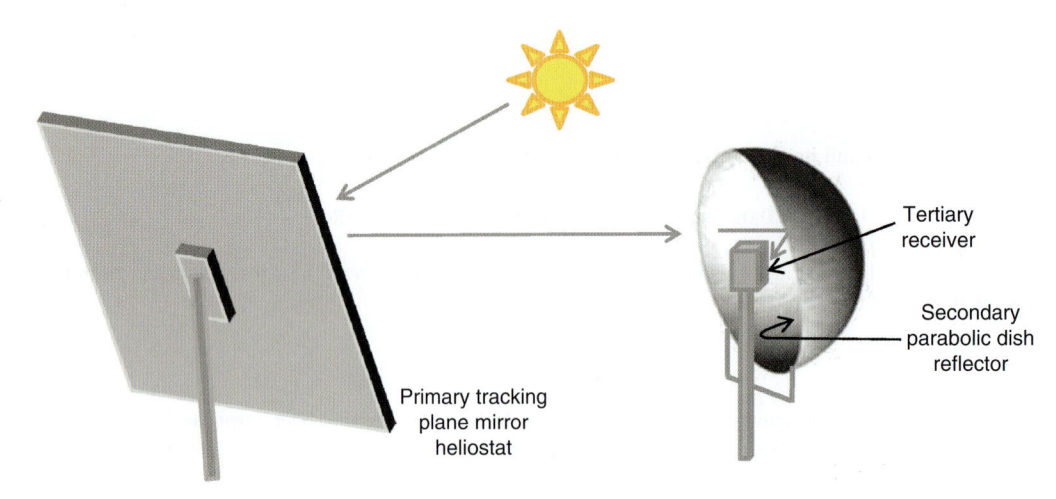

Figure 22 A solar furnace [57].

semiconductors and superconductors, to commodity products such as cement. None of these processes have achieved mainstream commercial adoption.

A solar furnace such as that shown in **Figure 22** can create a concentrated beam with intensity that is tens of thousands times the initial solar intensity. The surface of a material will be heated extremely rapidly when exposed to such a beam; the short heat pulse is dissipated largely by radiative heat transfer to the surroundings, avoiding heating the underlying substrate. Such rapid surface heating is necessary for chemical vapor deposition and ceramic metallization. In the latter, concentrated insolation can be used to bond thin layers of metal to a ceramic substrate to manufacture high-quality electronic components. Producing fullerenes in a solar furnace would use less energy than conventional production technologies. Solar-pumped lasers operate in the same manner as conventional lasers but use concentrated insolation for power instead of electricity. Potential applications include specialized materials processing and photochemistry. At a temperature of 1780 °C and under a N_2–H_2 atmosphere, grain growth and density increase have ensued after sintering alumina powder in a solar furnace located at the focus of a heliostat field [56].

3.17.8 Greenhouses

3.17.8.1 Achieving a Desired Interior Microclimate

A greenhouse is an enclosure designed to help create and maintain a suitable environment for enhancing the rates of growth of plants [58, 59]. These requirements vary according to the particular plant species and its stage of growth, and the approach to creating a specified environment depends on the prevailing ambient conditions and the value of the crop when harvested. The plant varieties chosen to be grown should suit the optimal artificial greenhouse environment that can be achieved economically. Multispan metal-framed modular greenhouses are the most prevalent commercially used form. Cheap Quonset-shaped 'polytunnels' and the less-common air-supported greenhouses, which utilize a lightweight transparent plastic film as the cover material, have been developed. Short-wave insolation transmitted through a greenhouse cover is absorbed by internal surfaces. These surfaces reemit longer wavelength radiation, to which the cover, traditionally of glass, is relatively opaque. The rate of heat loss from a polyethylene-covered greenhouse is thus 10–15% higher than from a similar glass greenhouse: when the cover is dry, this difference can be attributed largely to the transparency of polyethylene to long-wave radiation. Radiation trapping typically contributes only 10–25% of the total 'greenhouse effect', rather it is the suppression of convection losses by the presence of the enclosure itself that is usually the major cause of daytime temperature rises inside most greenhouses. The influences on the interior microclimate of a greenhouse can be categorized as shown in **Table 2**.

Heat losses may be reduced by the use of multiple-paned greenhouses and/or the nocturnal deployment of insulating screens [60, 61]. The ground temperature at a depth of about 1 m remains fairly constant throughout the year [54]. In suitable climates, fluid conveyed through the ground at this depth can be used to cool a greenhouse in summer and heat it in winter [62–64].

3.17.8.2 Greenhouse Heating and Cooling

The main source of heat for any greenhouse should be direct insolation. However, most greenhouses use supplementary heating systems for periods when solar heating is insufficient [65]. Heat storage is less frequently used although an air heating solar collector used to preheat air can readily be coupled with a rockpile to provide a sensible heat store. Such a system is particularly useful where daytime insolation levels are high and, due to nocturnal radiative cooling, the subsequent nights are cold. The ground itself can also

Table 2 Primary factors affecting the microclimate inside a greenhouse

Greenhouse microclimatic characteristics	Ambient climatic parameters	Structural parameters	Operational parameters
Temperature	Air temperature	Transmittance of cover to insolation and long-wave thermal radiation	Ventilation rate
	Wind speed	Thermal storage and heat-transmission properties of greenhouse	Heating and cooling systems
	Insolation		Presence of shades and thermal screens
Photosynthetically active radiation intensity	Insolation	Photosynthetically active radiation transmittance	Presence of shades
		Obstruction by opaque structural framework	Supplementary lighting
Atmospheric constituents	Levels of humidity, CO_2, NO_x, SO_2	Air tightness of the structure	Ventilation rate
			Humidity control
			CO_2 supplementation

be used for heat storage by ducting warm exhaust air from the greenhouse under the ground's surface [66]. Solar ponds have also been used for greenhouse heating.

In temperate climates, greenhouse cooling is achieved by increasing the rate of ventilation by opening ridge vents in conventional rigid-structured greenhouses to provide wind-induced and buoyancy-driven ventilation. On hot, calm days, fan-assisted ventilation is often used. On days of very high insolation, ventilation rates of over 60 air changes per hour may be necessary. Evaporative cooling techniques are often used in greenhouses, by either (1) directly wetting the air inside the greenhouse or (2) wetting the ground surface or the external cover of the greenhouse. A wide range of heating, cooling, and energy storage technologies are available for use in greenhouses [67, 68]. To reduce high solar gains, shades should be fitted externally, rather than internally, to reject their absorbed heat to the ambient environment. The use of an insulating glazing material that becomes opaque during periods of high insolation is technologically feasible, although currently not commercially viable [69].

3.17.9 Heating and Ventilation of Industrial and Agricultural Buildings

3.17.9.1 Solar Air Heating

Solar energy may be used for the space heating of agricultural buildings. The guiding economic principles are to first conserve energy, then adopt passive means of solar energy collection, distribution, and storage, and only then consider active solar technologies. The use of active solar technologies has been aided where the construction of farm building roofs can be modified readily to house air heating solar collectors. Low-cost roof-based air heating solar collectors are fabricated either from a transparent plastic film cover over a black plastic or metal absorber or from metal with glass covers. Farm-built metal solar air heaters range from unglazed low-temperature units for animal husbandry through to double-glazed medium-temperature systems for crop drying [8]. The principal attractions of farm-built roof-mounted air heating collectors are the low initial investment required giving low-cost availability of heated air for drying [70]. The disadvantages are that potentially suboptimal design of system components and poor fabrication quality lead to poor performance.

When a roof-space collector is formed by glazing the south-facing slope of a pitched roof, it enables the passive collection and active distribution of solar heat. Warmth is stored, to some extent, within the structural members of the roof-space collector. A roof-space collector can have a low initial capital cost as its physical construction may not differ greatly from that of a conventional pitched roof. In addition, a reduction in additional cost can arise when a roof-space collector is a preheater from the employment of components (i.e., fans and controls) that would be already present in an auxiliary air heating system.

Isolated gain collectors such as the thermosiphoning air panel [71] and transpired collectors overcome some of the disadvantages of indirect gain collectors by dispensing with heat storage and relying totally on convective heat gain. Heat input is almost immediate, while heat losses during nongain periods when the collector is isolated from the heated space are low. This design is suited to providing daytime heating in cool or cold climates. A thermosiphoning air panel operates in the same manner as the natural convection mode of a Trombe–Michel wall. However, the absorber is often made of metal, usually aluminum or steel, and the unit is insulated to prevent heat loss to, or from, the building. Heat output from a thermosiphoning air panel is controlled by full or partial manual closure of an inlet or existing vent.

3.17.9.2 Direct Solar Gain and Thermal Mass

Successful solar energy use is reconciled harmoniously with the diverse set of physical constraints (e.g., site and internal arrangement) and functional requirements (e.g., structure and use) that a particular industrial and agricultural building must satisfy. The immediate effect of direct solar gain can be ameliorated by thermal mass acting at different times as (1) primary mass is the wall and floor surfaces (masonry features or elements containing water or a phase change material) insolated directly by diurnal sun patch motion across the floor and the lower zones of the walls, (2) secondary mass irradiated by diffuse and reflected insolation and long-wave thermal radiation from directly insolated, primary mass surfaces, and (3) tertiary mass to which heat is transferred by solar heated air. For efficient overall operation, the auxiliary heating system must respond readily both to provide heating when the direct solar gains to particular zones cease and to switch off when solar gains resume.

3.17.10 Solar Cooking

3.17.10.1 Types of Solar Cooker

A classification of solar cookers is shown in **Figure 23**. In focusing cookers, a solar energy concentrator directs solar radiation on to a focal area at which the cooking vessel is located. In these cookers, the convection heat loss from the cooking vessel is large and the cooker utilizes only the direct solar radiation. Hot-box cookers consist of an insulated box painted black internally and double glazed. To enhance solar gain, plane sheet reflectors (single or multiple) may be employed. The adjustment of the cooker toward the sun is not required as frequently as in the case of focusing-type solar cookers. In most hot-box cookers, cooking can take a long time and many dishes cannot be prepared with this cooker as, depending on the weather, temperatures only in the range 50–80 °C are achieved. With indirect cookers, the problem of cooking outdoors is avoided as the solar heat is transferred directly to the cooking vessel in the kitchen. The cookers use either a flat-plate or focusing collector [72] from which collected solar heat is transferred to the cooking vessel. Methods for the design and characterization of solar cookers have been developed [73, 74]. Solar cooking has been advocated in many rural developing country contexts as a means of avoiding the use of wood for fuel, thereby limiting further deforestation and land erosion.

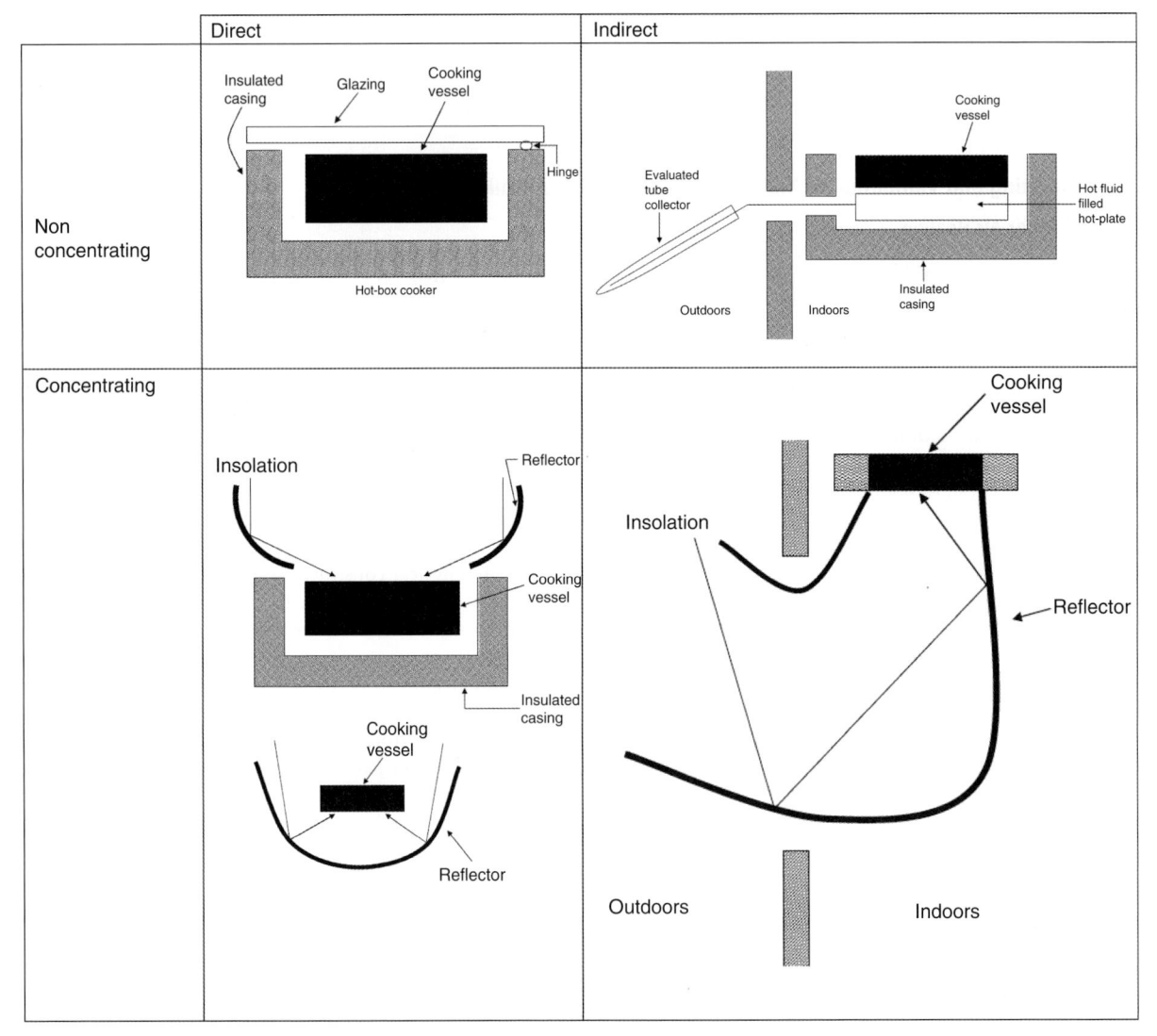

Figure 23 Classification of solar cookers.

3.17.10.2 Analysis of Solar Cookers

An energy balance of a simple solar cooker is [73]

$$mc_p \frac{d(T_p - T_a)}{dt} = \{\eta_o I - U(T_p - T_a)\}A \qquad [20]$$

where m is the mass of the pot (kg), c_p is the specific heat capacity at constant pressure (J kg^{-1} K^{-1}), $(T_p - T_a)$ is the temperature difference between the temperature of the pot content and the ambient temperature (K), η_o is the optical efficiency, I is the global solar radiation (W m^2), U is the overall heat loss coefficient (W m^{-2} K^{-1}), and A is the aperture area (m^2). The temperature rise above ambient at time t is thus given by

$$(T_p - T_a)_t = m\left(1 - e^{-IAt/mc}\right) \qquad [21]$$

Under conditions of constant insolation, the overall heat loss coefficient can be calculated from a heat loss test [73] as

$$U = \frac{mc_p}{t_{end} - t_{start}} \ln \frac{(T_p - T_a)_{start}}{(T_p - T_a)_{out}} \qquad [22]$$

where t_{start} and t_{end} are the times (in seconds) the test commenced and concluded, respectively. Alternatively, the overall heat loss coefficient can be determined for stagnation conditions under constant insolation from

$$U = \frac{\eta_o I}{T_{stag}} \qquad [23]$$

3.17.11 Solar Desalination

3.17.11.1 Solar Desalination Systems

Pollution of the rivers and lakes by industrial effluents and sewage has made freshwater scarce in parts of the third world and is becoming the single largest cause of freshwater shortages. About 79% of water available on the earth is salty, 20% is brackish, and only 1% is fresh. Many diseases are caused by unhygienic drinking water [75]. Over 2000 million people do not have ready access to an adequate supply of safe water. Conventional distillation plants are intensive users of fossil fuel energy. Many arid regions have underground brackish water resources or are close to seawater and have high annual levels of insolation. The production of potable water using solar energy has thus been well researched [76, 77] and in remote or isolated regions has been adopted practically. Among the most common solar desalination systems are (1) basin solar still shown in **Figure 24**, (2) multistage flush evaporation [77] shown in **Figure 25**, (3) reverse osmosis shown in **Figure 26**, and (4) multieffect evaporation shown in **Figure 27**.

Potable water extraction processes using solar energy include (1) passive solar stills and (2) multistage flash evaporation shown in **Figure 22**.

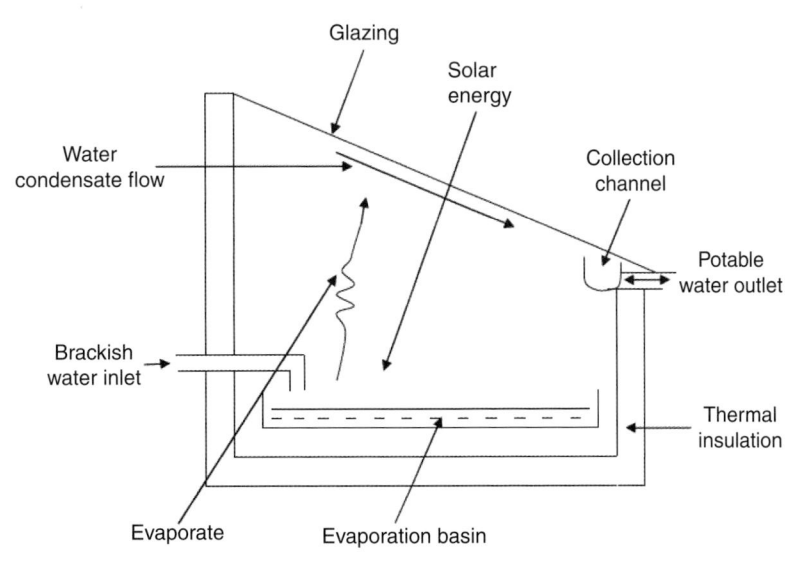

Figure 24 A single-slope basin solar still.

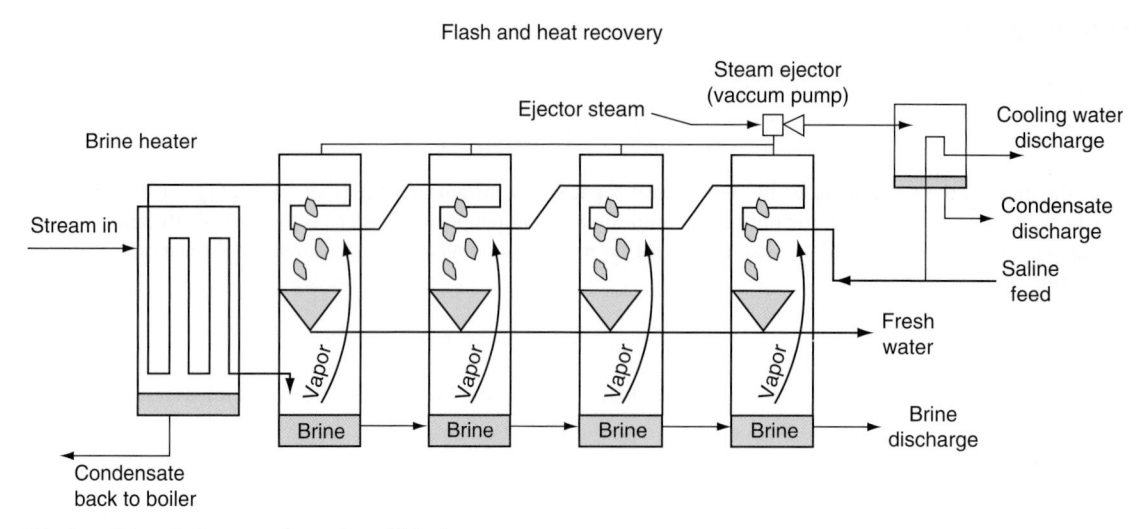

Figure 25 A multistage flash evaporation system with heat recovery.

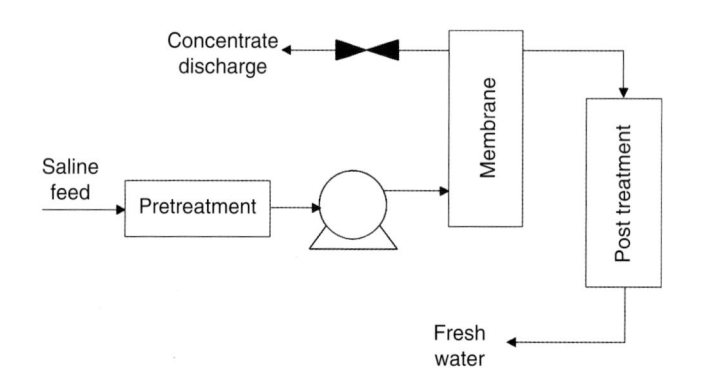

Figure 26 Reverse osmosis.

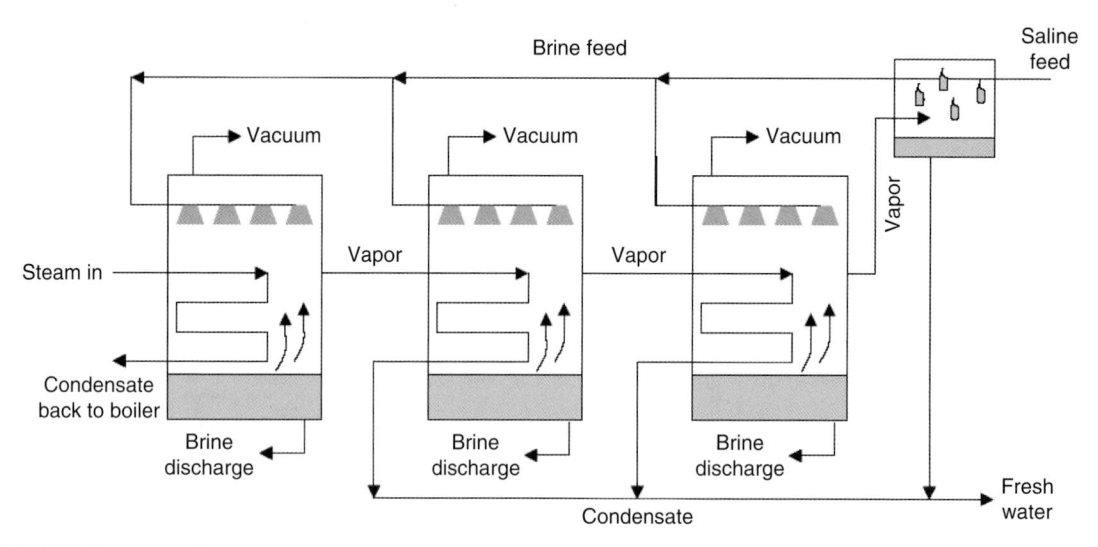

Figure 27 Multieffect evaporation.

In a vapor compression system, water vapor is compressed adiabatically producing a superheated vapor. This is first cooled to saturation temperature and then compressed, using mechanical energy, at constant pressure. In a reverse osmosis system, a pressure gradient across a membrane causes water molecules to pass from one side to the other, but larger mineral molecules cannot penetrate the membrane. A low-temperature solar organic Rankine cycle system for reverse osmosis desalination that operates continuously under intermittent solar energy has been shown experimentally to be a technically feasible concept [78]. In electrodialysis, a selective membrane containing positive and negative ions separates water from minerals using solar-generated electricity. A desalination system comprising a concentrating photovoltaic thermal collector and multieffect evaporation desalination plant [79] has been proposed. A feedback linearization control strategy has been developed and applied to a solar collector field supplying process heat to a multiple-effect seawater desalination plant [80]. Solar desalination systems are competitive economically when the solar collector field cost is very low and electricity prices are very high. These circumstances (particularly the latter) prevail in remote arid regions due to the low cost of land and distance from grid-connected electricity. Long-term economic viability is however dependent on effective operation and maintenance. Solar distillation may also be used for the treatment of brackish water withdrawn from wells using photovoltaic-powered pumps [81, 82].

3.17.11.2 Passive Basin Stills

Various diverse forms of passive basin stills using single-effect distillation can be used to supply water to isolated communities or for small supplies of water such as required for emergency drinking water, washing, and battery charging. A typical basin-type solar still consists of an insulated shallow basin lined or painted with a waterproof black material containing a shallow depth (5–20 cm) of saline or brackish water to be distilled and covered with a single-sloped glass aperture, as shown in **Figure 24**, or a double-sloped one, sealed tightly to reduce vapor leakage. A condensate channel along the lower edge of the glass pane collects the distillate. The still can be fed with saline water either continuously or intermittently, but the supply is generally kept at twice the amount of freshwater produced by the still, depending on initial salinity. Solar radiation transmitted through the transparent cover is absorbed in the water and basin causing the temperature of the water to be raised above that of the cover. Still temperatures above 70 °C reduce bacterial concentrations significantly [83]. The water loses heat by evaporation, convection, and radiation to the cover and by conduction through the base and edges of the still. The evaporation of water from the basin increases the moisture content in the enclosure and condensation ensues on the underside of the cover; the condensate is then collected via the condensate channels [84]. For passive basin stills, up to 20% of the potable water production can occur at night [85]. Models have been developed to calculate the solar fraction of single-stage passive solar stills [86].

Passive solar stills for water desalination can be self-operating, of simple construction, relatively maintenance-free, and avoid recurrent expenditure for fuel. The first system, built in Chile in 1872 [87], produced potable water for about 40 years. The advantages of simple passive solar stills are, however, offset by the small amounts of freshwater produced, approximately 2–3 l m^{-2} per day for the simple basin-type solar still [88] and the need for regular flushing of accumulated salts [76]. The performance of the simple basin-type solar still can be improved by integrating the unit with a water heating solar collector. Passing solar-heated water under the basin increases the evaporation rate by increasing the temperature difference between the saline water and the glass cover of the still [89]. Yields can be increased further using a concentrating collector; due to its smaller absorber surface area, thermal losses are reduced significantly resulting in increased thermal efficiency and higher productivity [90]. When a separate flat-plate or concentrating collector is used to increase the water temperature in a still, either pumped or thermosiphonic circulation may be employed to convey water between the still and the collector [91]. Passive solar distillation systems can have an overall efficiency higher than active solar distillation systems [92].

Integral systems replace both separate reflector and still components and their joining pipework with a single multifunctional fabrication leading to lower initial system costs and reduced heat losses. Extensive studies of inverted absorber solar concentrator systems for fluid heating applications [92–96] have shown that their performance can match that of comparable noninverted concentrators. For an inverted absorber solar distillation unit, a double-effect still has also been used successfully to improve output; latent heat of vaporization in the lower vessel was reused to heat the water mass in the upper vessel, which also enhanced condensation in the lower vessel as lower surface temperatures ensued [97]. The incorporation of a basin-type still with an inverted absorber line-axis asymmetric compound parabolic concentrating collector can achieve higher temperatures by minimizing thermal losses by convection suppression. Such systems have been fabricated and characterized experimentally in northern India [98]. An inverted absorber passive basin still as shown in **Figure 28** has been found to produce higher water

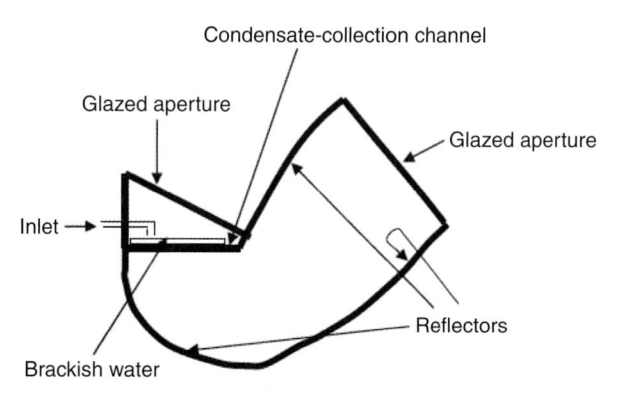

Figure 28 Inverted absorber CPC augmented basin solar still.

temperatures than comparable direct passive solar stills, thus increasing evaporation and condensation and ultimately producing more potable water based on the same basin area [84]. These higher water temperatures may also have the additional benefit of possibly eliminating more harmful bacteria.

3.17.12 Solar Refrigeration

3.17.12.1 Types of Solar Refrigeration

The solar operation of conventional electrical refrigerators, working on a compression cycle, requires the conversion of solar energy into electricity or the conversion of the direct current output of a photovoltaic array using an inverter to an alternating current.

Intermittent vapor absorption refrigeration plants work on a 24 h cycle comprising heating and refrigeration processes matched to the diurnal operation of the sun: undergoing heating process during the day and producing 'cooling' at night [99]. Porous solids, termed adsorbents, can physically and reversibly adsorb large volumes of a vapor, termed the adsorbate. The concentration of adsorbate vapors in a solid adsorbent is a function of the temperature of the 'working pair' (i.e., mixture of adsorbent and adsorbate) and the vapor pressure of the adsorbate. The dependence of adsorbate concentration on temperature under constant pressure conditions making it possible to adsorb or desorb the adsorbate by varying the temperature of the mixture forms the basis of the solar-powered intermittent vapor sorption refrigeration cycle [100]. An adsorbent–refrigerant working pair for a solar refrigerator requires the following characteristics: (1) a refrigerant with a large latent heat of vaporization; (2) a working pair with high thermodynamic efficiency; (3) a small heat of desorption under the envisaged operating pressure and temperature conditions; and (4) a low thermal capacity. In addition, the operating conditions of a solar-powered refrigerator (i.e., generator and condenser temperature) vary with its geographical location. Water–ammonia has been the most widely used sorption refrigeration pair. The efficiency of such systems is limited by the condensing temperature. For example, cooling towers or desiccant beds have to be used to produce cold water to condense ammonia at lower pressure. Among the other disadvantages inherent in using water and ammonia as the working pair are the following: heavy gauge pipe and vessel walls that are required to withstand the high pressure, the corrosiveness of ammonia, and the problem of rectification (i.e., removing water vapor from ammonia during generation).

When solid absorption using calcium chloride as the absorbent and ammonia as the refrigerant is employed, a reversible chemical reaction takes place when the refrigerant is absorbed by the solid absorbent. To overcome swelling of the volume of up to 400% when ammonia is absorbed into calcium chloride, a small quantity of another salt is added to the calcium chloride and then mixed with ammonia to prepare a paste, to be heated subsequently in a controlled manner to produce a new granulated absorbent. As the heat of adsorption and desorption for the working pair is high, almost twice the latent heat of evaporation of ammonia, a large combined solar collector/absorber area is required.

Solar refrigeration is employed to cool vaccine stores. The need for such systems is greatest in peripheral health centers in rural communities in the developing world [101, 102]. In the absence of grid-connected electricity, the vaccine cold chain can be extended to these areas with autonomous solar energy vaccine stores. Most of this provision is met by compression cycle refrigerators powered by photovoltaics. Solar thermal refrigeration systems have been the subject of extensive research [103, 104] but have, to date, only rarely led to commercially produced systems.

3.17.12.2 Uses of Solar Refrigeration

An example of practical solar ice making for commercial food storage in rural Mexico [105] illustrates the use of solar energy in remote, non-grid-connected areas. The system consists of seven double intermittent ammonia–water absorption cycle ice makers, three of which are ground-mounted to generate ice for processing fish and transporting it to market, and four, mounted on the roof of the storage building, to provide ice to cool a storage tank. Each double intermittent ammonia–water absorption cycle device is supplied with heat by a 12 m^2 aperture area parabolic trough concentrating solar collector and has produced about 68 kg of ice daily since late 1992. The 84 m^2 total parabolic trough solar collector area provides annually a 519 GJ heat input giving an annual 72.8 GJ of refrigeration.

Acknowledgmentss

The author would like to thank Professor Philip Eames, University of Loughborough, Professor Valentine Ekechukwu, University of Nigeria, Professor Yigsaw Yohanis, University of Ulster, Professor G. N. Tiwari, IIT Delhi, Dr. Mervyn Smyth, University of Ulster, and Dr. Steve Lo, University of Bath, for their various insights and collaborations on solar industrial and agricultural systems over many years. He would also like to thank Ms. Gillian Collins, who produced many of the diagrams and tables in this chapter.

Solar energy research undertaken by the author is supported by Science Foundation Ireland under grants SFI 07/RFP/ENE 719 and SFI 05/RFP/ENE 025.

References

[1] Kalogirou S (2003) The potential for solar industrial process heat applications. *Applied Energy* 76: 337–361.
[2] Weiss W, Schweiger H, and Battisti R (2005) Market potential and system designs for industrial heat applications. *Proceedings of ESTEC, 2005 – 2nd European Solar Thermal Energy Conference.* Freiburg, Germany, 21–22 June.
[3] Norton B (1999) Renewable electricity, what is the true cost? *IEE Power Engineering Journal* 13: 6–12.
[4] Butti K and Perlin J (1980) *A Golden Thread*. New York: Van Nostrand Reinhold Co.
[5] Rabl A (1985) *Active Solar Collectors and Their Application*. New York: Oxford University Press.
[6] Reddy TA (1987) *The Design and Sizing of Active Solar Thermal Systems*. Oxford, UK: Clarendon Press.
[7] Duffie JA and Beckman WA (1991) *Solar Engineering of Thermal Processes*, 2nd edn. New York Wiley Interscience.
[8] Norton B (1992) *Solar Energy Thermal Technology*. Heidelberg, Germany: Springer-Verlag.
[9] Goswami DY, Kreith F, and Kreider JF (1999) *Principles of Solar Engineering*, 2nd edn. New York: John Wiley and Sons.
[10] Norton B (2001) Solar process heat: Distillation, drying, agricultural and industrial uses. In: Gordon J (ed.) *Solar Process Heat: Distillation, Drying, Agricultural and Industrial Uses, Solar Energy; State of the Art*, pp. 477–496. London: James & James.
[11] Tiwari GN (2002) *Solar Energy, Fundamentals, Design, Modelling and Applications*. New York: CRC Press.
[12] Prapas DE, Norton B, and Probert SD (1986) Sensor system for aligning a single-axis tracker with direct solar insolation. *Applied Energy* 25: 1–8.
[13] Kim DH, Jenkins BM, Yore MW, and Kin NJ (2007) Salt recovery from agricultural drainage water using a liquid film solar-assisted concentrator – simulation and model validation. *Solar Energy* 81: 1314–1321.
[14] Dubener J, Helsh G, Moiseev A, and Bornhoft M (2008) Glasses for solar energy conversion systems. *Journal of the European Ceramic Society* 29: 1203–1210.
[15] Burek SAM, Norton B, and Probert SD (1989) Transmission and forward scattering of insolation through plastic (transparent and semi-transparent) materials. *Solar Energy* 42: 457–475.
[16] Norton B and Edmonds JEJ (1991) Aqueous propylene glycol concentrations for the freeze protection of thermosyphon solar energy water heaters. *Solar Energy* 47: 375–382.
[17] Häberbe A, Berger M, Luginsland F, and Zahler C (2008) Experience with linear concentrating Fresnel collectors for process heat applications. *14th International Symposium on Concentrating Solar Power and Chemical Energy Technologies.* Las Vegas, NV, USA.
[18] Alnaser W and Alnaser N (2009) Solar and wind potential in GCC countries and some related projects. *Journal of Renewable and Sustainable Energy* 1: 2.
[19] Russel JL, Schuster JR, and Eggers GH (1997) Development status of the fixed mirror solar concentrator. *Proceedings of the 12th Intersociety Energy Conversion Engineering Conference*, Honolulu, Hawaii, pp. 1141–1146.
[20] Martinez Moll V, Pujol Nadal R, Molá Pol A, and Schweiger H (2006) Analysis of a stationary parabolic linear concentrator with tracking absorber. *13th International Symposium on Concentrating Solar Power and Chemical Energy Technologies.* Seville, Spain.
[21] Abdel-Salam HEA, Probert SD, and Norton B (1986) Predicted performances of coffered solar ponds in the U.K. and Egypt. *International Journal of Physico-Chemical Hydrodynamics* 7: 217–233.
[22] Smyth M and Skates H (2009) A passive solar water heating system for vineyard front protection. *Solar Energy* 83: 400–408.
[23] Eames PC and Norton B (1998) The effect of tank geometry on thermally stratified sensible heat storage subject to low Reynolds number flows. *International Journal of Heat and Mass Transfer* 41: 2131–2142.
[24] Farrell AJ, Norton B, and Kennedy DM (2006) Corrosive effects of salt hydrates phase change materials used with aluminium and copper. *Journal of Materials Processing Technology* 175: 198–205.
[25] Yohanis YG, Popel O, Frid SE, and Norton B (2006a) Geographic variation of solar water heater performance in Europe. *Proceedings of the Institution of Mechanical Engineers, Part A, Journal of Power and Energy* 220: 395–407.
[26] Yohanis YG, Popel O, Frid SE, and Norton B (2006b) The annual number of days that solar heated water satisfies a specified demand temperature. *Solar Energy* 80(8): 1021–1030.
[27] Bourges B, Adnot J, Campana D, *et al.* (1980) Provision of long term average performance of low temperature solar systems: A synthetical review of existing methods and available meteorological data, ICBEM, Portugal.
[28] Luna D, Nadeau JP, and Jannot Y (2009) Solar timber kilns: State of the art and foreseeable developments. *Renewable and Sustainable Energy Reviews* 13: 1446–1455.
[29] Erbs DG, Klein SA, and Duffie JA (1982) Estimation of the diffuse radiation fraction for hourly, daily and monthly average global radiation. *Solar Energy* 25: 293–302.
[30] Karatasou S, Santamouris M, and Geros V (2006) On the calculation of solar utilizability for south oriented flat plate collectors tilted at an angle equal to the local latitude. *Solar Energy* 80: 1600–1610.
[31] Gordon JM and Rabl A (1982) Design, analysis and optimization of solar industrial process heat plants without storage. *Solar Energy* 28: 519–530.
[32] Braun JE, Klein SA, and Beckman WA (1981) Seasonal storage of energy in solar heating. *Solar Energy* 26: 403–411.
[33] Oliveira AC (2007) A new look at the long-term performance of general solar thermal systems. *Solar Energy* 81: 1361–1368.
[34] Klein SA, Beckman WA, and Duffie JA (1976) A design procedure for solar heating systems. *Solar Energy* 18: 113–127.
[35] Klein SA, Beckman WA, and Duffie JH (1977) A design procedure for solar air heating systems. *Solar Energy* 19: 509–512.
[36] Collares-Pereira M, Gordon JM, Rabl A, and Zarmi Y (1984) Design and optimisation of solar industrial hot water systems with storage. *Solar Energy* 32: 121–133.
[37] Baer D, Gordon JM, and Zarmi Y (1985) Design and optimization of solar steam systems for constant load applications. *Solar Energy* 35: 137–151.
[38] Kulkarni GN, Kedere SB, and Bandyopadhyay S (2008) Design of solar thermal systems utilising pressurised hot water storage for industrial applications. *Solar Energy* 82: 686–699.
[39] Klein SA, Beckmann B, and Duffie J, *et al.* (2009) *TRNSYS Program Manual*. Solar Energy Laboratory, University of Wisconsin–Madison, USA.
[40] Casavant TE and Côté RP (2004) Using chemical process simulation to design industrial ecosystems. *Journal of Cleaner Production* 12: 901–908.
[41] Kalogirou SA (2004) Optimisation of solar systems using artificial neural-networks and genetic algorithms. *Applied Energy* 77: 383–405.
[42] Tripathy PP and Kumar S (2008) A methodology for determination of temperature dependant mass transfer coefficients from drying kinetics: Application to solar drying. *Journal of Food Engineering* 90: 212–218.
[43] Sharma A, Chen CR, and Lan NV (2009) Solar-energy drying systems: A review. *Renewable and Sustainable Energy Reviews* 13: 1185–1210.
[44] Hassanain A, Norton B, and Eames PC (1998) An experimental investigation into solar chimney designs suitable to augment crop dryers. *Renewable Energy* 16: 2223–2226.
[45] Ferreira AG, Maia CB, Cortez MFB, and Valle RM (2008) Technical feasibility assessment of a solar chimney for food drying. *Solar Energy* 82: 198–205.
[46] Forson FK, Nacha MAA, and Rajakaruna H (2007) Modelling and experimental studies on a mixed-mode natural circulation solar crop-dryer. *Solar Energy* 81: 346–357.
[47] Ekechukwu OV and Norton B (1999) Effects of seasonal weather variations on the measured performance of a natural circulation solar energy tropical crop dryer. *Energy Conversion and Management* 39: 1265–1276.
[48] Hossain M and Bala BK (2007) Drying of hot chilli using solar tunnel drier. *Solar Energy* 81: 85–92.
[49] Suthi VP and Avosa S (2009) Improvement in greenhouse solar drying using inclined north wall reflection. *Solar Energy* 83: 1472–1484.
[50] Janjai S, Lamlest N, Intaivee P, *et al.* (2009) Experimental and simulated performance of a PV-ventilated solar greenhouse dryer for drying peeled longan and banana. *Solar Energy* 83: 1550–1565.
[51] Barnwal P and Tiwari A (2008) Design, construction and testing of hybrid photovoltaic integrated greenhouse dryer. *International Journal of Agricultural Research* 3: 110–120.
[52] Fargali H, El-Shafly A, Nafeh A, *et al.* (2008) Medicinal herb drying using a photovoltaic array and a solar thermal system. *Solar Energy* 82: 1154–1160.

[53] Cronin K, Norton B, Taylor J, et al. (1996) Development of a simulation tool to enable optimisation of the energy consumption of the industrial timber drying process. *Applied Energy* 53: 325–340.
[54] Khatry AK, Sodha MS, and Malik MAS (1978) Periodic variation of ground temperature with depth and time. *Solar Energy* 20: 425–427.
[55] Smitabhindu R (2008) Optimisation of Solar Assisted Drying System for Drying Bananas. PhD Thesis, Kasetsart University.
[56] Romàn R, Cañades I, Rodríguez J, et al. (2008) Solar sintering of alumina ceramics: Microstructural development. *Solar Energy* 82: 893–902.
[57] Haueter P, Seitz T, and Steinfeld A (1999) A new high flux solar furnace for high-temperature thermochemical research. *ASME Journal of Solar Energy Engineering* 121: 77–80.
[58] Hare JG, Norton B, and Probert SD (1984) Design of greenhouses; thermal aspects. *Applied Energy* 18: 49–82.
[59] Tiwari GN (2003) *Greenhouse Technology for Controlled Environment*. New Delhi, India: Narosa Publishing House.
[60] Abak KA, Bascetincelik A, Baytorun N, et al. (1994) Influence of double plastic cover and thermal screens on greenhouse temperature, yield and quality of tomato. *Acta Horticulturae* 369: 149–154.
[61] Bailey BJ (1981) The evaluation of thermal screens on greenhouses in commercial nurseries. *Acta Horticulturae* 115: 663–670.
[62] Santamouris M, Mihalakakou G, Balaras CA, et al. (1996) Energy conservation in greenhouses with buried pipes. *Solar Energy* 21: 353–360.
[63] Ghosal MK and Tiwari GN (2006) Modelling and parametric studies for thermal performance of an earth to air heat exchanger integrated with a greenhouse. *Energy Conservation and Management* 47: 1779–1798.
[64] Shukla A, Tiwari GM, and Sodha MS (2006) Thermal modeling for greenhouse heating by using thermal curtain and an earth–air heat exchanger. *Building and Environment* 41: 843–850.
[65] Santamouris M, Balaras CA, Dascalaki E, and Vallindras M (1994) Passive solar agricultural greenhouses: A worldwide classification and evaluation of technologies and systems used for heating purposes. *Solar Energy* 53: 411–426.
[66] Gauthier C, Lacroix M, and Bernier H (1997) Numerical simulation of soil heat exchanger – storage systems for greenhouses. *Solar Energy* 60: 333–346.
[67] Sethi VP and Sharma SK (2007) Survey of cooling technologies for worldwide agricultural greenhouses. *Solar Energy* 81: 1447–1459.
[68] Sethi VP and Sharma SK (2008) Survey and evaluation of heating technologies for worldwide agricultural greenhouse applications. *Solar Energy* 82: 832–859.
[69] Fang Y, Eames PC, Norton B, et al. (2008) The thermal performance of an electrochromic vacuum glazing with selected low-emittance coatings. *Thin Solid Films* 516: 1074–1081.
[70] Janjai S, Srisittipokakun N, and Bala BK (2007) Experimental and modeling performance of a roof-integrated solar drying system for drying herbs and spices. *Solar Energy* 33: 91–103.
[71] Norton B, Hobday RA, and Lo SNG (1992) Thermosyphoning air panels. *Advances in Solar Energy* 7: 495–571.
[72] Norton B, Eames PC, Yadav YP, and Griffiths PW (1997) Inverted absorber solar concentrators for rural applications. *International Journal of Ambient Energy* 18: 115–120.
[73] Schwarzer K and Vierada Silva ME (2008) Characterisation and design method of solar cookers. *Solar Energy* 82: 157–165.
[74] Funk PA and Larson DL (1998) Parametric model of solar cooker performance. *Solar Energy* 62: 63–68.
[75] WHO (1996) *Guidelines for Drinking-water Quality*, vol. 2, pp. 940–949. Geneva, Switzerland: World Health Organization.
[76] Malik MAS, Tiwari GN, Kumar A, and Sodha MS (1982) *Solar Distillation*. Oxford, U.K.: Pergamon Press.
[77] Kalogirou SA (2005) Seawater desalination using renewable energy sources. *Progress in Energy and Combustion Science* 31: 242–281.
[78] Monolakos D, Kosmadakis G, Kyritsis S, and Papadulis G (2009) On-site experimental evaluation of a low temperature solar organic Rankine cycle system for RO desalination. *Solar Energy* 83: 646–656.
[79] Mittelmen G, Kribus A, Mouchtan O, and Dayan A (2009) Water desalination with concentrating photovoltaic/thermal (CPVT) systems. *Solar Energy* 83: 1322–1334.
[80] Roca L, Berengivel M, Yebra L, and Alarcon-Padilla DC (2008) Solar field control for desalination plans. *Solar Energy* 82: 772–786.
[81] Odeh I, Yohanis YG, and Norton B (2006) Influence of pumping head, insolation and PV array size on PV water pumping system performance. *Solar Energy* 80: 51–64.
[82] Odeh I, Yohanis YG, and Norton B (2006) Economic viability of photovoltaic water pumping systems. *Solar Energy* 80: 850–860.
[83] Tiwari GN and Prasad B (1996) Thermal modelling of concentrator assisted solar distillation with water flow over the glass cover. *International Journal of Solar Energy* 18: 173–190.
[84] Smyth M, Norton B, and Byers W (2005) Measured effect of reflector augmentation of simple basin type passive solar skills. *International Journal of Ambient Energy* 25: 59–70.
[85] Yates A and Woto T (1988) *Small Scale Desalination for Areas of Botswana*. Ottawa, Canada: International Development Centre.
[86] Madlopa A and Johnstone C (2009) Model for computation of solar fraction in a single slope solar still. *Solar Energy* 83: 873–882.
[87] Harding J (1883) Apparatus for solar distillation. *Proceedings of the Institution of Civil Engineering* 73: 284–288.
[88] Zaki CM, Al-Turki A, and Fattani M (1992) Experimental investigation on concentrator assisted solar stills. *Solar Energy* 11: 193–199.
[89] Soleman SE (1976) Water Distillation by Solar Energy. PhD Thesis, Faculty of Engineering, Keio University.
[90] Zaki CM, Radhwan AM, and Balbeid AO (1993) Analysis of assisted coupled solar stills. *Solar Energy* 51(4): 277–258.
[91] Singh SK, Bhatnagar P, and Tiwari GN (1996) Design parameters for concentrator assisted solar distillation system. *Energy Conversion Management* 37(2): 247–252.
[92] Tiwari GN (1992) *Recent Advances in Solar Distillation. Solar Energy and Energy Conservation*. New Delhi, India: Wiley Eastern.
[93] Kothdiwala AF, Eames PC, and Norton B (1996) Optical performance of an asymmetric inverted absorber compound parabolic concentrating solar energy collector. *Renewable Energy* 9: 576–579.
[94] Kothdiwala AF, Eames PC, and Norton B (1997) Experimental analysis and performance of an asymmetric inverted absorber compound parabolic concentrating solar energy collector at various absorber gap configurations. *Renewable Energy* 10: 235–238.
[95] Kothdiwala AF, Eames PC, and Norton S (1999) Asymmetric line-axis inverted absorber compound parabolic concentrating optical parameter analysis. *Institution of Mechanical Engineering Journal of Mass, Power and Energy* 213(A): 143–148.
[96] Kothdiwala AF, Eames PC, Norton B, and Zacharopoulos A (1999) Comparison between inverted absorber arrangements and symmetric tubular absorber compound parabolic concentrating solar collectors. *Renewable Energy* 18: 277–281.
[97] Suneja S, Tiwari GN, and N Rai,S (1997) Parametric study of an inverted absorber double-effect solar distillation system. *Desalination* 109: 177–186.
[98] Yadav VP, Eames PC, and Norton B (1998) A double-evaporative single-basin solar still for high temperature solar distillation. *Proceedings of the 5th World Renewable Energy Congress*, pp. 2376–2379. Florence, Italy.
[99] Alghoul MA, Sulaiman MY, Azmi BZ, and Wahab MA (2007) Advances in multi purpose solar adsorption systems for domestic refrigeration and water heating. *Applied Thermal Engineering* 27: 813–822.
[100] Fan Y, Luo L, and Souyri B (2006) Review of solar sorption refrigeration technologies: Development and applications. *Renewable and Sustainable Energy Reviews* 11: 1758–1775.
[101] Wirkas T, Toikilik S, Miller N, et al. (2007) A vaccine cold chain freezing study in POVG highlights needs for hot climate countries. *Vaccine* 25: 691–697.
[102] Berhane Y and Demissie M (2000) Cold-chain status at immunisation centres in Ethiopia. *East Africa Medical Journal* 77: 476–479.
[103] Hammad M and Habali S (2000) Design and performance study of a solar energy powered vaccine cabinet. *Applied Thermal Engineering* 20: 1785–1798.
[104] Uppal AH, Norton B, and Probert SD (1986) A low-cost solar-energy stimulated absorption refrigerator for vaccine storage. *Applied Energy* 25: 167–174.
[105] Erickson DC (1994) Solar Icemakers in Maruata. *Solar Today*, July/August.

3.18 Concentrating Solar Power

B Hoffschmidt, S Alexopoulos, C Rau, J Sattler, A Anthrakidis, C Boura, B O'Connor, and P Hilger, Aachen University of Applied Sciences, Jülich, Germany

© 2012 Elsevier Ltd. All rights reserved.

3.18.1	Introduction	596
3.18.2	General Principles of Concentrating Systems	596
3.18.2.1	Concentration Effect	596
3.18.2.2	Energy and Mass Balance	597
3.18.2.3	Grid-Connected or Island Systems	597
3.18.2.4	Recooling	597
3.18.2.4.1	Closed-circuit recooling systems	597
3.18.2.4.2	Wet cooling systems	597
3.18.2.4.3	Mechanical draft cooling systems	598
3.18.2.4.4	Natural draft cooling towers	598
3.18.2.4.5	Hybrid cooling towers	599
3.18.2.4.6	Fan-assisted natural draft cooling towers	600
3.18.2.4.7	Air-driven condensers	600
3.18.3	Power Conversion Systems	600
3.18.3.1	Solar Only	600
3.18.3.1.1	Steam cycles	600
3.18.3.1.2	Organic Rankine cycles	603
3.18.3.1.3	Gas turbines	604
3.18.3.1.4	Solar dishes	605
3.18.3.2	Increase in Operational Hours	605
3.18.3.2.1	Hybridization	605
3.18.3.2.2	Storage	609
3.18.4	Cogeneration	611
3.18.4.1	Solar Cooling	611
3.18.4.1.1	Principles and technologies of solar cooling	612
3.18.4.1.2	Thermally driven cooling systems	612
3.18.4.1.3	Absorption chillers	612
3.18.4.1.4	Adsorption chillers	613
3.18.4.1.5	Best-practice examples for solar cooling	613
3.18.4.1.6	State of the art of solar cooling	614
3.18.4.1.7	Market expectations for solar cooling	614
3.18.4.2	Desalination	614
3.18.4.3	Off-Heat Usage	615
3.18.5	Examples	615
3.18.5.1	Commercial	615
3.18.5.1.1	SEGS	615
3.18.5.1.2	Andasol 1–3	616
3.18.5.1.3	PS10, PS20	617
3.18.5.1.4	STJ	619
3.18.5.1.5	Nevada Solar One	620
3.18.5.1.6	Sierra SunTower	620
3.18.5.1.7	Dish farm California	622
3.18.5.1.8	PE 1	622
3.18.5.1.9	AORA	622
3.18.5.1.10	Kimberlina solar thermal power plant	623
3.18.5.1.11	Others/under construction	623
3.18.5.2	Research	624
3.18.5.2.1	Solar One	624
3.18.5.2.2	Solar Two	625
3.18.5.2.3	CESA-1	626
3.18.5.2.4	DISS	626
3.18.5.2.5	STJ	627
3.18.5.2.6	SSPS	627

3.18.5.2.7		Others	627
3.18.5.3		Studies	629
3.18.5.3.1		GAST	629
3.18.5.3.2		PHOEBUS	629
3.18.6	**Economical Aspects**		629
3.18.7	**Environmental Aspects**		630
3.18.7.1		Emission	630
3.18.7.2		Impact on Flora and Fauna	630
3.18.7.3		Life Cycle Assessment	630
3.18.8	**Future Potential**		631
3.18.8.1		Desertec	631
3.18.8.2		United States and Europe	631
3.18.8.3		MENA Region	634
3.18.8.4		Future Research Fields	634
References			634

3.18.1 Introduction

Solar thermal energy is a booming field worldwide. Many gigawatts of such energy are currently being built. There are different competing technologies concerning the concentrator, heat transfer media, and power cycle.

Concentrating solar systems can be used for chemical reactions. Concentrated solar chemical applications include fuel production, for example, hydrogen, melting of metals which need high temperatures, and production of other chemical compounds.

The focus of this chapter is only the production of power and the use of the heat produced from concentrated solar thermal power systems.

3.18.2 General Principles of Concentrating Systems

3.18.2.1 Concentration Effect

Theoretically, concentrating solar systems can reach considerably higher temperatures without reducing their thermal efficiencies. According to Carnot's law, this means an improved conversion efficiency of the coupled thermodynamic cycle, so that the same amount of electricity can be produced by a smaller collector area.

The maximum thermal efficiency of a thermodynamic cycle is given by Carnot's law:

$$\eta_{\text{th, Carnot}} = \frac{T_P - T_A}{T_P}$$

where T_P and T_A are the process and ambient temperatures, respectively.

The upper boundary of the efficiency of solar thermal power plants is given by

$$\eta_{\max} = \eta_{\text{th, Carnot}} \cdot \eta_{\text{absorber}}$$

Figure 1 shows the theoretical possible achievable efficiency as a function of the absorber temperature. For simplicity, the absorber temperature is set equal to the process temperature. In reality, the process temperature is less due to losses. As can be seen from the

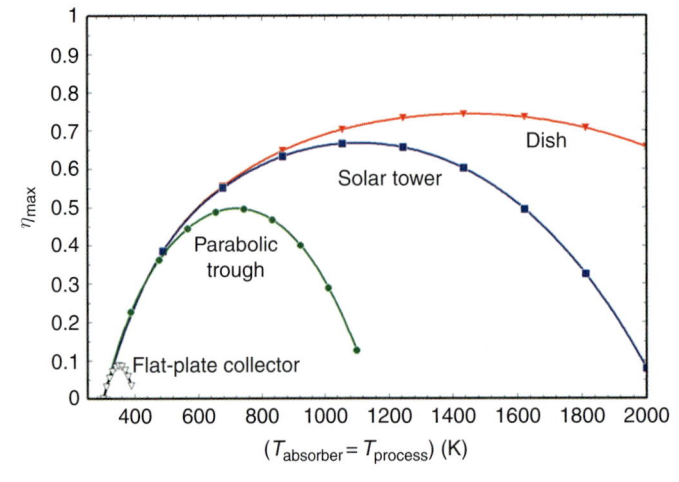

Figure 1 Upper boundary of solar thermal power plant efficiencies.

graph, the maximum efficiency increases when the process temperature is increased. Each solar thermal technology has a maximum efficiency. The highest efficiency is reached for the solar dish. In order to withstand such high temperatures as well as high temperature gradients, suitable materials have to be chosen. The solar tower reaches efficiencies above 60% and the operation temperatures match the operating temperatures of conventional power plants. In comparison, the parabolic trough has less efficiency; however, it has already resulted in a standard commercial application.

Another very useful dimension that characterizes solar thermal systems is the concentration ratio C. It is defined as the ratio of the collector aperture area to the receiver area. The whole collector field has to be considered.

$$C = \frac{\text{collector aperture area}}{\text{receiver area}}$$

Flat-plate collectors have a concentration ratio of 1, parabolic trough and Fresnel collectors about 100, solar towers up to or more than 1000, and solar dishes around 4000. For example, for the Solar Tower Plant of Jülich (STJ; see Section 3.18.5.1.4) in Germany with a receiver area of more than 20 m² and a heliostat field area of approximately 18 000 m², a concentration ratio of around 900 has been reached.

3.18.2.2 Energy and Mass Balance

In order to thermally analyze a solar thermal concentrating system, the mass and energy conservation law has to be considered for the whole system as well as for each component. Especially, the components of the solar cycle have to be considered in detail.

The thermal efficiency of solar thermal absorbers is given by the following equation:

$$\eta_{\text{absorber}} = \alpha_{\text{eff}} - \frac{\varepsilon \sigma_s T^4}{CS}$$

where ε is the emission coefficient, α_{eff} the effective absorptivity, σ the Stefan–Boltzmann constant, and S the solar input. The concentrated solar energy received by an absorber is absorbed to a large degree, but losses also occur. The losses at the receiver may be due to radiation, convection, and conduction, as well as thermal losses occur during the transport of heat transfer fluid (HTF).

A detailed energetic consideration of each solar absorber technology can be viewed in Chapter 3.06.

3.18.2.3 Grid-Connected or Island Systems

Solar thermal concentrated power systems can be connected in grid as well as in island systems. For small island systems, solar dish systems are a suitable solution. Parabolic trough collectors (PTCs), Fresnel collectors, and solar towers may be grid or island systems. Together with a thermal storage or after hybridization, dispatchable power can be provided.

3.18.2.4 Recooling

In a condensation power station, a main condenser or a turbine condenser, in which the steam flowing away from the turbine condenses out, can be used. Condensation heat must be led away from the system, to the ambient. This is done by the circulation of different coolants. Using different systems, heat is delivered either to the hydrosphere (heat removal directly by the main condenser) or to the atmosphere (heat removal indirectly by air-cooled heat exchangers).

3.18.2.4.1 Closed-circuit recooling systems

The closed-circuit recooling system is thermodynamically closed. By means of a finned tube bundle heat exchanger, the medium on the product side is cooled (**Figure 2**).

The use of finned tubes is necessary, because based on the low heat transfer coefficient of the air, a high air mass flow is necessary. The large need for air can be avoided by enlarging the air-side heat exchange surface compared with the surface on the coolant side. The big disadvantage of closed-circuit recoolers is the coolant temperature reached, which is close to ambient temperature. This affects the energy efficiency of the power station.

3.18.2.4.2 Wet cooling systems

Thermodynamically, this system is described as an open process. The warm coolant is injected into the cooling system and then conducted through a special fill material. The loss of heat occurs by means of convection and mass transport (**Figure 3**).

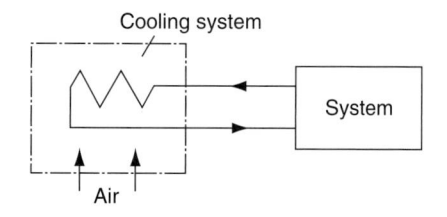

Figure 2 Closed-circuit recooling system.

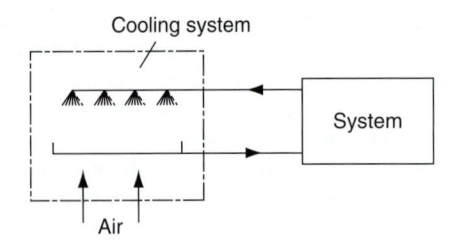

Figure 3 Wet cooling system.

In such a system, lower temperatures occur and smaller transfer surfaces can be reached compared with a system using the closed-circuit coolers due to cooling to the wet-bulb temperature. Disadvantages of wet coolers are vapor production and the demand for additional cooling water.

3.18.2.4.3 Mechanical draft cooling systems

As for air supply, there are two different cooling tower variations, supplying cooling air either by forced or by induced draft to the system. Both variations are used in the closed-circuit as well as in the wet recooling system. **Figure 4** shows different variations of arrangement.

- *Forced draft.* A mechanical draft recooling system with a blower-type fan at the intake. The fan forces air into the system. A forced draft design typically requires more power than an equivalent induced draft design. In combination with a wet recooling system, the fan on the intake of the cooling tower is more susceptible to complications due to freezing conditions.
- *Induced draft.* A mechanical draft recooling system with a fan at the discharge, which pulls air through the tower. The fan induces hot and wet air in combination with a wet cooling system.

3.18.2.4.4 Natural draft cooling towers

In the natural draft cooling tower, the necessary air mass flow is caused by density differences (buoyancy). **Figure 5** shows the function of a natural draft cooling tower with closed- and open-circuit cooling systems. The heat exchange surfaces are right in the lower part of

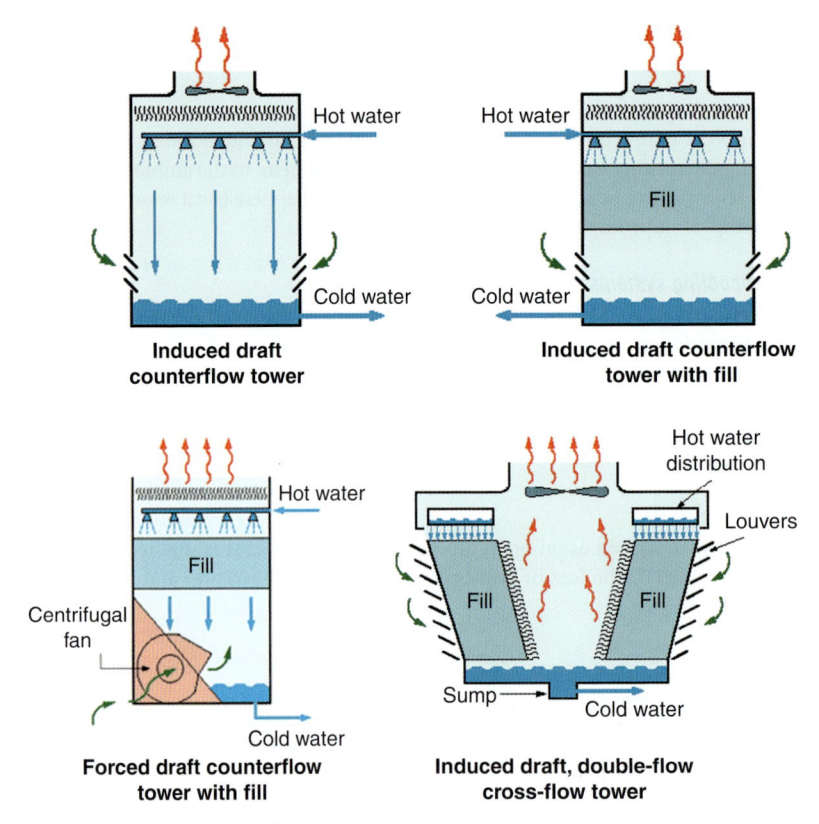

Figure 4 Wet cooling tower arrangements. Source: Geo4VA.

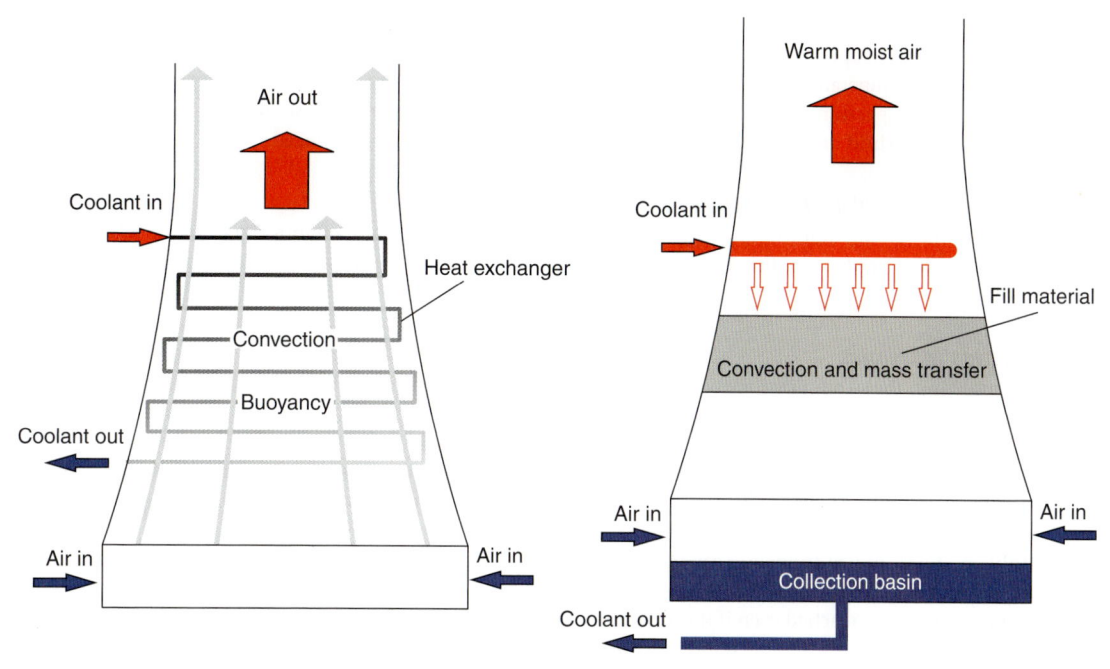

Figure 5 Natural draft cooling towers: closed circuit (left) and open circuit (right).

the tower, producing current by buoyancy. Compared with the mechanical draft system, the advantage is that the natural draft cooling tower does not demand power for the fans. The result is a positive impact on the achieved balance of the whole power station.

The natural draft wet cooling tower works in a similar way as the natural draft cooling tower with closed-circuit cooling system, but instead of the heat exchanger fill material is installed and the heat transfer mechanism functions in a different way.

3.18.2.4.5 Hybrid cooling towers

The hybrid cooling tower is a combination of a mechanical draft closed-circuit system and a wet recooling system. The warm coolant is partly injected into the cooling system; the other part is cooled down by an air-driven heat exchanger and can afterward be injected into the cooling system (**Figure 6**).

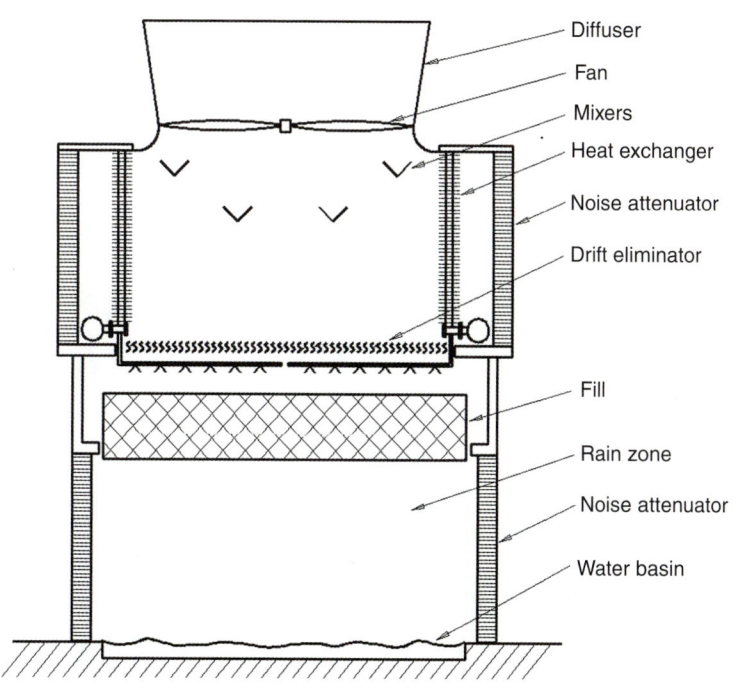

Figure 6 Hybrid cooling tower. Source: http://www.wetcooling.com.

The cooling tower can be operated according to the change in ambient temperature. At a low-level ambient temperature, only the air driven by heat exchanger is in operation. In case the ambient temperature increases, the wet cooling system can also be activated, to reach a very low coolant temperature. Hence, problems that occur in winter in the wet cooling systems can be avoided and in summer very low coolant temperatures can be reached. Moreover, the heat exchanger decreases fogging caused by the wet cooling system. When applying the hybrid driving mode, coolant consumption is considerably reduced.

3.18.2.4.6 Fan-assisted natural draft cooling towers

The design is similar to the natural draft cooling towers (**Figure 7**). In addition, big fans are introduced in the lower cooling tower. This additional air mass flow needs a smaller cooling tower. However, the mass flow caused by buoyancy is still very high, so that the fans are driven with low speed.

3.18.2.4.7 Air-driven condensers

In the air-driven condenser, the steam flowing away from the turbine condenses directly by means of a surface heat exchanger and the heat is transported directly to the ambient (**Figure 8**).

The heat exchanger tubes are finned to ensure better heat transfer. Cooling air supply is realized by mechanical draft. This system has the advantage that the steam is condensed directly so that no additional recooling system is required, and capital and operating costs decrease. Furthermore, such systems work without control, because the condensation occurs by itself. The disadvantage is that the accessible coolant temperature lies at ambient temperature level.

To fix this problem, the air-driven condenser can be combined with a hybrid cooling tower and a conventional surface condenser which transports the condensation heat to cooling water (**Figure 9**). This, however, requires higher capital costs. Thus, lower pressure in the condenser can be reached even if the ambient temperature is high. One such installed air-driven condenser, named LUKO of GEA Energietechnik GmbH, is shown in **Figure 10**.

3.18.3 Power Conversion Systems

3.18.3.1 Solar Only

3.18.3.1.1 Steam cycles

At present, most solar thermal power plants convert solar power into electricity applying Clausius–Rankine cycles. These steam cycles are basically of conventional technology and have only to be adjusted to the needs of the solar system. For example, the steam generator works with an HTF like thermal oil for the evaporation of water. When integrated with a solar cycle, some adjustments on the conventional cycle have to be made mainly in the heat recovery steam generator (HRSG), in order to consider the dynamical behavior of the solar part due to the changing weather conditions.

A steam cycle can be attached to almost all solar thermal systems except the solar dishes. **Figure 11** shows the operational scheme for a parabolic trough system with thermal oil as an HTF in combination with a conventional steam cycle.

Figure 12 shows the molten salt tower system with components of a conventional power plant, such as a steam generator.

Also a Fresnel system can be combined with the steam cycle of a conventional power plant.

Depending on the dimension of the power systems, one, two, or three pressure steam cycles in the steam are used. Taking into consideration the HTF used, one-cycle and two-cycle systems are applicable in order to transport the heat effectively to the steam turbine.

The main advantages of the conventional steam cycle are as follows:

Figure 7 Fan-assisted cooling tower. Source: GEA Energietechnik GmbH.

Concentrating Solar Power 601

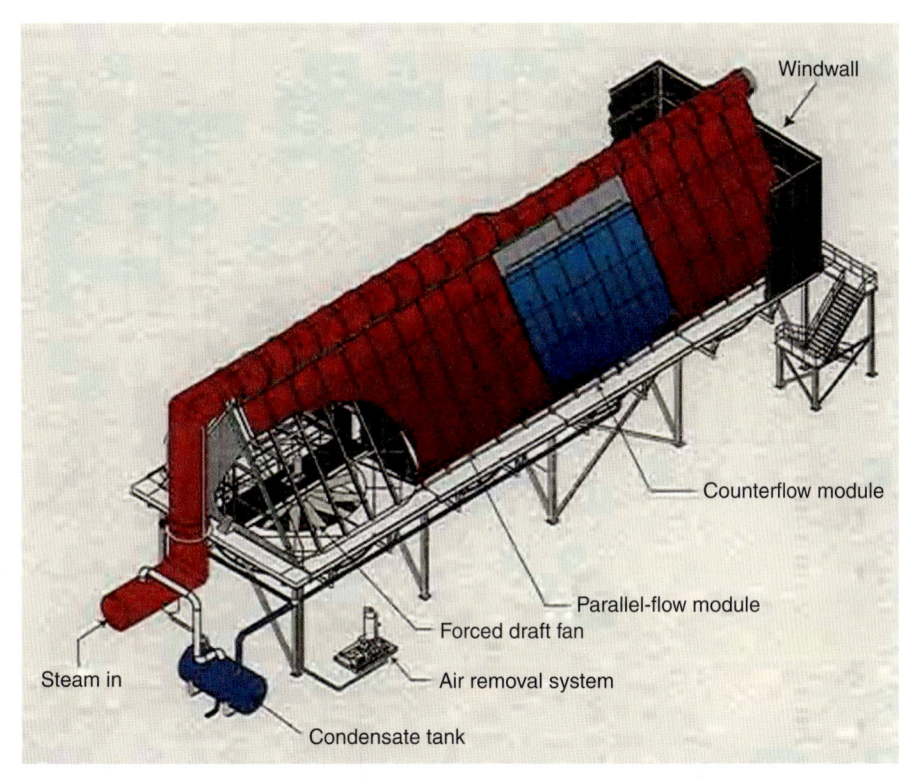

Figure 8 Two-stage, single-pressure air-driven dispenser. Source: GEA Energietechnik GmbH.

Figure 9 Parallel Condensing system (PAC®). Source: GEA Energietechnik GmbH.

Figure 10 Installed air-driven condenser. Source: GEA Energietechnik GmbH.

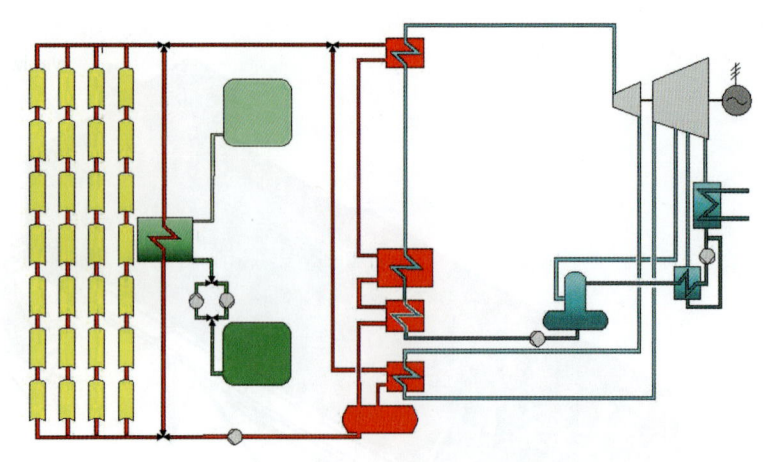

Figure 11 Process flow diagram of parabolic collector field combined with a steam power cycle.

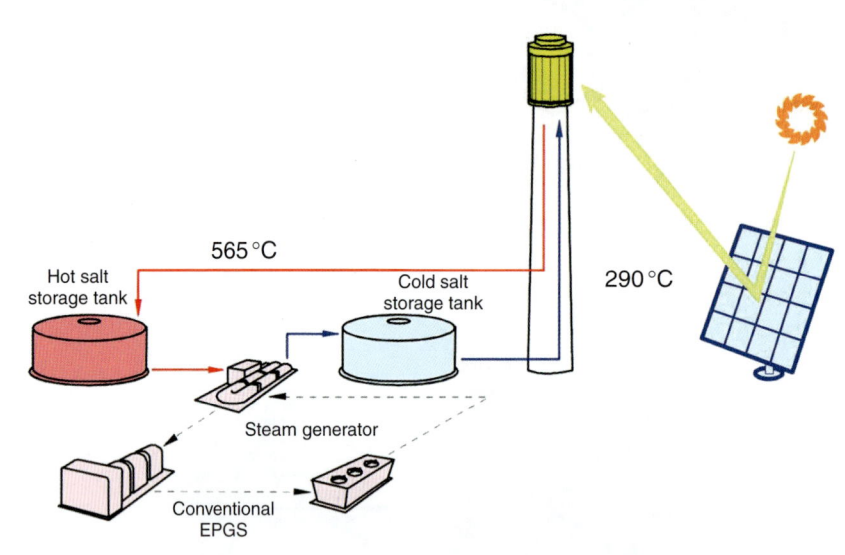

Figure 12 Process flow diagram of molten salt tower plant. EPGS, electric power generating system. Source: Sandia National Laboratories.

- Reasonably high efficiency of the steam cycle, especially the steam turbine
- High scale of power capacity from 1 MW to more than 1000 MW
- Applicable for the temperature ranges of solar thermal power plants
- Can be combined with hybrid systems as bottoming cycle to achieve higher efficiencies

The disadvantages are as follows:

- High water consumption for the cycle and/or for recooling
- Personnel need to have knowledge of the complex systems
- Can hardly be used as remote automatic power plant
- Not applicable for small-scale power plants

High efficiency is reached for large-dimension power plants due to the fact that for these plant sizes the components of the steam cycles are state of the art. But with appropriate adjustments to the conventional parts, even for small power plants good thermal efficiencies can be reached, and the high investment of the collector field is compensated.

For the efficiency of a Clausius–Rankine cycle, recooling is important, because the backpressure of the steam turbine reduces the possible expansion of the steam from high pressure to low pressure (vacuum). The backpressure is dependent on the recooling temperature. As solar power plants with recooling are located in regions with high ambient temperatures, this may have an impact when using recooling systems that use ambient air.

3.18.3.1.2 Organic Rankine cycles

Another alternative to conventional Clausius–Rankine cycles is the organic Rankine cycles (ORCs) used to convert thermal energy into electric energy. They work in a similar way but use an organic fluid for the cycle. These cycles are applied to lower temperature heat sources compared with water/steam cycles. ORCs are mainly used in combination with geothermal power or waste heat recovery in industrial processes. The range of the electrical power output is from some kilowatts to about 10 MW. Additionally, thermal energy can be produced, which does increase the overall efficiency. Due to the low temperatures, ORCs possess a lower theoretical Carnot efficiency at a maximum of 30% [1] than water/steam cycles. The temperatures of the working fluids are limited to about 250–350 °C due to thermal stability thresholds [1]. Working fluids include organic (hydrocarbon) fluids, namely, R-123, R-134a, R-245fa, R-717 (ammonia), R-601 (n-pentane), R-601a (isopentane), and C_6H_6 (benzene).

Generally, an ORC consists of components that are also included in a Clausius–Rankine cycle. The cycle consists of an evaporator, a superheater, a turbine/expander, a condenser behind the turbine, and a pump. Because of the organic fluids and their different freezing points, usually lower than that of water, the condenser does not work in subatmospheric pressures and is water- or air-cooled. In this configuration, ORCs with upper cycle temperatures of about 300 °C have an efficiency of about 12.5% [2]. The efficiency of the basic Rankine cycle can be increased by recuperation and reheating, which lead to efficiencies of 20.5% for the same boundary conditions [2]. In this case, the expanded fluid at the second turbine stage heats the fluid before entering the evaporator and is itself cooled down. Reheating takes place after the expansion in the first turbine stage by redirecting the heat to the boiler.

Additionally, when higher thermal energy source temperatures are available, the combination of two or three ORCs using different working fluids with different saturation temperatures can increase the overall cycle efficiency.

Reasonably high cycle efficiencies compared with other energy conversion techniques can be obtained by an ORC. Herein, the high turbine efficiency (up to 85% [1]) is the main advantage. Due to the low turbine speed, low mechanical stress, and absence of moisture in the vapor nozzles (thus no erosion of the blades), a long lifetime is guaranteed. Furthermore, the ORC has less operation and maintenance (O&M) costs and can be operated remotely because of the low pressures compared with steam cycles. Simple start–stop procedures and good part load behavior make the ORC an attractive energy conversion system.

Despite these advantages, the negative aspects have to be mentioned. The limited overall efficiency and the limited plant size due to the low source temperatures allow ORCs to be used only for certain applications. Using organic fluids may not be an environmentally friendly option, and some of these are forbidden by the Montreal Protocol as they are capable of destroying the ozone layer. Furthermore, dykes have to be installed to hinder fluid from entering the ground.

ORCs can work at lower temperatures, so the operating temperature of the parabolic trough can be reduced from about 400 to 300 °C. This allows to use inexpensive HTFs (e.g., Caloria) and combine it with a two-tank thermal energy storage system. Furthermore, lower operating temperatures result in lower capital cost for the solar components. By using organic fluids for the power cycle instead of water in combination with air cooling of the power cycle, the use of water is reduced to only the amount for cleaning the mirror surfaces, which is about 1.5% of the total water use at the solar electric generating systems (SEGSs) [2]. Another advantage, as mentioned before, is that the plant operation can be done remotely. This further reduces the O&M costs of solar thermal plants.

The combination of ORC and solar collectors follows a trade-off (**Figure 13**) between the single efficiencies to gain the maximum overall system efficiency. Increasing the temperature of the process will lead to a lower collector efficiency, but increases the ORC efficiency. Choosing the right medium temperature has a great impact on the overall system efficiency.

ORC installations have increased in the last few decades because of the optimization of the efficiency of industrial processes and the intensive application of renewable energies like biomass and geothermal. At present, the share of different applications in the ORC market is as follows: 48% biomass, 31% geothermal, 20% waste heat recovery, and 1% solar [3]. The solar thermal share of the ORC market is still low, but some applications have been installed. A choice of these installations is listed below:

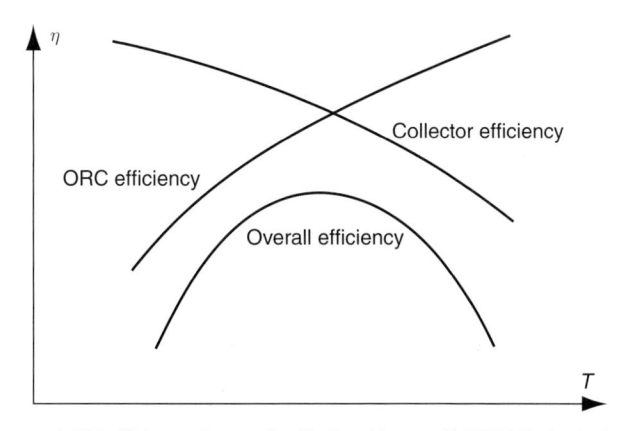

Figure 13 Trade-off between collector and ORC efficiency. Source: Quoilin S and Lemort V (2009) Technological and economical survey of organic Rankine cycle systems. In: *Proceedings of the 5th European Conference: Economics and Management of Energy in Industry.* Vilamoura, Algarve, Portugal, 14–17 April.

Figure 14 Solar ORC in Lesotho. Source: Solar Turbine Group.

- Arizona Public Service (APS) built a 1 MW$_e$ concentrated solar power (CSP) plant working with ORC in Arizona in 2006. Ormat International has supplied the 1.35 MW$_e$ gross power block and Solargenix Energy Inc. was the system integrator and the vendor of the 10 340 m^2 parabolic trough field [4]. The ORC runs with *n*-pentane as the working fluid and the peak solar-to-electrical efficiency is about 12.1% at the design point. The annual solar-to-electrical efficiency is 7.5% [5].
- Another prototype plant was built by GMK in Germany in 2005. The ORC power output is 250 kW$_e$, with the electrical efficiency of the system being about 15%. A parabolic trough field has not been built; instead, the solar system has been simulated by a natural gas boiler [3].
- The Solar Turbine Group developed small-scale systems for remote off-grid applications. **Figure 14** shows a 1 kW$_e$ system installed at Lesotho. Such systems have been developed to replace diesel generators in off-grid areas of developing countries. By using materials available in this country and designing an ORC that runs at medium temperatures, the levelized electricity cost (LEC) can be lowered (~0.12 $ kWh^{-1} compared with ~0.30 $ kWh^{-1} for diesel) [3].

3.18.3.1.3 Gas turbines

Introducing concentrated solar energy into a gas turbine (GT) system implements a new GT power plant concept. The GT can be combined with a dish/Brayton system as well as a solar tower. The receiver considered in both cases is a pressurized closed volumetric one. The heat transfer medium is forced through the receiver structure and is heated by convection.

In the combination of the GT with a dish/Brayton system, the solar radiation is focused by the dish concentrator and it enters the receiver through a quartz window. The window guarantees the closing of a pressure vessel. Air as an HTF enters the combustor and passes through the receiver, where it is heated up.

If required, an additional burner enables the daily operation of the plant. Hot air enters the turbine where it expands; the exiting hot air is connected to the GT combustor and the cycle is closed.

When the GT is combined with a solar tower (**Figure 15**), the receiver absorbs the concentrated solar irradiation and transfers the solar heat to pressurized air, which can be heated up to 1000 °C. The hot pressurized air from the solar receiver is directly fed into the combustion chamber of a GT, where natural gas is added to further heat the air to the turbine firing temperature design point.

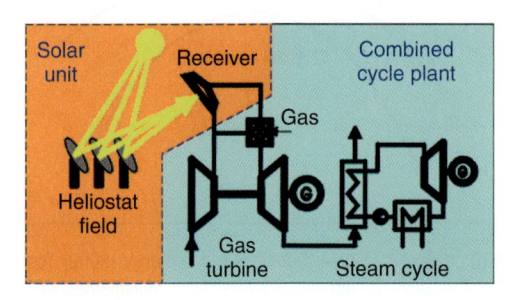

Figure 15 Scheme of solar hybrid GT system. Source: DLR.

The serial connection of pressurized solar air receivers with the combustion chamber of a GT allows a solar hybrid operation that can compensate for any deficiency in solar radiation. Thus, the power output of the solar-hybrid power plant can be guaranteed, independent of the sun's position or meteorological conditions, and still meets the utilities power demand requirements. Depending on the system configuration and operation strategy, the power output from solar energy can be between 40% and 90%, depending on the design conditions [6].

The concept of solar hybrid GT systems leads to the following advantages:

- High cost reduction potential due to the high conversion efficiency
- Low environmental impact due to low water consumption
  - GT Brayton cycle – no cooling water required
  - combined cycle configuration – up to 70% less cooling water required
- Reduced land use due to high conversion efficiency, which reduces collector area and land use
- Guaranteed dispatchable power

Different international projects like REFOS and SOLGATE have already been completed. Some are currently ongoing, like Solugas [7, 8].

The main objective of the Solugas project is to demonstrate the performance and cost reduction potential of a solar hybrid-driven GT system on a commercial scale. The German Aerospace Centre (DLR) and industrial partners, like GT manufacturer Turbomach and Abengoa Solar, participate.

3.18.3.1.4 Solar dishes

A dish/Stirling power plant is made of a parabolic dish concentrator, a solar receiver, and a Stirling engine. The system is hybrid, as it uses fuel to supplement solar power. **Figure 16** demonstrates the operational scheme of such a system. When solar energy is unavailable, the system can operate with fuel alone. Some dish/Stirling units have been tested and show tens or thousands of operation hours.

The Stirling engine can be replaced by a recuperated GT. In that case, a dish/Brayton system is formed as seen in **Figure 17**.

Many solar dishes, including Stirling or Brayton, can be combined together to form a solar dish power plant.

3.18.3.2 Increase in Operational Hours

3.18.3.2.1 Hybridization

Through hybridization, for example, by combustion of biofuel, the production of electricity can be increased up to 8600 h. It is expected that such hybrid power plants will have a high potential for market introduction in the next decade [10].

The concept of solar–fossil hybrid power plants offers a major option for accelerating the market introduction of solar thermal power technology. The advantage of solar–fossil hybrid power plants, compared with solar-only systems, lies in low additional investment costs due to an adaptable solar share and reduced technical and economical risks.

Many hybridization options are possible with natural gas combined cycle and coal-fired or oil-fired Rankine plants.

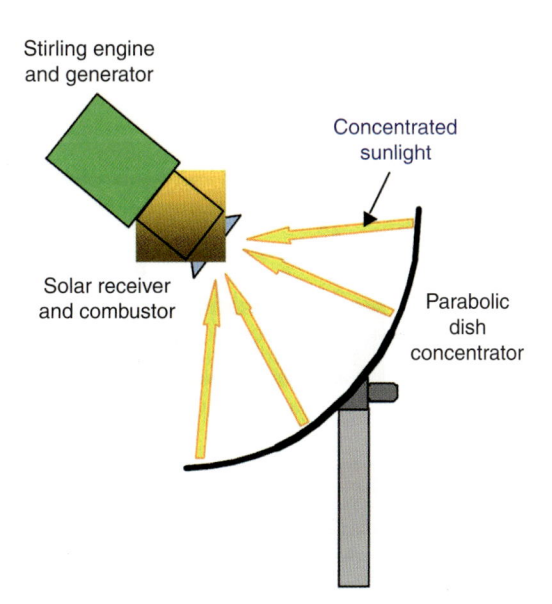

Figure 16 Operational scheme of a dish/Sterling system. Source: Pitz-Paal R, Dersch J, and Milow B (2005) European concentrated solar thermal road-mapping. *SES6-CT-2003-502578* [9].

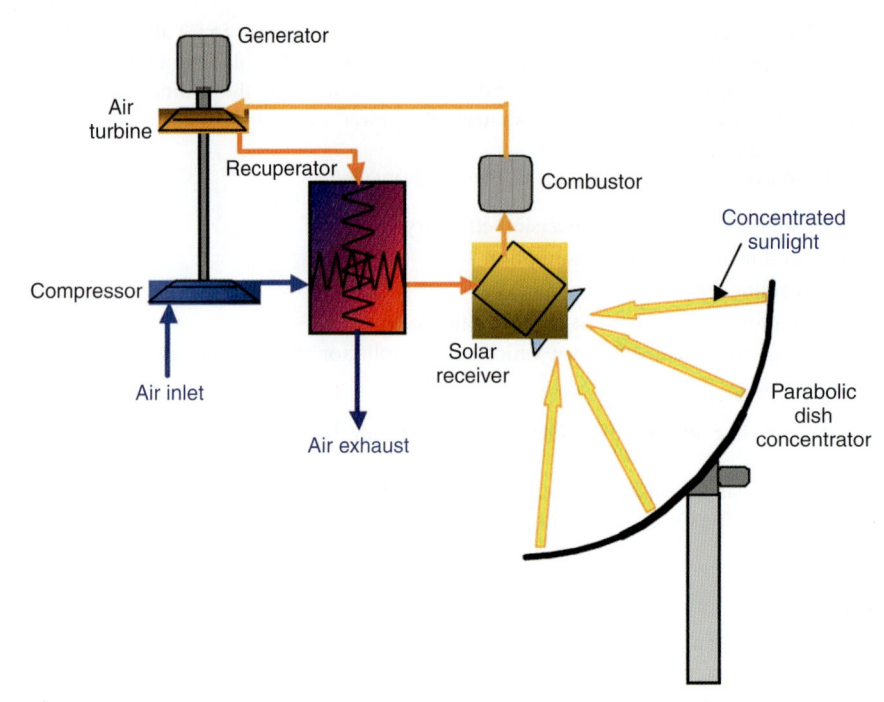

Figure 17 Operation scheme of a dish/Brayton system. Source: Pitz-Paal R, Dersch J, and Milow B (2005) European concentrated solar thermal road-mapping. *SES6-CT-2003-502578* [9].

An advantage of hybridization is that the power plant can be made dispatchable and this allows generation of electricity on demand. Hence, the plant can run more economically. Furthermore, hybridization leads to minimizing or neglecting thermal storage. Thus, the high costs of such a storage can be minimized.

3.18.3.2.1(i) Integrated solar combined cycle system

A hybrid solar power station is a solar thermal power station that uses a second energy source for heat production, besides the solar radiation. Non-fossil fuels, hydrogen, methanol, or fermentation gas can be used. These fuels are used when more electric energy is needed in case of low solar radiation. In addition, thermal energy can be stored to buffer the heat flows temporarily. The integrated solar combined cycle system (ISCCS; **Figure 18**) combines a solar parabolic through-collector field with a combined cycle power station.

The heat recovery boiler is modified to enable additional steam production by a solar steam generator or an afterburner. Solar heat is only partially used for steam production; in the absence of storage technologies, the annual solar heat produced in such types of power station is less than 20% (**Figure 19**).

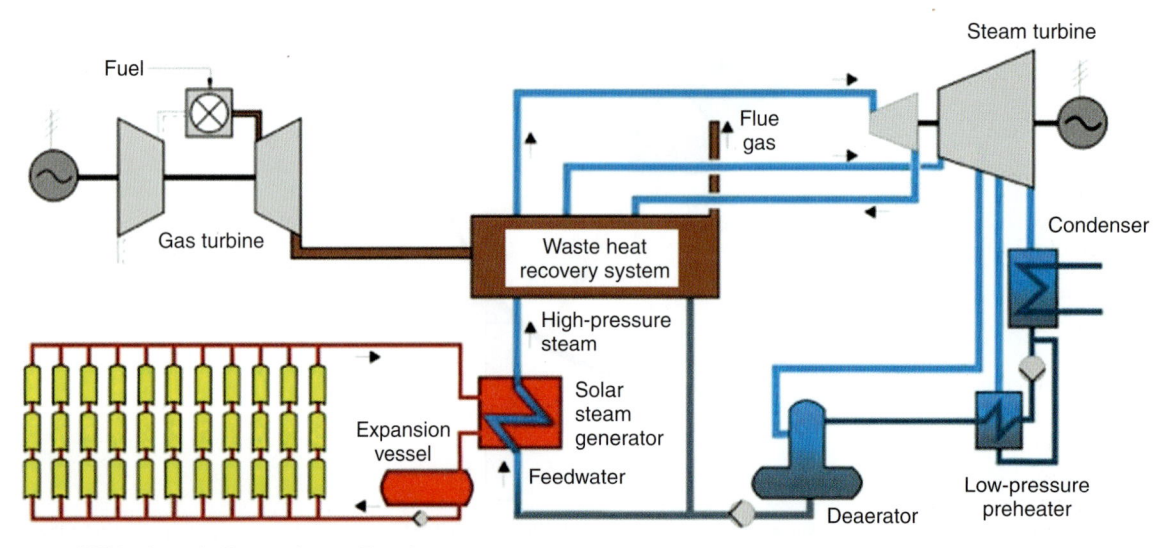

Figure 18 ISCCS schematic diagram. Source: Flagsol.

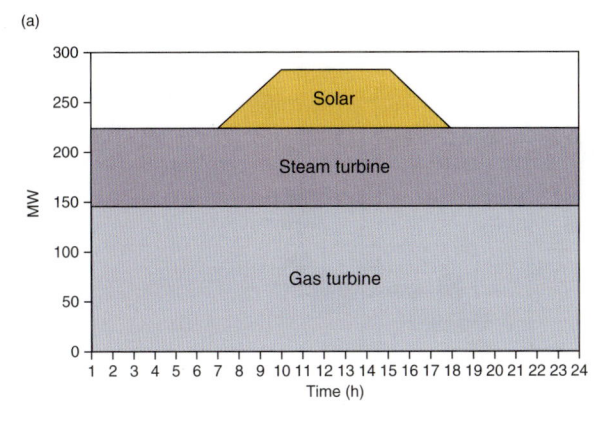

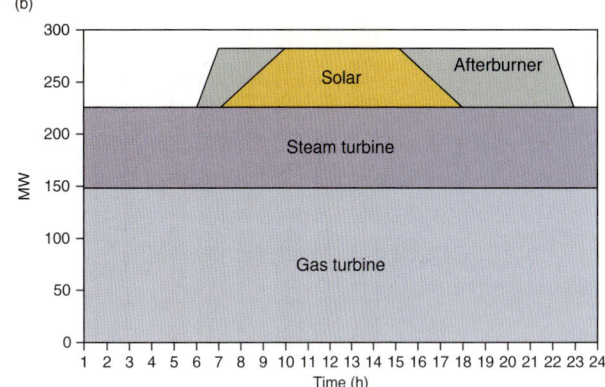

Figure 19 (a) Open-load and (b) base-load curves of ISCCS.

3.18.3.2.1(i)(a) Preheating for fossil power plants A solar thermal system may be a heat source, providing necessary heat for a heat exchanger of a steam power cycle, which might be a water preheater. On sunny days, the solar concentrated system provides the necessary heat; otherwise, fossil fuels in the conventional power plants take over. For preheating applications, Fresnel collectors, parabolic troughs, and solar towers are suitable. The collector area is specially dimensioned in order to match the required energy input. It may be located next to an existing coal or lignite power plant. Integration of a solar field enables reduction of CO_2 emission and saves fossil fuel.

3.18.3.2.1(i)(b) Gas engine Gas engines also enable hybridization of solar thermal power plants. Compared with other engines, gas engines may be of higher efficiency and there will be less environmental impact when using natural gas and biogas. A gas engine can work with biogas of low quality, which would be more difficult for GTs. Instead, GTs permit a higher variety in CH_4/CO_2 mixture. The advantages of using biogas compared with other biomass fuels are mainly the biomass-to-land use ratio due to the application of the whole plant, transport of biogas via pipeline, and the utilization in various machines and applications. Also hybridization of solar thermal power plants with biogas is of interest as the status of a renewable energy conversion plant is maintained.

Gas engines can be combined with parabolic trough as well as with tower power plants. Lower temperatures (in the range of 300 °C to almost 400 °C) of the flue gases of gas engines compared with those of GTs have to be considered. Due to this fact, gas engines are more applicable for parabolic troughs using thermo fluid. The flue gases of gas engines can also be integrated into other solar thermal plants, depending on their concept. In power plants running steam temperatures higher than 400 °C, the gas engine flue gases might be used for preheating. Compared with GTs, gas engines have a lower volume flow-to-installed capacity ratio because of almost stoichiometric combustion. Therefore, and due to efficiency of about 40% and more, the installed capacity of gas engines is higher to achieve a certain thermal power output. This capacity can be reached by using one or more engines that are connected. Possibly engines of capacities up to 100 MW_e may be installed to power parabolic trough power plants of 50 MW_e. More engines with less individual capacity can permit a better controllability of part load. Instead, in GTs, the combustion is over-stoichiometric, and additionally air is soaked in for cooling the turbine blades.

The use of gas engines for solar thermal power tower plants or Fresnel collectors with direct steam generation (DSG) depends on the live steam temperatures and the flue gas temperature of the engine. For DSG and power tower plants with water tube receiver and saturated steam production, the live steam parameters may be at about 400 °C where certain gas engines can produce flue gases at these temperatures. Nevertheless, even if the temperatures are too low for live steam production, gas engine flue gases can be heated up by an additional burner or can be used for preheating or evaporation. The flue gases' energy can be transmitted by a heat exchanger to the heat transport media or directly to the water/steam cycle. In combination with the open volumetric receiver concept of solar tower plants, the flue gases can be mixed with hot air which is heated up by the receiver and enter the HRSG. The hybridization of solar thermal power plants with gas engines predicts a dispatchable power plant which is independent of thermal storage, although the plant may include one for solar-only operation. At present, such hybridized plants speed up the market introduction of solar thermal power plants.

3.18.3.2.1(i)(c) Burner Hybridization is also possible with an additional burner in order to provide the steam parameters at the inlet of the steam turbine.

At the SEGS power plants, the hybridization with a burner was realized. **Figure 20** shows the schematic diagram of an optimal deployment of a burner in a parabolic trough system.

Thermal oil as an HTF is transported through the collector field and heated up. The heat is transported to water, and steam is produced in a boiler and expanded in the steam turbine, producing electricity. An additional burner provides the steam required on days with less solar radiation or at night.

The same hybridization may be realized when water/steam is used as an HTF. This concept has the advantage of leaving out heat exchangers, and is demonstrated in **Figure 21**.

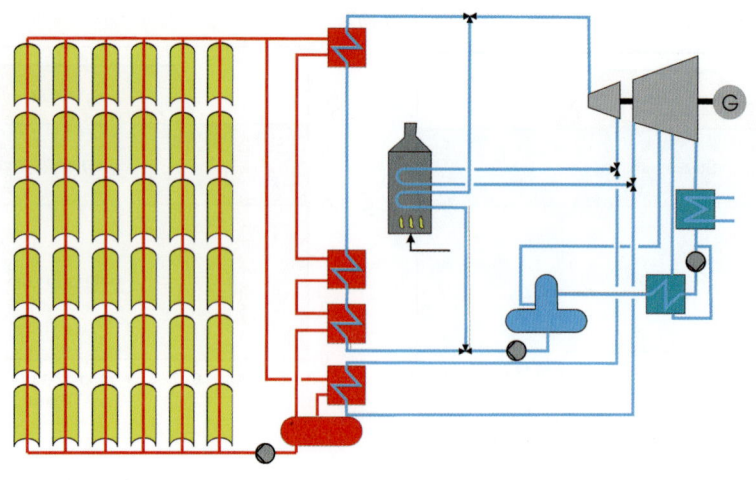

Figure 20 Additional burner for a PTC power plant. G, generator.

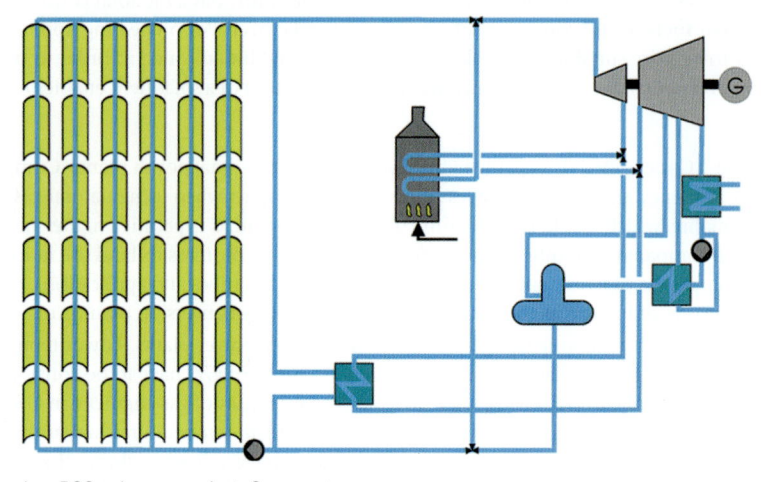

Figure 21 Additional burner in a DSG solar power plant. G, generator.

To achieve the gas parameters at the inlet of the HRSG, at a solar tower system with an open volumetric receiver, for nominal load even by less solar radiation, a channel burner is included. **Figure 22** shows the realization for such a hybrid system.

The burner heats up the preheated air from an open volumetric receiver to the desired temperature [11]. It can be operated in parallel or instead of the solar air receiver. Parallel means that on a day with little solar radiation, both components can provide the heat for the HRSG at the same time. In the other operation mode, the hybrid component is only switched on in the night or at times of no solar radiation.

3.18.3.2.1(i)(d) Gas turbine A GT can be combined with a solar tower with the use of open volumetric receiver. In the position of the burner, as shown in **Figure 22**, a GT is placed. The GT is in a position parallel to the receiver. The exhaust gas from the GT is mixed with the air from the receiver to get the nominal mass flow at a high temperature. After the HRSG, the exhaust gas is

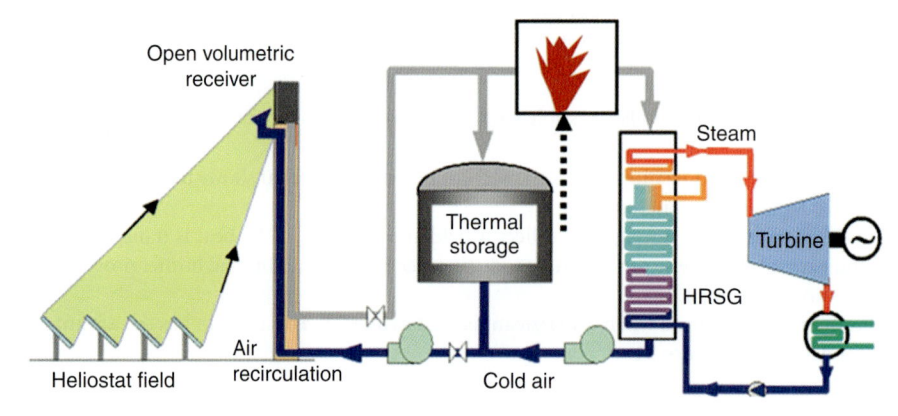

Figure 22 Schematic diagram of the Jülich demonstration plant with a channel burner. Source: SIJ.

recirculated to the receiver or can be passed to a stack. This hybridization concept has the advantages of combined cycles, like high efficiency, and additional power production by the GT. As fuel, natural gas or biogas (to maintain the status of the plant using renewable energies) can be used. In addition, the hybridization concepts can be used in different operation modes.

The combination of GT and closed volumetric receiver type for solar tower plants also permits hybridization. The compressed air is heated up by the concentrated irradiation and directed to the turbine. In case the solar power cannot heat the air to the needed turbine inlet temperature, a burner can be used to achieve the temperature by additional firing. This plant can also be operated in case of no solar radiation by using this setup as a conventional GT power plant.

3.18.3.2.2 Storage

Storages are classified as long- or short-term storages, according to their purpose.

While long-term storages are used to compensate for seasonal temperature fluctuations, short-term storages are intended for periods from a few minutes up to several days. Depending on the energy to be stored, there are a multitude of storage possibilities. Storage of electrical energy is either difficult to achieve or very expensive. The classic long-term storages in the energy sector are pumped storage plants.

A thermal storage system for solar power plants is used as a buffer. It stores thermal energy in times of high irradiation and enables the operation of the power plant after sunset and during periods of reduced solar input or cloud passages. By using storages, solar thermal power plants also gain the following advantages:

- Conservation of the conventional power plant components (protection of the turbine against increased loading due to constant starting up and shutting down)
- Cost savings for the power plant components – for example, due to the components of the steam cycle not having to be laid out for the maximum power rating of the receiver – which results in increased hours of operation of the steam cycle
- Possibility of various start-up strategies
- Enabling the supply of solar electricity at especially profitable times
- Flexibility – due to the storage and steam cycle having the same working temperature, the energy can usually be drawn faster from the storage and be directly supplied to the steam cycle; thus, warm-up times and delays in the process cycle are avoided

A great advantage of thermal power plants is the ability to store energy in many relatively low-priced ways. Economical thermal storage is a key technological issue for the future success of solar thermal technologies.

3.18.3.2.2(i) Solid media

The classic method of storing thermal energy is to choose a solid storage medium and increase its temperature by sensible heat transfer. Thermal storages with hot gases flowing through them have been in industrial operation for many years. These so-called regenerators are employed in flue gas cleaning and heat recovery in the metal industry.

This principle, as described in Reference 12, is implemented in the Jülich solar tower and serves as a heat storage for the solar tower power plant with an open volumetric receiver. The principle is depicted in the schematic diagram shown in **Figure 40**.

During charging, the HTF flows through the storage medium (**Figure 23**). For unloading, the flow direction is reversed. A temperature profile may develop over the height of the storage. This principle is illustrated in **Figure 24**. The steeper the temperature gradient, the greater the amount of storage medium that can be used for storage. The storage capacity varies mainly depending on the storage material chosen. In addition, the shape and distribution of the inventory materials are the decisive factors for the actual storage capacity per storage volume.

As mentioned in Reference 13, packed bed designs appear particularly attractive, but they have additional technical risks stemming from mechanical loads occurring during cyclic operations. A concrete heat storage developed by DLR offers low-cost prerequisites for heat storage for parabolic trough power plants with thermo oil as an HTF [14].

3.18.3.2.2(ii) Organic media

The term 'organic heat transfer media' describes hydrocarbon compounds as they are used in the ORC processes. Thermo oils used in current parabolic trough power plants also belong to this media group. Classical methods of heat storage for single-phase HTF are the one- and two-tank storage systems [15–17].

In the one-tank thermocline storage system, a single tank is used, which contains both the hot and cold heat transfer media. In order to prevent mixing of hot and cold fluids in the container, a thermocline stratification must be maintained. During charging of the storage, cold fluid is taken from the bottom of the tank, and after heating it flows back into the tank from the top.

During discharge, the flow direction is reversed. A simultaneous charging and discharging is theoretically possible if there are two sets of hot and cold pipes. In the two-tank system (hot/cold tank configuration), the hot and cold media are stored in separate tanks. In this way, a mixing, and therefore an exergy decrease, is prevented. This advantage, however, is achieved only with additional costs because of the need for two tanks.

3.18.3.2.2(iii) Phase-change materials

Due to their phase-change enthalpy, phase-change materials (PCMs) offer the greatest potential for large storage capacities per storage volume. In addition, during the entire melting time, this process provides an almost constant source temperature [18]. These materials have great advantages for operation with dual-phase HTFs. This technology is not as widespread as that of the sensitive heat storages

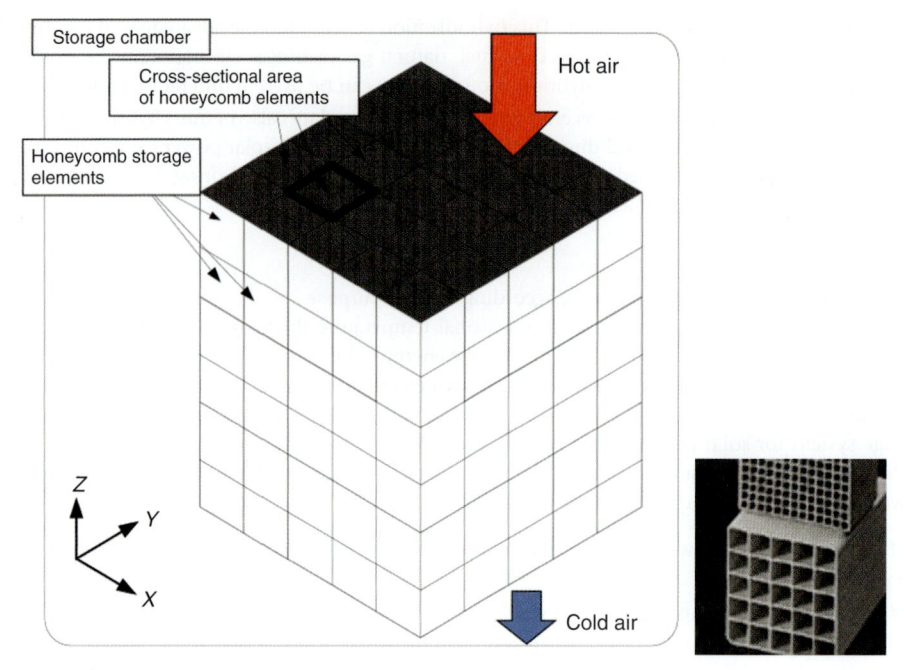

Figure 23 Storage layout and honeycomb element.

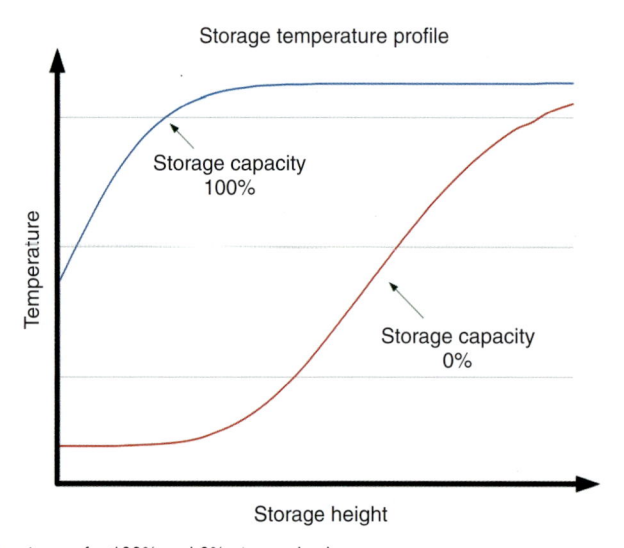

Figure 24 Temperature profile of the storage for 100% and 0% storage load.

(SHSs). The disadvantage is the usually lower heat transfer coefficient that can develop during loading and unloading. The reason is the solid–liquid interface, which moves away from the heat transfer surface during loading, causing an increase in the thermal resistance. A combination of PCM and SHS systems is the focus of current research [19].

There is an ongoing attempt to combine both advantages. Good heat transfer coefficients can be achieved with the SHS technology, and a high storage capacity can be reached using the latent heat storage (LHS) technology.

First, advanced storage materials based on PCM technology adapted to steam generation/condensation in the range of 200–300 °C have been tested by DLR in Almeria, Spain, in a plant with a power rating of 100 kW.

An expansion to 1000 kW with operating temperatures of 300 °C is being sought as described in Reference 19.

3.18.3.2.2(iv) Adiabatic pressurized air storage

Adiabatic pressurized air storage shows a new and low-cost possibility to store huge amounts of energy [20, 21]. This technology combines pressurized air storage with a heat exchanger. A standard method is to store pressurized air in caverns. A schematic diagram is shown in **Figure 25**.

During the charging process, ambient air is first compressed under high pressure and then in a subsequent step it passes the heat to a thermal storage system. When discharging, the stored heat is used. The pressurized air leaves the cavern and flows through the storage where it is heated up. Then the hot pressurized air is passed to a GT and electricity is produced. By this process, no additional

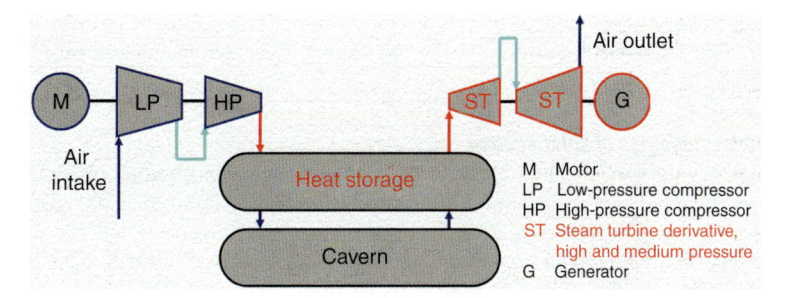

Figure 25 Schematic diagram of an adiabatic pressurized air storage system. Source: Bullough C, Gatzen C, Jakiel C, *et al.* (2004) Advanced adiabatic compressed air energy storage for the integration of wind energy. In: *Proceedings of the European Wind Energy Conference, EWEC 2004*. London, UK, 22–25 November.

heat is required. Since 1978, experience has been gained in the classical pressurized air storage technology [22]. This new technique, however, needs a pressure-resistant heat storage system (up to 200 bar), which has to withstand long operational periods and fluctuations of temperature of approximately 550 °C. Efforts for the construction of a 300 MW power plant are being made. The efficiency is estimated to be about 70% [20].

3.18.3.2.2(v)   Others

A high cost factor for all types of storages is the cost of the inventory materials. Considering future locations of solar power plants, raw sand which is almost free of charge would be an interesting storage medium. The concept of sand as a storage medium for a solar tower with a volumetric receiver has been evaluated to have high potential by DLR in Cologne (**Figure 26**). While in a ceramic storage one-third of the costs incurred are for the storage material, sand would be nearly free of charge and sufficiently available [13].

The key component is the air–sand heat exchanger. In recent years, a concept has been developed in the Solar-Institut Jülich (SIJ), and a test rig has been constructed [12]. In the cross-flow heat exchanger, sand flow is separated from the airflow channels by ceramic and woven-metal filter walls. The air flows through the sand bed, thus generating a temperature profile.

The sand which is heated up in the air–sand heat exchanger to approximately 800 °C (not directly irradiated as with a particle receiver [23]) flows to the hot storage through a downpipe and further to the fluid bed cooler. The fluid bed cooler, a unit which is a standard component of fluidized bed combustion units, is the driving element of the steam cycle. The generated steam is finally fed to the steam turbine for power generation. The cooled sand exits from the fluid bed cooler at a temperature of approximately 150 °C and either returns to the air–sand heat exchanger or is stored in the cold storage tank [12].

3.18.4   Cogeneration

3.18.4.1   Solar Cooling

Solar cooling can be either realized electrically or thermally driven. With respect to CSP technology, in general, both solutions are technically feasible. But when focusing on cogeneration options of CSP, only thermally driven cooling is relevant. Cooling with

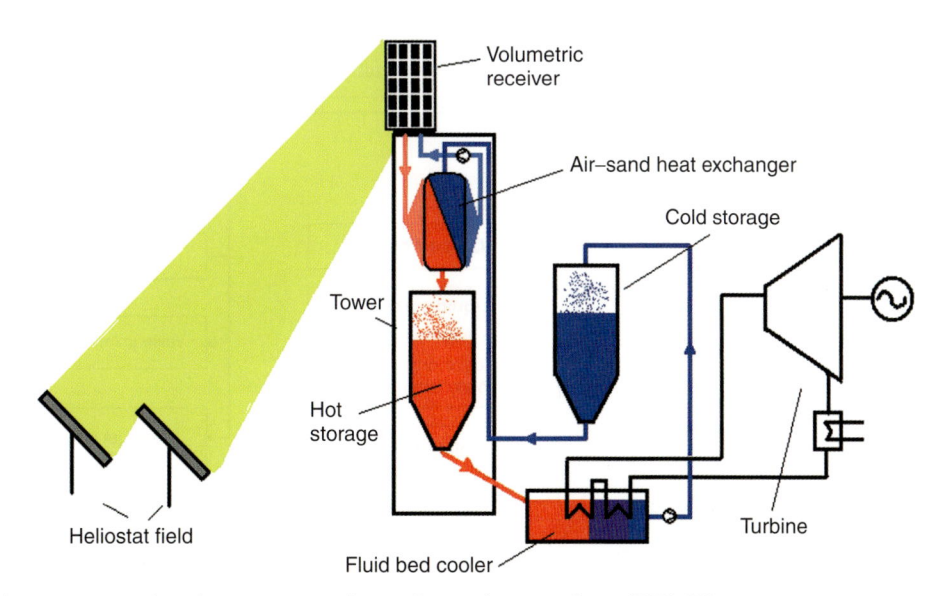

Figure 26 Sand storage concept for solar power towers. Source: German Aerospace Centre (DLR), SIJ.

solar energy is feasible without the use of ozone-depleting chlorofluorocarbons (CFCs) and helps lower the emission of greenhouse gases (GHGs). The global cooling demand is steadily increasing and varying. The potential in Europe for solar heating and cooling is presented in Reference 24.

3.18.4.1.1 Principles and technologies of solar cooling
The driving heat for any thermally driven chiller can be produced by solar energy with the appropriate technology, concentrated or not concentrated, that allows different temperature levels for the inlet heat. Varying cooling demand and intensity of solar radiation show the same pattern at many geographical sites which can be regarded as a benefiting coincidence. Another benefit is the fact that the use factor of the solar appliances (collectors, concentrators, and complete plants) can be easily increased when cogenerating heat and cold. The variation in principles is huge. **Figure 27** is an overview of different groups of solar cooling principles.

3.18.4.1.2 Thermally driven cooling systems
Well-proven thermally driven cooling technologies for cold production are absorption and adsorption chillers. Absorption cooling uses a liquid sorption material or a solid material (dry absorption). Solar thermal energy changes the refrigerant into a vapor.

Adsorption cooling uses a solid sorption material (water/silica gel or water/zeolite). Solar thermal energy dries out or regenerates the desiccant. The process is called the desiccant cycle. The cycles can be both continuous and intermittent.

3.18.4.1.3 Absorption chillers
In absorption chillers, a thermochemical process is used to drive a vapor compression cycle. The refrigerant in an absorption chiller dissolves in an absorbent solution for which it has a high chemical affinity. Two common refrigerant/absorbent combinations are water and lithium bromide (LiBr–H$_2$O) (used in water-cooled absorption systems) and ammonia and water (NH$_3$–H$_2$O) (used in air-cooled systems). Thermal energy for the absorption process can be supplied in different ways, for example, by gas burners and by recovering thermal energy from concentrated solar thermal power plants (cogeneration). The number of heat exchangers within the absorption chiller distinguishes the system as either single-effect or double-effect absorption chiller. Single-effect absorption chiller systems consist of an evaporator, an absorber, a generator, a separator, and a condenser and is shown in **Figure 28**.

The evaporator generates chilled water at 4–10 °C that is pumped to air conditioning units in the air distribution system. Solar flat-plate, evacuated tube, or parabolic trough collectors can be used to heat water from 77 to 99 °C, which is circulated through the generator to heat the refrigerant/lithium bromide solution.

Double-effect absorption chiller systems use a high-temperature generator and a low-temperature generator to improve the thermodynamic efficiency of the absorption cooling cycle. Operation of the evaporator and the absorber is the same as that of the single-effect system. The high temperature for the heating cycle of a two-stage chiller requires concentrating solar collectors, like PTCs. Steam units operate with a pressure of 3.5–9 bar, which can be produced directly by a field of trough collectors. In triple-effect absorption chiller systems, two single-effect absorption circuits are combined. A basic figure to describe the quality of the conversion of heat into cold is the thermal coefficient of performance (COP). It is defined as the useful cold (Q_{cold}) per unit of invested driving heat (Q_{heat}). Single-effect lithium bromide chillers operate with thermal COP that is limited to about 0.7. Double-effect chillers can have thermal COP in the range of 1.0–1.5.

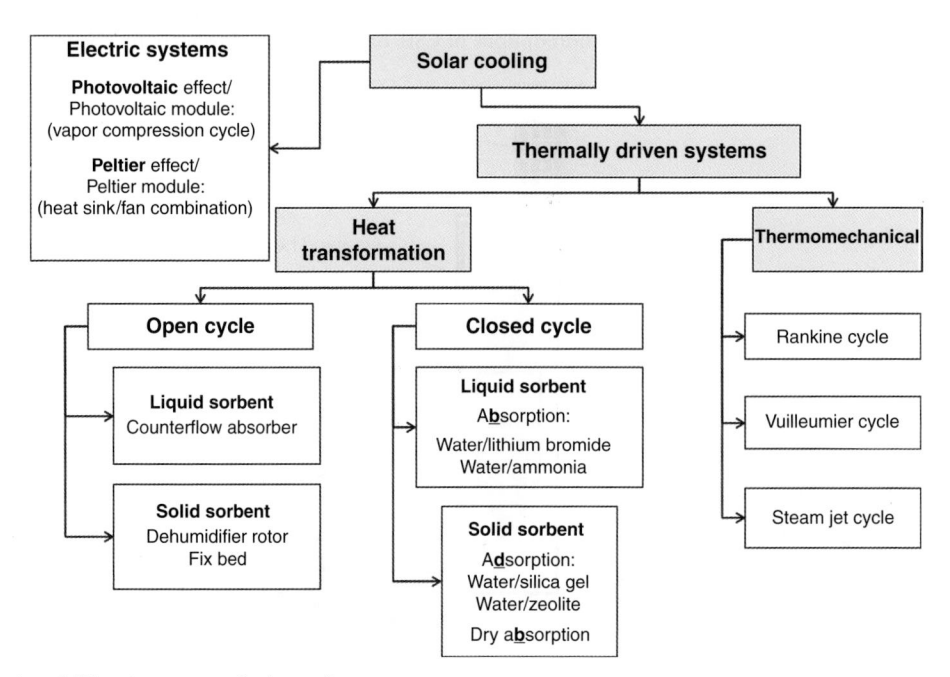

Figure 27 Overview of different processes of solar cooling.

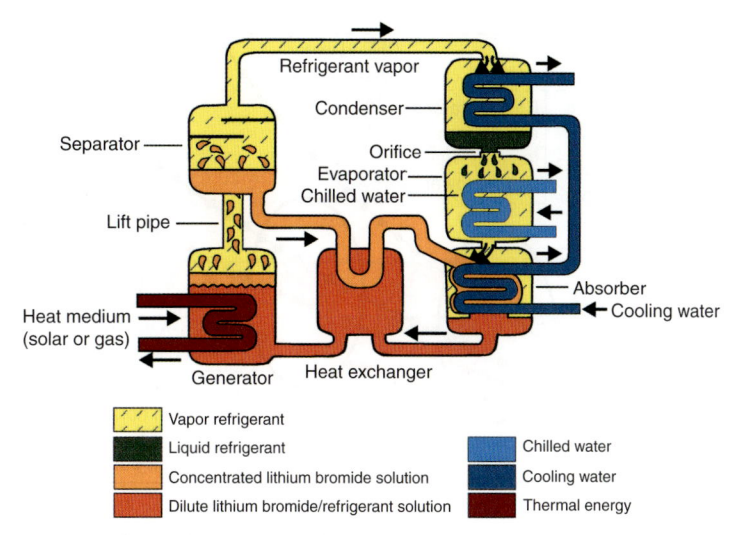

Figure 28 Single-effect absorption chiller. Source: http://www.yazakienergy.com.

3.18.4.1.4 Adsorption chillers

The adsorption cycle needs a lower heat source temperature than the absorption cycle. It operates with silica gel/water or with zeolite/water as working pairs. Adsorption and desorption take place in reversible cycles. Large heat exchange surfaces permit a mode of operation close to the thermodynamic limits. An adsorption chiller consists of two or four chambers, a condenser, and an evaporator. **Figure 29** shows a simplified schematic of an adsorption chiller with two chambers.

In the system shown in the figure, the water, bounded to the silica gel, is driven out of the right chamber while heat is being transferred into the same stage. Subsequently, the water is liquefied in the condenser. The heat is transferred to the cooling water. In the low heat chamber (left), the water vapor is adsorbed and the resulting heat is dissipated to the cooling water. The inlet temperature of the hot water side of an adsorption chiller can be below 75 °C. Thus, solar or waste heat of a low temperature level can drive an adsorption chiller [25].

3.18.4.1.5 Best-practice examples for solar cooling

The increasing demand for small-scale solar heating and cooling systems results in a number of installed systems for air conditioning in residential houses or small offices. Within IEA Task 38, a large number of these systems are included in the monitoring and evaluation procedures [26]. To date, 23 systems have been identified which cover all relevant technologies and a broad range of different climatic conditions. An overview of installed solar cooling systems worldwide is given in Reference 27. The AEE Institute for Sustainable Technologies (Austria) runs a project with several partners to demonstrate industrial cooling technology using a solar-driven steam jet ejector chiller (SJEC). The steam uses water as a refrigerant. An operation between 150 and 200 °C is planned. Therefore, PTCs are being coupled.

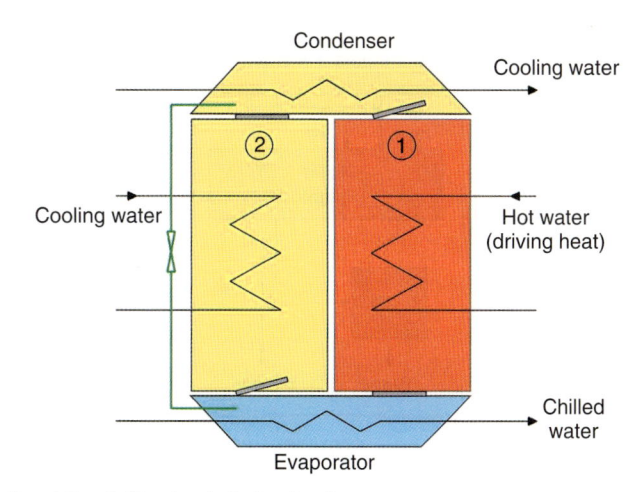

Figure 29 Schematic of an adsorption chiller. 1, Chamber 1; 2, chamber 2.

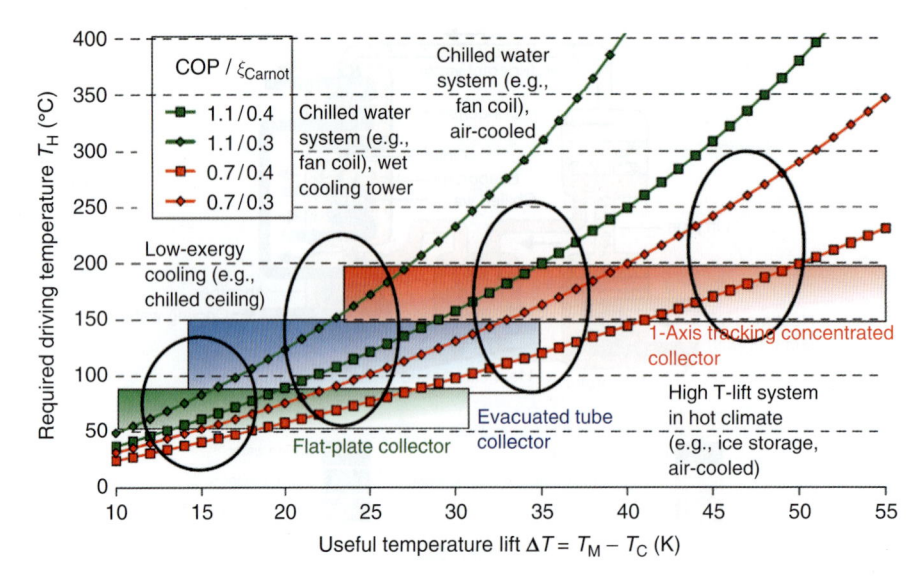

Figure 30 Required heat source temperature as a function of the required temperature lift between required temperature of cold production (low-temperature heat source) and temperature for heat rejection. Curves refer to different COP/ξ_{Carnot} ratios (ξ_{Carnot} is the Carnot efficiency factor). Typical operation temperature ranges of different solar collector technologies are marked by colored areas. The ellipses indicate different system designs [28].

3.18.4.1.6 State of the art of solar cooling

Some of the cooling technologies described are still in the status of pilot projects or system testing. **Figure 30** gives an overview, which compares the different systems with respect to different driving temperatures according to temperature lift showing the suitable combination of solar collector and cooling technology with their expected COP.

3.18.4.1.7 Market expectations for solar cooling

The growing demand for air conditioning in homes and small office buildings is producing a growing market for different types and scales of solar-assisted cooling technologies. Basic and applied research in the field of thermally driven cooling is currently dominated by Japan and, increasingly, China. Europe lagged behind for some time, but due to advances in the efficiency of energy transformation chains, European R&D institutes and universities have been increasing their efforts on thermally driven cooling technology, and specifically on its operation in combination with solar energy. Today, Europe is one of the global leaders in the implementation of solar thermal cooling technology [29].

3.18.4.2 Desalination

A number of CSP systems including the solar tower technology can be used for desalination as well [30]. There are different ways for the exploitation of the heliostat field for producing clean water (**Figure 31**).

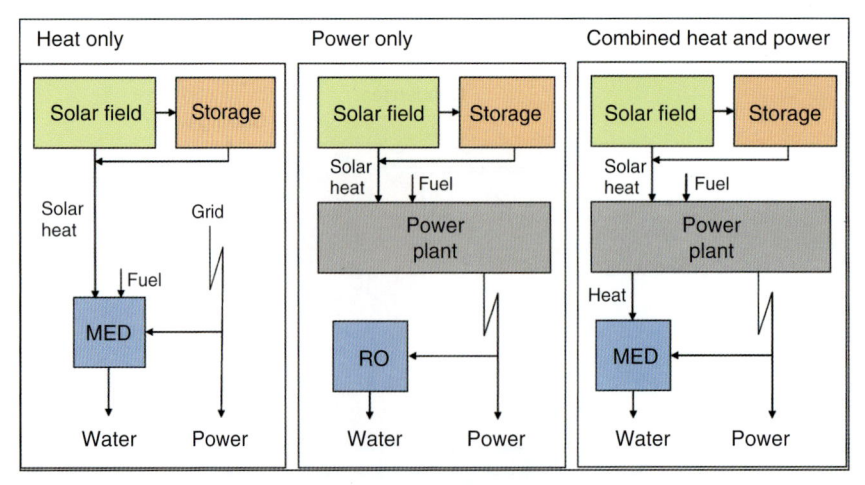

Figure 31 Desalination systems combined with solar tower. Source: (2007) AQUA-CSP concentrating solar power for desalination. *Final Report by German Aerospace Center (DLR)*. Stuttgart, Germany, November.

Worldwide, a large number of different desalination technologies are available and applied [30]. Only some of these technologies reached a semicommercial state and can be applied in large units in order to be effectively combined with CSP plants.

At present, either multieffect desalination (MED) systems or reverse osmosis (RO) units are used. The MED system needs electricity and heat, whereas RO needs only electricity.

MED is a thermal distillation process and has gained attention due to its better thermal performance [31]. MED plants can be configured for high- or low-temperature operation and can be coupled to a condenser of a steam cycle. The MED process is composed of a number of elements, which are called effects. As described in Reference 32, the steam from one effect is used in order to heat another effect which, while condensing, causes evaporation of a part of the salty solution. The produced steam goes through the next effect, where the same condensing and evaporating phenomena take place.

RO is a membrane separation process that recovers water from a saline solution pressurized to a point greater than the osmotic pressure of the solution. Membrane layers hold back the salt ions from the pressurized solution, allowing only the water to pass.

Figure 31 shows three different desalination systems combined with a CSP. The first desalination system in combination with a solar tower (see **Figure 31**, left) uses only the heat from the solar cycle for the supply of the MED system with heat and the electricity is provided by the grid. In the second system, the solar tower provides only the electricity necessary for the RO unit (see **Figure 31**, middle). The RO plant uses electricity generated by a solar thermal power block to work the pumps. The only high energy requirement is to pump the feedwater at a pressure above the osmotic pressure. High pressures must be used, typically 50–80 bar, in order to have a sufficient amount of water pass through a unit area of membrane [33].

The third MED system (see **Figure 31**, right) includes the conventional cycle for supplying the desalination system with heat and electricity.

These three systems may find application in islands and coastal areas that face water shortage problems.

Desalination plants are to be operated nonstop. Therefore, a solar tower power plant should be in operation day and night [34]. This is possible only with an additional storage unit or with the hybridization of the plant.

3.18.4.3 Off-Heat Usage

In all thermodynamic cycles, it is beneficial to use as much of the heat produced as possible, since this increases the efficiency of the cycle as a whole. This is especially important in solar thermal power plants, since they are usually built in areas with little access to cooling water. By reducing the temperature of the waste steam as much as possible, the condensation power required for the recycling of the process steam can be reduced.

The sources of waste heat in a CSP plant are either steam or heated air, depending on the type of plant and individual thermodynamic cycles.

Apart from the previously discussed cogeneration applications of desalination and cooling, waste heat can also be profitably used for other applications. Possibly the simplest and most obvious use of this energy is the same process carried out in every thermal power plant, that is, the preheating of the feedwater for the power production cycle. This is one of the highest temperature applications of waste heat and is carried out by a heat exchanger between the steam exiting the steam turbine and the feedwater entering the boiler.

The applications suitable for the waste heat are determined by its source temperature. Low-temperature heat (<100 °C) is suitable for hot water and space heating in residential, commercial, and institutional buildings, schools, hotels, and swimming pools as well as for crop drying.

CSP plants often suffer the disadvantage of variable solar irradiance, which results in unstable steam or hot air parameters. This could prove to be a severe disadvantage for applications such as crop drying, since these require very precisely controlled air temperatures. However, the advantage of these lower temperature applications is that even with fluctuating power process parameters, low-temperature applications (of up to approximately 100 °C) are practically always sustainable.

Higher temperature waste heat (>100 °C) can be used for industrial processes, for example, in the paper and food industries and sterilization.

In the best-case scenario, solar tower power plants will be run on a combined cycle similar to many modern fossil-fueled power plants, with a GT topping and a steam turbine bottoming cycle. Only then will the true potential of the technology be harnessed. In this case, the waste heat of the GT will be the energy supply for the steam production for the steam turbine, and waste heat from both heated air and steam will be readily available.

A further possibility for central receiver power plants is that waste heat may be obtained from the peripheral areas of the receiver, where air can be heated to 200 or 300 °C, containing enough thermal energy to drive waste heat processes but not enough to produce power in a steam turbine or GT.

3.18.5 Examples

3.18.5.1 Commercial

3.18.5.1.1 SEGS

In the years between 1985 and 1991, the nine commercial parabolic trough power plants SEGS I–IX were commissioned in California, USA. In total, the plants generate an electrical power of 354 MW$_e$, which is fed into the grid. The first of the plants, SEGS I,

Figure 32 The parabolic troughs used in the SEGS. Source: Sandia National Laboratories.

generates 13.8 MW$_e$, the plants SEGS II–VII generate 30 MW$_e$, and plants SEGS VII–IX deliver 80 MW$_e$. The reflective aperture area varies between 83 000 m^2 for SEGS I and 484 000 m^2 for SEGS IX.

The parabolic troughs which are used in the SEGS plant are shown in **Figure 32**.

For these plants, no thermal storage system is installed. However, all nine plants are operated in gas hybrid mode, that is, in a gas operation that enables a continuous plant operation during periods of overcast or night hours. When in gas operation mode, the steam quality is improved. As an example, SEGS IX produces a steam temperature of 371 °C at a pressure of 100 bar in solar mode, but a far higher steam temperature of 510 °C at a pressure of 105 bar is produced in gas mode. However, the solar energy is already sufficient to generate superheated steam for the plants SEGS II–IX when in solar mode. **Figure 33** shows a view of the SEGS parabolic trough system.

3.18.5.1.2 Andasol 1–3

In Andalusia, Spain, Europe's first parabolic trough power plant – Andasol 1 – with an electrical power capacity of 50 MW$_e$ was constructed, which – with an area of 510 000 m^2 – has the largest collector area in the world when compared with other parabolic trough-type power plants. It has been planned to construct two more similar plants with the same electrical power output as

Figure 33 A view of the SEGS parabolic trough system. Source: Sandia National Laboratories.

Figure 34 A view of Andasol 1 and Andasol 2. Source: ESTELA.

Andasol 1, which will be named Andasol 2 and Andasol 3. **Figure 34** shows both Andasol 1 and Andasol 2 parabolic trough power plants.

The field size of each of the three power plants is 510 120 m^2. A total of 209 664 mirrors and 22 464 receivers (absorption pipes), each with a length of 4 m, will be installed.

A heat storage system using 28 500 tons of molten salt (mixture of potassium, sodium, and nitrate salts) consisting of a hot salt and a cold salt tank will deliver a storage capacity of 7.5 peak load hours when using the stored heat for electricity generation. This enables the operation of the power plant well into the night hours and allows the buffering of short and longer periods of cloud passages or overcasts.

The size of the solar field is large enough so that there is sufficient collector area for running the plant's steam turbine at nominal load and also for simultaneously charging the thermal storages during the day. In the two-tank system, the molten salt in the hot salt tank is heated up to 390 °C, and by keeping a minimal temperature of 290 °C, solidification of the salt is prevented. **Figure 35** shows the schematic diagram of the Andasol power plant. With the aid of the thermal storage, 3500 peak load hours of operation should be realized [35].

The thermal storage system is being loaded during the day. During the night, the power plant can be operated with the stored energy.

3.18.5.1.3 PS10, PS20

The plant Planta Solar 10 (PS10), on the Plataforma Solar de Sanlúcar la Mayor (PSSM), has been connected to the grid since June 2007. It is located near Seville, Spain, and went into operation in 2006. It delivers a nominal gross power of 11.5 MW$_e$ and produces an estimated 24.3 GWh of electricity per year – enough to supply 6000 households. A total of 624 heliostats, each with a surface area of 120 m^2, concentrate the incident direct normal irradiation (DNI) onto a saturated steam receiver.

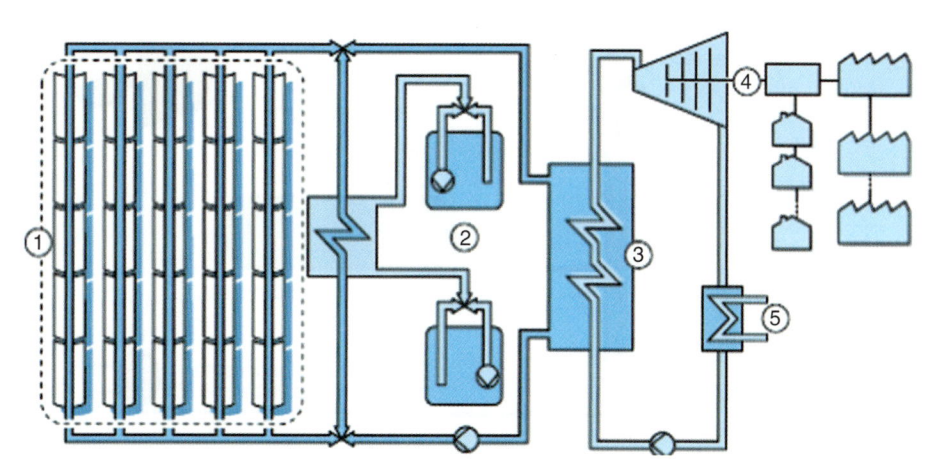

Figure 35 Schematic diagram of the Andasol power plant. Source: Solar Millennium AG. 1, Solar collector field; 2, storage; 3, heat exchanger; 4, steam turbine; 5, condenser.

Figure 36 Bird's-eye view of PS10. Source: (2006) 10 MW solar thermal power plant for southern Spain. *Final Technical Progress Report.* November.

This direct evaporation receiver uses water/steam as an HTF and is installed at a height of 100 m from the foot of the tower, which has a total height of 115 m. **Figure 36** provides a bird's-eye view of PS10. The heliostat field has a total area of 75 216 m². The heliostats are positioned in a north-only array in 35 concentric rows [36].

The PS10 solar tower was the first commercial solar tower in Europe. PS10 has been designed on a very conservative approach. The schematic diagram of the plant is shown in **Figure 37**.

It works on a conventional and reliable concept based on direct saturated steam generation in the receiver. The generated steam leaves the receiver in saturated state at 250 °C, at a pressure of 40 bar, and is passed over a steam turbine, whose shaft drives the generator to produce electricity. The operational availability of the plant in the first months, between 21 June 2007 and 24 October 2007, was 98%.

A thermal storage allows the buffering of cloud passages for 50 min, however, only at half of the turbine workload [36]. Spanish law allows for a gas cocombustion of up to 15%. On clear days such as those referred to above, no cocombustion is necessary. However, on days of variable DNI, cocombustion guarantees constant and reliable operation of the plant. During the night, the plant shuts down. By the operation of the plant, approximately 20 000 tons of CO_2 emissions are avoided per year.

PS20 is located right next to PS10 and went into operation in 2009. It generates 20 MW_e gross power with an energy turnover of 50 600 MWh a^{-1}. A direct evaporation receiver, also using water/steam as an HTF, is installed at the top of the 161 m tower. The heliostat field consists of 1255 heliostats, each with a reflective mirror area of 120 m², totaling to an area of 150 000 m². The heliostats are positioned in a north-only array in concentric rows.

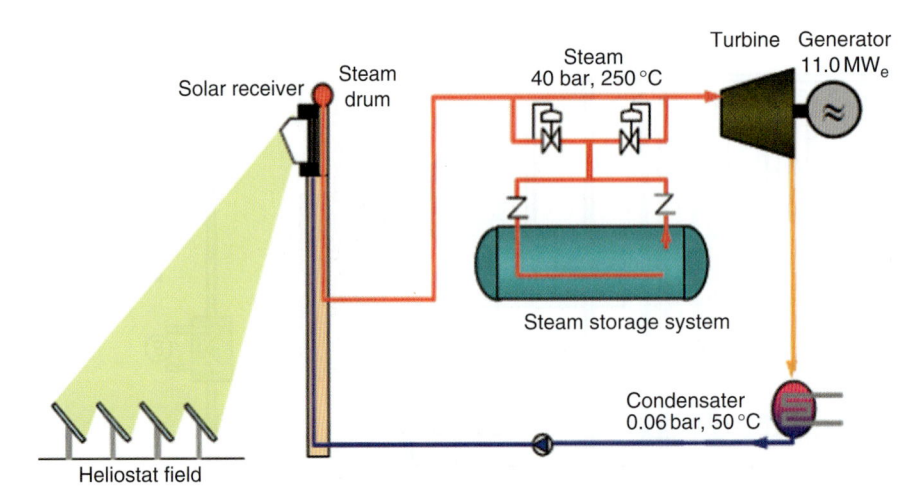

Figure 37 Schematic diagram of PS10. Source: (2006) 10 MW solar thermal power plant for southern Spain. *Final Technical Progress Report.* November.

The generated steam leaves the cavity receiver in saturated state at 250–300 °C at a pressure of 45 bar and is passed over a steam turbine. A thermal storage allows the buffering of cloud passages for 1 h.

3.18.5.1.4 STJ

In Germany, the construction of a 1.5 MW$_e$ solar tower power plant began in 2008. It has been operational since December 2008 and started the production of electricity in the spring of 2009.

Professor Bernhard Hoffschmidt was the initiator of the project and he set the basis for the realization of the construction of the first solar tower power plant, which uses air as an HTF. The plant as seen in **Figure 38** was built by Kraftanlagen München and is operated by the local utility Stadtwerke Jülich. The SIJ of the Aachen University of Applied Sciences and the DLR conduct the accompanying research. The location of Jülich was chosen not only because it is close to the research institutions involved but also because of its fluctuating direct solar radiation that allows and requires investigation of the system operation strategy under transient conditions – especially in combination with thermal storage.

The objective of the solar power tower project in Jülich is to demonstrate the entire system. The whole venture is funded by the finance ministries of the states of North Rhine-Westphalia and Bavaria and the German Ministry of Environment.

The Jülich central receiver plant has been designed to deliver up to 11 MW$_e$ of thermal energy, which will supply the grid with a nominal power of 1.5 MW$_e$. **Figure 39** shows a bird's-eye view of the STJ. The concentrator system consists of 2150 sun-tracking heliostats of about 8 m^2 reflective surface each and reflects the sunlight onto a 22 m^2 receiver aperture in the shape of an inclined segment of a cylinder. The applied open volumetric receiver technology is used to heat up ambient air to high temperatures for steam generation in a boiler of a conventional steam turbine cycle. The porous absorber located at the top of a 60 m tower traps the highly concentrated solar radiation inside the structure, allowing the heat to be transferred to air very effectively. The receiver is made up of identical subreceivers, in which the absorber modules can easily be exchanged in case of failure or to test innovative modules [12].

The advantages of this technology are simplicity and scalability, the ability to include a thermal storage, the low thermal capacity (quick start-up), and a high efficiency potential due to high achievable temperatures.

Figure 38 The STJ in operation. Source: Kraftanlagen München GmbH.

Figure 39 Bird's-eye view of the STJ. Source: M. Kraus University of Applied Science Aachen.

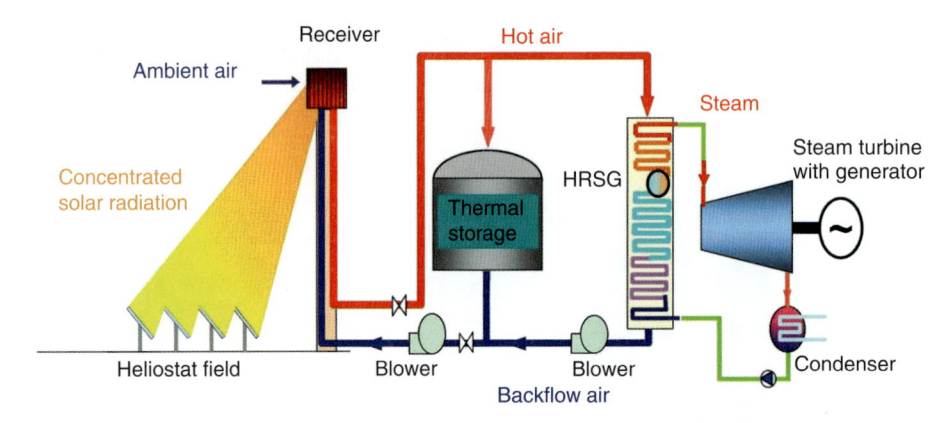

Figure 40 Schematic diagram of the Test and Demonstration Power Plant Jülich. Source: SIJ.

Figure 40 shows a schematic diagram of the Test and Demonstration Power Plant Jülich. The heat is transferred to air, which is sucked through the receiver structure. The hot air is transported to the storage system or the HRSG.

In the conventional cycle, steam is produced in the boiler and thermal energy is transported to a steam turbine. The steam expands in the turbine, producing mechanical work which is then converted into electrical energy by a generator. The exhaust steam from the turbine is then condensed in a condenser, and the condensate is thereafter pumped to the boiler where it receives heat from the solar receiver again, and the cycle is repeated.

A thermal storage unit is integrated into the air cycle, through which the operation of the power plant can be held for a certain time at constant power, depending on the storage dimensions. In principle, this thermal storage can be designed with an unlimited capacity, securing a continuous power plant operation. It is used as a buffer that stores energy in times of high irradiation and enables operation of the plant after sunset or during periods of reduced solar input.

3.18.5.1.5 Nevada Solar One

Nevada Solar One is a 64 MW$_e$ commercial-scale solar energy parabolic trough power plant located near Boulder City, Nevada, USA, which started operation in June 2006. The parabolic trough receiver uses oil as an HTF, which is heated to a temperature of 300 °C. The oil is passed over a steam generator where steam is generated to drive a 75 MW Siemens reheat steam turbine. The plant can keep the steam temperature stable during times of cloud passages by using a natural gas backup [37].

Figure 41 gives a view of the parabolic trough field.

3.18.5.1.6 Sierra SunTower

The Sierra SunTower Solar Generating Station is located in Lancaster, California, about 80 km northeast of Los Angeles (**Figure 42**).

The project site occupies approximately 8 ha on a 34 ha property in an arid valley in the western corner of the Mojave Desert. **Figure 43** shows a panoramic view of the heliostat field and the tower, approximately 50 m in height, of the Sierra SunTower plant.

Figure 41 Nevada Solar One. Source: Acciona.

Figure 42 Sierra SunTower power plant of eSolar in California. Source: eSolar.

Figure 43 Panoramic view of the eSolar heliostat field together with the solar tower. Source: eSolar.

Plant construction was initiated in June 2008. Near the end of 2008, 24 360 heliostats were installed, with the tower and receiver installation completed by April 2009. The first full-power receiver operation began in June 2009 [38].

The plant produces 5 MW$_e$ of electricity, powering up to 4000 homes. Design inlet steam conditions are 420 °C and 42 bar. The solar power generating facility is interconnected to the Southern California Edison (SCE) grid, and the output of Sierra SunTower will reduce CO$_2$ emissions by 7000 tons per year [39].

3.18.5.1.7 Dish farm California

The development of dish/Stirling systems has been going on for about 40 years. The combination of solar concentrated energy and the already almost 200-year-old technology of a Stirling motor has proved to be favorable. Although these techniques were known for a long time, such systems have been built only in small noncommercial demo plants. Only one midscale plant has been built by the LaJet Energy Company in Abilene, Texas. This dish farm Solar Plant 1 was constructed in 1984 consisting of 700 dishes, type LEC-460, in total. The plant was built close to Warner Springs, northeast of San Diego, California. **Figure 44** shows a view of the dish farm at this location in the United States.

The electrical output is 4.92 MW$_e$, produced by two different collector fields. The first field produces water steam with a temperature of 276 °C, which is superheated to 371 °C by the second dish field. The generated steam drives two steam turbines, of which the first has a nominal power of 3.68 MW$_e$ and the second is designed for 1.24 MW$_e$. For start-up, shutdown, and at low solar radiation, the second turbine is used, while, additionally, the first one produces electricity when there is enough solar-generated steam. Other prototypes have been constructed, but they were all smaller compared with the electrical power output.

3.18.5.1.8 PE 1

NOVATEC BIOSOL has commissioned PE 1 (**Figure 45**), a solar thermal power plant located in southern Spain. It is based on linear Fresnel collector technology and has an electrical capacity of 1.4 MW$_e$. Since March 2009, it has been connected to the local grid and is selling electricity to the local network provider [40].

PE 1 consists of two rows of linear Fresnel collectors of about 807 m length each. The net aperture area is about 18 490 m^2 and the optical efficiency in the first year of operation is 67%. The nominal power of the plant is 1.4 MW$_e$ and the projected power production is 2000 MWh a^{-1}.

An absorber tube is positioned in the focal line of the mirror field in which water is evaporated directly into saturated steam at 270 °C and at a pressure of 55 bar by the concentrated solar energy.

3.18.5.1.9 AORA

A concentrated solar tower plant is located in southern Israel. This tulip-shaped power plant as shown in **Figure 46** has an electrical power output of only 100 kW.

The corresponding technology was developed at the Weizmann Institute of Science (WIS) in Israel and was introduced to the market by the Israeli company AORA, with the aim of supplying CSP plants at the community level.

The developed technology enables to position an industry-standard micro-GT (Brayton thermodynamic cycle) on top of a 30 m tower. Radiation is concentrated onto the tower by reflecting sunlight from an array of sun-tracking mirrors into a solar receiver, where it heats compressed air that drives the GT. The microturbine of the solar unit provides both 100 kW of electric power and 170 kW of thermal power [41]. Fuel combustion is used only when solar input is insufficient (e.g., cloud cover and sunrise/sunset).

Figure 44 Dish farm Solar Plant 1. Source: Sandia National Laboratories.

Figure 45 The PE 1 Fresnel power plant in Spain. Source: NOVATEC BIOSOL.

Figure 46 AORA tower power plant in Israel. Source: AORA.

The mirrors, with a total surface of 800 m^2, can be mounted on less than 2000 m^2 of land [42]. Each mirror is located by a GPS and the computer system takes into account the different positions.

3.18.5.1.10 Kimberlina solar thermal power plant
Kimberlina is the first compact linear Fresnel reflector (CLFR) project in North America. Located in Bakersfield, California, Ausra began construction of the power plant in March 2008, with the plant beginning operation in October 2008 [43]. Situated in an area of 12 acres, the demonstration plant generates 5 MW$_e$. The solar field aperture area is 26 000 m^2 and the absorber length of each of the three lines is 385 m. As an HTF, water/steam is used.

3.18.5.1.11 Others/under construction
3.18.5.1.11(i) Gemasolar
Gemasolar will become Spain's first commercial molten salt central receiver power plant. Construction of the plant began in 2008 in Fuentes de Andalucía, Seville, and could be completed in 2011. **Figure 47** shows a picture of Gemasolar during erection of the power plant.

The installation covers 185 ha and will be able to generate 17 MW when it is up and running. The energy generated (approximately 100 GWh yr^{-1}) will power 25 000 homes in Andalusia. Furthermore, the savings on carbon dioxide (CO$_2$) emissions in comparison with other conventional plants are around 30 000 tons per year [44]. The heliostat field consists of 2650 heliostats, each with 120 m^2 reflective mirror area, totaling to 318 000 m^2 of mirror area for the entire field. The receiver, which will use molten salt as an HTF, will be installed on top of the tower whose height will be 150 m [45].

Same as the other molten salt solar towers, Gemasolar also has a two-tank molten salt (sodium and potassium nitrate) storage system. In the cold tank, molten salt is kept at a minimal temperature of 290 °C (to keep it from solidifying). From there, the molten

Figure 47 Gemasolar tower plant (in September 2010). Source: Torresol Energy.

salt is pumped to the receiver and it exits at a temperature of 565 °C. The hot molten salt is then pumped into a hot salt tank. The steam is produced in a steam generator using the salt from the hot salt tank. The salt leaving the steam generator is then pumped into the cold salt tank. Gemasolar will have a 15 h storage capacity, which means that it can be operated day and night [45]. The plant is designed to be in operation 6700 h a^{-1}, which accounts for an availability of nearly 75% [46].

3.18.5.2 Research

3.18.5.2.1 Solar One

The experimental solar tower power plant Solar One (**Figure 48**) was built in Barstow, California, USA, and operated from 1982 until 1988, when it was replaced by Solar Two. Solar One was designed to generate an electric power of 10 MW$_e$, but exceeded this goal as it generated a net electric power of up to 11.7 MW$_e$. The height of the tower including the receiver was 90 m [47, 48].

The receiver was a cylindrical-shaped single-pass superheat boiler, designed to generate steam at 510 °C and a pressure of 102 bar. Corresponding to the receiver shape, a surround-type heliostat field was used. The heliostat field consisted of 1818 heliostats, each having a reflective area of 39 m^2, totaling to an area of 71 100 m^2 for the entire field [48].

During its 3-year power production phase, the Solar One pilot plant had annual availabilities above 80%, and during its last year, the availability was 96% [49].

Figure 48 Solar One, near Barstow, California, USA. Source: Sandia National Laboratories.

3.18.5.2.2 Solar Two

Solar Two was converted and adapted from Solar One and operated from 1996 to 1999 [50]. The function of Solar Two (**Figure 49**) was to encourage the development of molten salt technology, which required several changes to be made to the Solar One construction. The Solar One receiver, which was a cylindrical-shaped single-pass superheat boiler, could no longer be used and thus an entire new molten salt–heat transfer system had to be installed, as well as a new control system. The heat transfer system included the receiver, piping, thermal storage, and a steam generator.

The surround-type heliostat field from Solar One was kept as it was and further 108 heliostats of a new type with an area of 95 m^2 were added. Due to the surrounding field, a cylindrical receiver shape was used. **Figure 50** shows Solar Two in operation.

The receiver was made up of 24 panels surrounding the internal piping, instrumentation, and salt holding vessels like a shell. Each of the panels comprised 32 thin-walled, stainless-steel tubes that were connected on either end by flow distribution manifolds.

The receiver was able to withstand rapid temperature changes during cloud passages without damage. The thermal storage medium consisted of 1500 tons of nitrate salt consisting of 60 wt.% NaNO$_3$ and 40 wt.% KNO$_3$. In molten salt power plants, there were two thermal storages. There was a hot salt storage in which the salt had a temperature of 565 °C and a cold salt storage tank of 290 °C. The temperature in the cold storage tank was kept at this level, as below that temperature the molten salt would solidify. From the cold storage tank, the molten salt was pumped back into the receiver [51].

Figure 49 Solar Two in the United States. Source: US Department of Energy.

Figure 50 Solar Two in operation. Source: Sandia National Laboratories.

3.18.5.2.3 CESA-1

The CESA-1 solar tower was built on the Plataforma Solar de Almería (PSA), Spain, in 1983 and generated 1.2 MW$_e$. The tower height was 80 m and had the receiver fitted at 60 m. With a thermal power of 4.95 MW$_{th}$ on the cavity receiver, the receiver's HTF steam was brought to 520 °C and 100 bar. The heliostat field consisted of 300 heliostats, each with a reflective mirror area of 39.6 m^2, and thus the total reflective area was 11 880 m^2. **Figure 51** shows the heliostats and the tower of the CESA-1 plant.

The plant had a thermal storage, which uses molten salt as a storage medium. The capacity of the thermal storage is 2.7 MWh in full-load operation [47].

3.18.5.2.4 DISS

The project Direct Solar Steam (DISS) focuses on testing a 300 kW (thermal) parabolic trough test loop, using water as a heat transfer medium. This test plant as seen in **Figure 52** is located at the PSA in Almeria, Spain. A single row of solar collectors, capable of producing 300 kW (thermal), was built with water as the HTF within a test loop to extract steam. The row was divided into water evaporation and superheated steam sections. In the first section, the water is evaporated by passing through nine solar collectors, whereas in the second section consisting of three collectors, superheated steam – that is, steam at a temperature of above 400 °C – is produced [52].

The solar field is composed of a single north–south-oriented row of 11 PTCs connected in series, with a total length of 550 m and 3000 m^2 of reflecting mirror [53]. At the DISS test facility, the once-through, injection, and recirculation operation modes have been tested since the beginning of the 1990s.

Figure 51 View of the CESA-1 at the PSA in Spain. Source: Sandia National Laboratories.

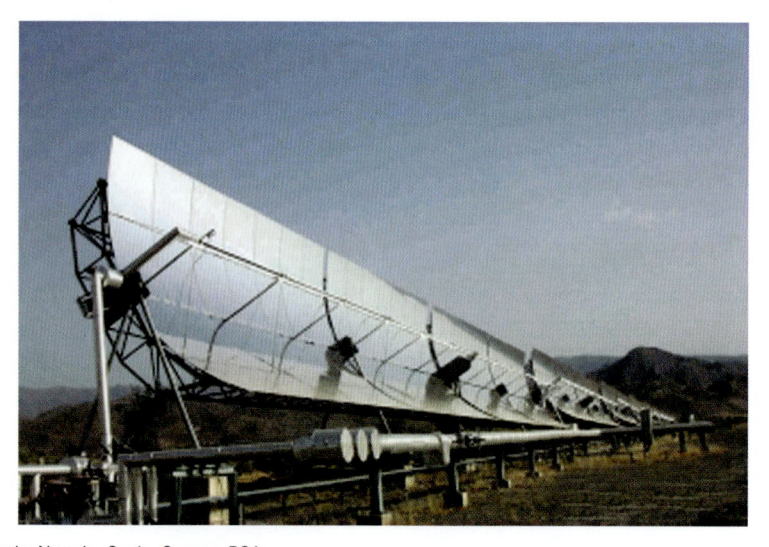

Figure 52 DISS test facility in Almeria, Spain. Source: PSA.

3.18.5.2.5 STJ

The commercial operation of the STJ is accompanied by an intensive R&D program to facilitate the market introduction in larger plants.

The STJ power plant has been built to test the power plant as a whole and to investigate the systems' operation. Start-up and shutdown procedures, varying solar input, and storage operation are aspects that have to be investigated in the context of this process.

The solar thermal power plant's operation is accompanied by computer simulations, which are validated by the power plant's operational data. Thus, the operation can be computed and new research aspects can be identified. Furthermore, upscaling to larger plants can be done by using these results.

The following new innovations and upcoming improvements are currently under investigation in the STJ [54]:

- new heliostat concepts and new means of control
- new absorber structures with high efficiencies
- storage concepts based on sand
- hybridization with fossil or fuels produced from biomass
- custom-made boilers for the integration of GTs

3.18.5.2.6 SSPS

The SSPS (small solar power system) plant was the first central receiver plant in Europe and was built in 1981 on the PSA in Almeria, southern Spain, by the International Energy Agency (IEA).

The plant had a design power rating of 500 kW$_e$ and used liquid sodium as a heat transfer medium. The key feature of sodium as a molten salt working fluid is that it provides efficient, low-cost thermal energy storage. The SSPS plant was reliable and proved to have good operational characteristics but suffered from safety and maintenance problems. After a sodium fire in 1986, the plant was rebuilt without the sodium components. The plant is still in use as a test facility.

The LEC of the SSPS, at approximately 0.48 € kWh^{-1}, is considerably higher than the one corresponding to the larger SEGS parabolic trough plants and the Solar One tower plant which were built in California [55].

This facility consisted of two parabolic trough solar fields with a total mirror aperture area of 7602 m^2. The fields used the single-axis tracking Acurex collectors and the double-axis tracking PTCs developed by M.A.N. of Munich, Germany [56].

3.18.5.2.7 Others

3.18.5.2.7(i) Themis

The 2 MW$_e$ Themis solar tower power plant is a research and development center located near the village of Targassonne, southern France. The focus of the research center lies not only in solar towers but also in photovoltaic (PV) power [57].

The plant was operated from 1983 to 1986. The 10 MW$_{th}$ receiver used molten salt as an HTF, generating steam with a temperature of 440 °C at 42 bar. The heliostat field consisted of 200 heliostats which had an area of 54 m^2 each, totaling to a reflective mirror area of 10 800 m^2 [57]. **Figure 53** shows a bird's-eye view of the Themis solar tower.

The tower had two experimental areas, where the project PEGASE (production of electricity from gas and solar energy) was realized [58].

Figure 53 Bird's-eye view of the Themis solar tower. Source: CNIM Division Energy Solaire.

Figure 54 Solar tower at the Solar Research Facility in Rehovot, Israel. Source: WIS.

3.18.5.2.7(ii) Solar Research Facility Unit

The Solar Research Facility of the WIS, shown in **Figure 54**, is located in Israel and its major feature is a solar power tower containing a heliostat field of 64 large, multifaceted mirrors of 56 m² each.

Each heliostat tracks the movement of the sun independently and reflects its light onto a selected target on a 54 m high tower containing five separate experimental stations, each of which can house several experiments. Light can be reflected toward any or all of these stations, allowing a number of experiments to be carried out simultaneously [59]. The central receiver research facility has been in full operation since 1988 and provided power of up to 3 MW$_{th}$ at equinox noon [60].

3.18.5.2.7(iii) EURELIOS

In late 1980, the construction of the power plant EURELIOS was completed in Adrano, Sicily, Italy, and was operated until 1984. The nominal output was stated to be 1 MW$_e$ at an insolation of 1 kW m^{-2} at noon in equinox. The receiver used was a cavity-type boiler that used water/steam directly as an HTF. The steam reached a temperature of 512 °C at a pressure of 64 bar. In an optimization process, the tower, which was constructed from steel, was raised from 50 to 55 m to the center of the receiver aperture. Two types of heliostats were used. The first type consisted of 70 CETHEL heliostats that had a reflective mirror area of 52 m². The other type consisted of 112 MBB heliostats that had a reflective mirror area of 23 m² [61].

The thermal storage system had a capacity of 30 min of reduced electrical output. The storage system consisted of a salt tank and a water reservoir. The salt storage system had a cold and a hot tank and used 1250 kg of a salt known as Hitec salt. The water reservoir held 4300 kg of vapor [61].

3.18.5.2.7(iv) SEDC

In June 2008, BrightSource Energy opened the Solar Energy Development Center (SEDC), a fully operational solar demonstration facility used to test equipment, materials, and procedures as well as construction and operating methods. The SEDC is located in the Rotem Industrial Park in Israel's Negev Desert, about 100 km southeast of Jerusalem. The 4–6 MW test facility utility-grade superheated steam is piped from the boiler to a standard steam turbine.

3.18.5.2.7(vi) CSIRO

A close-packed heliostat field of more than 800 m² reflector area was installed in 2006 at the CSIRO (**Figure 55**) solar tower at the National Solar Energy Centre (NSEC) in Newcastle, Australia.

The NSEC solar tower facility at the CSIRO comprises three main elements [62]:

- A high-concentration tower solar array that uses 200 mirrors to generate more than 500 kW of energy. It will be capable of achieving peak temperatures of over 1000 °C.
- A linear concentrator solar array that generates a hot fluid at temperatures around 250 °C to power a small turbine generator or adsorption chiller.
- A control room facility that houses the center's communications and control systems and serves as an elevated viewing platform.

In late 2010, a second field was commissioned adjacent to the existing field. This field consisted of 450 heliostats, with a thermal capacity of 1.2 MW$_{th}$ and will be used to demonstrate a 200 kW Brayton cycle GT [63].

Figure 55 CSIRO with the solar tower test facility. Source: CSIRO.

3.18.5.2.7(vii) Sunshine
The solar tower, located in Nio Town, Japan, began operation in 1981. It has a nominal power of 1 MW$_e$. The heliostat field consists of 807 heliostats, each with a mirror area of 16 m^2. The open receiver has an aperture area of 15.4 m^2. Steam is used as an HTF and a mixture of salt and water is used as a storage medium. The water is heated up in the receiver of the tower from 38 to 512 °C [64].

3.18.5.2.7(viii) SPP-5
The solar tower SPP-5 is located in Krim, Ukraine. It was constructed in 1986 and has a nominal power of 5 MW$_e$. A total of 1600 heliostats with 25 m^2 mirror surface each concentrate the solar radiation to the receiver. The open receiver uses water/steam as an HTF and a storage medium [64].

3.18.5.3 Studies

3.18.5.3.1 GAST
A German–Spanish project named GAST coordinated by the companies Interatom and Asinel proposed in the late 1980s the construction of a 20 MW solar power plant in Spain using a tubular panel air-cooled receiver [65]. For that reason, several components were tested at the PSA in Almeria. As described in Reference 66, the high estimated investment costs and the low incident solar fluxes permitted by the tubes made it impractical to pursue the construction of the plant.

3.18.5.3.2 PHOEBUS
PHOEBUS was an open volumetric receiver study on a solar tower. Air was considered as the HTF [67]. It was one of the bases for further development that resulted in the erection of the first solar tower plant STJ (Jülich, Germany), which uses air in an open volumetric receiver in Jülich, Germany. In the PHOEBUS study, an all-around heliostat field of 1000 heliostats with 150 m^2 each was considered. The receiver included hexagonal conic absorber modules. Atmospheric air was considered as the HTF, and it was heated up by passing it through a metal wire mesh receiver to temperatures on the order of 700 °C and used to produce steam. The designed power plant had a tower height of 130 m and consisted of two thermal cycles: an air and a water/steam loop. Together with this study, a PHOEBUS consortium was formed with companies from Germany, Switzerland, Spain, and the United States, and at the end of the 1980s it made a prefeasibility study for the erection of a 30 MW$_e$ tower plant in Jordan [68]. Unfortunately, the project could not obtain the necessary grants and financial support and did not come to eventual construction.

Technological development of key components followed through the German TSA Consortium Technology Program Solar Air Receiver, under the leadership of the company Steinmüller. A 2.5 MW$_{th}$ air receiver facility comprising the complete PHOEBUS power plant cycle that included air recirculation loop, thermal storage, and steam generator was assembled on top of the CESA-1 tower in Spain at the end of 1991 [66]. The plant was successfully operated by DLR and CIEMAT for nearly 400 h between April and December 1993, and for shorter periods in 1994 and 1999, demonstrating that a receiver outlet temperature of 700 °C could easily be achieved within 20 min of plant start-up [69].

3.18.6 Economical Aspects

Detailed cost data are not always available for most of the commercial solar thermal power plants. This is the case, for example, for the first commercial SEGS plants. This is partially because Luz did not actually track expenses against individual projects. However, information on the financed sales price of the SEGS plants is available [70]. For example, SEGS I cost 4400\$ kW$_e^{-1}$ in 1984, and if normalized to 2003 dollars using the consumer price index, it corresponds to 7738 \$ kW$_e^{-1}$.

Another possibility is to use estimations from studies. Some years ago, a very important study, named ECOSTAR, made cost estimations for all available solar thermal technologies. Among these technologies, the most mature technology today is the parabolic trough system that uses thermal oil as an HTF. The ECOSTAR evaluation estimates LECs of 0.17–0.18 € kWh^{-1} for parabolic trough power plants of 50 MW$_e$ [9]. Parabolic trough and solar tower technologies have similar LEC values that vary between 0.15 and 0.18 € kWh^{-1}. The LECs for solar dish systems in the same large size are more than 10¢ higher. If middle power plant size of 15 MW$_e$ is considered, the LEC is significantly higher, ranging from 0.19 to 0.28 € kWh^{-1}. For a system of a solar tower integrated into a GT/combined cycle, LEC values below 0.09 € kWh^{-1} are achievable, but the technology neither is yet available nor is demonstrated in a realistic size.

In the conventional power market, the CSP competes with mid-load power in the range of 0.03–0.05 € kWh^{-1}. Competitiveness is influenced not only by the cost of technology but also by a rise in the price of fossil energy and by the internalization of associated environmental costs such as CO_2 emissions.

At present, the cost of power generated by solar power plants including its transport via high-voltage direct current (HVDC) transmission lines amounts to 0.10–0.20 € kWh^{-1} – depending on the location, technology, and form of operation [71].

However, these costs will drop significantly with economies of scale, refinements in the technologies, and increased research activities.

A further study made by the Sargent & Lundy Consulting Group for the US Department of Energy showed that trough and tower solar power plants can compete with technologies that provide bulk power and will reach values of LEC under 0.06 $ kWh^{-1} by the year 2020 for large power scales. Especially for tower technology, the study implies that if commercial development is successful, then the LEC for deployment in 2020 will be less than for trough technology [72].

The latest report of the European Renewable Energy Council (EREC) and Greenpeace demonstrates that depending on the level of irradiation and mode of operation, long-term future electricity generation costs of 0.06–0.10 € kWh^{-1} can be achieved [73]. This presupposes rapid market introduction in the next few years.

3.18.7 Environmental Aspects

3.18.7.1 Emission

The most significant difference in the environmental impact of solar thermal power plants compared with fossil-fired power stations is that in solar-only operation, electricity is produced without emission of CO_2, SO_2, or NO_x to the atmosphere.

Life cycle CO_2 emissions of solar-only CSP plants are assessed at 17 g kWh^{-1} against, for example, 776 g kWh^{-1} for coal plants and 396 g kWh^{-1} for natural gas combined cycle plants [74]. However, to the extent that some fossil fuel is used as a backup, a CSP plant or an ISCCS cannot be qualified as a 'zero-emitting' plant. If the power plant is hybridized with a conventional fossil plant, emissions will be released from the nonsolar portion of the plant, but if biomass hybridization of a CSP is realized, then the direct emissions remain zero.

3.18.7.2 Impact on Flora and Fauna

In a solar tower, land use, although significant, is typically much less than that required for hydropower and is generally less than that required for fossil power (e.g., oil, coal, and natural gas), when the mining and exploration of land are included [75].

No hazardous gaseous or liquid emissions that affect the environment are released during operation of a solar power tower plant. For example, when melting salt is used as an HTF, if a salt spill occurs, the salt will freeze before significant contamination of the soil occurs. Salt is picked up with a shovel and can be recycled if necessary. Nevertheless, the use of molten salts and synthetic oil in a CSP plant bears some risk of spillage or fire. This may in turn hinder acceptance of a project by the local population. The use of air as an HTF, on the other hand, does not have environmental impacts at all.

In a CSP located in a desert, impacts will occur on water supplies and resources, if water is piped from limited aquatic systems, and these will directly affect desert flora and fauna, some of which may have declining populations. In general, the impact of a CSP on flora and fauna is negligible, given that installations are not done in national reserved areas.

3.18.7.3 Life Cycle Assessment

It would appear sensible to align the restructuring of the energy supply not only with climate protection goals but rather to duly take other aspects of sustainable development into consideration. It is important to consider water, material, and energy demand for the erection and operation of a CSP.

Concerning water demand, an 80 MW trough plant requires about 1.2 million cubic meters of water per year, mostly for cooling the steam cycle and for cleaning the mirrors. Dry air cooling systems could considerably reduce water consumption.

To achieve this, the resource productivity of the various installations and the possibilities for their augmentation must be investigated on a mutual scale. This also provides a background against which decisions about financial investment and funding can be made.

The sustainability of a solar power plant can be investigated using two methods. First of all, the resource intensity can be examined using the material input per service unit (MIPS) method, and second, the cumulative fossil energy input of the power plant can be examined. Both methods can be used for the whole life cycle phases of the power plant, which means that the construction, operation, and dismantling of the plant are all taken into account for the calculations.

In order to assess the sustainability of the plant, it is necessary to compare the results with those of other energy converters. MIPS calculations were compiled for solar thermal parabolic trough power plants and PV installations in the 1990s. A comparison of the MIPS calculations of three types of power plants (parabolic trough, solar tower, and PV) was carried out by Fricke in 2008 [76]. The comparison of the cumulative energy input returned considerably lower values for the solar tower power plant than for the PV installations.

The results showed that investment in the construction and development of solar thermal power plants has a large contribution to the restructuring of the energy supply structures with a view to enabling improved sustainability.

3.18.8 Future Potential

The sun-rich areas of the so-called Sun Belt of the Earth are ideal for the economically feasible employment of solar thermal power plants. According to various studies, by 2010 at least 2000 MW of solar thermal power plants will be installed worldwide, and by 2020 there will be at least 20 000 MW. According to a study by Greenpeace and EREC, predictions are for 138 000 MW to be installed by 2030 and 267 000 MW by 2040.

The industries involved predict that with the constant development of up to 15–20 GW worldwide and with the simultaneous advancement of research and development, the full competitiveness against fossil fuels for mid-load electricity supply will be achieved in good locations by 2020 and that the same will be achieved for base-load electricity by 2030.

Solar thermal power plants, with their inherent storage capability and hybridization solutions, will play a key role in providing sustainable electricity globally in the twenty-first century.

3.18.8.1 Desertec

In particular, the possibility of integrating low-cost energy storages or the additional firing of fossil or fuels produced from biomass in order to produce electricity on demand allows for the supply of a large portion of long-term requirements by solar thermal power plants. Production locations for solar thermal power plant technologies are in the sunny regions of the earth, whereby the long-term target area for Europe is North Africa.

Along with the rapidly growing energy markets of the world's Sun Belt, the technical requirements also exist in order to be able to use the electricity produced there in Central Europe when the appropriate network capacities for HVDC transmission have been built. A detailed consideration of such solutions has been already done as can be seen in Reference 77.

According to the ESTELA study, it is possible to build 20 GW of solar thermal power plants in North African states, since the technology is commercially available. Moreover, such a plan will promote the industrial development of the North African region, because many components can be produced there.

Much of the electricity produced in North Africa can be transported to Europe. Such technology is already used in many offshore projects in Europe and is expected to achieve a further improvement in terms of price and performance.

A further step was the Desertec concept (**Figure 56**), which schedules the use of renewable, mainly solar and wind, energy from the deserts.

A unique industry initiative to develop a reliable, sustainable, and climate-friendly energy supply from the deserts in the Middle East and North Africa (MENA) took place in 2009. In this initiative, 12 German, Spanish, and Algerian shareholders participate.

The Desertec concept describes the perspective of a sustainable supply of electricity for Europe (EU), the Middle East (ME), and North Africa (NA) up to the year 2050. The long-term objective is to cover a substantial part of the MENA electricity demand and 15% of the EU electricity demand by 2050 [71]. A huge amount will be recovered from electricity generated from CSP plants.

The initial plans consider the construction of CSP plants in Morocco and the transport of electricity to Spain and Germany.

3.18.8.2 United States and Europe

One CSP project is proposed by Abengoa Solar Inc., the sole member of Mojave Solar LLC, for a nominal 250 MW solar electric generating facility to be located near Harper Dry Lake in an unincorporated area of San Bernardino County (**Figure 57**). The sun will provide 100% of the power supplied to the project through solar thermal collectors; no supplementary fossil-based energy source is proposed for electrical power production. The plant is under construction and will start production in 2013 [45].

Beacon Solar, LLC, a Delaware limited liability company, is proposing to construct, own, and operate the Beacon Solar Energy Project. The project is a concentrated solar electric generating facility of parabolic trough technology proposed on an approximately 2012-acre site in Kern County, California. This project will have a nominal electrical output of 250 MW, and commercial operation is planned to commence by 2014 [45].

The proposed Victorville 2 project would have a net electrical output of 563 MW. Primary equipment for the generating facility would include two natural gas-fired combustion turbine generators (CTGs) rated at 154 MW each, two HRSGs, one steam turbine

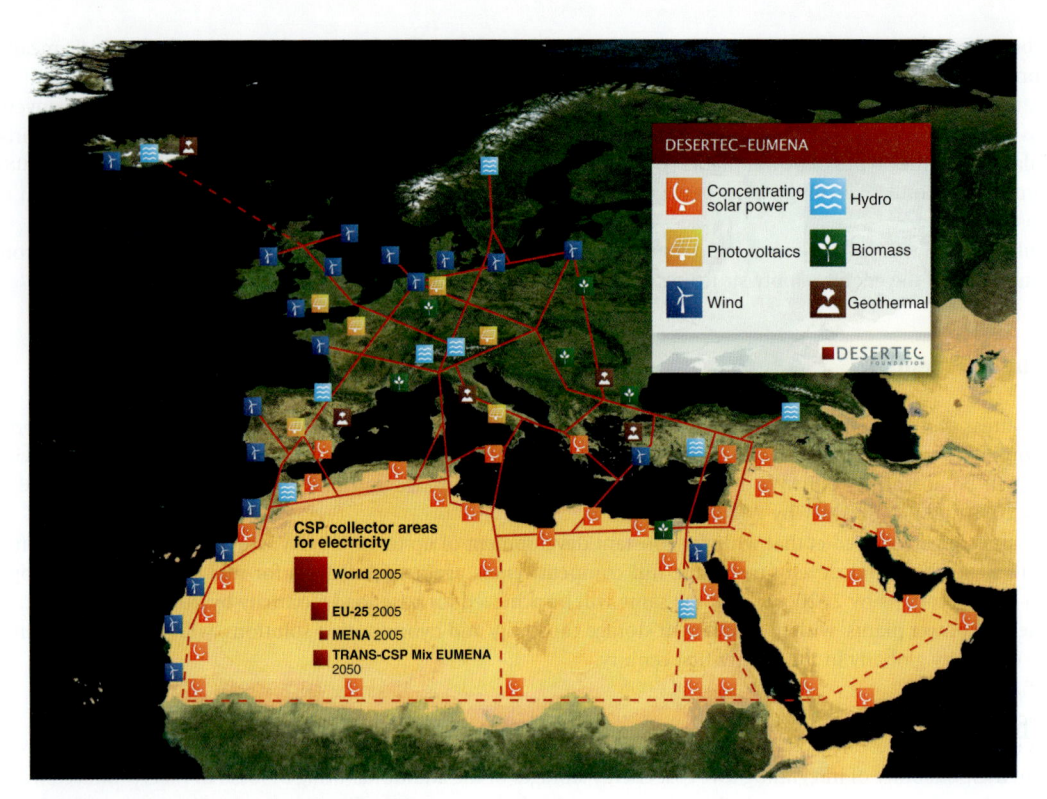

Figure 56 The Desertec concept. Source: Desertec Foundation.

Figure 57 Plan for the Abengoa Mojave Solar Project Power Plant. Source: CEC.

generator (STG) rated at 268 MW, and 250 acres of parabolic solar thermal collectors with associated heat transfer equipment. The solar thermal collectors would contribute up to 50 MW of the STG's 268 MW output.

Projects under review would generate more than 3000 MW. Among them is the Ivanpah Solar Electric Generating System using solar tower technology. The proposed project of BrightSource Energy and Solar Partners includes three concentrating solar tower power plants. Each 100 MW site would require approximately 850 acres and would have three tower receivers and arrays (**Figure 58**); the 200 MW site would require approximately 1600 acres (or 2.5 square miles) and would have four tower receivers and arrays.

The Rice project could break ground as early as spring of 2011 creating 450 construction jobs during the 2-year construction period. The project will employ 45 permanent operations staff and will have an annual operating budget of more than $5.0 million.

Figure 58 Plan for the Ivanpah Solar Electric Generating System. Source: CEC.

In the field of solar dishes also, several large projects with Stirling engine technology are now being developed. Stirling Energy Systems Inc. (SES) has announced plans for two large Stirling plants in California with a total capacity of 1600 MW. Solar One has a capacity of up to 850 MW, which will be constructed in two phases of 500 and 350 MW consisting of 34 000 SunCatcher dishes. SES has a PPA with SCE for this plant planned to be installed in the Mojave Desert. The second plant, Solar Two, is designed to generate 750 MW, also included in a PPA with San Diego Gas & Electric (SDG&E). In the first phase 12 000 dishes (300 MW) will be built, and in the second phase 18 000 SunCatcher with 450 MW will be built. These commercial-scale plants would be the first solar dish/Stirling plants that are in a reasonable megawatt scale.

As described in Reference 78, a new 100 MW solar energy project will be located near the town of Tonopah in Nye County, Nevada. When completed, Tonopah Solar Energy's facility will supply approximately 480 000 MWh of clean, renewable electricity annually – enough to power up to 75 000 homes during peak electricity periods – utilizing its innovative energy storage capabilities. The solar tower plant will be developed and owned by a SolarReserve's subsidiary, Tonopah Solar Energy.

Another company, eSolar, is developing solar thermal tower power plants of 46 MW (and above) across the southwestern United States and globally. The innovation of eSolar, as demonstrated through the Sierra SunTower facility, has led to a broad, global footprint of projects. In New Mexico, eSolar has partnered with NRG Energy to develop a 92 MW solar power plant under a PPA with El Paso Electric Corporation. This contract is the first and only contract to deliver solar thermal energy in New Mexico and will help El Paso Electric to meet its renewable portfolio goals. eSolar has further projects under development with NRG in California.

Internationally, eSolar executed an exclusive licensing agreement with the ACME Group, a leader in the field of infrastructure in India, to develop up to 1000 MW of solar thermal power plants in India over the next 10 years. ACME recently announced that commissioning will begin on the first eSolar power plant in the first quarter of 2010. In January 2010, eSolar announced a partnership with Penglai Electric, a privately owned Chinese electrical power equipment manufacturer, to build 2 GW of solar thermal power plants in China by 2021.

In Europe, mostly in Spain, 1000 MW of CSP are planned to be operational by around 2011. The greatest European market for CSP is located there. An additional 10 000 GW are under planning and development, which could all go online by 2017. By 2013, with 2400 MW of CSP projects, Spain will topple the United States as the global leader for installed CSP capacity. Most of these systems will include a storage system, and parabolic troughs make more than 90% of this capacity. Spanish government intervention with feed-in tariffs has driven this growth [79].

SolarReserve, a US-based developer of utility-scale solar energy projects, and Preneal, a Madrid-based developer of renewable energy projects, announced in November 2009 that the autonomous government of Castilla-La Mancha has issued an environmental permit necessary for the construction of a 50 MW solar thermal power project. This Alcázar Solar Thermal Power Project is being developed near the town of Alcázar de San Juan, about 180 km south of Madrid. The project will generate more than 300 000 MWh of electricity per year or enough electricity to power almost 70 000 homes in the region [45, 80]. The project started construction in 2011 and will bring significant local economic and employment benefits to the region.

A forecast for European countries by 2020, National Allowance Plans (NAPs), shows that more than 5000 MW will come from CSP in Spain, about 500 MW each for Portugal and France, and 600 MW for Italy and Greece together with Cyprus with more than 300 MW.

Even with a set of moderate assumptions for future market development, the world would have a combined solar power capacity of over 830 GW by 2050, with annual deployments of 41 GW. This would represent 3.0–3.6% of global demand in 2030 and 8.5–11.8% in 2050.

3.18.8.3 MENA Region

In MENA countries currently, there are four CSP power plants under construction, of which three are ISCC power plants. These are in Kuraymat (Egypt), Ain Béni Mathar (Morocco), and Hassi R'mel (Algeria). The fourth project is the Shams One Solar Thermal Power Plant (Emirate of Abu Dhabi), a hybridization of parabolic trough technology with fossil-fired superheating [81].

The ISCC Kuraymat is located about 87 km south of Cairo, Egypt, on the eastern side of the river Nile. The ISCC Kuraymat power plant has been under construction since January 2008 and commercial operation is scheduled for the end of 2012 [45, 81]. The concept includes 160 SKAL-ET PTCs arranged in 40 loops and a combined cycle power plant consisting of one GT, one HRSG, one steam turbine, solar heat exchangers, and all associated auxiliaries. Under reference conditions, the solar cycle will generate about 50 MW of solar heat, which will enable the ISCC to generate 125.7 MW$_e$ of net electric power output.

The ISCC Ain Béni Mathar (integrated solar combined cycle power plant) is located in Ain Béni Mathar, about 90 km south of Oujda (Morocco) close to the Algerian border [82]. In reference day mode operation, the solar parabolic trough cycle will generate about 58.7 MW of solar heat at a temperature of 393 °C; this enables the ISCC to generate 472.3 MW$_e$ of net electricity. Without solar heat, the plant will generate 450.2 MW$_e$ of net electricity.

The ISCC Hassi R'mel power plant project is located about 60 km from Ghardaia in the northern central region of Algeria. The ISCC Hassi R'mel uses parabolic trough and has a total gross electric power generation of 150 MW$_e$, with a solar share of approximately 20 MW$_e$.

The Shams One Solar Power Plant will be located in the Emirate of Abu Dhabi (UAE), about 100 km southwest of Abu Dhabi and 10 km from Madinat Zayed. The Shams One Project started in June 2010 and the commercial operation is estimated for the third quarter of 2012. The concept includes 768 Abengoa solar parabolic collectors arranged in 192 loops, and fossil-fired backup HTF heaters [81]. Under reference conditions, the plant will generate 100 MW$_e$ of net electricity.

3.18.8.4 Future Research Fields

For the successful deployment of concentrated solar thermal technology, basic research is needed, manufacturing industry providing hardware from mature production techniques as well as engineering services. Basic research is provided both by research groups at universities and by research organizations.

Improving efficiency and reducing costs are top priorities for researchers trying to make CSP a reality. The major challenge is increasing the operating temperature of the plants while maintaining efficiency.

In the future, researchers will try to strike the right balance between high efficiency, low pressure drop, high durability, and low cost. Ongoing research projects aim also to discover more effective HTFs [83]. They focus on the research of ideal HTFs, which provide a high thermal capacity, low viscosity, low melting point, and minimal corrosion of the system.

Another very important field of research activities will be the design and development of concepts for increasing the load hours of solar power plants. Among them are the fields of hybridization and the search for appropriate storage materials. In order to commercialize CSP as a dispatchable energy, industry has developed hybrid models that use natural gas or fossil fuel in combination with the solar resource. But in view of long-term scarcity and related price volatility of fossil fuels, this approach provides only a medium-term solution.

Instead, industry players are now examining how CSP can be hybridized with biomass energy to achieve around-the-clock 100% renewable energy [84].

A huge research potential is also the adjustment of the conventional part, for example, of a steam turbine, an HRSG, or a GT, in order to operate under conditions with dynamical thermal behavior and gradients which are common for solar thermal power stations.

References

[1] Bini R and Manciana E (1996) Organic Rankine cycle turbogenerators for combined heat and power production from biomass. Presented at the *3rd Munich Discussion Meeting 'Energy Conversion from Biomass Fuels: Current Trends and Future Systems'*. Munich, Germany, 22–23 October.
[2] Hassani V and Price HW (2001) Modular trough power plants. In: *Proceedings of Solar Forum 2001, Solar Energy: The Power to Choose*. Washington, DC, USA, 21–25 April.
[3] Quoilin S and Lemort V (2009) Technological and economical survey of organic Rankine cycle systems. In: *Proceedings of the 5th European Conference: Economics and Management of Energy in Industry*. Vilamoura, Algarve, Portugal, 14–17 April.
[4] Sinai J and Fisher U (2007) 1 MW solar power plant using Ormat energy converter. In: *Proceedings of the 14th Sede Boqer Symposium on Solar Electricity Production 53*. 19–21 February.
[5] Canada S, Cohen G, Cable R, et al. (2004) Parabolic trough organic Rankine cycle solar power plant. Presented at the *2004 DOE Solar Energy Technologies, Program Review Meeting*. Denver, CO, USA, 25–28 October.
[6] Solugas Project Consortium (2010). www.solugas.com (accessed 1 December 2011).
[7] Buck R, Lüpfert E, and Telez F (2010) Receiver for solar hybrid gas turbine and CC systems (REFOS). In: *Proceedings of the 10th International Symposium on Solar Thermal*. Sydney, NSW, Australia, 8–10 March.
[8] European Commission (2005) SOLGATE solar hybrid gas turbine electric power system. Project partly funded by the European Community under the *5th RTD Framework Programme (1998–2002)*, Brussels.
[9] Pitz-Paal R, Dersch J, and Milow B (2005) European concentrated solar thermal road-mapping. *SES6-CT-2003-502578*. Deutsches Zentrum fur Luft- und Raumfahrt, Roadmap Document, Brussels.

[10] Alexopoulos S, Hoffschmidt B, Rau C, and Schwarzbözl P (2009) Simulation results for a hybridization concept of a small solar tower power plant. In: *SolarPACES Symposium*. Berlin, Germany, 15–18 September.
[11] Alexopoulos S, Hoffschmidt B, Göttsche J, *et al.* (2008) First simulation results for the hybridization of small solar power tower plants. In: *Proceedings of the 1st International Conference on Solar Heating, Cooling and Buildings*. Lisboa, Portugal, 7–10 October.
[12] Alexopoulos S, Göttsche J, Hoffschmidt B, *et al.* (2009) Solar tower power plant Jülich first experience with an open volumetric receiver plant and presentation of future enhancements. In: *Proceedings of the Conference on Renewable World Europe*. Cologne, Germany, 26–28 May.
[13] Zunft S, Hänel M, Krüger M, and Dreißigacker V (2009) High-temperature heat storage for air-cooled solar central receiver plants: A design study. In: *SolarPACES 2009*. Berlin, Germany, 15–18 September.
[14] Laing D, Lehmann D, Fiß M, and Bahl C (2009) Test results of concrete thermal energy storage for parabolic trough power plants. *Journal of Solar Energy Engineering* 131: 041007/1–6.
[15] Price H and Hassani V (2002) Modular trough power plant cycle and systems analysis. *National Renewable Energy Laboratory Technical Report*. Operated by Midwest Research Institute, Battelle, Bechtel, Golden, CO, USA, January.
[16] Winter C-J, Sizmann RL, and Vant-Hull LL (1991) *Solar Power Plants*. Berlin: Springer-Verlag.
[17] Khartchenko N (1995) *Thermische Solaranlagen*. Berlin: Springer.
[18] Technology Program GAST (1988) Gas-cooled solar tower power station (in German). *Technical Report*. Bergisch-Gladbach (D), Germany: Interatom GmbH.
[19] Steinmann W-D, Laing D, and Tamme R (2009) Development of PCM storage for process heat and power generation. *Journal of Solar Energy Engineering* 131: 041009/1–3.
[20] Bullough C, Gatzen C, Jakiel C, *et al.* (2004) Advanced adiabatic compressed air energy storage for the integration of wind energy. In: *Proceedings of the European Wind Energy Conference, EWEC 2004*. London, UK, 22–25 November.
[21] Gatzen C (2004) Modellgestutzte Wirtschaftlichkeitsanalyse innovativer Speichertechnologien am Beispiel eines adiabaten Druckluftspeichers. In: *Proceedings Symposium Energieinnovation 'Erfolgreiche Energieinnovationsprozesse'*. Graz, Austria, February.
[22] Crotogino F, Mohmeyer K-U, and Scharf R (2001) Huntorf CAES: More than 20 years of successful operation. In: *Proceedings of the SMRI Spring Meeting*. Orlando, FL, USA, 15–18 April; (2009) *Journal of Solar Energy Engineering* 131.
[23] Siegel N, Kolb G, Kim J, *et al.* (2007) Solid particle receiver flow characterization studies. In: *Proceedings of the 2007 ASME Energy Sustainability Conference*. Long Beach, CA, USA, 27–30 June.
[24] Weiss W and Biermayr P (2007) Potential of solar thermal in Europe. *Study within the Framework of the EU-Funded Project RESTMAC*.
[25] Teng Y, Wang RZ, and Wu JY (1997) Study of the fundamentals of adsorption systems. *Applied Thermal Engineering* 17(4): 327–338.
[26] IEA Task http://www.iea-shc.org/task38/index.html (accessed 1 April 2010).
[27] AEE – Institut für Nachhaltige Technologie http://www.aee-intec.at (accessed 1 April 2010).
[28] Henning H-M, Häberle A, Lodi A, and Motta M (2006) Solar cooling and refrigeration with high temperature lifts – Thermodynamic background and technical solution. In: *Proceedings of the 61st National ATI Congress, ATI-IIR International Session 'Solar Heating and Cooling'*, pp. 63–68. Perugia, Italy, 14 September.
[29] (2010) Solar heating and cooling for a sustainable energy future in Europe (FP6). *European Solar Thermal Technology Platform (ESTTP) and European Solar Thermal Industry Federation (ESTIF)*. Belgium.
[30] Kalogirou S (2005) Seawater desalination using renewable energy sources. *Progress in Energy and Combustion Science* 31(3): 242–281.
[31] (2007) AQUA-CSP concentrating solar power for desalination. *Final Report by German Aerospace Center (DLR)*. Stuttgart, Germany, November.
[32] Kalogirou S (1997) Survey of solar desalination systems and system selection. *Energy* 22(1): 69–81.
[33] Spiegler KS and Laird ADK (1980) *Principles of Desalination, Part B*. New York: Academic Press.
[34] Alexopoulos S and Hoffschmidt B (2009) Solar tower power plant in Germany and future perspectives of the development of the technology in Greece and Cyprus. *Renewable Energy* 35(7): 1352–1356.
[35] Solar Millennium AG (2010) The parabolic trough power plants Andasol 1 to 3 (information provided in the internet under www.solarmillennium.de).
[36] (2006) 10 MW solar thermal power plant for southern Spain. *Final Technical Progress Report*. November.
[37] Broehl J (2006) A new chapter begins for concentrated solar power. *Journal Renewable Energy World*, 11 February.
[38] eSolar (2010) Sierra SunTower Report on the First Six Months. March (information provided in the internet under www.esolar.com).
[39] eSolar (2009) Sierra SunTower. A new blue print for solar energy. Fact Sheet (information provided in the internet under www.esolar.com).
[40] NOVATEC BIOSOL AG (2009) PE 1 – World's first Fresnel solar power plant in commercial operation. Information Brochure (information provided by the company).
[41] AORA (2010) Bringing solar thermal technology to every community under the sun. Information Brochure (information provided in the internet under www.aora-solar.com).
[42] Augsten E (2009) Make the desert bloom. *Sun & Wind Energy* 9: 52–53.
[43] Mehos MS (2009) Part 3: Task I – Solar thermal electric systems. *SolarPACES, Annual Report*.
[44] Torresol Energy. Press Dossier SENER 2010 (information provided in the internet under www.torresolenergy.com).
[45] NREL Project Details. 17 April 2009 (information provided in the internet under www.nrel.gov).
[46] Martín JC (2007) *SENER, NREL, CSP Technology Workshop*. Denver, CO, USA, 7 March.
[47] Khartchenko NV (2004) *Thermische Solaranlagen*. Berlin: Springer.
[48] Duffie JA and Beckman WA (2006) *Solar Engineering of Thermal Processes*. Hoboken, NJ: John Wiley & Sons.
[49] Kolb GJ and Lopez CW (1988) Reliability of the Solar One plant during the power production phase. *Report SAND88-2664*. Albuquerque, NM: Sandia National Laboratories.
[50] Sun Lab (2000) Solar Two demonstrates clean power for the future. *Report SAND2000-0613*. Washington, DC: Sandia National Laboratories.
[51] Tyner C, Kolb G, Prairie M, *et al.* (1996) *Solar Power Tower Development: Recent Experiences. Report SAND96-2662C*. Albuquerque, NM: Sandia National Laboratories.
[52] European Commission (2007) Concentrating solar power – From research to implementation. Luxembourg: Office for Official Publications of the European Communities.
[53] Zarza E, Valenzuela L, León J, *et al.* (2001) The DISS project: Direct steam generation in parabolic troughs – Operation and Maintenance Experience and Update on Project Status. In: *Proceedings of Solar Forum 2001, Solar Energy: The Power to Choose*. Washington, DC, USA, 21–25 April.
[54] Schmitz M (2009) Salt-free solar: CSP tower using air. *Renewable Energy World*, January–February, pp. 51–52.
[55] Riffelmann K-J, Krüger D, and Pitz-Paal R (2002) *Solar Thermal Plants – Power and Process Heat. 6th International Summer School*, Klagenfurt (Austria), July 21–August 4, 2000.
[56] SolarPACES (2010) Solar parabolic trough. http://www.solarpaces.org (accessed 1 December 2011).
[57] CNIM Division Energy Solaire (2010) Concentrating solar power plants. http://www.cnim.com/en/cnim-and-solar-energy.aspx (last accessed 1 November 2011).
[58] Processes, Materials and Solar Energy Laboratory (PROMES) (2010) A laboratory of CNRS, France (National Centre for Scientific Research). http://www.sollab.eu/promes.html (last accessed 1 October 2011).
[59] Weizmann Institute of Science (WIS). http://www.weizmann.ac.il/weizsites/solarenergy/ (accessed 18 June 2007).
[60] Becker M, Gupta B, Meinecke W, and Bohn M (1995) *Solar Energy Concentrating Systems: Applications and Technologies*. Heidelberg, Germany: Muller Verlag.
[61] Strub AS, Gretz J, and Palz W; (Commission of the European Communities 1984) Eurelios, the 1 MWe experimental solar thermal electric power plant of the European Community. *Final Report of the Construction of EURELIOS, assembled by the Industrial Consortium for the Implementation of the European Solar Power Plant*.
[62] CSIRO (2006) New solar energy research facility in the limelight. Reference: 06/52, Media Release, 31 March.
[63] Stein W, Kim J-S, Burton A, *et al.* (2010) Design and construction of a 200 kWe tower Brayton cycle pilot plant. In: *Proceedings of the 16th Concentrating Solar Power SolarPACES Symposium*. Perpignan, France, 21–24 September.
[64] Mohr M and Svoboda P (1999) *Praxis solarthermischer Kraftwerke*. Berlin, Springer.

[65] Becker M, Gupta B, Meinecke W, and Bohn M (1995) *Solar Energy Concentrating Systems*. Heidelberg, Germany: Muller Verlag.
[66] Romero M, Buck R, and Pacheco JE (2002) An update on solar central receiver systems, projects and technologies. *Transactions of the ASME* 124: 98–108.
[67] Keintzel G and Finker A (1995) PHOEBUS: Ein Solarturmkraftwerk vor der Markteinführung. In: *VDI Berichte, Solarthermsiche Kraftwerke II*, pp. 35–51, Nr. 1200.
[68] Heinrich P and Schmitz-Goeb M (1995) 2,5 MW-Demonstrationsprogramm zum air receiver PHOEBUS. In: *VDI Berichte, Solarthermsiche Kraftwerke II*, pp. 23–34, Nr. 1200.
[69] Haeger M (1994) Phoebus technology program: Solar air receiver TSA. *PSA Technical Report: PSA-TR02/94*. July.
[70] Luz International Limited (1990) *SEGS IX Proposal for Project Debt*. January.
[71] Desertec Foundation Red Paper (2009) *An Overview of the Desertec Concept*. Berlin, Germany.
[72] Sargent & Lundy Consulting Group (2003) Assessment of parabolic trough and power tower solar technology cost and performance forecasts. *Final Report*. NREL Report NREL/SR-550-34440 US Department of Energy, October.
[73] EREC (2008) Lead authors: Teske S, Schafer O, and Zervos A. Energy [r]evolution: A sustainable global energy outlook. *Greenpeace Report*. Brussels, Ocober.
[74] Renewable Energy Essentials (2009) Concentrating solar thermal power. IEA, CSP Brochure.
[75] Anderson D and Ahmed K (1995) The case for the solar energy investments. *World Bank Technical Paper Number 279 – Energy Series*. Washington, DC: World Bank.
[76] Fricke B (2007) *Vergleich der Zukunftsfähigkeit eines Solarturm-Kraftwerks mit der anderer Energiekonverter anhand des Material-Inputs-Pro-Serviceeinheit (MIPS) und des kumulierten Energieaufwands (KEA)*. Diplomarbeit, Jülich, Germany, Juli.
[77] Zweibel K, Mason J, and Fthenakis V (2007) A solar grand plan – By 2050 solar power could end U.S. dependence on foreign oil and slash greenhouse gas emissions. *Scientific American Magazine*, 16 December.
[78] SolarReserve signs power contract with NV Energy for utility scale solar power project in Nevada. Press Release, 22 December.
[79] Price T (2010) Spain's CSP policy: Do we follow the leader? *CSP Today*, 5 March.
[80] SolarReserve (2009) SolarReserve and Preneal receive environmental permit for 50 MW solar energy project in Spain. Press Release, 17 November (information provided in the internet under www.solarreserve.com).
[81] Brakmann G, Dolejsi M, Kretschmann J, and Klingler R (2010) CSP in the Middle East and North Africa (MENA). In: *Proceedings of the 16th Concentrating Solar Power SolarPACES Symposium*. Perpignan, France, 21–24 September.
[82] Brakmann G, Badaoui N-E, Dolejsi M, and Klingler R (2010) Construction of ISCC Ain Béni Mathar in Morocco. In: *Proceedings of the 16th Concentrating Solar Power SolarPACES Symposium*. Perpignan, France, 21–24 September.
[83] Cohn L and Smit R (2008) The future: Widespread use of CSP? *Sun & Wind Energy* 2: 42–53.
[84] Chhabara R (2009) CSP–biomass hybridisation: A truly sustainable solution? *CSP Today*, 29 December.

3.19 Passive Solar Architecture

D Kolokotsa, Technical University of Crete, Crete, Greece
M Santamouris, A Synnefa, and T Karlessi, National and Kapodistrian University of Athens, Athens, Greece

© 2012 Elsevier Ltd. All rights reserved.

3.19.1	Introduction	637
3.19.1.1	Energy and Urbanization	637
3.19.1.2	Solar Architecture – History and Concepts	638
3.19.1.3	Solar Architecture – Comprehensive Design and Operation	639
3.19.1.3.1	Passive solar heating	639
3.19.1.3.2	Passive cooling	642
3.19.2	Role of Solar Architecture in Urban Buildings	644
3.19.2.1	Development of Cool-Colored Materials	644
3.19.2.2	Use of Phase Change Materials to Enhance the Performance of Cool-Colored Coatings	646
3.19.2.3	Development of Thermochromic Coatings	648
3.19.2.4	Development and Testing of Colored Thin-Film Layers of Asphalt	648
3.19.2.5	Green Spaces for Urban Buildings	651
3.19.2.6	Discussion	653
3.19.3	Control Systems for Solar Architecture	654
3.19.3.1	Controlled Parameters and Control Variables in Passive Solar Architecture	655
3.19.3.2	Control Strategies in Solar Architecture	656
3.19.3.2.1	Conventional control for solar architecture	656
3.19.3.2.2	Advanced control	657
3.19.3.2.3	Intelligent systems	659
3.19.4	Conclusion and Future Prospects	663
References		663

Glossary

Cool materials Cool materials are materials with high solar reflectance (high ability to reflect sunlight) and high thermal emittance (high ability to radiate heat) and stay cool in the sun.

Intelligent control systems in solar architecture Intelligent control systems are defined as intelligence in automation exhibited by an artificial entity. Neural networks, genetic programming, fuzzy logic, computer vision, heuristic search, etc. and combinations of any of the above are some of the available technologies used to optimize the performance of solar buildings.

Urban heat island is a city region which is significantly warmer than its surrounding suburban regions. By altering the nature of the city's surface and generating large amounts of heat, urbanized areas modify the microclimate and air quality. The urban heat island serves as a trap for atmospheric pollutants, deteriorates the quality of life and has a direct impact on the energy demand.

Urbanization The increase of urban population and the physical growth of urban areas as a result of global change. Urbanization is also defined by the United Nations as movement of people from rural to urban areas with population growth equating to urban migration.

3.19.1 Introduction

3.19.1.1 Energy and Urbanization

In recent years, concerns regarding the shortage of traditional energy reserves, the rising demand for energy, fueled partly by the development of new economies, and obvious concerns regarding the effect of irrational energy use and human activity on the environment have made the topic of energy efficiency almost ubiquitous.

Population growth is commonly assumed to be a key issue of unsustainable consumption. The current world population is at around 6 billion people, and is steadily growing by 220 000 each day. At the present rate, it is estimated to reach 8 billion by the year 2030. However, energy consumption is not simply determined by population growth, but also by economic activity, technology choices, social values, institutions, and policies.

Migration of people from rural areas to cities has been on the rise and will likely continue unabated in the so-called less developed countries as a result of increased opportunities being constantly offered in the urban environment and the degradation of the rural economies and societies. Nowadays, approximately 50–60% of the world's population lives in cities and towns. The second half of the last century was a period of more intensive urbanization that our planet had never experienced. In fact, urban population has increased from 160 million to about 3 billion in just 100 years, and it is expected to increase to about 5 billion by 2025.

This has resulted in the energy consumed in buildings to account for 40% of the energy used worldwide, and it has become a widely accepted fact that measures and changes in the building *modus operandi* can yield substantial energy savings. Evidently, even very modest reductions can have a significant impact. Advances in the design, operational optimization, and control of energy-influencing building elements (e.g., building design and services, solar energy, fuel cells, shading, and natural ventilation) unleashed the potential for realization of significant energy savings and efficiencies in the operation of both new and existing building sites worldwide.

Moreover, buildings constitute a major part of the economic sector in the world and the quality of buildings shapes the life of citizens. Although there is an important and substantial increase in the budget allocation toward construction, the United Nations estimates [1] that more than 1 billion urban citizens live in inappropriate houses – mostly in squatter and slum settlements – while in most of the cities in the less developed countries, between one-third and two-thirds of the population live in poor quality and overcrowded housing [2]. Even in the developed world, the percentage of people living in low-income households is quite high. The average percentage of low-income households in the European Union is close to 15%, while in some countries like Ireland it may go up to 21%. Inappropriate housing is characterized by poor indoor environmental conditions such as extremely low or high temperatures and lack of ventilation. In parallel, heat-island conditions in dense urban areas increase ambient temperatures and the thermal stress to buildings, especially during the summer period [3].

The aforementioned international framework along with the possibility of local energy generation with the exploitation of renewable energy sources has led to the concept of solar architecture [4], that is, the design of buildings that consume less than 15 kWh m^{-2} energy by applying bioclimatic principles combined with locally installed (renewable) energy-generating sources to produce part of their energy demands.

This leads to the 'Passive House concept', which aims to provide a satisfactory indoor environmental quality in terms of indoor air quality (IAQ) and thermal comfort at minimum energy demand and cost [5]. Minimizing energy and costs at the same time is not possible with conventional improvements. Significant energy efficiency and energy cost reduction can be achieved by the integration of innovative design and operational aspects that contribute simultaneously to the required balance among indoor quality and energy demand.

3.19.1.2 Solar Architecture – History and Concepts

Extensive research is recorded in the literature concerning solar techniques for the reduction of energy consumption in buildings. The solar techniques can be categorized as passive and active solar systems.

Active solar systems incorporate electrical or mechanical equipment, such as pumps and fans, to forward the energy produced by the sun to the buildings. Active thermal solar systems are systems using solar collectors (either flat or evacuated tubes), solar concentrators (parabolic trough), and so on. Active cooling systems are solar devices coupled with chillers, solar-assisted air conditioners, and roof-integrated water or air solar collectors (**Figure 1**). In any case, the production of electricity is performed via photovoltaics (PV).

Solar architecture and passive house concepts are not new. The solar insolation and path has always influenced a building's orientation, location, shape, constructional elements, and materials used. Climate is one of the major parameters that influenced

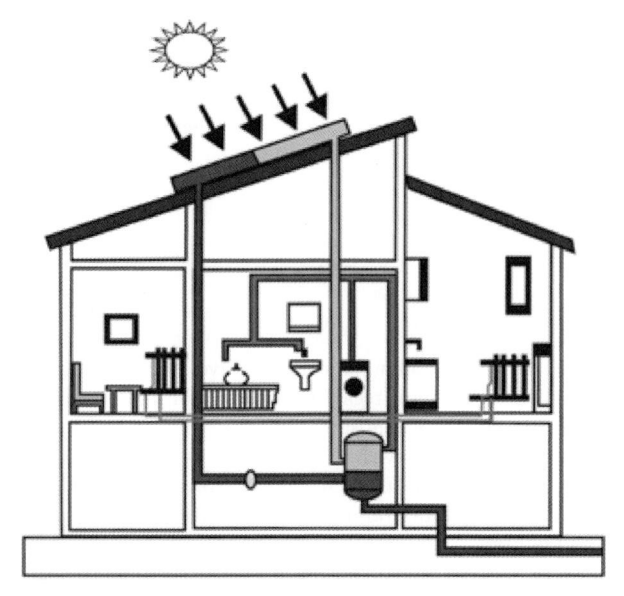

Figure 1 Active solar systems incorporated in the building fabric.

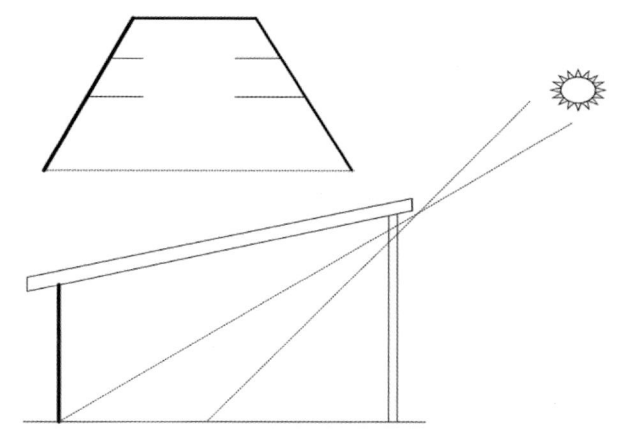

Figure 2 The solar architectural concepts in Socrates solar house (470–399 BC).

the evolution of construction types and buildings' design techniques. One example is the Socrates solar house [6], which incorporates the following features as shown in **Figure 2**:

- trapezoidal plan with increased south facade,
- compact form,
- solar zoning with cool rooms on the north side and warm rooms on the south side,
- shading protection against solar radiation during the summer period, and
- utilization of thermal mass.

3.19.1.3 Solar Architecture – Comprehensive Design and Operation

The basic guidelines for the design and operation of green buildings are as follows:

- Enhance living by creating a comfortable environment for the building occupants and users.
- Consume minimum energy and consider the damage that can be caused by the building to the natural environment over its life cycle.
- Minimize the generation of buildings' waste.
- Use energy from renewable sources to cover the overall energy needs.

Passive solar architecture is a design-and-operational approach which seeks to make buildings and their adjacent spaces to function in harmony with the environment by taking advantage of the sun's energy for the heating and cooling of living spaces. In this approach, the building itself takes advantage of natural energy characteristics in materials and air created by its exposure to the sun. Passive solar features add little or even nothing to the overall cost, are simple, have few moving parts, and require minimal maintenance as usually the mechanical parts are limited.

The main design-and-operational issues behind passive solar architecture are as follows:

- site analysis and building's form and orientation [7];
- building fabric characteristics [8]; and
- appropriate services and control systems [9].

Some basic guidelines for passive buildings are as follows:

- The building should be elongated on an east–west axis (**Figure 3**).
- Interior spaces that require the most light, heating, and cooling should be along the south face of the building.
- Less used spaces should be located on the north.
- An open floor plan optimizes passive system operation.
- Shading is recommended to prevent summer overheating.

In the following sections, passive heating and cooling technologies are analyzed.

3.19.1.3.1 *Passive solar heating*

For passive solar heating, the building should combine the following characteristics:

- increased insulation and air tightness to minimize heat losses,
- large south-facing glazing facade,

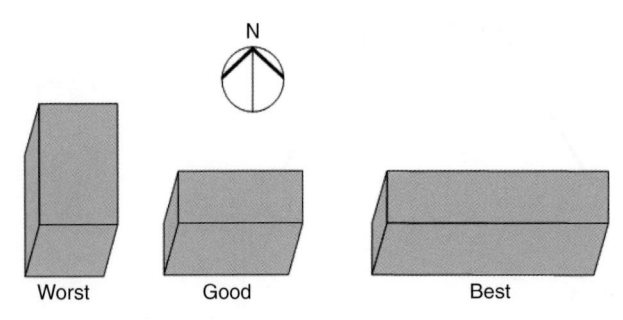

Figure 3 Orientation and building's form.

- minimization of shading in winter,
- thermal mass to store solar heat, and
- responsive and efficient heating system.

Passive solar heating is accomplished via the following procedures:

- solar collection,
- thermal storage, and
- thermal energy distribution.

Solar collection depends upon the orientation and the surface area of glazings as well as the glazings' light transmittance.

Thermal storage systems for passive solar heating are distinguished as direct systems, indirect systems, and sunspaces.

The direct gain/thermal storage system is the living space which acts as solar collector, heat absorber, and distribution system. South-facing glass admits solar energy into the house, where it strikes directly and indirectly thermal mass materials in the house. The direct system utilizes almost 60–75% of the sun's energy striking the windows (**Figure 4**). In a direct storage system, the thermal mass walls and floors are functional parts of the house. It is also possible to use water containers inside the house to store heat. However, it is more difficult to integrate water storage containers in the design of the house. The thermal mass will absorb and store the heat during the day. At night, the thermal mass will radiate the stored heat into the living space.

Indirect passive solar systems include solar walls. A solar wall is a south-facing wall specially designed to collect solar energy and transmit it to the buildings. Although a number of configurations are available, the most representative are the mass wall and the Trombe wall.

The mass wall (**Figure 5**) is a solid south-facing wall that absorbs solar radiation and transmits it into the building. These walls may be of stone, concrete, or other materials, and they have a black mat surface to absorb solar radiation. These walls are glazed to the outside to reduce heat losses to the environment. Mass walls should be well shaded during summer to protect the building from overheating.

A Trombe wall, shown in **Figure 6**, is a mass wall with a vent at its top and bottom to allow air to circulate between the glass-wall gap and the building. Vents should be open during the day and closed during the night to avoid reverse circulation, which may reduce the indoor temperature of the heating space.

Sunspaces are isolated gain systems which are completely separate from the main living area. It is a glazed enclosure adjacent in the south facade of the building. The isolated gain system will utilize 15–30% of the sunlight striking the glazing toward heating the adjoining living areas. Solar energy is also retained in the sunroom itself.

Sunspaces or solar greenhouses, shown in **Figure 7**, employ a combination of direct gain and indirect gain system features. Sunlight entering the sunroom is retained in the thermal mass and air of the room. Sunlight is brought into the house by means of

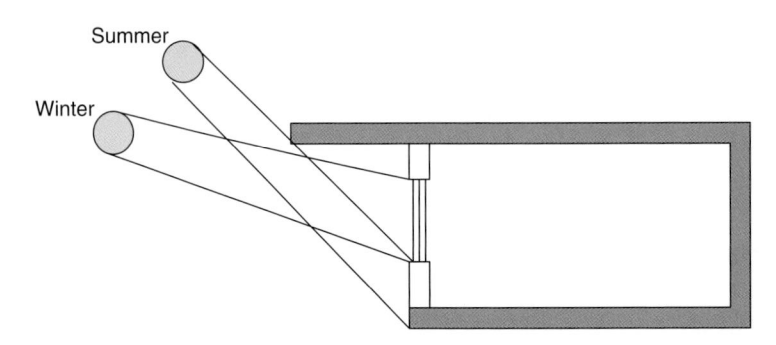

Figure 4 Direct passive solar systems.

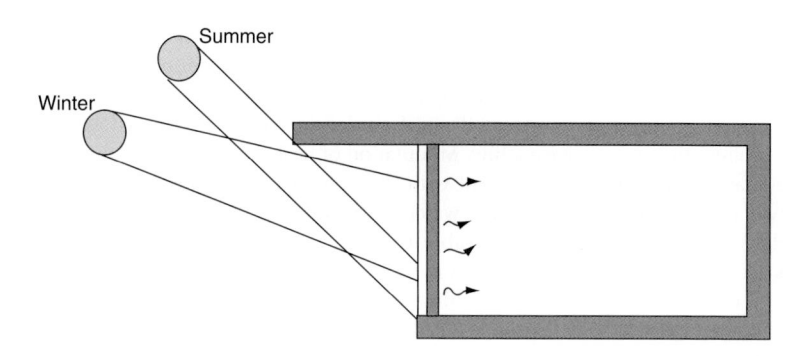

Figure 5 Mass wall.

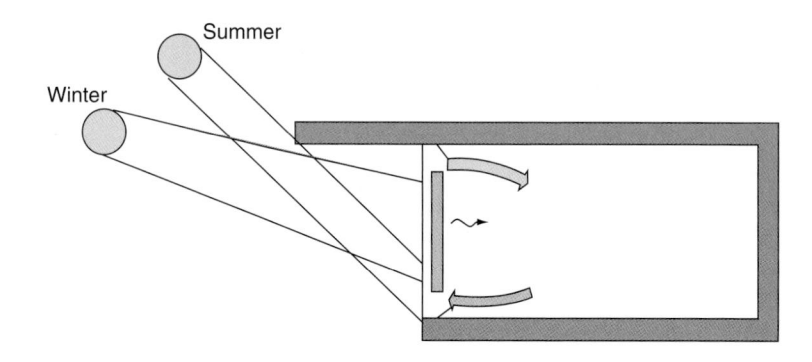

Figure 6 Trombe wall.

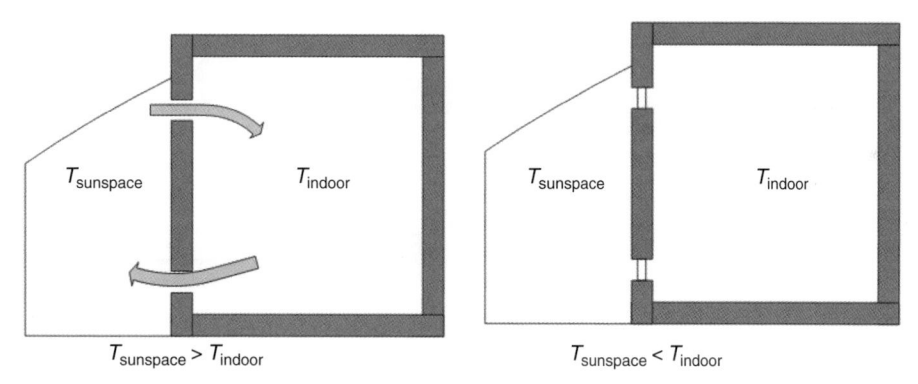

Figure 7 The sunspaces operation as passive.

conduction through a shared mass wall in the rear of the sunroom, or by vents that permit the air between the sunroom and living space to be exchanged by convection.

Recent developments in passive heating include mass walls, solar chimneys (**Figure 8**), increased insulation [11], innovative glazing systems [12], double-skin facades [13], and so on.

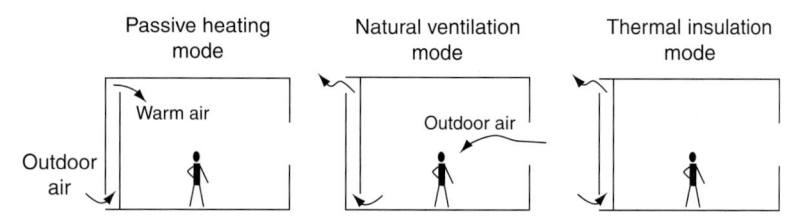

Figure 8 Passive heating via solar chimney [10].

3.19.1.3.2 Passive cooling

Passive cooling relies on the use of techniques for solar and heat control, heat amortization, and heat dissipation. Solar and heat protection techniques may involve thermal improvement by the use of outdoor and semi-outdoor spaces, layout and external finishing, solar control and shading of building surfaces, thermal insulation, control of internal gains, night ventilation strategies (see **Figure 11**), radiative cooling, and evaporative cooling. Modulation of heat gains deals with the thermal storage capacity of the building structure, while heat dissipation techniques deal with the potential for disposal of excess heat of the building to an environmental sink of lower temperature, like the ground, water, ambient air, or the sky.

The main passive cooling techniques are tabulated in **Table 1**.

Evaporative cooling is realized by the interaction of hot air with water. Water vaporization causes a drop in air temperature and an increase in humidity. This effect is maximized by establishing pools or fountains adjacent to the buildings. Evaporative cooling is not suitable for humid climates (**Figure 9**).

Ground cooling is a certain procedure where air is cooled before entering the building by passing through underground ducts. Since the temperature of the ground below a certain depth is lower than the ambient air temperature, cooling is achieved by convection or even evaporation if the ground is damp (**Figure 10**).

Table 1 Main passive cooling techniques

Passive cooling technique	Heat sink	Heat transfer method
Radiative cooling	Space	Radiation
Evaporative cooling	Water–air	Convection
Ventilation	Air	Convection
Earth cooling	Ground	Conduction

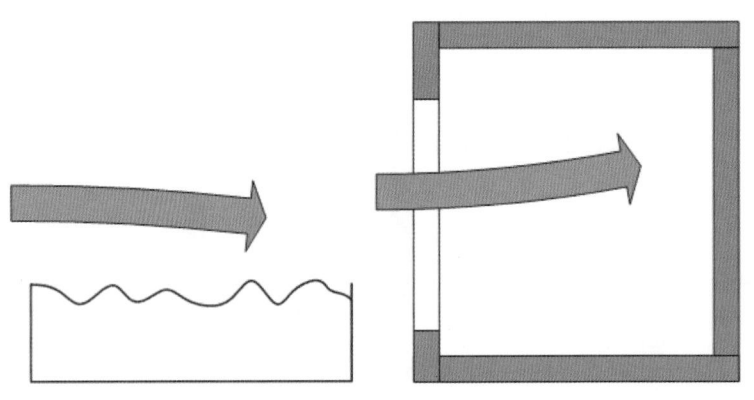

Figure 9 Evaporative cooling.

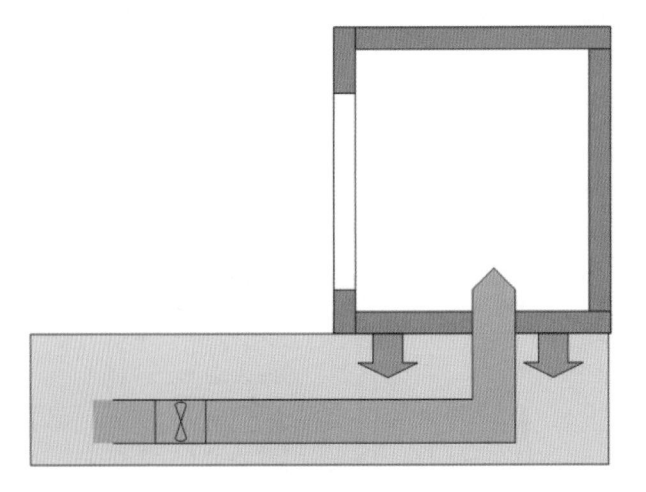

Figure 10 Ground cooling.

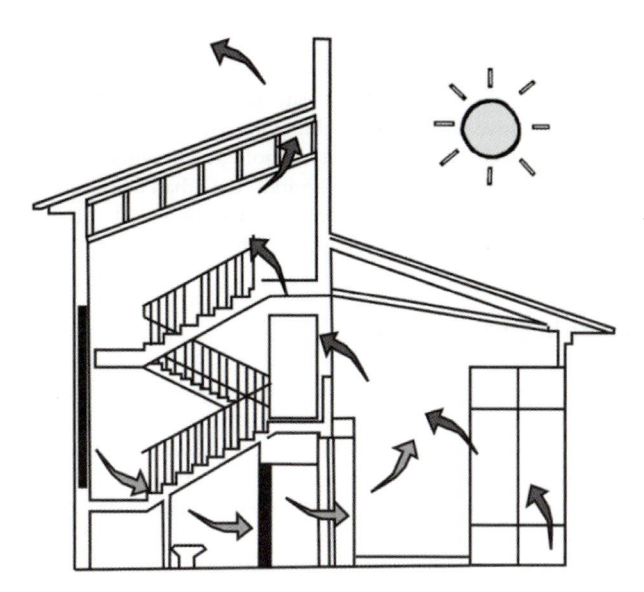

Figure 11 Passive cooling via ventilation.

Ventilation contributes to cooling by forwarding fresh air into the building either naturally (due to pressure or temperature difference) or mechanically. Passive cooling via ventilation is performed by (1) side ventilation, where the air cross-ventilation and the pressure difference move the air into the building; (2) cross-ventilation, where the air is passed through the building due to pressure difference between two openings; or (3) stack ventilation, which allows the air to move into the building due to temperature difference [14] (see **Figure 11**).

Radiative cooling occurs when two adjacent masses have different temperatures. Therefore, since the sky is usually colder than the various building surfaces, a significant amount of heat which has gathered in the building during the day is radiated to the sky during the night. The overall procedure is depicted in **Figure 12**.

State-of-the-art passive cooling technologies incorporate innovative glazing, light-colored walls and roofs, using high-albedo cool materials [15], green roofs [16, 17] and shaded roof [18], cooled ceiling systems [19, 20], passive cooling of the buildings [21], natural ventilation [22], solar control of buildings such as shading with plants and proper tree plantation [23], and insulating envelopes and external surfaces of the buildings [24, 25], which are effective ways for reducing cooling loads of the buildings. Moreover, advanced materials are used in the building fabric. This varies from the application of Fresnel lenses for temperature and illumination control [26] to the incorporation of cool materials and green spaces [15, 23, 27–29]. The Fresnel lenses are incorporated into the building as transparent material to separate the direct from the diffuse solar radiation and can be combined

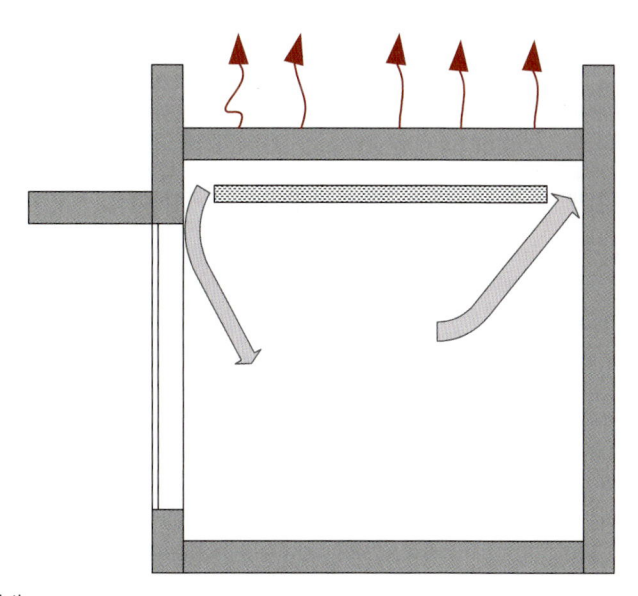

Figure 12 Passive cooling via radiation.

with solar radiation absorbers (T), PV, or hybrid PV/T. The application of cool materials and green spaces in the building fabric has become the object of serious research during the very last period. Integrated solar systems that combine heating and cooling are also proposed [30]. The solution combines solar collectors with a hot water storage tank and a gas boiler backup to provide hot water, which is used either for space heating or to drive an absorption chiller for space cooling.

Based on the above analysis, this chapter focuses on the recent technological developments in the improvement of the building fabric and control systems for the solar architecture. The state of the art in the urban fabric and dynamic facade materials including cool materials, thermochromic coatings, and green spaces are analyzed in Section 3.19.2. The evolution of control systems in the solar architecture is discussed in Section 3.19.3. Section 3.19.4 analyzes the research trends and the state of the art is concluded.

3.19.2 Role of Solar Architecture in Urban Buildings

Increased urban temperatures have an important impact on the energy consumption of buildings, mainly during the summer period. Heat island is the most documented phenomenon of climatic change. Heat island is related to the increase of urban temperatures compared to the suburban areas because of the positive heat balance. Hundreds of studies have been performed all over the world, and data for many European, American, and other cities are available [3].

Higher urban temperatures increase the peak electricity demand for cooling and the concentration of pollutants in cities.

Several techniques have been proposed to mitigate heat islands, of which two appear to be especially significant: the use of green spaces and the use of appropriate materials in buildings and the urban fabric.

Heat island intensity can be considerably reduced by decreasing the amount of solar radiation absorbed by the urban fabric. The use of proper materials for buildings and the urban fabric that present high reflectivity to solar radiation may contribute significantly to a decrease in the temperature of cities. These 'cool materials' have become the subject of much research recently [31, 32].

In parallel, the development of dynamic facade materials, like the thermochromic coatings, may contribute to reduce the cooling load of buildings and, in parallel, decrease the corresponding heating needs.

This section analyzes the role of passive cooling in the urban buildings and focuses on the techniques used to increase albedo, such as the use of cool materials and green spaces in the urban structure.

3.19.2.1 Development of Cool-Colored Materials

The use of cool materials for heat-island mitigation has gained a lot of interest during the past few years. Cool materials are characterized by high solar reflectance (SR) and infrared emittance values. These two properties mainly affect the temperature of a surface. Increasing the reflectance and/or the emittance of the covering contributes to lower the surface temperature, which in turn decreases the heat penetrating into the building, if it is a surface of the building envelope, or contributes to decrease the temperature of the ambient air as heat convection intensity from a cooler surface is lower.

During the last year, the development of cool-colored materials has gained increasing acceptance, because in many cases the aesthetics of darker colors is preferred. Cool nonwhite coatings absorb light in the visible range in order to appear having a specific color, but they should be highly reflective in the near-infrared (NIR) part of the electromagnetic spectrum to maintain a high SR. This is very important considering the fact that about half of all solar power arrives as invisible NIR radiation. Specialized, complex inorganic color pigments that are dark in color but have the ability to reflect strongly the NIR portion of the solar spectrum have been created by pigment manufacturers and they are used in order to develop cool-colored coatings with higher SR compared to conventionally pigmented coatings.

Cool-colored coatings can be applied on building envelopes and other surfaces of the urban environment as exterior finishes and paints or they can be used to manufacture building materials that reflect more sunlight than conventionally pigmented products. City-scale application of cool materials will increase surface albedo. This means that surface temperatures will be lower as well as near-surface air temperatures.

Ten prototype cool-colored coatings were created at the National and Kapodistrian University of Athens using special NIR reflective color pigments and were tested in comparison to color-matched, conventionally pigmented coatings [27]. All coatings tested are acryl-based coatings and they can be applied on building envelopes (roofs and walls) and other surfaces of the urban environment. The coatings were applied on white concrete pavement tiles. The tiles had a size of 40 × 40 cm. In order to study the optical properties and the thermal performance of the coatings, the following parameters were measured:

1. The surface temperature of the samples on a 24 h basis. The basic experimental equipment consists of surface temperature sensors (thermocouples type K) connected to a data logging system. Instantaneous values were measured and saved on a computer hard disk every 10 min. The temperature sensors were placed on the center of the surface of each tile.
2. The infrared emittance of the samples, with the use of the Devices & Services emissometer model AE. This emittance device determines the total thermal emittance, in comparison with standard high- and low-emittance materials.
3. The spectral reflectance of the samples, using UV/VIS/NIR spectrophotometer (Varian Cary 5000) fitted with a 150 mm-diameter integrating sphere (Labsphere DRA 2500) that collects both specular and diffuse radiation. The reference standard reflectance material used for the measurement was a polytetrafluoroethylene (PTFE) plate (Labsphere).

Table 2 SR of cool and color-matched standard coatings and % increase in SR between them

Color	SR (%) Cool	SR (%) Standard	% Increase in SR$_{(cool-standard)}$
Orange	63	53	19
Light blue	42	40	5
Blue	33	18	83
Green	27	20	35
Black (1)	12	6	100
Anthracite	26	7	271
Brown	34	23	48
Chocolate brown	27	9	200
Light brown	36	22	64
Black (2)	27	5	440

SR, solar reflectance.

During the experimental period, the ambient meteorological conditions were characterized by high temperatures, low relative humidity, low wind speeds, and clear sky. The samples were placed on a horizontal platform, insulated from below in order to eliminate the heat transfer effects between the platform and the samples. The experimental procedure took place during the months of August to October of 2005.

Based on the results of the spectrophotometric measurements, the SR of each sample was calculated. The calculation was done by the weighted averaging method, using a standard solar spectrum as the weighting function. The spectrum employed is that suggested by American Society for Testing and Materials (ASTM) (ASTM E903-96, ASTM G159-98)). The values of SR for each sample are shown in **Table 2**. All the coatings containing infrared reflective pigments have SR values higher than those of the standard coatings. The highest difference in the SR was observed between cool black (2) coating (SR = 27%) and standard black (2) (SR = 5%). The percentage increase of SR was 440%. In contrast, the smaller difference in the SR was observed between cool light blue coating (SR = 42%) and standard light blue (SR = 40%), with a percentage increase of SR of only 5%. In general, the increase in SR varies with the color of the coating, but it appears to be higher for dark colors.

Spectral reflectance measurements showed that the reflectance curves for each standard and its corresponding cool coating coincide in the visible range, indicating that the coatings are color-matched, that is, they appear to have the same color. Furthermore, almost all of the standard coatings exhibit low or modest reflectance in the NIR range, while the cool-colored coatings exhibit a more selective absorption band, reflecting significantly the NIR radiation.

During the day, it was found that all the cool-colored coatings had surface temperatures lower than those of the color-matched standard coatings. The best performing cool coatings were black (2), chocolate brown, blue, and anthracite, which maintained a difference in mean daily surface temperature from their standard color-matched coatings by 5.2, 4.7, 4.7, and 2.8 °C, respectively, for the month of August. The highest temperature difference was observed between cool and standard black (2) and was equal to 10.2 °C, corresponding to a difference in their SR of 22. The lowest temperature difference was observed between cool and standard green (2) and was equal to 1.6 °C (for August), corresponding to a difference in their SR of 7%.

This temperature difference between the cool and the standard coatings can easily be explained. If a coating appears, for example, black, this means that it must absorb in the entire range of the visible spectrum. The light energy that is absorbed is converted to heat energy, resulting in an increase in the surface temperature of the sample. The same applies for the cool and standard black coatings that both have strong absorptance in the visible range. In the NIR range, the standard black coating continues to show very low reflectance, absorbing not only all the visible light that enters its surface but also the infrared part of the solar energy. In contrast, a coating containing infrared reflective pigments exhibits a more selective absorption band (like the cool black). Therefore, although it still absorbs all of the visible wavelengths, a large part of the NIR radiation is reflected rather than absorbed. If we consider the fact that almost half of the solar energy that arrives to earth is infrared, it becomes evident that the black coating that absorbs this part will become hotter than the coating that reflects it.

The temperature difference between the cool and standard coatings decreases from August to October, as the monthly average daily global solar radiation decreases too, and the impact of the infrared reflective pigments in the coatings becomes less evident. It was found that the coatings with higher values of SR demonstrated lower surface temperatures. A strong correlation ($R^2 = 0.92$) was found between the maximum daily surface temperature and the SR of the samples. We can therefore assume that the main factor affecting the thermal performance of the samples during the day is their SR.

During the night when there is no solar radiation, the surface temperature of the samples was found to be quite uniform due to the fact that all the coatings have an emissivity of about 0.88. However, cool-colored coatings remain cooler (by 0.1–1.6 °C) than the standard color-matched coatings, probably because they have absorbed smaller amounts of solar radiation during the day. Small variations in the measured emissivity explain the variations in the night surface temperature.

646 Applications

3.19.2.2 Use of Phase Change Materials to Enhance the Performance of Cool-Colored Coatings

Phase change materials (PCMs) may store heat in their mass under the form of latent heat. PCMs are widely used in solar applications as well as in building materials, like plaster, to absorb the excess heat in buildings. Microencapsulated PCMs are commercially developed and are available at a particle size ranging between 17 and 20 μm. Microparticles include a phase change ingredient, usually paraffins, in their core and a polymer or a plastic in the exterior shell. The melting temperature may vary according to the specific needs.

Phase change microparticles have been used to further enhance the performance of cool color coatings. They have been used to develop coatings based on infrared reflective pigments doped with PCMs [33]. Six different colored pigments have been tested while investigations have been performed regarding the melting temperature of the microcapsules and the weight percentage of the materials. The PCM-doped coatings as well as the conventional infrared reflective and the common coatings have been used to paint concrete tiles, and their surface temperature has been measured during the summer of 2008 (**Figure 13**). Surface temperature sensors and infrared thermography techniques have been used.

Measurements have shown that the PCM-doped materials present a peak daily temperature of up to 4 °C lower compared to conventional infrared reflective coatings and up to 9 °C compared to common coatings.

Figure 14 shows the daily variation of the surface temperature of black tiles, coated with PCM-doped, conventional infrared reflective, and common black coatings, for 10 consecutive days of measurements. As shown, during the whole measurement period, the peak surface temperature of PCM-doped coatings was in all cases 2–4 °C lower than that of the conventional infrared reflective

Figure 13 Picture of the tested cool phase change coatings.

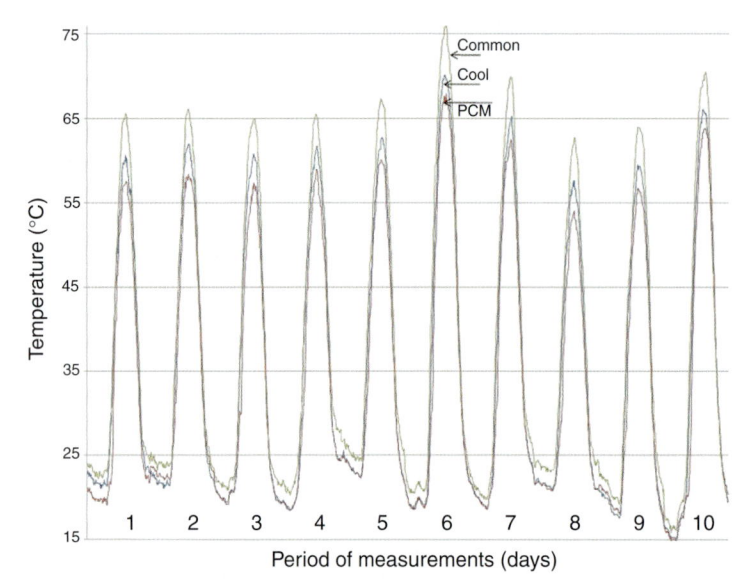

Figure 14 Daily variation of the surface temperature of black tiles coated with phase change material (PCM)-doped, conventional infrared reflective, and common black coatings.

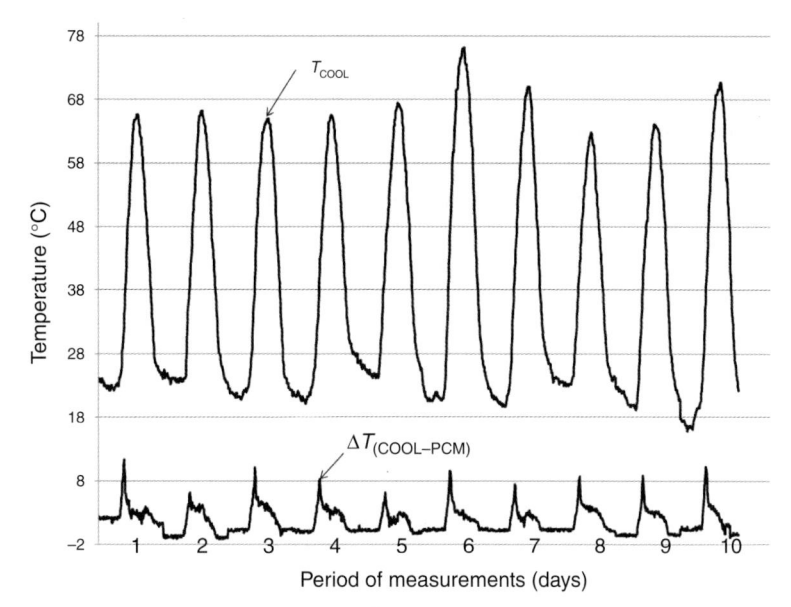

Figure 15 Daily variation of the surface temperature difference between the phase change material (PCM)-doped and the conventional infrared reflective coatings. Also, the daily variation of the conventional infrared reflective material is shown.

coatings. During the night period, both the PCM-doped and the conventional infrared reflective coatings presented substantially lower surface temperatures than the common black paints.

The measured temperature difference between the PCM-doped and the conventional infrared reflective coatings varies during the day, presenting its maximum during the morning hours when the surface temperature approaches the melting point of the PCM.

Figure 15 shows the daily variation of the surface temperature difference between the PCM-doped and the conventional infrared reflective coatings together with the daily variation of the temperature of the conventional infrared reflective material. As shown, the maximum temperature difference between the two coatings is seen at about 9.30 a.m. when the temperature of the material reaches the fusion temperature of the PCM. At that time, the temperature difference between the two materials varies between 8 and 10 °C.

Figure 16 shows the daily variation of both the PCM-doped and the conventional infrared reflective materials. During the night period, both materials present a similar temperature. At about 8.00 a.m., the PCM starts to melt and the surface temperature of this coating presents a much lower increase than that of the conventional one, until 9.30 a.m., when the maximum surface temperature difference is achieved. At that time, convective phenomena between the tiles and the ambient air are much more intensive for the PCM-doped coating as its surface temperature is considerably lower. Thus, the rate of increase of the surface temperature of the PCM-doped material starts to be much higher than that of the conventional coating and this continues until the early afternoon period when surface temperatures reach their maximum. In the afternoon period, the rate of decrease of the surface temperature of the

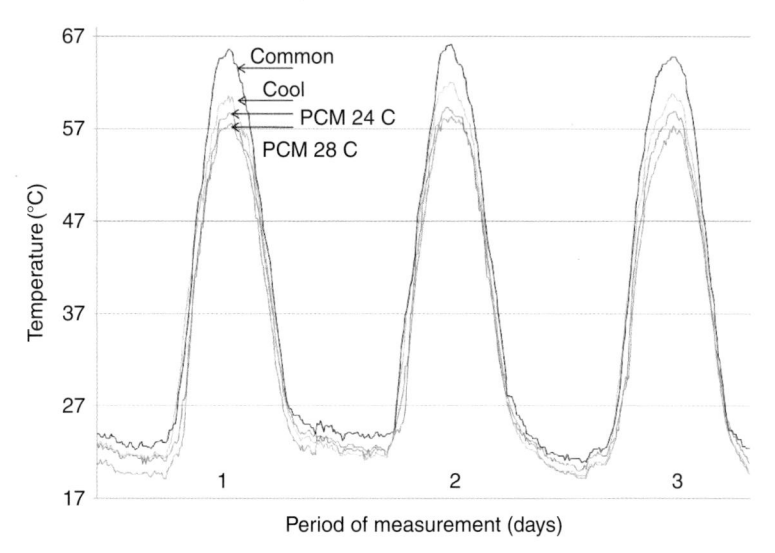

Figure 16 Daily variation of the surface temperature of the common, conventional infrared reflective, and phase change material (PCM) 28 °C and PCM 24 °C doped infrared reflective black coatings.

PCM-doped material is quite lower until the sunset when both materials present almost a similar temperature. During the night period, latent heat released by the PCM-doped material does not have any significant impact on the surface temperature of the coating.

3.19.2.3 Development of Thermochromic Coatings

Highly reflective materials contribute substantially to decrease the cooling load of buildings; however, they may also increase the heating needs during the winter period. The development of coatings that respond thermally to the environment and may change reversibly their color could present high advantages. Materials that may present high absorptance during winter and high reflectance during summer could contribute to decrease both the heating and cooling needs of buildings. Thermochromic coatings present a thermally reversible transformation of their molecular structure that causes a spectral change of visible color [34–36].

Thermochromic materials are based on organic leuco dye mixtures composed of three main components:

1. a solvent, which usually is an alcohol or an ester, the melting point of which defines the transition temperature at which the coating changes its color;
2. a color former, which usually is a cyclic ester that defines the color of the coating in its colored state; and
3. a color developer, which is a weak acid responsible for the color intensity of the product.

To protect the thermochromic system from the chemicals used in a coating and to prevent aging and oxidation, the mixture is encapsulated in microspheres of less than 15 μm [35–44]. However, aging is a major problem for thermochromic materials as absorption of ultraviolet (UV) energy can cause the breaking and/or cross-linking of the polymer chains, leading to altered chemical and mechanical properties [45].

Thermochromic coatings for the outdoor environment have been developed and tested by Ma et al. [46, 47]. It has been found that for temperatures above the transition temperature of the thermochromic system, its surface temperature was 4 °C lower than that of the ordinary colored coating. Karlessi et al. [33] have developed and tested thermochromic coatings for buildings and urban structures. The color transition temperature of the coatings was 30 °C. Microencapsulated pigments having a particle size close to 5 μm have been used while the slurry form contained almost 50% of solid thermochromic compound. Two types of coatings have been prepared and tested: the first comprised only the thermochromic pigments and the binder, while in the second, titanium dioxide (TiO_2) has been added to avoid transparency of the coating at the warm state. Coatings of six different colors with and without TiO_2 have been developed and tested.

Measurements of the spectral reflectance of all the prepared coatings, shown in **Figure 17**, in both the colored and colorless state, have shown that in the visible range of the colored state, the thermochromic coatings present almost similar reflectance with the cool and common coatings. In parallel, all thermochromic coatings presented a very high reflection in the NIR and a very strong absorption in the near UV. Comparison between the reflectance curves of thermochromic coatings at their colored phase and their colorless phase shows that thermochromic coatings can absorb solar energy at lower temperatures and reduce the absorption at higher temperatures. The SR of each developed thermochromic coating, shown in **Table 3**, is higher in both the colored and colorless phases than the cool and common coatings. In particular, green thermochromic coating with TiO_2 presents an increase of its SR at the white phase by 43%, while for the yellow coating the increase was only of 4%. The infrared emittance of all thermochromic coatings range from 0.83 to 0.91 and no significant differences are observed against the cool and common coatings.

Comparative testing of the surface temperature of the developed thermochromic coatings against common and cool coatings has shown that thermochromic materials present much lower surface temperatures, as shown in **Figure 18**. A detailed comparison of the measured mean and maximum daily surface temperatures as well as of the mean nocturnal temperatures for the thermochromic as well as for the cool and common coatings is given in **Tables 4–6**. As shown, temperature differences range from 2.2 °C for thermochromic and cool yellow to 9.2 °C for thermochromic and cool brown and from 4.2 °C for thermochromic and common yellow to 11.4 °C for thermochromic and common green. In parallel, thermochromic coatings demonstrate 10–15 °C lower mean maximum daily temperatures than cool coatings, and 18–20 °C lower than common coatings. For yellow coatings, the $\Delta T_{max(cool-thermo)}$ was close to 1.5 °C, and $\Delta T_{max(common-thermo)}$ was 6.8 °C. Also, for blue coatings, the $\Delta T_{max(common-thermo)}$ was equal to 10.1 °C. Nocturnal temperature differences between thermochromic, cool, and common coatings are not found to be significant. **Figure 19** shows the mean surface temperature profile of all the green coatings for August.

By applying statistical methods, it is found that the mean surface temperatures of both groups of thermochromic coatings (with TiO_2 and without TiO_2) are significantly different from that of the cool and common coatings, at a significant level of 0.05.

Aging tests have been performed and various techniques have been tested to decrease the degradation of the thermochromic coatings. Although an important improvement has been achieved, further research to stabilize the optimal properties of the materials is necessary.

3.19.2.4 Development and Testing of Colored Thin-Film Layers of Asphalt

The reflectivity of asphalt may be increased and its surface temperature can be reduced significantly when colors are mixed with binder or lighter colored aggregates are used. Also, chip seals and emulsions of lighter colors can be used to increase the reflectivity of the asphaltic products.

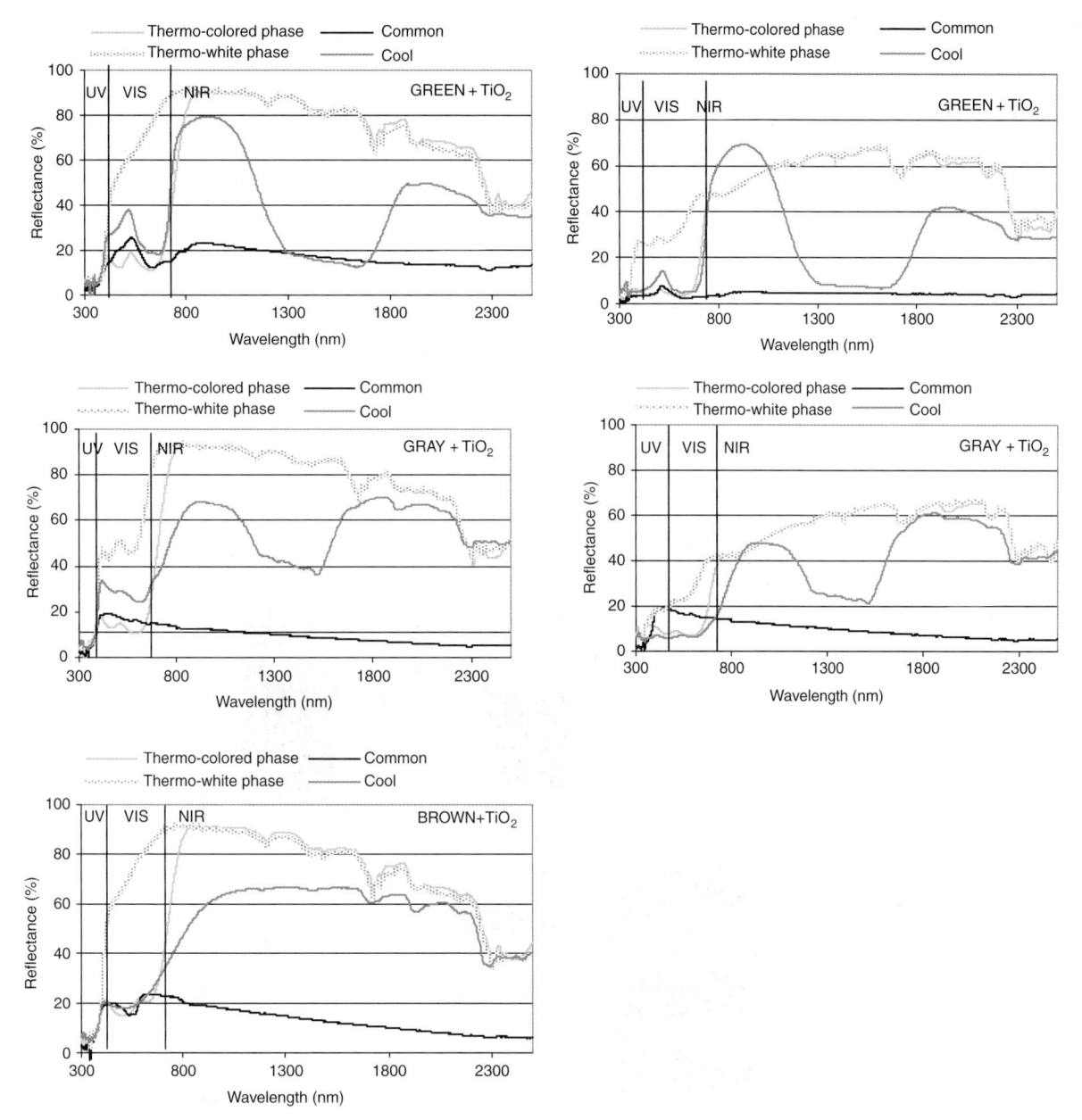

Figure 17 Spectral reflectance of thermochromic, cool, and common coatings of the same color.

Twenty-six asphalt pavements composed of different aggregates and of five different colors (whitish, green, red, yellow, and natural) have been developed and tested to investigate their heat-island mitigation potential [48]. As shown in **Figure 20**, the reflectivity of the developed asphalt pavements is much higher than that of the common asphalt. In particular, colored asphalt materials present a reflectivity in the visible range between 20% and 70%, while the corresponding reflectivity of common asphalt is not higher than 4%. In parallel, in the infrared spectrum, the reflectivity of the colored asphalt products varies between 40% and 55%, while the conventional material presents a reflectivity close to 6%. The measured reflectivity of representative colored asphalt materials in the UV, visible, and infrared parts is given in **Table 7**. The total SR of the colored asphalt materials varies between 27% and 55%, while the corresponding value for the conventional black asphalt is 4%.

All developed colored asphalt materials have been exposed to the outdoor environment during the summer of 2008 and their surface temperature has been measured for about a month. The maximum daily temperature of representative colored and black asphalt materials is given in **Figure 21**. As shown, colored asphalt products present a reduction of the maximum daily temperature, which ranges between 5.6 and 16.5 °C. The daily variation of the surface temperature of representative colored and black asphalt materials is given in **Figure 22**.

The use of colored asphalt materials may reduce the surface temperatures in the urban environment and contribute highly to mitigate heat island in cities.

650 Applications

Table 3 SR and % increase in the SR of thermochromic, cool, and common coatings

SR (%)		Thermochromic Colored phase	Colorless phase	% Increase SR $_{(colorless-colored)}$	Cool	% Increase SR $_{(thermocolored-cool)}$	Common	% Increase SR $_{(thermocolored-common)}$
Green	With TiO$_2$	51	73	43	41	24	18	183
	Without TiO$_2$	33	45	36	27	22	4	725
Yellow	With TiO$_2$	78	81	4	73	7	64	22
	Without TiO$_2$	70	73	4	69	1	64	9
Brown	With TiO$_2$	55	76	38	41	34	18	206
Black	With TiO$_2$	40	53	33	17	135	3	1233
	Without TiO$_2$	40	47	18	12	233	3	1233
Blue	With TiO$_2$	59	71	20	53	11	51	16
	Without TiO$_2$	41	54	32	32	28	21	95
Gray	With TiO$_2$	55	73	33	44	25	13	323
	Without TiO$_2$	34	40	18	25	36	13	162

SR, solar reflectance.

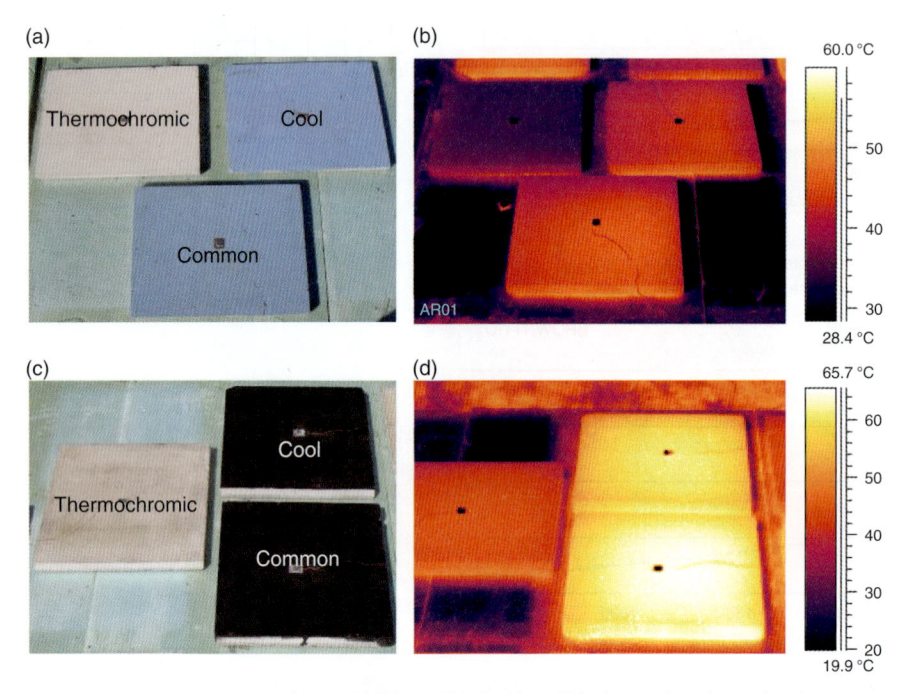

Figure 18 Visible (a), (c) and infrared (b), (d) images of blue with TiO$_2$ and black without TiO$_2$ thermochromic, cool, and common coatings, respectively.

Table 4 Mean daily surface temperatures (°C) for thermochromic, cool, and common coatings in August

	Mean daily surface temperature (°C) in August					
	Thermochromic		Cool		Common	
	With TiO$_2$	Without TiO$_2$	With TiO$_2$	Without TiO$_2$	Light	Dark
Green	33.2	36.0	40.9	43.8	44.6	48.5
Yellow	32.2	32.5	34.4	35.3	36.4	
Brown	31.0		40.2		42.3	
Black	37.6	38.4	44.6	45.2		47.5
Blue	33.1	37.4	38.7	42.4	39.0	43.9
Gray	34.1	35.5	40.4	44.4	45.1	

Table 5 Mean maximum daily surface temperatures (°C) for thermochromic, cool, and common coatings in August

	Mean maximum daily surface temperature (°C) in August					
	Thermochromic		Cool		Common	
	With TiO$_2$	Without TiO$_2$	With TiO$_2$	Without TiO$_2$	Light	Dark
Green	44.2	49.5	57.0	61.1	63.6	69.8
Yellow	42.5	43.8	44.0	46.7	49.3	
Brown	40.2		54.9		59.2	
Black	50.3	51.5	63.8	64.4		68.0
Blue	42.7	49.6	52.3	59.2	52.8	62.6
Gray	44.3	46.7	56.1	63.0	64.3	

Table 6 Mean nocturnal surface temperatures (°C) for thermochromic, cool, and common coatings in August

	Mean nocturnal surface temperature (°C) in August					
	Thermochromic		Cool		Common	
	With TiO$_2$	Without TiO$_2$	With TiO$_2$	Without TiO$_2$	Light	Dark
Green	18.0	17.8	20.2	21.6	20.2	20.7
Yellow	18.5	18.0	17.6	20.5	20.2	
Brown	18.6		21.0		20.6	
Black	21.3	21.1	20.4	20.6		21.1
Blue	20.0	20.6	20.7	20.5	20.9	20.2
Gray	21.0	20.5	20.2	20.8	20.3	

3.19.2.5 Green Spaces for Urban Buildings

The importance of green spaces to mitigate urban heat island has been stressed by many researchers. Trees create a favorable thermal balance for humans and enhance outdoor thermal comfort [49]. Papadakis *et al.* [29] have conducted measurements to investigate the ability of trees to control solar radiation on vertical facades in Greece. It is reported that almost 70–85% of the incident radiation was intercepted by the trees while the ambient temperature behind the shaded area was relatively lower than those without the trees.

Building-integrated green spaces are mainly green rooftops. A typical green roof consists of a soil mixture and a drainage layer (see **Figure 23**). Green roofs can be categorized as intensive and extensive, depending upon the use, the depth of plantation, and the required maintenance. Intensive green roofs are usually traditional roof gardens that require a relatively thick soil to grow large plants and they require increased irrigation, feeding, and other maintenance. They are normally accessible as a recreation space for residents and so incorporate areas of paving, seating, and other architectural features. In contrast, extensive green roofs feature a lightweight growing medium and self-generative plants. They are designed to be self-sustaining and require only a minimum of maintenance, perhaps a once-yearly weeding or an application of slow-release fertilizer to boost growth. Extensive roofs are usually only accessed for maintenance.

Planted roofs can contribute highly to mitigate heat island. Planted roofs present much lower temperatures than hard surfaces and contribute to decrease the ambient temperature through convection and evapotranspiration.

Eumorfopoulou and Aravantinos have simulated various planted roof elements with different heights of plants and different drainage and they have performed comparisons between a bare roof and a planted roof. It is concluded that the planted roof contributes highly to the thermal protection of buildings but cannot replace the thermal insulation layer [50].

Niachou *et al.* have reported extensive measurements of a planted roof in Greece and they concluded that it contributes to reduce seriously the cooling load of buildings. The application of the green roof reduced the percentage of maximum indoor air temperature exceeding 30 °C to 15% from 68% without the green rooftop. The energy efficiency due to green roofs for a noninsulated building was 37–48%, while for an insulated building it was quite low (5%) [22].

The benefits of an intensive rooftop garden installation in a tropical environment were investigated by Wong *et al.* through field measurements carried out in Singapore. The analysis reveals that the temperature measured under the vegetation depends upon the plants' leaf area index. Lower temperatures were measured under vegetation with increased leaf area index. The cooling effect of plants was also confirmed by the ambient air temperature reduction observed at different heights. A maximum temperature difference of 4.2 °C was obtained between the locations with and without the plants [51].

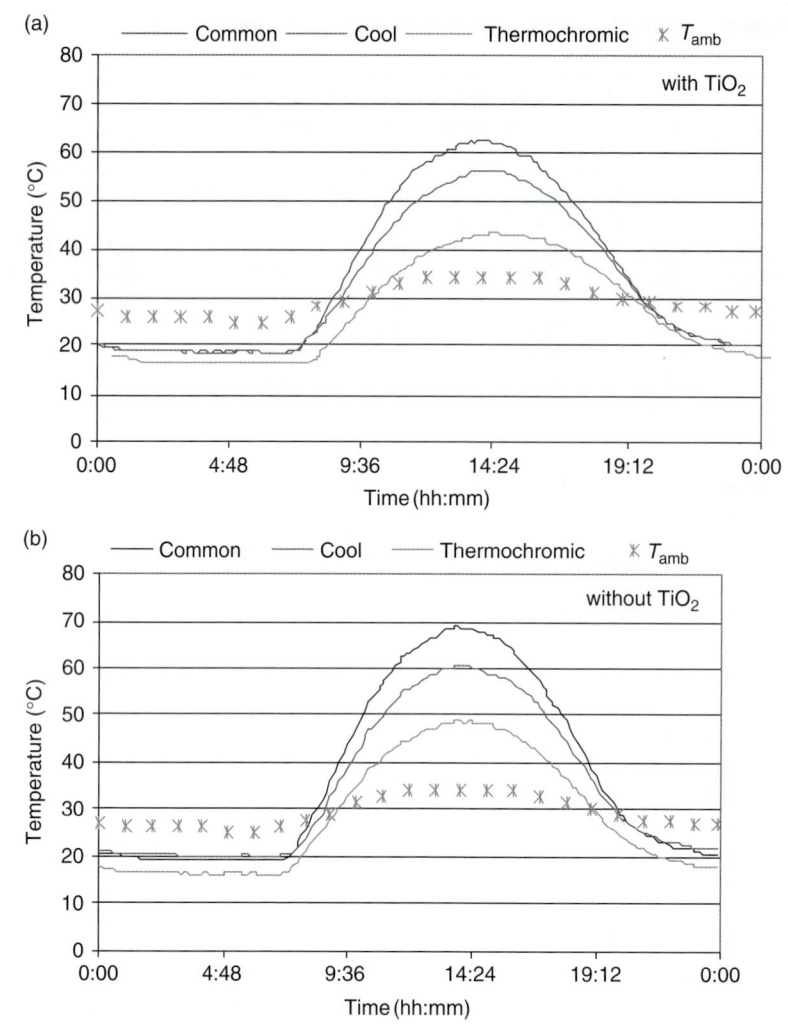

Figure 19 Mean daily surface temperature profile of ambient temperature (T_{amb}) and of green-colored thermochromic, cool, and common coatings with TiO$_2$ (a) and without TiO$_2$ (b) in August.

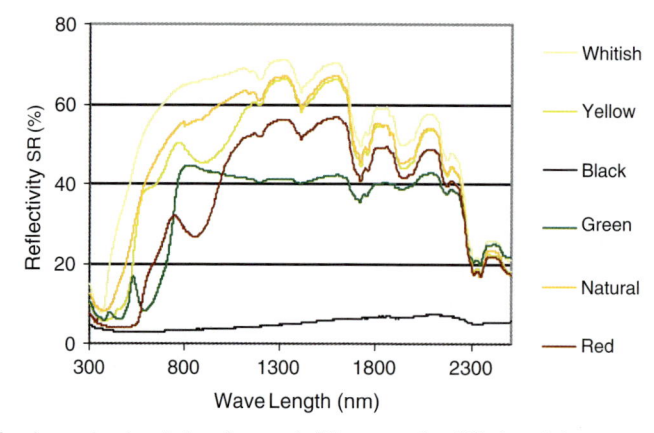

Figure 20 Spectral reflectance of various colored asphalt surfaces and of the conventional black asphalt.

Wong *et al.* also carried out energy simulations to estimate the energy savings for a commercial building in Singapore with an intensive green roof. The annual energy savings were estimated to be around 15%. Increase of soil thickness contributes to the increase of energy savings and more than 60% of heat gain was intercepted by the rooftop system [52].

It is therefore more than obvious that green spaces and green rooftops constitute a feasible mitigation strategy for urban heat island leading to a substantial decrease in energy consumption.

Table 7 Measured reflectivity of colored and conventional asphalt materials

Product	SR (%)	SR_{UV} (%)	SR_{VIS} (%)	SR_{NIR} (%)
Whitish	55	10	45	63
Yellow	40	8	26	51
Green	27	8	10	39
Black conventional	4	4	3	4
Natural	45	10	31	56
Red	27	6	10	40

SR, solar reflectance; SR_{NIR}, solar reflectance in the near-infrared region; SR_{UV}, solar reflectance in the ultraviolet region; SR_{VIS}, solar reflectance in the visible region.

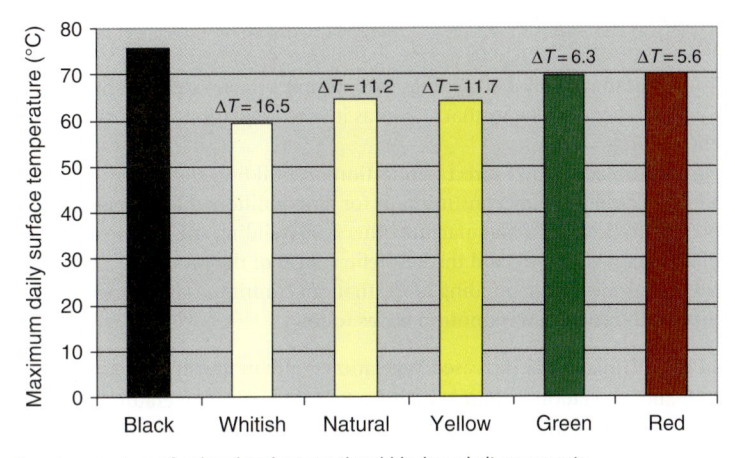

Figure 21 Maximum daily surface temperature of colored and conventional black asphalt pavements.

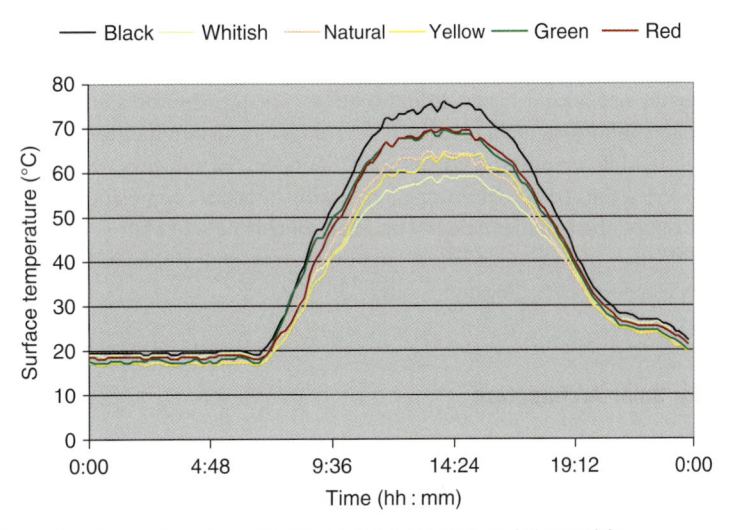

Figure 22 Daily variation of the surface temperature of representative colored and black asphalt materials.

3.19.2.6 Discussion

The mitigation of the heat-island effect can be achieved by decreasing the thermal gains in the urban environment, and in particular, the amount of the absorbed solar radiation. This can be done by increasing the albedo of cities using materials for buildings and the urban fabric that have high SR values. In order to meet the building market's aesthetic preferences, cool nonwhite materials are needed. The results of the relevant research indicate significant success in developing cool-colored coatings doped or not with PCM microcapsules, thermochromic materials, and cool asphalt coatings that have the same visible reflectance as the standard coatings,

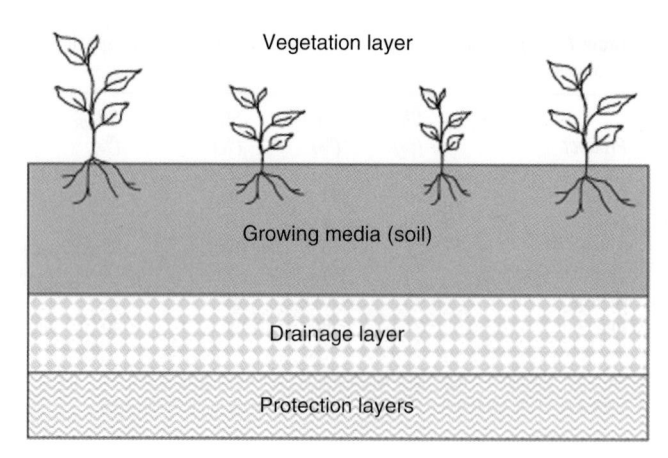

Figure 23 A green roof structure [17].

appearing to have the same color, but for the colored coatings they exhibit a more selective absorption band in the infrared part of the spectrum, reflecting large parts of the solar energy that arrives as infrared radiation rather than absorbing it. This results in lower surface temperatures for all the coatings.

The use of cool coatings is not limited to their direct application on building envelopes, resulting in the reduction of surface temperatures and leading to lower cooling energy consumption for air-conditioned buildings and increased thermal comfort for unconditioned building; they can also be used to manufacture other cool building and paving materials. The use of cool coatings is a passive solution that combines energy efficiency and the aesthetic appeal of the products.

Therefore, solar architecture techniques in the building fabric that can contribute simultaneously to the mitigation of the urban heat island and to the reduction of the energy consumption are as follows:

- Improvement of the urban microclimate and increased vegetation – urban greening. Many studies have been carried out on the cooling benefits of trees and vegetation within the cities. Surface peak temperature reductions of up to 20 °C may be possible on hot, sunny days. Vegetation augmentation and reduction of impervious surface cover in urban environments can be accomplished through residential and municipal tree planting programs, addition or expansion of ecoroofs (or green roofs), and implementation of pervious pavements. While many studies focus on the evapotranspiration benefits of urban trees, it is important to note that trees also affect wind patterns within cities. Thus, by changing wind patterns, trees may alter the effectiveness of cooling breezes and can play an important role in dispersion processes as well as pollutant removal by deposition.
- Increase of surface albedo by the use of cool materials and coatings. The primary surfaces in the urban environment that are amenable to albedo increase are rooftops. In order to assess potential for albedo modification, various studies have estimated the composition of the urban fabric. This composition varies for different land use subtypes within a city and depends on whether one is concerned with the plan view data (as seen from a plane) or with the actual composition under the canopy. With respect to the plan view composition of cities, these studies typically find that roughly 20% of a city's surface is rooftop. 30% is pavement, and the remainder is a combination of vegetation canopy and other surfaces. It is this underlying composition that limits the potential effectiveness of any albedo-related mitigation strategy.

3.19.3 Control Systems for Solar Architecture

The main challenge in the design of control systems for energy performance of buildings is to find the balance between implementation costs, operation costs, energy consumption, indoor climate quality, users' satisfaction, and contribution to sustainable building. Intelligently designed buildings are those that involve environmentally responsive design, taking into account the surroundings and building usage and involving the selection of appropriate building services and control systems to further enhance building operation with a view to the reduction of energy consumption and environmental impact over its lifetime. This procedure requires advanced control techniques to establish a balance among the following (see **Figure 24**):

- user comfort requirements,
- energy consumption,
- passive solar design concepts,
- solar heating and cooling technologies, and
- PV.

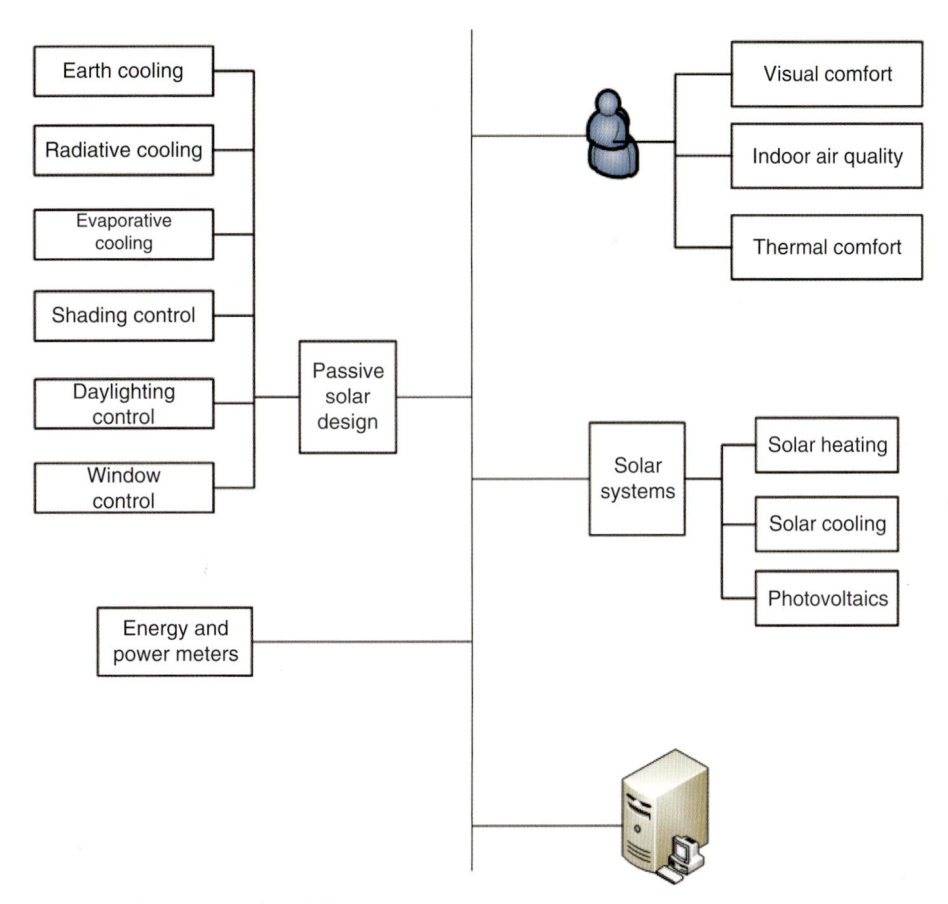

Figure 24 The advanced control systems in solar buildings.

Various control strategies are used for the regulation of the above. The combined control of active and passive systems, as, for example, night ventilation for cooling and mechanical cooling or hybrid ventilation, generally requires the use of the so-called 'logic control' implemented by various rules in order to determine which of the passive or active systems should be operated.

Many digital controllers offer this possibility to implement logic control rules as well as ON–OFF or proportional–integral–derivative (PID) control [53, 54]. Modern control systems provide optimized operation of the energy systems while satisfying indoor comfort. Recent technological developments based on artificial intelligence techniques offer several advantages compared with the classical control systems. The use of fuzzy logic and artificial neural networks (ANNs) in various building-related applications has been growing significantly over the years [55–62]. The results have revealed the potential usefulness of the advanced control strategies for the energy management of houses and buildings. Evolutionary computing techniques, namely, genetic algorithms (GAs), are employed in buildings since they have proved to be robust and efficient in finding near-optimal solutions in complex problem spaces [63, 64]. Predictive control techniques are also applied [65].

Finally, optimization methods such as dynamic programming [66], multiobjective techniques [67], and simulation-assisted multicriteria analysis [68] are widely adopted due to buildings' nonlinearity.

3.19.3.1 Controlled Parameters and Control Variables in Passive Solar Architecture

Passive solar architecture cannot be implemented without taking into account the various controlled parameters that the overall system will regulate. The most widely used in the literature concern occupants' thermal, visual, and acoustic comfort as well as the IAQ. The building's occupants have a direct impact on the passive design operation and the effectiveness of passive solar architecture. For example, the influence of occupants' behavior on the energy consumption is studied by Foster *et al.* [69]. In this chapter, the interaction between the occupants and the venetian blinds is examined as blinds are the key element in the passive control of glare, daylighting, and overheating, all of which affect both the occupants' comfort and the energy consumption.

The American Society of Heating, Refrigerating and Air-Conditioning Engineers (ASHRAE) Standard 55 describes thermal comfort as 'the condition of mind which expresses satisfaction with the thermal environment'. The environmental variables that influence thermal comfort are the air temperature, the mean radiant temperature, the air velocity, and the water vapor pressure in ambient air. Two other important variables are the person's activity level and clothing. Most of the above are combined in the predicted mean vote

(PMV), which provides information on the degree of discomfort experienced in a thermal environment with an extra invocator, the percentage of people dissatisfied (PPD) [70, 71]. Regarding thermal comfort, the controlled parameters found in the literature involve

- PMV [72–74],
- the PPD [75],
- indoor temperature [76],
- maximum daily discomfort in degree hours [77], and
- zone operative temperature [75].

Regarding visual comfort, the control involves passive shading targeting the regulation of workplane illuminance [65, 78]. Additionally, the daylight glare index regulated through the adjustment of shading and electric lighting is proposed as the controlled variable for visual comfort [79].

Regarding the solar system operation, the following controlled parameters are found:

- tank water temperature for solar collectors for the simultaneous control of indoor environment and water circuit [76] and
- supply and return temperature of passive solar systems' collector [75].

In terms of energy consumption, the controlled variables may be

- seasonal building load profiles [77],
- buildings' heating or cooling balance points (i.e., the temperature above or below which cooling or heating is necessary) [77], and
- building load coefficient [67].

Other parameters that are taken into account in the formulation of the control strategy include

- climatic conditions either measured or predicted [80] and
- presence of detectors.

The control variables differ according to the passive system. The most representative are the following [74, 76, 81]:

- heating, ventilating, and air conditioning (HVAC) ON–OFF,
- boilers or chillers,
- coils and valves,
- water pumps,
- supply and exhaust fans,
- electric lighting control,
- shading control, and
- window motors.

All the above environmental parameters and control variables are integrated into the various control strategies described in the next section targeting to minimize the energy consumption and create a comfortable and qualitative environment for the building users.

3.19.3.2 Control Strategies in Solar Architecture

The control theory for linear systems has been considered for quite a long time as a well-established scientific discipline with different techniques for analyzing and designing controllers.

The main problems in applying the linear control theory for solar architecture are caused by the fact that (1) linear mathematical models are needed and cannot be straightforwardly extracted, (2) the developed mathematical models of such complicated processes cannot take into account all aspects of reality and therefore simplifications and assumptions are necessary, (3) most processes for solar architecture techniques are not linear, and (4) due to continuous changes of the climatic conditions, solar system processes vary dynamically with time.

The control techniques used for solar architecture can be divided into different categories (tabulated in **Table 8**) [82, 83], and these are explained below.

3.19.3.2.1 Conventional control for solar architecture

Conventional control strategies for solar architecture include the widely used ON–OFF and conventional PID methods [84]. The conventional control strategies are still very attractive when they involve a small number of environmental parameters' regulation and a limited number of solar techniques. For example, active ON–OFF control is proposed by Tzempelikos and Athienitis [78] for the regulation of electric lighting consumption in a simulation-based thermal and daylight analysis for office spaces. The ON–OFF system is based on occupancy sensors, while the buildings are designed to exploit the daylight availability via window sizing, orientation, and window-to-wall ratio.

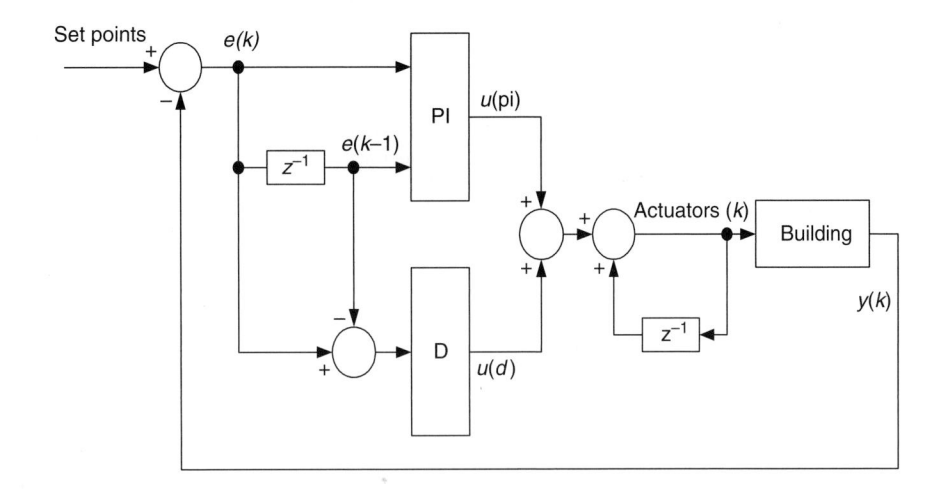

Figure 25 The proportional–integral–derivative control diagram.

Due to the dynamic characteristics of the technologies involved in the solar architecture, it is quite difficult to obtain a satisfactory performance when an integrated approach is established where a combination of passive heating and cooling techniques is considered. The use of PID controllers (**Figure 25**) with fixed gains K_P, K_I, K_D although applied in numerous cases [85] cannot deal with nominal operation of the various components without including a feedforward term in the control loop to account for the effect of the quite significant disturbances and time variations. Gain scheduling proportional–integral (PI) controllers, adaptive PID controllers, and fuzzy logic- or neural network (NN)-based PID controllers are some examples of PID feedforward actions and adaptations to buildings' dynamic characteristics [86].

Classical PID as well as ON–OFF control has been proved to be energy 'inefficient' due to the fact that the controlled variable creates overshootings and oscillations once the reference signal is reached [85]. Overshootings and oscillations are the main cause of energy waste.

3.19.3.2.2 Advanced control

Based on the categorization in **Table 8**, advanced control for solar architecture includes model-based predictive control and adaptive control. Predictive control in solar architecture uses a model to estimate and predict the optimum control strategy to be implemented (**Figure 26**).

While the online control systems can react only to the actual building conditions, a model-based predictive control can move forward in time to predict the buildings' reaction to alternative control schemes. Therefore, different control scenarios can be evaluated based on suitable objective functions and create a control state space that corresponds to a building's performance space.

A model can be either a 'black box' or a 'physical' model. In the 'black box' or nonphysical model approaches, self-learning algorithms, reinforced learning [87], or NNs [88] are some of the methodologies found in the literature. The benefits of the mentioned approaches are low computational time and the fact that they do not require any specific building modeling expertise, while their limitations are that, on the one hand, NNs require reliable training data that may not be available and, on the other hand, self-learning algorithms cannot move beyond the limits of their experience. When physical models are utilized, the expert has the opportunity to understand the cause-and-effect relationship between the various building components, the control strategies, and the climatic conditions. The physical models approach can use stochastic mathematical models [89] or simulation-assisted predictive control [90]. Some physical models, though, require high computational skills and effort. For this reason, integration of

Table 8 Control strategies for solar architecture

Control category	Control strategies
Conventional control	ON–OFF
	Proportional–integral–derivative control
	Feedforward control
Advanced control	Model-based predictive control
	Adaptive control
Intelligent techniques	Optimal control
	Fuzzy logic
	Neural network

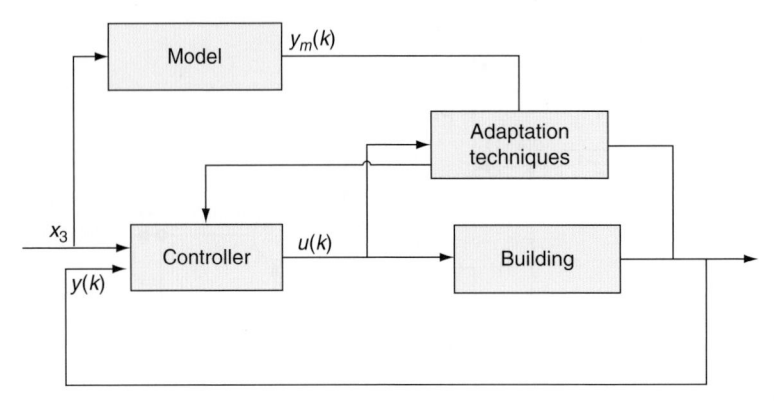

Figure 26 Model-based predictive control.

whole-building thermal models with (cognitive-based) control is quite interesting and with significant potential – see References 91 and 92 for some efforts.

Adaptive control has been developed for decades, and now it has become a rigorous and mature discipline which mainly focuses on dealing with uncertainties in control systems. Since adaptive control usually involves adaptive estimation algorithms, it can deal with relatively large uncertainties and gain flexibility to fit the unknown system, therefore playing a role of 'learning' in some sense.

The adaptive control systems in solar buildings are used to modify the controller dynamically during its operation, that is, adjusting the controller to building users' preferences, modifying the control actions so as to fit to specific operational, usually predefined, performance (**Figure 27**).

Therefore, the main advantage of adaptive control comes from the fact that adaptive controllers can adjust themselves to modify the control law based on estimation of unknown parameters by identification algorithms. Consequently, the adaptive control field is very closely connected to the systems' (in our case, building components) identification algorithms, in which an area is aiming at providing and investigating mathematical tools and algorithms that build dynamical models from measured data.

Typically, in system identification, a certain model structure which contains some unknown parameters is selected by the user and then by the use of some recursive algorithms which are based on specific model characteristics, statistical data, and noise, these unknown parameters are extracted. The methods or algorithms developed in system identification are borrowed in adaptive control in order to estimate the unknown parameters in the closed loop. For convenience, the parameter estimation methods or algorithms adopted in adaptive control are often referred to as adaptive estimation methods. Adaptive estimation and system identification share many similar characteristics; for example, both of them originate and benefit from the development of statistics. One typical example is the least-squares algorithm that is applied to system identification, statistics, or adaptive control and gives parameter estimation by minimizing the sum of squared errors.

As an example of the above, a bilinear model-based predictive control is proposed by Kolokotsa *et al.* [65], so as to achieve optimum indoor environmental conditions while minimizing energy costs by the prioritization of natural ventilation for cooling, shading regulation for optimum daylight utilization, and window operation for a building energy management system. The control diagram depicted in **Figure 28** includes the actuators (A) and the overall installation (P), where k is the sample time, $x(k)$ the state vector, $y(k)$ the measurements vector, $n(k)$ the unknown noise for the measurements, $u(k)$ the control vector, $d(k)$ the disturbances vector (casual gains, door opening, people smoking, etc.), and x_s the set point vector.

Bilinear models are developed for the thermal comfort, visual comfort, and IAQ where the indoor temperature, relative humidity, indoor carbon dioxide concentration, and indoor illuminance behavior are modeled. The least-squares estimation is

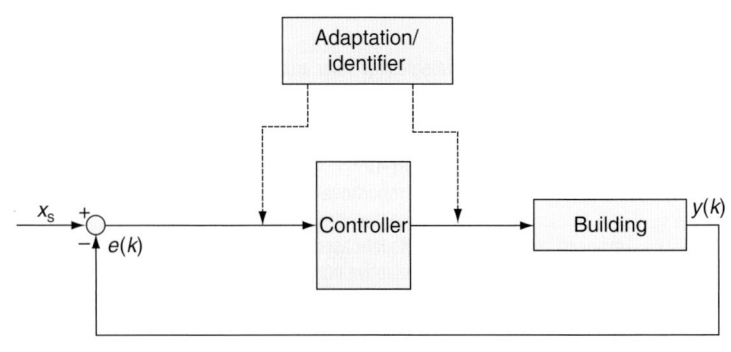

Figure 27 Self-tuning controller.

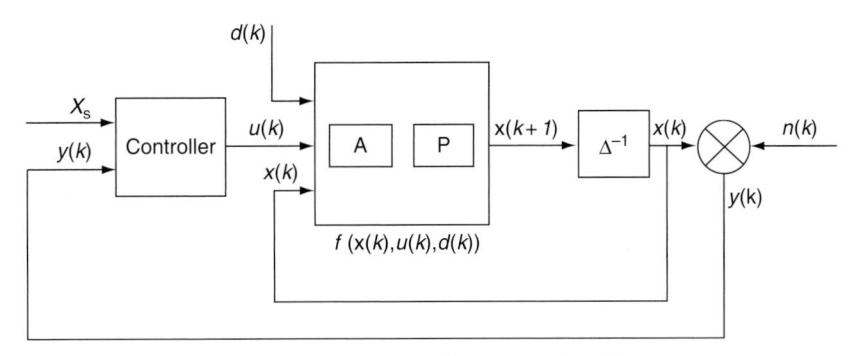

Figure 28 Model-based predictive control for indoor comfort and energy efficiency regulation [65].

performed separately for each actuator that influences the corresponding environmental parameter by putting the building energy management systems (BEMS) in continuous operation mode for at least 48 h.

Following the identification procedure, the BEMS controller is designed to minimize the performance index $J(k)$ which aims to keep the environmental variables as close as possible to the defined set points x_s and simultaneously minimize the energy consumption. $J(k)$ is defined as

$$J(k) = \|x_{in}(k+1) - x_s\|_Q^2 + \|u(k)\|_R^2 \qquad [1]$$

where Q and R are weight matrices corresponding to the set points' proximity and the actuators' electric energy cost, respectively. The bilinear model-based predictive control's response to fluctuations in the environmental variables is found to be fast and stable. Finally, the controller's performance is tested by an installation in specific building where comfort, weather data, and prediction model are integrated into a common architecture (**Figure 29**); the controller's performance is found to be quite satisfactory and selects the optimum solutions based on the energy consumption and the set point proximity by satisfying the performance index J (**Figure 30**).

3.19.3.2.3 Intelligent systems

Recent research in building-related artificial intelligence topics has shown that artificial intelligence techniques such as fuzzy systems and NNs can contribute to a significant reduction of energy consumption while maintaining indoor comfort in acceptable margins by regulating the operation of the various building-integrated solar systems or by giving priority to passive means in order to cover the comfort or energy requirements.

Fuzzy logic (**Figure 31**) is based on the way the human brain deals with inexact information. Fuzzy systems are structured numerical estimators. They start from formalized insights about the structure of categories that exist in the real world and then formulate the fuzzy IF–THEN rules that represent expert knowledge. They combine fuzzy sets with fuzzy rules and they produce complex nonlinear behavior. Fuzziness is often confused with probability. The main difference between fuzzy logic and probability is that fuzziness deals with deterministic plausibility while probability concerns the likelihood of nondeterministic and stochastic events. Fuzziness expresses the uncertainty in the definition of phenomena such as 'tall person' and 'large room'. The major feature of fuzzy logic is its ability to express the ambiguity in human thinking, subjectivity, and knowledge in a comparatively accurate manner.

As a result of the above, the use of fuzziness in buildings' solar architecture systems and components is applicable for the following reasons:

- A fuzzy description of the operational characteristics under study fits naturally to the problem.
- The systems to be controlled are usually nonlinear.

ANNs imitate the operation of the human brain's neurons. They are composed of a number of elements/neurons operating in parallel and are inspired by the biological nervous systems. A schematic diagram of typical multilayer feedforward ANN architecture is shown in **Figure 32**. The network as depicted in **Figure 32** usually consists of an input layer, the hidden layers, and an output layer. The number of hidden layers depends on the complexity of the problem under study. Each neuron is connected to other neurons of a previous layer through adaptable synaptic weights. Usually, the biggest challenge faced when designing an NN is to find the right number of neurons in the hidden layer. This depends on the number of inputs and outputs and also on the number of training cases.

The GAs are adaptive search and optimization algorithms that work by mimicking the principles of natural genetics. GAs are very different from traditional search and optimization methods used in engineering design problems [93]. Fundamental ideas of genetics are borrowed and used artificially to construct search algorithms that are robust and require minimal problem information.

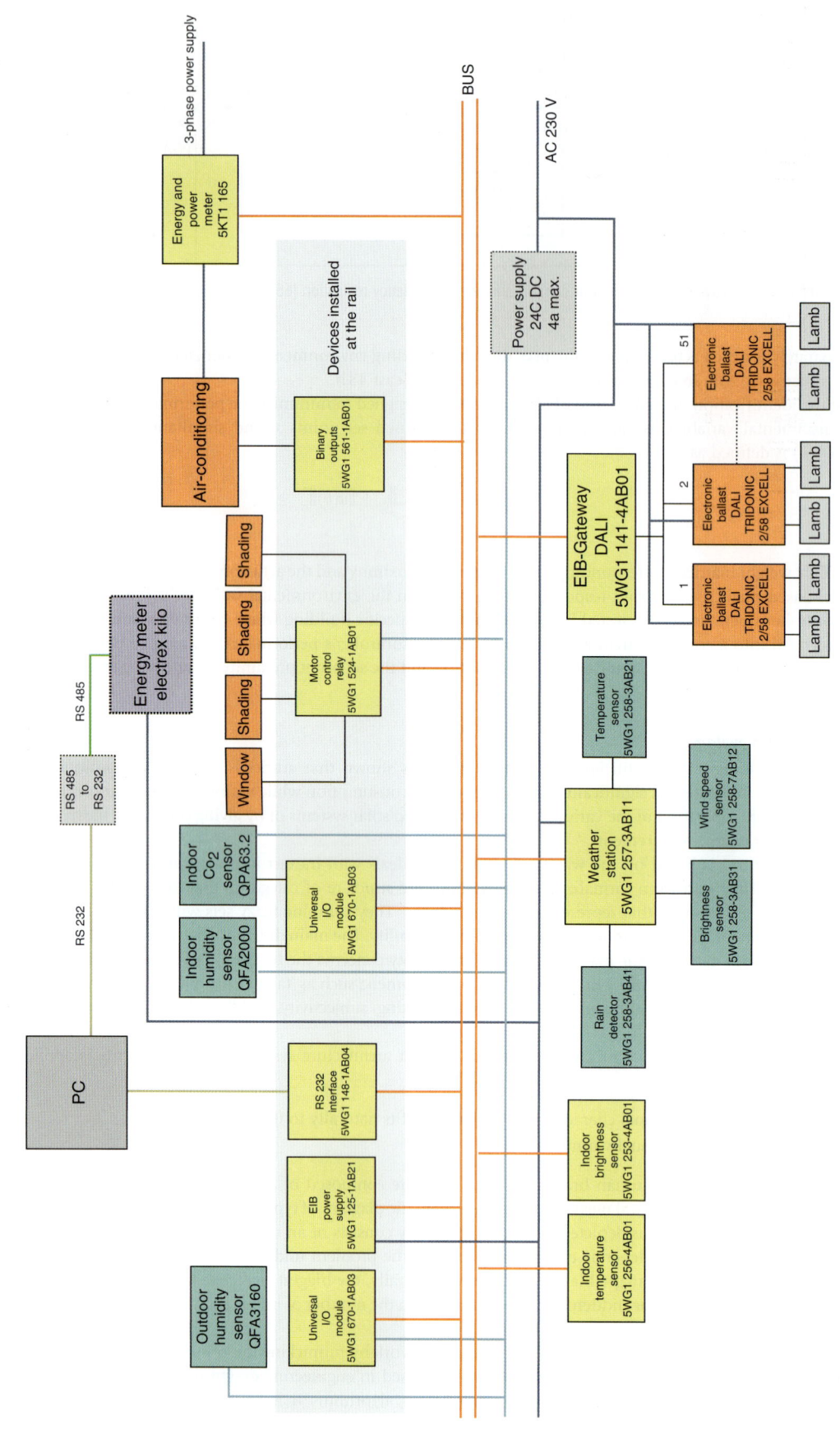

Figure 29 The bilinear model-based predictive control BEMS architecture [65].

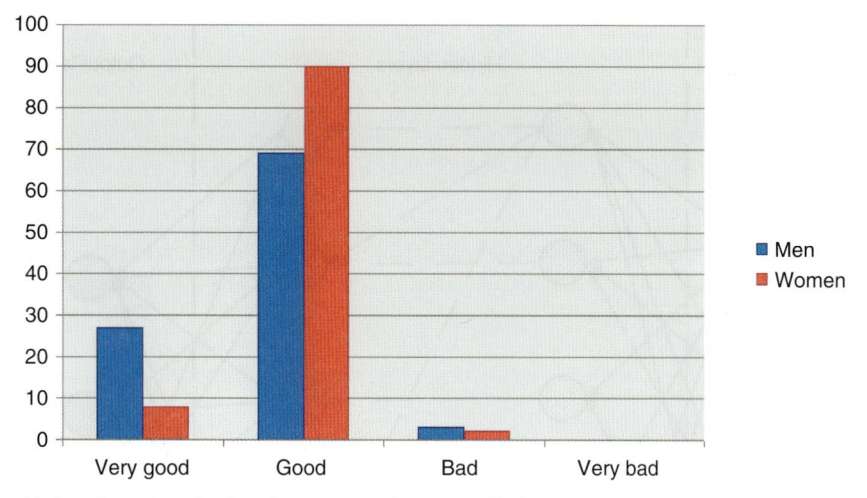

Figure 30 Perception of indoor thermal comfort based on occupants' responses [65].

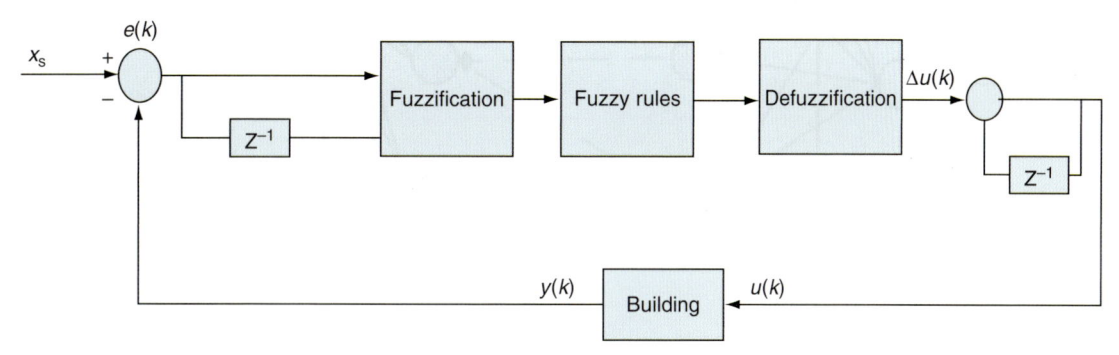

Figure 31 The fuzzy control system.

A typical unconstrained, single variable optimization problem can be outlined as follows:

$$\text{maximize } f(x)$$
$$x_{\min} \leq x \leq x_{\max} \tag{2}$$

The GA, as any evolution program, for a particular problem must have the following five components:

- a generic representation for potential solutions to the problem;
- a way to create an initial population of potential solutions;
- an evaluation function that plays the role of the environment, rating solutions in terms of their 'fitness';
- genetic operators (such as crossover and mutation) that alter the composition of children; and
- applying genetic operators, and so on.

Indicatively, artificial intelligence in solar buildings control is found in the following applications:

- Lah *et al.* designed a fuzzy control system for the regulation of a movable shade roller blind, targeting the harmonization of thermal and optical flows. They aimed to combine minimization of energy use with comfortable living and working conditions. The control algorithm consisted of thermal and lighting parts, each one containing conventional and fuzzy controllers. The impact on thermal light behavior was analyzed with adaptable window geometry. The controller is designed and adjusted so as to adjust the inside daylight illumination level with moderate continuous movement of the roller blind. The overheating is reduced by the roller blind regulation and the desired illuminance is reached [94].
- In the same route of the regulation of thermal and visual comfort is the work proposed by Kristl *et al.* [95]. A fuzzy controller for the regulation of a roller blind is tested and tuned in an experimental chamber. A thermal comfort loop and an illumination loop are developed and then these loops are merged to harmonize the results.

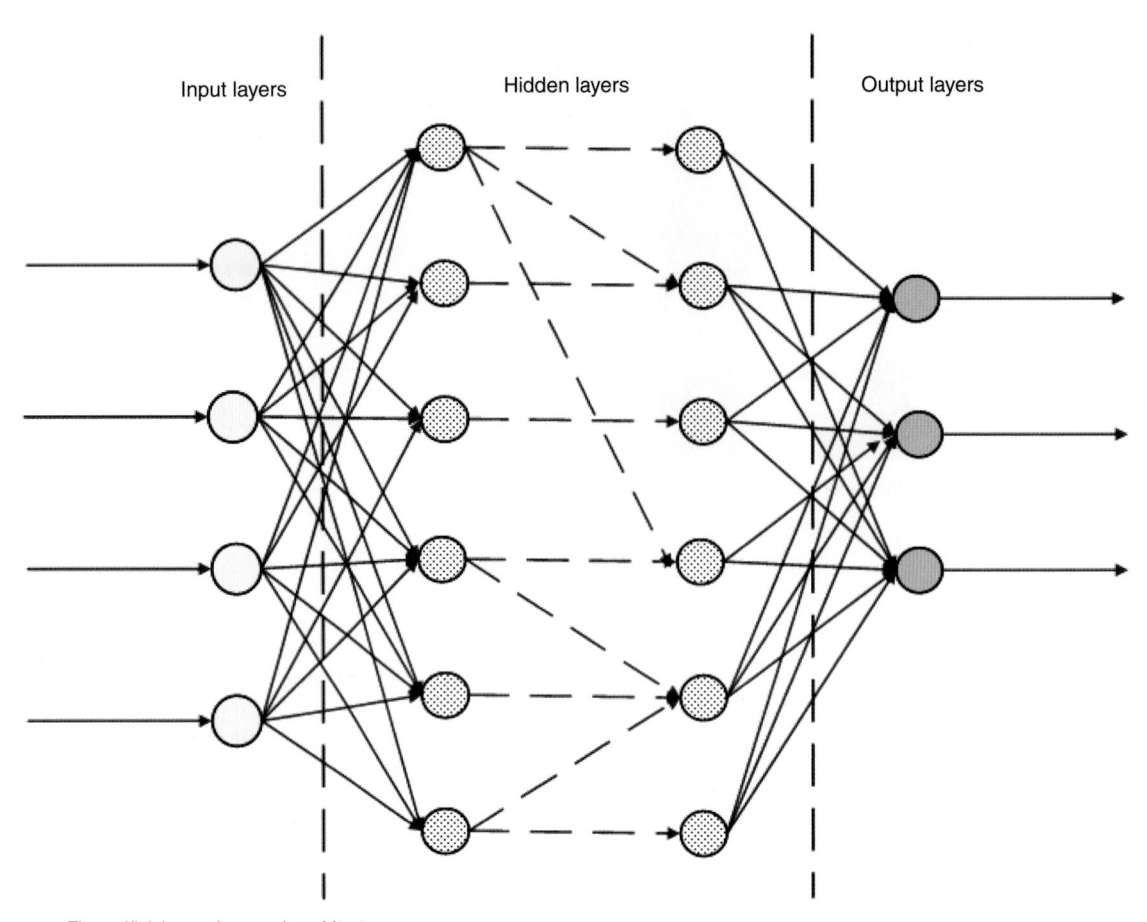

Figure 32 The artificial neural network architecture.

- A quasi-adaptive fuzzy controller for space heating in passive solar buildings that is responsive to the lagging effects of solar energy inputs is proposed by Gouda et al. [96]. The controller is divided into two main modules: a conventional static fuzzy controller and feedforward NN with a singular value decomposition (SVD) algorithm. An estimation of the internal air temperature at least 1 h ahead in time and within typical measurement uncertainty is provided by an ANN. Experimental results of the fuzzy controller are compared to simulations of the conventional PI heating system. The fuzzy controller follows the variable set point more accurately without overshootings, thus reducing the afternoon overheating and the energy costs significantly, compared to the conventional control problems.
- An NN model is proposed by Kazanasmaz et al. to predict daylighting levels in office buildings. The input parameters used in the model included date, hour, outdoor temperature, solar radiation, humidity, UV index, distance to windows, number of windows, orientation of rooms, floor identification, room dimensions, and point identification. The model was tested for specific office buildings, providing quite satisfactory results. The specific model can be used by architects and designers to determine illuminance and light distribution in solar architecture without the need for a detailed model development [97].
- A fuzzy and feedforward controller for operating a hybrid thermal energy storage system (HTESS) is presented by LeBreux et al. [98]. The storage system accumulates solar energy during daytime and releases it during the night or during cloudy days and, simultaneously, it stores electrical energy during off-peak periods and releases it later during on-peak hours. The control strategy takes into account the weather forecasts for solar radiation and outdoor air temperature, and optimizes the off-peak and the on-peak periods for electrical heating. The thermal comfort of the room is maintained in all situations and at all times. Finally, the electricity consumption for space heating is minimized and 95% of this electricity is consumed during off-peak hours.
- Guillemin and Morel developed a self-adaptive integrated system for building energy and comfort management. The fuzzy expert system consists of a shading device controller, an artificial lighting controller, and a heating controller. When the user is present, priority is given to visual comfort, and when absent, priority is given to thermal aspects (heating/cooling energy saving). The models used in the controller are adapted regularly in order to meet the requirements of the building and of the environment. A process of adaptation is performed each night using GAs in order to identify the most appropriate parameters of the controller. The operation of the controller is compared to that of a conventional controller (no automatic blind control and artificial lighting control, and a

proportional controller for heating). The energy consumption of the fuzzy controller is 20–25% less than that of a conventional controller. Additionally, Guillemin and Morel presented a controller with inputs of the users' set points and the weather data of the room. The ANNs are included for the prediction of room temperature. The thermal comfort level is kept high and the visual comfort is improved by the fuzzy control system. An energy efficiency of 19% is estimated, compared to conventional control [74].

- Kubota *et al.* developed a prediction system based on genetic programming and fuzzy inference systems. Genetic programming is applied for the feature extraction and selection, and fuzzy inference is used for the building energy load prediction. The method is compared to the Kalman filtering algorithm and a feedforward NN with four layers. Although the NN is better for load prediction, the proposed method can extract meaningful information from the measured data and can predict the building energy load corresponding to the next day [99].

The application of advanced control strategies in passive solar buildings has a significant impact on the energy consumption compared to conventional techniques. In all cases, the energy consumption is reduced by at least 18–20%, when an optimal control strategy is applied [100].

3.19.4 Conclusion and Future Prospects

Buildings are increasingly expected to meet higher and potentially more complex levels of performance. They should be sustainable, use zero net energy, be healthy and comfortable, grid-friendly, yet economical to build and maintain. Ensuring any one of these is challenging in itself, but achieving all would seem to be overwhelming. Various technologies are mature and can be considered for the improvement of the energy efficiency and indoor comfort in buildings. These technologies may be distinguished into the following basic categories:

- measures for the improvement of the building's envelope (addition or improvement of insulation, change of color, placement of heat-insulating door and window frames, increase of thermal mass, building shaping, superinsulated building envelopes, etc.);
- incorporation of high-efficiency heating and cooling equipment, for example, air-conditioning equipment with higher energy efficiency ratio (EER) and high-efficiency condensing boilers;
- use of renewables (solar thermal systems, building's integrated photovoltaics, hybrid systems, etc.);
- use of 'intelligent' energy management, that is, advanced sensors, energy control (zone heating and cooling), and monitoring systems;
- measures for the improvement of the indoor comfort conditions in parallel with minimization of the energy requirements (increase in the ventilation rate, use of mechanical ventilation with heat recovery, improvement of boilers and air-conditioning efficiency, use of multifunctional equipment, i.e., integrated water heating with space cooling, etc.); and
- use of energy-efficient appliances, including compact fluorescent lighting, light emitting diode (LED) lighting, and so on.

Nowadays, passive solar design is moving toward zero- or even positive-energy buildings. Zero-energy buildings have become a high priority for architects and multidisciplinary researchers related to building engineering and physics. A zero-energy building refers to a building with a net energy consumption of zero over a typical year [101]. It implies that the energy demand for heat and electrical power is reduced, and this reduced demand is met on an annual basis from renewable energy supply. The renewable energy supply can be either integrated into the building design or specifically provided for the building, for example, as part of a community renewable energy supply system. Additionally, this normally implies that the grid is used to supply electrical power when there is no renewable power available, and the building will export power back to the grid when it has excess power generation. This 'two-way' flow should result in a net positive or zero export of power from the building to the grid. The zero-energy building design concept is a progression from passive sustainable design. The objective of a zero-energy building is not only to minimize the energy consumption of the building with passive design methods, but also to design a building that balances energy requirements with active techniques and renewable technologies (e.g., building-integrated PV, solar, thermal, or wind turbines). It is usually measured in terms of primary energy consumption or carbon emissions.

In the road toward zero-energy buildings, passive solar architecture and intelligent control systems will play the most critical roles, since, on the one hand, a building's energy demand should initially become as low as possible and, on the other hand, intelligent-predictive control schemes should be progressed to perform the necessary generation–consumption matching under real-time dynamic conditions.

References

[1] United Nations Council for Human Settlements (2001) UNCHS, Nairobi, Kenya: The State of the World Cities.
[2] Santamouris M, Pavlou K, Synnefa A, *et al.* (2007) Recent progress on passive cooling techniques. Advanced technological developments to improve survivability levels in low-income households. *Energy and Buildings* 39(7): 859–866.
[3] Santamouris M (2007) Heat island research in Europe: The state of the art. *Advances in Building Energy Research* 1(1): 123–150.
[4] Athienitis AK and Santamouris M (2002) *Thermal Analysis and Design of Passive Solar Buildings.* London, UK: James and James Publisher.

[5] Feist W, Schnieders J, Dorer V, and Haas A (2005) Re-inventing air heating: Convenient and comfortable within the frame of the Passive House concept. *Energy and Buildings* 37(11 SPEC. ISS): 1186–1203.
[6] Florides GA, Tassou SA, Kalogirou SA, and Wrobel LC (2002) Review of solar and low energy cooling technologies for buildings. *Renewable and Sustainable Energy Reviews* 6(6): 557–572.
[7] Yezioro A (2009) A knowledge based CAAD system for passive solar architecture. *Renewable Energy* 34(3): 769–779.
[8] Stathopoulou M, Synnefa A, Cartalis C, et al. (2009) A surface heat island study of Athens using high-resolution satellite imagery and measurements of the optical and thermal properties of commonly used building and paving materials. *International Journal of Sustainable Energy* 28(1–3): 59–76.
[9] Kolokotsa D (2007) Artificial intelligence in buildings: A review on the application of fuzzy logic. *Advances in Building Energy Research* 1(1): 29–54.
[10] Miyazaki T, Akisawa A, and Kashiwagi T (2006) The effects of solar chimneys on thermal load mitigation of office buildings under the Japanese climate. *Renewable Energy* 31(7): 987–1010.
[11] Filippín C, Flores Larsen S, and Lopez Gay E (2008) Energy improvement of a conventional dwelling in Argentina through thermal simulation. *Renewable Energy* 33(10): 2246–2257.
[12] Papaefthimiou S, Leftheriotis G, Yianoulis P, et al. (2006) Development of electrochromic evacuated advanced glazing. *Energy and Buildings* 38(12): 1455–1467.
[13] Zhou J and Chen Y (2009) A review on applying ventilated double-skin facade to buildings in hot-summer and cold-winter zone in China. *Renewable and Sustainable Energy Reviews* 14(4): 1321–1328.
[14] Allard F, Santamouris M, Alvarez S, et al. (1998) *Natural Ventilation in Buildings*. London, UK: James and James.
[15] Akbari H, Bretz SE, Kurn DM, and Hanford JW (1997) Peak power and cooling energy savings of high-albedo roofs. *Energy and Buildings* 25(2): 117–126.
[16] Theodosiou TG (2003) Summer period analysis of the performance of a planted roof as a passive cooling technique. *Energy and Buildings* 35(9): 909–917.
[17] Theodosiou T (2009) Green roofs in buildings: Thermal and environmental behaviour. *Advances in Building Energy Research* 3(1): 271–288.
[18] Lam JC (2000) Shading effects due to nearby buildings and energy implications. *Energy Conversion and Management* 41(7): 647–659.
[19] Niu JL, Zhang LZ, and Zuo HG (2002) Energy savings potential of chilled-ceiling combined with desiccant cooling in hot and humid climates. *Energy and Buildings* 34(5): 487–495.
[20] Novoselac A and Srebric J (2002) A critical review on the performance and design of combined cooled ceiling and displacement ventilation systems. *Energy and Buildings* 34(5): 497–509.
[21] Gan G (1998) A parametric study of Trombe walls for passive cooling of buildings. *Energy and Buildings* 27(1): 37–43.
[22] Niachou A, Papakonstantinou K, Santamouris M, et al. (2001) Analysis of the green roof thermal properties and investigation of its energy performance. *Energy and Buildings* 33(7): 719–729.
[23] Akbari H, Kurn DM, Bretz SE, and Hanford JW (1997) Peak power and cooling energy savings of shade trees. *Energy and Buildings* 25(2): 139–148.
[24] Bojic M, Yik F, and Sat P (2001) Influence of thermal insulation position in building envelope on the space cooling of high-rise residential buildings in Hong Kong. *Energy and Buildings* 33(6): 569–581.
[25] Bojic M, Yik F, Wan K, and Burnett J (2002) Influence of envelope and partition characteristics on the space cooling of high-rise residential buildings in Hong Kong. *Building and Environment* 37(4): 347–355.
[26] Tripanagnostopoulos Y, Siabekou C, and Tonui JK (2007) The Fresnel lens concept for solar control of buildings. *Solar Energy* 81(5): 661–675.
[27] Synnefa A, Santamouris M, and Apostolakis K (2007) On the development, optical properties and thermal performance of cool colored coatings for the urban environment. *Solar Energy* 81(4): 488–497.
[28] Synnefa A, Santamouris M, and Livada I (2006) A study of the thermal performance of reflective coatings for the urban environment. *Solar Energy* 80(8): 968–981.
[29] Papadakis G, Tsamis P, and Kyritsis S (2001) An experimental investigation of the effect of shading with plants for solar control of buildings. *Energy and Buildings* 33(8): 831–836.
[30] Mateus T and Oliveira AC (2009) Energy and economic analysis of an integrated solar absorption cooling and heating system in different building types and climates. *Applied Energy* 86(6): 949–957.
[31] Akbari H, Davis S, Dorsano S, et al. (1992) *Cooling Our Communities: A Guidebook on Tree Planting and Light Colored Surfacing*. San Franscisco, CA: US Environmental Protection Agency, Office of Policy Analysis, Climate Change Division.
[32] Bretz SE and Akbari H (1997) Long-term performance of high-albedo roof coatings. *Energy and Buildings* 25(2): 159–167.
[33] Karlessi T, Santamouris M, Apostolakis K, et al. (2009) Development and testing of thermochromic coatings for buildings and urban structures. *Solar Energy* 83(4): 538–551.
[34] McNaught A and Wilkinson A (1997) *Compendium of Chemical Terminology, IUPAC*, 2nd edn. The Royal Society of Chemistry. Cambridge, UK: Blackwell Science.
[35] Aitken D, Burkinshaw SM, Griffiths J, and Towns AD (1996) Textile applications of thermochromic systems. *Review of Progress in Coloration and Related Topics* 26: 1–8.
[36] White MA and LeBlanc M (1999) Thermochromism in commercial products. *Journal of Chemical Education* 76(9): 1201–1205.
[37] Bamfield P (2001) *Chromic Phenomena, Technological Applications of Color Chemistry*, pp. 33–41. Cambridge: Royal Society of Chemistry.
[38] Yoshikawa K, Fukuo H, and Kuroda J (1986) Thermochromic Compositions. US Patent 4,620,941.
[39] Novinson T (1996) Reversible Thermochromic Pigments. US Patent 5,480,482.
[40] Fujita K and Senga K (2002) Thermochromic Microencapsulated Pigments. US Patent 6,494,950.
[41] Shibahashi Y, Nakasuji N, Kataota T, et al. (1984) Thermochromic Materials. US Patent 4,425,161.
[42] MacLaren DC and White MA (2003a) Competition between dye–developer and solvent–developer interactions in a reversible thermochromic system. *Journal of Materials Chemistry* 13(7): 1701–1704.
[43] MacLaren DC and White MA (2003b) Dye–developer interactions in the crystal violet lactone–lauryl gallate binary system: Implications for thermochromism. *Journal of Materials Chemistry* 13(7): 1695–1700.
[44] White G, Zartman D, and Bonicamp J (2000) A serious look at changeable silly putty. *Journal of Chemical Educator* 5: 2–7.
[45] Pospíšil J and Nešpurek S (2000) Photostabilization of coatings. Mechanisms and performance. *Progress in Polymer Science (Oxford)* 25(9): 1261–1335.
[46] Ma Y, Zhang X, Zhu B, and Wu K (2002) Research on reversible effects and mechanism between the energy-absorbing and energy-reflecting states of chameleon-type building coatings. *Solar Energy* 72(6): 511–520.
[47] Ma Y, Zhu B, and Wu K (2001) Preparation and solar reflectance spectra of chameleon-type building coatings. *Solar Energy* 70(5): 417–422.
[48] Synnefa A, Karlesi T, and Santamouris M (2008) Development and testing of colored asphalt materials. Final Report. University of Athens (in Greek).
[49] Picot X (2004) Thermal comfort in urban spaces: Impact of vegetation growth. Case study: Piazza della Scienza, Milan, Italy. *Energy and Buildings* 36(4): 329–334.
[50] Eumorfopoulou E and Aravantinos D (1998) The contribution of a planted roof to the thermal protection of buildings in Greece. *Energy and Buildings* 27(1): 29–36.
[51] Wong NH, Chen Y, Ong CL, and Sia A (2003) Investigation of thermal benefits of rooftop garden in the tropical environment. *Building and Environment* 38(2): 261–270.
[52] Wong NH, Cheong DKW, Yan H, et al. (2003) The effects of rooftop garden on energy consumption of a commercial building in Singapore. *Energy and Buildings* 35(4): 353–364.
[53] Levermore GJ (2000) *Energy Management Systems and Direct Digital Control*. New York: E & FN Spon.
[54] Dounis AI and Caraiscos C (2009) Advanced control systems engineering for energy and comfort management in a building environment – a review. *Renewable and Sustainable Energy Reviews* 13(6–7): 1246–1261.
[55] Kalogirou SA and Bojic M (2000) Artificial neural networks for the prediction of the energy consumption of a passive solar building. *Energy* 25(5): 479–491.
[56] Kalogirou SA (2000) Applications of artificial neural-networks for energy systems. *Applied Energy* 67(1–2): 17–35.
[57] Kalogirou SA (2009) Artificial neural networks and genetic algorithms in energy applications in buildings. *Advances in Building Energy Research* 3(1): 83–120.
[58] Doukas H, Patlitzianas KD, Iatropoulos K, and Psarras J (2007) Intelligent building energy management system using rule sets. *Building and Environment* 42(10): 3562–3569.

[59] Dounis AI and Manolakis DE (2001) Design of a fuzzy system for living space thermal-comfort regulation. *Applied Energy* 69(2): 119–144.
[60] Dounis AI, Bruant M, Guarracino G, et al. (1996) Indoor air-quality control by a fuzzy-reasoning machine in naturally ventilated buildings. *Applied Energy* 54(1): 11–28.
[61] Dounis AI, Santamouris MJ, Lefas CC, and Argiriou A (1995) Design of a fuzzy set environment comfort system. *Energy and Buildings* 22(1): 81–87.
[62] Kolokotsa D, Stavrakakis G, and Agoris D (2003) Optimized fuzzy controller for indoor comfort control and energy management in buildings implemented with PLC and local operating networks (LON) technology. *Computer Science and Technology Conference.* Cancun, Mexico.
[63] Wright JA, Loosemore HA, and Farmani R (2002) Optimization of building thermal design and control by multi-criterion genetic algorithm. *Energy and Buildings* 34(9): 959–972.
[64] Kolokotsa D, Stavrakakis GS, Kalaitzakis K, and Agoris D (2002) Genetic algorithms optimized fuzzy controller for the indoor environmental management in buildings implemented using PLC and local operating networks. *Engineering Applications of Artificial Intelligence* 15(5): 417–428.
[65] Kolokotsa D, Pouliezos A, Stavrakakis G, and Lazos C (2009) Predictive control techniques for energy and indoor environmental quality management in buildings. *Building and Environment* 44(9): 1850–1863.
[66] Caldas LG and Norford LK (2003) Genetic algorithms for optimization of building envelopes and the design and control of HVAC systems. *Journal of Solar Energy Engineering, Transactions of the ASME* 125(3): 343–351.
[67] Diakaki C, Grigoroudis E, and Kolokotsa D (2008) Towards a multi-objective optimization approach for improving energy efficiency in buildings. *Energy and Buildings* 40(9): 1747–1754.
[68] Blondeau P, Spérandio M, and Allard F (2002) Multicriteria analysis of ventilation in summer period. *Building and Environment* 37(2): 165–176.
[69] Foster M and Oreszczyn T (2001) Occupant control of passive systems: The use of venetian blinds. *Building and Environment* 36(2): 149–155.
[70] Fanger PO (1973) Practical application of the comfort equation. *The Building Services Engineer* 41: 132–138.
[71] Olesen BW (2004) International standards for the indoor environment. *Indoor Air* 14(supplement 7): 18–26.
[72] Dounis AI, Santamouris MJ, and Lefas CC (1992) Implementation of artificial intelligence techniques in thermal comfort control for passive solar buildings. *Energy Conversion and Management* 33(3): 175–182.
[73] Kolokotsa D, Tsiavos D, Stavrakakis GS, et al. (2001) Advanced fuzzy logic controllers design and evaluation for buildings' occupants thermal–visual comfort and indoor air quality satisfaction. *Energy and Buildings* 33(6): 531–543.
[74] Guillemin A and Morel N (2002) Experimental results of a self-adaptive integrated control system in buildings: A pilot study. *Solar Energy* 72(5): 397–403.
[75] Kummert M, André P, and Nicolas J (2000) Optimal heating control in a passive solar commercial building. *Solar Energy* 69(supplement): 103–116.
[76] Yu Z and Dexter A (2010) Hierarchical fuzzy control of low-energy building systems. *Solar Energy* 84(4): 538–548.
[77] Perez R, Hoff T, Herig C, and Shah J (2003) Maximizing PV peak shaving with solar load control: Validation of a web-based economic evaluation tool. *Solar Energy* 74(5): 409–415.
[78] Tzempelikos A and Athienitis AK (2007) The impact of shading design and control on building cooling and lighting demand. *Solar Energy* 81(3): 369–382.
[79] Dounis AI, Santamouris MJ, Lefas CC, and Manolakis DE (1994) Thermal-comfort degradation by a visual comfort fuzzy-reasoning machine under natural ventilation. *Applied Energy* 48(2): 115–130.
[80] Argiriou AA, Bellas-Velidis I, Kummert M, and André P (2004) A neural network controller for hydronic heating systems of solar buildings. *Neural Networks* 17(3): 427–440.
[81] Guillemin A and Morel N (2001) Innovative lighting controller integrated in a self-adaptive building control system. *Energy and Buildings* 33(5): 477–487.
[82] Camacho EF, Rubio FR, Berenguel M, and Valenzuela L (2007) A survey on control schemes for distributed solar collector fields. Part I: Modeling and basic control approaches. *Solar Energy* 81(10): 1240–1251.
[83] Camacho EF, Rubio FR, Berenguel M, and Valenzuela L (2007) A survey on control schemes for distributed solar collector fields. Part II: Advanced control approaches. *Solar Energy* 81(10): 1252–1272.
[84] Dounis AI, Bruant M, Santamouris M, et al. (1996) Comparison of conventional and fuzzy control of indoor air quality in buildings. *Journal of Intelligent and Fuzzy Systems* 4(2): 131–140.
[85] Dounis AI, Lefas CC, and Argiriou A (1995) Knowledge-based versus classical control for solar-building designs. *Applied Energy* 50(4): 281–292.
[86] Kolokotsa D (2003) Comparison of the performance of fuzzy controllers for the management of the indoor environment. *Building and Environment* 38(12): 1439–1450.
[87] Dalamagkidis K, Kolokotsa D, Kalaitzakis K, and Stavrakakis GS (2007) Reinforcement learning for energy conservation and comfort in buildings. *Building and Environment* 42(7): 2686–2698.
[88] Karatasou S, Santamouris M, and Geros V (2006) Modeling and predicting building's energy use with artificial neural networks: Methods and results. *Energy and Buildings* 38(8): 949–958.
[89] Loveday DL and Virk GS (1992) Artificial intelligence for buildings. *Applied Energy* 41(3): 201–221.
[90] Clarke JA, Cockroft J, Conner S, et al. (2002) Simulation-assisted control in building energy management systems. *Energy and Buildings* 34(9): 933–940.
[91] Spindler HC and Norford LK (2009) Naturally ventilated and mixed-mode buildings – Part I: Thermal modeling. *Building and Environment* 44(4): 736–749.
[92] Spindler HC and Norford LK (2009) Naturally ventilated and mixed-mode buildings – Part II: Optimal control. *Building and Environment* 44(4): 750–761.
[93] Michalewicz Z (1994) *Genetic Algorithms + Data Structures = Evolution Programs*, 2nd edn. New York: Springer-Verlag.
[94] Lah MT, Zupančič B, and Krainer A (2005) Fuzzy control for the illumination and temperature comfort in a test chamber. *Building and Environment* 40(12): 1626–1637.
[95] Kristl Z, Košir M, Trobec Lah M, and Krainer A (2008) Fuzzy control system for thermal and visual comfort in building. *Renewable Energy* 33(4): 694–702.
[96] Gouda MM, Danaher S, and Underwood CP (2006) Quasi-adaptive fuzzy heating control of solar buildings. *Building and Environment* 41(12): 1881–1891.
[97] Kazanasmaz T, Günaydin M, and Binol S (2009) Artificial neural networks to predict daylight illuminance in office buildings. *Building and Environment* 44(8): 1751–1757.
[98] LeBreux M, Lacroix M, and Lachiver G (2009) Control of a hybrid solar/electric thermal energy storage system. *International Journal of Thermal Sciences* 48(3): 645–654.
[99] Kubota N, Hashimoto S, Kojima F, and Taniguchi K (2000) GP-preprocessed fuzzy inference for the energy load prediction. *Proceedings of the IEEE Conference on Evolutionary Computation, ICEC 1*, pp. 1–6. La Jolla, CA, USA.
[100] Kolokotsa D, Niachou K, Geros V, et al. (2005) Implementation of an integrated indoor environment and energy management system. *Energy and Buildings* 37(1): 93–99.
[101] Wang L, Gwilliam J, and Jones P (2009) Case study of zero energy house design in UK. *Energy and Buildings* 41(11): 1215–1222.